CALCULUS
GRAPHICAL, NUMERICAL, ALGEBRAIC

SOLUTIONS MANUAL

Prentice
Hall

Glenview, Illinois
Needham, Massachusetts
Upper Saddle River, New Jersey

Introduction

This publication provides complete, worked out solutions for Quick Review, Excercises, and lesson Explorations, including Cumulative Review and Appendices exercises.

Many of the analytic solutions could alternatively be done graphically. Teachers are encouraged to accept creative, graphical solutions that show understanding of the graphing utilities. In general, the solutions in the manual provide one possible method of solution.

ISBN 0-13-067810-4

1 2 3 4 5 6 7 8 9 10   06 05 04 03 02 01

C O N T E N T S

Chapter 1
Prerequisites for Calculus

■ Section 1.1 Lines (pp. 1–9)

Quick Review 1.1

1. $y = -2 + 4(3 - 3) = -2 + 4(0) = -2 + 0 = -2$

2. $3 = 3 - 2(x + 1)$
$3 = 3 - 2x - 2$
$2x = -2$
$x = -1$

3. $m = \dfrac{2 - 3}{5 - 4} = \dfrac{-1}{1} = -1$

4. $m = \dfrac{2 - (-3)}{3 - (-1)} = \dfrac{5}{4}$

5. (a) $3(2) - 4\left(\dfrac{1}{4}\right) \overset{?}{=} 5$
$6 - 1 = 5$ Yes

(b) $3(3) - 4(-1) \overset{?}{=} 5$
$13 \neq 5$ No

6. (a) $7 \overset{?}{=} -2(-1) + 5$
$7 = 2 + 5$ Yes

(b) $1 = -2(-2) + 5$
$1 \neq 9$ No

7. $d = \sqrt{(x_2 - x_1)^2 + (y_2 - y_1)^2}$
$= \sqrt{(0 - 1)^2 + (1 - 0)^2}$
$= \sqrt{2}$

8. $d = \sqrt{(x_2 - x_1)^2 + (y_2 - y_1)^2}$
$= \sqrt{(1 - 2)^2 + \left(-\dfrac{1}{3} - 1\right)^2}$
$= \sqrt{(-1)^2 + \left(-\dfrac{4}{3}\right)^2}$
$= \sqrt{1 + \dfrac{16}{9}}$
$= \sqrt{\dfrac{25}{9}}$
$= \dfrac{5}{3}$

9. $4x - 3y = 7$
$-3y = -4x + 7$
$y = \dfrac{4}{3}x - \dfrac{7}{3}$

10. $-2x + 5y = -3$
$5y = 2x - 3$
$y = \dfrac{2}{5}x - \dfrac{3}{5}$

Section 1.1 Exercises

1. $\Delta x = -1 - 1 = -2$
$\Delta y = -1 - 2 = -3$

2. $\Delta x = -1 - (-3) = 2$
$\Delta y = -2 - 2 = -4$

3. $\Delta x = -8 - (-3) = -5$
$\Delta y = 1 - 1 = 0$

4. $\Delta x = 0 - 0 = 0$
$\Delta y = -2 - 4 = -6$

5. (a, c)

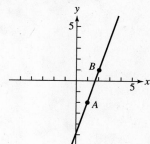

(b) $m = \dfrac{1 - (-2)}{2 - 1} = \dfrac{3}{1} = 3$

6. (a, c)

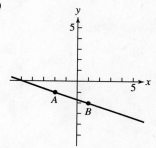

(b) $m = \dfrac{-2 - (-1)}{1 - (-2)} = \dfrac{-1}{3} = -\dfrac{1}{3}$

7. (a, c)

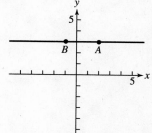

(b) $m = \dfrac{3 - 3}{-1 - 2} = \dfrac{0}{-3} = 0$

8. (a, c)

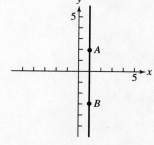

8. continued

(b) $m = \dfrac{-3-2}{1-1} = \dfrac{-5}{0}$ (undefined)

This line has no slope.

9. (a) $x = 2$

   (b) $y = 3$

10. (a) $x = -1$

   (b) $y = \dfrac{4}{3}$

11. (a) $x = 0$

   (b) $y = -\sqrt{2}$

12. (a) $x = -\pi$

   (b) $y = 0$

13. $y = 1(x - 1) + 1$

14. $y = -1[x - (-1)] + 1$
   $y = -1(x + 1) + 1$

15. $y = 2(x - 0) + 3$

16. $y = -2[x - (-4)] + 0$
   $y = -2(x + 4) + 0$

17. $m = \dfrac{3-0}{2-0} = \dfrac{3}{2}$

   $y = \dfrac{3}{2}(x - 0) + 0$

   $y = \dfrac{3}{2}x$

   $2y = 3x$

   $3x - 2y = 0$

18. $m = \dfrac{1-1}{2-1} = \dfrac{0}{1} = 0$

   $y = 0(x - 1) + 1$

   $y = 1$

19. $m = \dfrac{-2-0}{-2-(-2)} = \dfrac{-2}{0}$ (undefined)

   Vertical line: $x = -2$

20. $m = \dfrac{-2-1}{2-(-2)} = \dfrac{-3}{4} = -\dfrac{3}{4}$

   $y = -\dfrac{3}{4}[x - (-2)] + 1$

   $4y = -3(x + 2) + 4$

   $4y = -3x - 2$

   $3x + 4y = -2$

21. $y = 3x - 2$

22. $y = -1x + 2$ or $y = -x + 2$

23. $y = -\dfrac{1}{2}x - 3$

24. $y = \dfrac{1}{3}x - 1$

25. The line contains $(0, 0)$ and $(10, 25)$.

   $m = \dfrac{25-0}{10-0} = \dfrac{25}{10} = \dfrac{5}{2}$

   $y = \dfrac{5}{2}x$

26. The line contains $(0, 0)$ and $(5, 2)$.

   $m = \dfrac{2-0}{5-0} = \dfrac{2}{5}$

   $y = \dfrac{2}{5}x$

27. $3x + 4y = 12$

   $4y = -3x + 12$

   $y = -\dfrac{3}{4}x + 3$

   (a) Slope: $-\dfrac{3}{4}$

   (b) y-intercept: 3

   (c)

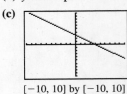

   $[-10, 10]$ by $[-10, 10]$

28. $x + y = 2$
   $y = -x + 2$

   (a) Slope: -1

   (b) y-intercept: 2

   (c)

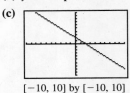

   $[-10, 10]$ by $[-10, 10]$

29. $\dfrac{x}{3} + \dfrac{y}{4} = 1$

   $\dfrac{y}{4} = -\dfrac{x}{3} + 1$

   $y = -\dfrac{4}{3}x + 4$

   (a) Slope: $-\dfrac{4}{3}$

   (b) y-intercept: 4

   (c)

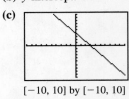

   $[-10, 10]$ by $[-10, 10]$

30. $y = 2x + 4$

   (a) Slope: 2

   (b) y-intercept: 4

   (c)

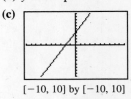

   $[-10, 10]$ by $[-10, 10]$

31. (a) The desired line has slope -1 and passes through $(0, 0)$:
$$y = -1(x - 0) + 0 \text{ or } y = -x.$$

(b) The desired line has slope $\dfrac{-1}{-1} = 1$ and passes through $(0, 0)$:
$$y = 1(x - 0) + 0 \text{ or } y = x.$$

32. (a) The given equation is equivalent to $y = -2x + 4$. The desired line has slope -2 and passes through $(-2, 2)$:
$$y = -2(x + 2) + 2 \text{ or } y = -2x - 2.$$

(b) The desired line has slope $\dfrac{-1}{-2} = \dfrac{1}{2}$ and passes through $(-2, 2)$:
$$y = \frac{1}{2}(x + 2) + 2 \text{ or } y = \frac{1}{2}x + 3.$$

33. (a) The given line is vertical, so we seek a vertical line through $(-2, 4)$: $x = -2$.

(b) We seek a horizontal line through $(-2, 4)$: $y = 4$.

34. (a) The given line is horizontal, so we seek a horizontal line through $\left(-1, \dfrac{1}{2}\right)$: $y = \dfrac{1}{2}$.

(b) We seek a vertical line through $\left(-1, \dfrac{1}{2}\right)$: $x = -1$.

35. $m = \dfrac{9 - 2}{3 - 1} = \dfrac{7}{2}$

$f(x) = \dfrac{7}{2}(x - 1) + 2 = \dfrac{7}{2}x - \dfrac{3}{2}$

Check: $f(5) = \dfrac{7}{2}(5) - \dfrac{3}{2} = 16$, as expected.

Since $f(x) = \dfrac{7}{2}x - \dfrac{3}{2}$, we have $m = \dfrac{7}{2}$ and $b = -\dfrac{3}{2}$.

36. $m = \dfrac{-4 - (-1)}{4 - 2} = \dfrac{-3}{2} = -\dfrac{3}{2}$

$f(x) = -\dfrac{3}{2}(x - 2) + (-1) = -\dfrac{3}{2}x + 2$

Check: $f(6) = -\dfrac{3}{2}(6) + 2 = -7$, as expected.

Since $f(x) = -\dfrac{3}{2}x + 2$, we have $m = -\dfrac{3}{2}$ and $b = 2$.

37.
$$-\frac{2}{3} = \frac{y - 3}{4 - (-2)}$$
$$-\frac{2}{3}(6) = y - 3$$
$$-4 = y - 3$$
$$-1 = y$$

38.
$$2 = \frac{2 - (-2)}{x - (-8)}$$
$$2(x + 8) = 4$$
$$x + 8 = 2$$
$$x = -6$$

39. (a) $y = 0.680x + 9.013$

(b) The slope is 0.68. It represents the approximate average weight gain in pounds per month.

(c)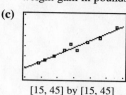

[15, 45] by [15, 45]

(d) When $x = 30$, $y \approx 0.680(30) + 9.013 = 29.413$. She weighs about 29 pounds.

40. (a) $y = 1{,}060.4233x - 2{,}077{,}548.669$

(b) The slope is 1,060.4233. It represents the approximate rate of increase in earnings in dollars per year.

(c)

[1975, 1995] by [20,000, 35,000]

(d) When $x = 2000$,
$y \approx 1{,}060.4233(2000) - 2{,}077{,}548.669 \approx 43{,}298$. In 2000, the construction workers' average annual compensation will be about \$43,298.

41. $y = 1 \cdot (x - 3) + 4$
$y = x - 3 + 4$
$y = x + 1$
This is the same as the equation obtained in Example 5.

42. (a) When $y = 0$, we have $\dfrac{x}{c} = 1$, so $x = c$.
When $x = 0$, we have $\dfrac{y}{d} = 1$, so $y = d$.

(b) When $y = 0$, we have $\dfrac{x}{c} = 2$, so $x = 2c$.
When $x = 0$, we have $\dfrac{y}{d} = 2$, so $y = 2d$.
The x-intercept is $2c$ and the y-intercept is $2d$.

43. (a) The given equations are equivalent to $y = -\dfrac{2}{k}x + \dfrac{3}{k}$ and $y = -x + 1$, respectively, so the slopes are $-\dfrac{2}{k}$ and -1. The lines are parallel when $-\dfrac{2}{k} = -1$, so $k = 2$.

(b) The lines are perpendicular when $-\dfrac{2}{k} = \dfrac{-1}{-1}$, so $k = -2$.

44. (a) $m \approx \dfrac{68 - 69.5}{0.4 - 0} = \dfrac{-1.5}{0.4} = -3.75$ degrees/inch

(b) $m \approx \dfrac{9 - 68}{4 - 0.4} = \dfrac{-59}{3.6} \approx -16.1$ degrees/inch

(c) $m \approx \dfrac{4 - 9}{4.7 - 4} = \dfrac{-5}{0.7} \approx -7.1$ degrees/inch

(d) Best insulator: Fiberglass insulation
Poorest insulator: Gypsum wallboard
The best insulator will have the largest temperature change per inch, because that will allow larger temperature differences on opposite sides of thinner layers.

45. Slope: $k = \dfrac{\Delta p}{\Delta d} = \dfrac{10.94 - 1}{100 - 0} = \dfrac{9.94}{100}$
$= 0.0994$ atmospheres per meter

At 50 meters, the pressure is

$p = 0.0994(50) + 1 = 5.97$ atmospheres.

46. (a) $d(t) = 45t$

(b)

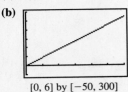

[0, 6] by [−50, 300]

(c) The slope is 45, which is the speed in miles per hour.

(d) Suppose the car has been traveling 45 mph for several hours when it is first observed at point P at time $t = 0$.

(e) The car starts at time $t = 0$ at a point 30 miles past P.

47. (a) $y = 5632x - 11,080,280$

(b) The rate at which the median price is increasing in dollars per year

(c) $y = 2732x - 5,362,360$

(d) The median price is increasing at a rate of about \$5632 per year in the Northeast, and about \$2732 per year in the Midwest. It is increasing more rapidly in the Northeast.

48. (a) Suppose $x°$F is the same as $x°$C.

$x = \dfrac{9}{5}x + 32$

$\left(1 - \dfrac{9}{5}\right)x = 32$

$-\dfrac{4}{5}x = 32$

$x = -40$

Yes, $-40°$F is the same as $-40°$C.

(b)

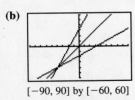

[−90, 90] by [−60, 60]

It is related because all three lines pass through the point $(-40, -40)$ where the Fahrenheit and Celsius temperatures are the same.

49. The coordinates of the three missing vertices are $(5, 2)$, $(-1, 4)$ and $(-1, -2)$, as shown below.

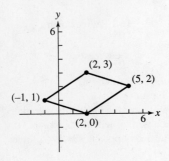

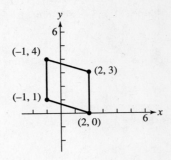

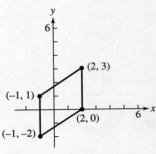

50.

Suppose that the vertices of the given quadrilateral are (a, b), (c, d), (e, f), and (g, h). Then the midpoints of the consecutive sides are $W\left(\dfrac{a+c}{2}, \dfrac{b+d}{2}\right)$, $X\left(\dfrac{c+e}{2}, \dfrac{d+f}{2}\right)$, $Y\left(\dfrac{e+g}{2}, \dfrac{f+h}{2}\right)$, and $Z\left(\dfrac{g+a}{2}, \dfrac{h+b}{2}\right)$. When these four points are connected, the slopes of the sides of the resulting figure are:

WX: $\dfrac{\dfrac{d+f}{2} - \dfrac{b+d}{2}}{\dfrac{c+e}{2} - \dfrac{a+c}{2}} = \dfrac{f-b}{e-a}$

XY: $\dfrac{\dfrac{f+h}{2} - \dfrac{d+f}{2}}{\dfrac{e+g}{2} - \dfrac{c+e}{2}} = \dfrac{h-d}{g-c}$

ZY: $\dfrac{\dfrac{f+h}{2} - \dfrac{h+b}{2}}{\dfrac{e+g}{2} - \dfrac{g+a}{2}} = \dfrac{f-b}{e-a}$

WZ: $\dfrac{\dfrac{h+b}{2} - \dfrac{b+d}{2}}{\dfrac{g+a}{2} - \dfrac{a+c}{2}} = \dfrac{h-d}{g-c}$

Opposite sides have the same slope and are parallel.

51. The radius through $(3, 4)$ has slope $\dfrac{4 - 0}{3 - 0} = \dfrac{4}{3}$.

The tangent line is tangent to this radius, so its slope is $\dfrac{-1}{4/3} = -\dfrac{3}{4}$. We seek the line of slope $-\dfrac{3}{4}$ that passes through $(3, 4)$.

$$y = -\frac{3}{4}(x - 3) + 4$$
$$y = -\frac{3}{4}x + \frac{9}{4} + 4$$
$$y = -\frac{3}{4}x + \frac{25}{4}$$

52. (a) The equation for line L can be written as

$y = -\dfrac{A}{B}x + \dfrac{C}{B}$, so its slope is $-\dfrac{A}{B}$. The perpendicular line has slope $\dfrac{-1}{-A/B} = \dfrac{B}{A}$ and passes through (a, b), so its equation is
$y = \dfrac{B}{A}(x - a) + b$.

(b) Substituting $\dfrac{B}{A}(x - a) + b$ for y in the equation for line L gives:

$$Ax + B\left[\frac{B}{A}(x - a) + b\right] = C$$
$$A^2x + B^2(x - a) + ABb = AC$$
$$(A^2 + B^2)x = B^2a + AC - ABb$$
$$x = \frac{B^2a + AC - ABb}{A^2 + B^2}$$

Substituting the expression for x in the equation for line L gives:

$$A\left(\frac{B^2a + AC - ABb}{A^2 + B^2}\right) + By = C$$
$$By = \frac{-A(B^2a + AC - ABb)}{A^2 + B^2} + \frac{C(A^2 + B^2)}{A^2 + B^2}$$
$$By = \frac{-AB^2a - A^2C + A^2Bb + A^2C + B^2C}{A^2 + B^2}$$
$$By = \frac{A^2Bb + B^2C - AB^2a}{A^2 + B^2}$$
$$y = \frac{A^2b + BC - ABa}{A^2 + B^2}$$

The coordinates of Q are $\left(\dfrac{B^2a + AC - ABb}{A^2 + B^2}, \dfrac{A^2b + BC - ABa}{A^2 + B^2}\right)$.

(c) Distance $= \sqrt{(x - a)^2 + (y - b)^2}$

$$= \sqrt{\left(\frac{B^2a + AC - ABb}{A^2 + B^2} - a\right)^2 + \left(\frac{A^2b + BC - ABa}{A^2 + B^2} - b\right)^2}$$
$$= \sqrt{\left(\frac{B^2a + AC - ABb - a(A^2 + B^2)}{A^2 + B^2}\right)^2 + \left(\frac{A^2b + BC - ABa - b(A^2 + B^2)}{A^2 + B^2}\right)^2}$$
$$= \sqrt{\left(\frac{AC - ABb - A^2a}{A^2 + B^2}\right)^2 + \left(\frac{BC - ABa - B^2b}{A^2 + B^2}\right)^2}$$
$$= \sqrt{\left(\frac{A(C - Bb - Aa)}{A^2 + B^2}\right)^2 + \left(\frac{B(C - Aa - Bb)}{A^2 + B^2}\right)^2}$$
$$= \sqrt{\frac{A^2(C - Aa - Bb)^2}{(A^2 + B^2)^2} + \frac{B^2(C - Aa - Bb)^2}{(A^2 + B^2)^2}}$$
$$= \sqrt{\frac{(A^2 + B^2)(C - Aa - Bb)^2}{(A^2 + B^2)^2}}$$
$$= \sqrt{\frac{(C - Aa - Bb)^2}{A^2 + B^2}}$$
$$= \frac{|C - Aa - Bb|}{\sqrt{A^2 + B^2}}$$
$$= \frac{|Aa + Bb - C|}{\sqrt{A^2 + B^2}}$$

■ Section 1.2 Functions and Graphs

(pp. 9–19)

Exploration 1   Composing Functions

1. $y_3 = g \circ f, y_4 = f \circ g$

2. Domain of y_3: $[-2, 2]$ Range of y_3: $[0, 2]$

y_1:
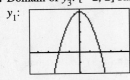
$[-4.7, 4.7]$ by $[-2, 4.2]$

y_2:
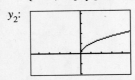
$[-4.7, 4.7]$ by $[-2, 4.2]$

y_3:
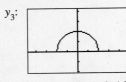
$[-4.7, 4.7]$ by $[-2, 4.2]$

3. Domain of y_4: $[0, \infty)$; Range of y_4: $(-\infty, 4]$

y_4:
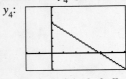
$[-2, 6]$ by $[-2, 6]$

4. $y_3 = y_2 (y_1(x)) = \sqrt{y_1(x)} = \sqrt{4 - x^2}$
$y_4 = y_1(y_2(x)) = 4 - (y_2(x))^2 = 4 - (\sqrt{x})^2 = 4 - x, x \geq 0$

Quick Review 1.2

1. $3x - 1 \leq 5x + 3$
$-2x \leq 4$
$x \geq -2$
Solution: $[-2, \infty)$

2. $x(x - 2) > 0$
Solutions to $x(x - 2) = 0$: $x = 0, x = 2$
Test $x = -1$: $-1(-1 - 2) = 3 > 0$
   $x(x - 2) > 0$ is true when $x < 0$.
Test $x = 1$: $1(1 - 2) = -1 < 0$
   $x(x - 2) > 0$ is false when $0 < x < 2$.
Test $x = 3$: $3(3 - 2) = 3 > 0$
   $x(x - 2) > 0$ is true when $x > 2$.
Solution set: $(-\infty, 0) \cup (2, \infty)$

3. $|x - 3| \leq 4$
$-4 \leq x - 3 \leq 4$
$-1 \leq x \leq 7$
Solution set: $[-1, 7]$

4. $|x - 2| \geq 5$
$x - 2 \leq -5$ or $x - 2 \geq 5$
$x \leq -3$ or $x \geq 7$
Solution set: $(-\infty, -3] \cup [7, \infty)$

5. $x^2 < 16$
Solutions to $x^2 = 16$: $x = -4, x = 4$
Test $x = -6$ $(-6)^2 = 36 > 16$
   $x^2 < 16$ is false when $x < -4$
Test $x = 0$: $0^2 = 0 < 16$
   $x^2 < 16$ is true when $-4 < x < 4$
Test $x = 6$: $6^2 = 36 > 16$
   $x^2 < 16$ is false when $x > 4$.
Solution set: $(-4, 4)$

6. $9 - x^2 \geq 0$
Solutions to $9 - x^2 = 0$: $x = -3, x = 3$
Test $x = -4$: $9 - (-4)^2 = 9 - 16 = -7 < 0$
   $9 - x^2 \geq 0$ is false when $x < -3$.
Test $x = 0$: $9 - 0^2 = 9 > 0$
   $9 - x^2 \geq 0$ is true when $-3 < x < 3$.
Test $x = 4$: $9 - 4^2 = 9 - 16 = -7 < 0$
   $9 - x^2 \geq 0$ is false when $x > 3$.
Solution set: $[-3, 3]$

7. Translate the graph of f 2 units left and 3 units downward.

8. Translate the graph of f 5 units right and 2 units upward.

9. (a) $f(x) = 4$
         $x^2 - 5 = 4$
         $x^2 - 9 = 0$
$(x + 3)(x - 3) = 0$
         $x = -3$ or $x = 3$

   (b) $f(x) = -6$
         $x^2 - 5 = -6$
         $x^2 = -1$
No real solution

10. (a) $f(x) = -5$
       $\dfrac{1}{x} = -5$
       $x = -\dfrac{1}{5}$

   (b) $f(x) = 0$
       $\dfrac{1}{x} = 0$
No solution

11. (a) $f(x) = 4$
       $\sqrt{x + 7} = 4$
         $x + 7 = 16$
             $x = 9$
Check: $\sqrt{9 + 7} = \sqrt{16} = 4$; it checks.

   (b) $f(x) = 1$
       $\sqrt{x + 7} = 1$
         $x + 7 = 1$
             $x = -6$
Check: $\sqrt{-6 + 7} = 1$; it checks.

12. (a) $f(x) = -2$
       $\sqrt[3]{x - 1} = -2$
         $x - 1 = -8$
             $x = -7$

   (b) $f(x) = 3$
       $\sqrt[3]{x - 1} = 3$
         $x - 1 = 27$
             $x = 28$

Section 1.2 Exercises

1. Since $A = \pi r^2 = \pi\left(\dfrac{d}{2}\right)^2$, the formula is $A = \dfrac{\pi d^2}{4}$, where A represents area and d represents diameter.

2. Let h represent height and let s represent side length.

$$h^2 + \left(\frac{s}{2}\right)^2 = s^2$$
$$h^2 = s^2 - \frac{1}{4}s^2$$
$$h^2 = \frac{3}{4}s^2$$
$$h = \pm\frac{\sqrt{3}}{2}s$$

Since side length and height must be positive, the formula is $h = \dfrac{\sqrt{3}}{2}s$.

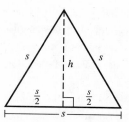

3. $S = 6e^2$, where S represents surface area and e represents edge length.

4. $V = \dfrac{4}{3}\pi r^3$, where V represents volume and r represents radius.

5. (a) $(-\infty, \infty)$ or all real numbers
   (b) $(-\infty, 4]$
   (c)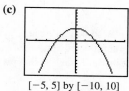
   $[-5, 5]$ by $[-10, 10]$
   (d) Symmetric about y-axis (even)

6. (a) $(-\infty, \infty)$ or all real numbers
   (b) $[-9, \infty)$
   (c)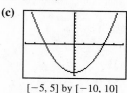
   $[-5, 5]$ by $[-10, 10]$
   (d) Symmetric about the y-axis (even)

7. (a) Since we require $x - 1 \geq 0$, the domain is $[1, \infty)$.
   (b) $[2, \infty)$
   (c)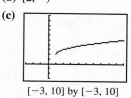
   $[-3, 10]$ by $[-3, 10]$
   (d) None

8. (a) Since we require $-x \geq 0$, the domain is $(-\infty, 0]$.
   (b) $(-\infty, 0]$
   (c)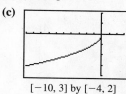
   $[-10, 3]$ by $[-4, 2]$
   (d) None

9. (a) Since we require $3 - x \geq 0$, the domain is $(-\infty, 3]$.
   (b) $[0, \infty)$
   (c)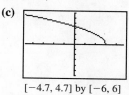
   $[-4.7, 4.7]$ by $[-6, 6]$
   (d) None

10. (a) Since we require $x - 2 \neq 0$, the domain is $(-\infty, 2) \cup (2, \infty)$.
    (b) Since $\dfrac{1}{x - 2}$ can assume any value except 0, the range is $(-\infty, 0) \cup (0, \infty)$.
    (c)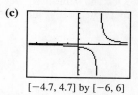
    $[-4.7, 4.7]$ by $[-6, 6]$
    (d) None

11. (a) $(-\infty, \infty)$ or all real numbers
    (b) $(-\infty, \infty)$ or all real numbers
    (c)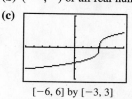
    $[-6, 6]$ by $[-3, 3]$
    (d) None

12. (a) $(-\infty, \infty)$ or all real numbers
    (b) The maximum function value is attained at the point $(0, 1)$, so the range is $(-\infty, 1]$.
    (c)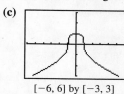
    $[-6, 6]$ by $[-3, 3]$
    (d) Symmetric about the y-axis (even)

13. (a) Since we require $-x \geq 0$, the domain is $(-\infty, 0]$.

 (b) $[0, \infty)$

 (c)

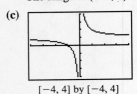

 $[-10, 3]$ by $[-1, 2]$

 (d) None

14. (a) Since we require $x \neq 0$, the domain is $(-\infty, 0) \cup (0, \infty)$.

 (b) Note that $\frac{1}{x}$ can assume any value except 0, so $1 + \frac{1}{x}$

 can assume any value except 1.
 The range is $(-\infty, 1) \cup (1, \infty)$.

 (c)

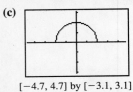

 $[-4, 4]$ by $[-4, 4]$

 (d) None

15. (a) Since we require $4 - x^2 \geq 0$, the domain is $[-2, 2]$.

 (b) Since $4 - x^2$ will be between 0 and 4, inclusive (for x in the domain), its square root is between 0 and 2, inclusive. The range is $[0, 2]$.

 (c)

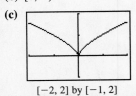

 $[-4.7, 4.7]$ by $[-3.1, 3.1]$

 (d) Symmetric about the y-axis (even)

16. (a) This function is equivalent to $y = \sqrt[3]{x^2}$, so its domain is all real numbers.

 (b) $[0, \infty)$

 (c)

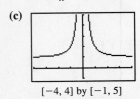

 $[-2, 2]$ by $[-1, 2]$

 (d) Symmetric about the y-axis (even)

17. (a) Since we require $x^2 \neq 0$, the domain is $(-\infty, 0) \cup (0, \infty)$

 (b) Since $\frac{1}{x^2} > 0$ for all x, the range is $(1, \infty)$.

 (c)

 $[-4, 4]$ by $[-1, 5]$

 (d) Symmetric about the y-axis (even)

18. (a) This function is equivalent to $y = \sqrt{x^3}$, so its domain is $[0, \infty)$.

 (b) $[0, \infty)$

 (c)

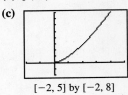

 $[-2, 5]$ by $[-2, 8]$

 (d) None

19. Even, since the function is an even power of x.

20. Neither, since the function is a sum of even and odd powers of x.

21. Neither, since the function is a sum of even and odd powers of x $(x^1 + 2x^0)$.

22. Even, since the function is a sum of even powers of x $(x^2 - 3x^0)$.

23. Even, since the function involves only even powers of x.

24. Odd, since the function is a sum of odd powers of x.

25. Odd, since the function is a quotient of an odd function (x^3) and an even function $(x^2 - 1)$.

26. Neither, since, (for example), $y(-2) = 4^{1/3}$ and $y(2) = 0$.

27. Neither, since, (for example), $y(-1)$ is defined and $y(1)$ is undefined.

28. Even, since the function involves only even powers of x.

29. (a)

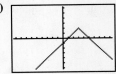

 $[-9.4, 9.4]$ by $[-6.2, 6.2]$

 Note that $f(x) = -|x - 3| + 2$, so its graph is the graph of the absolute value function reflected across the x-axis and then shifted 3 units right and 2 units upward.

 (b) $(-\infty, \infty)$

 (c) $(-\infty, 2]$

30. (a) The graph of $f(x)$ is the graph of the absolute value function stretched vertically by a factor of 2 and then shifted 4 units to the left and 3 units downward.

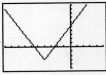

 $[-10, 5]$ by $[-5, 10]$

 (b) $(-\infty, \infty)$ or all real numbers

 (c) $[-3, \infty)$

31. (a)

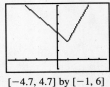

 $[-4.7, 4.7]$ by $[-1, 6]$

 (b) $(-\infty, \infty)$ or all real numbers

 (c) $[2, \infty)$

32. (a)

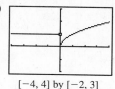

[−4, 4] by [−2, 3]

(b) $(-\infty, \infty)$ or all real numbers

(c) $[0, \infty)$

33. (a)

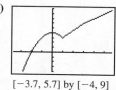

[−3.7, 5.7] by [−4, 9]

(b) $(-\infty, \infty)$ or all real numbers

(c) $(-\infty, \infty)$ or all real numbers

34. (a)

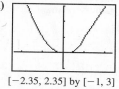

[−2.35, 2.35] by [−1, 3]

(b) $(-\infty, \infty)$ or all real numbers

(c) $[0, \infty)$

35. Because if the vertical line test holds, then for each x-coordinate, there is at most one y-coordinate giving a point on the curve. This y-coordinate would correspond to the value assigned to the x-coordinate. Since there is only one y-coordinate, the assignment would be unique.

36. If the curve is not $y = 0$, there must be a point (x, y) on the curve where $y \neq 0$. That would mean that (x, y) and $(x, -y)$ are two different points on the curve and it is not the graph of a function, since it fails the vertical line test.

37. No

38. Yes

39. Yes

40. No

41. Line through $(0, 0)$ and $(1, 1)$: $y = x$
Line through $(1, 1)$ and $(2, 0)$: $y = -x + 2$
$$f(x) = \begin{cases} x, & 0 \le x \le 1 \\ -x + 2, & 1 < x \le 2 \end{cases}$$

42. $f(x) = \begin{cases} 2, & 0 \le x < 1 \\ 0, & 1 \le x < 2 \\ 2, & 2 \le x < 3 \\ 0, & 3 \le x \le 4 \end{cases}$

43. Line through $(0, 2)$ and $(2, 0)$: $y = -x + 2$

Line through $(2, 1)$ and $(5, 0)$: $m = \dfrac{0 - 1}{5 - 2} = \dfrac{-1}{3} = -\dfrac{1}{3}$,

so $y = -\dfrac{1}{3}(x - 2) + 1 = -\dfrac{1}{3}x + \dfrac{5}{3}$

$$f(x) = \begin{cases} -x + 2, & 0 < x \le 2 \\ -\dfrac{1}{3}x + \dfrac{5}{3}, & 2 < x \le 5 \end{cases}$$

44. Line through $(-1, 0)$ and $(0, -3)$:
$$m = \frac{-3 - 0}{0 - (-1)} = \frac{-3}{1} = -3, \text{ so } y = -3x - 3$$
Line through $(0, 3)$ and $(2, -1)$:
$$m = \frac{-1 - 3}{2 - 0} = \frac{-4}{2} = -2, \text{ so } y = -2x + 3$$
$$f(x) = \begin{cases} -3x - 3, & -1 < x \le 0 \\ -2x + 3, & 0 < x \le 2 \end{cases}$$

45. Line through $(-1, 1)$ and $(0, 0)$: $y = -x$

Line through $(0, 1)$ and $(1, 1)$: $y = 1$

Line through $(1, 1)$ and $(3, 0)$:
$$m = \frac{0 - 1}{3 - 1} = \frac{-1}{2} = -\frac{1}{2},$$
so $y = -\dfrac{1}{2}(x - 1) + 1 = -\dfrac{1}{2}x + \dfrac{3}{2}$
$$f(x) = \begin{cases} -x, & -1 \le x < 0 \\ 1, & 0 < x \le 1 \\ -\dfrac{1}{2}x + \dfrac{3}{2}, & 1 < x < 3 \end{cases}$$

46. Line through $(-2, -1)$ and $(0, 0)$: $y = \dfrac{1}{2}x$

Line through $(0, 2)$ and $(1, 0)$: $y = -2x + 2$

Line through $(1, -1)$ and $(3, -1)$: $y = -1$
$$f(x) = \begin{cases} \dfrac{1}{2}x, & -2 \le x \le 0 \\ -2x + 2, & 0 < x \le 1 \\ -1, & 1 < x \le 3 \end{cases}$$

47. Line through $\left(\dfrac{T}{2}, 0\right)$ and $(T, 1)$:
$$m = \frac{1 - 0}{T - (T/2)} = \frac{2}{T}, \text{ so } y = \frac{2}{T}\left(x - \frac{T}{2}\right) + 0 = \frac{2}{T}x - 1$$
$$f(x) = \begin{cases} 0, & 0 \le x \le \dfrac{T}{2} \\ \dfrac{2}{T}x - 1, & \dfrac{T}{2} < x \le T \end{cases}$$

48. $f(x) = \begin{cases} A, & 0 \le x < \dfrac{T}{2} \\ -A, & \dfrac{T}{2} \le x < T \\ A, & T \le x < \dfrac{3T}{2} \\ -A, & \dfrac{3T}{2} \le x \le 2T \end{cases}$

49. (a) $f(g(x)) = (x^2 - 3) + 5 = x^2 + 2$

(b) $g(f(x)) = (x + 5)^2 - 3$
$= (x^2 + 10x + 25) - 3$
$= x^2 + 10x + 22$

(c) $f(g(0)) = 0^2 + 2 = 2$

(d) $g(f(0)) = 0^2 + 10 \cdot 0 + 22 = 22$

(e) $g(g(-2)) = [(-2)^2 - 3]^2 - 3 = 1^2 - 3 = -2$

(f) $f(f(x)) = (x + 5) + 5 = x + 10$

50. (a) $f(g(x)) = (x - 1) + 1 = x$

(b) $g(f(x)) = (x + 1) - 1 = x$

(c) $f(g(x)) = 0$

(d) $g(f(0)) = 0$

(e) $g(g(-2)) = (-2 - 1) - 1 = -3 - 1 = -4$

(f) $f(f(x)) = (x + 1) + 1 = x + 2$

51. (a) Enter $y_1 = f(x) = x - 7$, $y_2 = g(x) = \sqrt{x}$,
$y_3 = (f \circ g)(x) = y_1(y_2(x))$,
and $y_4 = (g \circ f)(x) = y_2(y_1(x))$

$f \circ g$:

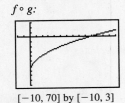

[−10, 70] by [−10, 3]

Domain: $[0, \infty)$
Range: $[-7, \infty)$

$g \circ f$:

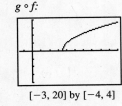

[−3, 20] by [−4, 4]

Domain: $[7, \infty)$
Range: $[0, \infty)$

(b) $(f \circ g)(x) = \sqrt{x} - 7$ $(g \circ f)(x) = \sqrt{x - 7}$

52. (a) Enter $y_1 = f(x) = 1 - x^2$, $y_2 = g(x) = \sqrt{x}$,
$y_3 = (f \circ g)(x) = y_1(y_2(x))$,
and $y_4 = (g \circ f)(x) = y_2(y_1(x))$

$f \circ g$:

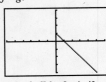

[−6, 6] by [−4, 4]

Domain: $[0, \infty)$
Range: $(-\infty, 1]$

$g \circ f$:

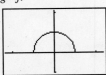

[−2.35, 2.35] by [−1, 2.1]

Domain: $[-1, 1]$
Range: $[0, 1]$

(b) $(f \circ g)(x) = 1 - (\sqrt{x})^2 = 1 - x, x \ge 0$
$(g \circ f)(x) = \sqrt{1 - x^2}$

53. (a) Enter $y_1 = f(x) = x^2 - 3$, $y_2 = g(x) = \sqrt{x + 2}$,
$y_3 = (f \circ g)(x) = y_1(y_2(x))$,
and $y_4 = (g \circ f)(x) = y_2(y_1(x))$.

$f \circ g$:

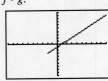

[−10, 10] by [−10, 10]

Domain: $[-2, \infty)$
Range: $[-3, \infty)$

$g \circ f$:

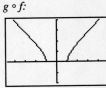

[−4.7, 4.7] by [−2, 4]

Domain: $(-\infty, -1] \cup [1, \infty)$
Range: $[0, \infty)$

(b) $(f \circ g)(x) = (\sqrt{x + 2})^2 - 3$
$= (x + 2) - 3, x \ge -2$
$= x - 1, x \ge -2$
$(g \circ f)(x) = \sqrt{(x^2 - 3) + 2} = \sqrt{x^2 - 1}$

54. (a) Enter $y_1(x) = f(x) = \dfrac{2x - 1}{x + 3}$, $y_2 = \dfrac{3x + 1}{2 - x}$,

$y_3 = (f \circ g)(x) = y_1(y_2(x))$,
and $y_4 = (g \circ f)(x) = y_2(y_1(x))$.
Use a "decimal window" such as the one shown.

$f \circ g$:

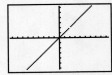

[−9.4, 9.4] by [−6.2, 6.2]

Domain: $(-\infty, 2) \cup (2, \infty)$
Range: $(-\infty, 2) \cup (2, \infty)$

$g \circ f$:

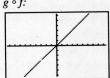

[−9.4, 9.4] by [−6.2, 6.2]

Domain: $(-\infty, -3) \cup (-3, \infty)$
Range: $(-\infty, -3) \cup (-3, \infty)$

(b) $(f \circ g)(x) = \dfrac{2\left(\dfrac{3x + 1}{2 - x}\right) - 1}{\dfrac{3x + 1}{2 - x} + 3}$

$= \dfrac{2(3x + 1) - (2 - x)}{(3x + 1) + 3(2 - x)}, x \ne 2$

$= \dfrac{7x}{7}, x \ne 2$

$= x, x \ne 2$

$(g \circ f)(x) = \dfrac{3\left(\dfrac{2x - 1}{x + 3}\right) + 1}{2 - \dfrac{2x - 1}{x + 3}}$

$= \dfrac{3(2x - 1) + (x + 3)}{2(x + 3) - (2x - 1)}, x \ne -3$

$= \dfrac{7x}{7}, x \ne -3$

$= x, x \ne -3$

55.

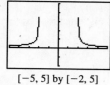

[−5, 5] by [−2, 5]

We require $x^2 - 4 \geq 0$ (so that the square root is defined) and $x^2 - 4 \neq 0$ (to avoid division by zero), so the domain is $(-\infty, -2) \cup (2, \infty)$. For values of x in the domain, $x^2 - 4$ $\left(\text{and hence } \sqrt{x^2 - 4} \text{ and } \dfrac{1}{\sqrt{x^2 - 4}}\right)$ can attain any positive value, so the range is $(0, \infty)$. (Note that grapher failure may cause the range to appear as a finite interval on a grapher.

56.

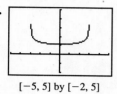

[−5, 5] by [−2, 5]

We require $9 - x^2 \geq 0$ (so that the fourth root is defined) and $9 - x^2 \neq 0$ (to avoid division by zero), so the domain is $(-3, 3)$. For values of x in the domain, $9 - x^2$ can attain any value in $(0, 9]$. Therefore, $\sqrt[4]{9 - x^2}$ can attain any value in $(0, \sqrt{3}]$, and $\dfrac{2}{\sqrt[4]{9 - x^2}}$ can attain any value in $\left[\dfrac{2}{\sqrt{3}}, \infty\right)$. The range is $\left[\dfrac{2}{\sqrt{3}}, \infty\right)$ or approximately $[1.15, \infty)$. (Note that grapher failure may cause the range to appear as a finite interval on a grapher.)

57.

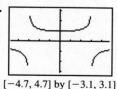

[−4.7, 4.7] by [−3.1, 3.1]

We require $9 - x^2 \neq 0$, so the domain is $(-\infty, -3) \cup (-3, 3) \cup (3, \infty)$. For values of x in the domain, $9 - x^2$ can attain any value in $(-\infty, 0) \cup (0, 9]$, so $\sqrt[3]{9 - x^2}$ can attain any value in $(-\infty, 0) \cup (0, \sqrt[3]{9}]$. Therefore, $\dfrac{2}{\sqrt[3]{9 - x^2}}$ can attain any value in $(-\infty, 0) \cup \left[\dfrac{2}{\sqrt[3]{9}}, \infty\right)$. The range is $(-\infty, 0) \cup \left[\dfrac{2}{\sqrt[3]{9}}, \infty\right)$ or approximately $(-\infty, 0) \cup [0.96, \infty)$. (Note that grapher failure can cause the intervals in the range to appear as finite intervals on a grapher.)

58.

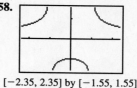

[−2.35, 2.35] by [−1.55, 1.55]

We require $x^2 - 1 \neq 0$, so the domain is $(-\infty, -1) \cup (-1, 1) \cup (1, \infty)$. For values of x in the domain, $x^2 - 1$ can attain any value in $[-1, 0) \cup (0, \infty)$, so $\sqrt[3]{x^2 - 1}$ can also attain any value in $[-1, 0) \cup (0, \infty)$. Therefore, $\dfrac{1}{\sqrt[3]{x - 1}}$ can attain any value in $(-\infty, -1] \cup (0, \infty)$. The range is $(-\infty, -1] \cup (0, \infty)$. (Note that grapher failure can cause the intervals in the range to appear as finite intervals on a grapher.)

59. (a)

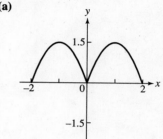

(b)

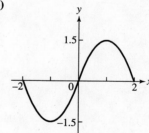

60. (a)

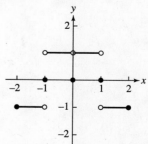

60. continued

(b)

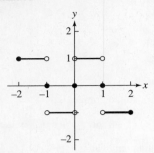

61. (a)

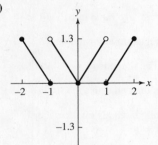

(b)

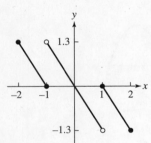

62. (a)

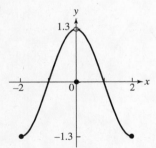

(b)

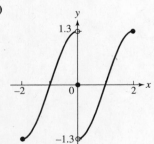

63. (a) Since $(f \circ g)(x) = \sqrt{g(x) - 5} = \sqrt{x^2 - 5}$, $g(x) = x^2$.

(b) Since $(f \circ g)(x) = 1 + \dfrac{1}{g(x)} = x$, we know that
$\dfrac{1}{g(x)} = x - 1$, so $g(x) = \dfrac{1}{x - 1}$.

(c) Since $(f \circ g)(x) = f\!\left(\dfrac{1}{x}\right) = x$, $f(x) = \dfrac{1}{x}$.

(d) Since $(f \circ g)(x) = f(\sqrt{x}) = |x|$, $f(x) = x^2$.
The completed table is shown. Note that the absolute value sign in part (d) is optional.

$g(x)$	$f(x)$	$(f \circ g)(x)$
x^2	$\sqrt{x - 5}$	$\sqrt{x^2 - 5}$
$\dfrac{1}{x - 1}$	$1 + \dfrac{1}{x}$	$x,\ x \neq -1$
$\dfrac{1}{x}$	$\dfrac{1}{x}$	$x,\ x \neq 0$
$\sqrt{x}$	x^2	$|x|,\ x \geq 0$

64. (a) Note that the data in the table begins at $x = 20$. (We do not include the initial investment in the data.) The power regression equation is $y = 27.1094x^{2.651044}$.

(b)

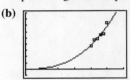

$[0, 30]$ by $[-20{,}000, 180{,}000]$

(c) When $x = 30$, $y \approx 223{,}374$. According to the power regression equation, the investment will grow to approximately \$223,374.

(d) The linear regression equation is
$y = 12{,}577.97x - 177{,}275.52$. When
$x = 30$, $y \approx 200{,}064$. According to the linear regression equation, the investment will grow to approximately \$200,064.

65. (a) Because the circumference of the original circle was 8π and a piece of length x was removed.

(b) $r = \dfrac{8\pi - x}{2\pi} = 4 - \dfrac{x}{2\pi}$

(c) $h = \sqrt{16 - r^2}$

$= \sqrt{16 - \left(4 - \dfrac{x}{2\pi}\right)^2}$

$= \sqrt{16 - \left(16 - \dfrac{4x}{\pi} + \dfrac{x^2}{4\pi^2}\right)}$

$= \sqrt{\dfrac{4x}{\pi} - \dfrac{x^2}{4\pi^2}}$

$= \sqrt{\dfrac{16\pi x}{4\pi^2} - \dfrac{x^2}{4\pi^2}}$

$= \dfrac{\sqrt{16\pi x - x^2}}{2\pi}$

(d) $V = \dfrac{1}{3}\pi r^2 h$

$= \dfrac{1}{3}\pi\left(\dfrac{8\pi - x}{2\pi}\right)^2 \cdot \dfrac{\sqrt{16\pi x - x^2}}{2\pi}$

$= \dfrac{(8\pi - x)^2 \sqrt{16\pi x - x^2}}{24\pi^2}$

66. (a) Note that 2 mi = 10,560 ft, so there are $\sqrt{800^2 + x^2}$ feet of river cable at \$180 per foot and $(10{,}560 - x)$ feet of land cable at \$100 per foot. The cost is
$$C(x) = 180\sqrt{800^2 + x^2} + 100(10{,}560 - x)$$

(b)
$$C(0) = \$1{,}200{,}000$$
$$C(500) \approx \$1{,}175{,}812$$
$$C(1000) \approx \$1{,}186{,}512$$
$$C(1500) \approx \$1{,}212{,}000$$
$$C(2000) \approx \$1{,}243{,}732$$
$$C(2500) \approx \$1{,}278{,}479$$
$$C(3000) \approx \$1{,}314{,}870$$

Values beyond this are all larger. It would appear that the least expensive location is less than 2000 ft from point P.

67. (a)

[−3, 3] by [−1, 3]

(b) Domain of y_1: $[0, \infty)$
Domain of y_2: $(-\infty, 1]$
Domain of y_3: $[0, 1]$

(c) The functions $y_1 - y_2$, $y_2 - y_1$, and $y_1 \cdot y_2$ all have domain $[0, 1]$, the same as the domain of $y_1 + y_2$ found in part (b).

Domain of $\dfrac{y_1}{y_2}$: $[0, 1)$

Domain of $\dfrac{y_2}{y_1}$: $(0, 1]$

(d) The domain of a sum, difference, or product of two functions is the intersection of their domains.

The domain of a quotient of two functions is the intersection of their domains with any zeros of the denominator removed.

68. (a) Yes. Since
$$(f \cdot g)(-x) = f(-x) \cdot g(-x) = f(x) \cdot g(x) = (f \cdot g)(x),$$
the function $(f \cdot g)(x)$ will also be even.

(b) The product will be even, since
$$\begin{aligned}(f \cdot g)(-x) &= f(-x) \cdot g(-x)\\ &= (-f(x)) \cdot (-g(x))\\ &= f(x) \cdot g(x)\\ &= (f \cdot g)(x).\end{aligned}$$

■ Section 1.3 Exponential Functions

(pp. 20–26)

Exploration 1   Exponential Functions

1.

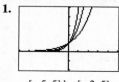

[−5, 5] by [−2, 5]

2. $x > 0$

3. $x < 0$

4. $x = 0$

5.

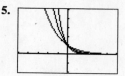

[−5, 5] by [−2, 5]

6. $2^{-x} < 3^{-x} < 5^{-x}$ for $x < 0$; $2^{-x} > 3^{-x} > 5^{-x}$ for $x > 0$; $2^{-x} = 3^{-x} = 5^{-x}$ for $x = 0$.

Quick Review 1.3

1. Using a calculator, $5^{2/3} \approx 2.924$.

2. Using a calculator, $3^{\sqrt{2}} \approx 4.729$.

3. Using a calculator, $3^{-1.5} \approx 0.192$.

4. $x^3 = 17$
$x = \sqrt[3]{17}$
$x \approx 2.5713$

5. $x^5 = 24$
$x = \sqrt[5]{24}$
$x \approx 1.8882$

6. $x^{10} = 1.4567$
$x = \pm\sqrt[10]{1.4567}$
$x \approx \pm 1.0383$

7. $500(1.0475)^5 \approx \$630.58$

8. $1000(1.063)^3 \approx \$1201.16$

9. $\dfrac{(x^{-3}y^2)^2}{(x^4y^3)^3} = \dfrac{x^{-6}y^4}{x^{12}y^9}$
$= x^{-6-12}y^{4-9}$
$= x^{-18}y^{-5}$
$= \dfrac{1}{x^{18}y^5}$

10. $\left(\dfrac{a^3b^{-2}}{c^4}\right)^2\left(\dfrac{a^4c^{-2}}{b^3}\right)^{-1} = \dfrac{a^6b^{-4}}{c^8} \cdot \dfrac{b^3}{a^4c^{-2}}$
$= \dfrac{a^6}{b^4c^8} \cdot \dfrac{b^3c^2}{a^4}$
$= a^{6-4}b^{-4+3}c^{-8+2}$
$= a^2b^{-1}c^{-6} = \dfrac{a^2}{bc^6}$

Section 1.3 Exercises

1. The graph of $y = 2^x$ is increasing from left to right and has the negative x-axis as an asymptote. (a)

2. The graph of $y = 3^{-x}$ or, equivalently, $y = \left(\dfrac{1}{3}\right)^x$, is decreasing from left to right and has the positive x-axis as an asymptote. (d)

3. The graph of $y = -3^{-x}$ is the reflection about the x-axis of the graph in Exercise 2. (e)

4. The graph of $y = -0.5^{-x}$ or, equivalently, $y = -2^x$, is the reflection about the x-axis of the graph in Exercise 1. (c)

5. The graph of $y = 2^{-x} - 2$ is decreasing from left to right and has the line $y = -2$ as an asymptote. (b)

6. The graph of $y = 1.5^x - 2$ is increasing from left to right and has the line $y = -2$ as an asymptote. (f)

7.

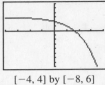

$[-4, 4]$ by $[-8, 6]$

Domain: $(-\infty, \infty)$
Range: $(-\infty, 3)$
x-intercept: ≈ 1.585
y-intercept: 2

8.

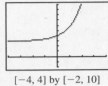

$[-4, 4]$ by $[-2, 10]$

Domain: $(-\infty, \infty)$
Range: $(3, \infty)$
x-intercept: None
y-intercept: 4

9.

$[-4, 4]$ by $[-4, 8]$

Domain: $(-\infty, \infty)$
Range: $(-2, \infty)$
x-intercept: ≈ 0.405
y-intercept: 1

10.

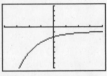

$[-4, 4]$ by $[-8, 4]$

Domain: $(-\infty, \infty)$
Range: $(-\infty, -1)$
x-intercept: None
y-intercept: -2

11. $9^{2x} = (3^2)^{2x} = 3^{4x}$

12. $16^{3x} = (2^4)^{3x} = 2^{12x}$

13. $\left(\dfrac{1}{8}\right)^{2x} = (2^{-3})^{2x} = 2^{-6x}$

14. $\left(\dfrac{1}{27}\right)^{x} = (3^{-3})^{x} = 3^{-3x}$

15.

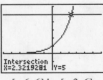

Intersection
X=2.3219281 Y=5

$[-6, 6]$ by $[-2, 6]$

$x \approx 2.3219$

16.

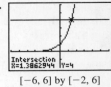

Intersection
X=1.3862944 Y=4

$[-6, 6]$ by $[-2, 6]$

$x \approx 1.3863$

17.

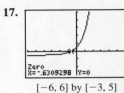

Zero
X=-.6309298 Y=0

$[-6, 6]$ by $[-3, 5]$

$x \approx -0.6309$

18.

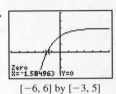

Zero
X=-1.584963 Y=0

$[-6, 6]$ by $[-3, 5]$

$x \approx -1.5850$

19.

x	y	Δy
1	-1	
		2
2	1	
		2
3	3	
		2
4	5	

20.

x	y	Δy
1	1	
		-3
2	-2	
		-3
3	-5	
		-3
4	-8	

21.

x	y	Δy
1	1	
		3
2	4	
		5
3	9	
		7
4	16	

22.

x	y	ratio
1	8.155	
		2.718
2	22.167	
		2.718
3	60.257	
		2.718
4	163.794	

23. Let t be the number of years. Solving $500,000(1.0375)^t = 1,000,000$ graphically, we find that $t \approx 18.828$. The population will reach 1 million in about 19 years.

24. (a) The population is given by $P(t) = 6250(1.0275)^t$, where t is the number of years after 1890.
Population in 1915: $P(25) \approx 12,315$
Population in 1940: $P(50) \approx 24,265$

(b) Solving $P(t) = 50,000$ graphically, we find that $t \approx 76.651$. The population reached 50,000 about 77 years after 1890, in 1967.

25. (a) $A(t) = 6.6\left(\dfrac{1}{2}\right)^{t/14}$

(b) Solving $A(t) = 1$ graphically, we find that $t \approx 38.1145$. There will be 1 gram remaining after about 38.1145 days.

26. Let t be the number of years. Solving $2300(1.06)^t = 4150$ graphically, we find that $t \approx 10.129$. It will take about 10.129 years. (If the interest is not credited to the account until the end of each year, it will take 11 years.)

27. Let A be the amount of the initial investment, and let t be the number of years. We wish to solve $A(1.0625)^t = 2A$, which is equivalent to $1.0625^t = 2$. Solving graphically, we find that $t \approx 11.433$. It will take about 11.433 years. (If the interest is credited at the end of each year, it will take 12 years.)

28. Let A be the amount of the initial investment, and let t be the number of years. We wish to solve
$$A\left(1 + \frac{0.0625}{12}\right)^{12t} = 2A,\text{ which is equivalent to}$$
$$\left(1 + \frac{0.0625}{12}\right)^{12t} = 2.\text{ Solving graphically, we find that}$$
$t \approx 11.119$. It will take about 11.119 years. (If the interest is credited at the end of each month, it will take 11 years 2 months.)

29. Let A be the amount of the initial investment, and let t be the number of years. We wish to solve $Ae^{0.0625t} = 2A$, which is equivalent to $e^{0.0625t} = 2$. Solving graphically, we find that $t \approx 11.090$. It will take about 11.090 years.

30. Let A be the amount of the initial investment, and let t be the number of years. We wish to solve $A(1.0575)^t = 3A$, which is equivalent to $1.0575^t = 3$. Solving graphically, we find that $t \approx 19.650$. It will take about 19.650 years. (If the interest is credited at the end of each year, it will take 20 years.)

31. Let A be the amount of the initial investment, and let t be the number of years. We wish to solve
$$A\left(1 + \frac{0.0575}{365}\right)^{365t} = 3A,\text{ which is equivalent to}$$
$$\left(1 + \frac{0.0575}{365}\right)^{365t} = 3.\text{ Solving graphically, we find that}$$
$t \approx 19.108$. It will take about 19.108 years.

32. Let A be the amount of the initial investment, and let t be the number of years. We wish to solve $Ae^{0.0575t} = 3A$, which is equivalent to $e^{0.0575t} = 3$. Solving graphically, we find that $t \approx 19.106$. It will take about 19.106 years.

33. After t hours, the population is $P(t) = 2^{t/0.5}$ or, equivalently, $P(t) = 2^{2t}$. After 24 hours, the population is $P(24) = 2^{48} \approx 2.815 \times 10^{14}$ bacteria.

34. (a) Each year, the number of cases is $100\% - 20\% = 80\%$ of the previous year's number of cases. After t years, the number of cases will be $C(t) = 10,000(0.8)^t$. Solving $C(t) = 1000$ graphically, we find that $t \approx 10.319$. It will take about 10.319 years.

(b) Solving $C(t) = 1$ graphically, we find that $t \approx 41.275$. It will take about 41.275 years.

35. Since $\Delta x = 1$, the corresponding value of Δy is equal to the slope of the line. If the changes in x are constant for a linear function, then the corresponding changes in y are constant as well.

36. (a) When $t = 0$, $B = 100e^0 = 100$. There were 100 bacteria present initially.

(b) When $t = 6$, $B = 100e^{0.693(6)} \approx 6394.351$. After 6 hours, there are about 6394 bacteria.

(c) Solving $100e^{0.693t} = 200$ graphically, we find that $t \approx 1.000$. The population will be 200 after about 1 hour. Since the population doubles (from 100 to 200) in about 1 hour, the doubling time is about 1 hour.

37. (a) Let $x = 0$ represent 1900, $x = 1$ represent 1901, and so on. The regression equation is $P(x) = 6.033(1.030)^x$.

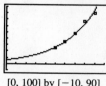

[0, 100] by [−10, 90]

(b) The regression equation gives an estimate of $P(0) \approx 6.03$ million, which is not very close to the actual population.

(c) Since the equation is of the form $P(x) = P(0) \cdot 1.030^x$, the annual rate of growth is about 3%.

38. (a) The regression equation is $P(x) = 4.831(1.019)^x$.

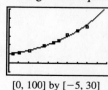

[0, 100] by [−5, 30]

(b) $P(90) \approx 26.3$ million

(c) Since the equation is of the form $P(x) = P(0) \cdot 1.019^x$, the annual rate of growth is approximately 1.9%.

39. $5422(1.018)^{19} \approx 7609.7$ million

40. (a)

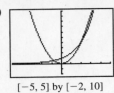

$[-5, 5]$ by $[-2, 10]$

In this window, it appears they cross twice, although a third crossing off-screen appears likely.

(b)

x	change in $Y1$	change in $Y2$
1		
	3	2
2		
	5	4
3		
	7	8
4		

It happens by the time $x = 4$.

(c) Solving graphically, $x \approx -0.7667$, $x = 2$, $x = 4$.

(d) The solution set is approximately $(-0.7667, 2) \cup (4, \infty)$.

41. Since $f(1) = 4.5$ we have $ka = 4.5$, and since $f(-1) = 0.5$ we have $ka^{-1} = 0.5$.
Dividing, we have

$$\frac{ka}{ka^{-1}} = \frac{4.5}{0.5}$$
$$a^2 = 9$$

$$a = \pm 3$$

Since $f(x) = k \cdot a^x$ is an exponential function, we require $a > 0$, so $a = 3$. Then $ka = 4.5$ gives $3k = 4.5$, so $k = 1.5$. The values are $a = 3$ and $k = 1.5$.

42. Since $f(1) = 1.5$ we have $ka = 1.5$, and since $f(-1) = 6$ we have $ka^{-1} = 6$. Dividing, we have

$$\frac{ka}{ka^{-1}} = \frac{1.5}{6}$$
$$a^2 = 0.25$$

$$a = \pm 0.5$$

Since $f(x) = k \cdot a^x$ is an exponential function, we require $a > 0$, so $a = 0.5$. Then $ka = 1.5$ gives $0.5k = 1.5$, so $k = 3$. The values are $a = 0.5$ and $k = 3$.

■ Section 1.4 Parametric Equations (pp. 26–31)

Exploration 1 Parametrizing Circles

1. Each is a circle with radius $|a|$. As $|a|$ increases, the radius of the circle increases.

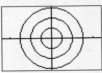

$[-4.7, 4.7]$ by $[-3.1, 3.1]$

2. $0 \le t \le \frac{\pi}{2}$:

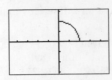

$[-4.7, 4.7]$ by $[-3.1, 3.1]$

$0 \le t \le \pi$:

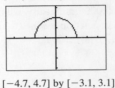

$[-4.7, 4.7]$ by $[-3.1, 3.1]$

$0 \le t \le \frac{3\pi}{2}$:

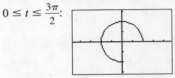

$[-4.7, 4.7]$ by $[-3.1, 3.1]$

$2\pi \le t \le 4\pi$:

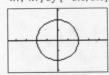

$[-4.7, 4.7]$ by $[-3.1, 3.1]$

$0 \le t \le 4\pi$:

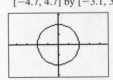

$[-4.7, 4.7]$ by $[-3.1, 3.1]$

Let d be the length of the parametric interval. If $d < 2\pi$, you get $\frac{d}{2\pi}$ of a complete circle. If $d = 2\pi$, you get the complete circle. If $d > 2\pi$, you get the complete circle but portions of the circle will be traced out more than once. For example, if $d = 4\pi$ the entire circle is traced twice.

3.

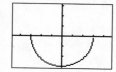

$$\frac{\pi}{2} \le t \le \frac{3\pi}{2}$$
initial point: (0, 3)
terminal point: (0, −3)

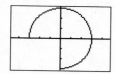

$$\pi \le t \le 2\pi$$
initial point: (−3, 0)
terminal point: (3, 0)

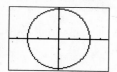

$$\frac{3\pi}{2} \le t \le 3\pi$$
initial point: (0, −3)
terminal point: (−3, 0)

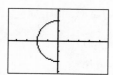

$$\pi \le t \le 5\pi$$
initial point: (−3, 0)
terminal point: (−3, 0)

4. For $0 \le t \le 2\pi$ the complete circle is traced once clockwise beginning and ending at (2, 0).
For $\pi \le t \le 3\pi$ the complete circle is traced once clockwise beginning and ending at (−2, 0).

For $\frac{\pi}{2} \le t \le \frac{3\pi}{2}$ the half circle below is traced clockwise

starting at (0, −2) and ending at (0, 2).

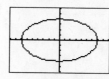

Exploration 2   Parametrizing Ellipses

1. $a = 2, b = 3$:

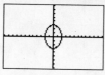

$[-12, 12]$ by $[-8, 8]$

$a = 2, b = 4$:

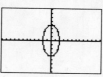

$[-12, 12]$ by $[-8, 8]$

$a = 2, b = 5$:

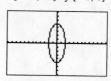

$[-12, 12]$ by $[-8, 8]$

$a = 2, b = 6$:

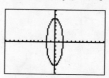

$[-12, 12]$ by $[-8, 8]$

2. $a = 3, b = 4$:

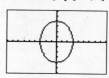

$[-9, 9]$ by $[-6, 6]$

$a = 5, b = 4$:

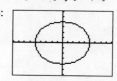

$[-9, 9]$ by $[-6, 6]$

$a = 6, b = 4$:

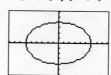

$[-9, 9]$ by $[-6, 6]$

$a = 7, b = 4$:

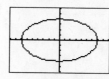

$[-9, 9]$ by $[-6, 6]$

3. If $|a| > |b|$, then the major axis is on the x-axis and the
minor on the y-axis. If $|a| < |b|$, then the major axis is on
the y-axis and the minor on the x-axis.

4. $0 \le t \le \dfrac{\pi}{2}$:

[−6, 6] by [−4, 4]

$0 \le t \le \pi$:

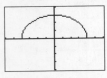

[−6, 6] by [−4, 4]

$0 \le t \le \dfrac{3\pi}{2}$:

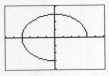

[−6, 6] by [−4, 4]

$0 \le t \le 4\pi$:

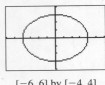

[−6, 6] by [−4, 4]

Let d be the length of the parametric interval. If $d < 2\pi$, you get $\dfrac{d}{2\pi}$ of a complete ellipse. If $d = 2\pi$, you get the complete ellipse. If $d > 2\pi$, you get the complete ellipse but portions of the ellipse will be traced out more than once. For example, if $d = 4\pi$ the entire ellipse is traced twice.

5. $0 \le t \le 2\pi$:

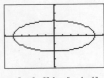

[−6, 6] by [−4, 4]

initial point: (5, 0)
terminal point: (5, 0)

$\pi \le t \le 3\pi$:

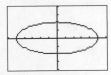

[−6, 6] by [−4, 4]

initial point: (−5, 0)
terminal point: (−5, 0)

$\dfrac{\pi}{2} \le t \le \dfrac{3\pi}{2}$:

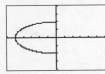

[−6, 6] by [−4, 4]

initial point: (0, −2)
terminal point: (0, 2)

Each curve is traced clockwise from the initial point to the terminal point.

Exploration 3   Graphing the Witch of Agnesi

1. We used the parameter interval $[0, \pi]$ because our graphing calculator ignored the fact that the curve is not defined when $t = 0$ or π. The curve is traced from right to left across the screen. x ranges from $-\infty$ to ∞.

2. $-\dfrac{\pi}{2} \le t \le \dfrac{\pi}{2}$:

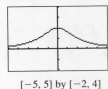

[−5, 5] by [−2, 4]

$0 < t \le \dfrac{\pi}{2}$:

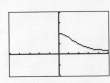

[−5, 5] by [−2, 4]

$\dfrac{\pi}{2} \le t < \pi$:

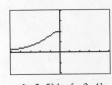

[−5, 5] by [−2, 4]

For $-\dfrac{\pi}{2} \le t \le \dfrac{\pi}{2}$, the entire graph described in part 1 is drawn. The left branch is drawn from right to left across the screen starting at the point (0, 2). Then the right branch is drawn from right to left across the screen stopping at the point (0, 2). If you leave out $-\dfrac{\pi}{2}$ and $\dfrac{\pi}{2}$, then the point (0, 2) is not drawn.

For $0 < t \le \dfrac{\pi}{2}$, the right branch is drawn from right to left across the screen stopping at the point (0, 2). If you leave out $\dfrac{\pi}{2}$, then the point (0, 2) is not drawn.

For $\dfrac{\pi}{2} \le t < \pi$, the left branch is drawn from right to left across the screen starting at the point (0, 2). If you leave out $\dfrac{\pi}{2}$, then the point (0, 2) is not drawn.

3. If you replace $x = 2 \cot t$ by $x = -2 \cot t$, the same graph is drawn except it is traced from left to right across the screen. If you replace $x = 2 \cot t$ by $x = 2 \cot (\pi - t)$, the same graph is drawn except it is traced from left to right across the screen.

Quick Review 1.4

1. $m = \dfrac{3 - 8}{4 - 1} = \dfrac{-5}{3} = -\dfrac{5}{3}$

$y = -\dfrac{5}{3}(x - 1) + 8$

$y = -\dfrac{5}{3}x + \dfrac{29}{3}$

2. $y = -4$

3. $x = 2$

4. When $y = 0$, we have $\frac{x^2}{9} = 1$, so the x-intercepts are -3 and 3. When $x = 0$, we have $\frac{y^2}{16} = 1$, so the y-intercepts are -4 and 4.

5. When $y = 0$, we have $\frac{x^2}{16} = 1$, so the x-intercepts are -4 and 4. When $x = 0$, we have $-\frac{y^2}{9} = 1$, which has no real solution, so there are no y-intercepts.

6. When $y = 0$, we have $0 = x + 1$, so the x-intercept is -1. When $x = 0$, we have $2y^2 = 1$, so the y-intercepts are $-\frac{1}{\sqrt{2}}$ and $\frac{1}{\sqrt{2}}$.

7. (a) $2(1)^2(1) + 1^2 \overset{?}{=} 3$
$$3 = 3 \quad \text{Yes}$$

(b) $2(-1)^2(-1) + (-1)^2 \overset{?}{=} 3$
$$-2 + 1 \overset{?}{=} 3$$
$$-1 \neq 3 \quad \text{No}$$

(c) $2\left(\frac{1}{2}\right)^2(-2) + (-2)^2 \overset{?}{=} 3$
$$-1 + 4 \overset{?}{=} 3$$
$$3 = 3 \quad \text{Yes}$$

8. (a) $9(1)^2 - 18(1) + 4(3)^2 = 27$
$$9 - 18 + 36 \overset{?}{=} 27$$
$$27 = 27 \quad \text{Yes}$$

(b) $9(1)^2 - 18(1) + 4(-3)^2 \overset{?}{=} 27$
$$9 - 18 + 36 \overset{?}{=} 27$$
$$27 = 27 \quad \text{Yes}$$

(c) $9(-1)^2 - 18(-1) + 4(3)^2 \overset{?}{=} 27$
$$9 + 18 + 36 \overset{?}{=} 27$$
$$63 \neq 27 \quad \text{No}$$

9. (a) $2x + 3t = -5$
$$3t = -2x - 5$$
$$t = \frac{-2x - 5}{3}$$

(b) $3y - 2t = -1$
$$-2t = -3y - 1$$
$$2t = 3y + 1$$
$$t = \frac{3y + 1}{2}$$

10. (a) The equation is true for $a \geq 0$.

(b) The equation is equivalent to "$\sqrt{a^2} = a$ or $\sqrt{a^2} = -a$." Since $\sqrt{a^2} = a$ is true for $a \geq 0$ and $\sqrt{a^2} = -a$ is true for $a \leq 0$, at least one of the two equations is true for all real values of a. Therefore, the given equation $\sqrt{a^2} = \pm a$ is true for all real values of a.

(c) The equation is true for all real values of a.

Section 1.4 Exercises

1. Graph (c). Window: $[-4, 4]$ by $[-3, 3]$, $0 \leq t \leq 2\pi$

2. Graph (a). Window: $[-2, 2]$ by $[-2, 2]$, $0 \leq t \leq 2\pi$

3. Graph (d). Window: $[-10, 10]$ by $[-10, 10]$, $0 \leq t \leq 2\pi$

4. Graph (b). Window: $[-15, 15]$ by $[-15, 15]$, $0 \leq t \leq 2\pi$

5. (a) The resulting graph appears to be the right half of a hyperbola in the first and fourth quadrants. The parameter a determines the x-intercept. The parameter b determines the shape of the hyperbola. If b is smaller, the graph has less steep slopes and appears "sharper." If b is larger, the slopes are steeper and the graph appears more "blunt." The graphs for $a = 2$ and $b = 1, 2$, and 3 are shown.

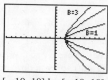

$[-10, 10]$ by $[-10, 10]$

(b)

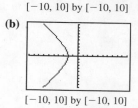

$[-10, 10]$ by $[-10, 10]$

This appears to be the left half of the same hyberbola.

(c)

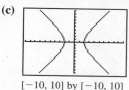

$[-10, 10]$ by $[-10, 10]$

One must be careful because both $\sec t$ and $\tan t$ are discontinuous at these points. This might cause the grapher to include extraneous lines (the asymptotes of the hyperbola) in its graph. The extraneous lines can be avoided by using the grapher's dot mode instead of connected mode.

(d) Note that $\sec^2 t - \tan^2 t = 1$ by a standard trigonometric identity. Substituting $\frac{x}{a}$ for $\sec t$ and $\frac{y}{b}$ for $\tan t$ gives $\left(\frac{x}{a}\right)^2 - \left(\frac{y}{b}\right)^2 = 1$.

(e) This changes the orientation of the hyperbola. In this case, b determines the y-intercept of the hyperbola, and a determines the shape. The parameter interval $\left(-\frac{\pi}{2}, \frac{\pi}{2}\right)$ gives the upper half of the hyperbola. The parameter interval $\left(\frac{\pi}{2}, \frac{3\pi}{2}\right)$ gives the lower half. The same values of t cause discontinuities and may add extraneous lines to the graph. Substituting $\frac{y}{b}$ for $\sec t$ and $\frac{x}{a}$ for $\tan t$ in the identity $\sec^2 t - \tan^2 t = 1$ gives $\left(\frac{y}{b}\right)^2 - \left(\frac{x}{a}\right)^2 = 1$.

6. (a)

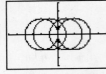

[−6, 6] by [−4, 4]

The graph is a circle of radius 2 centered at $(h, 0)$. As h changes, the graph shifts horizontally.

(b)

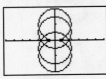

[−6, 6] by [−4, 4]

The graph is a circle of radius 2 centered at $(0, k)$. At k changes, the graph shifts vertically.

(c) Since the circle is to be centered at $(2, -3)$, we use $h = 2$ and $k = -3$. Since a radius of 5 is desired, we need to change the coefficients of $\cos t$ and $\sin t$ to 5.
$x = 5\cos t + 2, y = 5\sin t - 3, 0 \le t \le 2\pi$

(d) $x = 5\cos t - 3, y = 2\sin t + 4, 0 \le t \le 2\pi$

7. (a)

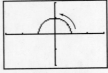

[−3, 3] by [−2, 2]

Initial point: $(1, 0)$
Terminal point: $(-1, 0)$

(b) $x^2 + y^2 = \cos^2 t + \sin^2 t = 1$
The parametrized curve traces the upper half of the circle defined by $x^2 + y^2 = 1$ (or all of the semicircle defined by $y = \sqrt{1 - x^2}$).

8. (a)

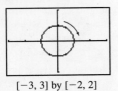

[−3, 3] by [−2, 2]

Initial and terminal point: $(0, 1)$

(b) $x^2 + y^2 = \sin^2(2\pi t) + \cos^2(2\pi t) = 1$
The parametrized curve traces all of the circle defined by $x^2 + y^2 = 1$.

9. (a)

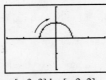

[−3, 3] by [−2, 2]

Initial point: $(-1, 0)$
Terminal point: $(0, 1)$

(b) $x^2 + y^2 = \cos^2(\pi - t) + \sin^2(\pi - t) = 1$
The parametrized curve traces the upper half of the circle defined by $x^2 + y^2 = 1$ (or all of the semicircle defined by $y = \sqrt{1 - x^2}$).

10. (a)

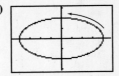

[−4.7, 4.7] by [−3.1, 3.1]

Initial and terminal point: $(4, 0)$

(b) $\left(\dfrac{x}{4}\right)^2 + \left(\dfrac{y}{2}\right)^2 = \cos^2 t + \sin^2 t = 1$

The parametrized curve traces all of the ellipse defined by $\left(\dfrac{x}{4}\right)^2 + \left(\dfrac{y}{2}\right)^2 = 1$.

11. (a)

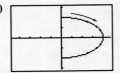

[−4.7, 4.7] by [−3.1, 3.1]

Initial point: $(0, 2)$
Terminal point: $(0, -2)$

(b) $\left(\dfrac{x}{4}\right)^2 + \left(\dfrac{y}{2}\right)^2 = \sin^2 t + \cos^2 t = 1$

The parametrized curve traces the right half of the ellipse defined by $\left(\dfrac{x}{4}\right)^2 + \left(\dfrac{y}{2}\right)^2 = 1$ (or all of the curve defined by $x = 2\sqrt{4 - y^2}$).

12. (a)

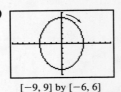

[−9, 9] by [−6, 6]

Initial and terminal point: $(0, 5)$

(b) $\left(\dfrac{x}{4}\right)^2 + \left(\dfrac{y}{5}\right)^2 = \sin^2 t + \cos^2 t = 1$

The parametrized curve traces all of the ellipse defined by $\left(\dfrac{x}{4}\right)^2 + \left(\dfrac{y}{5}\right)^2 = 1$.

13. (a)

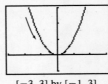

[−3, 3] by [−1, 3]

No initial or terminal point.

(b) $y = 9t^2 = (3t)^2 = x^2$
The parametrized curve traces all of the parabola defined by $y = x^2$.

14. (a)

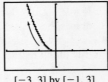

[−3, 3] by [−1, 3]

Initial point: $(0, 0)$
Terminal point: None

(b) $y = t = (-\sqrt{t})^2 = x^2$

The parametrized curve traces the left half of the parabola defined by $y = x^2$ (or all of the curve defined by $x = -\sqrt{y}$).

15. (a)

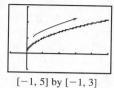

$[-1, 5]$ by $[-1, 3]$

Initial point: $(0, 0)$
Terminal point: None

(b) $y = \sqrt{t} = \sqrt{x}$

The parametrized curve traces all of the curve defined by $y = \sqrt{x}$ (or the upper half of the parabola defined by $x = y^2$).

16. (a)

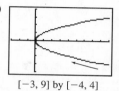

$[-3, 9]$ by $[-4, 4]$

No initial or terminal point.

(b) $x = \sec^2 t - 1 = \tan^2 t = y^2$

The parametrized curve traces all of the parabola defined by $x = y^2$.

17. (a)

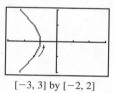

$[-3, 3]$ by $[-2, 2]$

No initial or terminal point. Note that it may be necessary to use a t-interval such as $[-1.57, 1.57]$ or use dot mode in order to avoid "asymptotes" showing on the calculator screen.

(b) $x^2 - y^2 = \sec^2 t - \tan^2 t = 1$

The parametrized curve traces the left branch of the hyperbola defined by $x^2 - y^2 = 1$ (or all of the curve defined by $x = -\sqrt{y^2 + 1}$).

18. (a)

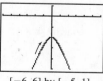

$[-6, 6]$ by $[-5, 1]$

No initial or terminal point. Note that it may be necessary to use a t-interval such as $[-1.57, 1.57]$ or use dot mode in order to avoid "asymptotes" showing on the calculator screen.

(b) $\left(\dfrac{y}{2}\right)^2 - x^2 = \sec^2 t - \tan^2 t = 1$

The parametrized curve traces the lower branch of the hyperbola defined by $\left(\dfrac{y}{2}\right)^2 - x^2 = 1$ (or all of the curve defined by $y = -2\sqrt{x^2 + 1}$).

19. (a)

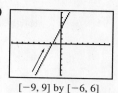

$[-9, 9]$ by $[-6, 6]$

No initial or terminal point.

(b) $y = 4t - 7 = 2(2t - 5) + 3 = 2x + 3$

The parametrized curve traces all of the line defined by $y = 2x + 3$.

20. (a)

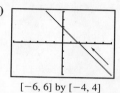

$[-6, 6]$ by $[-4, 4]$

No initial or terminal point.

(b) $y = 1 + t = 2 - (1 - t) = 2 - x = -x + 2$

The parametrized curve traces all of the line defined by $y = -x + 2$.

21. (a)

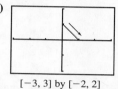

$[-3, 3]$ by $[-2, 2]$

Initial point: $(0, 1)$
Terminal point: $(1, 0)$

(b) $y = 1 - t = 1 - x = -x + 1$

The Cartesian equation is $y = -x + 1$. The portion traced by the parametrized curve is the segment from $(0, 1)$ to $(1, 0)$.

22. (a)

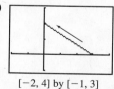

$[-2, 4]$ by $[-1, 3]$

Initial point: $(3, 0)$
Terminal point: $(0, 2)$

(b) $y = 2t = (2t - 2) + 2 = -\dfrac{2}{3}(3 - 3t) + 2 = -\dfrac{2}{3}x + 2$

The Cartesian equation is $y = -\dfrac{2}{3}x + 2$. The portion traced by the curve is the segment from $(3, 0)$ to $(0, 2)$.

23. (a)

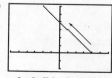

$[-6, 6]$ by $[-2, 6]$

Initial point: $(4, 0)$
Terminal point: None

(b) $y = \sqrt{t} = 4 - (4 - \sqrt{t}) = 4 - x = -x + 4$

The parametrized curve traces the portion of the line defined by $y = -x + 4$ to the left of $(4, 0)$, that is, for $x \le 4$.

24. (a)

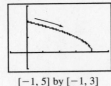

[−1, 5] by [−1, 3]

Initial point: (0, 2)
Terminal point: (4, 0)

(b) $y = \sqrt{4 - t^2} = \sqrt{4 - x}$
The parametrized curve <u>traces</u> the right portion of the curve defined by $y = \sqrt{4 - x}$, that is, for $x \geq 0$.

25. (a)

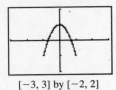

[−3, 3] by [−2, 2]

No initial or terminal point, since the t-interval has no beginning or end. The curve is traced and retraced in both directions.

(b) $y = \cos 2t$
$= \cos^2 t - \sin^2 t$
$= 1 - 2\sin^2 t$
$= 1 - 2x^2$
$= -2x^2 + 1$
The parametrized curve traces the portion of the parabola defined by $y = -2x^2 + 1$ corresponding to $-1 \leq x \leq 1$.

26. (a)

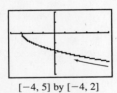

[−4, 5] by [−4, 2]

Initial point: None
Terminal point: (−3, 0)

(b) $x = t^2 - 3 = y^2 - 3$
The parametrized curve traces the lower half of the parabola defined by $x = y^2 - 3$ (or all of the curve defined by $y = -\sqrt{x + 3}$).

27. Using $(-1, -3)$ we create the parametric equations $x = -1 + at$ and $y = -3 + bt$, representing a line which goes through $(-1, -3)$ at $t = 0$. We determine a and b so that the line goes through $(4, 1)$ when $t = 1$.
Since $4 = -1 + a, a = 5$.
Since $1 = -3 + b, b = 4$.
Therefore, one possible parametrization is $x = -1 + 5t$, $y = -3 + 4t, 0 \leq t \leq 1$.

28. Using $(-1, 3)$ we create the parametric equations $x = -1 + at$ and $y = 3 + bt$, representing a line which goes through $(-1, 3)$ at $t = 0$. We determine a and b so that the line goes through $(3, -2)$ at $t = 1$.
Since $3 = -1 + a, a = 4$.
Since $-2 = 3 + b, b = -5$.
Therefore, one possible parametrization is $x = -1 + 4t$, $y = 3 - 5t, 0 \leq t \leq 1$.

29. The lower half of the parabola is given by $x = y^2 + 1$ for $y \leq 0$. Substituting t for y, we obtain one possible parametrization: $x = t^2 + 1, y = t, t \leq 0$.

30. The vertex of the parabola is at $(-1, -1)$, so the left half of the parabola is given by $y = x^2 + 2x$ for $x \leq -1$. Substituting t for x, we obtain one possible parametrization: $x = t, y = t^2 + 2t, t \leq -1$.

31. For simplicity, we assume that x and y are linear functions of t and that the point (x, y) starts at $(2, 3)$ for $t = 0$ and passes through $(-1, -1)$ at $t = 1$. Then $x = f(t)$, where $f(0) = 2$ and $f(1) = -1$.

Since slope $= \dfrac{\Delta x}{\Delta t} = \dfrac{-1 - 2}{1 - 0} = -3$,

$x = f(t) = -3t + 2 = 2 - 3t$. Also, $y = g(t)$, where

$g(0) = 3$ and $g(1) = -1$.

Since slope $= \dfrac{\Delta y}{\Delta t} = \dfrac{-1 - 3}{1 - 0} = -4$,

$y = g(t) = -4t + 3 = 3 - 4t$.

One possible parametrization is:

$x = 2 - 3t, y = 3 - 4t, t \geq 0$.

32. For simplicity, we assume that x and y are linear functions of t and that the point (x, y) starts at $(-1, 2)$ for $t = 0$ and passes through $(0, 0)$ at $t = 1$. Then $x = f(t)$, where $f(0) = -1$ and $f(1) = 0$.

Since slope $= \dfrac{\Delta x}{\Delta t} = \dfrac{0 - (-1)}{1 - 0} = 1$,

$x = f(t) = 1t + (-1) = -1 + t$.

Also, $y = g(t)$, where $g(0) = 2$ and $g(1) = 0$.

Since slope $= \dfrac{\Delta y}{\Delta t} = \dfrac{0 - 2}{1 - 0} = -2$,

$y = g(t) = -2t + 2 = 2 - 2t$.

One possible parametrization is:

$x = -1 + t, y = 2 - 2t, t \geq 0$.

33. The graph is in Quadrant I when $0 < y < 2$, which corresponds to $1 < t < 3$. To confirm, note that $x(1) = 2$ and $x(3) = 0$.

34. The graph is in Quadrant II when $2 < y \leq 4$, which corresponds to $3 < t \leq 5$. To confirm, note that $x(3) = 0$ and $x(5) = -2$.

35. The graph is in Quadrant III when $-6 \leq y < -4$, which corresponds to $-5 \leq t < -3$. To confirm, note that $x(-5) = -2$ and $x(-3) = 0$.

36. The graph is in Quadrant IV when $-4 < y < 0$, which corresponds to $-3 < t < 1$. To confirm, note that $x(-3) = 0$ and $x(1) = 2$.

37. The graph of $y = x^2 + 2x + 2$ lies in Quadrant I for all $x > 0$. Substituting t for x, we obtain one possible parametrization:
$x = t, y = t^2 + 2t + 2, t > 0$.

38. The graph of $y = \sqrt{x + 3}$ lies in Quadrant I for all $x \geq 0$. Substituting t for x, we obtain one possible parametrization:
$x = t, y = \sqrt{t + 3}, t > 0$.

39. Possible answers:

    (a) $x = a \cos t, \ y = -a \sin t, \ 0 \le t \le 2\pi$

    (b) $x = a \cos t, \ y = a \sin t, \ 0 \le t \le 2\pi$

    (c) $x = a \cos t, \ y = -a \sin t, \ 0 \le t \le 4\pi$

    (d) $x = a \cos t, \ y = a \sin t, \ 0 \le t \le 4\pi$

40. Possible answers:

    (a) $x = -a \cos t, \ y = b \sin t, \ 0 \le t \le 2\pi$

    (b) $x = -a \cos t, \ y = -b \sin t, \ 0 \le t \le 2\pi$

    (c) $x = -a \cos t, \ y = b \sin t, \ 0 \le t \le 4\pi$

    (d) $x = -a \cos t, \ y = -b \sin t, \ 0 \le t \le 4\pi$

41. Note that $m\angle OAQ = t$, since alternate interior angles formed by a transversal of parallel lines are congruent.

Therefore, $\tan t = \dfrac{OQ}{AQ} = \dfrac{2}{x}$, so $x = \dfrac{2}{\tan t} = 2 \cot t$.

Now, by equation (iii), we know that

$$
\begin{aligned}
AB &= \frac{(AQ)^2}{AO} \\
&= \left(\frac{AQ}{AO}\right)(AQ) \\
&= (\cos t)(x) \\
&= (\cos t)(2 \cot t) \\
&= \frac{2 \cos^2 t}{\sin t}.
\end{aligned}
$$

Then equation (ii) gives

$$ y = 2 - AB \sin t = 2 - \frac{2 \cos^2 t}{\sin t} \cdot \sin t = 2 - 2 \cos^2 t $$

$$ = 2 \ \sin^2 t. $$

The parametric equations are:

$$ x = 2 \cot t, \ y = 2 \ \sin^2 t, \ 0 < t < \pi $$

Note: Equation (iii) may not be immediately obvious, but it may be justified as follows. Sketch segment QB. Then $\angle OBQ$ is a right angle, so $\triangle ABQ \sim \triangle AQO$, which gives $\dfrac{AB}{AQ} = \dfrac{AQ}{AO}$.

42. (a) If $x_2 = x_1$ then the line is a vertical line and the first parametric equation gives $x = x_1$, while the second will give all real values for y since it cannot be the case that $y_2 = y_1$ as well.

Otherwise, solving the first equation for t gives $t = (x - x_1)/(x_2 - x_1)$.
Substituting that into the second equation gives
$y = y_1 + [(y_2 - y_1)/(x_2 - x_1)](x - x_1)$
which is the point-slope form of the equation for the line through (x_1, y_1) and (x_2, y_2).

Note that the first equation will cause x to take on all real values, because $(x_2 - x_1)$ is not zero. Therefore, all of the points on the line will be traced out.

(b) Use the equations for x and y given in part (a), with $0 \le t \le 1$.

■ Section 1.5 Functions and Logarithms
(pp. 32–40)

Exploration 1   Testing for Inverses Graphically

1. It appears that $(f \circ g)(x) = (g \circ f)(x) = x$, suggesting that f and g may be inverses of each other.

    (a) f and g:

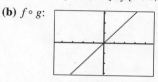

$[-4.7, 4.7]$ by $[-3.1, 3.1]$

    (b) $f \circ g$:

$[-4.7, 4.7]$ by $[-3.1, 3.1]$

    (c) $g \circ f$:

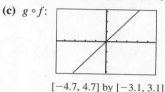

$[-4.7, 4.7]$ by $[-3.1, 3.1]$

2. It appears that $f \circ g = g \circ f = g$, suggesting that f may be the identity function.

    (a) f and g:

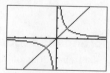

$[-4.7, 4.7]$ by $[-3.1, 3.1]$

    (b) $f \circ g$:

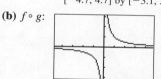

$[-4.7, 4.7]$ by $[-3.1, 3.1]$

    (c) $g \circ f$:

$[-4.7, 4.7]$ by $[-3.1, 3.1]$

3. It appears that $(f \circ g)(x) = (g \circ f)(x) = x$, suggesting that f and g may be inverses of each other.

    (a) f and g:

$[-4.7, 4.7]$ by $[-3.1, 3.1]$

    (b) $f \circ g$:

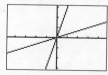

$[-4.7, 4.7]$ by $[-3.1, 3.1]$

3. continued

(c) $g \circ f$:

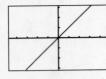

[−4.7, 4.7] by [−3.1, 3.1]

4. It appears that $(f \circ g)(x) = (g \circ f)(x) = x$, suggesting that f and g may be inverse of each other. (Notice that the domain of $f \circ g$ is $(0, \infty)$ and the domain of $g \circ f$ is $(-\infty, \infty)$.)

(a) f and g:

[−4.7, 4.7] by [−3.1, 3.1]

(b) $f \circ g$:

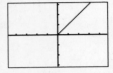

[−4.7, 4.7] by [−3.1, 3.1]

(c) $g \circ f$:

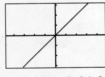

[−4.7, 4.7] by [−3.1, 3.1]

Exploration 2   Supporting the Product Rule

1. They appear to be vertical translations of each other.

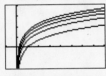

[−1, 8] by [−2, 4]

2. This graph suggests that each difference $(y_3 = y_1 - y_2)$ is a constant.

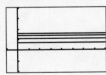

[−1, 8] by [−2, 4]

3. $y_3 = y_1 - y_2 = \ln(ax) - \ln x = \ln a + \ln x - \ln x = \ln a$
Thus, the difference $y_3 = y_1 - y_2$ is the constant $\ln a$.

Quick Review 1.5

1. $(f \circ g)(1) = f(g(1)) = f(2) = 1$

2. $(g \circ f)(-7) = g(f(-7)) = g(-2) = 5$

3. $(f \circ g)(x) = f(g(x)) = f(x^2 + 1) = \sqrt[3]{(x^2 + 1) - 1}$
$= \sqrt[3]{x^2} = x^{2/3}$

4. $(g \circ f)(x) = g(f(x)) = g(\sqrt[3]{x - 1})$
$= (\sqrt[3]{x - 1})^2 + 1$
$= (x - 1)^{2/3} + 1$

5. Substituting t for x, one possible answer is:
$$x = t, \ y = \frac{1}{t - 1}, \ t \geq 2.$$

6. Substituting t for x, one possible answer is:
$x = t, y = t, t < -3.$

7.

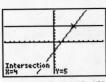

[−10, 10] by [−10, 10]

(4, 5)

8.

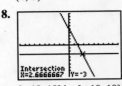

[−10, 10] by [−10, 10]

$\left(\dfrac{8}{3}, -3\right) \approx (2.67, -3)$

9. (a)

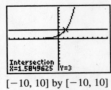

[−10, 10] by [−10, 10]

(1.58, 3)

(b) No points of intersection, since $2^x > 0$ for all values of x.

10. (a)

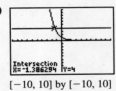

[−10, 10] by [−10, 10]

(−1.39, 4)

(b) No points of intersection, since $e^{-x} > 0$ for all values of x.

Section 1.5 Exercises

1. No, since (for example) the horizontal line $y = 2$ intersects the graph twice.

2. Yes, since each horizontal line intersects the graph only once.

3. Yes, since each horizontal line intersects the graph at most once.

4. No, since (for example) the horizontal line $y = 0.5$ intersects the graph twice.

5. Yes, since each horizontal line intersects the graph only once.

6. No, since (for example) the horizontal line $y = 2$ intersects the graph at more than one point.

7.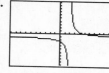

[−10, 10] by [−10, 10]

Yes, the function is one-to-one since each horizontal line intersects the graph at most once, so it has an inverse function.

8.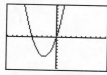

[−10, 10] by [−10, 10]

No, the function is not one-to-one since (for example) the horizontal line $y = 0$ intersects the graph twice, so it does not have an inverse function.

9.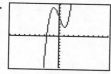

[−10, 10] by [−10, 10]

No, the function is not one-to-one since (for example) the horizontal line $y = 5$ intersects the graph more than once, so it does not have an inverse function.

10.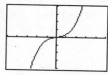

[−5, 5] by [−20, 20]

Yes, the function is one-to-one since each horizontal line intersects the graph only once, so it has an inverse function.

11.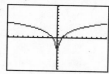

[−10, 10] by [−10, 10]

No, the function is not one-to-one since each horizontal line intersects the graph twice, so it does not have an inverse function.

12.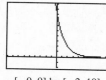

[−9, 9] by [−2, 10]

Yes, the function is one-to-one since each horizontal line intersects the graph at most once, so it has an inverse function.

13. $y = 2x + 3$

$y - 3 = 2x$

$\dfrac{y - 3}{2} = x$

Interchange x and y.

$\dfrac{x - 3}{2} = y$

$f^{-1}(x) = \dfrac{x - 3}{2}$.

Verify.

$$(f \circ f^{-1})(x) = f\left(\dfrac{x - 3}{2}\right)$$
$$= 2\left(\dfrac{x - 3}{2}\right) + 3$$
$$= (x - 3) + 3$$
$$= x$$

$$(f^{-1} \circ f)(x) = f^{-1}(2x + 3)$$
$$= \dfrac{(2x + 3) - 3}{2}$$
$$= \dfrac{2x}{2}$$
$$= x$$

14. $y = 5 - 4x$

$4x = 5 - y$

$x = \dfrac{5 - y}{4}$

Interchange x and y.

$y = \dfrac{5 - x}{4}$

$f^{-1}(x) = \dfrac{5 - x}{4}$

Verify.

$$(f \circ f^{-1})(x) = f\left(\dfrac{5 - x}{4}\right) = 5 - 4\left(\dfrac{5 - x}{4}\right)$$
$$= 5 - (5 - x)$$
$$= x$$

$$(f^{-1} \circ f)(x) = f^{-1}(5 - 4x)$$
$$= \dfrac{5 - (5 - 4x)}{4}$$
$$= \dfrac{4x}{4}$$
$$= x$$

15. $y = x^3 - 1$

$y + 1 = x^3$

$(y + 1)^{1/3} = x$

Interchange x and y.

$(x + 1)^{1/3} = y$

$f^{-1}(x) = (x + 1)^{1/3}$ or $\sqrt[3]{x + 1}$

Verify.

$$(f \circ f^{-1})(x) = f(\sqrt[3]{x + 1})$$
$$= (\sqrt[3]{x + 1})^3 - 1 = (x + 1) - 1 = x$$

$$(f^{-1} \circ f)(x) = f^{-1}(x^3 - 1)$$
$$= \sqrt[3]{(x^3 - 1) + 1} = \sqrt[3]{x^3} = x$$

16. $y = x^2 + 1$, $x \geq 0$

$y - 1 = x^2$, $x \geq 0$

$\sqrt{y - 1} = x$

Interchange x and y.

$\sqrt{x - 1} = y$

$f^{-1}(x) = \sqrt{x - 1}$ or $(x - 1)^{1/2}$

Verify. For $x \geq 1$ (the domain of f^{-1}),

$(f \circ f^{-1})(x) = f(\sqrt{x - 1})$

$\qquad = (\sqrt{x - 1})^2 + 1$

$\qquad = (x - 1) + 1 = x$

For $x > 0$, (the domain of f),

$(f^{-1} \circ f)(x) = f^{-1}(x^2 + 1)$

$\qquad = \sqrt{(x^2 + 1) - 1}$

$\qquad = \sqrt{x^2} = |x| = x$

17. $y = x^2$, $x \leq 0$

$x = -\sqrt{y}$

Interchange x and y.

$y = -\sqrt{x}$

$f^{-1}(x) = -\sqrt{x}$ or $-x^{1/2}$

Verify.

For $x \geq 0$ (the domain of f^{-1}),

$(f \circ f^{-1})(x) = f(-\sqrt{x}) = (-\sqrt{x})^2 = x$

For $x \leq 0$, (the domain of f),

$(f^{-1} \circ f)(x) = f^{-1}(x^2) = -\sqrt{x^2} = -|x| = x$

18. $y = x^{2/3}$, $x \geq 0$

$y^{3/2} = (x^{2/3})^{3/2}$, $x \geq 0$

$y^{3/2} = x$

Interchange x and y.

$x^{3/2} = y$

$f^{-1}(x) = x^{3/2}$

Verify.

For $x \geq 0$ (the domain of f^{-1}),

$(f \circ f^{-1})(x) = f(x^{3/2}) = (x^{3/2})^{2/3} = x$

for $x \geq 0$, (the domain of f),

$(f^{-1} \circ f)(x) = f^{-1}(x^{2/3}) = (x^{2/3})^{3/2} = |x| = x$

19. $y = -(x - 2)^2$, $x \leq 2$

$(x - 2)^2 = -y$, $x \leq 2$

$x - 2 = -\sqrt{-y}$

$x = 2 - \sqrt{-y}$

Interchange x and y.

$y = 2 - \sqrt{-x}$

$f^{-1}(x) = 2 - \sqrt{-x}$ or $2 - (-x)^{1/2}$

Verify.

For $x \leq 0$ (the domain of f^{-1})

$(f \circ f^{-1})(x) = f(2 - \sqrt{-x})$

$\qquad = -[(2 - \sqrt{-x}) - 2]^2$

$\qquad = -(-\sqrt{-x})^2 = -|x| = x$

For $x \leq 2$ (the domain of f),

$(f^{-1} \circ f)(x) = f^{-1}(-(x - 2)^2)$

$\qquad = 2 - \sqrt{(x - 2)^2}$

$\qquad = 2 - |x - 2| = 2 + (x - 2) = x$

20. $y = (x^2 + 2x + 1)$, $x \geq -1$

$y = (x + 1)^2$, $x \geq -1$

$\sqrt{y} = x + 1$

$\sqrt{y} - 1 = x$

Interchange x and y.

$\sqrt{x} - 1 = y$

$f^{-1}(x) = \sqrt{x} - 1$ or $x^{1/2} - 1$

Verify.

For $x \geq 0$ (the domain of f^{-1}),

$(f \circ f^{-1})(x) = f(\sqrt{x} - 1)$

$\qquad = [(\sqrt{x} - 1)^2 + 2(\sqrt{x} - 1) + 1]$

$\qquad = (\sqrt{x})^2 - 2\sqrt{x} + 1 + 2\sqrt{x} - 2 + 1$

$\qquad = (\sqrt{x})^2 = x$

For $x \geq -1$ (the domain of f),

$(f^{-1} \circ f)(x) = f^{-1}(x^2 + 2x + 1)$

$\qquad = \sqrt{x^2 + 2x + 1} - 1$

$\qquad = \sqrt{(x + 1)^2} - 1$

$\qquad = |x + 1| - 1$

$\qquad = (x + 1) - 1 = x$

21. $y = \frac{1}{x^2}$, $x > 0$

$x^2 = \frac{1}{y}$, $x > 0$

$x = \sqrt{\frac{1}{y}} = \frac{1}{\sqrt{y}}$

Interchange x and y.

$y = \frac{1}{\sqrt{x}}$

$f^{-1}(x) = \frac{1}{\sqrt{x}}$ or $\frac{1}{x^{1/2}}$

Verify.

For $x > 0$ (the domain of f^{-1}),

$(f \circ f^{-1})(x) = f\left(\frac{1}{\sqrt{x}}\right) = \frac{1}{(1/\sqrt{x})^2} = x$

For $x > 0$ (the domain of f),

$(f^{-1} \circ f)(x) = f^{-1}\left(\frac{1}{x^2}\right) = \frac{1}{\sqrt{1/x^2}} = \sqrt{x^2} = |x| = x$

22. $y = \frac{1}{x^3}$

$x^3 = \frac{1}{y}$

$x = \sqrt[3]{\frac{1}{y}} = \frac{1}{\sqrt[3]{y}}$

Interchange x and y.

$y = \frac{1}{\sqrt[3]{x}}$

$f^{-1}(x) = \frac{1}{\sqrt[3]{x}}$ or $\frac{1}{x^{1/3}}$

Verify.

$(f \circ f^{-1})(x) = f\left(\frac{1}{\sqrt[3]{x}}\right) = \frac{1}{(1/\sqrt[3]{x})^3} = x$

$(f^{-1} \circ f)(x) = f^{-1}\left(\frac{1}{x^3}\right) = \frac{1}{\sqrt[3]{1/x^3}} = x$

23. $y = \dfrac{2x + 1}{x + 3}$

$xy + 3y = 2x + 1$

$xy - 2x = 1 - 3y$

$(y - 2)x = 1 - 3y$

$x = \dfrac{1 - 3y}{y - 2}$

Interchange x and y.

$y = \dfrac{1 - 3x}{x - 2}$

$f^{-1}(x) = \dfrac{1 - 3x}{x - 2}$

Verify.

$(f \circ f^{-1})(x) = f\left(\dfrac{1 - 3x}{x - 2}\right)$

$= \dfrac{2\left(\dfrac{1 - 3x}{x - 2}\right) + 1}{\dfrac{1 - 3x}{x - 2} + 3}$

$= \dfrac{2(1 - 3x) + (x - 2)}{(1 - 3x) + 3(x - 2)}$

$= \dfrac{-5x}{-5} = x$

$(f^{-1} \circ f)(x) = f^{-1}\left(\dfrac{2x + 1}{x + 3}\right)$

$= \dfrac{1 - 3\left(\dfrac{2x + 1}{x + 3}\right)}{\dfrac{2x + 1}{x + 3} - 2}$

$= \dfrac{(x + 3) - 3(2x + 1)}{(2x + 1) - 2(x + 3)}$

$= \dfrac{-5x}{-5} = x$

24. $y = \dfrac{x + 3}{x - 2}$

$xy - 2y = x + 3$

$xy - x = 2y + 3$

$x(y - 1) = 2y + 3$

$x = \dfrac{2y + 3}{y - 1}$

Interchange x and y.

$y = \dfrac{2x + 3}{x - 1}$

$f^{-1}(x) = \dfrac{2x + 3}{x - 1}$

Verify.

$(f \circ f^{-1})(x) = f\left(\dfrac{2x + 3}{x - 1}\right)$

$= \dfrac{\dfrac{2x + 3}{x - 1} + 3}{\dfrac{2x + 3}{x - 1} - 2}$

$= \dfrac{(2x + 3) + 3(x - 1)}{(2x + 3) - 2(x - 1)}$

$= \dfrac{5x}{5} = x$

$(f^{-1} \circ f)(x) = f^{-1}\left(\dfrac{x + 3}{x - 2}\right)$

$= \dfrac{2\left(\dfrac{x + 3}{x - 2}\right) + 3}{\dfrac{x + 3}{x - 2} - 1}$

$= \dfrac{2(x + 3) + 3(x - 2)}{(x + 3) - (x - 2)}$

$= \dfrac{5x}{5} = x$

25. Graph of f: $x_1 = t$, $y_1 = e^t$

Graph of f^{-1}: $x_2 = e^t$, $y_2 = t$

Graph of $y = x$: $x_3 = t$, $y_3 = t$

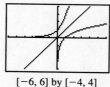

$[-6, 6]$ by $[-4, 4]$

26. Graph of f: $x_1 = t$, $y_1 = 3^t$

Graph of f^{-1}: $x_2 = 3^t$, $y_2 = t$

Graph of $y = x$: $x_3 = t$, $y_3 = t$

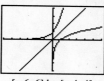

$[-6, 6]$ by $[-4, 4]$

27. Graph of f: $x_1 = t$, $y_1 = 2^{-t}$
Graph of f^{-1}: $x_2 = 2^{-t}$, $y_2 = t$
Graph of $y = x$: $x_3 = t$, $y_3 = t$

$[-4.5, 4.5]$ by $[-3, 3]$

28. Graph of f: $x_1 = t$, $y_1 = 3^{-t}$
Graph of f^{-1}: $x_2 = 3^{-t}$, $y_2 = t$
Graph of $y = x$: $x_3 = t$, $y_3 = t$

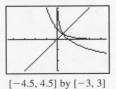

$[-4.5, 4.5]$ by $[-3, 3]$

29. Graph of f: $x_1 = t$, $y_1 = \ln t$
Graph of f^{-1}: $x_2 = \ln t$, $y_2 = t$
Graph of $y = x$: $x_3 = t$, $y_3 = t$

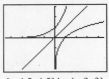

$[-4.5, 4.5]$ by $[-3, 3]$

30. Graph of f: $x_1 = t$, $y_1 = \log t$
Graph of f^{-1}: $x_2 = \log t$, $y_2 = t$
Graph of $y = x$: $x_3 = t$, $y_3 = t$

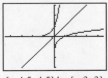

$[-4.5, 4.5]$ by $[-3, 3]$

31. Graph of f: $x_1 = t$, $y_1 = \sin^{-1} t$
Graph of f^{-1}: $x_2 = \sin^{-1} t$, $y_2 = t$
Graph of $y = x$: $x_3 = t$, $y_3 = t$

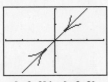

$[-3, 3]$ by $[-2, 2]$

32. Graph of f: $x_1 = t$, $y_1 = \tan^{-1} t$
Graph of f^{-1}: $x_2 = \tan^{-1} t$, $y_2 = t$
Graph of $y = x$: $x_3 = t$, $y_3 = t$

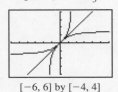

$[-6, 6]$ by $[-4, 4]$

33.

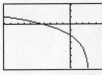

$[-10, 5]$ by $[-7, 3]$
Domain: $(-\infty, 3)$
Range: $(-\infty, \infty)$

34.

$[-5, 10]$ by $[-5, 5]$
Domain: $(-2, \infty)$
Range: $(-\infty, \infty)$

35.

$[-3, 6]$ by $[-2, 4]$
Domain: $(-1, \infty)$
Range: $(-\infty, \infty)$

36.

$[-2, 10]$ by $[-2, 4]$
Domain: $(4, \infty)$
Range: $(-\infty, \infty)$

37. $(1.045)^t = 2$
$\ln(1.045)^t = \ln 2$
$t \ln 1.045 = \ln 2$
$t = \dfrac{\ln 2}{\ln 1.045} \approx 15.75$
Graphical support:

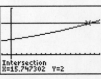

Intersection
X=15.747302 Y=2
$[-2, 18]$ by $[-1, 3]$

38. $e^{0.05t} = 3$
$\ln e^{0.05t} = \ln 3$
$0.05t = \ln 3$
$t = \dfrac{\ln 3}{0.05} = 20 \ln 3 \approx 21.97$
Graphical support:

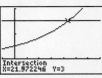

Intersection
X=21.972246 Y=3
$[-5, 35]$ by $[-1, 4]$

39. $e^x + e^{-x} = 3$

$e^x - 3 + e^{-x} = 0$

$e^x(e^x - 3 + e^{-x}) = e^x(0)$

$(e^x)^2 - 3e^x + 1 = 0$

$e^x = \dfrac{3 \pm \sqrt{(-3)^2 - 4(1)(1)}}{2(1)}$

$e^x = \dfrac{3 \pm \sqrt{5}}{2}$

$x = \ln\left(\dfrac{3 \pm \sqrt{5}}{2}\right) \approx -0.96 \text{ or } 0.96$

Graphical support:

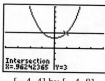

Intersection
X=.96242365   Y=3
[−4, 4] by [−4, 8]

40. $2^x + 2^{-x} = 5$

$2^x - 5 + 2^{-x} = 0$

$2^x(2^x - 5 + 2^{-x}) = 2^x(0)$

$(2^x)^2 - 5(2^x) + 1 = 0$

$2^x = \dfrac{5 \pm \sqrt{(-5)^2 - 4(1)(1)}}{2(1)}$

$2^x = \dfrac{5 \pm \sqrt{21}}{2}$

$x = \log_2\left(\dfrac{5 \pm \sqrt{21}}{2}\right) \approx -2.26 \text{ or } 2.26$

Graphical support:

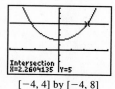

Intersection
X=2.2604135   Y=5
[−4, 4] by [−4, 8]

41. $\ln y = 2t + 4$

$e^{\ln y} = e^{2t + 4}$

$y = e^{2t + 4}$

42. $\ln(y - 1) - \ln 2 = x + \ln x$

$\ln(y - 1) = x + \ln x + \ln 2$

$e^{\ln(y-1)} = e^{x + \ln x + \ln 2}$

$y - 1 = e^x(x)(2)$

$y = 2xe^x + 1$

43. $y = \dfrac{100}{1 + 2^{-x}}$

$1 + 2^{-x} = \dfrac{100}{y}$

$2^{-x} = \dfrac{100}{y} - 1$

$\log_2(2^{-x}) = \log_2\left(\dfrac{100}{y} - 1\right)$

$-x = \log_2\left(\dfrac{100}{y} - 1\right)$

$x = -\log_2\left(\dfrac{100}{y} - 1\right)$

$= -\log_2\left(\dfrac{100 - y}{y}\right)$

$= \log_2\left(\dfrac{y}{100 - y}\right)$

Interchange x and y.

$y = \log_2\left(\dfrac{x}{100 - x}\right)$

$f^{-1}(x) = \log_2\left(\dfrac{x}{100 - x}\right)$

Verify.

$(f \circ f^{-1})(x) = f\left(\log_2 \dfrac{x}{100 - x}\right)$

$= \dfrac{100}{1 + 2^{-\log_2\left(\frac{x}{100 - x}\right)}}$

$= \dfrac{100}{1 + 2^{\log_2\left(\frac{100 - x}{x}\right)}}$

$= \dfrac{100}{1 + \dfrac{100 - x}{x}}$

$= \dfrac{100x}{x + (100 - x)} = \dfrac{100x}{100} = x$

$(f^{-1} \circ f)(x) = f^{-1}\left(\dfrac{100}{1 + 2^{-x}}\right)$

$= \log_2\left(\dfrac{\dfrac{100}{1 + 2^{-x}}}{100 - \dfrac{100}{1 + 2^{-x}}}\right)$

$= \log_2\left(\dfrac{100}{100(1 + 2^{-x}) - 100}\right)$

$= \log_2\left(\dfrac{1}{2^{-x}}\right) = \log_2(2^x) = x$

44. $y = \dfrac{50}{1 + 1.1^{-x}}$

$1 + 1.1^{-x} = \dfrac{50}{y}$

$1.1^{-x} = \dfrac{50}{y} - 1$

$\log_{1.1}(1.1^{-x}) = \log_{1.1}\left(\dfrac{50}{y} - 1\right)$

$-x = \log_{1.1}\left(\dfrac{50}{y} - 1\right)$

$x = -\log_{1.1}\left(\dfrac{50}{y} - 1\right) = -\log_{1.1}\left(\dfrac{50 - y}{y}\right) = \log_{1.1}\left(\dfrac{y}{50 - y}\right)$

Interchange x and y:

$y = \log_{1.1}\left(\dfrac{x}{50 - x}\right)$

$f^{-1}(x) = \log_{1.1}\left(\dfrac{x}{50 - x}\right)$

Verify.

$(f \circ f^{-1})(x) = f\left(\log_{1.1}\left(\dfrac{x}{50 - x}\right)\right)$

$= \dfrac{50}{1 + 1.1^{-\log_{1.1}\left(\frac{x}{50-x}\right)}}$

$= \dfrac{50}{1 + 1.1^{\log_{1.1}\left(\frac{50-x}{x}\right)}}$

$= \dfrac{50}{1 + \dfrac{50 - x}{x}}$

$= \dfrac{50x}{x + (50 - x)} = \dfrac{50x}{50} = x$

$(f^{-1} \circ f)(x) = f^{-1}\left(\dfrac{50}{1 + 1.1^{-x}}\right)$

$= \log_{1.1}\left(\dfrac{\dfrac{50}{1 + 1.1^{-x}}}{50 - \dfrac{50}{1 + 1.1^{-x}}}\right)$

$= \log_{1.1}\left(\dfrac{50}{50(1 + 1.1^{-x}) - 50}\right)$

$= \log_{1.1}\left(\dfrac{1}{1.1^{-x}}\right) = \log_{1.1}(1.1^{x}) = x$

45. (a) $f(f(x)) = \sqrt{1 - (f(x))^2}$

$= \sqrt{1 - (1 - x^2)}$

$= \sqrt{x^2} = |x| = x$, since $x \geq 0$

(b) $f(f(x)) = f\left(\dfrac{1}{x}\right) = \dfrac{1}{1/x} = x$ for all $x \neq 0$

46. (a) Amount $= 8\left(\dfrac{1}{2}\right)^{t/12}$

(b) $8\left(\dfrac{1}{2}\right)^{t/12} = 1$

$\left(\dfrac{1}{2}\right)^{t/12} = \dfrac{1}{8}$

$\left(\dfrac{1}{2}\right)^{t/12} = \left(\dfrac{1}{2}\right)^3$

$\dfrac{t}{12} = 3$

$t = 36$

There will be 1 gram remaining after 36 hours.

47. $500(1.0475)^t = 1000$

$1.0475^t = 2$

$\ln(1.0475^t) = \ln 2$

$t \ln 1.0475 = \ln 2$

$t = \dfrac{\ln 2}{\ln 1.0475} \approx 14.936$

It will take about 14.936 years. (If the interest is paid at the end of each year, it will take 15 years.)

48. $375,000(1.0225)^t = 1,000,000$

$1.0225^t = \dfrac{8}{3}$

$\ln(1.0225^t) = \ln\left(\dfrac{8}{3}\right)$

$t \ln 1.0225 = \ln\left(\dfrac{8}{3}\right)$

$t = \dfrac{\ln(8/3)}{\ln 1.0225} \approx 44.081$

It will take about 44.081 years.

49. (a) $y = -2539.852 + 636.896 \ln x$

(b) When $x = 75$, $y \approx 209.94$. About 209.94 million metric tons were produced.

(c) $-2539.852 + 636.896 \ln x = 400$

$636.896 \ln x = 2939.852$

$\ln x = \dfrac{2939.852}{636.896}$

$x = e^{\frac{2939.852}{636.896}} \approx 101.08$

According to the regression equation, Saudi Arabian oil production will reach 400 million metric tons when $x \approx 101.08$, in about 2001.

50. (a) $y = -590.969 + 152.817 \ln x$

   (b) When $x = 85$, $y \approx 87.94$.
   About 87.94 million metric tons were produced.

   (c) $-590.969 + 152.817 \ln x = 120$

   $$152.817 \ln x = 710.969$$

   $$\ln x = \frac{710.969}{152.817}$$

   $$x = e^{\frac{710.969}{152.817}} \approx 104.84$$

   According to the regression equation, oil production will reach 120 million metric tons when $x \approx 104.84$, in about 2005.

51. (a) Suppose that $f(x_1) = f(x_2)$. Then $mx_1 + b = mx_2 + b$ so $mx_1 = mx_2$. Since $m \neq 0$, this gives $x_1 = x_2$.

   (b) $y = mx + b$

   $$y - b = mx$$

   $$\frac{y - b}{m} = x$$

   Interchange x and y.

   $$\frac{x - b}{m} = y$$

   $$f^{-1}(x) = \frac{x - b}{m}$$

   The slopes are reciprocals.

   (c) If the original functions both have slope m, each of the inverse functions will have slope $\frac{1}{m}$. The graphs of the inverses will be parallel lines with nonzero slope.

   (d) If the original functions have slopes m and $-\frac{1}{m}$, respectively, then the inverse functions will have slopes $\frac{1}{m}$ and $-m$, respectively. Since each of $\frac{1}{m}$ and $-m$ is the negative reciprocal of the other, the graphs of the inverses will be perpendicular lines with nonzero slopes.

52. (a) y_2 is a vertical shift (upward) of y_1, although it's difficult to see that near the vertical asymptote at $x = 0$. One might use "trace" or "table" to verify this.

   (b) Each graph of y_3 is a horizontal line.

   (c) The graphs of y_4 and $y = a$ are the same.

   (d) $e^{y_2 - y_1} = a$, $\ln(e^{y_2 - y_1}) = \ln a$,
   $y_2 - y_1 = \ln a$, $y_1 = y_2 - \ln a = \ln x - \ln a$

53. If the graph of $f(x)$ passes the horizontal line test, so will the graph of $g(x) = -f(x)$ since it's the same graph reflected about the x-axis.
   Alternate answer: If $g(x_1) = g(x_2)$ then
   $-f(x_1) = -f(x_2)$, $f(x_1) = f(x_2)$, and $x_1 = x_2$
   since f is one-to-one.

54. Suppose that $g(x_1) = g(x_2)$. Then $\frac{1}{f(x_1)} = \frac{1}{f(x_2)}$,
   $f(x_1) = f(x_2)$, and x_1 and x_2 since f is one-to-one.

55. (a) The expression $a(b^{c-x}) + d$ is defined for all values of x, so the domain is $(-\infty, \infty)$. Since b^{c-x} attains all positive values, the range is (d, ∞) if $a > 0$ and the range is $(-\infty, d)$ if $a < 0$.

   (b) The expression $a \log_b(x - c) + d$ is defined when $x - c > 0$, so the domain is (c, ∞).
   Since $a \log_b(x - c) + d$ attains every real value for some value of x, the range is $(-\infty, \infty)$.

56. (a) Suppose $f(x_1) = f(x_2)$. Then:

   $$\frac{ax_1 + b}{cx_1 + d} = \frac{ax_2 + b}{cx_2 + d}$$

   $$(ax_1 + b)(cx_2 + d) = (ax_2 + b)(cx_1 + d)$$

   $$acx_1x_2 + adx_1 + bcx_2 + bd$$

   $$\qquad = acx_1x_2 + adx_2 + bcx_1 + bd$$

   $$adx_1 + bcx_2 = adx_2 + bcx_1$$

   $$(ad - bc)x_1 = (ad - bc)x_2$$

   Since $ad - bc \neq 0$, this means that $x_1 = x_2$.

   (b) $y = \frac{ax + b}{cx + d}$

   $$cxy + dy = ax + b$$

   $$(cy - a)x = -dy + b$$

   $$x = \frac{-dy + b}{cy - a}$$

   Interchange x and y:

   $$y = \frac{-dx + b}{cx - a}$$

   $$f^{-1}(x) = \frac{-dx + b}{cx - a}$$

   (c) As $x \to \pm\infty$, $f(x) = \frac{ax + b}{cx + d} \to \frac{a}{c}$, so the horizontal asymptote is $y = \frac{a}{c}$ $(c \neq 0)$. Since $f(x)$ is undefined at $x = -\frac{d}{c}$, the vertical asymptote is $x = -\frac{d}{c}$.

   (d) As $x \to \pm\infty$, $f^{-1}(x) = \frac{-dx + b}{cx - a} \to -\frac{d}{c}$, so the horizontal asymptote is $y = -\frac{d}{c}$ $(c \neq 0)$. Since $f^{-1}(x)$ is undefined at $x = \frac{a}{c}$, the vertical asymptote is $x = \frac{a}{c}$.
   The horizontal asymptote of f becomes the vertical asymptote of f^{-1} and vice versa due to the reflection of the graph about the line $y = x$.

■ Section 1.6 Trigonometric Functions (pp. 41–51)

Exploration 1   Unwrapping Trigonometric Functions

1. (x_1, y_1) is the circle of radius 1 centered at the origin (unit circle). (x_2, y_2) is one period of the graph of the sine function.

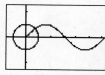

2. The y-values are the same in the interval $0 \le t \le 2\pi$.

3. The y-values are the same in the interval $0 \le t \le 4\pi$.

4. The x_1-values and the y_2-values are the same in each interval.

5. $y_2 = \tan t$:

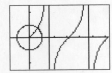

$y_2 = \csc t$:

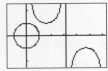

$y_2 = \sec t$:

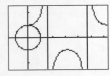

$y_2 = \cot t$:

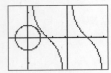

For each value of t, the value of $y_2 = \tan t$ is equal to the ratio $\dfrac{y_1}{x_1}$.

For each value of t, the value of $y_2 = \csc t$ is equal to the ratio $\dfrac{1}{y_1}$.

For each value of t, the value of $y_2 = \sec t$ is equal to the ratio $\dfrac{1}{x_1}$.

For each value of t, the value of $y_2 = \cot t$ is equal to the ratio $\dfrac{x_1}{y_1}$.

Exploration 2   Finding Sines and Cosines

1. The decimal viewing window $[-4.7, 4.7]$ by $[-3.1, 3.1]$ is square on the TI-82/83 and many other calculators. There are many other possibilities.

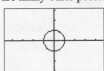

$[-4.7, 4.7]$ by $[-3.1, 3.1]$

2. Using the Ask table setting for the independent variable on the TI-83 we obtain

T	X₁ᴛ	Y₁ᴛ
.5	.87758	.47943
1	.5403	.84147
2	-.4161	.9093
3.5	-.9365	-.3508
6.2	.99654	-.0831

X₁ᴛ**◼**cos(T)

3.

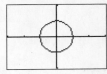

$[-3, 3]$ by $[-2, 2]$

Using trace, $\cos t$ and $\sin t$ are being computed for 0, 15, 30, ... , 360 degrees.

Quick Review 1.6

1. $\dfrac{\pi}{3} \cdot \dfrac{180°}{\pi} = 60°$

2. $-2.5 \cdot \dfrac{180°}{\pi} = \left(-\dfrac{450}{\pi}\right)° \approx -143.24°$

3. $-40° \cdot \dfrac{\pi}{180°} = -\dfrac{2\pi}{9}$

4. $45° \cdot \dfrac{\pi}{180°} = \dfrac{\pi}{4}$

5.

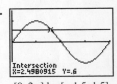

$[0, 2\pi]$ by $[-1.5, 1.5]$

$x \approx 0.6435,\ x \approx 2.4981$

6.

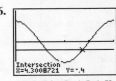

$[0, 2\pi]$ by $[-1.5, 1.5]$

$x \approx 1.9823,\ x \approx 4.3009$

7.

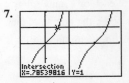

$\left[-\dfrac{\pi}{2}, \dfrac{3\pi}{2}\right]$ by $[-2, 2]$

$x \approx 0.7854 \left(\text{or } \dfrac{\pi}{4}\right),\ x \approx 3.9270 \left(\text{or } \dfrac{5\pi}{4}\right)$

8. $f(-x) = 2(-x)^2 - 3 = 2x^2 - 3 = f(x)$

The graph is symmetric about the y-axis because if a point (a, b) is on the graph, then so is the point $(-a, b)$.

9. $f(-x) = (-x)^3 - 3(-x)$
$= -x^3 + 3x$
$= -(x^3 - 3x) = -f(x)$

The graph is symmetric about the origin because if a point (a, b) is on the graph, then so is the point $(-a, -b)$.

10. $x \ge 0$

Section 1.6 Exercises

1. Arc length $= \left(\dfrac{5\pi}{8}\right)(2) = \dfrac{5\pi}{4}$

2. Radius $= \dfrac{10}{175°\left(\dfrac{\pi}{180°}\right)} = \dfrac{72}{7\pi} \approx 3.274$

3. Angle $= \dfrac{7}{14} = \dfrac{1}{2}$ radian or about 28.65°

4. Angle $= \dfrac{3\pi/2}{6} = \dfrac{\pi}{4}$ radian or 45°

5. (a) The period of $y = \sec x$ is 2π, so the window should have length 4π.
One possible answer: $[0, 4\pi]$ by $[-3, 3]$

   (b) The period of $y = \csc x$ is 2π, so the window should have length 4π.
One possible answer: $[0, 4\pi]$ by $[-3, 3]$

   (c) The period of $y = \cot x$ is π, so the window should have length 2π.
One possible answer: $[0, 2\pi]$ by $[-3, 3]$

6. (a) The period of $y = \sin x$ is 2π, so the window should have length 4π.
One possible answer: $[0, 4\pi]$ by $[-2, 2]$

   (b) The period of $y = \cos x$ is 2π, so the window should have length 4π.
One possible answer: $[0, 4\pi]$ by $[-2, 2]$

   (c) The period of $y = \tan x$ is π, so the window should have length 2π.
One possible answer: $[0, 2\pi]$ by $[-3, 3]$

7. Since $\dfrac{\pi}{6}$ is in the range $\left[-\dfrac{\pi}{2}, \dfrac{\pi}{2}\right]$ of $y = \sin^{-1} x$ and $\sin \dfrac{\pi}{6} = 0.5$, $\sin^{-1}(0.5) = \dfrac{\pi}{6}$ radian or $\dfrac{\pi}{6} \cdot \dfrac{180°}{\pi} = 30°$.

8. Since $-\dfrac{\pi}{4}$ is the range $\left[-\dfrac{\pi}{2}, \dfrac{\pi}{2}\right]$ of $y = \sin^{-1} x$ and $\sin\left(-\dfrac{\pi}{4}\right) = -\dfrac{\sqrt{2}}{2}$, $\sin^{-1}\left(-\dfrac{\sqrt{2}}{2}\right) = -\dfrac{\pi}{4}$ radian or $-\dfrac{\pi}{4} \cdot \dfrac{180°}{\pi} = -45°$.

9. Using a calculator, $\tan^{-1}(-5) \approx -1.3734$ radians or $-78.6901°$.

10. Using a calculator, $\cos^{-1}(0.7) \approx 0.7954$ radian or $45.5730°$.

11. (a) Period $= \dfrac{2\pi}{2} = \pi$
   (b) Amplitude $= 1.5$
   (c) $[-2\pi, 2\pi]$ by $[-2, 2]$

12. (a) Period $= \dfrac{2\pi}{3}$
   (b) Amplitude $= 2$
   (c) $\left[-\dfrac{2\pi}{3}, \dfrac{2\pi}{3}\right]$ by $[-4, 4]$

13. (a) Period $= \dfrac{2\pi}{2} = \pi$
   (b) Amplitude $= 3$
   (c) $[-2\pi, 2\pi]$ by $[-4, 4]$

14. (a) Period $= \dfrac{2\pi}{1/2} = 4\pi$
   (b) Amplitude $= 5$
   (c) $[-4\pi, 4\pi]$ by $[-10, 10]$

15. (a) Period $= \dfrac{2\pi}{\pi/3} = 6$
   (b) Amplitude $= 4$
   (c) $[-3, 3]$ by $[-5, 5]$

16. (a) Period $= \dfrac{2\pi}{\pi} = 2$
   (b) Amplitude $= 1$
   (c) $[-4, 4]$ by $[-2, 2]$

17. (a) Period $= \dfrac{2\pi}{3}$

   (b) Domain: Since $\csc(3x + \pi) = \dfrac{1}{\sin(3x + \pi)}$, we require $3x + \pi \neq k\pi$, or $x \neq \dfrac{(k-1)\pi}{3}$. This requirement is equivalent to $x \neq \dfrac{k\pi}{3}$ for integers k.

   (c) Since $|\csc(3x + \pi)| \geq 1$, the range excludes numbers between $-3 - 2 = -5$ and $3 - 2 = 1$. The range is $(-\infty, -5] \cup [1, \infty)$.

   (d)
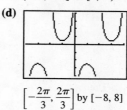
$\left[-\dfrac{2\pi}{3}, \dfrac{2\pi}{3}\right]$ by $[-8, 8]$

18. (a) Period $= \dfrac{2\pi}{4} = \dfrac{\pi}{2}$

   (b) Domain: $(-\infty, \infty)$

   (c) Since $|\sin(4x + \pi)| \leq 1$, the range extends from $-2 + 3 = 1$ to $2 + 3 = 5$. The range is $[1, 5]$.

   (d)
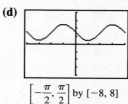
$\left[-\dfrac{\pi}{2}, \dfrac{\pi}{2}\right]$ by $[-8, 8]$

19. (a) Period $= \dfrac{\pi}{3}$

   (b) Domain: We require $3x + \pi \neq \dfrac{k\pi}{2}$ for odd integers k. Therefore, $x \neq \dfrac{(k-2)\pi}{6}$ for odd integers k. This requirement is equivalent to $x \neq \dfrac{k\pi}{6}$ for odd integers k.

   (c) Since the tangent function attains all real values, the range is $(-\infty, \infty)$.

   (d)
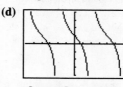
$\left[-\dfrac{\pi}{2}, \dfrac{\pi}{2}\right]$ by $[-8, 8]$

20. (a) Period $= \dfrac{2\pi}{2} = \pi$

   (b) Domain: $(-\infty, \infty)$

   (c) Range: Since $\left|\sin\left(2x + \dfrac{\pi}{3}\right)\right| \leq 1$, the range is $[-2, 2]$.

   (d)
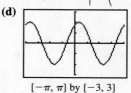
$[-\pi, \pi]$ by $[-3, 3]$

21. Note that $\sqrt{8^2 + 15^2} = 17$.

Since $\sin \theta = \frac{8}{17}$ and $-\frac{\pi}{2} \le \theta \le \frac{\pi}{2}$,

$\cos \theta = \sqrt{1 - \sin^2 \theta} = \sqrt{1 - \left(\frac{8}{17}\right)^2} = \frac{15}{17}$.

Therefore: $\sin \theta = \frac{8}{17}$, $\cos \theta = \frac{15}{17}$, $\tan \theta = \frac{\sin \theta}{\cos \theta} = \frac{8}{15}$,

$\cot \theta = \frac{1}{\tan \theta} = \frac{15}{8}$, $\sec \theta = \frac{1}{\cos \theta} = \frac{17}{15}$, $\csc \theta = \frac{1}{\sin \theta} = \frac{17}{8}$

22. Note that $\sqrt{5^2 + 12^2} = 13$.

Since $\tan \theta = -\frac{5}{12} = \frac{-5/13}{12/13} = \frac{\sin \theta}{\cos \theta}$ and $-\frac{\pi}{2} \le \theta \le \frac{\pi}{2}$, we

have $\sin \theta = -\frac{5}{13}$ and $\cos \theta = \frac{12}{13}$. In summary:

$\sin \theta = -\frac{5}{13}$, $\cos \theta = \frac{12}{13}$, $\tan \theta = -\frac{5}{12}$,

$\cot \theta = \frac{1}{\tan \theta} = -\frac{12}{5}$, $\sec \theta = \frac{1}{\cos \theta} = \frac{13}{12}$,

$\csc \theta = \frac{1}{\sin \theta} = -\frac{13}{5}$

23. Note that $r = \sqrt{(-3)^2 + 4^2} = 5$. Then:

$\sin \theta = \frac{y}{r} = \frac{4}{5}$, $\cos \theta = \frac{x}{r} = -\frac{3}{5}$, $\tan \theta = \frac{y}{x} = -\frac{4}{3}$,

$\cot \theta = \frac{x}{y} = -\frac{3}{4}$, $\sec \theta = \frac{r}{x} = -\frac{5}{3}$, $\csc \theta = \frac{r}{y} = \frac{5}{4}$

24. Note that $r = \sqrt{(-2)^2 + 2^2} = 2\sqrt{2}$. Then:

$\sin \theta = \frac{y}{r} = \frac{2}{2\sqrt{2}} = \frac{1}{\sqrt{2}}$ $\cos \theta = \frac{x}{r} = \frac{-2}{2\sqrt{2}} = -\frac{1}{\sqrt{2}}$,

$\tan \theta = \frac{y}{x} = \frac{2}{-2} = -1$, $\cot \theta = \frac{x}{y} = \frac{-2}{2} = -1$,

$\sec \theta = \frac{r}{x} = \frac{2\sqrt{2}}{-2} = -\sqrt{2}$, $\csc \theta = \frac{r}{y} = \frac{2\sqrt{2}}{2} = \sqrt{2}$

25. The angle $\tan^{-1}(2.5) \approx 1.190$ is the solution to this

equation in the interval $-\frac{\pi}{2} < x < \frac{\pi}{2}$. Another solution in

$0 \le x < 2\pi$ is $\tan^{-1}(2.5) + \pi \approx 4.332$. The solutions are

$x \approx 1.190$ and $x \approx 4.332$.

26. The angle $\cos^{-1}(-0.7) \approx 2.346$ is the solution to this
equation in the interval $0 \le x \le \pi$. Since the cosine
function is even, the value $-\cos^{-1}(-0.7) \approx -2.346$ is also
a solution, so any value of the form $\pm\cos^{-1}(-0.7) + 2k\pi$
is a solution, where k is an integer. In $2\pi \le x < 4\pi$ the
solutions are $x = \cos^{-1}(-0.7) + 2\pi \approx 8.629$ and
$x = -\cos^{-1}(-0.7) + 4\pi \approx 10.220$.

27. This equation is equivalent to $\sin x = \frac{1}{2}$, so the solutions in

the interval $0 \le x < 2\pi$ are $x = \frac{\pi}{6}$ and $x = \frac{5\pi}{6}$.

28. This equation is equivalent to $\cos x = -\frac{1}{3}$, so the solution

in the interval $0 \le x \le \pi$ is $y = \cos^{-1}\left(-\frac{1}{3}\right) \approx 1.911$.

Since the cosine function is even, the solutions in the

interval $-\pi \le x < \pi$ are $x \approx -1.911$ and $x \approx 1.911$.

29. The solutions in the interval $0 \le x < 2\pi$ are $x = \frac{7\pi}{6}$ and

$x = \frac{11\pi}{6}$. Since $y = \sin x$ has period 2π, the solutions are

all of the form $x = \frac{7\pi}{6} + 2k\pi$ or $x = \frac{11\pi}{6} + 2k\pi$, where k

is any integer.

30. The equation is equivalent to $\tan x = \frac{1}{-1} = -1$, so the

solution in the interval $-\frac{\pi}{2} < x < \frac{\pi}{2}$ is

$x = \tan^{-1}(-1) = -\frac{\pi}{4}$. Since the period of $y = \tan x$ is π,

all solutions are of the form $x = -\frac{\pi}{4} + k\pi$, where k is any

integer. This is equivalent to $x = \frac{3\pi}{4} + k\pi$, where k is any

integer.

31. Let $\theta = \cos^{-1}\left(\frac{7}{11}\right)$. Then $0 \le \theta \le \pi$ and $\cos \theta = \frac{7}{11}$, so

$\sin\left(\cos^{-1}\left(\frac{7}{11}\right)\right) = \sin \theta = \sqrt{1 - \cos^2 \theta} = \sqrt{1 - \left(\frac{7}{11}\right)^2}$

$= \frac{\sqrt{72}}{11} = \frac{6\sqrt{2}}{11} \approx 0.771$.

32. Let $\theta = \sin^{-1}\left(\frac{9}{13}\right)$. Then $-\frac{\pi}{2} \le \theta \le \frac{\pi}{2}$ and $\sin \theta = \frac{9}{13}$, so

$\cos \theta = \sqrt{1 - \sin^2 \theta} = \sqrt{1 - \left(\frac{9}{13}\right)^2} = \frac{\sqrt{88}}{13}$. Therefore,

$\tan\left(\sin^{-1}\left(\frac{9}{13}\right)\right) = \tan \theta = \frac{\sin \theta}{\cos \theta} = \frac{9/13}{\sqrt{88}/13} = \frac{9}{\sqrt{88}} \approx 0.959$.

33. (a) Using a graphing calculator with the sinusoidal
regression feature, the equation is
$y = 1.543 \sin(2468.635x - 0.494) + 0.438$.

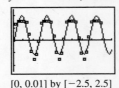

$[0, 0.01]$ by $[-2.5, 2.5]$

(b) The frequency is 2468.635 radians per second, which is

equivalent to $\frac{2468.635}{2\pi} \approx 392.9$ cycles per second (Hz).

The note is a "G."

34. (a) $b = \frac{2\pi}{12} = \frac{\pi}{6}$

(b) It's half of the difference, so $a = \frac{80 - 30}{2} = 25$.

(c) $k = \frac{80 + 30}{2} = 55$

(d) The function should have its minimum at $t = 2$ (when

the temperature is 30°F) and its maximum at $t = 8$

(when the temperature is 80°F). The value of h is

$\frac{2 + 8}{2} = 5$. Equation: $y = 25 \sin\left[\frac{\pi}{6}(x - 5)\right] + 55$

(e)

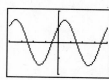

$[-1, 13]$ by $[-10, 100]$

35. (a) Amplitude = 37

(b) Period = $\dfrac{2\pi}{(2\pi/365)} = 365$

(c) Horizontal shift = 101

(d) Vertical shift = 25

36. (a) Highest: $25 + 37 = 62°F$
Lowest: $25 - 37 = -12°F$

(b) Average = $\dfrac{62 + (-12)}{2} = 25°F$

This average is the same as the vertical shift because the average of the highest and lowest values of $y = \sin x$ is 0.

37. (a) $\cot(-x) = \dfrac{\cos(-x)}{\sin(-x)} = \dfrac{\cos(x)}{-\sin(x)} = -\cot(x)$

(b) Assume that f is even and g is odd.
Then $\dfrac{f(-x)}{g(-x)} = \dfrac{f(x)}{-g(x)} = -\dfrac{f(x)}{g(x)}$ so $\dfrac{f}{g}$ is odd. The situation is similar for $\dfrac{g}{f}$.

38. (a) $\csc(-x) = \dfrac{1}{\sin(-x)} = \dfrac{1}{-\sin(x)} = -\csc(x)$

(b) Assume that f is odd.
Then $\dfrac{1}{f(-x)} = \dfrac{1}{-f(x)} = -\dfrac{1}{f(x)}$ so $\dfrac{1}{f}$ is odd.

39. Assume that f is even and g is odd.
Then $f(-x)g(-x) = (f(x))(-g(x)) = -f(x)g(x)$ so (fg) is odd.

40. If (a, b) is the point on the unit circle corresponding to the angle θ, then $(-a, -b)$ is the point on the unit circle corresponding to the angle $(\theta + \pi)$ since it is exactly half way around the circle. This means that both $\tan(\theta)$ and $\tan(\theta + \pi)$ have the same value, $\dfrac{b}{a}$.

41. (a) Using a graphing calculator with the sinusoidal regression feature, the equation is
$y = 3.0014 \sin(0.9996x + 2.0012) + 2.9999$.

(b) $y = 3\sin(x + 2) + 3$

42. (a)

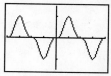

$[-2\pi, 2\pi]$ by $[-2, 2]$

The graph is a sine/cosine type graph, but it is shifted and has an amplitude greater than 1.

(b) Amplitude ≈ 1.414 (that is, $\sqrt{2}$)

Period $= 2\pi$

Horizontal shift $\approx -0.785 \left(\text{that is, } -\dfrac{\pi}{4}\right)$
or 5.498 $\left(\text{that is, } \dfrac{7\pi}{4}\right)$

Vertical shift: 0

(c) $\sin\left(x + \dfrac{\pi}{4}\right) = (\sin x)\left(\cos\dfrac{\pi}{4}\right) + (\cos x)\left(\sin\dfrac{\pi}{4}\right)$
$= (\sin x)\left(\dfrac{1}{\sqrt{2}}\right) + (\cos x)\left(\dfrac{1}{\sqrt{2}}\right)$
$= \dfrac{1}{\sqrt{2}}(\sin x + \cos x)$

Therefore, $\sin x + \cos x = \sqrt{2}\sin\left(x + \dfrac{\pi}{4}\right)$.

43. (a) $\sqrt{2}\sin\left(ax + \dfrac{\pi}{4}\right)$

(b) See part (a).

(c) It works.

(d) $\sin\left(ax + \dfrac{\pi}{4}\right) = (\sin ax)\left(\cos\dfrac{\pi}{4}\right) + (\cos ax)\left(\sin\dfrac{\pi}{4}\right)$
$= (\sin ax)\left(\dfrac{1}{\sqrt{2}}\right) + (\cos ax)\left(\dfrac{1}{\sqrt{2}}\right)$
$= \dfrac{1}{\sqrt{2}}(\sin ax + \cos ax)$
So, $\sin(ax) + \cos(ax) = \sqrt{2}\sin\left(ax + \dfrac{\pi}{4}\right)$.

44. (a) One possible answer:
$y = \sqrt{a^2 + b^2}\sin\left(x + \tan^{-1}\left(\dfrac{b}{a}\right)\right)$

(b) See part (a).

(c) It works.

(d) $\sin\left(x + \tan^{-1}\left(\dfrac{b}{a}\right)\right)$
$= \sin(x)\cos\left(\tan^{-1}\left(\dfrac{b}{a}\right)\right) + \cos(x)\sin\left(\tan^{-1}\left(\dfrac{b}{a}\right)\right)$
$= \sin(x)\left(\dfrac{a}{\sqrt{a^2+b^2}}\right) + \cos(x)\left(\dfrac{b}{\sqrt{a^2+b^2}}\right)$
$= \dfrac{1}{\sqrt{a^2+b^2}}\cdot(a\sin x + b\cos x)$

and multiplying through by the square root gives the desired result. Note that the substitutions
$\cos\left(\tan^{-1}\dfrac{b}{a}\right) = \dfrac{a}{\sqrt{a^2+b^2}}$ and
$\sin\left(\tan^{-1}\dfrac{b}{a}\right) = \dfrac{b}{\sqrt{a^2+b^2}}$ depend on the requirement that a is positive. If a is negative, the formula does not work.

45. Since $\sin x$ has period 2π, $\sin^3(x + 2\pi) = \sin^3(x)$. This function has period 2π. A graph shows that no smaller number works for the period.

$[-2\pi, 2\pi]$ by $[-1.5, 1.5]$

46. Since $\tan x$ has period π, $|\tan (x + \pi)| = |\tan x|$. This function has period π. A graph shows that no smaller number works for the period.

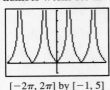

$[-2\pi, 2\pi]$ by $[-1, 5]$

47. The period is $\dfrac{2\pi}{60} = \dfrac{\pi}{30}$. One possible graph:

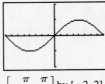

$\left[-\dfrac{\pi}{60}, \dfrac{\pi}{60}\right]$ by $[-2, 2]$

48. The period is $\dfrac{2\pi}{60\pi} = \dfrac{1}{30}$. One possible graph:

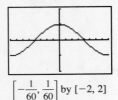

$\left[-\dfrac{1}{60}, \dfrac{1}{60}\right]$ by $[-2, 2]$

■ Chapter 1 Review Exercises
(pp. 52–53)

1. $y = 3(x - 1) + (-6)$
$y = 3x - 9$

2. $y = -\dfrac{1}{2}(x + 1) + 2$
$y = -\dfrac{1}{2}x + \dfrac{3}{2}$

3. $x = 0$

4. $m = \dfrac{-2 - 6}{1 - (-3)} = \dfrac{-8}{4} = -2$
$y = -2(x + 3) + 6$
$y = -2x$

5. $y = 2$

6. $m = \dfrac{5 - 3}{-2 - 3} = \dfrac{2}{-5} = -\dfrac{2}{5}$
$y = -\dfrac{2}{5}(x - 3) + 3$
$y = -\dfrac{2}{5} + \dfrac{21}{5}$

7. $y = -3x + 3$

8. Since $2x - y = -2$ is equivalent to $y = 2x + 2$, the slope of the given line (and hence the slope of the desired line) is 2.
$y = 2(x - 3) + 1$
$y = 2x - 5$

9. Since $4x + 3y = 12$ is equivalent to $y = -\dfrac{4}{3}x + 4$, the slope of the given line (and hence the slope of the desired line) is $-\dfrac{4}{3}$.
$y = -\dfrac{4}{3}(x - 4) - 12$
$y = -\dfrac{4}{3}x - \dfrac{20}{3}$

10. Since $3x - 5y = 1$ is equivalent to $y = \dfrac{3}{5}x - \dfrac{1}{5}$, the slope of the given line is $\dfrac{3}{5}$ and the slope of the perpendicular line is $-\dfrac{5}{3}$.
$y = -\dfrac{5}{3}(x + 2) - 3$
$y = -\dfrac{5}{3}x - \dfrac{19}{3}$

11. Since $\dfrac{1}{2}x + \dfrac{1}{3}y = 1$ is equivalent to $y = -\dfrac{3}{2}x + 3$, the slope of the given line is $-\dfrac{3}{2}$ and the slope of the perpendicular line is $\dfrac{2}{3}$.
$y = \dfrac{2}{3}(x + 1) + 2$
$y = \dfrac{2}{3}x + \dfrac{8}{3}$

12. The line passes through $(0, -5)$ and $(3, 0)$
$m = \dfrac{0 - (-5)}{3 - 0} = \dfrac{5}{3}$
$y = \dfrac{5}{3}x - 5$

13. $m = \dfrac{2 - 4}{2 - (-2)} = \dfrac{-2}{4} = -\dfrac{1}{2}$
$f(x) = -\dfrac{1}{2}(x + 2) + 4$
$f(x) = -\dfrac{1}{2}x + 3$
Check: $f(4) = -\dfrac{1}{2}(4) + 3 = 1$, as expected.

14. The line passes through $(4, -2)$ and $(-3, 0)$.
$m = \dfrac{0 - (-2)}{-3 - 4} = \dfrac{2}{-7} = -\dfrac{2}{7}$
$y = -\dfrac{2}{7}(x - 4) - 2$
$y = -\dfrac{2}{7}x - \dfrac{6}{7}$

15.

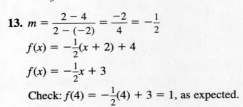

$[-3, 3]$ by $[-2, 2]$
Symmetric about the origin.

16.

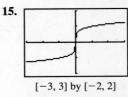

$[-3, 3]$ by $[-2, 2]$
Symmetric about the y-axis.

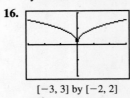

17.

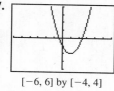

[−6, 6] by [−4, 4]

Neither

18.

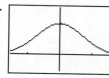

[−1.5, 1.5] by [−0.5, 1.5]

Symmetric about the y-axis.

19. $y(-x) = (-x)^2 + 1 = x^2 + 1 = y(x)$
Even

20. $y(-x) = (-x)^5 - (-x)^3 - (-x) = -x^5 + x^3 + x = -y(x)$
Odd

21. $y(-x) = 1 - \cos(-x) = 1 - \cos x = y(x)$
Even

22. $y(-x) = \sec(-x)\tan(-x)$

$\quad = \dfrac{\sin(-x)}{\cos^2(-x)} = \dfrac{-\sin x}{\cos^2 x}$

$\quad = -\sec x \tan x = -y(x)$

Odd

23. $y(-x) = \dfrac{(-x)^4 + 1}{(-x)^3 - 2(-x)} = \dfrac{x^4 + 1}{-x^3 + 2x} = -\dfrac{x^4 + 1}{x^3 - 2x} = -y(x)$
Odd

24. $y(-x) = 1 - \sin(-x) = 1 + \sin x$
Neither even nor odd

25. $y(-x) = -x + \cos(-x) = -x + \cos x$
Neither even nor odd

26. $y(-x) = \sqrt{(-x)^4 - 1} = \sqrt{x^4 - 1}$
Even

27. (a) The function is defined for all values of x, so the domain is $(-\infty, \infty)$.

  (b) Since $|x|$ attains all nonnegative values, the range is $[-2, \infty)$.

  (c)

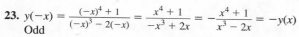

[−10, 10] by [−10, 10]

28. (a) Since the square root requires $1 - x \geq 0$, the domain is $(-\infty, 1]$.

  (b) Since $\sqrt{1 - x}$ attains all nonnegative values, the range is $[-2, \infty)$.

  (c)

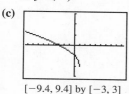

[−9.4, 9.4] by [−3, 3]

29. (a) Since the square root requires $16 - x^2 \geq 0$, the domain is $[-4, 4]$.

  (b) For values of x in the domain, $0 \leq 16 - x^2 \leq 16$, so $0 \leq \sqrt{16 - x^2} \leq 4$. The range is $[0, 4]$.

  (c)

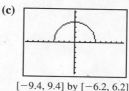

[−9.4, 9.4] by [−6.2, 6.2]

30. (a) The function is defined for all values of x, so the domain is $(-\infty, \infty)$.

  (b) Since 3^{2-x} attains all positive values, the range is $(1, \infty)$.

  (c)

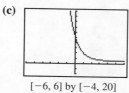

[−6, 6] by [−4, 20]

31. (a) The function is defined for all values of x, so the domain is $(-\infty, \infty)$.

  (b) Since $2e^{-x}$ attains all positive values, the range is $(-3, \infty)$.

  (c)

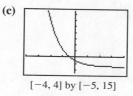

[−4, 4] by [−5, 15]

32. (a) The function is equivalent to $y = \tan 2x$, so we require $2x \neq \dfrac{k\pi}{2}$ for odd integers k. The domain is given by $x \neq \dfrac{k\pi}{4}$ for odd integers k.

  (b) Since the tangent function attains all values, the range is $(-\infty, \infty)$.

  (c)

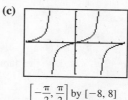

$\left[-\dfrac{\pi}{2}, \dfrac{\pi}{2}\right]$ by [−8, 8]

33. (a) The function is defined for all values of x, so the domain is $(-\infty, \infty)$.

  (b) The sine function attains values from -1 to 1, so $-2 \leq 2\sin(3x + \pi) \leq 2$, and hence $-3 \leq 2\sin(3x + \pi) - 1 \leq 1$. The range is $[-3, 1]$.

  (c)

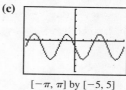

[−π, π] by [−5, 5]

34. (a) The function is defined for all values of x, so the domain is $(-\infty, \infty)$.

(b) The function is equivalent to $y = \sqrt[5]{x^2}$, which attains all nonnegative values. The range is $[0, \infty)$.

(c)

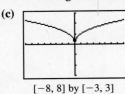

$[-8, 8]$ by $[-3, 3]$

35. (a) The logarithm requires $x - 3 > 0$, so the domain is $(3, \infty)$.

(b) The logarithm attains all real values, so the range is $(-\infty, \infty)$.

(c)

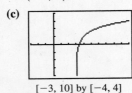

$[-3, 10]$ by $[-4, 4]$

36. (a) The function is defined for all values of x, so the domain is $(-\infty, \infty)$.

(b) The cube root attains all real values, so the range is $(-\infty, \infty)$.

(c)

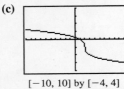

$[-10, 10]$ by $[-4, 4]$

37. (a) The function is defined for $-4 \le x \le 4$, so the domain is $[-4, 4]$.

(b) The function is equivalent to $y = \sqrt{|x|}$, $-4 \le x \le 4$, which attains values from 0 to 2 for x in the domain. The range is $[0, 2]$.

(c)

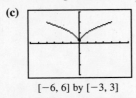

$[-6, 6]$ by $[-3, 3]$

38. (a) The function is defined for $-2 \le x \le 2$, so the domain is $[-2, 2]$.

(b) See the graph in part (c). The range is $[-1, 1]$.

(c)

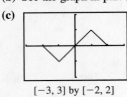

$[-3, 3]$ by $[-2, 2]$

39. First piece: Line through $(0, 1)$ and $(1, 0)$

$$m = \frac{0 - 1}{1 - 0} = \frac{-1}{1} = -1$$

$$y = -x + 1 \text{ or } 1 - x$$

Second piece:
Line through $(1, 1)$ and $(2, 0)$

$$m = \frac{0 - 1}{2 - 1} = \frac{-1}{1} = -1$$

$$y = -(x - 1) + 1$$

$$y = -x + 2 \text{ or } 2 - x$$

$$f(x) = \begin{cases} 1 - x, & 0 \le x < 1 \\ 2 - x, & 1 \le x \le 2 \end{cases}$$

40. First piece: Line through $(0, 0)$ and $(2, 5)$

$$m = \frac{5 - 0}{2 - 0} = \frac{5}{2}$$

$$y = \frac{5}{2}x$$

Second piece: Line through $(2, 5)$ and $(4, 0)$

$$m = \frac{0 - 5}{4 - 2} = \frac{-5}{2} = -\frac{5}{2}$$

$$y = -\frac{5}{2}(x - 2) + 5$$

$$y = -\frac{5}{2}x + 10 \text{ or } 10 - \frac{5x}{2}$$

$$f(x) = \begin{cases} \dfrac{5x}{2}, & 0 \le x < 2 \\ 10 - \dfrac{5x}{2}, & 2 \le x \le 4 \end{cases}$$

(Note: $x = 2$ can be included on either piece.)

41. (a) $(f \circ g)(-1) = f(g(-1)) = f\left(\dfrac{1}{\sqrt{-1 + 2}}\right) = f(1) = \dfrac{1}{1} = 1$

(b) $(g \circ f)(2) = g(f(2)) = g\left(\dfrac{1}{2}\right) = \dfrac{1}{\sqrt{1/2 + 2}} = \dfrac{1}{\sqrt{2.5}}$ or $\sqrt{\dfrac{2}{5}}$

(c) $(f \circ f)(x) = f(f(x)) = f\left(\dfrac{1}{x}\right) = \dfrac{1}{1/x} = x,\ x \ne 0$

(d) $(g \circ g)(x) = g(g(x)) = g\left(\dfrac{1}{\sqrt{x + 2}}\right) = \dfrac{1}{\sqrt{1/\sqrt{x + 2} + 2}}$

$$= \dfrac{\sqrt[4]{x + 2}}{\sqrt{1 + 2\sqrt{x + 2}}}$$

42. (a) $(f \circ g)(-1) = f(g(-1))$

$$= f(\sqrt[3]{-1 + 1})$$

$$= f(0) = 2 - 0 = 2$$

(b) $(g \circ f)(2) = g(f(2)) = g(2 - 2) = g(0) = \sqrt[3]{0 + 1} = 1$

(c) $(f \circ f)(x) = f(f(x)) = f(2 - x) = 2 - (2 - x) = x$

(d) $(g \circ g)(x) = g(g(x)) = g(\sqrt[3]{x + 1}) = \sqrt[3]{\sqrt[3]{x + 1} + 1}$

43. (a)
$$(f \circ g)(x) = f(g(x))$$
$$= f(\sqrt{x + 2})$$
$$= 2 - (\sqrt{x + 2})^2$$
$$= -x, \, x \geq -2$$
$$(g \circ f)(x) = g(f(x))$$
$$= g(2 - x^2)$$
$$= \sqrt{(2 - x^2) + 2} = \sqrt{4 - x^2}$$

(b) Domain of $f \circ g$: $[-2, \infty)$
Domain of $g \circ f$: $[-2, 2]$

(c) Range of $f \circ g$: $(-\infty, 2]$
Range of $g \circ f$: $[0, 2]$

44. (a)
$$(f \circ g)(x) = f(g(x))$$
$$= f(\sqrt{1 - x})$$
$$= \sqrt{\sqrt{1 - x}}$$
$$= \sqrt[4]{1 - x}$$
$$(g \circ f)(x) = g(f(x)) = g(\sqrt{x}) = \sqrt{1 - \sqrt{x}}$$

(b) Domain of $f \circ g$: $(-\infty, 1]$
Domain of $g \circ f$: $[0, 1]$

(c) Range of $f \circ g$: $[0, \infty)$
Range of $g \circ f$: $[0, 1]$

45. (a)

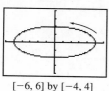

$[-6, 6]$ by $[-4, 4]$

Initial point: (5, 0)
Terminal point: (5, 0)
The ellipse is traced exactly once in a counterclockwise direction starting and ending at the point (5, 0).

(b) Substituting $\cos t = \frac{x}{5}$ and $\sin t = \frac{y}{2}$ in the identity $\cos^2 t + \sin^2 t = 1$ gives the Cartesian equation
$$\left(\frac{x}{5}\right)^2 + \left(\frac{y}{2}\right)^2 = 1.$$
The entire ellipse is traced by the curve.

46. (a)

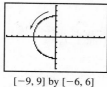

$[-9, 9]$ by $[-6, 6]$

Initial point: (0, 4)
Terminal point: None (since the endpoint $\frac{3\pi}{2}$ is not included in the t-interval)
The semicircle is traced in a counterclockwise direction starting at (0, 4) and extending to, but not including, (0, −4).

(b) Substituting $\cos t = \frac{x}{4}$ and $\sin t = \frac{y}{4}$ in the identity $\cos^2 t + \sin^2 t = 1$ gives the Cartesian equation $\left(\frac{x}{4}\right)^2 + \left(\frac{y}{4}\right)^2 = 1$, or $x^2 + y^2 = 16$. The left half of the circle is traced by the parametrized curve.

47. (a)

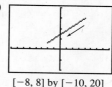

$[-8, 8]$ by $[-10, 20]$

Initial point: (4, 15)
Terminal point: (−2, 3)
The line segment is traced from right to left starting at (4, 15) and ending at (−2, 3).

(b) Substituting $t = 2 - x$ into $y = 11 - 2t$ gives the Cartesian equation $y = 11 - 2(2 - x)$, or $y = 2x + 7$. The part of the line from (4, 15) to (−2, 3) is traced by the parametrized curve.

48. (a)

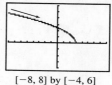

$[-8, 8]$ by $[-4, 6]$

Initial point: None
Terminal point: (3, 0)
The curve is traced from left to right ending at the point (3, 0).

(b) Substituting $t = x - 1$ into $y = \sqrt{4 - 2t}$ gives the Cartesian equation $y = \sqrt{4 - 2(x - 1)}$, or $y = \sqrt{6 - 2x}$. The entire curve is traced by the parametrized curve.

49. (a) For simplicity, we assume that x and y are linear functions of t, and that the point (x, y) starts at $(-2, 5)$ for $t = 0$ and ends at $(4, 3)$ for $t = 1$. Then $x = f(t)$, where $f(0) = -2$ and $f(1) = 4$. Since
$$\text{slope} = \frac{\Delta x}{\Delta t} = \frac{4 - (-2)}{1 - 0} = 6,$$
$$x = f(t) = 6t - 2 = -2 + 6t.$$
Also, $y = g(t)$, where $g(0) = 5$ and $g(1) = 3$. Since
$$\text{slope} = \frac{\Delta y}{\Delta t} = \frac{3 - 5}{1 - 0} = -2,$$
$$y = g(t) = -2t + 5 = 5 - 2t.$$
One possible parametrization is:
$$x = -2 + 6t, \, y = 5 - 2t, \, 0 \leq t \leq 1$$

50. For simplicity, we assume that x and y are linear functions of t and that the point (x, y) passes through $(-3, -2)$ for $t = 0$ and $(4, -1)$ for $t = 1$. Then $x = f(t)$, where $f(0) = -3$ and $f(1) = 4$. Since

$$\text{slope} = \frac{\Delta x}{\Delta t} = \frac{4 - (-3)}{1 - 0} = 7,$$

$$x = f(t) = 7t - 3 = -3 + 7t.$$

Also, $y = g(t)$, where $g(0) = -2$ and $g(1) = -1$. Since

$$\text{slope} = \frac{\Delta y}{\Delta t} = \frac{-1 - (-2)}{1 - 0} = 1$$

$$y = g(t) = t - 2 = -2 + t.$$

One possible parametrization is:
$$x = -3 + 7t, \, y = -2 + t, \, -\infty < t < \infty.$$

51. For simplicity, we assume that x and y are linear functions of t and that the point (x, y) starts at $(2, 5)$ for $t = 0$ and passes through $(-1, 0)$ for $t = 1$. Then $x = f(t)$, where $f(0) = 2$ and $f(1) = -1$. Since

$$\text{slope} = \frac{\Delta x}{\Delta t} = \frac{-1 - 2}{1 - 0} = -3, \, x = f(t) = -3t + 2 = 2 - 3t.$$

Also, $y = g(t)$, where $g(0) = 5$ and $g(1) = 0$. Since

$$\text{slope} = \frac{\Delta y}{\Delta t} = \frac{0 - 5}{1 - 0} = -5, \, y = g(t) = -5t + 5 = 5 - 5t.$$

One possible parametrization is:
$$x = 2 - 3t, \, y = 5 - 5t, \, t \geq 0.$$

52. One possible parametrization is:
$$x = t, \, y = t(t - 4), \, t \leq 2.$$

53. (a) $y = 2 - 3x$

$$3x = 2 - y$$

$$x = \frac{2 - y}{3}$$

Interchange x and y.

$$y = \frac{2 - x}{3}$$

$$f^{-1}(x) = \frac{2 - x}{3}$$

Verify.

$$(f \circ f^{-1})(x) = f(f^{-1}(x))$$

$$= f\left(\frac{2 - x}{3}\right)$$

$$= 2 - 3\left(\frac{2 - x}{3}\right)$$

$$= 2 - (2 - x) = x$$

$$(f^{-1} \circ f)(x) = f^{-1}(f(x))$$

$$= f^{-1}(2 - 3x)$$

$$= \frac{2 - (2 - 3x)}{3}$$

$$= \frac{3x}{3} = x$$

(b)

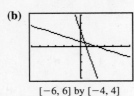

$$[-6, 6] \text{ by } [-4, 4]$$

54. (a) $y = (x + 2)^2, \, x \geq -2$

$$\sqrt{y} = x + 2$$

$$x = \sqrt{y} - 2$$

Interchange x and y.

$$y = \sqrt{x} - 2$$

$$f^{-1}(x) = \sqrt{x} - 2$$

Verify.

For $x \geq 0$ (the domain of f^{-1})

$$(f \circ f^{-1})(x) = f(f^{-1}(x))$$

$$= f(\sqrt{x} - 2)$$

$$= [(\sqrt{x} - 2) + 2]^2$$

$$= (\sqrt{x})^2 = x$$

For $x \geq -2$ (the domain of f),

$$(f^{-1} \circ f)(x) = f^{-1}(f(x))$$

$$= f^{-1}((x + 2)^2)$$

$$= \sqrt{(x + 2)^2} - 2$$

$$= |x + 2| - 2$$

$$= (x + 2) - 2 = x$$

(b)

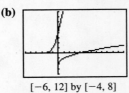

$$[-6, 12] \text{ by } [-4, 8]$$

55. Using a calculator, $\sin^{-1}(0.6) \approx 0.6435$ radians or $36.8699°$.

56. Using a calculator, $\tan^{-1}(-2.3) \approx -1.1607$ radians or $-66.5014°$.

57. Since $\cos \theta = \frac{3}{7}$ and $0 \leq \theta \leq \pi$,

$$\sin \theta = \sqrt{1 - \cos^2 \theta} = \sqrt{1 - \left(\frac{3}{7}\right)^2} = \sqrt{\frac{40}{49}} = \frac{\sqrt{40}}{7}.$$

Therefore,

$$\sin \theta = \frac{\sqrt{40}}{7}, \cos \theta = \frac{3}{7}, \tan \theta = \frac{\sin \theta}{\cos \theta} = \frac{\sqrt{40}}{3},$$

$$\cot \theta = \frac{1}{\tan \theta} = \frac{3}{\sqrt{40}}, \sec \theta = \frac{1}{\cos \theta} = \frac{7}{3},$$

$$\csc \theta = \frac{1}{\sin \theta} = \frac{7}{\sqrt{40}}$$

58. (a) Note that $\sin^{-1}(-0.2) \approx -0.2014$. In $[0, 2\pi)$, the solutions are $x = \pi - \sin^{-1}(-0.2) \approx 3.3430$ and $x = \sin^{-1}(-0.2) + 2\pi \approx 6.0818$.

(b) Since the period of $\sin x$ is 2π, the solutions are $x \approx 3.3430 + 2k\pi$ and $x \approx 6.0818 + 2k\pi$, k any integer.

59. $e^{-0.2x} = 4$

$$\ln e^{-0.2x} = \ln 4$$

$$-0.2x = \ln 4$$

$$x = \frac{\ln 4}{-0.2} = -5 \ln 4$$

60. (a) The given graph is reflected about the y-axis.

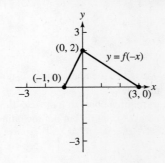

(b) The given graph is reflected about the x-axis.

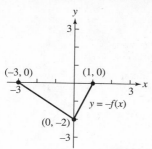

(c) The given graph is shifted left 1 unit, stretched vertically by a factor of 2, reflected about the x-axis, and then shifted upward 1 unit.

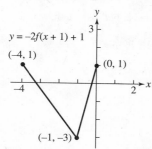

(d) The given graph is shifted right 2 units, stretched vertically by a factor of 3, and then shifted downward 2 units.

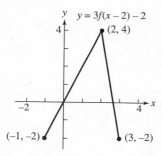

61. (a)

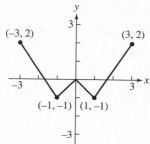

(b)

62. (a) $V = 100,000 - 10,000x, \ 0 \le x \le 10$

(b)
$$V = 55,000$$
$$100,000 - 10,000x = 55,000$$
$$-10,000x = -45,000$$
$$x = 4.5$$
The value is \$55,000 after 4.5 years.

63. (a) $f(0) = 90$ units

(b) $f(2) = 90 - 52 \ln 3 \approx 32.8722$ units

(c)

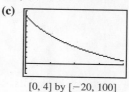

$[0, 4]$ by $[-20, 100]$

64. $1500(1.08)^t = 5000$

$$1.08^t = \frac{5000}{1500} = \frac{10}{3}$$
$$\ln (1.08)^t = \ln \frac{10}{3}$$
$$t \ln 1.08 = \ln \frac{10}{3}$$
$$t = \frac{\ln (10/3)}{\ln 1.08}$$
$$t \approx 15.6439$$

It will take about 15.6439 years. (If the bank only pays interest at the end of the year, it will take 16 years.)

65. (a) $N(t) = 4 \cdot 2^t$

(b) 4 days: $4 \cdot 2^4 = 64$ guppies
1 week: $4 \cdot 2^7 = 512$ guppies

(c)
$$N(t) = 2000$$
$$4 \cdot 2^t = 2000$$
$$2^t = 500$$
$$\ln 2^t = \ln 500$$
$$t \ln 2 = \ln 500$$
$$t = \frac{\ln 500}{\ln 2} \approx 8.9658$$

There will be 2000 guppies after 8.9658 days, or after nearly 9 days.

(d) Because it suggests the number of guppies will continue to double indefinitely and become arbitrarily large, which is impossible due to the finite size of the tank and the oxygen supply in the water.

66. (a) $y = 20.627x + 338.622$

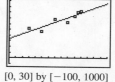

$[0, 30]$ by $[-100, 1000]$

(b) When $x = 30$, $y \approx 957.445$. According to the regression equation, about 957 degrees will be earned.

(c) The slope is 20.627. It represents the approximate annual increase in the number of doctorates earned by Hispanic Americans per year.

67. (a) $y = 14.60175 \cdot 1.00232^x$

(b) Solving $y = 25$ graphically, we obtain $x \approx 232$. According to the regression equation, the population will reach 25 million in the year 2132.

(c) 0.232%

Chapter 2
Limits and Continuity

■ Section 2.1 Rates of Change and Limits
(pp. 55–65)

Quick Review 2.1

1. $f(2) = 2(2^3) - 5(2)^2 + 4 = 0$

2. $f(2) = \dfrac{4(2)^2 - 5}{2^3 + 4} = \dfrac{11}{12}$

3. $f(2) = \sin\left(\pi \cdot \dfrac{2}{2}\right) = \sin\pi = 0$

4. $f(2) = \dfrac{1}{2^2 - 1} = \dfrac{1}{3}$

5. $|x| < 4$
$-4 < x < 4$

6. $|x| < c^2$
$-c^2 < x < c^2$

7. $|x - 2| < 3$
$-3 < x - 2 < 3$
$-1 < x < 5$

8. $|x - c| < d^2$
$-d^2 < x - c < d^2$
$-d^2 + c < x < d^2 + c$

9. $\dfrac{x^2 - 3x - 18}{x + 3} = \dfrac{(x + 3)(x - 6)}{x + 3} = x - 6, \ x \neq -3$

10. $\dfrac{2x^2 - x}{2x^2 + x - 1} = \dfrac{x(2x - 1)}{(2x - 1)(x + 1)} = \dfrac{x}{x + 1}, \ x \neq \dfrac{1}{2}$

Section 2.1 Exercises

1. (a) $\lim\limits_{x \to 3^-} f(x) = 3$

(b) $\lim\limits_{x \to 3^+} f(x) = -2$

(c) $\lim\limits_{x \to 3} f(x)$ does not exist, because the left- and
right-hand limits are not equal.

(d) $f(3) = 1$

2. (a) $\lim\limits_{t \to -4^-} g(t) = 5$

(b) $\lim\limits_{t \to -4^+} g(t) = 2$

(c) $\lim\limits_{t \to -4} g(t)$ does not exist, because the left- and
right-hand limits are not equal.

(d) $g(-4) = 2$

3. (a) $\lim\limits_{h \to 0^-} f(h) = -4$

(b) $\lim\limits_{h \to 0^+} f(h) = -4$

(c) $\lim\limits_{h \to 0} f(h) = -4$

(d) $f(0) = -4$

4. (a) $\lim\limits_{s \to -2^-} p(s) = 3$

(b) $\lim\limits_{s \to -2^+} p(s) = 3$

(c) $\lim\limits_{s \to -2} p(s) = 3$

(d) $p(-2) = 3$

5. (a) $\lim\limits_{x \to 0^-} F(x) = 4$

(b) $\lim\limits_{x \to 0^+} F(x) = -3$

(c) $\lim\limits_{x \to 0} F(x)$ does not exist, because the left- and
right-hand limits are not equal.

(d) $F(0) = 4$

6. (a) $\lim\limits_{x \to 2^-} G(x) = 1$

(b) $\lim\limits_{x \to 2^+} G(x) = 1$

(c) $\lim\limits_{x \to 2} G(x) = 1$

(d) $G(2) = 3$

7. $\lim\limits_{x \to -1/2} 3x^2(2x - 1) = 3\left(-\dfrac{1}{2}\right)^2\left[2\left(-\dfrac{1}{2}\right) - 1\right] = 3\left(\dfrac{1}{4}\right)(-2)$
$= -\dfrac{3}{2}$

Graphical support:

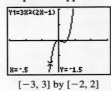

$[-3, 3]$ by $[-2, 2]$

8. $\lim\limits_{x \to -4} (x + 3)^{1998} = (-4 + 3)^{1998} = (-1)^{1998} = 1$

Graphical support:

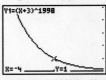

$[-4.001, -3.999]$ by $[0, 5]$

9. $\lim\limits_{x \to 1} (x^3 + 3x^2 - 2x - 17) = (1)^3 + 3(1)^2 - 2(1) - 17$
$= 1 + 3 - 2 - 17 = -15$

Graphical support:

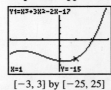

$[-3, 3]$ by $[-25, 25]$

10. $\displaystyle\lim_{y\to 2}\frac{y^2+5y+6}{y+2}=\frac{2^2+5(2)+6}{2+2}=\frac{20}{4}=5$

Graphical support:

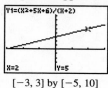

$[-3, 3]$ by $[-5, 10]$

11. $\displaystyle\lim_{y\to -3}\frac{y^2+4y+3}{y^2-3}=\frac{(-3)^2+4(-3)+3}{(-3)^2-3}=\frac{0}{6}=0$

Graphical support:

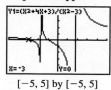

$[-5, 5]$ by $[-5, 5]$

12. $\displaystyle\lim_{x\to 1/2}\operatorname{int}x=\operatorname{int}\frac{1}{2}=0$

Note that substitution cannot always be used to find limits of the int function. Its use here can be justified by the Sandwich Theorem, using $g(x)=h(x)=0$ on the interval $(0, 1)$.

Graphical support:

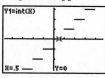

$[-4.7, 4.7]$ by $[-3.1, 3.1]$

13. $\displaystyle\lim_{x\to -2}(x-6)^{2/3}=(-2-6)^{2/3}=\sqrt[3]{(-8)^2}=\sqrt[3]{64}=4$

Graphical support:

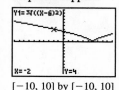

$[-10, 10]$ by $[-10, 10]$

14. $\displaystyle\lim_{x\to 2}\sqrt{x+3}=\sqrt{2+3}=\sqrt{5}$

Graphical support:

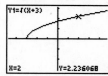

$[-4.7, 4.7]$ by $[-3.1, 3.1]$

15. $\displaystyle\lim_{x\to 0}(e^x\cos x)=e^0\cos 0=1\cdot 1=1$

Graphical support:

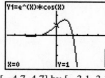

$[-4.7, 4.7]$ by $[-3.1, 3.1]$

16. $\displaystyle\lim_{x\to \pi/2}\ln(\sin x)=\ln\left(\sin\frac{\pi}{2}\right)=\ln 1=0$

Graphical support:

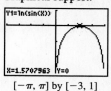

$[-\pi, \pi]$ by $[-3, 1]$

17. You cannot use substitution because the expression $\sqrt{x-2}$ is not defined at $x=-2$. Since the expression is not defined at points near $x=-2$, the limit does not exist.

18. You cannot use substitution because the expression $\frac{1}{x^2}$ is not defined at $x=0$. Since $\frac{1}{x^2}$ becomes arbitrarily large as x approaches 0 from either side, there is no (finite) limit. (As we shall see in Section 2.2, we may write $\displaystyle\lim_{x\to 0}\frac{1}{x^2}=\infty$.)

19. You cannot use substitution because the expression $\frac{|x|}{x}$ is not defined at $x=0$. Since $\displaystyle\lim_{x\to 0^-}\frac{|x|}{x}=-1$ and $\displaystyle\lim_{x\to 0^+}\frac{|x|}{x}=1$, the left- and right-hand limits are not equal and so the limit does not exist.

20. You cannot use substitution because the expression $\frac{(4+x)^2-16}{x}$ is not defined at $x=0$. Since $\frac{(4+x)^2-16}{x}=\frac{8x+x^2}{x}=8+x$ for all $x\neq 0$, the limit exists and is equal to $\displaystyle\lim_{x\to 0}(8+x)=8+0=8$.

21.

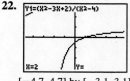

$[-4.7, 4.7]$ by $[-3.1, 3.1]$

$\displaystyle\lim_{x\to 1}\frac{x-1}{x^2-1}=\frac{1}{2}$

Algebraic confirmation:

$\displaystyle\lim_{x\to 1}\frac{x-1}{x^2-1}=\lim_{x\to 1}\frac{x-1}{(x+1)(x-1)}=\lim_{x\to 1}\frac{1}{x+1}=\frac{1}{1+1}=\frac{1}{2}$

22.

$[-4.7, 4.7]$ by $[-3.1, 3.1]$

$\displaystyle\lim_{t\to 2}\frac{t^2-3t+2}{t^2-4}=\frac{1}{4}$

Algebraic confirmation:

$\displaystyle\lim_{t\to 2}\frac{t^2-3t+2}{t^2-4}=\lim_{t\to 2}\frac{(t-1)(t-2)}{}=\lim_{t\to 2}\frac{t-1}{t+2}=\frac{2-1}{2+2}=\frac{1}{4}$

23.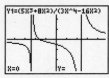

$[-4.7, 4.7]$ by $[-3.1, 3.1]$

$$\lim_{x \to 0} \frac{5x^3 + 8x^2}{3x^4 - 16x^2} = -\frac{1}{2}$$

Algebraic confirmation:

$$\lim_{x \to 0} \frac{5x^3 + 8x^2}{3x^4 - 16x^2} = \lim_{x \to 0} \frac{x^2(5x + 8)}{x^2(3x^2 - 16)}$$
$$= \lim_{x \to 0} \frac{5x + 8}{3x^2 - 16}$$
$$= \frac{5(0) + 8}{3(0)^2 - 16}$$
$$= \frac{8}{-16} = -\frac{1}{2}$$

24.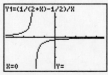

$[-4.7, 4.7]$ by $[-3.1, 3.1]$

$$\lim_{x \to 0} \frac{\frac{1}{2 + x} - \frac{1}{2}}{x} = -\frac{1}{4}$$

Algebraic confirmation:

$$\lim_{x \to 0} \frac{\frac{1}{2 + x} - \frac{1}{2}}{x} = \lim_{x \to 0} \frac{2 - (2 + x)}{x}$$
$$= \lim_{x \to 0} \frac{-x}{x(2 + x)(2)}$$
$$= \lim_{x \to 0} \frac{-1}{2(2 + x)}$$
$$= \frac{-1}{2(2 + 0)} = -\frac{1}{4}$$

25.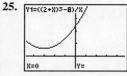

$[-4.7, 4.7]$ by $[-5, 20]$

$$\lim_{x \to 0} \frac{(2 + x)^3 - 8}{x} = 12$$

Algebraic confirmation:

$$\lim_{x \to 0} \frac{(2 + x)^3 - 8}{x} = \lim_{x \to 0} \frac{12x + 6x^2 + x^3}{x}$$
$$= \lim_{x \to 0} (12 + 6x + x^2)$$
$$= 12 + 6(0) + (0)^2 = 12$$

26.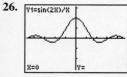

$[-4.7, 4.7]$ by $[-3.1, 3.1]$

$$\lim_{x \to 0} \frac{\sin 2x}{x} = 2$$

Algebraic confirmation:

$$\lim_{x \to 0} \frac{\sin 2x}{x} = 2 \lim_{x \to 0} \frac{\sin 2x}{2x} = 2(1) = 2$$

27.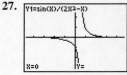

$[-4.7, 4.7]$ by $[-3.1, 3.1]$

$$\lim_{x \to 0} \frac{\sin x}{2x^2 - x} = -1$$

Algebraic confirmation:

$$\lim_{x \to 0} \frac{\sin x}{2x^2 - x} = \lim_{x \to 0} \left(\frac{\sin x}{x} \cdot \frac{1}{2x - 1} \right)$$
$$= \left(\lim_{x \to 0} \frac{\sin x}{x} \right) \left(\lim_{x \to 0} \frac{1}{2x - 1} \right) = (1)\left(\frac{1}{2(0) - 1} \right) = -1$$

28.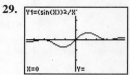

$[-4.7, 4.7]$ by $[-3.1, 3.1]$

$$\lim_{x \to 0} \frac{x + \sin x}{x} = 2$$

Algebraic confirmation:

$$\lim_{x \to 0} \frac{x + \sin x}{x} = \lim_{x \to 0} \left(1 + \frac{\sin x}{x} \right)$$
$$= \left(\lim_{x \to 0} 1 \right) + \left(\lim_{x \to 0} \frac{\sin x}{x} \right)$$
$$= 1 + 1 = 2$$

29.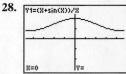

$[-4.7, 4.7]$ by $[-3.1, 3.1]$

$$\lim_{x \to 0} \frac{\sin^2 x}{x} = 0$$

Algebraic confirmation:

$$\lim_{x \to 0} \frac{\sin^2 x}{x} = \lim_{x \to 0} \left(\sin x \cdot \frac{\sin x}{x} \right)$$
$$= \left(\lim_{x \to 0} \sin x \right) \cdot \left(\lim_{x \to 0} \frac{\sin x}{x} \right)$$
$$= (\sin 0)(1) = 0$$

30.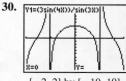

$[-2, 2]$ by $[-10, 10]$

$$\lim_{x \to 0} \frac{3 \sin 4x}{\sin 3x} = 4$$

Algebraic confirmation:

$$\lim_{x \to 0} \frac{3 \sin 4x}{\sin 3x} = 4 \lim_{x \to 0} \left(\frac{\sin 4x}{4x} \cdot \frac{3x}{\sin 3x} \right)$$
$$= 4 \left(\lim_{x \to 0} \frac{\sin 4x}{4x} \right) \div \left(\lim_{x \to 0} \frac{\sin 3x}{3x} \right)$$
$$= 4(1) \div (1) = 4$$

31. **(a)** True

(b) True

(c) False, since $\lim\limits_{x\to 0^-} f(x) = 0$.

(d) True, since both are equal to 0.

(e) True, since (d) is true.

(f) True

(g) False, since $\lim\limits_{x\to 0} f(x) = 0$.

(h) False, $\lim\limits_{x\to 1^-} f(x) = 1$, but $\lim\limits_{x\to 1} f(x)$ is undefined.

(i) False, $\lim\limits_{x\to 1^+} f(x) = 0$, but $\lim\limits_{x\to 1} f(x)$ is undefined.

(j) False, since $\lim\limits_{x\to 2^-} f(x) = 0$.

32. **(a)** True

(b) False, since $\lim\limits_{x\to 2} f(x) = 1$.

(c) False, since $\lim\limits_{x\to 2} f(x) = 1$.

(d) True

(e) True

(f) True, since $\lim\limits_{x\to 1^-} f(x) \ne \lim\limits_{x\to 1^+} f(x)$.

(g) True, since both are equal to 0.

(h) True

(i) True, since $\lim\limits_{x\to c} f(x) = 1$ for all c in (1, 3).

33. $y_1 = \dfrac{x^2 + x - 2}{x - 1} = \dfrac{(x-1)(x+2)}{x-1} = x + 2,\ x \ne 1$

(c)

34. $y_1 = \dfrac{x^2 - x - 2}{x - 1} = \dfrac{(x+1)(x-2)}{x-1}$

(b)

35. $y_1 = \dfrac{x^2 - 2x + 1}{x - 1} = \dfrac{(x-1)^2}{x-1} = x - 1,\ x \ne 1$

(d)

36. $y_1 = \dfrac{x^2 + x - 2}{x + 1} = \dfrac{(x-1)(x+2)}{x+1}$

(a)

37. Since int $x = 0$ for x in (0, 1), $\lim\limits_{x\to 0^+}$ int $x = 0$.

38. Since int $x = -1$ for x in (−1, 0), $\lim\limits_{x\to 0^-}$ int $x = -1$.

39. Since int $x = 0$ for x in (0, 1), $\lim\limits_{x\to 0.01}$ int $x = 0$.

40. Since int $x = 1$ for x in (1, 2), $\lim\limits_{x\to 2^-}$ int $x = 1$.

41. Since $\dfrac{x}{|x|} = 1$ for $x > 0$, $\lim\limits_{x\to 0^+} \dfrac{x}{|x|} = 1$.

42. Since $\dfrac{x}{|x|} = -1$ for $x < 0$, $\lim\limits_{x\to 0^-} \dfrac{x}{|x|} = -1$.

43. **(a)** $\lim\limits_{x\to 4}(g(x) + 3) = \left(\lim\limits_{x\to 4} g(x)\right) + \left(\lim\limits_{x\to 4} 3\right) = 3 + 3 = 6$

(b) $\lim\limits_{x\to 4} xf(x) = \left(\lim\limits_{x\to 4} x\right)\left(\lim\limits_{x\to 4} f(x)\right) = 4 \cdot 0 = 0$

(c) $\lim\limits_{x\to 4} g^2(x) = \left(\lim\limits_{x\to 4} g(x)\right)^2 = 3^2 = 9$

(d) $\lim\limits_{x\to 4} \dfrac{g(x)}{f(x) - 1} = \dfrac{\lim\limits_{x\to 4} g(x)}{\left(\lim\limits_{x\to 4} f(x)\right) - \left(\lim\limits_{x\to 4} 1\right)} = \dfrac{3}{0 - 1} = -3$

44. **(a)** $\lim\limits_{x\to b}(f(x) + g(x)) = \left(\lim\limits_{x\to b} f(x)\right) + \left(\lim\limits_{x\to b} g(x)\right)$

$= 7 + (-3) = 4$

(b) $\lim\limits_{x\to b}(f(x) \cdot g(x)) = \left(\lim\limits_{x\to b} f(x)\right)\left(\lim\limits_{x\to b} g(x)\right)$

$= (7)(-3) = -21$

(c) $\lim\limits_{x\to b} 4g(x) = 4\lim\limits_{x\to b} g(x) = 4(-3) = -12$

(d) $\lim\limits_{x\to b} \dfrac{f(x)}{g(x)} = \dfrac{\lim\limits_{x\to b} f(x)}{\lim\limits_{x\to b} g(x)} = \dfrac{7}{-3} = -\dfrac{7}{3}$

45. **(a)**

[−3, 6] by [−1, 5]

(b) $\lim\limits_{x\to 2^+} f(x) = 2;\ \lim\limits_{x\to 2^-} f(x) = 1$

(c) No, because the two one-sided limits are different.

46. **(a)**

[−3, 6] by [−1, 5]

(b) $\lim\limits_{x\to 2^+} f(x) = 1;\ \lim\limits_{x\to 2^-} f(x) = 1$

(c) Yes. The limit is 1.

47. **(a)**

[−5, 5] by [−4, 8]

(b) $\lim\limits_{x\to 1^+} f(x) = 4;\ \lim\limits_{x\to 1^-} f(x)$ does not exist.

(c) No, because the left-hand limit does not exist.

48. **(a)**

[−4.7, 4.7] by [−3.1, 3.1]

48. continued

(b) $\lim_{x \to -1^+} f(x) = 0$; $\lim_{x \to -1^-} f(x) = 0$

(c) Yes. The limit is 0.

49. (a)

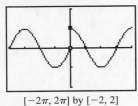

$[-2\pi, 2\pi]$ by $[-2, 2]$

(b) $(-2\pi, 0) \cup (0, 2\pi)$

(c) $c = 2\pi$

(d) $c = -2\pi$

50. (a)

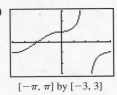

$[-\pi, \pi]$ by $[-3, 3]$

(b) $\left(-\pi, \dfrac{\pi}{2}\right) \cup \left(\dfrac{\pi}{2}, \pi\right)$

(c) $c = \pi$ (d) $c = -\pi$

51. (a)

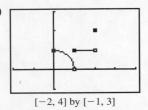

$[-2, 4]$ by $[-1, 3]$

(b) $(0, 1) \cup (1, 2)$

(c) $c = 2$ (d) $c = 0$

52. (a)

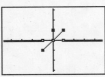

$[-4.7, 4.7]$ by $[-3.1, 3.1]$

(b) $(-\infty, -1) \cup (-1, 1) \cup (1, \infty)$

(c) None   (d) None

53.

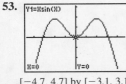

$[-4.7, 4.7]$ by $[-3.1, 3.1]$

$\lim_{x \to 0} (x \sin x) = 0$

Confirm using the Sandwich Theorem, with $g(x) = -|x|$ and $h(x) = |x|$.

$|x \sin x| = |x| \cdot |\sin x| \le |x| \cdot 1 = |x|$
$-|x| \le x \sin x \le |x|$

Because $\lim_{x \to 0} (-|x|) = \lim_{x \to 0} |x| = 0$, the Sandwich Theorem gives $\lim_{x \to 0} (x \sin x) = 0$.

54.

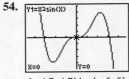

$[-4.7, 4.7]$ by $[-5, 5]$

$\lim_{x \to 0} (x^2 \sin x) = 0$

Confirm using the Sandwich Theorem, with $g(x) = -x^2$ and $h(x) = x^2$.

$|x^2 \sin x| = |x^2| \cdot |\sin x| \le |x^2| \cdot 1 = x^2$.
$-x^2 \le x^2 \sin x \le x^2$

Because $\lim_{x \to 0} (-x^2) = \lim_{x \to 0} x^2 = 0$, the Sandwich Theorem

gives $\lim_{x \to 0} (x^2 \sin x) = 0$

55.

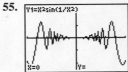

$[-0.5, 0.5]$ by $[-0.25, 0.25]$

$\lim_{x \to 0} \left(x^2 \sin \dfrac{1}{x^2} \right) = 0$

Confirm using the Sandwich Theorem, with $g(x) = -x^2$ and $h(x) = x^2$.

$\left| x^2 \sin \dfrac{1}{x^2} \right| = |x^2| \cdot \left| \sin \dfrac{1}{x^2} \right| \le |x^2| \cdot 1 = x^2$.

$-x^2 \le x^2 \sin \dfrac{1}{x^2} \le x^2$

Because $\lim_{x \to 0} (-x^2) = \lim_{x \to 0} x^2 = 0$, the Sandwich Theorem

give $\lim_{x \to 0} \left(x^2 \sin \dfrac{1}{x^2} \right) = 0$.

56.

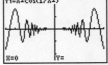

$[-0.5, 0.5]$ by $[-0.25, 0.25]$

$\lim_{x \to 0} \left(x^2 \cos \dfrac{1}{x^2} \right) = 0$

Confirm using the Sandwich Theorem, with $g(x) = -x^2$ and $h(x) = x^2$.

$\left| x^2 \cos \dfrac{1}{x^2} \right| = |x^2| \cdot \left| \cos \dfrac{1}{x^2} \right| \le |x^2| \cdot 1 = x^2$.

$-x^2 \le x^2 \cos \dfrac{1}{x^2} \le x^2$

Because $\lim_{x \to 0} (-x^2) = \lim_{x \to 0} x^2 = 0$, the Sandwich Theorem

give $\lim_{x \to 0} \left(x^2 \cos \dfrac{1}{x^2} \right) = 0$.

57. (a) In three seconds, the ball falls $4.9(3)^2 = 44.1$ m, so its

average speed is $\dfrac{44.1}{3} = 14.7$ m/sec.

(b) The average speed over the interval from time $t = 3$ to time $3 + h$ is

$$\frac{\Delta y}{\Delta t} = \frac{4.9(3 + h)^2 - 4.9(3)^2}{(3 + h) - 3} = \frac{4.9(6h + h^2)}{h}$$
$$= 29.4 + 4.9h$$

Since $\lim_{h \to 0} (29.4 + 4.9h) = 29.4$, the instantaneous speed is 29.4 m/sec.

58. (a) $y = gt^2$

$20 = g(4^2)$

$g = \dfrac{20}{16} = \dfrac{5}{4}$ or 1.25

(b) Average speed $= \dfrac{20}{4} = 5$ m/sec

(c) If the rock had not been stopped, its average speed over the interval from time $t = 4$ to time $t = 4 + h$ is

$$\frac{\Delta y}{\Delta t} = \frac{1.25(4 + h)^2 - 1.25(4)^2}{(4 + h) - 4} = \frac{1.25(8h + h^2)}{h}$$
$$= 10 + 1.25h$$

Since $\lim_{h \to 0} (10 + 1.25h) = 10$, the instantaneous speed is 10 m/sec.

59. (a)

x	-0.1	-0.01	-0.001	-0.0001
$f(x)$	-0.054402	-0.005064	-0.000827	-0.000031

(b)

x	0.1	0.01	0.001	0.0001
$f(x)$	-0.054402	-0.005064	-0.000827	-0.000031

The limit appears to be 0.

60. (a)

x	-0.1	-0.01	-0.001	-0.0001
$f(x)$	0.5440	0.5064	-0.8269	0.3056

(b)

x	0.1	0.01	0.001	0.0001
$f(x)$	-0.5440	-0.5064	0.8269	-0.3056

There is no clear indication of a limit.

61. (a)

x	-0.1	-0.01	-0.001	-0.0001
$f(x)$	2.0567	2.2763	2.2999	2.3023

(b)

x	0.1	0.01	0.001	0.0001
$f(x)$	2.5893	2.3293	2.3052	2.3029

The limit appears to be approximately 2.3.

62. (a)

x	-0.1	-0.01	-0.001	-0.0001
$f(x)$	0.074398	-0.009943	0.000585	0.000021

(b)

x	0.1	0.01	0.001	0.0001
$f(x)$	-0.074398	0.009943	-0.000585	-0.000021

The limit appears to be 0.

63. (a) Because the right-hand limit at zero depends only on the values of the function for positive x-values near zero.

(b) Area of $\triangle OAP = \dfrac{1}{2}$(base)(height) $= \dfrac{1}{2}(1)(\sin \theta) = \dfrac{\sin \theta}{2}$

Area of sector $OAP = \dfrac{(\text{angle})(\text{radius})^2}{2} = \dfrac{\theta(1)^2}{2} = \dfrac{\theta}{2}$

Area of $\triangle OAT = \dfrac{1}{2}$(base)(height) $= \dfrac{1}{2}(1)(\tan \theta) = \dfrac{\tan \theta}{2}$

(c) This is how the areas of the three regions compare.

(d) Multiply by 2 and divide by $\sin \theta$.

(e) Take reciprocals, remembering that all of the values involved are positive.

(f) The limits for $\cos \theta$ and 1 are both equal to 1. Since $\dfrac{\sin \theta}{\theta}$ is between them, it must also have a limit of 1.

(g) $\dfrac{\sin (-\theta)}{-\theta} = \dfrac{-\sin \theta}{-\theta} = \dfrac{\sin (\theta)}{\theta}$

(h) If the function is symmetric about the y-axis, and the right-hand limit at zero is 1, then the left-hand limit at zero must also be 1.

(i) The two one-sided limits both exist and are equal to 1.

64. (a) The limit can be found by substitution.

$$\lim_{x \to 2} f(x) = f(2) = \sqrt{3(2) - 2} = \sqrt{4} = 2$$

(b) The graphs of $y_1 = f(x)$, $y_2 = 1.8$, and $y_3 = 2.2$ are shown.

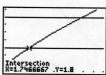

[1.5, 2.5] by [1.5, 2.3]

The intersections of y_1 with y_2 and y_3 are at $x \approx 1.7467$ and $x = 2.28$, respectively, so we may choose any value of a in [1.7467, 2) (approximately) and any value of b in (2, 2.28].
One possible answer: $a = 1.75$, $b = 2.28$.

(c) The graphs of $y_1 = f(x)$, $y_2 = 1.99$, and $y_3 = 2.01$ are shown.

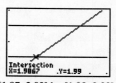

[1.97, 2.03] by [1.98, 2.02]

The intersections of y_1 with y_2 and y_3 are at $x = 1.9867$ and $x \approx 2.0134$, respectively, so we may choose any value of a in [1.9867, 2) and any value of b in (2, 2.0134] (approximately).
One possible answer: $a = 1.99$, $b = 2.01$

65. (a) $f\left(\dfrac{\pi}{6}\right) = \sin\dfrac{\pi}{6} = \dfrac{1}{2}$

(b) The graphs of $y_1 = f(x)$, $y_2 = 0.3$, and $y_3 = 0.7$ are shown.

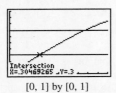

[0, 1] by [0, 1]

The intersections of y_1 with y_2 and y_3 are at $x \approx 0.3047$ and $x \approx 0.7754$, respectively, so we may choose any value of a in $\left[0.3047, \dfrac{\pi}{6}\right)$ and any value of b in $\left(\dfrac{\pi}{6}, 0.7754\right]$, where the interval endpoints are approximate.

One possible answer: $a = 0.305$, $b = 0.775$

(c) The graphs of $y_1 = f(x)$, $y_2 = 0.49$, and $y_3 = 0.51$ are shown.

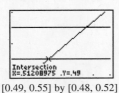

[0.49, 0.55] by [0.48, 0.52]

The intersections of y_1 with y_2 and y_3 are at $x \approx 0.5121$ and $x \approx 0.5352$, respectively, so we may choose any value of a in $\left[0.5121, \dfrac{\pi}{6}\right)$, and any value of b in $\left(\dfrac{\pi}{6}, 0.5352\right]$, where the interval endpoints are approximate.

One possible answer: $a = 0.513$, $b = 0.535$

66. Line segment OP has endpoints $(0, 0)$ and (a, a^2), so its midpoint is $\left(\dfrac{0 + a}{2}, \dfrac{0 + a^2}{2}\right) = \left(\dfrac{a}{2}, \dfrac{a^2}{2}\right)$ and its slope is $\dfrac{a^2 - 0}{a - 0} = a$. The perpendicular bisector is the line through $\left(\dfrac{a}{2}, \dfrac{a^2}{2}\right)$ with slope $-\dfrac{1}{a}$, so its equation is $y = -\dfrac{1}{a}\left(x - \dfrac{a}{2}\right) + \dfrac{a^2}{2}$, which is equivalent to $y = -\dfrac{1}{a}x + \dfrac{1 + a^2}{2}$. Thus the y-intercept is $b = \dfrac{1 + a^2}{2}$. As the point P approaches the origin along the parabola, the value of a approaches zero. Therefore,

$$\lim_{P \to 0} b = \lim_{a \to 0} \dfrac{1 + a^2}{2} = \dfrac{1 + 0^2}{2} = \dfrac{1}{2}.$$

■ Section 2.2 Limits Involving Infinity
(pp. 65–73)

Exploration 1   Exploring Theorem 5

1. Neither $\lim\limits_{x \to \infty} f(x)$ or $\lim\limits_{x \to \infty} g(x)$ exist. In this case, we can describe the behavior of f and g as $x \to \infty$ by writing $\lim\limits_{x \to \infty} f(x) = \infty$ and $\lim\limits_{x \to \infty} g(x) = \infty$. We cannot apply the quotient rule because both limits must exist. However, from Example 5,

$$\lim_{x \to \infty} \dfrac{5x + \sin x}{x} = \lim_{x \to \infty}\left(5 + \dfrac{\sin x}{x}\right) = 5 + 0 = 5,$$

so the limit of the quotient exists.

2. Both f and g oscillate between 0 and 1 as $x \to \infty$, taking on each value infinitely often. We cannot apply the sum rule because neither limit exists. However,

$$\lim_{x \to \infty} (\sin^2 x + \cos^2 x) = \lim_{x \to \infty} (1) = 1,$$

so the limit of the sum exists.

3. The limt of f and g as $x \to \infty$ do not exist, so we cannot apply the difference rule to $f - $ g. We can say that $\lim\limits_{x \to \infty} f(x) = \lim\limits_{x \to \infty} g(x) = \infty$. We can write the difference as

$$f(x) - g(x) = \ln (2x) - \ln (x + 1) = \ln \dfrac{2x}{x + 1}.$$

We can use graphs or tables to convince ourselves that this limit is equal to $\ln 2$.

4. The fact that the limits of f and g as $x \to \infty$ do not exist does not necessarily mean that the limits of $f + g$, $f - g$ or $\dfrac{f}{g}$ do not exist, just that Theorem 5 cannot be applied.

Quick Review 2.2

1. $y = 2x - 3$

$y + 3 = 2x$

$\dfrac{y + 3}{2} = x$

Interchange x and y.

$\dfrac{x + 3}{2} = y$

$f^{-1}(x) = \dfrac{x + 3}{2}$

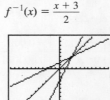

[−12, 12] by [−8, 8]

2. $y = e^x$
$\ln y = x$
Interchange x and y.
$\ln x = y$
$f^{-1}(x) = \ln x$

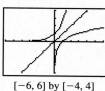

[−6, 6] by [−4, 4]

3. $y = \tan^{-1}x$

$\tan y = x, \ -\dfrac{\pi}{2} < y < \dfrac{\pi}{2}$

Interchange x and y.

$\tan x = y, \ -\dfrac{\pi}{2} < x < \dfrac{\pi}{2}$

$f^{-1}(x) = \tan x, \ -\dfrac{\pi}{2} < x < \dfrac{\pi}{2}$

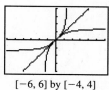

[−6, 6] by [−4, 4]

4. $y = \cot^{-1}x$
$\cot y = x, \ 0 < x < \pi$
Interchange x and y.
$\cot x = y, \ 0 < y < \pi$
$f^{-1}(x) = \cot x, \ 0 < x < \pi$

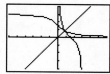

[−6, 6] by [−4, 4]

5.

$$3x^3 + 4x - 5\overline{)2x^3 - 3x^2 + x - 1} \quad \tfrac{2}{3}$$

$$2x^3 + 0x^2 + \tfrac{8}{3}x - \tfrac{10}{3}$$

$$\overline{{-3x^2 - \tfrac{5}{3}x + \tfrac{7}{3}}}$$

$q(x) = \dfrac{2}{3}$

$r(x) = -3x^2 - \dfrac{5}{3}x + \dfrac{7}{3}$

6.

$$x^3 - x^2 + 1\overline{)2x^5 + 0x^4 - x^3 + 0x^2 + x - 1} \quad 2x^2 + 2x + 1$$

$$2x^5 - 2x^4 + 0x^3 + 2x^2$$

$$\overline{2x^4 - x^3 - 2x^2 + x - 1}$$

$$2x^4 - 2x^3 + 0x^2 + 2x$$

$$\overline{x^3 - 2x^2 - x - 1}$$

$$x^3 - x^2 + 0x + 1$$

$$\overline{{-x^2 - x - 2}}$$

$q(x) = 2x^2 + 2x + 1$
$r(x) = -x^2 - x - 2$

7. (a) $f(-x) = \cos(-x) = \cos x$

   (b) $f\left(\dfrac{1}{x}\right) = \cos\left(\dfrac{1}{x}\right)$

8. (a) $f(-x) = e^{-(-x)} = e^x$

   (b) $f\left(\dfrac{1}{x}\right) = e^{-1/x}$

9. (a) $f(-x) = \dfrac{\ln(-x)}{-x} = -\dfrac{\ln(-x)}{x}$

   (b) $f\left(\dfrac{1}{x}\right) = \dfrac{\ln 1/x}{1/x} = x \ln x^{-1} = -x \ln x$

10. (a) $f(-x) = \left(-x + \dfrac{1}{-x}\right)\sin(-x) = -\left(x + \dfrac{1}{x}\right)(-\sin x)$

   $= \left(x + \dfrac{1}{x}\right)\sin x$

   (b) $f\left(\dfrac{1}{x}\right) = \left(\dfrac{1}{x} + \dfrac{1}{1/x}\right)\sin\left(\dfrac{1}{x}\right) = \left(\dfrac{1}{x} + x\right)\sin\left(\dfrac{1}{x}\right)$

Section 2.2 Exercises

1.

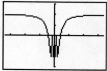

[−5, 5] by [−1.5, 1.5]

X	Y1
100	.99995
200	.99999
300	.99999
400	1
-100	.99995
-200	.99999
-300	.99999

Y1■cos(1/X)

   (a) $\lim\limits_{x \to \infty} f(x) = 1$

   (b) $\lim\limits_{x \to -\infty} f(x) = 1$

   (c) $y = 1$

2.

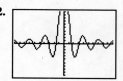

[−10, 10] by [−1, 1]

X	Y1
100	-.0087
200	-.0043
500	.00165
1000	9.3E-4
-100	-.0087
-200	-.0043
-500	.00165

Y1■sin(2X)/X

   (a) $\lim\limits_{x \to \infty} f(x) = 0$

   (b) $\lim\limits_{x \to -\infty} f(x) = 0$

   (c) $y = 0$

3.

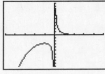

$[-5, 5]$ by $[-10, 10]$

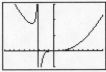

$Y_1 \blacksquare e^{\wedge}(-X)/X$

(a) $\lim\limits_{x \to \infty} f(x) = 0$

(b) $\lim\limits_{x \to -\infty} f(x) = -\infty$

(c) $y = 0$

4.

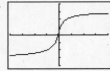

$[-10, 10]$ by $[-100, 300]$

$Y_1 \blacksquare (3X^3 - X + 1)/(X \ldots$

(a) $\lim\limits_{x \to \infty} f(x) = \infty$

(b) $\lim\limits_{x \to -\infty} f(x) = \infty$

(c) No horizontal asymptotes.

5.

$[-20, 20]$ by $[-4, 4]$

$Y_1 \blacksquare (3X + 1)/(abs(\ldots$

(a) $\lim\limits_{x \to \infty} f(x) = 3$

(b) $\lim\limits_{x \to -\infty} f(x) = -3$

(c) $y = 3, y = -3$

6.

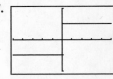

$[-20, 20]$ by $[-4, 4]$

$Y_1 \blacksquare (2X - 1)/(abs(\ldots$

(a) $\lim\limits_{x \to \infty} f(x) = 2$

(b) $\lim\limits_{x \to -\infty} f(x) = -2$

(c) $y = 2, y = -2$

7.

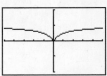

$[-5, 5]$ by $[-2, 2]$

$Y_1 \blacksquare X/abs(X)$

(a) $\lim\limits_{x \to \infty} f(x) = 1$

(b) $\lim\limits_{x \to -\infty} f(x) = -1$

(c) $y = 1, y = -1$

8.

$[-5, 5]$ by $[-2, 2]$

$Y_1 \blacksquare abs(X)/(abs(\ldots$

(a) $\lim\limits_{x \to \infty} f(x) = 1$

(b) $\lim\limits_{x \to -\infty} f(x) = 1$

(c) $y = 1$

9.

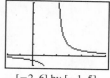

[−2, 6] by [−1, 5]

X	Y1
2.8	1.25
2.4	2.5
2.2	5
2.1	10
2.01	100
2.001	1000
2.0001	10000

Y1**▉**1/(X−2)

$$\lim_{x \to 2^+} \frac{1}{x-2} = \infty$$

10.

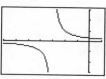

[−2, 6] by [−3, 3]

X	Y1
1.2	-1.5
1.6	-4
1.8	-9
1.9	-19
1.99	-199
1.999	-1999
1.9999	-19999

Y1**▉**X/(X−2)

$$\lim_{x \to 2^-} \frac{x}{x-2} = -\infty$$

11.

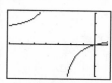

[−7, 1] by [−3, 3]

X	Y1
-3.8	-1.25
-3.4	-2.5
-3.3	-3.333
-3.2	-5
-3.1	-10
-3.01	-100
-3.001	-1000

Y1**▉**1/(X+3)

$$\lim_{x \to -3^-} \frac{1}{x+3} = -\infty$$

12.

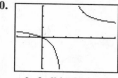

[−7, 1] by [−3, 3]

X	Y1
-2.2	-2.75
-2.6	-6.5
-2.7	-9
-2.8	-14
-2.9	-29
-2.99	-299
-2.999	-2999

Y1**▉**X/(X+3)

$$\lim_{x \to -3^+} \frac{x}{x+3} = -\infty$$

13.

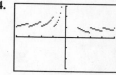

[−4, 4] by [−3, 3]

X	Y1
.8	0
.4	0
.2	0
.1	0
.01	0
.001	0
1E-4	0

Y1**▉**int(X)/X

$$\lim_{x \to 0^+} \frac{\text{int } x}{x} = 0$$

14.

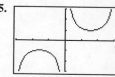

[−4, 4] by [−3, 3]

X	Y1
-.8	1.25
-.4	2.5
-.2	5
-.1	10
-.01	100
-.001	1000
-1E-4	10000

Y1**▉**int(X)/X

$$\lim_{x \to 0^-} \frac{\text{int } x}{x} = \infty$$

15.

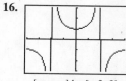

[−3, 3] by [−3, 3]

X	Y1
.8	1.394
.4	2.5679
.2	5.0335
.1	10.017
.01	100
.001	1000
1E-4	10000

Y1**▉**1/sin(X)

$$\lim_{x \to 0^+} \csc x = \infty$$

16.

[−π, π] by [−3, 3]

X	Y1
1.6	-34.25
1.59	-52.08
1.58	-108.7
1.576	-192.2
1.572	-830.8
1.571	-4910
1.5708	-2.7E5

Y1**▉**1/cos(X)

$$\lim_{x \to (\pi/2)^+} \sec x = -\infty$$

17.

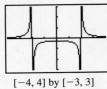

$[-4, 4]$ by $[-3, 3]$

(a) $x = -2$, $x = 2$

(b) Left-hand limit at -2 is ∞.
Right-hand limit at -2 is $-\infty$.
Left-hand limit at 2 is $-\infty$.
Right-hand limit at 2 is ∞.

18.

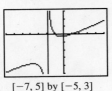

$[-7, 5]$ by $[-5, 3]$

(a) $x = -2$

(b) Left-hand limit at -2 is $-\infty$.
Right-hand limit at -2 is ∞.

19.

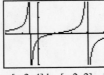

$[-6, 6]$ by $[-12, 6]$

(a) $x = -1$

(b) Left-hand limit at -1 is $-\infty$.
Right-hand limit at -1 is ∞.

20.

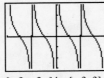

$[-2, 4]$ by $[-2, 2]$

(a) $x = -\dfrac{1}{2}$, $x = 3$

(b) Left-hand limit at $-\dfrac{1}{2}$ is ∞.

Right-hand limit at $-\dfrac{1}{2}$ is $-\infty$.

Left-hand limit at 3 is ∞.

Right-hand limit at 3 is $-\infty$.

21.

$[-2\pi, 2\pi]$ by $[-3, 3]$

(a) $x = k\pi$, k any integer

(b) at each vertical asymptote:
Left-hand limit is $-\infty$.
Right-hand limit is ∞.

22.

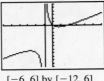

$[-2\pi, 2\pi]$ by $[-3, 3]$

(a) $x = \dfrac{\pi}{2} + n\pi$, n any integer

(b) If n is even:
Left-hand limit is ∞.
Right-hand limit is $-\infty$.

If n is odd:
Left-hand limit is $-\infty$.
Right-hand limit is ∞.

23. $y = \left(2 - \dfrac{x}{x+1}\right)\left(\dfrac{x^2}{5+x^2}\right) = \left(\dfrac{2(x+1)-x}{x+1}\right)\left(\dfrac{x^2}{5+x^2}\right)$

$\quad = \left(\dfrac{x+2}{x+1}\right)\left(\dfrac{x^2}{5+x^2}\right) = \dfrac{x^3 + 2x^2}{x^3 + x^2 + 5x + 5}$

An end behavior model for y is $\dfrac{x^3}{x^3} = 1$.

$\displaystyle\lim_{x\to\infty} y = \lim_{x\to\infty} 1 = 1$

$\displaystyle\lim_{x\to-\infty} y = \lim_{x\to-\infty} 1 = 1$

24. $y = \left(\dfrac{2}{x} + 1\right)\left(\dfrac{5x^2 - 1}{x^2}\right) = \left(\dfrac{2+x}{x}\right)\left(\dfrac{5x^2 - 1}{x^2}\right)$

$\quad = \dfrac{5x^3 + 10x^2 - x - 2}{x^3}$

An end behavior model for y is $\dfrac{5x^3}{x^3} = 5$.

$\displaystyle\lim_{x\to\infty} y = \lim_{x\to\infty} 5 = 5$

$\displaystyle\lim_{x\to-\infty} y = \lim_{x\to-\infty} 5 = 5$

25. Use the method of Example 10 in the text.

$\displaystyle\lim_{x\to\infty} \dfrac{\cos\left(\dfrac{1}{x}\right)}{1 + \dfrac{1}{x}} = \lim_{x\to 0^+} \dfrac{\cos x}{1 + x} = \dfrac{\cos(0)}{1 + 0} = \dfrac{1}{1} = 1$

$\displaystyle\lim_{x\to-\infty} \dfrac{\cos\left(\dfrac{1}{x}\right)}{1 + \dfrac{1}{x}} = \lim_{x\to 0^-} \dfrac{\cos x}{1 + x} = \dfrac{\cos(0)}{1 + 0} = \dfrac{1}{1} = 1$

26. Note that $y = \dfrac{2x + \sin x}{x} = 2 + \dfrac{\sin x}{x}$.

So, $\displaystyle\lim_{x\to\infty} y = \lim_{x\to\infty} 2 + \lim_{x\to\infty} \dfrac{\sin x}{x} = 2 + 0 = 2$.

Similarly, $\displaystyle\lim_{x\to-\infty} y = 2$.

27. Use $y = \dfrac{\sin x}{2x^2 + x} = \dfrac{\sin x}{x} \cdot \dfrac{1}{2x + 1}$

$\displaystyle\lim_{x \to \pm\infty} \frac{\sin x}{x} = 0$

$\displaystyle\lim_{x \to \pm\infty} \frac{1}{2x + 1} = 0$

So, $\displaystyle\lim_{x \to \infty} y = 0$ and $\displaystyle\lim_{x \to -\infty} y = 0$.

28. $y = \dfrac{1}{2}\dfrac{\sin x}{x} + \dfrac{1}{x}\dfrac{\sin x}{x}$

So, $\displaystyle\lim_{x \to \infty} y = 0$ and $\displaystyle\lim_{x \to -\infty} y = 0$.

29. An end behavior model is $\dfrac{2x^3}{x} = 2x^2$. (a)

30. An end behavior model is $\dfrac{x^5}{2x^2} = 0.5x^3$. (c)

31. An end behavior model is $\dfrac{2x^4}{-x} = -2x^3$. (d)

32. An end behavior model is $\dfrac{x^4}{-x^2} = -x^2$. (b)

33. (a) $3x^2$

  (b) None

34. (a) $-4x^3$

  (b) None

35. (a) $\dfrac{x}{2x^2} = \dfrac{1}{2x}$

  (b) $y = 0$

36. (a) $\dfrac{3x^2}{x^2} = 3$

  (b) $y = 3$

37. (a) $\dfrac{4x^3}{x} = 4x^2$

  (b) None

38. (a) $\dfrac{-x^4}{x^2} = -x^2$

  (b) None

39. (a) The function $y = e^x$ is a right end behavior model

  because $\displaystyle\lim_{x \to \infty} \frac{e^x - 2x}{e^x} = \lim_{x \to \infty}\left(1 - \frac{2x}{e^x}\right) = 1 - 0 = 1.$

  (b) The function $y = -2x$ is a left end behavior model

  because $\displaystyle\lim_{x \to -\infty} \frac{e^x - 2x}{-2x} = \lim_{x \to -\infty}\left(-\frac{e^x}{2x} + 1\right) = 0 + 1 = 1.$

40. (a) The function $y = x^2$ is a right end behavior model

  because $\displaystyle\lim_{x \to \infty} \frac{x^2 + e^{-x}}{x^2} = \lim_{x \to \infty}\left(1 + \frac{e^{-x}}{x^2}\right) = 1 + 0 = 1.$

  (b) The function $y = e^{-x}$ is a left end behavior model

  because $\displaystyle\lim_{x \to -\infty} \frac{x^2 + e^{-x}}{e^{-x}} = \lim_{x \to -\infty}\left(\frac{x^2}{e^{-x}} + 1\right)$

  $= \displaystyle\lim_{x \to -\infty}(x^2 e^x + 1) = 0 + 1 = 1.$

41. (a, b) The function $y = x$ is both a right end behavior

  model and a left end behavior model because

  $\displaystyle\lim_{x \to \pm\infty}\left(\frac{x + \ln|x|}{x}\right) = \lim_{x \to \pm\infty}\left(1 + \frac{\ln|x|}{x}\right) = 1 + 0 = 1.$

42. (a, b) The function $y = x^2$ is both a right end behavior

  model and a left end behavior model because

  $\displaystyle\lim_{x \to \pm\infty}\left(\frac{x^2 + \sin x}{x^2}\right) = \lim_{x \to \pm\infty}\left(1 + \frac{\sin x}{x^2}\right) = 1.$

43.

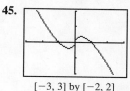

$[-4, 4]$ by $[-1, 3]$

The graph of $y = f\left(\dfrac{1}{x}\right) = \dfrac{1}{x}e^{1/x}$ is shown.

$\displaystyle\lim_{x \to \infty} f(x) = \lim_{x \to 0^+} f\left(\frac{1}{x}\right) = \infty$

$\displaystyle\lim_{x \to \infty^-} f(x) = \lim_{x \to 0^-} f\left(\frac{1}{x}\right) = 0$

44.

$[-4, 4]$ by $[-1, 3]$

The graph of $y = f\left(\dfrac{1}{x}\right) = \dfrac{1}{x^2}e^{-1/x}$ is shown.

$\displaystyle\lim_{x \to \infty} f(x) = \lim_{x \to 0^+} f\left(\frac{1}{x}\right) = 0$

$\displaystyle\lim_{x \to -\infty} f(x) = \lim_{x \to 0^-} f\left(\frac{1}{x}\right) = \infty$

45.

$[-3, 3]$ by $[-2, 2]$

The graph of $y = f\left(\dfrac{1}{x}\right) = x \ln\left|\dfrac{1}{x}\right|$ is shown.

$\displaystyle\lim_{x \to \infty} f(x) = \lim_{x \to 0^+} f\left(\frac{1}{x}\right) = 0$

$\displaystyle\lim_{x \to -\infty} f(x) = \lim_{x \to 0^-} f\left(\frac{1}{x}\right) = 0$

46.

$[-5, 5]$ by $[-1.5, 1.5]$

The graph of $y = f\left(\dfrac{1}{x}\right) = \dfrac{\sin x}{x}$ is shown.

$\displaystyle\lim_{x \to \infty} f(x) = \lim_{x \to 0^+} f\left(\frac{1}{x}\right) = 1$

$\displaystyle\lim_{x \to -\infty} f(x) = \lim_{x \to 0^-} f\left(\frac{1}{x}\right) = 1$

47. (a) $\lim\limits_{x\to-\infty} f(x) = \lim\limits_{x\to-\infty}\left(\dfrac{1}{x}\right) = 0$

(b) $\lim\limits_{x\to\infty} f(x) = \lim\limits_{x\to\infty}(-1) = -1$

(c) $\lim\limits_{x\to0^-} f(x) = \lim\limits_{x\to0^-}\dfrac{1}{x} = -\infty$

(d) $\lim\limits_{x\to0^+} f(x) = \lim\limits_{x\to0^+}(-1) = -1$

48. (a) $\lim\limits_{x\to-\infty} f(x) = \lim\limits_{x\to-\infty}\dfrac{x-2}{x-1} = \lim\limits_{x\to-\infty}\dfrac{x}{x} = 1$

(b) $\lim\limits_{x\to\infty} f(x) = \lim\limits_{x\to\infty}\dfrac{1}{x^2} = 0$

(c) $\lim\limits_{x\to0^-} f(x) = \lim\limits_{x\to0^-}\dfrac{x-2}{x-1} = \dfrac{0-2}{0-1} = 2$

(d) $\lim\limits_{x\to0^+} f(x) = \lim\limits_{x\to0^+}\dfrac{1}{x^2} = \infty$

49. One possible answer:

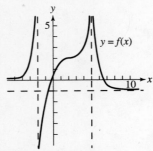

50. One possible answer:

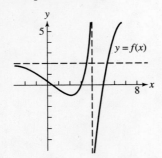

51. Note that $\dfrac{f_1(x)/f_2(x)}{g_1(x)/g_2(x)} = \dfrac{f_1(x)g_2(x)}{g_1(x)f_2(x)} = \dfrac{f_1(x)/g_1(x)}{f_2(x)/g_2(x)}$.

As x becomes large, $\dfrac{f_1}{g_1}$ and $\dfrac{f_2}{g_2}$ both approach 1. Therefore, using the above equation, $\dfrac{f_1/f_2}{g_1/g_2}$ must also approach 1.

52. Yes. The limit of $(f + g)$ will be the same as the limit of g. This is because adding numbers that are very close to a given real number L will not have a significant effect on the value of $(f + g)$ since the values of g are becoming arbitrarily large.

53. (a) Using 1980 as $x = 0$:
$y = -2.2316x^3 + 54.7134x^2 - 351.0933x + 733.2224$

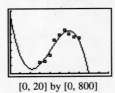

[0, 20] by [0, 800]

(b) Again using 1980 as $x = 0$:
$y = 1.458561x^4 - 60.5740x^3 + 905.8877x^2$
$\quad - 5706.0943x + 12967.6288$

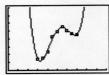

[0, 20] by [0, 800]

(c) Cubic: approximately -2256 dollars
Quartic: approximately 9979 dollars

(d) Cubic: End behavior model is $-2.2316x^3$.
This model predicts that the grants will become negative by 1996.

Quartic: End behavior model is $1.458561x^4$.
This model predicts that the size of the grants will grow very rapidly after 1995.

Neither of these seems reasonable. There is no reason to expect the grants to disappear (become negative) based on the data. Similarly, the data give no indication that a period of rapid growth is about to occur.

54. (a) Note that $fg = f(x)g(x) = 1$.
$f \to -\infty$ as $x \to 0^-$, $f \to \infty$ as $x \to 0^+$, $g \to 0$, $fg \to 1$

(b) Note that $fg = f(x)g(x) = -8$.
$f \to \infty$ as $x \to 0^-$, $f \to -\infty$ as $x \to 0^+$, $g \to 0$, $fg \to -8$

(c) Note that $fg = f(x)g(x) = 3(x - 2)^2$.
$f \to -\infty$ as $x \to 2^-$, $f \to \infty$ as $x \to 2^+$, $g \to 0$, $fg \to 0$

(d) Note that $fg = f(x)g(x) = \dfrac{5}{(x - 3)^2}$.
$f \to \infty$, $g \to 0$, $fg \to \infty$

(e) Nothing – you need more information to decide.

55. (a) This follows from $x - 1 < \text{int } x \le x$, which is true for all x. Dividing by x gives the result.

(b, c) Since $\lim\limits_{x\to\pm\infty}\dfrac{x-1}{x} = \lim\limits_{x\to\pm\infty} 1 = 1$, the Sandwich Theorem gives $\lim\limits_{x\to\infty}\dfrac{\text{int } x}{x} = \lim\limits_{x\to-\infty}\dfrac{\text{int } x}{x} = 1$.

56. For $x > 0$, $0 < e^{-x} < 1$, so $0 < \dfrac{e^{-x}}{x} < \dfrac{1}{x}$.

Since both 0 and $\dfrac{1}{x}$ approach zero as $x \to \infty$, the Sandwich Theorem states that $\dfrac{e^{-x}}{x}$ must also approach zero.

57. This is because as x approaches infinity, $\sin x$ continues to oscillate between 1 and -1 and doesn't approach any given real number.

58. $\lim\limits_{x\to\infty}\dfrac{\ln x^2}{\ln x} = 2$, because $\dfrac{\ln x^2}{\ln x} = \dfrac{2\ln x}{\ln x} = 2$.

59. $\lim\limits_{x\to\infty}\dfrac{\ln x}{\log x}=\ln(10)$, since $\dfrac{\ln x}{\log x}=\dfrac{\ln x}{(\ln x)/(\ln 10)}$

$=\ln 10$.

60. $\lim\limits_{x\to\infty}\dfrac{\ln(x+1)}{\ln x}=1$

Since $\ln(x+1)=\ln\left[x\left(1+\dfrac{1}{x}\right)\right]=\ln x+\ln\left(1+\dfrac{1}{x}\right)$,

$\dfrac{\ln(x+1)}{\ln x}=\dfrac{\ln x+\ln\left(1+\dfrac{1}{x}\right)}{\ln x}=1+\dfrac{\ln\left(1+\dfrac{1}{x}\right)}{\ln x}$

But as $x\to\infty$, $1+1/x$ approaches 1, so $\ln(1+1/x)$ approaches $\ln(1)=0$. Also, as $x\to\infty$, $\ln x$ approaches infinity. This means the second term above approaches 0 and the limit is 1.

■ Section 2.3 Continuity

(pp. 73–81)

Exploration 1   Removing a Discontinuity

1. $x^2-9=(x-3)(x+3)$. The domain of f is $(-\infty,-3)\cup(-3,3)\cup(3,\infty)$ or all $x\neq\pm3$.

2. It appears that the limit of f as $x\to3$ exists and is a little more than 3.

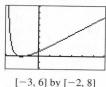

[−3, 6] by [−2, 8]

3. $f(3)$ should be defined as $\dfrac{10}{3}$.

4. $x^3-7x-6=(x-3)(x+1)(x+2)$, x^2-9

$=(x-3)(x+3)$, so $f(x)=\dfrac{(x+1)(x+2)}{x+3}$ for $x\neq3$.

Thus, $\lim\limits_{x\to3}\dfrac{(x+1)(x+2)}{x+3}=\dfrac{20}{6}=\dfrac{10}{3}$.

5. $\lim\limits_{x\to3}g(x)=\dfrac{10}{3}=g(3)$, so g is continuous at $x=3$.

Quick Review 2.3

1. $\lim\limits_{x\to-1}\dfrac{3x^2-2x+1}{x^3+4}=\dfrac{3(-1)^2-2(-1)+1}{(-1)^3+4}=\dfrac{6}{3}=2$

2. (a) $\lim\limits_{x\to-1^-}f(x)=\lim\limits_{x\to-1^-}\text{int}(x)=-2$

(b) $\lim\limits_{x\to-1^+}f(x)=\lim\limits_{x\to-1^+}f(x)=-1$

(c) $\lim\limits_{x\to-1}f(x)$ does not exist, because the left- and right-hand limits are not equal.

(d) $f(-1)=\text{int}(-1)=-1$

3. (a) $\lim\limits_{x\to2^-}f(x)=\lim\limits_{x\to2^-}(x^2-4x+5)=2^2-4(2)+5=1$

(b) $\lim\limits_{x\to2^+}f(x)=\lim\limits_{x\to2^+}(4-x)=4-2=2$

(c) $\lim\limits_{x\to2}f(x)$ does not exist, because the left- and right-hand limits are not equal.

(d) $f(2)=4-2=2$

4. $(f\circ g)(x)=f(g(x))=f\left(\dfrac{1}{x}+1\right)=\dfrac{2\left(\dfrac{1}{x}+1\right)-1}{\left(\dfrac{1}{x}+1\right)+5}$

$=\dfrac{2(1+x)-x}{(1+x)+5x}=\dfrac{x+2}{6x+1},x\neq0$

$(g\circ f)(x)=g(f(x))=g\left(\dfrac{2x-1}{x+5}\right)=\dfrac{1}{\dfrac{2x-1}{x+5}}+1$

$=\dfrac{x+5}{2x-1}+\dfrac{2x-1}{2x-1}=\dfrac{3x+4}{2x-1},x\neq-5$

5. Note that $\sin x^2=(g\circ f)(x)=g(f(x))=g(x^2)$.
Therefore: $g(x)=\sin x,x\geq0$
$(f\circ g)(x)=f(g(x))=f(\sin x)=(\sin x)^2$ or $\sin^2 x,x\geq0$

6. Note that $\dfrac{1}{x}=(g\circ f)(x)=g(f(x))=\sqrt{f(x)-1}$.

Therefore, $\sqrt{f(x)-1}=\dfrac{1}{x}$ for $x>0$. Squaring both sides

gives $f(x)-1=\dfrac{1}{x^2}$. Therefore, $f(x)=\dfrac{1}{x^2}+1,x>0$.

$(f\circ g)(x)=f(g(x))=\dfrac{1}{(\sqrt{x-1})^2}+1=\dfrac{1}{x-1}+1$

$=\dfrac{1+x-1}{x-1}=\dfrac{x}{x-1},x>1$

7. $2x^2+9x-5=0$

$(2x-1)(x+5)=0$

Solutions: $x=\dfrac{1}{2},x=-5$

8.

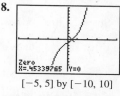

Zero
X=.45339765 Y=0

[−5, 5] by [−10, 10]

Solution: $x\approx0.453$

9. For $x\leq3$, $f(x)=4$ when $5-x=4$, which gives $x=1$. (Note that this value is, in fact, ≤3.)

For $x>3$, $f(x)=4$ when $-x^2+6x-8=4$, which gives $x^2-6x+12=0$. The discriminant of this equation is $b^2-4ac=(-6)^2-4(1)(12)=-12$. Since the discriminant is negative, the quadratic equation has no solution.

The only solution to the original equation is $x=1$.

10.

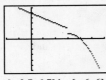

$[-2.7, 6.7]$ by $[-6, 6]$

A graph of $f(x)$ is shown. The range of $f(x)$ is $(-\infty, 1) \cup [2, \infty)$. The values of c for which $f(x) = c$ has no solution are the values that are excluded from the range. Therefore, c can be any value in $[1, 2)$.

Section 2.3 Exercises

1. The function $y = \dfrac{1}{(x + 2)^2}$ is continuous because it is a quotient of polynomials, which are continuous. Its only point of discontinuity occurs where it is undefined. There is an infinite discontinuity at $x = -2$.

2. The function $y = \dfrac{x + 1}{x^2 - 4x + 3}$ is continuous because it is a quotient of polynomials, which are continuous. Its only points of discontinuity occur where it is undefined, that is, where the denominator $x^2 - 4x + 3 = (x - 1)(x - 3)$ is zero. There are infinite discontinuities at $x = 1$ and at $x = 3$.

3. The function $y = \dfrac{1}{x^2 + 1}$ is continuous because it is a quotient of polynomials, which are continuous. Furthermore, the domain is all real numbers because the denominator, $x^2 + 1$, is never zero. Since the function is continuous and has domain $(-\infty, \infty)$, there are no points of discontinuity.

4. The function $y = |x - 1|$ is a composition $(f \circ g)(x)$ of the continuous functions $f(x) = |x|$ and $g(x) = x - 1$, so it is continuous. Since the function is continuous and has domain $(-\infty, \infty)$, there are no points of discontinuity.

5. The function $y = \sqrt{2x + 3}$ is a composition $(f \circ g)(x)$ of the continuous functions $f(x) = \sqrt{x}$ and $g(x) = 2x + 3$, so it is continuous. Its points of discontinuity are the points not in the domain, i.e., all $x < -\dfrac{3}{2}$.

6. The function $y = \sqrt[3]{2x - 1}$ is a composition $(f \circ g)(x)$ of the continuous functions $f(x) = \sqrt[3]{x}$ and $g(x) = 2x - 1$, so it is continuous. Since the function is continuous and has domain $(-\infty, \infty)$, there are no points of discontinuity.

7. The function $y = \dfrac{|x|}{x}$ is equivalent to
$$y = \begin{cases} -1, & x < 0 \\ 1, & x > 0. \end{cases}$$
It has a jump discontinuity at $x = 0$.

8. The function $y = \cot x$ is equivalent to $y = \dfrac{\cos x}{\sin x}$, a quotient of continuous functions, so it is continuous. Its only points of discontinuity occur where it is undefined. It has infinite discontinuities at $x = k\pi$ for all integers k.

9. The function $y = e^{1/x}$ is a composition $(f \circ g)(x)$ of the continuous functions $f(x) = e^x$ and $g(x) = \dfrac{1}{x}$, so it is continuous. Its only point of discontinuity occurs at $x = 0$, where it is undefined. Since $\lim\limits_{x \to 0^+} e^{1/x} = \infty$, this may be considered an infinite discontinuity.

10. The function $y = \ln(x + 1)$ is a composition $(f \circ g)(x)$ of the continuous functions $f(x) = \ln x$ and $g(x) = x + 1$, so it is continuous. Its points of discontinuity are the points not in the domain, i.e., $x < -1$.

11. (a) Yes, $f(-1) = 0$.

    (b) Yes, $\lim\limits_{x \to -1^+} = 0$.

    (c) Yes

    (d) Yes, since -1 is a left endpoint of the domain of f and $\lim\limits_{x \to -1^+} f(x) = f(-1)$, f is continuous at $x = -1$.

12. (a) Yes, $f(1) = 1$.

    (b) Yes, $\lim\limits_{x \to 1} f(x) = 2$.

    (c) No

    (d) No

13. (a) No

    (b) No, since $x = 2$ is not in the domain.

14. Everywhere in $[-1, 3)$ except for $x = 0, 1, 2$.

15. Since $\lim\limits_{x \to 2} f(x) = 0$, we should assign $f(2) = 0$.

16. Since $\lim\limits_{x \to 1} f(x) = 2$, we should reassign $f(1) = 2$.

17. No, because the right-hand and left-hand limits are not the same at zero.

18. Yes. Assign the value 0 to $f(3)$. Since 3 is a right endpoint of the extended function and $\lim\limits_{x \to 3^-} f(x) = 0$, the extended function is continuous at $x = 3$.

19.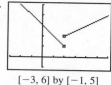

$[-3, 6]$ by $[-1, 5]$

(a) $x = 2$

(b) Not removable, the one-sided limits are different.

20.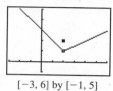

$[-3, 6]$ by $[-1, 5]$

(a) $x = 2$

(b) Removable, assign the value 1 to $f(2)$.

21.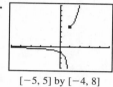

$[-5, 5]$ by $[-4, 8]$

(a) $x = 1$

(b) Not removable, it's an infinite discontinuity.

22.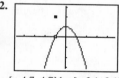

$[-4.7, 4.7]$ by $[-3.1, 3.1]$

(a) $x = -1$

(b) Removable, assign the value 0 to $f(-1)$.

23. (a) All points not in the domain along with $x = 0, 1$

(b) $x = 0$ is a removable discontinuity, assign $f(0) = 0$. $x = 1$ is not removable, the one-sided limits are different.

24. (a) All points not in the domain along with $x = 1, 2$

(b) $x = 1$ is not removable, the one-sided limits are different. $x = 2$ is a removable discontinuity, assign $f(2) = 1$.

25. For $x \neq -3$, $f(x) = \dfrac{x^2 - 9}{x + 3} = \dfrac{(x + 3)(x - 3)}{x + 3} = x - 3$.

The extended function is $y = x - 3$.

26. For $x \neq 1$, $f(x) = \dfrac{x^3 - 1}{x^2 - 1}$

$= \dfrac{(x - 1)(x^2 + x + 1)}{(x + 1)(x - 1)}$

$= \dfrac{x^2 + x + 1}{x + 1}$.

The extended function is $y = \dfrac{x^2 + x + 1}{x + 1}$.

27. Since $\lim\limits_{x \to 0} \dfrac{\sin x}{x} = 1$, the extended function is

$$y = \begin{cases} \dfrac{\sin x}{x}, & x \neq 0 \\ 1, & x = 0. \end{cases}$$

28. Since $\lim\limits_{x \to 0} \dfrac{\sin 4x}{x} = 4 \lim\limits_{x \to 0} \dfrac{\sin 4x}{4x} = 4(1) = 4$, the extended function is

$$y = \begin{cases} \dfrac{\sin 4x}{x}, & x \neq 0 \\ 4, & x = 0. \end{cases}$$

29. For $x \neq 4$ (and $x > 0$),

$$f(x) = \frac{x - 4}{\sqrt{x} - 2} = \frac{(\sqrt{x} + 2)(\sqrt{x} - 2)}{\sqrt{x} - 2} = \sqrt{x} + 2.$$

The extended function is $y = \sqrt{x} + 2$.

30. For $x \neq 2$ (and $x \neq -2$),

$$f(x) = \frac{x^3 - 4x^2 - 11x + 30}{x^2 - 4}$$

$$= \frac{(x - 2)(x - 5)(x + 3)}{(x - 2)(x + 2)}$$

$$= \frac{(x - 5)(x + 3)}{x + 2}$$

$$= \frac{x^2 - 2x - 15}{x + 2}.$$

The extended function is $y = \dfrac{x^2 - 2x - 15}{x + 2}$.

31. One possible answer:
Assume $y = x$, constant functions, and the square root function are continuous.

By the sum theorem, $y = x + 2$ is continuous.

By the composite theorem, $y = \sqrt{x + 2}$ is continuous.

By the quotient theorem, $y = \dfrac{1}{\sqrt{x + 2}}$ is continuous.

Domain: $(-2, \infty)$

32. One possible answer:
Assume $y = x$, constant functions, and the cube root function are continuous.

By the difference theorem, $y = 4 - x$ is continuous.
By the composite theorem, $y = \sqrt[3]{4 - x}$ is continuous.
By the product theorem, $y = x^2 = x \cdot x$ is continuous.
By the sum theorem, $y = x^2 + \sqrt[3]{4 - x}$ is continuous.
Domain: $(-\infty, \infty)$

33. Possible answer:
Assume $y = x$ and $y = |x|$ are continuous.

By the product theorem, $y = x^2 = x \cdot x$ is continuous.
By the constant multiple theorem, $y = 4x$ is continuous.
By the difference theorem, $y = x^2 - 4x$ is continuous.
By the composite theorem, $y = |x^2 - 4x|$ is continuous.
Domain: $(-\infty, \infty)$

34. One possible answer:

Assume $y = x$ and $y = 1$ are continuous.

Use the product, difference, and quotient theorems. One also needs to verify that the limit of this function as x approaches 1 is 2.

Alternately, observe that the function is equivalent to $y = x + 1$ (for all x), which is continuous by the sum theorem.

Domain: $(-\infty, \infty)$

35. One possible answer:

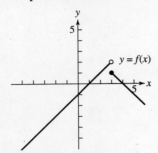

36. One possible answer:

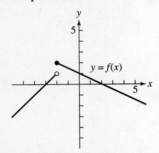

37. One possible answer:

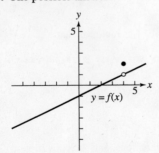

38. One possible answer:

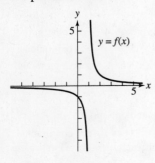

39.

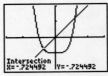

[−3, 3] by [−2, 2]

Solving $x = x^4 - 1$, we obtain the solutions $x \approx -0.724$ and $x \approx 1.221$.

40.

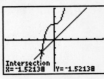

[−6, 6] by [−4, 4]

Solving $x = x^3 + 2$, we obtain the solution $x \approx -1.521$.

41. We require that $\lim\limits_{x \to 3^+} 2ax = \lim\limits_{x \to 3^-} (x^2 - 1)$:

$$2a(3) = 3^2 - 1$$
$$6a = 8$$
$$a = \frac{4}{3}$$

42. Consider $f(x) = x - e^{-x}$. f is continuous, $f(0) = -1$, and $f(1) = 1 - \dfrac{1}{e} > 0.5$. By the Intermediate Value Theorem, for some c in $(0, 1)$, $f(c) = 0$ and $e^{-c} = c$.

43. (a) Sarah's salary is $\$36,500 = \$36,500(1.035)^0$ for the first year ($0 \le t < 1$), $\$36,500(1.035)$ for the second year ($1 \le t < 2$), $\$36,500(1.035)^2$ for the third year ($2 \le t < 3$), and so on. This corresponds to $y = 36,500(1.035)^{\text{int } t}$.

(b)

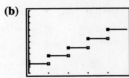

[0, 4.98] by [35,000, 45,000]

The function is continuous at all points in the domain [0, 5) except at $t = 1, 2, 3, 4$.

44. (a) We require:

$$f(x) = \begin{cases} 0 & x = 0 \\ 1.10, & 0 < x \le 1 \\ 2.20, & 1 < x \le 2 \\ 3.30, & 2 < x \le 3 \\ 4.40, & 3 < x \le 4 \\ 5.50, & 4 < x \le 5 \\ 6.60, & 5 < x \le 6 \\ 7.25, & 6 < x \le 24. \end{cases}$$

This may be written more compactly as

$$f(x) = \begin{cases} -1.10 \text{ int}(-x), & 0 \le x \le 6 \\ 7.25, & 6 < x \le 24 \end{cases}$$

(b)

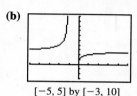

[0, 24] by [0, 9]

This is continuous for all values of x in the domain [0, 24] except for $x = 0, 1, 2, 3, 4, 5, 6$.

45. (a) The function is defined when $1 + \dfrac{1}{x} > 0$, that is, on $(-\infty, -1) \cup (0, \infty)$. (It can be argued that the domain should also include certain values in the interval $(-1, 0)$, namely, those rational numbers that have odd denominators when expressed in lowest terms.)

(b)

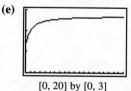

[−5, 5] by [−3, 10]

(c) If we attempt to evaluate $f(x)$ at these values, we obtain
$$f(-1) = \left(1 + \frac{1}{-1}\right)^{-1} = 0^{-1} = \frac{1}{0} \text{ (undefined) and}$$
$$f(0) = \left(1 + \frac{1}{0}\right)^{0} \text{ (undefined). Since } f \text{ is undefined at}$$
these values due to division by zero, both values are points of discontinuity.

(d) The discontinuity at $x = 0$ is removable because the right-hand limit is 0. The discontinuity at $x = -1$ is not removable because it is an infinite discontinuity.

(e)

[0, 20] by [0, 3]

X	Y1
10	2.5937
100	2.7048
1000	2.7169
10000	2.7181
100000	2.7183
1E6	2.7183
1E7	2.7183

Y1 ∎(1+1/X)^X

The limit is about 2.718, or e.

46. This is because $\displaystyle\lim_{h \to 0} f(a + h) = \lim_{x \to a} f(x)$.

47. Suppose not. Then f would be negative somewhere in the interval and positive somewhere else in the interval. So, by the Intermediate Value Theorem, it would have to be zero somewhere in the interval, which contradicts the hypothesis.

48. Since the absolute value function is continuous, this follows from the theorem about continuity of composite functions.

49. For any real number a, the limit of this function as x approaches a cannot exist. This is because as x approaches a, the values of the function will continually oscillate between 0 and 1.

■ Section 2.4 Rates of Change and Tangent Lines (pp. 82–90)

Quick Review 2.4

1. $\Delta x = 3 - (-5) = 8$
$\Delta y = 5 - 2 = 3$

2. $\Delta x = a - 1$
$\Delta y = b - 3$

3. $m = \dfrac{-1 - 3}{5 - (-2)} = \dfrac{-4}{7} = -\dfrac{4}{7}$

4. $m = \dfrac{3 - (-1)}{3 - (-3)} = \dfrac{4}{6} = \dfrac{2}{3}$

5. $y = \dfrac{3}{2}[x - (-2)] + 3$
$y = \dfrac{3}{2}x + 6$

6. $m = \dfrac{-1 - 6}{4 - 1} = \dfrac{-7}{3} = -\dfrac{7}{3}$
$y = -\dfrac{7}{3}(x - 1) + 6$
$y = -\dfrac{7}{3}x + \dfrac{25}{3}$

7. $y = -\dfrac{3}{4}(x - 1) + 4$
$y = -\dfrac{3}{4}x + \dfrac{19}{4}$

8. $m = -\dfrac{1}{-3/4} = \dfrac{4}{3}$
$y = \dfrac{4}{3}(x - 1) + 4$
$y = \dfrac{4}{3}x + \dfrac{8}{3}$

9. Since $2x + 3y = 5$ is equivalent to $y = -\dfrac{2}{3}x + \dfrac{5}{3}$, we use
$m = -\dfrac{2}{3}$.
$y = -\dfrac{2}{3}[x - (-1)] + 3$
$y = -\dfrac{2}{3}x + \dfrac{7}{3}$

10. $\dfrac{b - 3}{4 - 2} = \dfrac{5}{3}$
$b - 3 = \dfrac{10}{3}$
$b = \dfrac{19}{3}$

Section 2.4 Exercises

1. (a) $\dfrac{\Delta f}{\Delta x} = \dfrac{f(3) - f(2)}{3 - 2} = \dfrac{28 - 9}{1} = 19$

(b) $\dfrac{\Delta f}{\Delta x} = \dfrac{f(1) - f(-1)}{1 - (-1)} = \dfrac{2 - 0}{2} = 1$

2. (a) $\dfrac{\Delta f}{\Delta x} = \dfrac{f(2) - f(0)}{2 - 0} = \dfrac{3 - 1}{2} = 1$

(b) $\dfrac{\Delta f}{\Delta x} = \dfrac{f(12) - f(10)}{12 - 10} = \dfrac{7 - \sqrt{41}}{2} \approx 0.298$

3. (a) $\dfrac{\Delta f}{\Delta x} = \dfrac{f(0) - f(-2)}{0 - (-2)} = \dfrac{1 - e^{-2}}{2} \approx 0.432$

(b) $\dfrac{\Delta f}{\Delta x} = \dfrac{f(3) - f(1)}{3 - 1} = \dfrac{e^3 - e}{2} \approx 8.684$

4. (a) $\dfrac{\Delta f}{\Delta x} = \dfrac{f(4) - f(1)}{4 - 1} = \dfrac{\ln 4 - 0}{3} = \dfrac{\ln 4}{3} \approx 0.462$

(b) $\dfrac{\Delta f}{\Delta x} = \dfrac{f(103) - f(100)}{103 - 100} = \dfrac{\ln 103 - \ln 100}{3} = \dfrac{1}{3} \ln \dfrac{103}{100}$

$= \dfrac{1}{3} \ln 1.03 \approx 0.0099$

5. (a) $\dfrac{\Delta f}{\Delta x} = \dfrac{f(3\pi/4) - f(\pi/4)}{(3\pi/4) - (\pi/4)} = \dfrac{-1 - 1}{\pi/2} = -\dfrac{4}{\pi} \approx -1.273$

(b) $\dfrac{\Delta f}{\Delta x} = \dfrac{f(\pi/2) - f(\pi/6)}{(\pi/2) - (\pi/6)} = \dfrac{0 - \sqrt{3}}{\pi/3} = -\dfrac{3\sqrt{3}}{\pi} \approx -1.654$

6. (a) $\dfrac{\Delta f}{\Delta x} = \dfrac{f(\pi) - f(0)}{\pi - 0} = \dfrac{1 - 3}{\pi} = -\dfrac{2}{\pi} \approx -0.637$

(b) $\dfrac{\Delta f}{\Delta x} = \dfrac{f(\pi) - f(-\pi)}{\pi - (-\pi)} = \dfrac{1 - 1}{2\pi} = 0$

7. We use $Q_1 = (10, 225)$, $Q_2 = (14, 375)$, $Q_3 = (16.5, 475)$, $Q_4 = (18, 550)$, and $P = (20, 650)$.

(a) Slope of PQ_1: $\dfrac{650 - 225}{20 - 10} \approx 43$

Slope of PQ_2: $\dfrac{650 - 375}{20 - 14} \approx 46$

slope of PQ_3: $\dfrac{650 - 475}{20 - 16.5} = 50$

Slope of PQ_4: $\dfrac{650 - 550}{20 - 18} = 50$

Secant	Slope
PQ_1	43
PQ_2	46
PQ_3	50
PQ_4	50

The appropriate units are meters per second.

(b) Approximately 50 m/sec

8. We use $Q_1 = (5, 20)$, $Q_2 = (7, 38)$, $Q_3 = (8.5, 56)$, $Q_4 = (9.5, 72)$, and $P = (10, 80)$.

(a) Slope of PQ_1: $\dfrac{80 - 20}{10 - 5} = 12$

Slope of PQ_2: $\dfrac{80 - 38}{10 - 7} = 14$

Slope of PQ_3: $\dfrac{80 - 56}{10 - 8.5} = 16$

Slope of PQ_4: $\dfrac{80 - 72}{10 - 9.5} = 16$

Secant	Slope
PQ_1	12
PQ_2	14
PQ_3	16
PQ_4	16

The appropriate units are meters per second.

(b) Approximately 16 m/sec

9. (a) $\displaystyle\lim_{h \to 0} \dfrac{y(-2 + h) - y(-2)}{h} = \lim_{h \to 0} \dfrac{(-2 + h)^2 - (-2)^2}{h}$

$= \displaystyle\lim_{h \to 0} \dfrac{4 - 4h + h^2 - 4}{h}$

$= \displaystyle\lim_{h \to 0} \dfrac{-4h + h^2}{h}$

$= \displaystyle\lim_{h \to 0} (-4 + h)$

$= -4$

(b) The tangent line has slope -4 and passes through $(-2, y(-2)) = (-2, 4)$.

$y = -4[x - (-2)] + 4$

$y = -4x - 4$

(c) The normal line has slope $-\dfrac{1}{-4} = \dfrac{1}{4}$ and passes through $(-2, y(-2)) = (-2, 4)$.

$y = \dfrac{1}{4}[x - (-2)] + 4$

$y = \dfrac{1}{4}x + \dfrac{9}{2}$

(d)
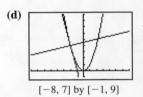

$[-8, 7]$ by $[-1, 9]$

10. (a) $\displaystyle\lim_{h \to 0} \dfrac{y(1 + h) - y(1)}{h}$

$= \displaystyle\lim_{h \to 0} \dfrac{[(1 + h)^2 - 4(1 + h)] - [1^2 - 4(1)]}{h}$

$= \displaystyle\lim_{h \to 0} \dfrac{1 + 2h + h^2 - 4 - 4h + 3}{h}$

$= \displaystyle\lim_{h \to 0} \dfrac{h^2 - 2h}{h}$

$= \displaystyle\lim_{h \to 0} (h - 2)$

$= -2$

(b) The tangent line has slope -2 and passes through $(1, y(1)) = (1, -3)$.

$y = -2(x - 1) - 3$

$y = -2x - 1$

(c) The normal line has slope $-\dfrac{1}{-2} = \dfrac{1}{2}$ and passes through $(1, y(1)) = (1, -3)$.

$y = \dfrac{1}{2}(x - 1) - 3$

$y = \dfrac{1}{2}x - \dfrac{7}{2}$

(d)
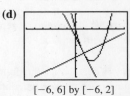

$[-6, 6]$ by $[-6, 2]$

11. (a)
$$\lim_{h\to0}\frac{y(2+h)-y(2)}{h}=\lim_{h\to0}\frac{\frac{1}{(2+h)-1}-\frac{1}{2-1}}{h}$$
$$=\lim_{h\to0}\frac{\frac{1}{h+1}-1}{h}$$
$$=\lim_{h\to0}\frac{1-(h+1)}{h(h+1)}$$
$$=\lim_{h\to0}\left(-\frac{1}{h+1}\right)$$
$$=-1$$

(b) The tangent line has slope -1 and passes through $(2, y(2)) = (2, 1)$.
$$y = -(x-2)+1$$
$$y = -x+3$$

(c) The normal line has slope $-\dfrac{1}{-1}=1$ and passes through $(2, y(2))=(2,1)$.
$$y = 1(x-2)+1$$
$$y = x-1$$

(d)

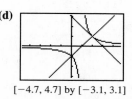

$[-4.7, 4.7]$ by $[-3.1, 3.1]$

12. (a)
$$\lim_{h\to0}\frac{y(0+h)-y(0)}{h}=\lim_{h\to0}\frac{(h^2-3h-1)-(-1)}{h}$$
$$=\lim_{h\to0}\frac{h^2-3h}{h}$$
$$=\lim_{h\to0}(h-3)$$
$$=-3$$

(b) The tangent line has slope -3 and passes through $(0, y(0))=(0,-1)$.
$$y = -3(x-0)-1$$
$$y = -3x-1$$

(c) The normal line has slope $-\dfrac{1}{-3}=\dfrac{1}{3}$ and passes through $(0, y(0))=(0,-1)$.
$$y = \frac{1}{3}(x-0)-1$$
$$y = \frac{1}{3}x-1$$

(d)

$[-6, 6]$ by $[-5, 3]$

13. (a) Near $x=2$, $f(x)=|x|=x$.
$$\lim_{h\to0}\frac{f(2+h)-f(2)}{h}=\lim_{h\to0}\frac{(2+h)-2}{h}=\lim_{h\to0}1=1$$

(b) Near $x=-3$, $f(x)=|x|=-x$.
$$\lim_{h\to0}\frac{f(-3+h)-f(-3)}{h}=\lim_{h\to0}\frac{(3-h)-3}{h}$$
$$=\lim_{h\to0}-1=-1$$

14. Near $x=1$, $f(x)=|x-2|=-(x-2)=2-x$.
$$\lim_{h\to0}\frac{f(1+h)-f(1)}{h}=\lim_{h\to0}\frac{[2-(1+h)]-(2-1)}{h}$$
$$=\lim_{h\to0}\frac{1-h-1}{h}=\lim_{h\to0}-1=-1$$

15. First, note that $f(0)=2$.
$$\lim_{h\to0^-}\frac{f(0+h)-f(0)}{h}=\lim_{h\to0^-}\frac{(2-2h-h^2)-2}{h}$$
$$=\lim_{h\to0^-}\frac{-2h-h^2}{h}$$
$$=\lim_{h\to0^-}(-2-h)$$
$$=-2$$

$$\lim_{h\to0^+}\frac{f(0+h)-f(0)}{h}=\lim_{h\to0^+}\frac{(2h+2)-2}{h}$$
$$=\lim_{h\to0^+}2$$
$$=2$$

No, the slope from the left is -2 and the slope from the right is 2. The two-sided limit of the difference quotient does not exist.

16. First, note that $f(0)=0$.
$$\lim_{h\to0^-}\frac{f(0+h)-f(0)}{h}=\lim_{h\to0^-}\frac{-h-0}{h}=-1$$
$$\lim_{h\to0^+}\frac{f(0+h)-f(0)}{h}=\lim_{h\to0^+}\frac{(h^2-h)-0}{h}$$
$$=\lim_{h\to0^+}(h-1)=-1$$

Yes. The slope is -1.

17. First, note that $f(2)=\dfrac{1}{2}$.
$$\lim_{h\to0^-}\frac{f(2+h)-f(2)}{h}=\lim_{h\to0^-}\frac{\frac{1}{2+h}-\frac{1}{2}}{h}$$
$$=\lim_{h\to0^-}\frac{2-(2+h)}{2h(2+h)}$$
$$=\lim_{h\to0^-}\frac{-h}{2h(2+h)}$$
$$=\lim_{h\to0^-}-\frac{1}{2(2+h)}$$
$$=-\frac{1}{4}$$

17. continued

$$\lim_{h\to 0^+} \frac{f(2+h)-f(2)}{h} = \lim_{h\to 0^+} \frac{\dfrac{4-(2+h)}{4} - \dfrac{1}{2}}{h}$$

$$= \lim_{h\to 0^+} \frac{[4-(2+h)]-2}{4h}$$

$$= \lim_{h\to 0^+} \frac{-h}{4h}$$

$$= -\frac{1}{4}$$

Yes. The slope is $-\dfrac{1}{4}$.

18. No. The function is discontinuous at $x = \dfrac{3\pi}{4}$

because $\lim_{x\to(3\pi/4)^-} f(x) = \lim_{x\to(3\pi/4)^-} \sin x = \sin\dfrac{3\pi}{4} = \dfrac{\sqrt{2}}{2}$

but $f\left(\dfrac{3\pi}{4}\right) = \cos\dfrac{3\pi}{4} = -\dfrac{\sqrt{2}}{2}$.

19. (a) $\lim_{h\to 0} \dfrac{f(a+h)-f(a)}{h} = \lim_{h\to 0} \dfrac{[(a+h)^2+2]-(a^2+2)}{h}$

$$= \lim_{h\to 0} \frac{a^2+2ah+h^2+2-a^2-2}{h}$$

$$= \lim_{h\to 0} \frac{2ah+h^2}{h}$$

$$= \lim_{h\to 0} (2a+h)$$

$$= 2a$$

(b) The slope of the tangent steadily increases as a increases.

20. (a) $\lim_{h\to 0} \dfrac{f(a+h)-f(a)}{h} = \lim_{h\to 0} \dfrac{\dfrac{2}{a+h}-\dfrac{2}{a}}{h}$

$$= \lim_{h\to 0} \frac{2a-2(a+h)}{ah(a+h)}$$

$$= \lim_{h\to 0} \frac{-2}{a(a+h)}$$

$$= -\frac{2}{a^2}$$

(b) The slope of the tangent is always negative. The tangents are very steep near $x = 0$ and nearly horizontal as a moves away from the origin.

21. (a) $\lim_{h\to 0} \dfrac{f(a+h)-f(a)}{h} = \lim_{h\to 0} \dfrac{\dfrac{1}{a+h-1}-\dfrac{1}{a-1}}{h}$

$$= \lim_{h\to 0} \frac{(a-1)-(a+h-1)}{h(a-1)(a+h-1)}$$

$$= \lim_{h\to 0} -\frac{1}{(a-1)(a+h-1)}$$

$$= -\frac{1}{(a-1)^2}$$

(b) The slope of the tangent is always negative. The tangents are very steep near $x = 1$ and nearly horizontal as a moves away from the origin.

22. (a) $\lim_{h\to 0} \dfrac{f(a+h)-f(a)}{h} = \lim_{h\to 0} \dfrac{[9-(a+h)^2]-(9-a^2)}{h}$

$$= \lim_{h\to 0} \frac{9-a^2-2ah-h^2-9+a^2}{h}$$

$$= \lim_{h\to 0} \frac{-2ah-h^2}{h}$$

$$= \lim_{h\to 0} (-2a-h)$$

$$= -2a$$

(b) The slope of the tangent steadily decreases as a increases.

23. Let $f(t) = 100 - 4.9t^2$.

$$\lim_{h\to 0} \frac{f(2+h)-f(2)}{h}$$

$$= \lim_{h\to 0} \frac{[100-4.9(2+h)^2]-[100-4.9(2)^2]}{h}$$

$$= \lim_{h\to 0} \frac{100-19.6-19.6h-4.9h^2-100+19.6}{h}$$

$$= \lim_{h\to 0} (-19.6-4.9h)$$

$$= -19.6$$

The object is falling at a speed of 19.6 m/sec.

24. Let $f(t) = 3t^2$.

$$\lim_{h\to 0} \frac{f(10+h)-f(10)}{h} = \lim_{h\to 0} \frac{3(10+h)^2-300}{h}$$

$$= \lim_{h\to 0} \frac{300+60h+3h^2-300}{h}$$

$$= \lim_{h\to 0} (60+3h)$$

$$= 60$$

The rocket's speed is 60 ft/sec.

25. Let $f(r) = \pi r^2$, the area of a circle of radius r.

$$\lim_{h\to 0} \frac{f(3+h)-f(3)}{h} = \lim_{h\to 0} \frac{\pi(3+h)^2-\pi(3)^2}{h}$$

$$= \lim_{h\to 0} \frac{9\pi+6\pi h+\pi h^2-9\pi}{h}$$

$$= \lim_{h\to 0} (6\pi+\pi h)$$

$$= 6\pi$$

The area is changing at a rate of 6π in^2/in., that is, 6π square inches of area per inch of radius.

26. Let $f(r) = \dfrac{4}{3}\pi r^3$.

$$\lim_{h\to 0} \frac{f(2+h)-f(2)}{h} = \lim_{h\to 0} \frac{\dfrac{4}{3}\pi(2+h)^3-\dfrac{4}{3}\pi(2)^3}{h}$$

$$= \frac{4}{3}\pi \lim_{h\to 0} \frac{(2+h)^3-2^3}{h}$$

$$= \frac{4}{3}\pi \lim_{h\to 0} \frac{8+12h+6h^2+h^3-8}{h}$$

$$= \frac{4}{3}\pi \lim_{h\to 0} (12+6h+h^2)$$

$$= \frac{4}{3}\pi \cdot 12$$

$$= 16\pi$$

The volume is changing at a rate of 16π in^3/in., that is, 16π cubic inches of volume per inch of radius.

27. $\lim\limits_{h\to 0}\dfrac{s(1+h)-s(1)}{h} = \lim\limits_{h\to 0}\dfrac{1.86(1+h)^2 - 1.86(1)^2}{h}$

$\qquad\qquad\qquad = \lim\limits_{h\to 0}\dfrac{1.86 + 3.72h + 1.86h^2 - 1.86}{h}$

$\qquad\qquad\qquad = \lim\limits_{h\to 0}(3.72 + 1.86h)$

$\qquad\qquad\qquad = 3.72$

The speed of the rock is 3.72 m/sec.

28. $\lim\limits_{h\to 0}\dfrac{s(2+h)-s(2)}{h} = \lim\limits_{h\to 0}\dfrac{11.44(2+h)^2 - 11.44(2)^2}{h}$

$\qquad\qquad\qquad = \lim\limits_{h\to 0}\dfrac{45.76 + 45.76h + 11.44h^2 - 45.76}{h}$

$\qquad\qquad\qquad = \lim\limits_{h\to 0}(45.76 + 11.44h)$

$\qquad\qquad\qquad = 45.76$

The speed of the rock is 45.76 m/sec.

29. First, find the slope of the tangent at $x = a$.

$\lim\limits_{h\to 0}\dfrac{f(a+h)-f(a)}{h}$

$= \lim\limits_{h\to 0}\dfrac{[(a+h)^2 + 4(a+h) - 1] - (a^2 + 4a - 1)}{h}$

$= \lim\limits_{h\to 0}\dfrac{a^2 + 2ah + h^2 + 4a + 4h - 1 - a^2 - 4a + 1}{h}$

$= \lim\limits_{h\to 0}\dfrac{2ah + h^2 + 4h}{h}$

$= \lim\limits_{h\to 0}(2a + h + 4)$

$= 2a + 4$

The tangent at $x = a$ is horizontal when $2a + 4 = 0$, or $a = -2$. The tangent line is horizontal at $(-2, f(-2)) = (-2, -5)$.

30. First, find the slope of the tangent at $x = a$.

$\lim\limits_{h\to 0}\dfrac{f(a+h)-f(a)}{h}$

$= \lim\limits_{h\to 0}\dfrac{[3 - 4(a+h) - (a+h)^2] - (3 - 4a - a^2)}{h}$

$= \lim\limits_{h\to 0}\dfrac{3 - 4a - 4h - a^2 - 2ah - h^2 - 3 + 4a + a^2}{h}$

$= \lim\limits_{h\to 0}\dfrac{-4h - 2ah - h^2}{h}$

$= \lim\limits_{h\to 0}(-4 - 2a - h)$

$= -4 - 2a$

The tangent at $x = a$ is horizontal when $-4 - 2a = 0$, or $a = -2$. The tangent line is horizontal at $(-2, f(-2)) = (-2, 7)$.

31. (a) From Exercise 21, the slope of the curve at $x = a$, is $-\dfrac{1}{(a-1)^2}$. The tangent has slope -1 when $-\dfrac{1}{(a-1)^2} = -1$, which gives $(a-1)^2 = 1$, so $a = 0$ or $a = 2$. Note that $y(0) = \dfrac{1}{0-1} = -1$ and $y(2) = \dfrac{1}{2-1} = 1$, so we need to find the equations of lines of slope -1 passing through $(0, -1)$ and $(2, 1)$, respectively.

At $x = 0$: $y = -1(x - 0) - 1$
$\qquad\qquad\;\; y = -x - 1$
At $x = 2$: $y = -1(x - 2) + 1$
$\qquad\qquad\;\; y = -x + 3$

(b) The normal has slope 1 when the tangent has slope $\dfrac{-1}{1} = -1$, so we again need to find lines through $(0, -1)$ and $(2, 1)$, this time using slope 1.

At $x = 0$: $y = 1(x - 0) - 1$
$\qquad\qquad\;\; y = x - 1$
At $x = 2$: $y = 1(x - 2) + 1$
$\qquad\qquad\;\; y = x - 1$

There is only one such line. It is normal to the curve at two points and its equation is $y = x - 1$.

32. Consider a line that passes through $(1, 12)$ and a point $(a, 9 - a^2)$ on the curve. Using the result of Exercise 22, this line will be tangent to the curve at a if its slope is $-2a$.

$$\dfrac{(9 - a^2) - 12}{a - 1} = -2a$$
$$9 - a^2 - 12 = -2a(a - 1)$$
$$-a^2 - 3 = -2a^2 + 2a$$
$$a^2 - 2a - 3 = 0$$
$$(a + 1)(a - 3) = 0$$
$$a = -1 \text{ or } a = 3$$

At $a = -1$ (or $x = -1$), the slope is $-2(-1) = 2$.
$$y = 2(x - 1) + 12$$
$$y = 2x + 10$$
At $a = 3$ (or $x = 3$), the slope is $-2(3) = -6$.
$$y = -6(x - 1) + 12$$
$$y = -6x + 18$$

33. (a) $\dfrac{2.1 - 1.5}{1995 - 1993} = 0.3$

The rate of change was 0.3 billion dollars per year.

(b) $\dfrac{3.1 - 2.1}{1997 - 1995} = 0.5$

The rate of change was 0.5 billion dollars per year.

(c) $y = 0.0571x^2 - 0.1514x + 1.3943$

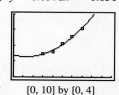

[0, 10] by [0, 4]

33. continued

(d) $\dfrac{y(5) - y(3)}{5 - 3} \approx 0.31$

$\dfrac{y(7) - y(5)}{7 - 5} \approx 0.53$

According to the regression equation, the rates were 0.31 billion dollars per year
and 0.53 billion dollars per year.

(e) $\displaystyle\lim_{h\to0} \frac{y(7+h) - y(7)}{h} = \lim_{h\to0} \frac{[0.0571(7+h)^2 - 0.1514(7+h) + 1.3943] - [0.0571(7)^2 - 0.1514(7) + 13943]}{h}$

$\displaystyle = \lim_{h\to0} \frac{0.0571(14h + h^2) - 0.1514h}{h}$

$\displaystyle = \lim_{h\to0} [0.0571(14) - 0.1514 + 0.0571h]$

≈ 0.65

The funding was growing at a rate of about 0.65 billion dollars per year.

34. (a)

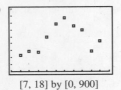

[7, 18] by [0, 900]

(b)

Q from year	Slope
1988	$\dfrac{440 - 225}{17 - 8} \approx 23.9$
1989	$\dfrac{440 - 289}{17 - 9} \approx 18.9$
1990	$\dfrac{440 - 270}{17 - 10} \approx 24.3$
1991	$\dfrac{440 - 493}{17 - 11} \approx -8.8$
1992	$\dfrac{440 - 684}{17 - 12} = -48.8$
1993	$\dfrac{440 - 763}{17 - 13} \approx -80.8$
1994	$\dfrac{440 - 651}{17 - 14} \approx -70.3$
1995	$\dfrac{440 - 600}{17 - 15} = -80.0$
1996	$\dfrac{440 - 296}{17 - 16} = 144.0$

(c) As Q gets closer to 1997, the slopes do not seem to be approaching a limit value.
The years 1995–97 seem to be very unusual and unpredictable.

35. (a) $\dfrac{f(1+h) - f(1)}{h} = \dfrac{e^{1+h} - e}{h}$

(b)

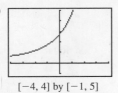

[−4, 4] by [−1, 5]

X	Y1
-.01	2.7047
-5E-4	2.7176
-1E-4	2.7181
0	ERROR
1E-4	2.7184
5E-4	2.719
.01	2.7319

Y1■(e^(1+X)−e^(...

Limit ≈ 2.718

(c) They're about the same.

(d) Yes, it has a tangent whose slope is about e.

36. (a) $\dfrac{f(1+h)-f(1)}{h} = \dfrac{2^{1+h}-2}{h}$

(b)

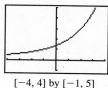

[−4, 4] by [−1, 5]

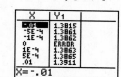

X	Y1
-.01	1.3815
-5E-4	1.3861
-1E-4	1.3862
0	ERROR
1E-4	1.3863
5E-4	1.3865
.01	1.3911

X= -.01

Limit ≈ 1.386

(c) They're about the same.

(d) Yes, it has a tangent whose slope is about ln 4.

37. Let $f(x) = x^{2/5}$. The graph of $y = \dfrac{f(0+h)-f(0)}{h} = \dfrac{f(h)}{h}$

is shown.

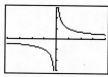

[−4, 4] by [−3, 3]

The left- and right-hand limits are $-\infty$ and ∞, respectively. Since they are not the same, the curve does not have a vertical tangent at $x = 0$. No.

38. Let $f(x) = x^{3/5}$. The graph of $y = \dfrac{f(0+h)-f(0)}{h} = \dfrac{f(h)}{h}$ is shown.

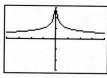

[−4, 4] by [−3, 3]

Yes, the curve has a vertical tangent at $x = 0$ because

$$\lim_{h \to 0} \frac{f(0+h)-f(0)}{h} = \infty.$$

39. Let $f(x) = x^{1/3}$. The graph of $y = \dfrac{f(0+h)-f(0)}{h} = \dfrac{f(h)}{h}$ is shown.

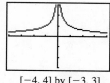

[−4, 4] by [−3, 3]

Yes, the curve has a vertical tangent at $x = 0$ because

$$\lim_{h \to 0} \frac{f(0+h)-f(0)}{h} = \infty.$$

40. Let $f(x) = x^{2/3}$. The graph of $y = \dfrac{f(0+h)-f(0)}{h} = \dfrac{f(h)}{h}$ is shown.

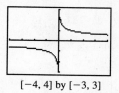

[−4, 4] by [−3, 3]

The left- and right-hand limits are $-\infty$ and ∞, respectively. Since they are not the same, the curve does not have a vertical tangent at $x = 0$. No.

41. This function has a tangent with slope zero at the origin. It is sandwiched between two functions, $y = x^2$ and $y = -x^2$, both of which have slope zero at the origin.

Looking at the difference quotient,

$$-h \le \frac{f(0+h)-f(0)}{h} \le h,$$

so the Sandwich Theorem tells us the limit is 0.

42. This function does not have a tangent line at the origin. As the function oscillates between $y = x$ and $y = -x$ infinitely often near the origin, there are an infinite number of difference quotients (secant line slopes) with a value of 1 and with a value of -1. Thus the limit of the difference quotient doesn't exist.

The difference quotient is $\dfrac{f(0+h)-f(0)}{h} = \sin\dfrac{1}{h}$ which oscillates between 1 and -1 infinitely often near zero.

43. Let $f(x) = \sin x$. The difference quotient is

$$\frac{f(1+h)-f(1)}{h} = \frac{\sin(1+h)-\sin(1)}{h}.$$

A graph and table for the difference quotient are shown.

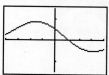

[−4, 4] by [−1.5, 1.5]

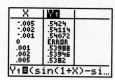

X	Y1
-.005	.5424
-.002	.54114
-.001	.54072
0	ERROR
.001	.53988
.002	.53946
.005	.5382

Y1■(sin(1+X)-si...

Since the limit as $h \to 0$ is about 0.540, the slope of $y = \sin x$ at $x = 1$ is about 0.540.

■ Chapter 2 Review Exercises
(pp. 91–93)

1. $\lim\limits_{x\to-2} (x^3 - 2x^2 + 1) = (-2)^3 - 2(-2)^2 + 1 = -15$

2. $\lim\limits_{x\to-2} \dfrac{x^2 + 1}{3x^2 - 2x + 5} = \dfrac{(-2)^2 + 1}{3(-2)^2 - 2(-2) + 5} = \dfrac{5}{21}$

3. No limit, because the expression $\sqrt{1 - 2x}$ is undefined for values of x near 4.

4. No limit, because the expression $\sqrt[4]{9 - x^2}$ is undefined for values of x near 5.

5. $\lim\limits_{x\to0} \dfrac{\frac{1}{2+x} - \frac{1}{2}}{x} = \lim\limits_{x\to0} \dfrac{2 - (2 + x)}{2x(2 + x)} = \lim\limits_{x\to0} \dfrac{-x}{2x(2 + x)}$

$= \lim\limits_{x\to0} \left(-\dfrac{1}{2(2 + x)}\right) = -\dfrac{1}{2(2 + 0)} = -\dfrac{1}{4}$

6. $\lim\limits_{x\to\pm\infty} \dfrac{2x^2 + 3}{5x^2 + 7} = \lim\limits_{x\to\pm\infty} \dfrac{2x^2}{5x^2} = \dfrac{2}{5}$

7. An end behavior model for $\dfrac{x^4 + x^3}{12x^3 + 128}$ is $\dfrac{x^4}{12x^3} = \dfrac{1}{12}x$.

Therefore:

$\lim\limits_{x\to\infty} \dfrac{x^4 + x^3}{12x^3 + 128} = \lim\limits_{x\to\infty} \dfrac{1}{12}x = \infty$

$\lim\limits_{x\to-\infty} \dfrac{x^4 + x^3}{12x^3 + 128} = \lim\limits_{x\to-\infty} \dfrac{1}{12}x = -\infty$

8. $\lim\limits_{x\to0} \dfrac{\sin 2x}{4x} = \dfrac{1}{2} \lim\limits_{x\to0} \dfrac{\sin 2x}{2x} = \dfrac{1}{2}(1) = \dfrac{1}{2}$

9. Multiply the numerator and denominator by $\sin x$.

$\lim\limits_{x\to0} \dfrac{x\csc x + 1}{x\csc x} = \lim\limits_{x\to0} \dfrac{x + \sin x}{x} = \lim\limits_{x\to0} \left(1 + \dfrac{\sin x}{x}\right)$

$= \left(\lim\limits_{x\to0} 1\right) + \left(\lim\limits_{x\to0} \dfrac{\sin x}{x}\right) = 1 + 1 = 2$

10. $\lim\limits_{x\to0} e^x \sin x = e^0 \sin 0 = 1 \cdot 0 = 0$

11. Let $x = \dfrac{7}{2} + h$, where h is in $\left(0, \dfrac{1}{2}\right)$. Then

$\text{int}\,(2x - 1) = \text{int}\left[2\left(\dfrac{7}{2}\right) + 2h - 1\right] = \text{int}\,(6 + 2h) = 6,$

because $6 + 2h$ is in $(6, 7)$.

Therefore, $\lim\limits_{x\to7/2^+} \text{int}\,(2x - 1) = \lim\limits_{x\to7/2^+} 6 = 6.$

12. Let $x = \dfrac{7}{2} + h$, where h is in $\left(-\dfrac{1}{2}, 0\right)$. Then

$\text{int}\,(2x - 1) = \text{int}\left[2\left(\dfrac{7}{2}\right) + 2h - 1\right] = \text{int}\,(6 + 2h) = 5,$

because $6 + 2h$ is in $(5, 6)$.

Therefore, $\lim\limits_{x\to7/2^-} \text{int}\,(2x - 1) = \lim\limits_{x\to7/2^-} 5 = 5$

13. Since $\lim\limits_{x\to\infty} (-e^{-x}) = \lim\limits_{x\to\infty} e^{-x} = 0$, and $-e^{-x} \le e^{-x} \cos x \le e^{-x}$ for all x, the Sandwich Theorem gives $\lim\limits_{x\to\infty} e^{-x} \cos x = 0$.

14. Since the expression x is an end behavior model for both $x + \sin x$ and $x + \cos x$, $\lim\limits_{x\to\infty} \dfrac{x + \sin x}{x + \cos x} = \lim\limits_{x\to\infty} \dfrac{x}{x} = 1$.

15. Limit exists.

16. Limit exists.

17. Limit exists.

18. Limit does not exist.

19. Limit exists.

20. Limit exists.

21. Yes

22. No

23. No

24. Yes

25. (a) $\lim\limits_{x\to3^-} g(x) = 1$

(b) $g(3) = 1.5$

(c) No, since $\lim\limits_{x\to3^-} g(x) \ne g(3)$.

(d) g is discontinuous at $x = 3$ (and at points not in the domain).

(e) Yes, the discontinuity at $x = 3$ can be removed by assigning the value 1 to $g(3)$.

26. (a) $\lim\limits_{x\to1^-} k(x) = 1.5$

(b) $\lim\limits_{x\to1^+} k(x) = 0$

(c) $k(1) = 0$

(d) No, since $\lim\limits_{x\to1^-} k(x) \ne k(1)$

(e) k is discontinuous at $x = 1$ (and at points not in the domain).

(f) No, the discontinuity at $x = 1$ is not removable because the one-sided limits are different.

27.

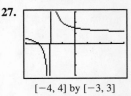

[−4, 4] by [−3, 3]

(a) Vertical asymptote: $x = -2$

(b) Left-hand limit $= \lim\limits_{x\to-2^-} \dfrac{x + 3}{x + 2} = -\infty$

Right-hand limit: $\lim\limits_{x\to-2^+} \dfrac{x + 3}{x + 2} = \infty$

28.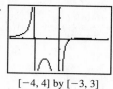

$[-4, 4]$ by $[-3, 3]$

(a) Vertical asymptotes: $x = 0$, $x = -2$

(b) At $x = 0$:

Left-hand limit $= \lim\limits_{x \to 0^-} \dfrac{x - 1}{x^2(x + 2)} = -\infty$

Right-hand limit $= \lim\limits_{x \to 0^+} \dfrac{x - 1}{x^2(x + 2)} = -\infty$

At $x = -2$:

Left-hand limit $= \lim\limits_{x \to -2^-} \dfrac{x - 1}{x^2(x + 2)} = \infty$

Right-hand limit $= \lim\limits_{x \to -2^+} \dfrac{x - 1}{x^2(x + 2)} = -\infty$

29. (a) At $x = -1$:

Left-hand limit $= \lim\limits_{x \to -1^-} f(x) = \lim\limits_{x \to -1^-} (1) = 1$

Right-hand limit $= \lim\limits_{x \to -1^+} f(x) = \lim\limits_{x \to -1^+} (-x) = 1$

At $x = 0$:

Left-hand limit $= \lim\limits_{x \to 0^-} f(x) = \lim\limits_{x \to 0^-} (-x) = 0$

Right-hand limit $= \lim\limits_{x \to 0^+} f(x) = \lim\limits_{x \to 0^+} (-x) = 0$

At $x = 1$:

Left-hand limit $= \lim\limits_{x \to 1^-} f(x) = \lim\limits_{x \to 1^-} (-x) = -1$

Right-hand limit $= \lim\limits_{x \to 1^+} f(x) = \lim\limits_{x \to 1^+} (1) = 1$

(b) At $x = -1$: Yes, the limit is 1.
At $x = 0$: Yes, the limit is 0.
At $x = 1$: No, the limit doesn't exist because the two one-sided limits are different.

(c) At $x = -1$: Continuous because $f(-1) =$ the limit.
At $x = 0$: Discontinuous because $f(0) \neq$ the limit.
At $x = 1$: Discontinuous because the limit does not exist.

30. (a) Left-hand limit $= \lim\limits_{x \to 1^-} f(x) = \lim\limits_{x \to 1^-} |x^3 - 4x|$

$= |(1)^3 - 4(1)| = |-3| = 3$

Right-hand limit $= \lim\limits_{x \to 1^+} f(x) = \lim\limits_{x \to 1^+} (x^2 - 2x - 2)$

$= (1)^2 - 2(1) - 2 = -3$

(b) No, because the two one-sided limits are different.

(c) Every place except for $x = 1$

(d) At $x = 1$

31. Since $f(x)$ is a quotient of polynomials, it is continuous and its points of discontinuity are the points where it is undefined, namely $x = -2$ and $x = 2$.

32. There are no points of discontinuity, since $g(x)$ is continuous and defined for all real numbers.

33. (a) End behavior model: $\dfrac{2x}{x^2}$, or $\dfrac{2}{x}$

(b) Horizontal asymptote: $y = 0$ (the x-axis)

34. (a) End behavior model: $\dfrac{2x^2}{x^2}$, or 2

(b) Horizontal asymptote: $y = 2$

35. (a) End behavior model: $\dfrac{x^3}{x}$, or x^2

(b) Since the end behavior model is quadratic, there are no horizontal asymptotes.

36. (a) End behavior model: $\dfrac{x^4}{x^3}$, or x

(b) Since the end behavior model represents a nonhorizontal line, there are no horizontal asymptotes.

37. (a) Since $\lim\limits_{x \to \infty} \dfrac{x + e^x}{e^x} = \lim\limits_{x \to \infty} \left(\dfrac{x}{e^x} + 1 \right) = 1$, a right end behavior model is e^x.

(b) Since $\lim\limits_{x \to -\infty} \dfrac{x + e^x}{x} = \lim\limits_{x \to -\infty} \left(1 + \dfrac{e^x}{x} \right) = 1$, a left end behavior model is x.

38. (a, b) Note that $\lim\limits_{x \to \pm\infty} \left(-\dfrac{1}{\ln|x|} \right) = \lim\limits_{x \to \pm\infty} \left(\dfrac{1}{\ln|x|} \right) = 0$ and $-\dfrac{1}{\ln|x|} < \dfrac{\sin x}{\ln|x|} < \dfrac{1}{\ln|x|}$ for all $x \neq 0$.

Therefore, the Sandwich Theorem gives

$\lim\limits_{x \to \pm\infty} \dfrac{\sin x}{\ln|x|} = 0$. Hence

$\lim\limits_{x \to \pm\infty} \dfrac{\ln|x| + \sin x}{\ln|x|} = \lim\limits_{x \to \pm\infty} \left(1 + \dfrac{\sin x}{\ln|x|} \right) = 1 + 0 = 1$,

so $\ln|x|$ is both a right end behavior model and a left end behavior model.

39. $\lim\limits_{x \to 3} f(x) = \lim\limits_{x \to 3} \dfrac{x^2 + 2x - 15}{x - 3} = \lim\limits_{x \to 3} \dfrac{(x - 3)(x + 5)}{x - 3}$

$= \lim\limits_{x \to 3} (x + 5) = 3 + 5 = 8$.

Assign the value $k = 8$.

40. $\lim\limits_{x \to 0} f(x) = \lim\limits_{x \to 0} \dfrac{\sin x}{2x} = \dfrac{1}{2} \lim\limits_{x \to 0} \dfrac{\sin x}{x} = \dfrac{1}{2}(1) = \dfrac{1}{2}$

Assign the value $k = \dfrac{1}{2}$.

41. One possible answer:

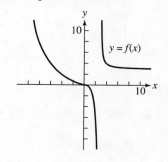

42. One possible answer:

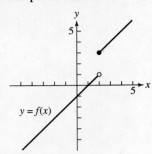

$y = f(x)$

43. $\dfrac{f(\pi/2) - f(0)}{\pi/2 - 0} = \dfrac{2 - 1}{\pi/2} = \dfrac{2}{\pi}$

44. $\displaystyle\lim_{h\to 0} \dfrac{V(a + h) - V(a)}{h} = \lim_{h\to 0} \dfrac{\frac{1}{3}\pi(a+h)^2 H - \frac{1}{3}\pi a^2 H}{h}$

$= \dfrac{1}{3}\pi H \displaystyle\lim_{h\to 0} \dfrac{a^2 + 2ah + h^2 - a^2}{h}$

$= \dfrac{1}{3}\pi H \displaystyle\lim_{h\to 0} (2a + h)$

$= \dfrac{1}{3}\pi H(2a)$

$= \dfrac{2}{3}\pi aH$

45. $\displaystyle\lim_{h\to 0} \dfrac{S(a + h) - S(a)}{h} = \lim_{h\to 0} \dfrac{6(a + h)^2 - 6a^2}{h}$

$= \displaystyle\lim_{h\to 0} \dfrac{6a^2 + 12ah + 6h^2 - 6a^2}{h}$

$= \displaystyle\lim_{h\to 0} (12a + 6h)$

$= 12a$

46. $\displaystyle\lim_{h\to 0} \dfrac{y(a + h) - y(a)}{h}$

$= \displaystyle\lim_{h\to 0} \dfrac{[(a + h)^2 - (a + h) - 2] - (a^2 - a - 2)}{h}$

$= \displaystyle\lim_{h\to 0} \dfrac{a^2 + 2ah + h^2 - a - h - 2 - a^2 + a + 2}{h}$

$= \displaystyle\lim_{h\to 0} \dfrac{2ah + h^2 - h}{h}$

$= \displaystyle\lim_{h\to 0} (2a + h - 1)$

$= 2a - 1$

47. (a) $\displaystyle\lim_{h\to 0} \dfrac{f(1 + h) - f(1)}{h} = \lim_{h\to 0} \dfrac{[(1 + h)^2 - 3(1 + h)] - (-2)}{h}$

$= \displaystyle\lim_{h\to 0} \dfrac{1 + 2h + h^2 - 3 - 3h + 2}{h}$

$= \displaystyle\lim_{h\to 0} (-1 + h)$

$= -1$

(b) The tangent at P has slope -1 and passes through $(1, -2)$.
$y = -1(x - 1) - 2$
$y = -x - 1$

(c) The normal at P has slope 1 and passes through $(1, -2)$.
$y = 1(x - 1) - 2$
$y = x - 3$

48. At $x = a$, the slope of the curve is

$\displaystyle\lim_{h\to 0} \dfrac{f(a + h) - f(a)}{h} = \lim_{h\to 0} \dfrac{[(a + h)^2 - 3(a + h)] - (a^2 - 3a)}{h}$

$= \displaystyle\lim_{h\to 0} \dfrac{a^2 + 2ah + h^2 - 3a - 3h - a^2 + 3a}{h}$

$= \displaystyle\lim_{h\to 0} \dfrac{2ah - 3h + h^2}{h}$

$= \displaystyle\lim_{h\to 0} (2a - 3 + h)$

$= 2a - 3$

The tangent is horizontal when $2a - 3 = 0$, at $a = \dfrac{3}{2}$ $\left(\text{or } x = \dfrac{3}{2}\right)$. Since $f\left(\dfrac{3}{2}\right) = -\dfrac{9}{4}$, the point where this occurs is $\left(\dfrac{3}{2}, -\dfrac{9}{4}\right)$.

49. (a) $p(0) = \dfrac{200}{1 + 7e^{-0.1(0)}} = \dfrac{200}{8} = 25$

Perhaps this is the number of bears placed in the reserve when it was established.

(b) $\displaystyle\lim_{t\to\infty} p(t) = \lim_{t\to\infty} \dfrac{200}{1 + 7e^{-0.1t}} = \dfrac{200}{1} = 200$

(c) Perhaps this is the maximum number of bears which the reserve can support due to limitations of food, space, or other resources. Or, perhaps the number is capped at 200 and excess bears are moved to other locations.

50. (a) $f(x) = \begin{cases} 3.20 - 1.35 \text{ int } (-x + 1), & 0 < x \le 20 \\ 0, & x = 0 \end{cases}$

(Note that we cannot use the formula $f(x) = 3.20 + 1.35 \text{ int } x$, because it gives incorrect results when x is an integer.)

(b)

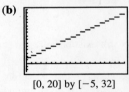

[0, 20] by [−5, 32]

f is discontinuous at integer values of x: 0, 1, 2, ..., 19.

51. (a) Cubic: $y = -1.644x^3 + 42.981x^2 - 254.369x + 300.232$
Quartic: $y = 2.009x^4 - 102.081x^3 + 1884.997x^2 - 14918.180x + 43004.464$

(b) Cubic: $-1.644x^3$, predicts spending will go to 0
Quartic: $2.009x^4$, predicts spending will go to ∞

52. Let $A = \displaystyle\lim_{x\to c} f(x)$ and $B = \lim_{x\to c} g(x)$. Then $A + B = 2$ and $A - B = 1$. Adding, we have $2A = 3$, so $A = \dfrac{3}{2}$, whence $\dfrac{3}{2} + B = 2$, which gives $B = \dfrac{1}{2}$. Therefore, $\displaystyle\lim_{x\to c} f(x) = \dfrac{3}{2}$ and $\displaystyle\lim_{x\to c} g(x) = \dfrac{1}{2}$.

53. (a)

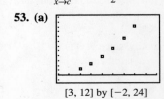

[3, 12] by [−2, 24]

(b)

Year of Q	Slope of PQ
1995	$\dfrac{20.1 - 2.7}{2000 - 1995} = 3.48$
1996	$\dfrac{20.1 - 4.8}{2000 - 1996} = 3.825$
1997	$\dfrac{20.1 - 7.8}{2000 - 1997} = 4.1$
1998	$\dfrac{20.1 - 11.2}{2000 - 1998} = 4.45$
1999	$\dfrac{20.1 - 15.2}{2000 - 1999} = 4.9$

(c) Approximately 5 billion dollars per year.

(d) $y = 0.3214x^2 - 1.3471x + 1.3857$

$$\lim_{h \to 0} \frac{y(10 + h) - y(10)}{h} = \lim_{h \to 0} \frac{[0.3214(10 + h)^2 - 1.3471(10 + h) + 1.3857] - [0.3214(10)^2 - 1.3471(10) + 1.3857]}{h}$$

$$= \lim_{h \to 0} \frac{0.3214(20h + h^2) - 1.3471h}{h}$$

$$= 0.3214(20) - 1.3471$$

$$\approx 5.081$$

The predicted rate of change in 2000 is about
5.081 billion dollars per year.

Chapter 3
Derivatives

■ Section 3.1 Derivative of a Function (pp. 95–104)

Exploration 1 Reading the Graphs

1. The graph in Figure 3.3b represents the rate of change of the depth of the water in the ditch with respect to time. Since y is measured in inches and x is measured in days, the derivative $\dfrac{dy}{dx}$ would be measured in inches per day. Those are the units that should be used along the y-axis in Figure 3.3b.

2. The water in the ditch is 1 inch deep at the start of the first day and rising rapidly. It continues to rise, at a gradually decreasing rate, until the end of the second day, when it achieves a maximum depth of 5 inches. During days 3, 4, 5, and 6, the water level goes down, until it reaches a depth of 1 inch at the end of day 6. During the seventh day it rises again, almost to a depth of 2 inches.

3. The weather appears to have been wettest at the beginning of day 1 (when the water level was rising fastest) and driest at the end of day 4 (when the water level was declining the fastest).

4. The highest point on the graph of the derivative shows where the water is rising the fastest, while the lowest point (most negative) on the graph of the derivative shows where the water is declining the fastest.

5. The y-coordinate of point C gives the maximum depth of the water level in the ditch over the 7-day period, while the x-coordinate of C gives the time during the 7-day period that the maximum depth occurred. The derivative of the function changes sign from positive to negative at C', indicating that this is when the water level stops rising and begins falling.

6. Water continues to run down sides of hills and through underground streams long after the rain has stopped falling. Depending on how much high ground is located near the ditch, water from the first day's rain could still be flowing into the ditch several days later. Engineers responsible for flood control of major rivers must take this into consideration when they predict when floodwaters will "crest," and at what levels.

Quick Review 3.1

1. $\lim\limits_{h\to 0} \frac{(2 + h)^2 - 4}{4} = \lim\limits_{h\to 0} \frac{(4 + 4h + h^2) - 4}{h}$
$\qquad\qquad = \lim\limits_{h\to 0} 4 + h$
$\qquad\qquad = 4 + 0 = 4$

2. $\lim\limits_{x\to 2^+} \frac{x + 3}{2} = \frac{2 + 3}{2} = \frac{5}{2}$

3. Since $\frac{|y|}{y} = -1$ for $y < 0$, $\lim\limits_{y\to 0^-} \frac{|y|}{y} = -1$.

4. $\lim\limits_{x\to 4} \frac{2x - 8}{\sqrt{x} - 2} = \lim\limits_{x\to 4} \frac{2(\sqrt{x} + 2)(\sqrt{x} - 2)}{\sqrt{x} - 2}$
$\qquad = \lim\limits_{h\to 4} 2(\sqrt{x} + 2) = 2(\sqrt{4} + 2) = 8$

5. The vertex of the parabola is at $(0, 1)$. The slope of the line

through $(0, 1)$ and another point $(h, h^2 + 1)$ on the parabola

is $\frac{(h^2 + 1) - 1}{h - 0} = h$. Since $\lim\limits_{h\to 0} h = 0$, the slope of the line

tangent to the parabola at its vertex is 0.

6. Use the graph of f in the window $[-6, 6]$ by $[-4, 4]$ to find
that $(0, 2)$ is the coordinate of the high point and $(2, -2)$ is
the coordinate of the low point. Therefore, f is increasing
on $(-\infty, 0]$ and $[2, \infty)$.

7. $\lim\limits_{x\to 1^+} f(x) = \lim\limits_{x\to 1^+} (x - 1)^2 = (1 - 1)^2 = 0$
$\lim\limits_{x\to 1^-} f(x) = \lim\limits_{x\to 1^-} (x + 2) = 1 + 2 = 3$

8. $\lim\limits_{h\to 0^+} f(1 + h) = \lim\limits_{x\to 1^+} f(x) = 0$

9. No, the two one-sided limits are different (see Exercise 7).

10. No, f is discontinuous at $x = 1$ because $\lim\limits_{x\to 1} f(x)$ does not

exist.

Section 3.1 Exercises

1. (a) The tangent line has slope 5 and passes through $(2, 3)$.
$\quad y = 5(x - 2) + 3$
$\quad y = 5x - 7$

(b) The normal line has slope $-\frac{1}{5}$ and passes through

$(2, 3)$.

$\quad y = -\frac{1}{5}(x - 2) + 3$
$\quad y = -\frac{1}{5}x + \frac{17}{5}$

2. $f'(3) = \lim\limits_{h\to 0} \frac{f(3 + h) - f(3)}{h}$
$\qquad = \lim\limits_{h\to 0} \frac{\frac{1}{3 + h} - \frac{1}{3}}{h}$
$\qquad = \lim\limits_{h\to 0} \frac{3 - (3 + h)}{3h(3 + h)}$
$\qquad = \lim\limits_{h\to 0} \frac{-1}{3(3 + h)} = -\frac{1}{9}$

3. $f'(3) = \lim\limits_{x\to 3} \frac{f(x) - f(3)}{x - 3}$
$\qquad = \lim\limits_{x\to 3} \frac{\frac{1}{x} - \frac{1}{3}}{x - 3}$
$\qquad = \lim\limits_{x\to 3} \frac{3 - x}{(x - 3)(x)(3)}$
$\qquad = \lim\limits_{x\to 3} -\frac{1}{3x} = -\frac{1}{9}$

4. $f'(x) = \lim\limits_{h\to 0} \frac{f(x + h) - f(x)}{h}$
$\qquad = \lim\limits_{h\to 0} \frac{[3(x + h) - 12] - (3x - 12)}{h}$
$\qquad = \lim\limits_{h\to 0} \frac{3h}{h} = \lim\limits_{h\to 0} 3 = 3$

5. $\frac{dy}{dx} = \lim\limits_{h\to 0} \frac{y(x + h) - y(x)}{h}$
$\qquad = \lim\limits_{h\to 0} \frac{7(x + h) - 7x}{h}$
$\qquad = \lim\limits_{h\to 0} \frac{7h}{h} = \lim\limits_{h\to 0} 7 = 7$

6. Let $f(x) = x^2$.

$\quad \frac{d}{dx}(x^2) = f'(x) = \lim\limits_{h\to 0} \frac{f(x + h) - f(x)}{h}$
$\qquad = \lim\limits_{h\to 0} \frac{(x + h)^2 - x^2}{h}$
$\qquad = \lim\limits_{h\to 0} \frac{x^2 + 2xh + h^2 - x^2}{h}$
$\qquad = \lim\limits_{h\to 0} (2x + h) = 2x$

7. The graph of $y = f_1(x)$ is decreasing for $x < 0$ and
increasing for $x > 0$, so its derivative is negative for $x < 0$
and positive for $x > 0$. (b)

8. The graph of $y = f_2(x)$ is always increasing, so its derivative
is always ≥ 0. (a)

9. The graph of $y = f_3(x)$ oscillates between increasing and
decreasing, so its derivative oscillates between positive and
negative. (d)

10. The graph of $y = f_4(x)$ is decreasing, then increasing, then
decreasing, and then increasing, so its derivative is
negative, then positive, then negative, and then positive. (c)

11. $\dfrac{dy}{dx} = \lim\limits_{h \to 0} \dfrac{y(x + h) - y(x)}{h}$

$= \lim\limits_{h \to 0} \dfrac{[2(x + h)^2 - 13(x + h) + 5] - (2x^2 - 13x + 5)}{h}$

$= \lim\limits_{h \to 0} \dfrac{2x^2 + 4xh + 2h^2 - 13x - 13h + 5 - 2x^2 + 13x - 5}{h}$

$= \lim\limits_{h \to 0} \dfrac{4xh + 2h^2 - 13h}{h}$

$= \lim\limits_{h \to 0} (4x + 2h - 13) = 4x - 13$

At $x = 3$, $\dfrac{dy}{dx} = 4(3) - 13 = -1$, so the tangent line has

slope -1 and passes through $(3, y(3)) = (3, -16)$.

$y = -1(x - 3) - 16$

$y = -x - 13$

12. Let $f(x) = x^3$.

$f'(1) = \lim\limits_{h \to 0} \dfrac{f(1 + h) - f(1)}{h}$

$= \lim\limits_{h \to 0} \dfrac{(1 + h)^3 - 1^3}{h}$

$= \lim\limits_{h \to 0} \dfrac{1 + 3h + 3h^2 + h^3 - 1}{h}$

$= \lim\limits_{h \to 0} (3 + 3h + h^2) = 3$

(a) The tangent line has slope 3 and passes through $(1, 1)$. Its equation is $y = 3(x - 1) + 1$, or $y = 3x - 2$.

(b) The normal line has slope $-\dfrac{1}{3}$ and passes through

$(1, 1)$. Its equation is $y = -\dfrac{1}{3}(x - 1) + 1$, or

$y = -\dfrac{1}{3}x + \dfrac{4}{3}$.

13. Since the graph of $y = x \ln x - x$ is decreasing for $0 < x < 1$ and increasing for $x > 1$, its derivative is negative for $0 < x < 1$ and positive for $x > 1$. The only one of the given functions with this property is $y = \ln x$. Note also that $y = \ln x$ is undefined for $x < 0$, which further agrees with the given graph. (ii)

14. Each of the functions $y = \sin x$, $y = x$, $y = \sqrt{x}$ has the

property that $y(0) = 0$ but the graph has nonzero slope (or

undefined slope) at $x = 0$, so none of these functions can be

its own derivative. The function $y = x^2$ is not its own

derivative because $y(1) = 1$ but

$y'(1) = \lim\limits_{h \to 0} \dfrac{(1 + h)^2 - 1^2}{h} = \lim\limits_{h \to 0} \dfrac{2h + h^2}{h}$

$= \lim\limits_{h \to 0} (2 + h) = 2$.

This leaves only e^x, which can plausibly be its own derivative because both the function value and the slope increase from very small positive values to very large values as we move from left to right along the graph. (iv)

15. (a) The amount of daylight is increasing at the fastest rate when the slope of the graph is largest. This occurs about one-fourth of the way through the year, sometime around April 1. The rate at this time is approximately $\dfrac{4 \text{ hours}}{24 \text{ days}}$ or $\dfrac{1}{6}$ hour per day.

(b) Yes, the rate of change is zero when the tangent to the graph is horizontal. This occurs near the beginning of the year and halfway through the year, around January 1 and July 1.

(c) Positive: January 1 through July 1
Negative: July 1 through December 31

16. The slope of the given graph is zero at $x \approx -2$ and at $x \approx 1$, so the derivative graph includes $(-2, 0)$ and $(1, 0)$. The slopes at $x = -3$ and at $x = 2$ are about 5 and the slope at $x = -0.5$ is about -2.5, so the derivative graph includes $(-3, 5)$, $(2, 5)$, and $(-0.5, -2.5)$. Connecting the points smoothly, we obtain the graph shown.

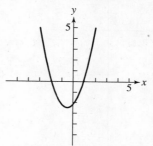

17. (a) Using Figure 3.10a, the number of rabbits is largest after 40 days and smallest from about 130 to 200 days. Using Figure 3.10b, the derivative is 0 at these times.

(b) Using Figure 3.10b, the derivative is largest after 20 days and smallest after about 63 days. Using Figure 3.10a, there were 1700 and about 1300 rabbits, respectively, at these times.

18. (a) The slope from $x = -4$ to $x = 0$ is $\dfrac{2 - 0}{0 - (-4)} = \dfrac{1}{2}$.

The slope from $x = 0$ to $x = 1$ is $\dfrac{-2 - 2}{1 - 0} = -4$.

The slope from $x = 1$ to $x = 4$ is $\dfrac{-2 - (-2)}{4 - 1} = 0$.

The slope from $x = 4$ to $x = 6$ is $\dfrac{2 - (-2)}{6 - 4} = 2$.

Note that the derivative is undefined at $x = 0$, $x = 1$, and $x = 4$. (The function is differentiable at $x = -4$ and at $x = 6$ because these are endpoints of the domain and the one-sided derivatives exist.) The graph of the derivative is shown.

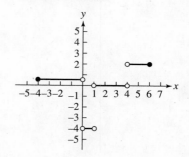

18. continued

(b) $x = 0, 1, 4$

19.

Midpoint of Interval (x)	Slope $\left(\dfrac{\Delta y}{\Delta x}\right)$
0.5	$\dfrac{3.3 - 0}{1 - 0} = 3.3$
1.5	$\dfrac{13.3 - 3.3}{2 - 1} = 10.0$
2.5	$\dfrac{29.9 - 13.3}{3 - 2} = 16.6$
3.5	$\dfrac{53.2 - 29.9}{4 - 3} = 23.3$
4.5	$\dfrac{83.2 - 53.2}{5 - 4} = 30.0$
5.5	$\dfrac{119.8 - 83.2}{6 - 5} = 36.6$
6.5	$\dfrac{163.0 - 119.8}{7 - 6} = 43.2$
7.5	$\dfrac{212.9 - 163.0}{8 - 7} = 49.9$
8.5	$\dfrac{269.5 - 212.9}{9 - 8} = 56.6$
9.5	$\dfrac{332.7 - 269.5}{10 - 9} = 63.2$

A graph of the derivative data is shown.

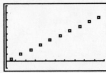

[0, 10] by [−10, 80]

(a) The derivative represents the speed of the skier.

(b) Since the distances are given in feet and the times are given in seconds, the units are feet per second.

(c) The graph appears to be approximately linear and passes through (0, 0) and (9.5, 63.2), so the slope is $\dfrac{63.2 - 0}{9.5 - 0} \approx 6.65$. The equation of the derivative is approximately $D = 6.65t$.

20. (a)

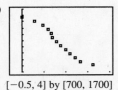

[−0.5, 4] by [700, 1700]

(b)

Midpoint of Interval (x)	Slope $\left(\dfrac{\Delta y}{\Delta x}\right)$
$\dfrac{0.00 + 0.56}{2} = 0.28$	$\dfrac{1512 - 1577}{0.56 - 0.00} \approx -116.07$
$\dfrac{0.56 + 0.92}{2} = 0.74$	$\dfrac{1448 - 1512}{0.92 - 0.56} \approx -177.78$
$\dfrac{0.92 + 1.19}{2} = 1.055$	$\dfrac{1384 - 1448}{1.19 - 0.92} \approx -237.04$
$\dfrac{1.19 + 1.30}{2} = 1.245$	$\dfrac{1319 - 1384}{1.30 - 1.19} \approx -590.91$
$\dfrac{1.30 + 1.39}{2} = 1.345$	$\dfrac{1255 - 1319}{1.39 - 1.30} \approx -711.11$
$\dfrac{1.39 + 1.57}{2} = 1.48$	$\dfrac{1191 - 1255}{1.57 - 1.39} \approx -355.56$
$\dfrac{1.57 + 1.74}{2} = 1.655$	$\dfrac{1126 - 1191}{1.74 - 1.57} \approx -382.35$
$\dfrac{1.74 + 1.98}{2} = 1.86$	$\dfrac{1062 - 1126}{1.98 - 1.74} \approx -266.67$
$\dfrac{1.98 + 2.18}{2} = 2.08$	$\dfrac{998 - 1062}{2.18 - 1.98} = -320.00$
$\dfrac{2.18 + 2.41}{2} = 2.295$	$\dfrac{933 - 998}{2.41 - 2.18} \approx -282.61$
$\dfrac{2.41 + 2.64}{2} = 2.525$	$\dfrac{869 - 933}{2.64 - 2.41} \approx -278.26$
$\dfrac{2.64 + 3.24}{2} = 2.94$	$\dfrac{805 - 869}{3.24 - 2.64} \approx -106.67$

A graph of the derivative data is shown.

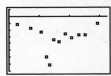

[0, 3.24] by [−800, 100]

(c) Since the elevation y is given in feet and the distance x down river is given in miles, the units of the gradiant are feet per mile.

(d) Since the elevation y is given in feet and the distance x downriver is given in miles, the units of the distance $\dfrac{dy}{dx}$ are feet per mile.

(e) Look for the steepest part of the curve. This is where the elevation is dropping most rapidly, and therefore the most likely location for significant "rapids."

(f) Look for the lowest point on the graph. This is where the elevation is dropping most rapidly, and therefore the most likely location for significant "rapids."

21.

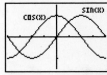

[−π, π] by [−1.5, 1.5]

The cosine function could be the derivative of the sine function. The values of the cosine are positive where the sine is increasing, zero where the sine has horizontal tangents, and negative where sine is decreasing.

22. We show that the right-hand derivative at 1 does not exist.

$$\lim_{h \to 0^+} \frac{f(1+h) - f(1)}{h} = \lim_{h \to 0^+} \frac{3(1+h) - (1)^3}{h}$$

$$= \lim_{h \to 0^+} \frac{2 + 3h}{h} = \lim_{h \to 0^+} \left(\frac{2}{h} + 3\right) = \infty$$

23. $\lim_{h \to 0^+} \dfrac{f(0+h) - f(0)}{h} = \lim_{h \to 0^+} \dfrac{\sqrt{h} - \sqrt{0}}{h} = \lim_{h \to 0^+} \dfrac{\sqrt{h}}{h}$

$= \lim_{h \to 0^+} \dfrac{1}{\sqrt{h}} = \infty$

Thus, the right-hand derivative at 0 does not exist.

24. Two parabolas are parallel if they have the same derivative at every value of x. This means that their tangent lines are parallel at each value of x.

Two such parabolas are given by $y = x^2$ and $y = x^2 + 4$. They are graphed below.

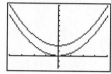

[−4, 4] by [−5, 20]

The parabolas are "everywhere equidistant," as long as the distance between them is always measured along a vertical line.

25. For $x > -1$, the graph of $y = f(x)$ must lie on a line of slope -2 that passes through $(0, -1)$: $y = -2x - 1$. Then $y(-1) = -2(-1) - 1 = 1$, so for $x < -1$, the graph of $y = f(x)$ must lie on a line of slope 1 that passes through $(-1, 1)$: $y = 1(x + 1) + 1$ or $y = x + 2$.

Thus $f(x) = \begin{cases} x + 2, & x < -1 \\ -2x - 1, & x \geq -1 \end{cases}$

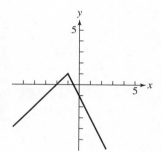

26. (a) $f'(x) = \lim_{h \to 0} \dfrac{f(x+h) - f(x)}{h}$

$= \lim_{h \to 0} \dfrac{(x+h)^2 - x^2}{h} = \lim_{h \to 0} \dfrac{2xh + h^2}{h}$

$= \lim_{h \to 0} (2x + h) = 2x$

(b) $f'(x) = \lim_{h \to 0} \dfrac{f(x+h) - f(x)}{h}$

$= \lim_{h \to 0} \dfrac{2(x+h) - 2x}{h} = \lim_{h \to 0} 2 = 2$

(c) $\lim_{x \to 1^-} f'(x) = \lim_{x \to 1^-} 2x = 2(1) = 2$

(d) $\lim_{x \to 1^+} f'(x) = \lim_{x \to 1^+} 2 = 2$

(e) Yes, the one-sided limits exist and are the same, so

$$\lim_{x \to 1} f'(x) = 2.$$

(f) $\lim_{h \to 0^-} \dfrac{f(1+h) - f(1)}{h} = \lim_{h \to 0^-} \dfrac{(1+h)^2 - 1^2}{h}$

$= \lim_{h \to 0^-} \dfrac{2h + h^2}{h} = \lim_{h \to 0^-} (2 + h) = 2$

(g) $\lim_{h \to 0^+} \dfrac{f(1+h) - f(1)}{h} = \lim_{h \to 0^-} \dfrac{2(1+h) - 1^2}{h}$

$= \lim_{h \to 0^-} \dfrac{1 + 2h}{h} = \lim_{h \to 0^-} \left(\dfrac{1}{h} + 2\right) = -\infty$

The right-hand derivative does not exist.

(h) It does not exist because the right-hand derivative does not exist.

27. The y-intercept of the derivative is $b - a$.

28. Since the function must be continuous at $x = 1$, we have $\lim_{x \to 1^+} (3x + k) = f(1) = 1$, so $3 + k = 1$, or $k = -2$.

This gives $f(x) = \begin{cases} x^3, & x \leq 1 \\ 3x - 2, & x > 1. \end{cases}$

Now we confirm that $f(x)$ is differentiable at $x = 1$.

$\lim_{h \to 0^-} \dfrac{f(1+h) - f(1)}{h} = \lim_{h \to 0^-} \dfrac{(1+h)^3 - (1)^3}{h}$

$= \lim_{h \to 0} \dfrac{3h + 3h^2 + h^3}{h}$

$= \lim_{h \to 0} (3 + 3h + h^2) = 3$

$\lim_{h \to 0^+} \dfrac{f(1+h) - f(1)}{h} = \lim_{h \to 0^+} \dfrac{[3(1+h) - 2] - (1)^3]}{h}$

$= \lim_{h \to 0^+} \dfrac{(1 + 3h) - 1}{h} = \lim_{h \to 0^+} 3 = 3$

Since the right-hand derivative equals the left-hand derivative at $x = 1$, the derivative exists (and is equal to 3) when $k = -2$.

29. (a) $1 \cdot \dfrac{364}{365} \cdot \dfrac{363}{365} \approx 0.992$

Alternate method: $\dfrac{_{365}P_3}{365^3} \approx 0.992$

(b) Using the answer to part (a), the probability is about $1 - 0.992 = 0.008$.

(c) Let P represent the answer to part (b), $P \approx 0.008$. Then the probability that three people all have different birthdays is $1 - P$. Adding a fourth person, the probability that all have different birthdays is $(1 - P)\left(\dfrac{362}{365}\right)$, so the probability of a shared birthday is $1 - (1 - P)\left(\dfrac{362}{365}\right) \approx 0.016$.

(d) No. Clearly February 29 is a much less likely birth date. Furthermore, census data do not support the assumption that the other 365 birth dates are equally likely. However, this simplifying assumption may still give us some insight into this problem even if the calculated probabilities aren't completely accurate.

■ Section 3.2 Differentiability (pp. 105–112)

Exploration 1   Zooming in to "See" Differentiability

1. Zooming in on the graph of f at the point $(0, 1)$ always produces a graph exactly like the one shown below, provided that a square window is used. The corner shows no sign of straightening out.

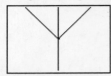

[−0.25, 0.25] by [0.836, 1.164]

2. Zooming in on the graph of g at the point $(0, 1)$ begins to reveal a smooth turning point. This graph shows the result of three zooms, each by a factor of 4 horizontally and vertically, starting with the window [−4, 4] by [−1.624, 3.624].

[−0.0625, 0.0625] by [0.959, 1.041]

3. On our grapher, the graph became horizontal after 8 zooms. Results can vary on different machines.

4. As we zoom in on the graphs of f and g together, the differentiable function gradually straightens out to resemble its tangent line, while the nondifferentiable function stubbornly retains its same shape.

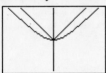

[−0.03125, 0.03125] by [0.9795, 1.0205]

Exploration 2   Looking at the Symmetric Difference Quotient Analytically

1. $\dfrac{f(10 + h) - f(10)}{h} = \dfrac{(10.01)^2 - 10^2}{0.01} = 20.01$

$f'(10) = 2 \cdot 10 = 20$

The difference quotient is 0.01 away from $f'(10)$.

2. $\dfrac{f(10 + h) - f(10 - h)}{2h} = \dfrac{(10.01)^2 - (9.99)^2}{0.02} = 20$

The symmetric difference quotient exactly equals $f'(10)$.

3. $\dfrac{f(10 + h) - f(10)}{h} = \dfrac{(10.01)^3 - 10^3}{0.01} = 300.3001.$

$f'(10) = 3 \cdot 10^2 = 300$

The difference quotient is 0.3001 away from $f'(10)$.

$\dfrac{f(10 + h) - f(10 - h)}{2h} = \dfrac{(10.01)^3 - (9.99)^3}{0.02} = 300.0001.$

The symmetric difference quotient is 0.0001 away from $f'(10)$.

Quick Review 3.2

1. Yes

2. No (The $f(h)$ term in the numerator is incorrect.)

3. Yes   4. Yes

5. No (The denominator for this expression should be $2h$).

6. All reals

7. $[0, \infty)$ 8. $[3, \infty)$

9. The equation is equivalent to $y = 3.2x + (3.2\pi + 5)$, so the slope is 3.2.

10. $\dfrac{f(3 + 0.001) - f(3 - 0.001)}{0.002} = \dfrac{5(3 + 0.001) - 5(3 - 0.001)}{0.002}$

$= \dfrac{5(0.002)}{0.002} = 5$

Section 3.2 Exercises

1. Left-hand derivative:

$\displaystyle\lim_{h \to 0^-} \dfrac{f(0 + h) - f(0)}{h} = \lim_{h \to 0^-} \dfrac{h^2 - 0}{h} = \lim_{h \to 0^-} h = 0$

Right-hand derivative:

$\displaystyle\lim_{h \to 0^+} \dfrac{f(0 + h) - f(0)}{h} = \lim_{h \to 0^+} \dfrac{h - 0}{h} = \lim_{h \to 0^+} 1 = 1$

Since $0 \neq 1$, the function is not differentiable at the point P.

2. Left-hand derivative:

$\displaystyle\lim_{h \to 0^-} \dfrac{f(1 + h) - f(1)}{h} = \lim_{h \to 0^-} \dfrac{2 - 2}{h} = \lim_{h \to 0^-} 0 = 0$

Right-hand derivative:

$\displaystyle\lim_{h \to 0^+} \dfrac{f(1 + h) - f(1)}{h} = \lim_{h \to 0^+} \dfrac{2(1 + h) - 2}{h} = \lim_{h \to 0^+} 2 = 2$

Since $0 \neq 2$, the function is not differentiable at the point P.

3. Left-hand derivative:

$\displaystyle\lim_{h \to 0^-} \dfrac{f(1 + h) - f(1)}{h} = \lim_{h \to 0^-} \dfrac{\sqrt{1 + h} - 1}{h}$

$= \lim_{h \to 0^-} \dfrac{(\sqrt{1 + h} - 1)(\sqrt{1 + h} + 1)}{h(\sqrt{1 + h} + 1)}$

$= \lim_{h \to 0^-} \dfrac{(1 + h) - 1}{h(\sqrt{1 + h} + 1)}$

$= \lim_{h \to 0^-} \dfrac{1}{\sqrt{1 + h} + 1} = \dfrac{1}{2}$

Right-hand derivative:

$\displaystyle\lim_{h \to 0^+} \dfrac{f(1 + h) - f(1)}{h} = \lim_{h \to 0^+} \dfrac{[2(1 + h) - 1] - 1}{h}$

$= \lim_{h \to 0^+} \dfrac{2h}{h}$

$= \lim_{h \to 0^+} 2 = 2$

Since $\dfrac{1}{2} \neq 2$, the function is not differentiable at the point P.

4. Left-hand derivative:

$$\lim_{h \to 0^-} \frac{f(1+h) - f(1)}{h} = \lim_{h \to 0^-} \frac{(1+h) - 1}{h} = \lim_{h \to 0^-} 1 = 1$$

Right-hand derivative:

$$\lim_{h \to 0^+} \frac{f(1+h) - f(1)}{h} = \lim_{h \to 0^+} \frac{\frac{1}{1+h} - 1}{h}$$

$$= \lim_{h \to 0^+} \frac{1 - (1+h)}{h(1+h)}$$

$$= \lim_{h \to 0^+} \frac{-h}{h(1+h)}$$

$$= \lim_{h \to 0^+} -\frac{1}{1+h} = -1$$

Since $1 \ne -1$, the function is not differentiable at the point P.

5. (a) All points in $[-3, 2]$

   (b) None

   (c) None

6. (a) All points in $[-2, 3]$

   (b) None

   (c) None

7. (a) All points in $[-3, 3]$ except $x = 0$

   (b) None

   (c) $x = 0$

8. (a) All points in $[-2, 3]$ except $x = -1, 0, 2$

   (b) $x = -1$

   (c) $x = 0, x = 2$

9. (a) All points in $[-1, 2]$ except $x = 0$

   (b) $x = 0$

   (c) None

10. (a) All points in $[-3, 3]$ except $x = -2, 2$

   (b) $x = -2, x = 2$

   (c) None

11. Since $\lim_{x \to 0} \tan^{-1} x = \tan^{-1} 0 = 0 \ne y(0)$, the problem is a discontinuity.

12. $\lim_{h \to 0^-} \frac{y(0+h) - y(0)}{h} = \lim_{h \to 0^-} \frac{h^{4/5}}{h} = \lim_{h \to 0^-} \frac{1}{h^{1/5}} = -\infty$

$\lim_{h \to 0^+} \frac{y(0+h) - y(0)}{h} = \lim_{h \to 0^+} \frac{h^{4/5}}{h} = \lim_{h \to 0^+} \frac{1}{h^{1/5}} = \infty$

The problem is a cusp.

13. Note that $y = x + \sqrt{x^2} + 2 = x + |x| + 2$

$$= \begin{cases} 2, & x \le 0 \\ 2x + 2, & x > 0. \end{cases}$$

$\lim_{h \to 0^-} \frac{y(0+h) - y(0)}{h} = \lim_{h \to 0^-} \frac{2 - 2}{h} = \lim_{h \to 0^-} 0 = 0$

$\lim_{h \to 0^+} \frac{y(0+h) - y(0)}{h} = \lim_{h \to 0^+} \frac{(2h+2) - 2}{h} = \lim_{h \to 0^+} 2 = 2$

The problem is a corner.

14. $\lim_{h \to 0} \frac{y(0+h) - y(0)}{h} = \lim_{h \to 0} \frac{(3 - \sqrt[3]{h}) - 3}{h} = \lim_{h \to 0} \frac{-\sqrt[3]{h}}{h}$

$= \lim_{h \to 0} \left(-\frac{1}{h^{2/3}}\right) = -\infty$

The problem is a vertical tangent.

15. Note that $y = 3x - 2|x| - 1 = \begin{cases} 5x - 1, & x \le 0 \\ x - 1, & x > 0 \end{cases}$

$\lim_{h \to 0^-} \frac{y(0+h) - y(0)}{h} = \lim_{h \to 0^-} \frac{(5h-1) - (-1)}{h} = \lim_{h \to 0^-} 5 = 5$

$\lim_{h \to 0^+} \frac{y(0+h) - y(0)}{h} = \lim_{h \to 0^+} \frac{(h-1) - (-1)}{h} = \lim_{h \to 0^+} 1 = 1$

The problem is a corner.

16. $\lim_{h \to 0^-} \frac{y(0+h) - y(0)}{h} = \lim_{h \to 0^-} \frac{\sqrt[3]{|h|} - 0}{h} = \lim_{h \to 0^-} \frac{-\sqrt[3]{h}}{h}$

$= \lim_{h \to 0^-} \left(-\frac{1}{h^{2/3}}\right) = -\infty$

$\lim_{h \to 0^+} \frac{y(0+h) - y(0)}{h} = \lim_{h \to 0^+} \frac{\sqrt[3]{|h|} - 0}{h} = \lim_{h \to 0^+} \frac{\sqrt[3]{h}}{h}$

$= \lim_{h \to 0^+} \frac{1}{h^{2/3}} = \infty$

The problem is a cusp.

17. Find the zeros of the denominator.

$$x^2 - 4x - 5 = 0$$
$$(x + 1)(x - 5) = 0$$
$$x = -1 \text{ or } x = 5$$

The function is a rational function, so it is differentiable for all x in its domain: all reals except $x = -1, 5$.

18. The function is differentiable except possibly where $3x - 6 = 0$, that is, at $x = 2$. We check for differentiability at $x = 2$, using k instead of the usual h, in order to avoid confusion with the function $h(x)$.

$$\lim_{k \to 0} \frac{h(2+k) - h(2)}{k} = \lim_{k \to 0} \frac{[\sqrt[3]{3(2+k) - 6} + 5] - 5}{k}$$

$$= \lim_{k \to 0} \frac{\sqrt[3]{3k}}{k} = \sqrt[3]{3} \lim_{k \to 0} \frac{1}{k^{2/3}} = \infty$$

The function has a vertical tangent at $x = 2$. It is differentiable for all reals except $x = 2$.

19. Note that the sine function is odd, so

$$P(x) = \sin(|x|) - 1 = \begin{cases} -\sin x - 1, & x < 0 \\ \sin x - 1, & x \ge 0. \end{cases}$$

The graph of $P(x)$ has a corner at $x = 0$. The function is differentiable for all reals except $x = 0$.

20. Since the cosine function is even, so $Q(x) = 3 \cos(|x|) = 3 \cos x$. The function is differentiable for all reals.

21. The function is piecewise-defined in terms of polynomials, so it is differentiable everywhere except possibly at $x = 0$ and at $x = 3$. Check $x = 0$:

$$\lim_{h \to 0^-} \frac{g(0+h) - g(0)}{h} = \lim_{h \to 0^-} \frac{(h+1)^2 - 1}{h} = \lim_{h \to 0^-} \frac{h^2 + 2h}{h}$$

$$= \lim_{h \to 0^-} (h + 2) = 2$$

$$\lim_{h \to 0^+} \frac{g(0+h) - g(0)}{h} = \lim_{h \to 0^+} \frac{(2h+1) - 1}{h} = \lim_{h \to 0^+} 2 = 2$$

The function is differentiable at $x = 0$.

21. continued

Check $x = 3$:

Since $g(3) = (4 - 3)^2 = 1$ and

$\lim\limits_{x \to 3^-} g(x) = \lim\limits_{x \to 3^-} (2x + 1) = 2(3) + 1 = 7$, the function is

not continuous (and hence not differentiable) at $x = 3$.

The function is differentiable for all reals except $x = 3$.

22. Note that $C(x) = x|x| = \begin{cases} -x^2, & x < 0 \\ x^2, & x \geq 0 \end{cases}$, so it is

differentiable for all x except possibly at $x = 0$.

Check $x = 0$:

$\lim\limits_{h \to 0} \dfrac{C(0 + h) - C(0)}{h} = \lim\limits_{h \to 0} \dfrac{h|h| - 0}{h} = \lim\limits_{h \to 0} |h| = 0$

The function is differentiable for all reals.

23. (a) $x = 0$ is not in their domains, or, they are both
discontinuous at $x = 0$.

(b) For $\dfrac{1}{x}$: NDER $\left(\dfrac{1}{x}, 0\right) = 1{,}000{,}000$

For $\dfrac{1}{x^2}$: NDER $\left(\dfrac{1}{x^2}, 0\right) = 0$

(c) It returns an incorrect response because even though
these functions are not defined at $x = 0$, they are
defined at $x = \pm 0.001$. The responses differ from each
other because $\dfrac{1}{x^2}$ is even (which automatically makes
NDER $\left(\dfrac{1}{x^2}, 0\right) = 0$) and $\dfrac{1}{x}$ is odd.

24.

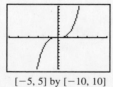

$[-5, 5]$ by $[-10, 10]$

$\dfrac{dy}{dx} = x^3$

25.

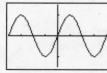

$[-2\pi, 2\pi]$ by $[-1.5, 1.5]$

$\dfrac{dy}{dx} = \sin x$

26.

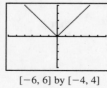

$[-6, 6]$ by $[-4, 4]$

$\dfrac{dy}{dx} = \text{abs}(x)$ or $|x|$

27.

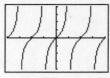

$[-2\pi, 2\pi]$ by $[-4, 4]$

$\dfrac{dy}{dx} = \tan x$

Note: Due to the way NDER is defined, the graph of
$y = $ NDER (x) actually has two asymptotes for each
asymptote of $y = \tan x$. The asymptotes of $y = $ NDER (x)
occur at $x = \dfrac{\pi}{2} + k\pi \pm 0.001$, where k is an integer. A
good window for viewing this behavior is $[1.566, 1.576]$ by
$[-1000, 1000]$.

28.

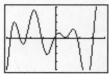

$[-2\pi, 2\pi]$ by $[-20, 20]$

The graph of NDER (x) does not look like the graph of any
basic function.

29. (a) $\lim\limits_{x \to 1^-} f(x) = f(1)$

$\lim\limits_{x \to 1^-} (3 - x) = a(1)^2 + b(1)$

$2 = a + b$

The relationship is $a + b = 2$.

(b) Since the function needs to be continuous, we may
assume that $a + b = 2$ and $f(1) = 2$.

$\lim\limits_{h \to 0^-} \dfrac{f(1 + h) - f(1)}{h} = \lim\limits_{h \to 0^-} \dfrac{3 - (1 + h) - 2}{h}$

$= \lim\limits_{h \to 0^-} (-1) = -1$

$\lim\limits_{h \to 0^+} \dfrac{f(1 + h) - f(1)}{h} = \lim\limits_{h \to 0^-} \dfrac{a(1 + h)^2 + b(1 + h) - 2}{h}$

$= \lim\limits_{h \to 0^-} \dfrac{a + 2ah + ah^2 + b + bh - 2}{h}$

$= \lim\limits_{h \to 0^-} \dfrac{2ah + ah^2 + bh + (a + b - 2)}{h}$

$= \lim\limits_{h \to 0^-} (2a + ah + b)$

$= 2a + b$

Therefore, $2a + b = -1$. Substituting $2 - a$ for b gives
$2a + (2 - a) = -1$, so $a = -3$.
Then $b = 2 - a = 2 - (-3) = 5$. The values are
$a = -3$ and $b = 5$.

30. The function $f(x)$ does not have the intermediate value
property. Choose some a in $(-1, 0)$ and b in $(0, 1)$. Then
$f(a) = 0$ and $f(b) = 1$, but f does not take on any value
between 0 and 1. Therefore, by the Intermediate Value
Theorem for Derivatives, f cannot be the derivative of any
function on $[-1, 1]$.

31. (a) Note that $-x \le \sin \dfrac{1}{x} \le x$, for all x,

so $\lim\limits_{x \to 0} \left(x \sin \dfrac{1}{x}\right) = 0$ by the Sandwich Theorem.

Therefore, f is continuous at $x = 0$.

(b) $\dfrac{f(0 + h) - f(0)}{h} = \dfrac{h \sin \dfrac{1}{h} - 0}{h} = \sin \dfrac{1}{h}$

(c) The limit does not exist because $\sin \dfrac{1}{h}$ oscillates

between -1 and 1 an infinite number of times

arbitrarily close to $h = 0$ (that is, for h in any open

interval containing 0).

(d) No, because the limit in part (c) does not exist.

(e) $\dfrac{g(0 + h) - g(0)}{h} = \dfrac{h^2 \sin\left(\dfrac{1}{h}\right) - 0}{h} = h \sin \dfrac{1}{h}$

As noted in part (a), the limit of this as x approaches

zero is 0, so $g'(0) = 0$.

■ Section 3.3 Rules for Differentiation

(pp. 112–121)

Quick Review 3.3

1. $(x^2 - 2)(x^{-1} + 1) = x^2 x^{-1} + x^2 \cdot 1 - 2x^{-1} - 2 \cdot 1$
$= x + x^2 - 2x^{-1} - 2$

2. $\left(\dfrac{x}{x^2 + 1}\right)^{-1} = \dfrac{x^2 + 1}{x} = \dfrac{x^2}{x} + \dfrac{1}{x} = x + x^{-1}$

3. $3x^2 - \dfrac{2}{x} + \dfrac{5}{x^2} = 3x^2 - 2x^{-1} + 5x^{-2}$

4. $\dfrac{3x^4 - 2x^3 + 4}{2x^2} = \dfrac{3x^4}{2x^2} - \dfrac{2x^3}{2x^2} + \dfrac{4}{2x^2} = \dfrac{3}{2}x^2 - x + 2x^{-2}$

5. $(x^{-1} + 2)(x^{-2} + 1) = x^{-1}x^{-2} + x^{-1} \cdot 1 + 2x^{-2} + 2 \cdot 1$
$= x^{-3} + x^{-1} + 2x^{-2} + 2$

6. $\dfrac{x^{-1} + x^{-2}}{x^{-3}} = x^3(x^{-1} + x^{-2}) = x^2 + x$

7.

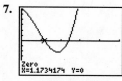

[0, 5] by [−6, 6]

At $x \approx 1.173$, $500x^6 \approx 1305$.
At $x \approx 2.394$, $500x^6 \approx 94{,}212$
After rounding, we have:
At $x \approx 1$, $500x^6 \approx 1305$.
At $x \approx 2$, $500x^6 \approx 94{,}212$.

8. (a) $f(10) = 7$

(b) $f(0) = 7$

(c) $f(x + h) = 7$

(d) $\lim\limits_{x \to a} \dfrac{f(x) - f(a)}{x - a} = \lim\limits_{x \to a} \dfrac{7 - 7}{x - a} = \lim\limits_{x \to a} 0 = 0$

9. These are all constant functions, so the graph of each
function is a horizontal line and the derivative of each
function is 0.

10. (a) $f'(x) = \lim\limits_{h \to 0} \dfrac{f(x + h) - f(x)}{h} = \lim\limits_{h \to 0} \dfrac{\dfrac{x + h}{\pi} - \dfrac{x}{\pi}}{h}$

$= \lim\limits_{h \to 0} \dfrac{x + h - x}{\pi h} = \lim\limits_{h \to 0} \dfrac{1}{\pi} = \dfrac{1}{\pi}$

(b) $f'(x) = \lim\limits_{h \to 0} \dfrac{f(x + h) - f(x)}{h} = \lim\limits_{h \to 0} \dfrac{\dfrac{\pi}{x + h} - \dfrac{\pi}{x}}{h}$

$= \lim\limits_{h \to 0} \dfrac{\pi x - \pi(x + h)}{hx(x + h)} = \lim\limits_{h \to 0} \dfrac{-\pi h}{hx(x + h)}$

$= \lim\limits_{h \to 0} -\dfrac{\pi}{x(x + h)} = -\dfrac{\pi}{x^2} = -\pi x^{-2}$

Section 3.3 Exercises

1. $\dfrac{dy}{dx} = \dfrac{d}{dx}(-x^2) + \dfrac{d}{dx}(3) = -2x + 0 = -2x$
$\dfrac{d^2y}{dx^2} = \dfrac{d}{dx}(-2x) = -2$

2. $\dfrac{dy}{dx} = \dfrac{d}{dx}\left(\dfrac{1}{3}x^3\right) - \dfrac{d}{dx}(x) = x^2 - 1$
$\dfrac{d^2y}{dx^2} = \dfrac{d}{dx}(x^2) - \dfrac{d}{dx}(1) = 2x - 0 = 2x$

3. $\dfrac{dy}{dx} = \dfrac{d}{dx}(2x) + \dfrac{d}{dx}(1) = 2 + 0 = 2$
$\dfrac{d^2y}{dx^2} = \dfrac{d}{dx}(2) = 0$

4. $\dfrac{dy}{dx} = \dfrac{d}{dx}(x^2) + \dfrac{d}{dx}(x) + \dfrac{d}{dx}(1) = 2x + 1 + 0 = 2x + 1$
$\dfrac{d^2y}{dx^2} = \dfrac{d}{dx}(2x) + \dfrac{d}{dx}(1) = 2 + 0 = 2$

5. $\dfrac{dy}{dx} = \dfrac{d}{dx}\left(\dfrac{1}{3}x^3\right) + \dfrac{d}{dx}\left(\dfrac{1}{2}x^2\right) + \dfrac{d}{dx}(x)$
$= x^2 + x + 1$
$\dfrac{d^2y}{dx^2} = \dfrac{d}{dx}(x^2) + \dfrac{d}{dx}(x) + \dfrac{d}{dx}(1) = 2x + 1 + 0 = 2x + 1$

6. $\dfrac{dy}{dx} = \dfrac{d}{dx}(1) - \dfrac{d}{dx}(x) + \dfrac{d}{dx}(x^2) - \dfrac{d}{dx}(x^3)$
$= 0 - 1 + 2x - 3x^2 = -1 + 2x - 3x^2$
$\dfrac{d^2y}{dx^2} = \dfrac{d}{dx}(-1) + \dfrac{d}{dx}(2x) - \dfrac{d}{dx}(3x^2)$
$= 0 + 2 - 6x = 2 - 6x$

7. $\dfrac{dy}{dx} = \dfrac{d}{dx}(x^4) - \dfrac{d}{dx}(7x^3) + \dfrac{d}{dx}(2x^2) + \dfrac{d}{dx}(15)$
$= 4x^3 - 21x^2 + 4x + 0 = 4x^3 - 21x^2 + 4x$
$\dfrac{d^2y}{dx^2} = \dfrac{d}{dx}(4x^3) - \dfrac{d}{dx}(21x^2) + \dfrac{d}{dx}(4x) = 12x^2 - 42x + 4$

8. $\dfrac{dy}{dx} = \dfrac{d}{dx}(5x^3) - \dfrac{d}{dx}(3x^5) = 15x^2 - 15x^4$
$\dfrac{d^2y}{dx^2} = \dfrac{d}{dx}(15x^2) - \dfrac{d}{dx}(15x^4) = 30x - 60x^3$

9. $\dfrac{dy}{dx} = \dfrac{d}{dx}(4x^{-2}) - \dfrac{d}{dx}(8x) + \dfrac{d}{dx}(1)$
$= -8x^{-3} - 8 + 0 = -8x^{-3} - 8$
$\dfrac{d^2y}{dx^2} = \dfrac{d}{dx}(-8x^{-3}) - \dfrac{d}{dx}(8) = 24x^{-4} - 0 = 24x^{-4}$

10. $\dfrac{dy}{dx} = \dfrac{d}{dx}\left(\dfrac{1}{4}x^{-4}\right) - \dfrac{d}{dx}\left(\dfrac{1}{3}x^{-3}\right) + \dfrac{d}{dx}\left(\dfrac{1}{2}x^{-2}\right) - \dfrac{d}{dx}(x^{-1})$

$\qquad + \dfrac{d}{dx}(3)$

$\qquad = -x^{-5} + x^{-4} - x^{-3} + x^{-2} + 0$

$\qquad = -x^{-5} + x^{-4} - x^{-3} + x^{-2}$

$\quad \dfrac{d^2y}{dx^2} = \dfrac{d}{dx}(-x^{-5}) + \dfrac{d}{dx}(x^{-4}) - \dfrac{d}{dx}(x^{-3}) + \dfrac{d}{dx}(x^{-2})$

$\qquad = 5x^{-6} - 4x^{-5} + 3x^{-4} - 2x^{-3}$

11. (a) $\dfrac{dy}{dx} = \dfrac{d}{dx}[(x+1)(x^2+1)]$

$\qquad = (x+1)\dfrac{d}{dx}(x^2+1) + (x^2+1)\dfrac{d}{dx}(x+1)$

$\qquad = (x+1)(2x) + (x^2+1)(1)$

$\qquad = 2x^2 + 2x + x^2 + 1$

$\qquad = 3x^2 + 2x + 1$

(b) $\dfrac{dy}{dx} = \dfrac{d}{dx}[(x+1)(x^2+1)]$

$\qquad = \dfrac{d}{dx}(x^3 + x^2 + x + 1)$

$\qquad = 3x^2 + 2x + 1$

12. (a) $\dfrac{dy}{dx} = \dfrac{d}{dx}\left(\dfrac{x^2+3}{x}\right)$

$\qquad = \dfrac{x\dfrac{d}{dx}(x^2+3) - (x^2+3)\dfrac{d}{dx}(x)}{x^2}$

$\qquad = \dfrac{x(2x) - (x^2+3)}{x^2}$

$\qquad = \dfrac{x^2 - 3}{x^2}$

(b) $\dfrac{dy}{dx} = \dfrac{d}{dx}\left(\dfrac{x^2+3}{x}\right) = \dfrac{d}{dx}(x + 3x^{-1}) = 1 - 3x^{-2}$

$\qquad = 1 - \dfrac{3}{x^2}$

This is equivalent to the answer in part (a).

13. $\dfrac{dy}{dx} = \dfrac{d}{dx}\dfrac{2x+5}{3x-2} = \dfrac{(3x-2)(2) - (2x+5)(3)}{(3x-2)^2} = -\dfrac{19}{(3x-2)^2}$

14. $\dfrac{dy}{dx} = \dfrac{d}{dx}\left(\dfrac{x^2+5x-1}{x^2}\right) = \dfrac{d}{dx}(1 + 5x^{-1} - x^{-2})$

$\qquad = 0 - 5x^{-2} + 2x^{-3} = -\dfrac{5}{x^2} + \dfrac{2}{x^3}$

15. $\dfrac{dy}{dx} = \dfrac{d}{dx}\left(\dfrac{(x-1)(x^2+x+1)}{x^3}\right) = \dfrac{d}{dx}\left(\dfrac{x^3-1}{x^3}\right)$

$\qquad = \dfrac{d}{dx}(1 - x^{-3}) = 0 + 3x^{-4} = \dfrac{3}{x^4}$

16. $\dfrac{dy}{dx} = \dfrac{d}{dx}\left(\dfrac{1-x}{1+x^2}\right) = \dfrac{(1+x^2)(-1) - (1-x)(2x)}{(1+x^2)^2}$

$\qquad = \dfrac{x^2 - 2x - 1}{(1+x^2)^2}$

17. $\dfrac{dy}{dx} = \dfrac{d}{dx}\left(\dfrac{x^2}{1-x^3}\right) = \dfrac{(1-x^3)(2x) - x^2(-3x^2)}{(1-x^3)^2} = \dfrac{x^4 + 2x}{(1-x^3)^2}$

18. $\dfrac{dy}{dx} = \dfrac{d}{dx}\left(\dfrac{\sqrt{x}-1}{\sqrt{x}+1}\right) = \dfrac{(\sqrt{x}+1)\dfrac{1}{2\sqrt{x}} - (\sqrt{x}-1)\dfrac{1}{2\sqrt{x}}}{(\sqrt{x}+1)^2}$

$\qquad = \dfrac{(\sqrt{x}+1) - (\sqrt{x}-1)}{2\sqrt{x}(\sqrt{x}+1)^2} = \dfrac{2}{2\sqrt{x}(\sqrt{x}+1)^2} = \dfrac{1}{\sqrt{x}(\sqrt{x}+1)^2}$

19. $\dfrac{dy}{dx} = \dfrac{d}{dx}\left(\dfrac{(x+1)(x+2)}{(x-1)(x-2)}\right) = \dfrac{d}{dx}\left(\dfrac{x^2+3x+2}{x^2-3x+2}\right)$

$\qquad = \dfrac{(x^2-3x+2)(2x+3) - (x^2+3x+2)(2x-3)}{(x^2-3x+2)^2}$

$\qquad = \dfrac{(2x^3-3x^2-5x+6) - (2x^3+3x^2-5x-6)}{(x^2-3x+2)^2}$

$\qquad = \dfrac{12 - 6x^2}{(x^2-3x+2)^2}$

20. (a) Let $f(x) = x$.

$\qquad \dfrac{d}{dx}(x) = f'(x) = \lim_{h\to 0}\dfrac{f(x+h)-f(x)}{h} = \lim_{h\to 0}\dfrac{(x+h)-x}{h}$

$\qquad = \lim_{h\to 0}\dfrac{h}{h} = \lim_{h\to 0}(1) = 1$

(b) Note that $u = u(x)$ is a function of x.

$\qquad \dfrac{d}{dx}(-u) = \lim_{h\to 0}\dfrac{-u(x+h)-[-u(x)]}{h}$

$\qquad = \lim_{h\to 0}\left(-\dfrac{u(x+h)-u(x)}{h}\right)$

$\qquad = -\lim_{h\to 0}\dfrac{u(x+h)-u(x)}{h} = -\dfrac{du}{dx}$

21. $\dfrac{d}{dx}(c\cdot f(x)) = c\cdot\dfrac{d}{dx}f(x) + f(x)\cdot\dfrac{d}{dx}(c)$

$\qquad = c\cdot\dfrac{d}{dx}f(x) + 0 = c\cdot\dfrac{d}{dx}f(x)$

22. $\dfrac{d}{dx}\left(\dfrac{1}{f(x)}\right) = \dfrac{f(x)\cdot 0 - 1\cdot\dfrac{d}{dx}f(x)}{[f(x)]^2} = -\dfrac{f'(x)}{[f(x)]^2}$

23. (a) At $x = 0$, $\dfrac{d}{dx}(uv) = u(0)v'(0) + v(0)u'(0)$

$\qquad = (5)(2) + (-1)(-3) = 13$

(b) At $x = 0$, $\dfrac{d}{dx}\left(\dfrac{u}{v}\right) = \dfrac{v(0)u'(0) - u(0)v'(0)}{[v(0)]^2}$

$\qquad = \dfrac{(-1)(-3) - (5)(2)}{(-1)^2} = -7$

(c) At $x = 0$, $\dfrac{d}{dx}\left(\dfrac{v}{u}\right) = \dfrac{u(0)v'(0) - v(0)u'(0)}{[u(0)]^2}$

$\qquad = \dfrac{(5)(2) - (-1)(-3)}{(5)^2} = \dfrac{7}{25}$

(d) At $x = 0$, $\dfrac{d}{dx}(7v - 2u) = 7v'(0) - 2u'(0)$

$\qquad = 7(2) - 2(-3) = 20$

24. (a) At $x = 2$, $\dfrac{d}{dx}(uv) = u(2)v'(2) + v(2)u'(2)$

$= (3)(2) + (1)(-4) = 2$

(b) At $x = 2$, $\dfrac{d}{dx}\left(\dfrac{u}{v}\right) = \dfrac{v(2)u'(2) - u(2)v'(2)}{[v(2)]^2}$

$= \dfrac{(1)(-4) - (3)(2)}{(1)^2} = -10$

(c) At $x = 2$, $\dfrac{d}{dx}\left(\dfrac{v}{u}\right) = \dfrac{u(2)v'(2) - v(2)u'(2)}{[u(2)]^2}$

$= \dfrac{(3)(2) - (1)(-4)}{(3)^2} = \dfrac{10}{9}$

(d) Use the result from part (a) for $\dfrac{d}{dx}(uv)$.

At $x = 2$, $\dfrac{d}{dx}(3u - 2v + 2uv)$

$= 3u'(2) - 2v'(2) + 2\dfrac{d}{dx}(uv)$

$= 3(-4) - 2(2) + 2(2)$

$= -12$

25. $y'(x) = 2x + 5$
$y'(3) = 2(3) + 5 = 11$
The slope is 11. (iii)

26. The given equation is equivalent to $y = \dfrac{3}{2}x + 6$, so the slope is $\dfrac{3}{2}$. (iii)

27. $y'(x) = 3x^2 - 3$
$y'(2) = 3(2)^2 - 3 = 9$

The tangent line has slope 9, so the perpendicular line has slope $-\dfrac{1}{9}$ and passes through (2, 3).

$y = -\dfrac{1}{9}(x - 2) + 3$

$y = -\dfrac{1}{9}x + \dfrac{29}{9}$

Graphical support:

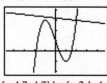

[−4.7, 4.7] by [−2.1, 4.1]

28. $y'(x) = 3x^2 + 1$
The slope is 4 when $3x^2 + 1 = 4$, at $x = \pm1$. The tangent at $x = -1$ has slope 4 and passes through $(-1, -2)$, so its equation is $y = 4(x + 1) - 2$, or $y = 4x + 2$. The tangent at $x = 1$ has slope 4 and passes through (1, 2), so its equation is $y = 4(x - 1) + 2$, or $y = 4x - 2$. The smallest slope occurs when $3x^2 + 1$ is minimized, so the smallest slope is 1 and occurs at $x = 0$.

Graphical support:

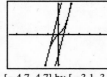

[−4.7, 4.7] by [−3.1, 3.1]

29. $y'(x) = 6x^2 - 6x - 12$
$= 6(x^2 - x - 2)$
$= 6(x + 1)(x - 2)$
The tangent is parallel to the x-axis when $y' = 0$, at $x = -1$ and at $x = 2$. Since $y(-1) = 27$ and $y(2) = 0$, the two points where this occurs are $(-1, 27)$ and $(2, 0)$.

Graphical support:

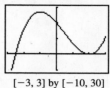

[−3, 3] by [−10, 30]

30. $y'(x) = 3x^2$
$y'(-2) = 12$

The tangent line has slope 12 and passes through $(-2, -8)$, so its equation is $y = 12(x + 2) - 8$, or $y = 12x + 16$. The x-intercept is $-\dfrac{4}{3}$ and the y-intercept is 16.

Graphical support:

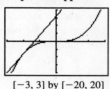

[−3, 3] by [−20, 20]

31. $y'(x) = \dfrac{(x^2 + 1)(4) - 4x(2x)}{(x^2 + 1)^2} = \dfrac{-4x^2 + 4}{(x^2 + 1)^2}$

At the origin: $y'(0) = 4$

The tangent is $y = 4x$.

At (1, 2): $y'(1) = 0$

The tangent is $y = 2$.

Graphical support:

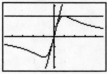

[−4.7, 4.7] by [−3.1, 3.1]

32. $y'(x) = \dfrac{(4 + x^2)(0) - 8(2x)}{(4 + x^2)^2} = -\dfrac{16x}{(4 + x^2)^2}$

$y'(2) = -\dfrac{1}{2}$

The tangent has slope $-\dfrac{1}{2}$ and passes through (2, 1). Its equation is $y = -\dfrac{1}{2}(x - 2) + 1$, or $y = -\dfrac{1}{2}x + 2$.

Graphical support:

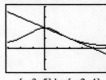

[−3, 5] by [−2, 4]

33. $\dfrac{dP}{dV} = \dfrac{d}{dV}\left(\dfrac{nRT}{V-nb} - \dfrac{an^2}{V^2}\right)$

$= \dfrac{(V-nb)\frac{d}{dV}(nRT) - (nRT)\frac{d}{dV}(V-nb)}{(V-nb)^2} - \dfrac{d}{dV}(an^2V^{-2})$

$= \dfrac{0 - nRT}{(V-nb)^2} + 2an^2V^{-3}$

$= -\dfrac{nRT}{(V-nb)^2} + \dfrac{2an^2}{V^3}$

34. $\dfrac{ds}{dt} = \dfrac{d}{dt}(4.9t^2) = 9.8t$

$\dfrac{d^2s}{dt^2} = \dfrac{d}{dt}(9.8t) = 9.8$

35. $\dfrac{dR}{dM} = \dfrac{d}{dM}\left[M^2\left(\dfrac{C}{2} - \dfrac{M}{3}\right)\right]$

$= \dfrac{d}{dM}\left(\dfrac{C}{2}M^2 - \dfrac{1}{3}M^3\right)$

$= CM - M^2$

36. If the radius of a circle is changed by a very small amount Δr, the change in the area can be thought of as a very thin strip with length given by the circumference, $2\pi r$, and width Δr. Therefore, the change in the area can be thought of as $(2\pi r)(\Delta r)$, which means that the change in the area divided by the change in the radius is just $2\pi r$.

37. If the radius of a sphere is changed by a very small amount Δr, the change in the volume can be thought of as a very thin layer with an area given by the surface area, $4\pi r^2$, and a thickness given by Δr. Therefore, the change in the volume can be thought of as $(4\pi r^2)(\Delta r)$, which means that the change in the volume divided by the change in the radius is just $4\pi r^2$.

38. Let $t(x)$ be the number of trees and $y(x)$ be the yield per tree x years from now. Then $t(0) = 156$, $y(0) = 12$, $t'(0) = 13$, and $y'(0) = 1.5$. The rate of increase of production is

$\dfrac{d}{dx}(ty) = t(0)y'(0) + y(0)t'(0) = (156)(1.5) + (12)(13)$

$= 390$ bushels of annual production per year.

39. Let $m(x)$ be the number of members and $c(x)$ be the pavillion cost x years from now. Then $m(0) = 65$, $c(0) = 250$, $m'(0) = 6$, and $c'(0) = 10$. The rate of change of each member's share is $\dfrac{d}{dx}\left(\dfrac{c}{m}\right) = \dfrac{m(0)c'(0) - c(0)m'(0)}{[m(0)]^2}$

$= \dfrac{(65)(10) - (250)(6)}{(65)^2} \approx -0.201$ dollars per year. Each

member's share of the cost is decreasing by approximately

20 cents per year.

40. (a) It is insignificant in the limiting case and can be treated as zero (and removed from the expression).

   (b) It was "rejected" because it is incomparably smaller than the other terms: $v\,du$ and $u\,dv$.

(c) $\dfrac{d}{dx}(uv) = v\dfrac{du}{dx} + u\dfrac{dv}{dx}$. This is equivalent to the product rule given in the text.

(d) Because dx is 'infinitely small,' and this could be thought of as dividing by zero.

(e) $d\left(\dfrac{u}{v}\right) = \dfrac{u + du}{v + dv} - \dfrac{u}{v}$

$= \dfrac{(u + du)(v) - (u)(v + dv)}{(v + dv)(v)}$

$= \dfrac{uv + vdu - uv - udv}{v^2 + vdv}$

$= \dfrac{vdu - udv}{v^2}$

■ Section 3.4 Velocity and Other Rates of Change (pp. 122–133)

Exploration 1   Growth Rings on a Tree

1. Figure 3.22 is a better model, as it shows rings of equal *area* as opposed to rings of equal *width*. It is not likely that a tree could sustain increased growth year after year, although climate conditions do produce some years of greater growth than others.

2. Rings of equal area suggest that the tree adds approximately the same amount of wood to its girth each year. With access to approximately the same raw materials from which to make the wood each year, this is how most trees actually grow.

3. Since change in area is constant, so also is $\dfrac{\text{change in area}}{2\pi}$. If we denote this latter constant by k, we have $\dfrac{k}{\text{change in radius}} = r$, which means that r varies inversely as the change in the radius. In other words, the change in radius must get smaller when r gets bigger, and vice-versa.

Exploration 2   Modeling Horizontal Motion

1. The particle reverses direction at about $t = 0.61$ and $t = 2.06$.

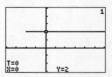

2. When the trace cursor is moving to the right the particle is moving to the right, and when the cursor is moving to the left the particle is moving to the left. Again we find the particle reverses direction at about $t = 0.61$ and $t = 2.06$.

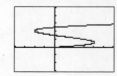

3. When the trace cursor is moving upward the particle is moving to the right, and when the cursor is moving downward the particle is moving to the left. Again we find the same values of t for when the particle reverses direction.

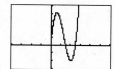

4. We can represent the velocity by graphing the parametric equations

$x_4(t) = x_1'(t) = 12t^2 - 32t + 15, \ y_4(t) = 2$ (part 1),
$x_5(t) = x_1'(t) = 12t^2 - 32t + 15, \ y_5(t) = t$ (part 2),
$x_6(t) = t, \ y_6(t) = x_1'(t) = 12t^2 - 32t + 15$ (part 3)

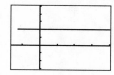

$[-8, 20]$ by $[-3, 5]$
(x_4, y_4)

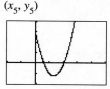

$[-8, 20]$ by $[-3, 5]$
(x_5, y_5)

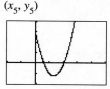

$[-2, 5]$ by $[-10, 20]$
(x_6, y_6)

For (x_4, y_4) and (x_5, y_5), the particle is moving to the right when the x-coordinate of the graph (velocity) is positive, moving to the left when the x-coordinate of the graph (velocity) is negative, and is stopped when the x-coordinate of the graph (velocity) is 0. For (x_6, y_6), the particle is moving to the right when the y-coordinate of the graph (velocity) is positive, moving to the left when the y-coordinate of the graph (velocity) is negative, and is stopped when the y-coordinate of the graph (velocity) is 0.

Exploration 3   Seeing Motion on a Graphing Calculator

1. Let tMin $= 0$ and tMax $= 10$.

2. Since the rock achieves a maximum height of 400 feet, set yMax to be slightly greater than 400, for example yMax $= 420$.

4. The grapher proceeds with constant increments of t (time), so pixels appear on the screen at regular time intervals. When the rock is moving more slowly, the pixels appear closer together. When the rock is moving faster, the pixels appear farther apart. We observe faster motion when the pixels are farther apart.

Quick Review 3.4

1. The coefficient of x^2 is negative, so the parabola opens downward.

Graphical support:

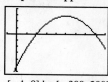

$[-1, 9]$ by $[-300, 200]$

2. The y-intercept is $f(0) = -256$.
See the solution to Exercise 1 for graphical support.

3. The x-intercepts occur when $f(x) = 0$.
$-16x^2 + 160x - 256 = 0$
$-16(x^2 - 10x + 16) = 0$
$-16(x - 2)(x - 8) = 0$
$x = 2$ or $x = 8$
The x-intercepts are 2 and 8. See the solution to Exercise 1 for graphical support.

4. Since $f(x) = -16(x^2 - 10x + 16)$
$= -16(x^2 - 10x + 25 - 9) = -16(x - 5)^2 + 144$,
the range is $(-\infty, 144]$.
See the solution to Exercise 1 for graphical support.

5. Since $f(x) = -16(x^2 - 10x + 16)$
$= -16(x^2 - 10x + 25 - 9) = -16(x - 5)^2 + 144$,
the vertex is at (5, 144). See the solution to Exercise 1 for graphical support.

6. $f(x) = 80$
$-16x^2 + 160x - 256 = 80$
$-16x^2 + 160x - 336 = 0$
$-16(x^2 - 10x + 21) = 0$
$-16(x - 3)(x - 7) = 0$
$x = 3$ or $x = 7$
$f(x) = 80$ at $x = 3$ and at $x = 7$.
See the solution to Exercise 1 for graphical support.

7. $\dfrac{dy}{dx} = 100$
$-32x + 160 = 100$
$60 = 32x$
$x = \dfrac{15}{8}$
$\dfrac{dy}{dx} = 100$ at $x = \dfrac{15}{8}$

Graphical support: the graph of NDER $f(x)$ is shown.

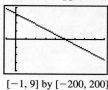

$[-1, 9]$ by $[-200, 200]$

8. $\dfrac{dy}{dx} > 0$
$-32x + 160 > 0$
$-32x > -160$
$x < 5$

$\dfrac{dy}{dx} > 0$ when $x < 5$.
See the solution to Exercise 7 for graphical support.

9. Note that $f'(x) = -32x + 160$.

$$\lim_{h \to 0} \frac{f(3 + h) - f(3)}{h} = f'(3) = -32(3) + 160 = 64$$

For graphical support, use the graph shown in the solution

to Exercise 7 and observe that NDER $(f(x), 3) \approx 64$.

10. $f'(x) = -32x + 160$
$f''(x) = -32$
At $x = 7$ (and, in fact, at any other of x),

$$\frac{d^2y}{dx^2} = -32.$$

Graphical support: the graph of NDER(NDER $f(x)$) is
shown.

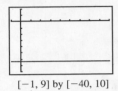

$[-1, 9]$ by $[-40, 10]$

Section 3.4 Exercises

1. Since $V = s^3$, the instantaneous rate of change is $\frac{dV}{ds} = 3s^2$.

2. (a) Displacement $= s(5) - s(0) = 12 - 2 = 10$ m

(b) Average velocity $= \dfrac{10 \text{ m}}{5 \text{ sec}} = 2$ m/sec

(c) Velocity $= s'(t) = 2t - 3$
At $t = 4$, velocity $= s'(4) = 2(4) - 3 = 5$ m/sec

(d) Acceleration $= s''(t) = 2$ m/sec^2

(e) The particle changes direction when

$s'(t) = 2t - 3 = 0$, so $t = \dfrac{3}{2}$ sec.

(f) Since the acceleration is always positive, the position s

is at a minimum when the particle changes direction, at

$t = \dfrac{3}{2}$ sec. Its position at this time is $s\left(\dfrac{3}{2}\right) = -\dfrac{1}{4}$ m.

3. (a) Velocity: $v(t) = \dfrac{ds}{dt} = \dfrac{d}{dt}(24t - 0.8t^2) = 24 - 1.6t$ m/sec

Acceleration: $a(t) = \dfrac{dv}{dt} = \dfrac{d}{dt}(24 - 1.6t) = -1.6$ m/sec^2

(b) The rock reaches its highest point when
$v(t) = 24 - 1.6t = 0$, at $t = 15$. It took 15 seconds.

(c) The maximum height was $s(15) = 180$ meters.

(d) $\qquad s(t) = \dfrac{1}{2}(180)$

$24t - 0.8t^2 = 90$

$0 = 0.8t^2 - 24t + 90$

$t = \dfrac{24 \pm \sqrt{(-24)^2 - 4(0.8)(90)}}{2(0.8)}$

$\approx 4.393, 25.607$

It took about 4.393 seconds to reach half its maximum

height.

(e) $\qquad s(t) = 0$
$24t - 0.8t^2 = 0$
$0.8t(30 - t) = 0$
$\qquad t = 0$ or $t = 30$
The rock was aloft from $t = 0$ to $t = 30$, so it was aloft
for 30 seconds.

4. On Mars:

Velocity $= \dfrac{ds}{dt} = \dfrac{d}{dt}(1.86t^2) = 3.72t$

Solving $3.72t = 16.6$, the downward velocity reaches

16.6 m/sec after about 4.462 sec.

On Jupiter:

Velocity $= \dfrac{ds}{dt} = \dfrac{d}{dt}(11.44t^2) = 22.88t$

Solving $22.88t = 16.6$, the downward velocity reaches

16.6 m/sec after about 0.726 sec.

5. The rock reaches its maximum height when the velocity
$s'(t) = 24 - 9.8t = 0$, at $t \approx 2.449$. Its maximum height is
about $s(2.449) \approx 29.388$ meters.

6. Moon:
$\qquad s(t) = 0$
$832t - 2.6t^2 = 0$
$2.6t(320 - t) = 0$
$\qquad t = 0$ or $t = 320$
It takes 320 seconds to return.
Earth:
$\qquad s(t) = 0$
$832t - 16t^2 = 0$
$16t(52 - t) = 0$
$\qquad t = 0$ or $t = 52$
It takes 52 seconds to return.

7. The following is one way to simulate the problem situation.
For the moon:
$x_1(t) = 3(t < 160) + 3.1(t \geq 160)$
$y_1(t) = 832t - 2.6t^2$
t-values: 0 to 320
window: $[0, 6]$ by $[-10{,}000, 70{,}000]$
For the earth:
$x_1(t) = 3(t < 26) + 3.1(t \geq 26)$
$y_1(t) = 832t - 16t^2$
t-values: 0 to 52
window: $[0, 6]$ by $[-1000, 11{,}000]$

8. The growth rate is given by
$b'(t) = 10^4 - 2 \cdot 10^3 t = 10{,}000 - 2000t$.
At $t = 0$: $b'(0) = 10{,}000$ bacteria/hour
At $t = 5$: $b'(5) = 0$ bacteria/hour
At $t = 10$: $b'(10) = -10{,}000$ bacteria/hour

9. $Q(t) = 200(30 - t)^2 = 200(900 - 60t + t^2)$
$= 180,000 - 12,000t + 200t^2$

$Q'(t) = -12,000 + 400t$

The rate of change of the amount of water in the tank after 10 minutes is $Q'(10) = -8000$ gallons per minute. Note that $Q'(10) < 0$, so the rate at which the water is running *out* is positive. The water is running out at the rate of 8000 gallons per minute.

The average rate for the first 10 minutes is

$\dfrac{Q(10) - Q(0)}{10 - 0} = \dfrac{80,000 - 180,000}{10} = -10,000$ gallons per minute.

The water is flowing out at an average rate of 10,000 gallons per minute over the first 10 min.

10. (a) Average cost $= \dfrac{c(100)}{100} = \dfrac{11,000}{100} = \$110$ per machine

(b) $c'(x) = 100 - 0.2x$
Marginal cost $= c'(100) = \$80$ per machine

(c) Actual cost of 101st machine is
$c(101) - c(100) = \$79.90$, which is very close to the marginal cost calculated in part (b).

11. (a)

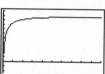

[0, 50] by [−500, 2200]

The values of x which make sense are the whole numbers, $x \geq 0$.

(b) Marginal revenue $= r'(x) = \dfrac{d}{dx}\left[2000\left(1 - \dfrac{1}{x + 1}\right)\right]$

$= \dfrac{d}{dx}\left(2000 - \dfrac{2000}{x + 1}\right)$

$= 0 - \dfrac{(x + 1)(0) - (2000)(1)}{(x + 1)^2} = \dfrac{2000}{(x + 1)^2}$

(c) $r'(5) = \dfrac{2000}{(5 + 1)^2} = \dfrac{2000}{36} \approx 55.56$

The increase in revenue is approximately $55.56.

(d) The limit is 0. This means that as x gets large, one reaches a point where very little extra revenue can be expected from selling more desks.

12. $v(t) = s'(t) = 3t^2 - 12t + 9$
$a(t) = v'(t) = 6t - 12$
Find when velocity is zero.
$3t^2 - 12t + 9 = 0$
$3(t^2 - 4t + 3) = 0$
$3(t - 1)(t - 3) = 0$
$t = 1$ or $t = 3$
At $t = 1$, the acceleration is $a(1) = -6$ m/sec^2
At $t = 3$, the acceleration is $a(3) = 6$ m/sec^2

13. $a(t) = v'(t) = 6t^2 - 18t + 12$
Find when acceleration is zero.
$6t^2 - 18t + 12 = 0$
$6(t^2 - 3t + 2) = 0$
$6(t - 1)(t - 2) = 0$
$t = 1$ or $t = 2$
At $t = 1$, the speed is $|v(1)| = |0| = 0$ m/sec.
At $t = 2$, the speed is $|v(2)| = |-1| = 1$ m/sec.

14. (a) $g'(x) = \dfrac{d}{dx}(x^3) = 3x^2$

$h'(x) = \dfrac{d}{dx}(x^3 - 2) = 3x^2$

$t'(x) = \dfrac{d}{dx}(x^3 + 3) = 3x^2$

(b) The graphs of NDER $g(x)$, NDER $h(x)$, and NDER $t(x)$ are all the same, as shown.

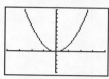

[−4, 4] by [−10, 20]

(c) $f(x)$ must be of the form $f(x) = x^3 + c$, where c is a constant.

(d) Yes. $f(x) = x^3$

(e) Yes. $f(x) = x^3 + 3$

15. (a)

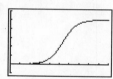

[0, 200] by [−2, 12]

(b) The values of x which make sense are the whole numbers, $x \geq 0$.

(c)

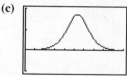

[0, 200] by [−0.1, 0.2]

P is most sensitive to changes in x when $|P'(x)|$ is largest. It is relatively sensitive to changes in x between approximately $x = 60$ and $x = 160$.

(d) The marginal profit, $P'(x)$, is greatest at $x \approx 106.44$. Since x must be an integer, $P(106) \approx 4.924$ thousand dollars or $4924.

(e) $P'(50) \approx 0.013$, or $13 per package sold
$P'(100) \approx 0.165$, or $165 per package sold
$P'(125) \approx 0.118$, or $118 per package sold
$P'(150) \approx 0.031$, or $31 per package sold
$P'(175) \approx 0.006$, or $6 per package sold
$P'(300) \approx 10^{-6}$, or $0.001 per package sold

(f) The limit is 10. The maximum possible profit is $10,000 monthly.

(g) Yes. In order to sell more and more packages, the company might need to lower the price to a point where they won't make any additional profit.

16. (a) 190 ft/sec

(b) 2 seconds

(c) After 8 seconds, and its velocity was 0 ft/sec then

(d) After about 11 seconds, and it was falling 90 ft/sec then

(e) About 3 seconds (from the rocket's highest point)

(f) The acceleration was greatest just before the engine stopped. The acceleration was constant from $t = 2$ to $t = 11$, while the rocket was in free fall.

17. Note that "downward velocity" is positive when McCarthy is falling downward. His downward velocity increases steadily until the parachute opens, and then decreases to a constant downward velocity. One possible sketch:

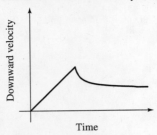

18. (a) We estimate the slopes at several points as follows, then connect the points to create a smooth curve.

t (days)	0	10	20	30	40	50
Slope (flies/day)	0.5	3.0	13.0	14.0	3.5	0.5

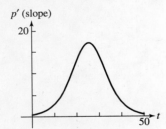

Horizontal axis: Days
Vertical axis: Flies per day

(b) Fastest: Around the 25th day
Slowest: Day 50 or day 0

19. The particle is at (5, 2) when $4t^3 - 16t^2 + 15t = 5$, which occurs at $t \approx 2.83$.

20. The motion can be simulated in parametric mode using $x_1(t) = 2t^3 - 13t^2 + 22t - 5$ and $y_1(t) = 2$ in $[-6, 8]$ by $[-3, 5]$.

(a) It begins at the point $(-5, 2)$ moving in the positive direction. After a little more than one second, it has moved a bit past (6, 2) and it turns back in the negative direction for approximately 2 seconds. At the end of that time, it is near $(-2, 2)$ and it turns back again in the positive direction. After that, it continues moving in the positive direction indefinitely, speeding up as it goes.

(b) The particle speeds up when its *speed* is increasing, which occurs during the approximate intervals $1.153 \le t \le 2.167$ and $t \ge 3.180$. It slows down during the approximate intervals $0 \le t \le 1.153$ and $2.167 \le t \le 3.180$. One way to determine the endpoints of these intervals is to use a grapher to find the minimums and maximums for the speed, $|\text{NDER } x(t)|$, using function mode in the window $[0, 5]$ by $[0, 10]$.

(c) The particle changes direction at $t \approx 1.153$ sec and at $t \approx 3.180$ sec.

(d) The particle is at rest "instantaneously" at $t \approx 1.153$ sec and at $t \approx 3.180$ sec.

(e) The velocity starts out positive but decreasing, it becomes negative, then starts to increase, and becomes positive again and continues to increase. The speed is decreasing, reaches 0 at $t \approx 1.15$ sec, then increases until $t \approx 2.17$ sec, decreases until $t \approx 3.18$ sec when it is 0 again, and then increases after that.

(f) The particle is at (5, 2) when $2t^3 - 13t^2 + 22t - 5 = 5$ at $t \approx 0.745$ sec, $t \approx 1.626$ sec, and at $t \approx 4.129$ sec.

21. (a)

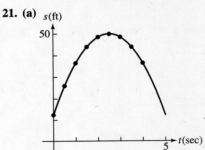

(b) $s'(1) = 18$, $s'(2.5) = 0$, $s'(3.5) = -12$

22. (a)

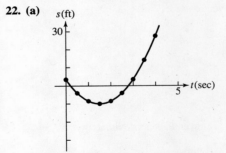

(b) $s'(1) = -6$, $s'(2.5) = 12$, $s'(3.5) = 24$

23. (a) The body reverses direction when v changes sign, at $t = 2$ and at $t = 7$.

(b) The body is moving at a constant speed, $|v| = 3$ m/sec, between $t = 3$ and $t = 6$.

(c) The speed graph is obtained by reflecting the negative portion of the velocity graph, $2 < t < 7$, about the x-axis.

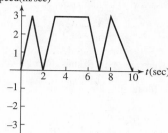

(d) For $0 \leq t < 1$: $a = \dfrac{3 - 0}{1 - 0} = 3$ m/sec^2

For $1 < t < 3$: $a = \dfrac{-3 - 3}{3 - 1} = -3$ m/sec^2

For $3 < t < 6$: $a = \dfrac{-3 - (-3)}{6 - 3} = 0$ m/sec^2

For $6 < t < 8$: $a = \dfrac{3 - (-3)}{8 - 6} = 3$ m/sec^2

For $8 < t \leq 10$: $a = \dfrac{0 - 3}{10 - 8} = -1.5$ m/sec^2

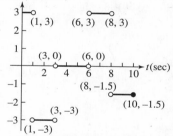

24. (a) The particle is moving left when the graph of s has negative slope, for $2 < t < 3$ and for $5 < t \leq 6$. The particle is moving right when the graph of s has positive slope, for $0 \leq t < 1$. The particle is standing still when the graph of s is horizontal, for $1 < t < 2$ and for $3 < t < 5$.

(b) For $0 \leq t < 1$: $v = \dfrac{2 - 0}{1 - 0} = 2$ cm/sec

Speed $= |v| = 2$ cm/sec

For $1 < t < 2$: $v = \dfrac{2 - 2}{2 - 1} = 0$ cm/sec

Speed $= |v| = 0$ cm/sec

For $2 < t < 3$: $v = \dfrac{-2 - 2}{3 - 2} = -4$ cm/sec

Speed $= |v| = 4$ cm/sec

For $3 < t < 5$: $v = \dfrac{-2 - (-2)}{5 - 3} = 0$ cm/sec

Speed $= |v| = 0$ cm/sec

For $5 < t \leq 6$: $v = \dfrac{-4 - (-2)}{6 - 5} = -2$ cm/sec

Speed $= |v| = 2$ cm/sec

Velocity graph:

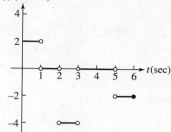

Speed graph:

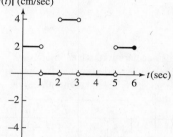

25. (a) The particle moves forward when $v > 0$, for $0 \leq t < 1$ and for $5 < t < 7$.
The particle moves backward when $v < 0$, for $1 < t < 5$.
The particle speeds up when v is negative and decreasing, for $1 < t < 2$, and when v is positive and increasing, for $5 < t < 6$.
The particle slows down when v is positive and decreasing, for $0 \leq t < 1$ and for $6 < t < 7$, and when v is negative and increasing, for $3 < t < 5$.

(b) Note that the acceleration $a = \dfrac{dv}{dt}$ is undefined at $t = 2$, $t = 3$, and $t = 6$.
The acceleration is positive when v is increasing, for $3 < t < 6$.
The acceleration is negative when v is decreasing, for $0 \leq t < 2$ and for $6 < t < 7$.
The acceleration is zero when v is constant, for $2 < t < 3$ and for $7 < t \leq 9$.

(c) The particle moves at its greatest speed when $|v|$ is maximized, at $t = 0$ and for $2 < t < 3$.

(d) The particle stands still for more than an instant when v stays at zero, for $7 < t \leq 9$.

26. (a) To graph the velocity, we estimate the slopes at several points as follows, then connect the points to create a smooth curve.

t (hours)	0	2.5	5	7.5	10	12.5	15
v (km/hour)	0	56	75	56	0	−94	−225

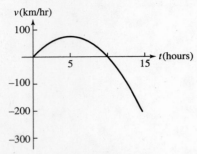

To graph the acceleration, we estimate the slope of the velocity graph at several points as follows, and then connect the points to create a smooth curve.

t (hours)	0	2.5	5	7.5	10	12.5	15
a (km/hour^2)	30	15	0	−15	−30	−45	−60

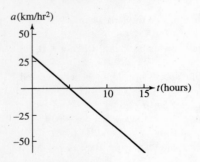

(b) $\dfrac{ds}{dt} = 30t - 3t^2$

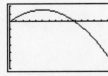

[0, 15] by [−300, 100]

$\dfrac{d^2s}{dt^2} = 30 - 6t$

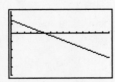

[0, 15] by [−100, 50]

The graphs are very similar.

27. (a) Solving $160 = 490t^2$ gives $t = \pm\dfrac{4}{7}$.

It took $\dfrac{4}{7}$ of a second. The average velocity was $\dfrac{160 \text{ cm}}{\left(\dfrac{4}{7}\right)}$ sec = 280 cm/sec.

(b) $v = s'(t) = 980t$

$a = s''(t) = 980$

The velocity was $s'\left(\dfrac{4}{7}\right) = 560$ cm/sec.

The acceleration was $s''\left(\dfrac{4}{7}\right) = 980$ cm/sec^2.

(c) Since there were about 16 flashes during $\dfrac{4}{7}$ of a second, the light was flashing at a rate of about 28 flashes per second.

28. Graph C is position, graph A is velocity, and graph B is acceleration.
A is the derivative of C because it is positive, negative, and zero where C is increasing, decreasing, and has horizontal tangents, respectively. The relationship between B and A is similar.

29. Graph C is position, graph B is velocity, and graph A is acceleration.
B is the derivative of C because it is negative and zero where C is decreasing and has horizontal tangents, respectively.
A is the derivative of B because it is positive, negative, and zero where B is increasing, decreasing, and has horizontal tangents, respectively.

30. (a) $\dfrac{dy}{dt} = \dfrac{d}{dt}\left[6\left(1 - \dfrac{t}{12}\right)^2\right]$

$= \dfrac{d}{dt}\left[6\left(1 - \dfrac{t}{6} + \dfrac{t^2}{144}\right)\right]$

$= \dfrac{d}{dt}\left(6 - t + \dfrac{1}{24}t^2\right)$

$= 0 - 1 + \dfrac{t}{12} = \dfrac{t}{12} - 1$

(b) The fluid level is falling fastest when $\dfrac{dy}{dt}$ is the most negative, at $t = 0$, when $\dfrac{dy}{dt} = -1$. The fluid level is falling slowest at $t = 12$, when $\dfrac{dy}{dt} = 0$.

(c)

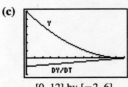

[0, 12] by [−2, 6]

y is decreasing and $\dfrac{dy}{dt}$ is negative over the entire interval. y decreases more rapidly early in the interval, and the magnitude of $\dfrac{dy}{dt}$ is larger then. $\dfrac{dy}{dt}$ is 0 at $t = 12$, where the graph of y seems to have a horizontal tangent.

31. (a) $\dfrac{dV}{dr} = \dfrac{d}{dr}\left(\dfrac{4}{3}\pi r^3\right) = 4\pi r^2$

When $r = 2$, $\dfrac{dV}{dr} = 4\pi(2)^2 = 16\pi$ cubic feet of

volume per foot of radius.

(b) The increase in the volume is

$\dfrac{4}{3}\pi(2.2)^3 - \dfrac{4}{3}\pi(2)^3 \approx 11.092$ cubic feet.

32. For $t > 0$, the speed of the aircraft in meters per second

after t seconds is $\dfrac{20}{9}t$. Multiplying by $\dfrac{3600 \text{ sec}}{1 \text{ h}} \cdot \dfrac{1 \text{ km}}{1000 \text{ m}}$,

we find that this is equivalent to $8t$ kilometers per hour.

Solving $8t = 200$ gives $t = 25$ seconds. The aircraft takes

25 seconds to become airborne, and the distance it travels

during this time is $D(25) \approx 694.444$ meters.

33. Let v_0 be the exit velocity of a particle of lava. Then

$s(t) = v_0 t - 16t^2$ feet, so the velocity is $\dfrac{ds}{dt} = v_0 - 32t$.

Solving $\dfrac{ds}{dt} = 0$ gives $t = \dfrac{v_0}{32}$. Then the maximum height, in

feet, is $s\left(\dfrac{v_0}{32}\right) = v_0\left(\dfrac{v_0}{32}\right) - 16\left(\dfrac{v_0}{32}\right)^2 = \dfrac{v_0{}^2}{64}$. Solving

$\dfrac{v_0{}^2}{64} = 1900$ gives $v_0 \approx \pm 348.712$. The exit velocity was

about 348.712 ft/sec. Multiplying by $\dfrac{3600 \text{ sec}}{1 \text{ h}} \cdot \dfrac{1 \text{ mi}}{5280 \text{ ft}}$, we

find that this is equivalent to about 237.758 mi/h.

34. By estimating the slope of the velocity graph at that point.

35. Since profit = revenue − cost, the Sum and Difference

Rule gives $\dfrac{d}{dx}(\text{profit}) = \dfrac{d}{dx}(\text{revenue}) - \dfrac{d}{dx}(\text{cost})$, where x is

the number of units produced. This means that marginal

profit = marginal revenue − marginal cost.

36. (a) It takes 135 seconds.

(b) Average speed $= \dfrac{\Delta F}{\Delta t} = \dfrac{5 - 0}{73 - 0} = \dfrac{5}{73}$

≈ 0.068 furlongs/sec.

(c) Using a symmetric difference quotient, the horse's

speed is approximately

$\dfrac{\Delta F}{\Delta t} = \dfrac{4 - 2}{59 - 33} = \dfrac{2}{26} = \dfrac{1}{13} \approx 0.077$ furlongs/sec.

(d) The horse is running the fastest during the last furlong
(between 9th and 10th furlong markers). This furlong
takes only 11 seconds to run, which is the least amount
of time for a furlong.

(e) The horse accelerates the fastest during the first furlong
(between markers 0 and 1).

37. (a) Assume that f is even. Then,

$f'(-x) = \lim\limits_{h \to 0} \dfrac{f(-x + h) - f(-x)}{h}$

$= \lim\limits_{h \to 0} \dfrac{f(x - h) - f(x)}{h}$, and substituting $k = -h$,

$= \lim\limits_{k \to 0} \dfrac{f(x + k) - f(x)}{-k}$

$= -\lim\limits_{k \to 0} \dfrac{f(x + k) - f(x)}{k} = -f'(x)$

So, f' is an odd function.

(b) Assume that f is odd. Then,

$f'(-x) = \lim\limits_{h \to 0} \dfrac{f(-x + h) - f(-x)}{h}$

$= \lim\limits_{h \to 0} \dfrac{-f(x - h) + f(x)}{h}$,

and substituting $k = -h$,

$= \lim\limits_{k \to 0} \dfrac{-f(x + k) + f(x)}{-k}$

$= \lim\limits_{k \to 0} \dfrac{f(x + k) - f(x)}{k} = f'(x)$

So, f' is an even function.

38. $\dfrac{d}{dx}(fgh) = \dfrac{d}{dx}[f(gh)] = f \cdot \dfrac{d}{dx}(gh) + gh \cdot \dfrac{d}{dx}(f)$

$= f\left(g \cdot \dfrac{dh}{dx} + h \cdot \dfrac{dg}{dx}\right) + gh \cdot \dfrac{df}{dx}$

$= \left(\dfrac{df}{dx}\right)gh + f\left(\dfrac{dg}{dx}\right)h + fg\left(\dfrac{dh}{dx}\right)$

■ Section 3.5 Derivatives of Trigonometric Functions (pp. 134–141)

Exploration 1   Making a Conjecture with NDER

1. When the graph of $\sin x$ is increasing, the graph of
NDER $(\sin x)$ is positive (above the x-axis).

2. When the graph of $\sin x$ is decreasing, the graph of
NDER $(\sin x)$ is negative (below the x-axis).

3. When the graph of $\sin x$ stops increasing and starts
decreasing, the graph of NDER $(\sin x)$ crosses the x-axis
from above to below.

4. The slope of the graph of $\sin x$ matches the value of
NDER $(\sin x)$ at these points.

5. We conjecture that NDER $(\sin x) = \cos x$. The graphs
coincide, supporting our conjecture.

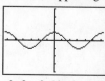

$[-2\pi, 2\pi]$ by $[-4, 4]$

6. When the graph of cos x is increasing, the graph of NDER (cos x) is positive (above the x-axis).

When the graph of cos x is decreasing, the graph of NDER (cos x) is negative (below the x-axis).

When the graph of cos x stops increasing and starts decreasing, the graph of NDER (cos x) crosses the x-axis from above to below.

The slope of the graph of cos x matches the value of NDER (cos x) at these points.

We conjecture that NDER (cos x) = $-\sin x$. The graphs coincide, supporting our conjecture.

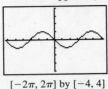

$[-2\pi, 2\pi]$ by $[-4, 4]$

Quick Review 3.5

1. $135° \cdot \dfrac{\pi}{180°} = \dfrac{3\pi}{4} \approx 2.356$

2. $1.7 \cdot \dfrac{180°}{\pi} = \left(\dfrac{306}{\pi}\right)° \approx 97.403°$

3. $\sin \dfrac{\pi}{3} = \dfrac{\sqrt{3}}{2}$

4. Domain: All reals
Range: $[-1, 1]$

5. Domain: $x \neq \dfrac{k\pi}{2}$ for odd integers k

Range: All reals

6. $\cos a = \pm\sqrt{1 - \sin^2 a} = \pm\sqrt{1 - (-1)^2} = \pm\sqrt{0} = 0$

7. If $\tan a = -1$, then $a = \dfrac{3\pi}{4} + k\pi$ for some integer k, so

$\sin a = \pm\dfrac{1}{\sqrt{2}}$.

8. $\dfrac{1 - \cos h}{h} = \dfrac{(1 - \cos h)(1 + \cos h)}{h(1 + \cos h)} = \dfrac{1 - \cos^2 h}{h(1 + \cos h)}$

$= \dfrac{\sin^2 h}{h(1 + \cos h)}$

9. $y'(x) = 6x^2 - 14x$
$y'(3) = 12$
The tangent line has slope 12 and passes through $(3, 1)$, so its equation is $y = 12(x - 3) + 1$, or $y = 12x - 35$.

10. $a(t) = v'(t) = 6t^2 - 14t$
$a(3) = 12$

Section 3.5 Exercises

1. $\dfrac{d}{dx}(1 + x - \cos x) = 0 + 1 - (-\sin x) = 1 + \sin x$

2. $\dfrac{d}{dx}(2 \sin x - \tan x) = 2 \cos x - \sec^2 x$

3. $\dfrac{d}{dx}\left(\dfrac{1}{x} + 5 \sin x\right) = -\dfrac{1}{x^2} + 5 \cos x$

4. $\dfrac{d}{dx}(x \sec x) = x\dfrac{d}{dx}(\sec x) + \sec x\dfrac{d}{dx}(x)$

$= x \sec x \tan x + \sec x$

5. $\dfrac{d}{dx}(4 - x^2 \sin x) = \dfrac{d}{dx}(4) - \left[x^2\dfrac{d}{dx}(\sin x) + (\sin x)\dfrac{d}{dx}(x^2)\right]$

$= 0 - [x^2 \cos x + (\sin x)(2x)]$

$= -x^2 \cos x - 2x \sin x$

6. $\dfrac{d}{dx}(3x + x \tan x) = \dfrac{d}{dx}(3x) + \left[x\dfrac{d}{dx}(\tan x) + (\tan x)\dfrac{d}{dx}(x)\right]$

$= 3 + x \sec^2 x + \tan x$

7. $\dfrac{d}{dx}\left(\dfrac{4}{\cos x}\right) = \dfrac{d}{dx}(4 \sec x) = 4 \sec x \tan x$

8. $\dfrac{d}{dx}\dfrac{x}{1 + \cos x} = \dfrac{(1 + \cos x)\dfrac{d}{dx}(x) - x\dfrac{d}{dx}(1 + \cos x)}{(1 + \cos x)^2}$

$= \dfrac{1 + \cos x + x \sin x}{(1 + \cos x)^2}$

9. $\dfrac{d}{dx}\dfrac{\cot x}{1 + \cot x} = \dfrac{(1 + \cot x)\dfrac{d}{dx}(\cot x) - (\cot x)\dfrac{d}{dx}(1 + \cot x)}{(1 + \cot x)^2}$

$= \dfrac{(1 + \cot x)(-\csc^2 x) - (\cot x)(-\csc^2 x)}{(1 + \cot x)^2}$

$= -\dfrac{\csc^2 x}{(1 + \cot x)^2} = -\dfrac{\csc^2 x \sin^2 x}{(1 + \cot x)^2 \sin^2 x} = -\dfrac{1}{(\sin x + \cos x)^2}$

10. $\dfrac{d}{dx}\dfrac{\cos x}{1 + \sin x} = \dfrac{(1 + \sin x)\dfrac{d}{dx}(\cos x) - (\cos x)\dfrac{d}{dx}(1 + \sin x)}{(1 + \sin x)^2}$

$= \dfrac{(1 + \sin x)(-\sin x) - (\cos x)(\cos x)}{(1 + \sin x)^2}$

$= \dfrac{-\sin x - \sin^2 x - \cos^2 x}{(1 + \sin x)^2}$

$= \dfrac{-(1 + \sin x)}{(1 + \sin x)^2}$

$= -\dfrac{1}{1 + \sin x}$

11. $y'(x) = \dfrac{d}{dx}(\sin x + 3) = \cos x$

$y'(\pi) = \cos \pi = -1$

The tangent line has slope -1 and passes through

$(\pi, \sin \pi + 3) = (\pi, 3)$.

Its equation is $y = -1(x - \pi) + 3$, or $y = -x + \pi + 3$.

12. $y'(x) = \dfrac{d}{dx}\dfrac{\tan x}{x} = \dfrac{x\frac{d}{dx}(\tan x) - \tan x\frac{d}{dx}(x)}{x^2}$

$= \dfrac{x\sec^2 x - \tan x}{x^2}$

$y'\left(\dfrac{\pi}{4}\right) = \dfrac{\frac{\pi}{4}\cdot(\sqrt{2})^2 - 1}{\left(\frac{\pi}{4}\right)^2} = \dfrac{8\pi - 16}{\pi^2}$

The normal line has slope $-\dfrac{\pi^2}{8\pi - 16} = \dfrac{\pi^2}{16 - 8\pi}$

and passes through $\left(\dfrac{\pi}{4}, \dfrac{\tan\left(\frac{\pi}{4}\right)}{\frac{\pi}{4}}\right) = \left(\dfrac{\pi}{4}, \dfrac{4}{\pi}\right)$.

Its equation is $y =$

$\dfrac{\pi^2}{16 - 8\pi}\left(x - \dfrac{\pi}{4}\right) + \dfrac{4}{\pi}$, or

$y = \dfrac{\pi^2}{16 - 8\pi}x - \dfrac{\pi^3}{64 - 32\pi} + \dfrac{4}{\pi}$.

Using decimals, this equation is approximately

$y = -1.081x + 2.122$.

13. $y'(x) = \dfrac{d}{dx}(x^2\sin x) = x^2\dfrac{d}{dx}(\sin x) + (\sin x)\dfrac{d}{dx}(x^2)$

$= x^2\cos x + 2x\sin x$

$y'(3) = 9\cos 3 + 6\sin 3$

The tangent line has slope $9\cos 3 + 6\sin 3$ and passes through $(3, 9\sin 3)$. Its equation is
$y = (9\cos 3 + 6\sin 3)(x - 3) + 9\sin 3$, or
$y = (9\cos 3 + 6\sin 3)x - 27\cos 3 - 9\sin 3$. Using decimals, this equation is approximately
$y = -8.063x + 25.460$.

14. $\lim\limits_{h\to 0}\dfrac{\cos(x + h) - \cos x}{h}$

$= \lim\limits_{h\to 0}\dfrac{(\cos x\cos h - \sin x\sin h) - \cos x}{h}$

$= \lim\limits_{h\to 0}\dfrac{\cos x(\cos h - 1) - \sin x\sin h}{h}$

$= \lim\limits_{h\to 0}\left((\cos x)\dfrac{\cos h - 1}{h} - (\sin x)\dfrac{\sin h}{h}\right)$

$= (\cos x)\left(\lim\limits_{h\to 0}\dfrac{\cos h - 1}{h}\right) - (\sin x)\left(\lim\limits_{h\to 0}\dfrac{\sin h}{h}\right)$

$= (\cos x)(0) - (\sin x)(1) = -\sin x$

15. (a) $\dfrac{d}{dx}\tan x = \dfrac{d}{dx}\dfrac{\sin x}{\cos x} = \dfrac{(\cos x)\frac{d}{dx}(\sin x) - (\sin x)\frac{d}{dx}(\cos x)}{(\cos x)^2}$

$= \dfrac{(\cos x)(\cos x) - (\sin x)(-\sin x)}{\cos^2 x}$

$= \dfrac{\cos^2 x + \sin^2 x}{\cos^2 x} = \dfrac{1}{\cos^2 x} = \sec^2 x$

(b) $\dfrac{d}{dx}\sec x = \dfrac{d}{dx}\dfrac{1}{\cos x} = \dfrac{(\cos x)\frac{d}{dx}(1) - (1)\frac{d}{dx}(\cos x)}{(\cos x)^2}$

$= \dfrac{(\cos x)(0) - (1)(-\sin x)}{\cos^2 x}$

$= \dfrac{\sin x}{\cos^2 x} = \sec x\tan x$

16. (a) $\dfrac{d}{dx}\cot x = \dfrac{d}{dx}\dfrac{\cos x}{\sin x}$

$= \dfrac{(\sin x)\frac{d}{dx}(\cos x) - (\cos x)\frac{d}{dx}(\sin x)}{(\sin x)^2}$

$= \dfrac{(\sin x)(-\sin x) - (\cos x)(\cos x)}{\sin^2 x}$

$= \dfrac{-(\sin^2 x + \cos^2 x)}{\sin^2 x}$

$= -\dfrac{1}{\sin^2 x} = -\csc^2 x$

(b) $\dfrac{d}{dx}\csc x = \dfrac{d}{dx}\dfrac{1}{\sin x}$

$= \dfrac{(\sin x)\frac{d}{dx}(1) - (1)\frac{d}{dx}(\sin x)}{(\sin x)^2}$

$= \dfrac{(\sin x)(0) - (1)(\cos x)}{\sin^2 x}$

$= -\dfrac{\cos x}{\sin^2 x} = -\csc x\cot x$

17. $\dfrac{d}{dx}\sec x = \sec x\tan x$ which is 0 at $x = 0$, so the slope of the tangent line is 0. $\dfrac{d}{dx}\cos x = -\sin x$ which is 0 at $x = 0$, so the slope of the tangent line is 0.

18. $\dfrac{d}{dx}\tan x = \sec^2 x = \dfrac{1}{\cos^2 x}$, which is never 0.
$\dfrac{d}{dx}\cot x = -\csc^2 x = -\dfrac{1}{\sin^2 x}$, which is never 0.

19. $y'(x) = \dfrac{d}{dx}(\sqrt{2}\cos x) = -\sqrt{2}\sin x$

$y'\left(\dfrac{\pi}{4}\right) = -\sqrt{2}\sin\dfrac{\pi}{4} = -\sqrt{2}\left(\dfrac{1}{\sqrt{2}}\right) = -1$

The tangent line has slope -1 and passes through

$\left(\dfrac{\pi}{4}, \sqrt{2}\cos\dfrac{\pi}{4}\right) = \left(\dfrac{\pi}{4}, 1\right)$, so its equation is

$y = -1\left(x - \dfrac{\pi}{4}\right) + 1$, or $y = -x + \dfrac{\pi}{4} + 1$.

The normal line has slope 1 and passes through $\left(\dfrac{\pi}{4}, 1\right)$, so

its equation is $y = 1\left(x - \dfrac{\pi}{4}\right) + 1$, or $y = x + 1 - \dfrac{\pi}{4}$.

20. $y'(x) = \dfrac{d}{dx}\tan x = \sec^2 x$

$y'(x) = \dfrac{d}{dx}(2x) = 2$

$\sec^2 x = 2$

$\sec x = \pm\sqrt{2}$

$\cos x = \pm\dfrac{1}{\sqrt{2}}$

On $\left(-\dfrac{\pi}{2}, \dfrac{\pi}{2}\right)$, the solutions are $x = \pm\dfrac{\pi}{4}$. The points on the

curve are $\left(-\dfrac{\pi}{4}, -1\right)$ and $\left(\dfrac{\pi}{4}, 1\right)$.

21. $y'(x) = \dfrac{d}{dx}(4 + \cot x - 2 \csc x)$

$= 0 - \csc^2 x + 2 \csc x \cot x$

$= -\csc^2 x + 2 \csc x \cot x$

(a) $y'\left(\dfrac{\pi}{2}\right) = -\csc^2 \dfrac{\pi}{2} + 2 \csc \dfrac{\pi}{2} \cot \dfrac{\pi}{2}$

$= -1^2 + 2(1)(0) = -1$

The tangent line has slope -1 and passes through

$P\left(\dfrac{\pi}{2}, 2\right)$. Its equation is $y = -1\left(x - \dfrac{\pi}{2}\right) + 2$, or

$y = -x + \dfrac{\pi}{2} + 2.$

(b) $y'(x) = 0$

$-\csc^2 x + 2 \csc x \cot x = 0$

$-\dfrac{1}{\sin^2 x} + \dfrac{2 \cos x}{\sin^2 x} = 0$

$\dfrac{1}{\sin^2 x}(2 \cos x - 1) = 0$

$\cos x = \dfrac{1}{2}$

$x = \dfrac{\pi}{3}$ at point Q

$y\left(\dfrac{\pi}{3}\right) = 4 + \cot \dfrac{\pi}{3} - 2 \csc \dfrac{\pi}{3}$

$= 4 + \dfrac{1}{\sqrt{3}} - 2\left(\dfrac{2}{\sqrt{3}}\right)$

$= 4 - \dfrac{3}{\sqrt{3}} = 4 - \sqrt{3}$

The coordinates of Q are $\left(\dfrac{\pi}{3}, 4 - \sqrt{3}\right)$.

The equation of the horizontal line is $y = 4 - \sqrt{3}$.

22. $y'(x) = \dfrac{d}{dx}(1 + \sqrt{2} \csc x + \cot x)$

$= 0 + \sqrt{2}(-\csc x \cot x) + (-\csc^2 x)$

$= -\sqrt{2} \csc x \cot x - \csc^2 x$

(a) $y'\left(\dfrac{\pi}{4}\right) = -\sqrt{2} \csc \dfrac{\pi}{4} \cot \dfrac{\pi}{4} - \csc^2 \dfrac{\pi}{4}$

$= -\sqrt{2}(\sqrt{2})(1) - (\sqrt{2})^2$

$= -2 - 2 = -4$

The tangent line has slope -4 and passes through

$P\left(\dfrac{\pi}{4}, 4\right)$. Its equation is $y = -4\left(x - \dfrac{\pi}{4}\right) + 4$, or

$y = -4x + \pi + 4.$

(b) $y'(x) = 0$

$-\sqrt{2} \csc x \cot x - \csc^2 x = 0$

$-\dfrac{\sqrt{2} \cos x}{\sin^2 x} - \dfrac{1}{\sin^2 x} = 0$

$-\dfrac{1}{\sin^2 x}(\sqrt{2} \cos x + 1) = 0$

$\cos x = -\dfrac{1}{\sqrt{2}}$

$x = \dfrac{3\pi}{4}$ at point Q

$y\left(\dfrac{3\pi}{4}\right) = 1 + \sqrt{2} \csc \dfrac{3\pi}{4} + \cot \dfrac{3\pi}{4}$

$= 1 + \sqrt{2}(\sqrt{2}) + (-1)$

$= 2$

The coordinates of Q are $\left(\dfrac{3\pi}{4}, 2\right)$.

The equation of the horizontal line is $y = 2$.

23. (a) Velocity: $s'(t) = -2 \cos t$ m/sec

Speed: $|s'(t)| = |2 \cos t|$ m/sec

Acceleration: $s''(t) = 2 \sin t$ m/sec^2

Jerk: $s'''(t) = 2 \cos t$ m/sec^3

(b) Velocity: $-2 \cos \dfrac{\pi}{4} = -\sqrt{2}$ m/sec

Speed: $|-\sqrt{2}| = \sqrt{2}$ m/sec

Acceleration: $2 \sin \dfrac{\pi}{4} = \sqrt{2}$ m/sec^2

Jerk: $2 \cos \dfrac{\pi}{4} = \sqrt{2}$ m/sec^3

(c) The body starts at 2, goes to 0 and then oscillates between 0 and 4.

Speed:

Greatest when $\cos t = \pm 1$ (or $t = k\pi$), at the center of the interval of motion.

Zero when $\cos t = 0$ (or $t = \dfrac{k\pi}{2}$, k odd), at the endpoints of the interval of motion.

Acceleration:

Greatest (in magnitude) when $\sin t = \pm 1$

(or $t = \dfrac{k\pi}{2}$, k odd)

Zero when $\sin t = 0$ (or $t = k\pi$)

Jerk:

Greatest (in magnitude) when $\cos t = \pm 1$ (or $t = k\pi$)

Zero when $\cos t = 0 \left(\text{or } t = \dfrac{k\pi}{2}, k \text{ odd}\right)$

24. (a) Velocity: $s'(t) = \cos t - \sin t$ m/sec

Speed: $|s'(t)| = |\cos t - \sin t|$ m/sec

Acceleration: $s''(t) = -\sin t - \cos t$ m/sec^2

Jerk: $s'''(t) = -\cos t + \sin t$ m/sec^3

(b) Velocity: $\cos\dfrac{\pi}{4} - \sin\dfrac{\pi}{4} = 0$ m/sec

Speed: $|0| = 0$ m/sec

Acceleration: $-\sin\dfrac{\pi}{4} - \cos\dfrac{\pi}{4} = -\sqrt{2}$ m/sec^2

Jerk: $-\cos\dfrac{\pi}{4} + \sin\dfrac{\pi}{4} = 0$ m/sec^3

(c) The body starts at 1, goes to $\sqrt{2}$ and then oscillates between $\pm\sqrt{2}$.

Speed:

Greatest when $t = \dfrac{3\pi}{4} + k\pi$

Zero when $t = \dfrac{\pi}{4} + k\pi$

Acceleration:

Greatest (in magnitude) when $t = \dfrac{\pi}{4} + k\pi$

Zero when $t = \dfrac{3\pi}{4} + k\pi$

Jerk:

Greatest (in magnitude) when $t = \dfrac{3\pi}{4} + k\pi$

Zero when $t = \dfrac{\pi}{4} + k\pi$

25. (a)

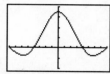

$[-360, 360]$ by $[-0.01, 0.02]$

The limit is $\dfrac{\pi}{180}$ because this is the conversion factor for changing from degrees to radians.

(b)

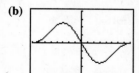

$[-360, 360]$ by $[-0.02, 0.02]$

This limit is still 0.

(c) $\dfrac{d}{dx}\sin x = \lim\limits_{h\to 0}\dfrac{\sin(x+h) - \sin x}{h}$

$= \lim\limits_{h\to 0}\dfrac{\sin x\cos h + \cos x\sin h - \sin x}{h}$

$= \lim\limits_{h\to 0}\dfrac{\sin x(\cos h - 1) + \cos x\sin h}{h}$

$= \left(\lim\limits_{h\to 0}\sin x\right)\left(\lim\limits_{h\to 0}\dfrac{\cos h - 1}{h}\right) + \left(\lim\limits_{h\to 0}\cos x\right)\left(\lim\limits_{h\to 0}\dfrac{\sin h}{h}\right)$

$= (\sin x)(0) + (\cos x)\left(\dfrac{\pi}{180}\right)$

$= \dfrac{\pi}{180}\cos x$

(d) $\dfrac{d}{dx}\cos x = \lim\limits_{h\to 0}\dfrac{\cos(x+h) - \cos x}{h}$

$= \lim\limits_{h\to 0}\dfrac{\cos x\cos h - \sin x\sin h - \cos x}{h}$

$= \lim\limits_{h\to 0}\dfrac{(\cos x)(\cos h - 1) - \sin x\sin h}{h}$

$= \left(\lim\limits_{h\to 0}\cos x\right)\left(\lim\limits_{h\to 0}\dfrac{\cos h - 1}{h}\right) - \left(\lim\limits_{h\to 0}\sin x\right)\left(\lim\limits_{h\to 0}\dfrac{\sin h}{h}\right)$

$= (\cos x)(0) - (\sin x)\left(\dfrac{\pi}{180}\right)$

$= -\dfrac{\pi}{180}\sin x$

(e) $\dfrac{d^2}{dx^2}\sin x = \dfrac{d}{dx}\dfrac{\pi}{180}\cos x = \dfrac{\pi}{180}\left(-\dfrac{\pi}{180}\sin x\right)$

$= -\dfrac{\pi^2}{180^2}\sin x$

$\dfrac{d^3}{dx^3}\sin x = \dfrac{d}{dx}\left(-\dfrac{\pi^2}{180^2}\sin x\right) = -\dfrac{\pi^2}{180^2}\left(\dfrac{\pi}{180}\cos x\right)$

$= -\dfrac{\pi^3}{180^3}\cos x$

$\dfrac{d^2}{dx^2}\cos x = \dfrac{d}{dx}\left(-\dfrac{\pi}{180}\sin x\right) = -\dfrac{\pi}{180}\left(\dfrac{\pi}{180}\cos x\right)$

$= -\dfrac{\pi^2}{180^2}\cos x$

$\dfrac{d^3}{dx^3}\cos x = \dfrac{d}{dx}\left(-\dfrac{\pi^2}{180^2}\cos x\right) = -\dfrac{\pi^2}{180^2}\left(-\dfrac{\pi}{180}\sin x\right)$

$= \dfrac{\pi^3}{180^3}\sin x$

26. $y' = \dfrac{d}{dx}\csc x = -\csc x\cot x$

$y'' = \dfrac{d}{dx}(-\csc x\cot x)$

$= -(\csc x)\dfrac{d}{dx}(\cot x) - (\cot x)\dfrac{d}{dx}(\csc x)$

$= -(\csc x)(-\csc^2 x) - (\cot x)(-\csc x\cot x)$

$= \csc^3 x + \csc x\cot^2 x$

27. $y' = \dfrac{d}{d\theta}(\theta\tan\theta)$

$= \theta\dfrac{d}{d\theta}(\tan\theta) + (\tan\theta)\dfrac{d}{d\theta}(\theta)$

$= \theta\sec^2\theta + \tan\theta$

$y'' = \dfrac{d}{d\theta}(\theta\sec^2\theta + \tan\theta)$

$= \theta\dfrac{d}{d\theta}[(\sec\theta)(\sec\theta)] + (\sec^2\theta)\dfrac{d}{d\theta}(\theta) + \dfrac{d}{d\theta}(\tan\theta)$

$= \theta\left[(\sec\theta)\dfrac{d}{d\theta}(\sec\theta) + (\sec\theta)\dfrac{d}{d\theta}(\sec\theta)\right] + \sec^2\theta +$

$\sec^2\theta$

$= 2\theta\sec^2\theta\tan\theta + 2\sec^2\theta$

$= (2\theta\tan\theta + 2)(\sec^2\theta)$

or, writing in terms of sines and cosines,

$= \dfrac{2 + 2\theta\tan\theta}{\cos^2\theta}$

$= \dfrac{2\cos\theta + 2\theta\sin\theta}{\cos^3\theta}$

28. Continuous:

Note that $g(0) = \lim\limits_{x \to 0^+} g(x) = \lim\limits_{x \to 0^+} \cos x = \cos(0) = 1$, and

$\lim\limits_{x \to 0^-} g(x) = \lim\limits_{x \to 0^-} (x + b) = b$. We require $\lim\limits_{x \to 0^-} g(x) = g(0)$,

so $b = 1$. The function is continuous if $b = 1$.

Differentiable:

For $b = 1$, the left-hand derivative is 1 and the right-hand derivative is $-\sin(0) = 0$, so the function is not differentiable. For other values of b, the function is discontinuous at $x = 0$ and there is no left-hand derivative. So, there is no value of b that will make the function differentiable at $x = 0$.

29. Observe the pattern:

$\dfrac{d}{dx} \cos x = -\sin x$ $\qquad$ $\dfrac{d^5}{dx^5} \cos x = -\sin x$

$\dfrac{d^2}{dx^2} \cos x = -\cos x$ $\qquad$ $\dfrac{d^6}{dx^6} \cos x = -\cos x$

$\dfrac{d^3}{dx^3} \cos x = \sin x$ $\qquad$ $\dfrac{d^7}{dx^7} \cos x = \sin x$

$\dfrac{d^4}{dx^4} \cos x = \cos x$ $\qquad$ $\dfrac{d^8}{dx^8} \cos x = \cos x$

Continuing the pattern, we see that

$\dfrac{d^n}{dx^n} \cos x = \sin x$ when $n = 4k + 3$ for any whole number k.

Since $999 = 4(249) + 3$, $\dfrac{d^{999}}{dx^{999}} \cos x = \sin x$.

30. Observe the pattern:

$\dfrac{d}{dx} \sin x = \cos x$ $\qquad$ $\dfrac{d^5}{dx^5} \sin x = \cos x$

$\dfrac{d^2}{dx^2} \sin x = -\sin x$ $\qquad$ $\dfrac{d^6}{dx^6} \sin x = -\sin x$

$\dfrac{d^3}{dx^3} \sin x = -\cos x$ $\qquad$ $\dfrac{d^7}{dx^7} \sin x = -\cos x$

$\dfrac{d^4}{dx^4} \sin x = \sin x$ $\qquad$ $\dfrac{d^8}{dx^8} \sin x = \sin x$

Continuing the pattern, we see that

$\dfrac{d^n}{dx^n} \sin x = \cos x$ when $n = 4k + 1$ for any whole number k.

Since $725 = 4(181) + 1$, $\dfrac{d^{725}}{dx^{725}} \sin x = \cos x$.

31. The line is tangent to the graph of $y = \sin x$ at $(0, 0)$. Since $y'(0) = \cos(0) = 1$,

the line has slope 1 and its equation is $y = x$.

32. (a) Using $y = x$, $\sin(0.12) \approx 0.12$.

(b) $\sin(0.12) \approx 0.1197122$; The approximation is within 0.0003 of the actual value.

33. $\dfrac{d}{dx} \sin 2x = \dfrac{d}{dx}(2 \sin x \cos x)$

$= 2 \dfrac{d}{dx}(\sin x \cos x)$

$= 2\left[(\sin x)\dfrac{d}{dx}(\cos x) + (\cos x)\dfrac{d}{dx}(\sin x)\right]$

$= 2[(\sin x)(-\sin x) + (\cos x)(\cos x)]$

$= 2(\cos^2 x - \sin^2 x)$

$= 2 \cos 2x$

34. $\dfrac{d}{dx} \cos 2x = \dfrac{d}{dx}[(\cos x)(\cos x) - (\sin x)(\sin x)]$

$= \left[(\cos x)\dfrac{d}{dx}(\cos x) + (\cos x)\dfrac{d}{dx}(\cos x)\right] - \left[(\sin x)\dfrac{d}{dx}(\sin x) + (\sin x)\dfrac{d}{dx}(\sin x)\right]$

$= 2(\cos x)(-\sin x) - 2(\sin x)(\cos x)$

$= -4 \sin x \cos x$

$= -2(2 \sin x \cos x)$

$= -2 \sin 2x$

35. $\lim\limits_{h \to 0} \dfrac{(\cos h - 1)}{h} = \lim\limits_{h \to 0} \dfrac{(\cos h - 1)(\cos h + 1)}{h(\cos h + 1)}$

$= \lim\limits_{h \to 0} \dfrac{\cos^2 h - 1}{h(\cos h + 1)}$

$= \lim\limits_{h \to 0} \dfrac{-\sin^2 h}{h(\cos h + 1)}$

$= -\left(\lim\limits_{h \to 0} \dfrac{\sin h}{h}\right)\left(\lim\limits_{h \to 0} \dfrac{\sin h}{\cos h + 1}\right)$

$= -(1)\left(\dfrac{0}{2}\right) = 0$

36. $y' = \dfrac{d}{dx}(A \sin x + B \cos x) = A \cos x - B \sin x$

$y'' = \dfrac{d}{dx}(A \cos x - B \sin x) = -A \sin x - B \cos x$

Solve: $\qquad\qquad\qquad\qquad\qquad y'' - y = \sin x$

$(-A \sin x - B \cos x) - (A \sin x + B \cos x) = \sin x$

$-2A \sin x - 2B \cos x = \sin x$

At $x = \dfrac{\pi}{2}$, this gives $-2A = 1$, so $A = -\dfrac{1}{2}$.

At $x = 0$, we have $-2B = 0$, so $B = 0$.

Thus, $A = -\dfrac{1}{2}$ and $B = 0$.

■ Section 3.6 Chain Rule (pp. 141–149)

Quick Review 3.6

1. $f(g(x)) = f(x^2 + 1) = \sin(x^2 + 1)$

2. $f(g(h(x))) = f(g(7x)) = f((7x)^2 + 1)$
$= \sin[(7x)^2 + 1] = \sin(49x^2 + 1)$

3. $(g \circ h)(x) = g(h(x)) = g(7x) = (7x)^2 + 1 = 49x^2 + 1$

4. $(h \circ g)(x) = h(g(x)) = h(x^2 + 1) = 7(x^2 + 1) = 7x^2 + 7$

5. $f\left(\dfrac{g(x)}{h(x)}\right) = f\left(\dfrac{x^2 + 1}{7x}\right) = \sin \dfrac{x^2 + 1}{7x}$

6. $\sqrt{\cos x + 2} = g(\cos x) = g(f(x))$

7. $\sqrt{3\cos^2 x + 2} = g(3\cos^2 x) = g(h(\cos x)) = g(h(f(x)))$

8. $3\cos x + 6 = 3(\cos x + 2) = 3(\sqrt{\cos x + 2})^2$
$= h(\sqrt{\cos x + 2}) = h(g(\cos x)) = h(g(f(x)))$

9. $\cos 27x^4 = f(27x^4) = f(3(3x^2)^2) = f(h(3x^2)) = f(h(h(x)))$

10. $\cos\sqrt{2 + 3x^2} = \cos\sqrt{3x^2 + 2} = f(\sqrt{3x^2 + 2})$
$= f(g(3x^2)) = f(g(h(x)))$

Section 3.6 Exercises

1. $\dfrac{dy}{dx} = \dfrac{d}{dx}\sin(3x + 1) = [\cos(3x+1)]\dfrac{d}{dx}(3x + 1)$
$= [\cos(3x + 1)](3) = 3\cos(3x + 1)$

2. $\dfrac{dy}{dx} = \dfrac{d}{dx}\sin(7 - 5x) = [\cos(7 - 5x)]\dfrac{d}{dx}(7 - 5x)$
$= [\cos(7 - 5x)](-5) = -5\cos(7 - 5x)$

3. $\dfrac{dy}{dx} = \dfrac{d}{dx}\cos(\sqrt{3}x) = [-\sin(\sqrt{3}x)]\dfrac{d}{dx}(\sqrt{3}x)$
$= [-\sin(\sqrt{3}x)](\sqrt{3}) = -\sqrt{3}\sin(\sqrt{3}x)$

4. $\dfrac{dy}{dx} = \dfrac{d}{dx}\tan(2x - x^3) = [\sec^2(2x - x^3)]\dfrac{d}{dx}(2x - x^3)$
$= [\sec^2(2x - x^3)](2 - 3x^2) = (2 - 3x^2)\sec^2(2x - x^3)$

5. $\dfrac{dy}{dx} = \dfrac{d}{dx}\left[5\cot\left(\dfrac{2}{x}\right)\right] = \left[-5\csc^2\left(\dfrac{2}{x}\right)\right]\dfrac{d}{dx}(2x^{-1})$
$= \left[-5\csc^2\left(\dfrac{2}{x}\right)\right](-2x^{-2}) = \dfrac{10}{x^2}\csc^2\left(\dfrac{2}{x}\right)$

6. $\dfrac{dy}{dx} = \dfrac{d}{dx}\left(\dfrac{\sin x}{1 + \cos x}\right)^2 = 2\left(\dfrac{\sin x}{1 + \cos x}\right)\dfrac{d}{dx}\left(\dfrac{\sin x}{1 + \cos x}\right)$

$= 2\left(\dfrac{\sin x}{1 + \cos x}\right)\left(\dfrac{(1 + \cos x)\frac{d}{dx}\sin x - \sin x\frac{d}{dx}(1 + \cos x)}{(1 + \cos x)^2}\right)$

$= 2\left(\dfrac{\sin x}{1 + \cos x}\right)\left(\dfrac{(1 + \cos x)(\cos x) - (\sin x)(-\sin x)}{(1 + \cos x)^2}\right)$

$= 2\left(\dfrac{\sin x}{1 + \cos x}\right)\left(\dfrac{\cos x + \cos^2 x + \sin^2 x}{(1 + \cos x)^2}\right)$

$= 2\left(\dfrac{\sin x}{1 + \cos x}\right)\left(\dfrac{1 + \cos x}{(1 + \cos x)^2}\right)$

$= 2\left(\dfrac{\sin x}{1 + \cos x}\right)\left(\dfrac{1}{1 + \cos x}\right)$

$= \dfrac{2\sin x}{(1 + \cos x)^2}$

7. $\dfrac{dy}{dx} = \dfrac{d}{dx}\cos(\sin x) = [-\sin(\sin x)]\dfrac{d}{dx}(\sin x)$
$= -\sin(\sin x)\cos x$

8. $\dfrac{dy}{dx} = \dfrac{d}{dx}\sec(\tan x) = \sec(\tan x)\tan(\tan x)\dfrac{d}{dx}(\tan x)$
$= \sec(\tan x)\tan(\tan x)\sec^2 x$

9. $\dfrac{dy}{dx} = \dfrac{d}{dx}(x + \sqrt{x})^{-2} = -2(x + \sqrt{x})^{-3}\dfrac{d}{dx}(x + \sqrt{x})$
$= -2(x + \sqrt{x})^{-3}\left(1 + \dfrac{1}{2\sqrt{x}}\right)$

10. $\dfrac{dy}{dx} = \dfrac{d}{dx}(\csc x + \cot x)^{-1}$
$= -(\csc x + \cot x)^{-2}\dfrac{d}{dx}(\csc x + \cot x)$
$= -\dfrac{1}{(\csc x + \cot x)^2}(-\cot x\csc x - \csc^2 x)$
$= \dfrac{(\csc x)(\cot x + \csc x)}{(\csc x + \cot x)^2} = \dfrac{\csc x}{\csc x + \cot x}$

11. $\dfrac{dy}{dx} = \dfrac{d}{dx}(\sin^{-5} x - \cos^3 x)$
$= (-5\sin^{-6} x)\dfrac{d}{dx}(\sin x) - (3\cos^2 x)\dfrac{d}{dx}(\cos x)$
$= -5\sin^{-6} x\cos x + 3\cos^2 x\sin x$

12. $\dfrac{dy}{dx} = \dfrac{d}{dx}[x^3(2x - 5)^4]$
$= (x^3)\dfrac{d}{dx}(2x - 5)^4 + (2x - 5)^4\dfrac{d}{dx}(x^3)$
$= (x^3)(4)(2x - 5)^3\dfrac{d}{dx}(2x - 5) + (2x - 5)^4(3x^2)$
$= (x^3)(4)(2x - 5)^3(2) + 3x^2(2x - 5)^4$
$= 8x^3(2x - 5)^3 + 3x^2(2x - 5)^4$
$= x^2(2x - 5)^3[8x + 3(2x - 5)]$
$= x^2(2x - 5)^3(14x - 15)$

13. $\dfrac{dy}{dx} = \dfrac{d}{dx}(\sin^3 x\tan 4x)$
$= (\sin^3 x)\dfrac{d}{dx}(\tan 4x) + (\tan 4x)\dfrac{d}{dx}(\sin^3 x)$
$= (\sin^3 x)(\sec^2 4x)\dfrac{d}{dx}(4x) + (\tan 4x)(3\sin^2 x)\dfrac{d}{dx}(\sin x)$
$= (\sin^3 x)(\sec^2 4x)(4) + (\tan 4x)(3\sin^2 x)(\cos x)$
$= 4\sin^3 x\sec^2 4x + 3\sin^2 x\cos x\tan 4x$

14. $\dfrac{dy}{dx} = \dfrac{d}{dx}(4\sqrt{\sec x + \tan x})$
$= 4\cdot\dfrac{1}{2\sqrt{\sec x + \tan x}}\dfrac{d}{dx}(\sec x + \tan x)$
$= \dfrac{2}{\sqrt{\sec x + \tan x}}(\sec x\tan x + \sec^2 x)$
$= 2\sec x\dfrac{\sec x + \tan x}{\sqrt{\sec x + \tan x}}$
$= 2\sec x\sqrt{\sec x + \tan x}$

15. $\dfrac{dy}{dx} = \dfrac{d}{dx}\left(\dfrac{3}{\sqrt{2x+1}}\right)$

$= \dfrac{(\sqrt{2x+1})\frac{d}{dx}(3) - 3\frac{d}{dx}(\sqrt{2x+1})}{(\sqrt{2x+1})^2}$

$= \dfrac{(\sqrt{2x+1})(0) - 3\left(\frac{1}{2\sqrt{2x+1}}\right)\frac{d}{dx}(2x+1)}{2x+1}$

$= \dfrac{-3\left(\frac{1}{2\sqrt{2x+1}}\right)(2)}{2x+1}$

$= -\dfrac{3}{(2x+1)\sqrt{2x+1}}$

$= -3(2x+1)^{-3/2}$

16. $\dfrac{dy}{dx} = \dfrac{d}{dx}\dfrac{x}{\sqrt{1+x^2}}$

$= \dfrac{(\sqrt{1+x^2})\frac{d}{dx}(x) - x\frac{d}{dx}(\sqrt{1+x^2})}{(\sqrt{1+x^2})^2}$

$= \dfrac{(\sqrt{1+x^2})(1) - x\left(\frac{1}{2\sqrt{1+x^2}}\right)\frac{d}{dx}(1+x^2)}{1+x^2}$

$= \dfrac{\sqrt{1+x^2} - x\left(\frac{1}{2\sqrt{1+x^2}}\right)(2x)}{1+x^2}$

$= \dfrac{(1+x^2) - x^2}{(1+x^2)(\sqrt{1+x^2})}$

$= (1+x^2)^{-3/2}$

17. The last step here uses the identity $2\sin a \cos a = \sin 2a$.

$\dfrac{dy}{dx} = \dfrac{d}{dx}\sin^2(3x-2)$

$= 2\sin(3x-2)\dfrac{d}{dx}\sin(3x-2)$

$= 2\sin(3x-2)\cos(3x-2)\dfrac{d}{dx}(3x-2)$

$= 2\sin(3x-2)\cos(3x-2)(3)$

$= 6\sin(3x-2)\cos(3x-2)$

$= 3\sin(6x-4)$

18. $\dfrac{dy}{dx} = \dfrac{d}{dx}(1+\cos 2x)^2 = 2(1+\cos 2x)\dfrac{d}{dx}(1+\cos 2x)$

$= 2(1+\cos 2x)(-\sin 2x)\dfrac{d}{dx}(2x)$

$= 2(1+\cos 2x)(-\sin 2x)(2)$

$= -4(1+\cos 2x)(\sin 2x)$

19. $\dfrac{dy}{dx} = \dfrac{d}{dx}(1+\cos^2 7x)^3$

$= 3(1+\cos^2 7x)^2\dfrac{d}{dx}(1+\cos^2 7x)$

$= 3(1+\cos^2 7x)^2(2\cos 7x)\dfrac{d}{dx}(\cos 7x)$

$= 3(1+\cos^2 7x)^2(2\cos 7x)(-\sin 7x)\dfrac{d}{dx}(7x)$

$= 3(1+\cos^2 7x)^2(2\cos 7x)(-\sin 7x)(7)$

$= -42(1+\cos^2 7x)^2\cos 7x \sin 7x$

20. $\dfrac{dy}{dx} = \dfrac{d}{dx}(\sqrt{\tan 5x}) = \dfrac{1}{2\sqrt{\tan 5x}}\dfrac{d}{dx}\tan 5x$

$= \dfrac{1}{2\sqrt{\tan 5x}}(\sec^2 5x)\dfrac{d}{dx}(5x)$

$= \dfrac{1}{2\sqrt{\tan 5x}}(\sec^2 5x)(5)$

$= \dfrac{5\sec^2 5x}{2\sqrt{\tan 5x}}$ or $\dfrac{5}{2}(\tan 5x)^{-1/2}\sec^2 5x$

21. $\dfrac{ds}{dt} = \dfrac{d}{dt}\cos\left(\dfrac{\pi}{2} - 3t\right)$

$= \left[-\sin\left(\dfrac{\pi}{2} - 3t\right)\right]\dfrac{d}{dt}\left(\dfrac{\pi}{2} - 3t\right)$

$= \left[-\sin\left(\dfrac{\pi}{2} - 3t\right)\right](-3)$

$= 3\sin\left(\dfrac{\pi}{2} - 3t\right)$

22. $\dfrac{ds}{dt} = \dfrac{d}{dt}[t\cos(\pi - 4t)]$

$= (t)\dfrac{d}{dt}[\cos(\pi - 4t)] + \cos(\pi - 4t)\dfrac{d}{dt}(t)$

$= t[-\sin(\pi - 4t)]\dfrac{d}{dt}(\pi - 4t) + \cos(\pi - 4t)(1)$

$= t[-\sin(\pi - 4t)](-4) + \cos(\pi - 4t)$

$= 4t\sin(\pi - 4t) + \cos(\pi - 4t)$

23. $\dfrac{ds}{dt} = \dfrac{d}{dt}\left(\dfrac{4}{3\pi}\sin 3t + \dfrac{4}{5\pi}\cos 5t\right)$

$= \dfrac{4}{3\pi}(\cos 3t)\dfrac{d}{dt}(3t) + \dfrac{4}{5\pi}(-\sin 5t)\dfrac{d}{dt}(5t)$

$= \dfrac{4}{3\pi}(\cos 3t)(3) + \dfrac{4}{5\pi}(-\sin 5t)(5)$

$= \dfrac{4}{\pi}\cos 3t - \dfrac{4}{\pi}\sin 5t$

24. $\dfrac{ds}{dt} = \dfrac{d}{dt}\left[\sin\left(\dfrac{3\pi}{2}t\right) + \cos\left(\dfrac{7\pi}{4}t\right)\right]$

$= \cos\left(\dfrac{3\pi}{2}t\right)\dfrac{d}{dt}\left(\dfrac{3\pi}{2}t\right) - \sin\left(\dfrac{7\pi}{4}t\right)\dfrac{d}{dt}\left(\dfrac{7\pi}{4}t\right)$

$= \dfrac{3\pi}{2}\cos\left(\dfrac{3\pi}{2}t\right) - \dfrac{7\pi}{4}\sin\left(\dfrac{7\pi}{4}t\right)$

25. $\dfrac{dr}{d\theta} = \dfrac{d}{d\theta}\tan(2-\theta) = \sec^2(2-\theta)\dfrac{d}{d\theta}(2-\theta)$

$= \sec^2(2-\theta)(-1) = -\sec^2(2-\theta)$

26. $\dfrac{dr}{d\theta} = \dfrac{d}{d\theta}(\sec 2\theta \tan 2\theta)$

$= (\sec 2\theta)\dfrac{d}{d\theta}(\tan 2\theta) + (\tan 2\theta)\dfrac{d}{d\theta}(\sec 2\theta)$

$= (\sec 2\theta)(\sec^2 2\theta)\dfrac{d}{d\theta}(2\theta) + (\tan 2\theta)(\sec 2\theta \tan 2\theta)\dfrac{d}{d\theta}(2\theta)$

$= 2\sec^3 2\theta + 2\sec 2\theta \tan^2 2\theta$

27. $\dfrac{dr}{d\theta} = \dfrac{d}{d\theta}\sqrt{\theta\sin\theta} = \dfrac{1}{2\sqrt{\theta\sin\theta}}\dfrac{d}{d\theta}(\theta\sin\theta)$

$= \dfrac{1}{2\sqrt{\theta\sin\theta}}\left[\theta\dfrac{d}{d\theta}(\sin\theta) + (\sin\theta)\dfrac{d}{d\theta}(\theta)\right]$

$= \dfrac{1}{2\sqrt{\theta\sin\theta}}(\theta\cos\theta + \sin\theta)$

$= \dfrac{\theta\cos\theta + \sin\theta}{2\sqrt{\theta\sin\theta}}$

28. $\dfrac{dr}{d\theta} = \dfrac{d}{d\theta}(2\theta\sqrt{\sec\theta})$

$= (2\theta)\dfrac{d}{d\theta}(\sqrt{\sec\theta}) + (\sqrt{\sec\theta})\dfrac{d}{d\theta}(2\theta)$

$= (2\theta)\left(\dfrac{1}{2\sqrt{\sec\theta}}\right)\dfrac{d}{d\theta}(\sec\theta) + 2\sqrt{\sec\theta}$

$= (2\theta)\left(\dfrac{1}{2\sqrt{\sec\theta}}\right)(\sec\theta\tan\theta) + 2\sqrt{\sec\theta}$

$= \theta(\sqrt{\sec\theta})(\tan\theta) + 2\sqrt{\sec\theta}$

$= \sqrt{\sec\theta}(\theta\tan\theta + 2)$

29. $y' = \dfrac{d}{dx}\tan x = \sec^2 x$

$y'' = \dfrac{d}{dx}\sec^2 x = (2\sec x)\dfrac{d}{dx}(\sec x)$

$= (2\sec x)(\sec x\tan x)$

$= 2\sec^2 x\tan x$

30. $y' = \dfrac{d}{dx}\cot x = -\csc^2 x$

$y'' = \dfrac{d}{dx}(-\csc^2 x) = (-2\csc x)\dfrac{d}{dx}(\csc x)$

$= (-2\csc x)(-\csc x\cot x)$

$= 2\csc^2 x\cot x$

31. $y' = \dfrac{d}{dx}\cot(3x - 1) = -\csc^2(3x - 1)\dfrac{d}{dx}(3x - 1)$

$= -3\csc^2(3x - 1)$

$y'' = \dfrac{d}{dx}[-3\csc^2(3x - 1)]$

$= -3[2\csc(3x - 1)]\dfrac{d}{dx}\csc(3x - 1)$

$= -3[2\csc(3x - 1)]\cdot$

$[-\csc(3x - 1)\cot(3x - 1)]\dfrac{d}{dx}(3x - 1)$

$= -3[2\csc(3x - 1)][-\csc(3x - 1)\cot(3x - 1)](3)$

$= 18\csc^2(3x - 1)\cot(3x - 1)$

32. $y' = \dfrac{d}{dx}\left[9\tan\left(\dfrac{x}{3}\right)\right] = 9\sec^2\left(\dfrac{x}{3}\right)\dfrac{d}{dx}\left(\dfrac{x}{3}\right)$

$= 3\sec^2\left(\dfrac{x}{3}\right)$

$y'' = \dfrac{d}{dx}\left[3\sec^2\left(\dfrac{x}{3}\right)\right] = 3\left[2\sec\left(\dfrac{x}{3}\right)\right]\dfrac{d}{dx}\sec\left(\dfrac{x}{3}\right)$

$= 6\left[\sec\left(\dfrac{x}{3}\right)\right]\left[\sec\left(\dfrac{x}{3}\right)\tan\left(\dfrac{x}{3}\right)\right]\dfrac{d}{dx}\left(\dfrac{x}{3}\right)$

$= 2\sec^2\left(\dfrac{x}{3}\right)\tan\left(\dfrac{x}{3}\right)$

33. $f'(u) = \dfrac{d}{du}(u^5 + 1) = 5u^4$

$g'(x) = \dfrac{d}{dx}(\sqrt{x}) = \dfrac{1}{2\sqrt{x}}$

$(f\circ g)'(1) = f'(g(1))g'(1) = f'(1)g'(1) = (5)\left(\dfrac{1}{2}\right) = \dfrac{5}{2}$

34. $f'(u) = \dfrac{d}{du}(1 - u^{-1}) = u^{-2} = \dfrac{1}{u^2}$

$g'(x) = \dfrac{d}{dx}(1 - x)^{-1} = -(1 - x)^{-2}\dfrac{d}{dx}(1 - x)$

$= -(1 - x)^{-2}(-1) = \dfrac{1}{(1 - x)^2}$

$(f\circ g)'(-1) = f'(g(-1))g'(-1) = f'\left(\dfrac{1}{2}\right)g'(-1)$

$= (4)\left(\dfrac{1}{4}\right) = 1$

35. $f'(u) = \dfrac{d}{du}\left(\cot\dfrac{\pi u}{10}\right) = -\csc^2\left(\dfrac{\pi u}{10}\right)\dfrac{d}{du}\left(\dfrac{\pi u}{10}\right)$

$= -\dfrac{\pi}{10}\csc^2\left(\dfrac{\pi u}{10}\right)$

$g'(x) = \dfrac{d}{dx}(5\sqrt{x}) = \dfrac{5}{2\sqrt{x}}$

$(f\circ g)'(1) = f'(g(1))g'(1) = f'(5)g'(1)$

$= -\dfrac{\pi}{10}\left[\csc^2\left(\dfrac{\pi}{2}\right)\right]\left(\dfrac{5}{2}\right)$

$= -\dfrac{\pi}{10}(1)\left(\dfrac{5}{2}\right) = -\dfrac{\pi}{4}$

36. $f'(u) = \dfrac{d}{du}[u + (\cos u)^{-2}]$

$= 1 - 2(\cos u)^{-3}\dfrac{d}{du}\cos u$

$= 1 + \dfrac{2\sin u}{\cos^3 u}$

$g'(x) = \dfrac{d}{dx}(\pi x) = \pi$

$(f\circ g)'\left(\dfrac{1}{4}\right) = f'(g(\tfrac{1}{4}))g'\left(\dfrac{1}{4}\right)$

$= f'\left(\dfrac{\pi}{4}\right)g'\left(\dfrac{1}{4}\right)$

$= \left(1 + \dfrac{\dfrac{2}{\sqrt{2}}}{\left(\dfrac{1}{\sqrt{2}}\right)^3}\right)(\pi)$

$= 5\pi$

37. $f'(u) = \dfrac{d}{du}\dfrac{2u}{u^2 + 1} = \dfrac{(u^2 + 1)\dfrac{d}{du}(2u) - (2u)\dfrac{d}{du}(u^2 + 1)}{(u^2 + 1)^2}$

$= \dfrac{(u^2 + 1)(2) - (2u)(2u)}{(u^2 + 1)^2} = \dfrac{-2u^2 + 2}{(u^2 + 1)^2}$

$g'(x) = \dfrac{d}{dx}(10x^2 + x + 1) = 20x + 1$

$(f\circ g)'(0) = f'(g(0))g'(0) = f'(1)g'(0) = (0)(1) = 0$

38. $f'(u) = \dfrac{d}{du}\left(\dfrac{u-1}{u+1}\right)^2 = 2\left(\dfrac{u-1}{u+1}\right)\dfrac{d}{du}\left(\dfrac{u-1}{u+1}\right)$

$ = 2\left(\dfrac{u-1}{u+1}\right)\dfrac{(u+1)\dfrac{d}{du}(u-1) - (u-1)\dfrac{d}{du}(u+1)}{(u+1)^2}$

$ = 2\left(\dfrac{u-1}{u+1}\right)\dfrac{(u+1) - (u-1)}{(u+1)^2} = \dfrac{4(u-1)}{(u+1)^3}$

$g'(x) = \dfrac{d}{dx}(x^{-2} - 1) = -2x^{-3}$

$(f \circ g)'(-1) = f'(g(-1))g'(-1)$

$ = f'(0)g'(-1)$

$ = (-4)(2) = -8$

39. (a) $\dfrac{dy}{dx} = \dfrac{dy}{du}\dfrac{du}{dx}$

$\phantom{\dfrac{dy}{dx}} = \dfrac{d}{du}(\cos u)\dfrac{d}{dx}(6x + 2)$

$\phantom{\dfrac{dy}{dx}} = (-\sin u)(6)$

$\phantom{\dfrac{dy}{dx}} = -6 \sin u$

$\phantom{\dfrac{dy}{dx}} = -6 \sin (6x + 2)$

(b) $\dfrac{dy}{dx} = \dfrac{dy}{du}\dfrac{du}{dx}$

$\phantom{\dfrac{dy}{dx}} = \dfrac{d}{du}(\cos 2u)\dfrac{d}{dx}(3x + 1)$

$\phantom{\dfrac{dy}{dx}} = (-\sin 2u)(2) \cdot (3)$

$\phantom{\dfrac{dy}{dx}} = -6 \sin 2u$

$\phantom{\dfrac{dy}{dx}} = -6 \sin (6x + 2)$

40. (a) $\dfrac{dy}{dx} = \dfrac{dy}{du}\dfrac{du}{dx}$

$\phantom{\dfrac{dy}{dx}} = \dfrac{d}{du}\sin (u + 1)\dfrac{d}{dx}(x^2)$

$\phantom{\dfrac{dy}{dx}} = \cos (u + 1)(1) \cdot 2x$

$\phantom{\dfrac{dy}{dx}} = 2x \cos (u + 1)$

$\phantom{\dfrac{dy}{dx}} = 2x \cos (x^2 + 1)$

(b) $\dfrac{dy}{dx} = \dfrac{dy}{du}\dfrac{du}{dx}$

$\phantom{\dfrac{dy}{dx}} = \dfrac{d}{du}(\sin u)\dfrac{d}{dx}(x^2 + 1)$

$\phantom{\dfrac{dy}{dx}} = (\cos u)(2x)$

$\phantom{\dfrac{dy}{dx}} = 2x \cos u$

$\phantom{\dfrac{dy}{dx}} = 2x \cos (x^2 + 1)$

41. $\dfrac{dx}{dt} = \dfrac{d}{dt}(2 \cos t) = -2 \sin t$

$\dfrac{dy}{dt} = \dfrac{d}{dt}(2 \sin t) = 2 \cos t$

$\dfrac{dy}{dx} = \dfrac{\dfrac{dy}{dt}}{\dfrac{dx}{dt}} = \dfrac{2 \cos t}{-2 \sin t} = -\cot t$

The line passes through $\left(2 \cos \dfrac{\pi}{4}, 2 \sin \dfrac{\pi}{4}\right) = (\sqrt{2}, \sqrt{2})$

and has slope $-\cot \dfrac{\pi}{4} = -1$. Its equation is

$y = -(x - \sqrt{2}) + \sqrt{2}$, or $y = -x + 2\sqrt{2}$.

42. $\dfrac{dx}{dt} = \dfrac{d}{dt}(\sin 2\pi t) = (\cos 2\pi t)\dfrac{d}{dt}(2\pi t) = 2\pi \cos 2\pi t$

$\dfrac{dy}{dt} = \dfrac{d}{dt}(\cos 2\pi t) = (-\sin 2\pi t)\dfrac{d}{dt}(2\pi t) = -2\pi \sin 2\pi t$

$\dfrac{dy}{dx} = \dfrac{\dfrac{dy}{dt}}{\dfrac{dx}{dt}} = \dfrac{-2\pi \sin 2\pi t}{2\pi \cos 2\pi t} = -\tan 2\pi t$

The line passes through $\left(\sin \dfrac{2\pi}{-6}, \cos \dfrac{2\pi}{-6}\right) = \left(-\dfrac{\sqrt{3}}{2}, \dfrac{1}{2}\right)$

and has slope $-\tan \dfrac{2\pi}{-6} = \sqrt{3}$. Its equation is

$y = \sqrt{3}\left(x + \dfrac{\sqrt{3}}{2}\right) + \dfrac{1}{2}$, or $y = \sqrt{3}x + 2$.

43. $\dfrac{dx}{dt} = \dfrac{d}{dt}(\sec^2 t - 1) = (2 \sec t)\dfrac{d}{dt}(\sec t)$

$\phantom{\dfrac{dx}{dt}} = (2 \sec t)(\sec t \tan t)$

$\phantom{\dfrac{dx}{dt}} = 2 \sec^2 t \tan t$

$\dfrac{dy}{dt} = \dfrac{d}{dt}\tan t = \sec^2 t$

$\dfrac{dy}{dx} = \dfrac{\dfrac{dy}{dt}}{\dfrac{dx}{dt}} = \dfrac{\sec^2 t}{2 \sec^2 t \tan t} = \dfrac{1}{2} \cot t.$

The line passes through

$\left(\sec^2 \left(-\dfrac{\pi}{4}\right) - 1, \tan \left(-\dfrac{\pi}{4}\right)\right) = (1, -1)$ and has

slope $\dfrac{1}{2} \cot \left(-\dfrac{\pi}{4}\right) = -\dfrac{1}{2}$. Its equation is

$y = -\dfrac{1}{2}(x - 1) - 1$, or $y = -\dfrac{1}{2}x - \dfrac{1}{2}$.

44. $\dfrac{dx}{dt} = \dfrac{d}{dt}\sec t = \sec t \tan t$

$\dfrac{dy}{dt} = \dfrac{d}{dt}\tan t = \sec^2 t$

$\dfrac{dy}{dx} = \dfrac{\dfrac{dy}{dt}}{\dfrac{dx}{dt}} = \dfrac{\sec^2 t}{\sec t \tan t} = \dfrac{\sec t}{\tan t} = \dfrac{1}{\sin t} = \csc t$

The line passes through $\left(\sec \dfrac{\pi}{6}, \tan \dfrac{\pi}{6}\right) = \left(\dfrac{2}{\sqrt{3}}, \dfrac{1}{\sqrt{3}}\right)$ and

has slope $\csc \dfrac{\pi}{6} = 2$. Its equation is $y = 2\left(x - \dfrac{2}{\sqrt{3}}\right) + \dfrac{1}{\sqrt{3}}$,

or $y = 2x - \sqrt{3}$.

45. $\dfrac{dx}{dt} = \dfrac{d}{dt}t = 1$

$\dfrac{dy}{dt} = \dfrac{d}{dt}\sqrt{t} = \dfrac{1}{2\sqrt{t}}$

$\dfrac{dy}{dx} = \dfrac{\frac{dy}{dt}}{\frac{dx}{dt}} = \dfrac{1/(2\sqrt{t})}{1} = \dfrac{1}{2\sqrt{t}}$

The line passes through $\left(\dfrac{1}{4}, \sqrt{\dfrac{1}{4}}\right) = \left(\dfrac{1}{4}, \dfrac{1}{2}\right)$ and has slope

$\dfrac{1}{2\sqrt{\frac{1}{4}}} = 1$. Its equation is $y = 1\left(x - \dfrac{1}{4}\right) + \dfrac{1}{2}$, or

$y = x + \dfrac{1}{4}$.

46. $\dfrac{dx}{dt} = \dfrac{d}{dt}(2t^2 + 3) = 4t$

$\dfrac{dy}{dt} = \dfrac{d}{dt}(t^4) = 4t^3$

$\dfrac{dy}{dx} = \dfrac{\frac{dy}{dt}}{\frac{dx}{dt}} = \dfrac{4t^3}{4t} = t^2$

The line passes through $(2(-1)^2 + 3, (-1)^4) = (5, 1)$ and has slope $(-1)^2 = 1$. Its equation is $y = 1(x - 5) + 1$, or $y = x - 4$.

47. $\dfrac{dx}{dt} = \dfrac{d}{dt}(t - \sin t) = 1 - \cos t$

$\dfrac{dy}{dt} = \dfrac{d}{dt}(1 - \cos t) = \sin t$

$\dfrac{dy}{dx} = \dfrac{\frac{dy}{dt}}{\frac{dx}{dt}} = \dfrac{\sin t}{1 - \cos t}$

The line passes through

$\left(\dfrac{\pi}{3} - \sin\dfrac{\pi}{3}, 1 - \cos\dfrac{\pi}{3}\right) = \left(\dfrac{\pi}{3} - \dfrac{\sqrt{3}}{2}, \dfrac{1}{2}\right)$ and has slope

$\dfrac{\sin\left(\frac{\pi}{3}\right)}{1 - \cos\left(\frac{\pi}{3}\right)} = \sqrt{3}$. Its equation is

$y = \sqrt{3}\left(x - \dfrac{\pi}{3} + \dfrac{\sqrt{3}}{2}\right) + \dfrac{1}{2}$, or

$y = \sqrt{3}x + 2 - \dfrac{\pi}{\sqrt{3}}$.

48. $\dfrac{dx}{dt} = \dfrac{d}{dt}\cos t = -\sin t$

$\dfrac{dy}{dt} = \dfrac{d}{dt}(1 + \sin t) = \cos t$

$\dfrac{dy}{dx} = \dfrac{\frac{dy}{dt}}{\frac{dx}{dt}} = \dfrac{\cos t}{-\sin t} = -\cot t$

The line passes through $\left(\cos\dfrac{\pi}{2}, 1 + \sin\dfrac{\pi}{2}\right) = (0, 2)$ and

has slope $-\cot\left(\dfrac{\pi}{2}\right) = 0$. Its equation is $y = 2$.

49. (a) $\dfrac{dx}{dt} = \dfrac{d}{dt}(t^2 + t) = 2t + 1$

$\dfrac{dy}{dt} = \dfrac{d}{dt}\sin t = \cos t$

$\dfrac{dy}{dx} = \dfrac{\frac{dy}{dt}}{\frac{dx}{dt}} = \dfrac{\cos t}{2t + 1}$

(b) $\dfrac{d}{dt}\left(\dfrac{dy}{dx}\right) = \dfrac{d}{dt}\dfrac{\cos t}{2t + 1}$

$= \dfrac{(2t + 1)\frac{d}{dt}(\cos t) - (\cos t)\frac{d}{dt}(2t + 1)}{(2t + 1)^2}$

$= \dfrac{(2t + 1)(-\sin t) - (\cos t)(2)}{(2t + 1)^2}$

$= -\dfrac{(2t + 1)(\sin t) + 2\cos t}{(2t + 1)^2}$

(c) Let $u = \dfrac{dy}{dx}$.

Then $\dfrac{du}{dt} = \dfrac{du}{dx}\dfrac{dx}{dt}$, so $\dfrac{du}{dx} = \dfrac{du}{dt} \div \dfrac{dx}{dt}$. Therefore,

$\dfrac{d}{dx}\left(\dfrac{dy}{dx}\right) = \dfrac{d}{dt}\left(\dfrac{dy}{dx}\right) \div \dfrac{dx}{dt}$

$= -\dfrac{(2t + 1)(\sin t) + 2\cos t}{(2t + 1)^2} \div (2t + 1)$

$= -\dfrac{(2t + 1)(\sin t) + 2\cos t}{(2t + 1)^3}$

(d) The expression in part (c).

50. Since the radius passes through $(0, 0)$ and $(2\cos t, 2\sin t)$,

it has slope given by $\tan t$. But the slope of the tangent line

is $\dfrac{dy}{dx} = \dfrac{\frac{dy}{dt}}{\frac{dx}{dt}} = \dfrac{2\cos t}{-2\sin t} = -\cot t$, which is the negative

reciprocal of $\tan t$. This means that the radius and the

tangent line are perpendicular. (The preceding argument

breaks down when $t = \dfrac{k\pi}{2}$, where k is an integer. At these

values, either the radius is horizontal and the tangent line is

vertical or the radius is vertical and the tangent line is

horizontal, so the result still holds.)

51. $\dfrac{ds}{dt} = \dfrac{ds}{d\theta}\dfrac{d\theta}{dt} = \dfrac{d}{d\theta}(\cos\theta)\dfrac{d\theta}{dt}$

$= (-\sin\theta)\left(\dfrac{d\theta}{dt}\right)$

When $\theta = \dfrac{3\pi}{2}$ and $\dfrac{d\theta}{dt} = 5$, $\dfrac{ds}{dt} = \left(-\sin\dfrac{3\pi}{2}\right)(5) = 5$.

52. $\dfrac{dy}{dt} = \dfrac{dy}{dx}\dfrac{dx}{dt} = \dfrac{d}{dx}(x^2 + 7x - 5)\dfrac{dx}{dt}$

$= (2x + 7)\left(\dfrac{dx}{dt}\right)$

When $x = 1$ and $\dfrac{dx}{dt} = \dfrac{1}{3}$, $\dfrac{dy}{dt} = [2(1) + 7]\left(\dfrac{1}{3}\right) = 3$.

53. $\dfrac{dy}{dx} = \dfrac{d}{dx} \sin \dfrac{x}{2} = \left(\cos \dfrac{x}{2}\right)\dfrac{d}{dx}\left(\dfrac{x}{2}\right) = \dfrac{1}{2}\cos \dfrac{x}{2}$

Since the range of the function $f(x) = \dfrac{1}{2}\cos\dfrac{x}{2}$ is $\left[-\dfrac{1}{2}, \dfrac{1}{2}\right]$,

the largest possible value of $\dfrac{dy}{dx}$ is $\dfrac{1}{2}$.

54. $\dfrac{dy}{dx} = \dfrac{d}{dx}(\sin mx) = (\cos mx)\dfrac{d}{dx}(mx) = m\cos mx$

The desired line has slope $y'(0) = m\cos 0 = m$ and passes

through $(0, 0)$, so its equation is $y = mx$.

55. $\dfrac{dy}{dx} = \dfrac{d}{dx} 2\tan\dfrac{\pi x}{4} = \left(2\sec^2 \dfrac{\pi x}{4}\right)\dfrac{d}{dx}\left(\dfrac{\pi x}{4}\right)$

$= \dfrac{\pi}{2}\sec^2\left(\dfrac{\pi x}{4}\right)$

$y'(1) = \dfrac{\pi}{2}\sec^2\left(\dfrac{\pi}{4}\right) = \dfrac{\pi}{2}(\sqrt{2})^2 = \pi.$

The tangent line has slope π and passes through

$\left(1, 2\tan\dfrac{\pi}{4}\right) = (1, 2)$. Its equation is $y = \pi(x - 1) + 2$, or

$y = \pi x - \pi + 2$.

The normal line has slope $-\dfrac{1}{\pi}$ and passes through $(1, 2)$. Its

equation is $y = -\dfrac{1}{\pi}(x - 1) + 2$, or $y = -\dfrac{1}{\pi}x + \dfrac{1}{\pi} + 2$.

Graphical support:

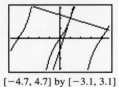

$[-4.7, 4.7]$ by $[-3.1, 3.1]$

56. (a) $\dfrac{d}{dx}[2\,f(x)] = 2f'(x)$

At $x = 2$, the derivative is $2f'(2) = 2\left(\dfrac{1}{3}\right) = \dfrac{2}{3}$.

(b) $\dfrac{d}{dx}[f(x) + g(x)] = f'(x) + g'(x)$

At $x = 3$, the derivative is $f'(3) + g'(3) = 2\pi + 5$.

(c) $\dfrac{d}{dx}[f(x)\cdot g(x)] = f(x)g'(x) + g(x)f'(x)$

At $x = 3$, the derivative is

$f(3)g'(3) + g(3)f'(3) = (3)(5) + (-4)(2\pi)$

$= 15 - 8\pi.$

(d) $\dfrac{d}{dx}\dfrac{f(x)}{g(x)} = \dfrac{g(x)f'(x) - f(x)g'(x)}{[g(x)]^2}$

At $x = 2$, the derivative is

$\dfrac{g(2)f'(2) - f(2)g'(2)}{[g(2)]^2} = \dfrac{(2)\left(\dfrac{1}{3}\right) - (8)(-3)}{(2)^2}$

$= \dfrac{\dfrac{74}{3}}{4} = \dfrac{37}{6}.$

(e) $\dfrac{d}{dx}f(g(x)) = f'(g(x))g'(x)$

At $x = 2$, the derivative is

$f'(g(2))g'(2) = f'(2)g'(2) = \left(\dfrac{1}{3}\right)(-3) = -1.$

(f) $\dfrac{d}{dx}\sqrt{f(x)} = \dfrac{1}{2\sqrt{f(x)}}\dfrac{d}{dx}f(x) = \dfrac{f'(x)}{2\sqrt{f(x)}}$

At $x = 2$, the derivative is

$\dfrac{f'(2)}{2\sqrt{f(2)}} = \dfrac{\dfrac{1}{3}}{2\sqrt{8}} = \dfrac{1}{6(2\sqrt{2})} = \dfrac{1}{12\sqrt{2}}.$

(g) $\dfrac{d}{dx}\dfrac{1}{g^2(x)} = \dfrac{d}{dx}[g(x)]^{-2} = -2[g(x)]^{-3}\dfrac{d}{dx}g(x) = -\dfrac{2g'(x)}{[g(x)]^3}$

At $x = 3$, the derivative is

$-\dfrac{2g'(3)}{[g(3)]^3} = -\dfrac{2(5)}{(-4)^3} = -\dfrac{10}{-64} = \dfrac{5}{32}.$

(h) $\dfrac{d}{dx}\sqrt{f^2(x) + g^2(x)} = \dfrac{1}{2\sqrt{f^2(x) + g^2(x)}}\dfrac{d}{dx}[f^2(x) + g^2(x)]$

$= \dfrac{1}{2\sqrt{f^2(x) + g^2(x)}}\left[2f(x)\dfrac{d}{dx}f(x) + 2g(x)\dfrac{d}{dx}g(x)\right]$

$= \dfrac{f(x)f'(x) + g(x)g'(x)}{\sqrt{f^2(x) + g^2(x)}}$

At $x = 2$, the derivative is

$\dfrac{f(2)f'(2) + g(2)g'(2)}{\sqrt{f^2(2) + g^2(2)}} = \dfrac{(8)\left(\dfrac{1}{3}\right) + (2)(-3)}{\sqrt{8^2 + 2^2}}$

$= \dfrac{-\dfrac{10}{3}}{\sqrt{68}} = \dfrac{-\dfrac{10}{3}}{2\sqrt{17}} = -\dfrac{5}{3\sqrt{17}}$

57. (a) $\dfrac{d}{dx}[5f(x) - g(x)] = 5f'(x) - g'(x)$

At $x = 1$, the derivative is

$5f'(1) - g'(1) = 5\left(-\dfrac{1}{3}\right) - \left(-\dfrac{8}{3}\right) = 1.$

(b) $\dfrac{d}{dx}f(x)g^3(x) = f(x)\dfrac{d}{dx}g^3(x) + g^3(x)\dfrac{d}{dx}f(x)$

$= f(x)[3g^2(x)]\dfrac{d}{dx}g(x) + g^3(x)f'(x)$

$= 3f(x)g^2(x)g'(x) + g^3(x)f'(x)$

At $x = 0$, the derivative is $3f(0)g^2(0)g'(0) + g^3(0)f'(0)$

$= 3(1)(1)^2\left(\dfrac{1}{3}\right) + (1)^3(5) = 6.$

(c) $\dfrac{d}{dx}\dfrac{f(x)}{g(x)+1} = \dfrac{[g(x)+1]\dfrac{d}{dx}f(x) - f(x)\dfrac{d}{dx}[g(x)+1]}{[g(x)+1]^2}$

$\qquad = \dfrac{[g(x)+1]f'(x) - f(x)g'(x)}{[g(x)+1]^2}$

At $x = 1$, the derivative is

$\dfrac{[g(1)+1]f'(1) - f(1)g'(1)}{[g(1)+1]^2} = \dfrac{(-4+1)\left(-\dfrac{1}{3}\right) - (3)\left(-\dfrac{8}{3}\right)}{(-4+1)^2}$

$\qquad\qquad = \dfrac{9}{9} = 1.$

(d) $\dfrac{d}{dx}f(g(x)) = f'(g(x))g'(x)$

At $x = 0$, the derivative is

$f'(g(0))g'(0) = f'(1)g'(0) = \left(-\dfrac{1}{3}\right)\left(\dfrac{1}{3}\right) = -\dfrac{1}{9}.$

(e) $\dfrac{d}{dx}g(f(x)) = g'(f(x))f'(x)$

At $x = 0$, the derivative is

$g'(f(0))f'(0) = g'(1)f'(0) = \left(-\dfrac{8}{3}\right)(5) = -\dfrac{40}{3}$

(f) $\dfrac{d}{dx}[g(x)+f(x)]^{-2} = -2[g(x)+f(x)]^{-3}\dfrac{d}{dx}[g(x)+f(x)]$

$\qquad = -\dfrac{2[g'(x)+f'(x)]}{[g(x)+f(x)]^3}$

At $x = 1$, the derivative is

$-\dfrac{2[g'(1)+f'(1)]}{[g(1)+f(1)]^3} = -\dfrac{2\left(-\dfrac{8}{3}-\dfrac{1}{3}\right)}{(-4+3)^3} = -\dfrac{-6}{-1} = -6.$

(g) $\dfrac{d}{dx}[f(x+g(x))] = f'(x+g(x))\dfrac{d}{dx}[x+g(x)]$

$\qquad = f'(x+g(x))(1+g'(x))$

At $x = 0$, the derivative is

$f'(0+g(0))(1+g'(0)) = f'(0+1)\left(1+\dfrac{1}{3}\right)$

$\qquad\qquad = f'(1)\left(\dfrac{4}{3}\right)$

$\qquad\qquad = \left(-\dfrac{1}{3}\right)\left(\dfrac{4}{3}\right) = -\dfrac{4}{9}.$

58. For $y = \sin 2x$, $y' = (\cos 2x)\dfrac{d}{dx}(2x) = 2\cos 2x$ and the slope at the origin is 2.

For $y = -\sin\dfrac{x}{2}$, $y' = \left(-\cos\dfrac{x}{2}\right)\dfrac{d}{dx}\left(\dfrac{x}{2}\right) = -\dfrac{1}{2}\cos\dfrac{x}{2}$ and the slope at the origin is $-\dfrac{1}{2}$. Since the slopes of the two tangent lines are 2 and $-\dfrac{1}{2}$, the lines are perpendicular and the curves are orthogonal.

A graph of the two curves along with the tangents $y = 2x$ and $y = -\dfrac{1}{2}x$ is shown.

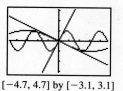

$[-4.7, 4.7]$ by $[-3.1, 3.1]$

59. Because the symbols $\dfrac{dy}{dx}, \dfrac{dy}{du},$ and $\dfrac{du}{dx}$ are not fractions. The individual symbols dy, dx, and du do not have numerical values.

60. Velocity: $s'(t) = -2\pi bA\sin(2\pi bt)$
acceleration: $s''(t) = -4\pi^2 b^2 A\cos(2\pi bt)$
jerk: $s'''(t) = 8\pi^3 b^3 A\sin(2\pi bt)$
The velocity, amplitude, and jerk are proportional to b, b^2, and b^3, respectively. If the frequency b is doubled, then the amplitude of the velocity is doubled, the amplitude of the acceleration is quadrupled, and the amplitude of the jerk is multiplied by 8.

61. (a) $y'(t) = \dfrac{d}{dt}37\sin\left[\dfrac{2\pi}{365}(x-101)\right] + \dfrac{d}{dt}(25)$

$\qquad = 37\cos\left[\dfrac{2\pi}{365}(x-101)\right]\cdot\dfrac{d}{dx}\left[\dfrac{2\pi}{365}(x-101)\right] + 0$

$\qquad = 37\cos\left[\dfrac{2\pi}{365}(x-101)\right]\cdot\dfrac{2\pi}{365}$

$\qquad = \dfrac{74\pi}{365}\cos\left[\dfrac{2\pi}{365}(x-101)\right]$

Since $\cos u$ is greatest when $u = 0, \pm 2\pi$, and so on, $y'(t)$ is greatest when $\dfrac{2\pi}{365}(x-101) = 0$, or $x = 101$. The temperature is increasing the fastest on day 101 (April 11).

(b) The rate of increase is

$y'(101) = \dfrac{74\pi}{365} \approx 0.637$ degrees per day.

62. Velocity: $s'(t) = \dfrac{d}{dt}\sqrt{1+4t} = \dfrac{1}{2\sqrt{1+4t}}\dfrac{d}{dt}(1+4t)$

$$= \dfrac{4}{2\sqrt{1+4t}} = \dfrac{2}{\sqrt{1+4t}}$$

At $t = 6$, the velocity is $\dfrac{2}{\sqrt{1+4(6)}} = \dfrac{2}{5}$ m/sec

Acceleration: $s''(t) = \dfrac{d}{dt}\dfrac{2}{\sqrt{1+4t}}$

$$= \dfrac{(\sqrt{1+4t})\dfrac{d}{dt}(2) - 2\dfrac{d}{dt}\sqrt{1+4t}}{(\sqrt{1+4t})^2}$$

$$= \dfrac{-2\left(\dfrac{1}{2\sqrt{1+4t}}\right)\dfrac{d}{dt}(1+4t)}{1+4t}$$

$$= \dfrac{\dfrac{-4}{\sqrt{1+4t}}}{1+4t} = -\dfrac{4}{(1+4t)^{3/2}}$$

At $t = 6$, the acceleration is $-\dfrac{4}{[1+4(6)]^{3/2}} = -\dfrac{4}{125}$ m/sec^2

63. Acceleration $= \dfrac{dv}{dt} = \dfrac{dv}{ds}\dfrac{ds}{dt} = \left(\dfrac{dv}{ds}\right)(v) = \left[\dfrac{d}{ds}(k\sqrt{s})\right](k\sqrt{s})$

$= \left(\dfrac{k}{2\sqrt{s}}\right)(k\sqrt{s}) = \dfrac{k^2}{2}$, a constant.

64. Note that this Exercise concerns itself with the slowing down caused by the earth's atmosphere, *not* the acceleration caused by gravity.

Given: $v = \dfrac{k}{\sqrt{s}}$

Acceleration $= \dfrac{dv}{dt} = \dfrac{dv}{ds}\dfrac{ds}{dt} = \left(\dfrac{dv}{ds}\right)(v) = (v)\left(\dfrac{dv}{ds}\right)$

$$= \left(\dfrac{k}{\sqrt{s}}\right)\dfrac{d}{ds}\dfrac{k}{\sqrt{s}}$$

$$= \left(\dfrac{k}{\sqrt{s}}\right)\left(\dfrac{\sqrt{s}\dfrac{d}{ds}(k) - k\dfrac{d}{ds}\sqrt{s}}{(\sqrt{s})^2}\right)$$

$$= \left(\dfrac{k}{\sqrt{s}}\right)\left(\dfrac{\dfrac{-k}{(2\sqrt{s})}}{s}\right)$$

$$= -\dfrac{k^2}{2s^2}, \; s \geq 0$$

Thus, the acceleration is inversely proportional to s^2.

65. Acceleration $= \dfrac{dv}{dt} = \dfrac{df(x)}{dt} = \dfrac{df(x)}{dx}\dfrac{dx}{dt} = f'(x)f(x)$

66. $\dfrac{dT}{du} = \dfrac{dT}{dL}\dfrac{dL}{du} = \left(\dfrac{d}{dL}2\pi\sqrt{\dfrac{L}{g}}\right)(kL)$

$$= \left(2\pi\dfrac{1}{2\sqrt{\dfrac{L}{g}}}\right)\left(\dfrac{d}{dL}\dfrac{L}{g}\right)(kL)$$

$$= \left(\dfrac{\pi}{\sqrt{\dfrac{L}{g}}}\right)\left(\dfrac{1}{g}\right)(kL) = k\pi\sqrt{\dfrac{L}{g}} = \dfrac{kT}{2}$$

67. No, this does not contradict the Chain Rule. The Chain Rule states that if two functions are differentiable at the appropriate points, then their composite must also be differentiable. It does not say: If a composite is differentiable, then the functions which make up the composite must all be differentiable.

68. Yes. Note that $\dfrac{d}{dx}f(g(x)) = f'(g(x))g'(x)$. If the graph of $y = f(g(x))$ has a horizontal tangent at $x = 1$, then $f'(g(1))g'(1) = 0$, so either $g'(1) = 0$ or $f'(g(1)) = 0$. This means that either the graph of $y = g(x)$ has a horizontal tangent at $x = 1$, or the graph of $y = f(u)$ has a horizontal tangent at $u = g(1)$.

69. For $h = 1$:

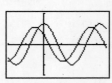

$[-2, 3.5]$ by $[-3, 3]$

For $h = 0.5$:

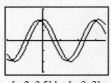

$[-2, 3.5]$ by $[-3, 3]$

For $h = 0.2$:

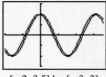

$[-2, 3.5]$ by $[-3, 3]$

As $h \to 0$, the second curve (the difference quotient) approaches the first ($y = 2\cos 2x$). This is because $2\cos 2x$ is the derivative of $\sin 2x$, and the second curve is the difference quotient used to define the derivative of $\sin 2x$. As $h \to 0$, the difference quotient expression should be approaching the derivative.

70. For $h = 1$:

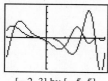

[−2, 3] by [−5, 5]

For $h = 0.7$:

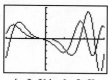

[−2, 3] by [−5, 5]

For $h = 0.3$:

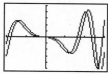

[−2, 3] by [−5, 5]

As $h \to 0$, the second curve (the difference quotient) approaches the first ($y = -2x \sin(x^2)$). This is because $-2x \sin(x^2)$ is the derivative of $\cos(x^2)$, and the second curve is the difference quotient used to define the derivative of $\cos(x^2)$. As $h \to 0$, the difference quotient expression should be approaching the derivative.

71. (a) Let $f(x) = |x|$.

Then

$$\frac{d}{dx}|u| = \frac{d}{dx}f(u) = f'(u)\frac{du}{dx} = \left(\frac{d}{du}|u|\right)\left(\frac{du}{dx}\right) = \frac{u}{|u|}u'.$$

The derivative of the absolute value function is $+1$ for

positive values, -1 for negative values, and undefined

at 0. So $f'(u) = \begin{cases} -1, & u < 0 \\ 1, & u > 0. \end{cases}$

But this is exactly how the expression $\frac{u}{|u|}$ evaluates.

(b) $f'(x) = \left[\frac{d}{dx}(x^2 - 9)\right] \cdot \frac{x^2 - 9}{|x^2 - 9|} = \frac{(2x)(x^2 - 9)}{|x^2 - 9|}$

$g'(x) = \frac{d}{dx}(|x| \sin x)$

$\quad = |x|\frac{d}{dx}(\sin x) + (\sin x)\frac{d}{dx}|x|$

$\quad = |x| \cos x + \frac{x \sin x}{|x|}$

Note: The expression for $g'(x)$ above is undefined at

$x = 0$, but actually

$g'(0) = \lim_{h \to 0}\frac{g(0 + h) - g(0)}{h} = \lim_{h \to 0}\frac{|h| \sin h}{h} = 0.$

Therefore, we may express the derivative as

$g'(x) = \begin{cases} |x| \cos x + \dfrac{x \sin x}{|x|}, & x \neq 0 \\ 0, & x = 0. \end{cases}$

72. $\dfrac{dG}{dx} = \dfrac{d}{dx}\sqrt{uv} = \dfrac{d}{dx}\sqrt{x(x + c)} = \dfrac{d}{dx}\sqrt{x^2 + cx}$

$\quad = \dfrac{1}{2\sqrt{x^2 + cx}}\dfrac{d}{dx}(x^2 + cx) = \dfrac{2x + c}{2\sqrt{x^2 + cx}} = \dfrac{x + (x + c)}{2\sqrt{x(x + c)}}$

$\quad = \dfrac{u + v}{2\sqrt{uv}} = \dfrac{A}{G}$

■ Section 3.7 Implicit Differentiation
(pp. 149–157)

Exploration 1   An Unexpected Derivative

1. $2x - 2y - 2xy' + 2yy' = 0$. Solving for y', we find that $\dfrac{dy}{dx} = 1$ (provided $y \neq x$).

2. With a constant derivative of 1, the graph would seem to be a line with slope 1.

3. Letting $x = 0$ in the original equation, we find that $y = \pm 2$. This would seem to indicate that this equation defines two lines implicitly, both with slope 1. The two lines are $y = x + 2$ and $y = x - 2$.

4. Factoring the original equation, we have
$[(x - y) - 2][(x - y) + 2] = 0$
$\therefore x - y - 2 = 0$ or $x - y + 2 = 0$
$\therefore y = x - 2$ or $y = x + 2$.
The graph is shown below.

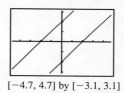

[−4.7, 4.7] by [−3.1, 3.1]

5. At each point (x, y) on either line, $\dfrac{dy}{dx} = 1$. The condition $y \neq x$ is true because both lines are parallel to the line $y = x$. The derivative is surprising because it does not depend on x or y, but there are no inconsistencies.

Quick Review 3.7

1. $x - y^2 = 0$
$\quad\quad x = y^2$
$\quad \pm\sqrt{x} = y$
$\quad\quad y_1 = \sqrt{x}, y_2 = -\sqrt{x}$

[−6, 6] by [−4, 4]

2. $4x^2 + 9y^2 = 36$

$$9y^2 = 36 - 4x^2$$

$$y^2 = \frac{36 - 4x^2}{9} = \frac{4}{9}(9 - x^2)$$

$$y = \pm\frac{2}{3}\sqrt{9 - x^2}$$

$$y_1 = \frac{2}{3}\sqrt{9 - x^2}, \, y_2 = -\frac{2}{3}\sqrt{9 - x^2}$$

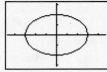

$[-4.7, 4.7]$ by $[-3.1, 3.1]$

3. $\qquad x^2 - 4y^2 = 0$

$$(x + 2y)(x - 2y) = 0$$

$$y = \pm\frac{x}{2}$$

$$y_1 = \frac{x}{2}, \, y_2 = -\frac{x}{2}$$

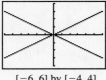

$[-6, 6]$ by $[-4, 4]$

4. $x^2 + y^2 = 9$

$$y^2 = 9 - x^2$$

$$y = \pm\sqrt{9 - x^2}$$

$$y_1 = \sqrt{9 - x^2}, \, y_2 = -\sqrt{9 - y^2}$$

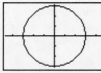

$[-4.7, 4.7]$ by $[-3.1, 3.1]$

5. $x^2 + y^2 = 2x + 3$

$$y^2 = 2x + 3 - x^2$$

$$y = \pm\sqrt{2x + 3 - x^2}$$

$$y_1 = \sqrt{2x + 3 - x^2}, \, y_2 = -\sqrt{2x + 3 - x^2}$$

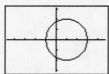

$[-4.7, 4.7]$ by $[-3.1, 3.1]$

6. $x^2y' - 2xy = 4x - y$

$$x^2y' = 4x - y + 2xy$$

$$y' = \frac{4x - y + 2xy}{x^2}$$

7. $y'\sin x - x\cos x = xy' + y$

$$y'\sin x - xy' = y + x\cos x$$

$$(\sin x - x)y' = y + x\cos x$$

$$y' = \frac{y + x\cos x}{\sin x - x}$$

8. $x(y^2 - y') = y'(x^2 - y)$

$$xy^2 = y'(x^2 - y + x)$$

$$y' = \frac{xy^2}{x^2 - y + x}$$

9. $\sqrt{x}(x - \sqrt[3]{x}) = x^{1/2}(x - x^{1/3})$
$$= x^{1/2}x - x^{1/2}x^{1/3}$$
$$= x^{3/2} - x^{5/6}$$

10. $\dfrac{x + \sqrt[3]{x^2}}{\sqrt{x^3}} = \dfrac{x + x^{2/3}}{x^{3/2}}$
$$= \frac{x}{x^{3/2}} + \frac{x^{2/3}}{x^{3/2}}$$
$$= x^{-1/2} + x^{-5/6}$$

Section 3.7 Exercises

1. $\dfrac{dy}{dx} = \dfrac{d}{dx}x^{9/4} = \dfrac{9}{4}x^{(9/4)-1} = \dfrac{9}{4}x^{5/4}$

2. $\dfrac{dy}{dx} = \dfrac{d}{dx}x^{-3/5} = -\dfrac{3}{5}x^{(-3/5)-1} = -\dfrac{3}{5}x^{-8/5}$

3. $\dfrac{dy}{dx} = \dfrac{d}{dx}\sqrt[3]{x} = \dfrac{d}{dx}x^{1/3} = \dfrac{1}{3}x^{(1/3)-1} = \dfrac{1}{3}x^{-2/3}$

4. $\dfrac{dy}{dx} = \dfrac{d}{dx}\sqrt[4]{x} = \dfrac{d}{dx}x^{1/4} = \dfrac{1}{4}x^{(1/4)-1} = \dfrac{1}{4}x^{-3/4}$

5. $\dfrac{dy}{dx} = \dfrac{d}{dx}(2x + 5)^{-1/2} = -\dfrac{1}{2}(2x + 5)^{(-1/2)-1}\dfrac{d}{dx}(2x + 5)$
$$= -\frac{1}{2}(2x + 5)^{-3/2}(2) = -(2x + 5)^{-3/2}$$

6. $\dfrac{dy}{dx} = \dfrac{d}{dx}(1 - 6x)^{2/3}$
$$= \frac{2}{3}(1 - 6x)^{(2/3)-1}\frac{d}{dx}(1 - 6x)$$
$$= \frac{2}{3}(1 - 6x)^{-1/3}(-6)$$
$$= -4(1 - 6x)^{-1/3}$$

7. $\dfrac{dy}{dx} = \dfrac{d}{dx}(x\sqrt{x^2 + 1})$
$$= x\frac{d}{dx}\sqrt{x^2 + 1} + \sqrt{x^2 + 1}\frac{d}{dx}(x)$$
$$= x\frac{d}{dx}(x^2 + 1)^{1/2} + (x^2 + 1)^{1/2}$$
$$= x \cdot \frac{1}{2}(x^2 + 1)^{-1/2}(2x) + (x^2 + 1)^{1/2}$$
$$= x^2(x^2 + 1)^{-1/2} + (x^2 + 1)^{1/2}$$

Note: This answer is equivalent to $\dfrac{2x^2 + 1}{\sqrt{x^2 + 1}}$.

8. $\dfrac{dy}{dx} = \dfrac{d}{dx}\dfrac{x}{\sqrt{x^2+1}} = \dfrac{(x^2+1)^{1/2}\frac{d}{dx}x - x\frac{d}{dx}(x^2+1)^{1/2}}{x^2+1}$

$\qquad = \dfrac{(x^2+1)^{1/2} - x \cdot \frac{1}{2}(x^2+1)^{-1/2}(2x)}{x^2+1}$

$\qquad = \dfrac{x^2+1-x^2}{(x^2+1)(x^2+1)^{1/2}}$

$\qquad = \dfrac{1}{(x^2+1)^{3/2}}$

$\qquad = (x^2+1)^{-3/2}$

9. $\qquad\qquad x^2y + xy^2 = 6$

$\qquad \dfrac{d}{dx}(x^2y) + \dfrac{d}{dx}(xy^2) = \dfrac{d}{dx}(6)$

$x^2\dfrac{dy}{dx} + y(2x) + x(2y)\dfrac{dy}{dx} + y^2(1) = 0$

$\qquad\qquad x^2\dfrac{dy}{dx} + 2xy\dfrac{dy}{dx} = -(2xy + y^2)$

$\qquad\qquad (2xy + x^2)\dfrac{dy}{dx} = -(2xy + y^2)$

$\qquad\qquad\qquad \dfrac{dy}{dx} = -\dfrac{2xy + y^2}{2xy + x^2}$

10. $\qquad\qquad x^3 + y^3 = 18xy$

$\qquad \dfrac{d}{dx}(x^3) + \dfrac{d}{dx}(y^3) = \dfrac{d}{dx}(18xy)$

$\qquad 3x^2 + 3y^2\dfrac{dy}{dx} = 18x\dfrac{dy}{dx} + 18y\,(1)$

$\qquad 3y^2\dfrac{dy}{dx} - 18x\dfrac{dy}{dx} = 18y - 3x^2$

$\qquad (3y^2 - 18x)\dfrac{dy}{dx} = 18y - 3x^2$

$\qquad\qquad \dfrac{dy}{dx} = \dfrac{18y - 3x^2}{3y^2 - 18x}$

$\qquad\qquad \dfrac{dy}{dx} = \dfrac{6y - x^2}{y^2 - 6x}$

11. $\quad y^2 = \dfrac{x-1}{x+1}$

$\quad \dfrac{d}{dx}y^2 = \dfrac{d}{dx}\dfrac{x-1}{x+1}$

$\quad 2y\dfrac{dy}{dx} = \dfrac{(x+1)(1) - (x-1)(1)}{(x+1)^2}$

$\quad 2y\dfrac{dy}{dx} = \dfrac{2}{(x+1)^2}$

$\quad \dfrac{dy}{dx} = \dfrac{1}{y(x+1)^2}$

12. $\qquad\qquad x^2 = \dfrac{x-y}{x+y}$

$\quad \dfrac{d}{dx}(x^2) = \dfrac{d}{dx}\dfrac{x-y}{x+y}$

$\quad 2x = \dfrac{(x+y)\left(1 - \frac{dy}{dx}\right) - (x-y)\left(1 + \frac{dy}{dx}\right)}{(x+y)^2}$

$\quad 2x = \dfrac{\left[x - x\frac{dy}{dx} + y - y\frac{dy}{dx}\right] - \left[x + x\frac{dy}{dx} - y - y\frac{dy}{dx}\right]}{(x+y)^2}$

$\quad 2x = \dfrac{2y - 2x\frac{dy}{dx}}{(x+y)^2}$

$\quad x(x+y)^2 = y - x\dfrac{dy}{dx}$

$\quad x\dfrac{dy}{dx} = y - x(x+y)^2$

$\quad \dfrac{dy}{dx} = \dfrac{y - x(x+y)^2}{x} = \dfrac{y}{x} - (x+y)^2$

Alternate solution:

$\qquad\qquad x^2 = \dfrac{x-y}{x+y}$

$\qquad\qquad x^2(x+y) = x-y$

$\qquad\qquad x^3 + x^2y = x-y$

$\quad \dfrac{d}{dx}(x^3) + \dfrac{d}{dx}(x^2y) = \dfrac{d}{dx}(x) - \dfrac{d}{dx}(y)$

$\quad 3x^2 + x^2\dfrac{dy}{dx} + y(2x) = 1 - \dfrac{dy}{dx}$

$\qquad\qquad (x^2+1)\dfrac{dy}{dx} = 1 - 3x^2 - 2xy$

$\qquad\qquad \dfrac{dy}{dx} = \dfrac{1 - 3x^2 - 2xy}{x^2+1}$

13. $\dfrac{dy}{dx} = \dfrac{d}{dx}(1 - x^{1/2})^{1/2}$

$\qquad = \dfrac{1}{2}(1 - x^{1/2})^{-1/2}\dfrac{d}{dx}(1 - x^{1/2})$

$\qquad = \dfrac{1}{2}(1 - x^{1/2})^{-1/2}\left(-\dfrac{1}{2}x^{-1/2}\right)$

$\qquad = -\dfrac{1}{4}(1 - x^{1/2})^{-1/2}x^{-1/2}$

14. $\dfrac{dy}{dx} = \dfrac{d}{dx}3(2x^{-1/2} + 1)^{-1/3}$

$\qquad = -(2x^{-1/2} + 1)^{-4/3}\dfrac{d}{dx}(2x^{-1/2} + 1)$

$\qquad = -(2x^{-1/2} + 1)^{-4/3}(-x^{-3/2})$

$\qquad = x^{-3/2}(2x^{-1/2} + 1)^{-4/3}$

15. $\dfrac{dy}{dx} = \dfrac{d}{dx}3(\csc x)^{3/2}$

$\qquad = \dfrac{9}{2}(\csc x)^{1/2}\dfrac{d}{dx}(\csc x)$

$\qquad = \dfrac{9}{2}(\csc x)^{1/2}(-\csc x \cot x)$

$\qquad = -\dfrac{9}{2}(\csc x)^{3/2}\cot x$

16. $\dfrac{dy}{dx} = \dfrac{d}{dx}[\sin{(x + 5)}]^{5/4}$

$\qquad = \dfrac{5}{4}[\sin{(x + 5)}]^{1/4}\dfrac{d}{dx}\sin{(x + 5)}$

$\qquad = \dfrac{5}{4}[\sin{(x + 5)}]^{1/4}\cos{(x + 5)}$

17. $\qquad x = \tan y$

$\qquad \dfrac{d}{dx}(x) = \dfrac{d}{dx}(\tan y)$

$\qquad\quad 1 = \sec^2 y\dfrac{dy}{dx}$

$\qquad \dfrac{dy}{dx} = \dfrac{1}{\sec^2 y} = \cos^2 y$

18. $\qquad x = \sin y$

$\qquad \dfrac{d}{dx}(x) = \dfrac{d}{dx}(\sin y)$

$\qquad\quad 1 = \cos y\dfrac{dy}{dx}$

$\qquad \dfrac{dy}{dx} = \dfrac{1}{\cos y} = \sec y$

19. $\qquad\qquad x + \tan xy = 0$

$\qquad \dfrac{d}{dx}(x) + \dfrac{d}{dx}(\tan xy) = \dfrac{d}{dx}(0)$

$\qquad 1 + \sec^2{(xy)}\dfrac{d}{dx}(xy) = 0$

$\qquad 1 + (\sec^2 xy)[x\dfrac{dy}{dx} + (y)(1)] = 0$

$\qquad (\sec^2 xy)(x)\dfrac{dy}{dx} = -1 - (\sec^2 xy)(y)$

$\qquad\qquad \dfrac{dy}{dx} = \dfrac{-1 - y\sec^2 xy}{x\sec^2 xy}$

$\qquad\qquad \dfrac{dy}{dx} = -\dfrac{1}{x}\cos^2 xy - \dfrac{y}{x}$

20. $\qquad\qquad x + \sin y = xy$

$\qquad \dfrac{d}{dx}(x) + \dfrac{d}{dx}(\sin y) = \dfrac{d}{dx}(xy)$

$\qquad 1 + (\cos y)\dfrac{dy}{dx} = x\dfrac{dy}{dx} + (y)(1)$

$\qquad (\cos y - x)\dfrac{dy}{dx} = -1 + y$

$\qquad\qquad \dfrac{dy}{dx} = \dfrac{-1 + y}{\cos y - x} = \dfrac{1 - y}{x - \cos y}$

21. (a) If $f(x) = \dfrac{3}{2}x^{2/3} - 3$, then

$\qquad f'(x) = x^{-1/3}$ and $f''(x) = -\dfrac{1}{3}x^{-4/3}$

$\qquad$ which contradicts the given equation $f''(x) = x^{-1/3}$.

(b) If $f(x) = \dfrac{9}{10}x^{5/3} - 7$, then

$\qquad f'(x) = \dfrac{3}{2}x^{2/3}$ and $f''(x) = x^{-1/3}$,

$\qquad$ which matches the given equation.

(c) Differentiating both sides of the given equation

$\qquad f''(x) = x^{-1/3}$ gives $f'''(x) = -\dfrac{1}{3}x^{-4/3}$, so it *must* be true

$\qquad$ that $f'''(x) = -\dfrac{1}{3}x^{-4/3}$.

(d) If $f'(x) = \dfrac{3}{2}x^{2/3} + 6$, then $f''(x) = x^{-1/3}$, which matches

$\qquad$ the given equation.

$\qquad$ Conclusion: (b), (c), and (d) could be true.

22. (a) If $g'(t) = 4\sqrt[4]{t} - 4$, then

$\qquad g''(t) = \dfrac{d}{dx}(4t^{1/4} - 4) = t^{-3/4} = \dfrac{1}{t^{3/4}}$, which matches the

$\qquad$ given equation.

(b) Differentiating both sides of the given equation

$\qquad g''(t) = \dfrac{1}{t^{3/4}} = t^{-3/4}$ gives $g'''(t) = -\dfrac{3}{4}t^{-7/4}$, which is not

$\qquad$ consistent with $g'''(t) = -\dfrac{4}{\sqrt[4]{t}}$.

(c) If $g(t) = t - 7 + \dfrac{16}{5}t^{5/4}$, then $g'(t) = 1 + 4t^{1/4}$ and

$\qquad g''(t) = t^{-3/4} = \dfrac{1}{t^{3/4}}$, which matches the given

$\qquad$ equation.

(d) If $g'(t) = \dfrac{1}{4}t^{1/4}$, then $g''(t) = \dfrac{1}{16}t^{-3/4}$, which

$\qquad$ contradicts the given equation.

$\qquad$ Conclusion: (a) and (c) could be true.

23. $\qquad\qquad x^2 + y^2 = 1$

$\qquad \dfrac{d}{dx}(x^2) + \dfrac{d}{dx}(y^2) = \dfrac{d}{dx}(1)$

$\qquad\qquad 2x + 2yy' = 0$

$\qquad\qquad\quad 2yy' = -2x$

$\qquad\qquad\quad\quad y' = -\dfrac{x}{y}$

$\qquad\qquad\quad\quad y'' = \dfrac{d}{dx}\left(-\dfrac{x}{y}\right)$

$\qquad\qquad\qquad = -\dfrac{(y)(1) - (x)(y')}{y^2}$

$\qquad\qquad\qquad = -\dfrac{y - x\left(-\dfrac{x}{y}\right)}{y^2}$

$\qquad\qquad\qquad = -\dfrac{x^2 + y^2}{y^3}$

Since our original equation was $x^2 + y^2 = 1$, we may

substitute 1 for $x^2 + y^2$, giving $y'' = -\dfrac{1}{y^3}$.

24. $x^{2/3} + y^{2/3} = 1$

$$\frac{d}{dx}(x^{2/3}) + \frac{d}{dx}(y^{2/3}) = \frac{d}{dx}(1)$$

$$\frac{2}{3}x^{-1/3} + \frac{2}{3}y^{-1/3}y' = 0$$

$$y' = -\frac{x^{-1/3}}{y^{-1/3}} = -\left(\frac{y}{x}\right)^{1/3}$$

$$y'' = \frac{d}{dx}\left[-\left(\frac{y}{x}\right)^{1/3}\right]$$

$$= -\frac{1}{3}\left(\frac{y}{x}\right)^{-2/3}\frac{d}{dx}\left(\frac{y}{x}\right)$$

$$= -\frac{1}{3}\left(\frac{y}{x}\right)^{-2/3}\frac{xy' - (y)(1)}{x^2}$$

$$= -\frac{1}{3}\frac{-(x)\left(\frac{y}{x}\right)^{1/3} - y}{x^{4/3}y^{2/3}}$$

$$= \frac{1}{3}\frac{x^{2/3}y^{1/3} + y}{x^{4/3}y^{2/3}}$$

$$= \frac{x^{2/3} + y^{2/3}}{3x^{4/3}y^{1/3}}$$

Since our original equation was $x^{2/3} + y^{2/3} = 1$, we may substitute 1 for $x^{2/3} + y^{2/3}$, giving $y'' = \frac{1}{3x^{4/3}y^{1/3}}$.

25. $y^2 = x^2 + 2x$

$$\frac{d}{dx}(y^2) = \frac{d}{dx}(x^2) + \frac{d}{dx}(2x)$$

$$2yy' = 2x + 2$$

$$y' = \frac{2x + 2}{2y} = \frac{x + 1}{y}$$

$$y'' = \frac{d}{dx}\left(\frac{x + 1}{y}\right)$$

$$= \frac{(y)(1) - (x + 1)y'}{y^2}$$

$$= \frac{y - (x + 1)\left(\frac{x + 1}{y}\right)}{y^2}$$

$$= \frac{y^2 - (x + 1)^2}{y^3}$$

Since our original equation was $y^2 = x^2 + 2x$, we may write $y^2 - (x + 1)^2 = (x^2 + 2x) - (x^2 + 2x + 1) = -1$, which gives $y'' = -\frac{1}{y^3}$.

26. $y^2 + 2y = 2x + 1$

$$\frac{d}{dx}(y^2 + 2y) = \frac{d}{dx}(2x + 1)$$

$$(2y + 2)y' = 2$$

$$y' = \frac{1}{y + 1}$$

$$y'' = \frac{d}{dx}\frac{1}{y + 1}$$

$$= -(y + 1)^{-2}y'$$

$$= -(y + 1)^{-2}\left(\frac{1}{y + 1}\right)$$

$$= -\frac{1}{(y + 1)^3}$$

27. $x^2 + xy - y^2 = 1$

$$\frac{d}{dx}(x^2) + \frac{d}{dx}(xy) - \frac{d}{dx}(y^2) = \frac{d}{dx}(1)$$

$$2x + x\frac{dy}{dx} + (y)(1) - 2y\frac{dy}{dx} = 0$$

$$(x - 2y)\frac{dy}{dx} = -2x - y$$

$$\frac{dy}{dx} = \frac{-2x - y}{x - 2y} = \frac{2x + y}{2y - x}$$

Slope at $(2, 3)$: $\frac{2(2) + 3}{2(3) - 2} = \frac{7}{4}$

(a) Tangent: $y = \frac{7}{4}(x - 2) + 3$ or $y = \frac{7}{4}x - \frac{1}{2}$

(b) Normal: $y = -\frac{4}{7}(x - 2) + 3$ or $y = -\frac{4}{7}x + \frac{29}{7}$

28. $x^2 + y^2 = 25$

$$\frac{d}{dx}(x^2) + \frac{d}{dx}(y^2) = \frac{d}{dx}(25)$$

$$2x + 2y\frac{dy}{dx} = 0$$

$$\frac{dy}{dx} = -\frac{x}{y}$$

Slope at $(3, -4)$: $-\frac{3}{-4} = \frac{3}{4}$

(a) Tangent: $y = \frac{3}{4}(x - 3) + (-4)$ or $y = \frac{3}{4}x - \frac{25}{4}$

(b) Normal: $y = -\frac{4}{3}(x - 3) + (-4)$ or $y = -\frac{4}{3}x$

29. $x^2y^2 = 9$

$$\frac{d}{dx}(x^2y^2) = \frac{d}{dx}(9)$$

$$(x^2)(2y)\frac{dy}{dx} + (y^2)(2x) = 0$$

$$2x^2y\frac{dy}{dx} = -2xy^2$$

$$\frac{dy}{dx} = -\frac{2xy^2}{2x^2y} = -\frac{y}{x}$$

Slope at $(-1, 3)$: $-\frac{3}{-1} = 3$

(a) Tangent: $y = 3(x + 1) + 3$ or $y = 3x + 6$

(b) Normal: $y = -\frac{1}{3}(x + 1) + 3$ or $y = -\frac{1}{3}x + \frac{8}{3}$

30. $y^2 - 2x - 4y - 1 = 0$

$$\frac{d}{dx}(y^2) - \frac{d}{dx}(2x) - \frac{d}{dx}(4y) - \frac{d}{dx}(1) = \frac{d}{dx}(0)$$

$$2y\frac{dy}{dx} - 2 - 4\frac{dy}{dx} - 0 = 0$$

$$(2y - 4)\frac{dy}{dx} = 2$$

$$\frac{dy}{dx} = \frac{1}{y - 2}$$

Slope at $(-2, 1)$: $\frac{1}{1 - 2} = -1$

(a) Tangent: $y = -(x + 2) + 1$ or $y = -x - 1$

(b) Normal: $y = 1(x + 2) + 1$ or $y = x + 3$

31.
$$6x^2 + 3xy + 2y^2 + 17y - 6 = 0$$

$$\frac{d}{dx}(6x^2) + \frac{d}{dx}(3xy) + \frac{d}{dx}(2y^2) + \frac{d}{dx}(17y) - \frac{d}{dx}(6) = \frac{d}{dx}(0)$$

$$12x + 3x\frac{dy}{dx} + (3y)(1) + 4y\frac{dy}{dx} + 17\frac{dy}{dx} - 0 = 0$$

$$3x\frac{dy}{dx} + 4y\frac{dy}{dx} + 17\frac{dy}{dx} = -12x - 3y$$

$$(3x + 4y + 17)\frac{dy}{dx} = -12x - 3y$$

$$\frac{dy}{dx} = \frac{-12x - 3y}{3x + 4y + 17}$$

Slope at $(-1, 0)$: $\dfrac{-12(-1) - 3(0)}{3(-1) + 4(0) + 17} = \dfrac{12}{14} = \dfrac{6}{7}$

(a) Tangent: $y = \dfrac{6}{7}(x + 1) + 0$ or $y = \dfrac{6}{7}x + \dfrac{6}{7}$

(b) Normal: $y = -\dfrac{7}{6}(x + 1) + 0$ or $y = -\dfrac{7}{6}x - \dfrac{7}{6}$

32.
$$x^2 - \sqrt{3}xy + 2y^2 = 5$$

$$\frac{d}{dx}(x^2) - \sqrt{3}\frac{d}{dx}(xy) + 2\frac{d}{dx}(y^2) = \frac{d}{dx}(5)$$

$$2x - \sqrt{3}(x)\frac{dy}{dx} - \sqrt{3}(y)(1) + 4y\frac{dy}{dx} = 0$$

$$(-x\sqrt{3} + 4y)\frac{dy}{dx} = y\sqrt{3} - 2x$$

$$\frac{dy}{dx} = \frac{y\sqrt{3} - 2x}{-x\sqrt{3} + 4y}$$

Slope at $(\sqrt{3}, 2)$: $\dfrac{2\sqrt{3} - 2\sqrt{3}}{-\sqrt{3}\sqrt{3} + 4(2)} = 0$

(a) Tangent: $y = 2$

(b) Normal: $x = \sqrt{3}$

33.
$$2xy + \pi \sin y = 2\pi$$

$$2\frac{d}{dx}(xy) + \pi\frac{d}{dx}(\sin y) = \frac{d}{dx}(2\pi)$$

$$2x\frac{dy}{dx} + 2y(1) + \pi \cos y \frac{dy}{dx} = 0$$

$$(2x + \pi \cos y)\frac{dy}{dx} = -2y$$

$$\frac{dy}{dx} = -\frac{2y}{2x + \pi \cos y}$$

Slope at $\left(1, \dfrac{\pi}{2}\right)$: $-\dfrac{2(\pi/2)}{2(1) + \pi \cos(\pi/2)} = -\dfrac{\pi}{2}$

(a) Tangent: $y = -\dfrac{\pi}{2}(x - 1) + \dfrac{\pi}{2}$ or $y = -\dfrac{\pi}{2}x + \pi$

(b) Normal: $y = \dfrac{2}{\pi}(x - 1) + \dfrac{\pi}{2}$ or $y = \dfrac{2}{\pi}x - \dfrac{2}{\pi} + \dfrac{\pi}{2}$

34. $x \sin 2y = y \cos 2x$

$$\frac{d}{dx}(x \sin 2y) = \frac{d}{dx}(y \cos 2x)$$

$$(x)(\cos 2y)(2)\frac{dy}{dx} + (\sin 2y)(1) =$$

$$(y)(-\sin 2x)(2) + (\cos 2x)\left(\frac{dy}{dx}\right)$$

$$(2x \cos 2y)\frac{dy}{dx} - (\cos 2x)\frac{dy}{dx} = -2y \sin 2x - \sin 2y$$

$$\frac{dy}{dx} = -\frac{2y \sin 2x + \sin 2y}{2x \cos 2y - \cos 2x}$$

Slope at $\left(\dfrac{\pi}{4}, \dfrac{\pi}{2}\right)$: $-\dfrac{2\left(\dfrac{\pi}{2}\right)\sin\left(\dfrac{\pi}{2}\right) + \sin(\pi)}{2\left(\dfrac{\pi}{4}\right)\cos(\pi) - \cos\left(\dfrac{\pi}{2}\right)}$

$$= -\frac{(\pi)(1) + 0}{\left(\dfrac{\pi}{2}\right)(-1) - 0} = 2$$

(a) Tangent: $y = 2\left(x - \dfrac{\pi}{4}\right) + \dfrac{\pi}{2}$ or $y = 2x$

(b) Normal: $y = -\dfrac{1}{2}\left(x - \dfrac{\pi}{4}\right) + \dfrac{\pi}{2}$ or $y = -\dfrac{1}{2}x + \dfrac{5\pi}{8}$

35.
$$y = 2 \sin(\pi x - y)$$

$$\frac{dy}{dx} = \frac{d}{dx}2 \sin(\pi x - y)$$

$$\frac{dy}{dx} = 2 \cos(\pi x - y)\left(\pi - \frac{dy}{dx}\right)$$

$$[1 + 2 \cos(\pi x - y)]\frac{dy}{dx} = 2\pi \cos(\pi x - y)$$

$$\frac{dy}{dx} = \frac{2\pi \cos(\pi x - y)}{1 + 2 \cos(\pi x - y)}$$

Slope at $(1, 0)$: $\dfrac{2\pi \cos \pi}{1 + 2 \cos \pi} = \dfrac{2\pi(-1)}{1 + 2(-1)} = 2\pi$

(a) Tangent: $y = 2\pi(x - 1) + 0$ or $y = 2\pi x - 2\pi$

(b) Normal: $y = -\dfrac{1}{2\pi}(x - 1) + 0$ or $y = -\dfrac{x}{2\pi} + \dfrac{1}{2\pi}$

36. $x^2 \cos^2 y - \sin y = 0$

$$\frac{d}{dx}(x^2 \cos^2 y) - \frac{d}{dx}(\sin y) = \frac{d}{dx}(0)$$

$$(x^2)(2 \cos y)(-\sin y)\left(\frac{dy}{dx}\right) + (\cos^2 y)(2x) - (\cos y)\frac{dy}{dx} = 0$$

$$-(2x^2 \cos y \sin y + \cos y)\frac{dy}{dx} = -2x \cos^2 y$$

$$\frac{dy}{dx} = \frac{2x \cos^2 y}{\cos y + 2x^2 \cos y \sin y} = \frac{2x \cos y}{1 + 2x^2 \sin y}$$

Slope at $(0, \pi)$: $\dfrac{2(0) \cos \pi}{1 + 2(0)^2 \sin \pi} = 0$

(a) Tangent: $y = \pi$

(b) Normal: $x = 0$

37. (a)
$$y^4 = y^2 - x^2$$

$$\frac{d}{dx}(y^4) = \frac{d}{dx}(y^2) - \frac{d}{dx}x^2$$

$$4y^3\frac{dy}{dx} = 2y\frac{dy}{dx} - 2x$$

$$(4y^3 - 2y)\frac{dy}{dx} = -2x$$

$$\frac{dy}{dx} = \frac{-2x}{4y^3 - 2y} = \frac{x}{y - 2y^3}$$

At $\left(\frac{\sqrt{3}}{4}, \frac{\sqrt{3}}{2}\right)$:

$$\text{Slope} = \frac{\dfrac{\sqrt{3}}{4}}{\dfrac{\sqrt{3}}{2} - 2\left(\dfrac{\sqrt{3}}{2}\right)^3}$$

$$= \frac{\dfrac{\sqrt{3}}{4}}{\dfrac{\sqrt{3}}{2} - \dfrac{3\sqrt{3}}{4}} \cdot \frac{\dfrac{4}{\sqrt{3}}}{\dfrac{4}{\sqrt{3}}} = \frac{1}{2 - 3} = -1$$

At $\left(\frac{\sqrt{3}}{4}, \frac{1}{2}\right)$:

$$\text{Slope} = \frac{\dfrac{\sqrt{3}}{4}}{\dfrac{1}{2} - 2\left(\dfrac{1}{2}\right)^3} = \frac{\dfrac{\sqrt{3}}{4}}{\dfrac{1}{2} - \dfrac{1}{4}} \cdot \frac{4}{4} = \frac{\sqrt{3}}{1} = \sqrt{3}$$

(b)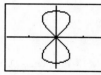

[−1.8, 1.8] by [−1.2, 1.2]

Parameter interval: $-1 \le t \le 1$

38. (a)
$$y^2(2 - x) = x^3$$

$$\frac{d}{dx}[y^2(2 - x)] = \frac{d}{dx}(x^3)$$

$$(y^2)(-1) + (2 - x)(2y)\frac{dy}{dx} = 3x^2$$

$$2y(2 - x)\frac{dy}{dx} = 3x^2 + y^2$$

$$\frac{dy}{dx} = \frac{3x^2 + y^2}{2y(2 - x)}$$

Slope at (1, 1): $\dfrac{3(1)^2 + (1)^2}{2(1)(2 - 1)} = \dfrac{4}{2} = 2$

Tangent: $y = 2(x - 1) + 1$ or $y = 2x - 1$

Normal: $y = -\dfrac{1}{2}(x - 1) + 1$ or $y = -\dfrac{1}{2}x + \dfrac{3}{2}$

(b) One way is to graph the equations $y = \pm\sqrt{\dfrac{x^3}{2 - x}}$.

39. (a) $(-1)^3(1)^2 = \cos(\pi)$ is true since both sides equal -1.

(b)
$$x^3y^2 = \cos(\pi y)$$

$$\frac{d}{dx}(x^3y^2) = \frac{d}{dx}\cos(\pi y)$$

$$(x^3)(2y)\frac{dy}{dx} + (y^2)(3x^2) = (-\sin \pi y)(\pi)\frac{dy}{dx}$$

$$(2x^3y + \pi \sin \pi y)\frac{dy}{dx} = -3x^2y^2$$

$$\frac{dy}{dx} = -\frac{3x^2y^2}{2x^3y + \pi \sin \pi y}$$

Slope at $(-1, 1)$: $-\dfrac{3(-1)^2(1)}{2(-1)^3(1) + \pi \sin \pi} = \dfrac{-3}{-2} = \dfrac{3}{2}$

The slope of the tangent line is $\dfrac{3}{2}$.

40. (a) When $x = 2$, we have $y^3 - 2y = -1$, or

$y^3 - 2y + 1 = 0$. Clearly, $y = 1$ is one solution, and

we may factor $y^3 - 2y + 1$ as $(y - 1)(y^2 + y - 1)$. The

solutions of $y^2 + y - 1 = 0$ are

$y = \dfrac{-1 \pm \sqrt{(1)^2 - 4(1)(-1)}}{2(1)} = \dfrac{-1 \pm \sqrt{5}}{2}$. Hence,

there are three possible y-values: 1, $\dfrac{-1 - \sqrt{5}}{2}$, and

$\dfrac{-1 + \sqrt{5}}{2}$.

(b)
$$y^3 - xy = -1$$

$$\frac{d}{dx}(y^3) - \frac{d}{dx}(xy) = \frac{d}{dx}(-1)$$

$$3y^2y' - xy' - (y)(1) = 0$$

$$(3y^2 - x)y' = y$$

$$y' = \frac{y}{3y^2 - x}$$

$$y'' = \frac{d}{dx}\frac{y}{3y^2 - x}$$

$$= \frac{(3y^2 - x)(y') - (y)(6y\,y' - 1)}{(3y^2 - x)^2}$$

$$= \frac{y - xy' - 3y^2\,y'}{(3y^2 - x)^2}$$

Since we are working with numerical information,
there is no need to write a general expression for y'' in
terms of x and y.

To evaluate $f'(2)$, evaluate the expression for y' using

$x = 2$ and $y = 1$:

$$f'(2) = \frac{1}{3(1)^2 - 2} = \frac{1}{1} = 1$$

To evaluate $f''(2)$, evaluate the expression for y'' using

$x = 2$, $y = 1$, and $y' = 1$:

$$f''(2) = \frac{(1) - 2(1) - 3(1)^2(1)}{[3(1)^2 - 2]^2} = \frac{-4}{1} = -4$$

41. Find the two points:

The curve crosses the x-axis when $y = 0$, so the equation becomes $x^2 + 0x + 0 = 7$, or $x^2 = 7$. The solutions are $x = \pm\sqrt{7}$, so the points are $(\pm\sqrt{7}, 0)$.

Show tangents are parallel:

$$x^2 + xy + y^2 = 7$$

$$\frac{d}{dx}(x^2) + \frac{d}{dx}(xy) + \frac{d}{dx}(y^2) = \frac{d}{dx}(7)$$

$$2x + x\frac{dy}{dx} + (y)(1) + 2y\frac{dy}{dx} = 0$$

$$(x + 2y)\frac{dy}{dx} = -(2x + y)$$

$$\frac{dy}{dx} = -\frac{2x + y}{x + 2y}$$

Slope at $(\sqrt{7}, 0)$: $-\dfrac{2\sqrt{7} + 0}{\sqrt{7} + 2(0)} = -2$

Slope at $(-\sqrt{7}, 0)$: $-\dfrac{2(-\sqrt{7}) + 0}{-\sqrt{7} + 2(0)} = -2$

The tangents at these points are parallel because they have the same slope. The common slope is -2.

42. $$x^2 + xy + y^2 = 7$$

$$\frac{d}{dx}(x^2) + \frac{d}{dx}(xy) + \frac{d}{dx}(y^2) = \frac{d}{dx}(7)$$

$$2x + x\frac{dy}{dx} + (y)(1) + 2y\frac{dy}{dx} = 0$$

$$(x + 2y)\frac{dy}{dx} = -(2x + y)$$

$$\frac{dy}{dx} = -\frac{2x + y}{x + 2y}$$

(a) The tangent is parallel to the x-axis when

$$\frac{dy}{dx} = -\frac{2x + y}{x + 2y} = 0, \text{ or } y = -2x.$$

Substituting $-2x$ for y in the original equation, we have

$$x^2 + xy + y^2 = 7$$
$$x^2 + (x)(-2x) + (-2x)^2 = 7$$
$$x^2 - 2x^2 + 4x^2 = 7$$
$$3x^2 = 7$$
$$x = \pm\sqrt{\frac{7}{3}}$$

The points are $\left(-\sqrt{\frac{7}{3}}, 2\sqrt{\frac{7}{3}}\right)$ and $\left(\sqrt{\frac{7}{3}}, -2\sqrt{\frac{7}{3}}\right)$.

(b) Since x and y are interchangeable in the original equation, $\frac{dx}{dy}$ can be obtained by interchanging x and y in the expression for $\frac{dy}{dx}$. That is, $\frac{dx}{dy} = -\frac{2y + x}{x + 2y}$. The tangent is parallel to the y-axis when $\frac{dx}{dy} = 0$, or $x = -2y$. Substituting $-2y$ for x in the original equation, we have:

$$x^2 + xy + y^2 = 7$$
$$(-2y)^2 + (-2y)(y) + y^2 = 7$$
$$4y^2 - 2y^2 + y^2 = 7$$
$$3y^2 = 7$$
$$y = \pm\sqrt{\frac{7}{3}}$$

The points are $\left(-2\sqrt{\frac{7}{3}}, \sqrt{\frac{7}{3}}\right)$ and $\left(2\sqrt{\frac{7}{3}}, -\sqrt{\frac{7}{3}}\right)$.

Note that these are the same points that would be obtained by interchanging x and y in the solution to part (a).

43. First curve:

$$2x^2 + 3y^2 = 5$$

$$\frac{d}{dx}(2x^2) + \frac{d}{dx}(3y^2) = \frac{d}{dx}(5)$$

$$4x + 6y\frac{dy}{dx} = 0$$

$$\frac{dy}{dx} = -\frac{4x}{6y} = -\frac{2x}{3y}$$

Second curve:

$$y^2 = x^3$$

$$\frac{d}{dx}y^2 = \frac{d}{dx}x^3$$

$$2y\frac{dy}{dx} = 3x^2$$

$$\frac{dy}{dx} = \frac{3x^2}{2y}$$

At $(1, 1)$, the slopes are $-\frac{2}{3}$ and $\frac{3}{2}$ respectively. At $(1, -1)$, the slopes are $\frac{2}{3}$ and $-\frac{3}{2}$ respectively. In both cases, the tangents are perpendicular. To graph the curves and normal lines, we may use the following parametric equations for $-\pi \le t \le \pi$:

First curve: $x = \sqrt{\frac{5}{2}}\cos t$, $y = \sqrt{\frac{5}{3}}\sin t$

Second curve: $x = \sqrt[3]{t^2}$, $y = t$

Tangents at $(1, 1)$: $x = 1 + 3t$, $y = 1 - 2t$
$\qquad\qquad\qquad x = 1 + 2t$, $y = 1 + 3t$

Tangents at $(1, -1)$: $x = 1 + 3t$, $y = -1 + 2t$
$\qquad\qquad\qquad x = 1 + 2t$, $y = -1 - 3t$

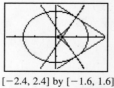

$[-2.4, 2.4]$ by $[-1.6, 1.6]$

44. $v(t) = s'(t) = \dfrac{d}{dt}(4 + 6t)^{3/2} = \dfrac{3}{2}(4 + 6t)^{1/2}(6)$

$\qquad = 9(4 + 6t)^{1/2}$

$a(t) = v'(t) = \dfrac{d}{dt}[9(4 + 6t)^{1/2}]$

$\qquad = \dfrac{9}{2}(4 + 6t)^{-1/2}(6) = 27(4 + 6t)^{-1/2}$

At $t = 2$, the velocity is $v(2) = 36$ m/sec and the

acceleration is $a(2) = \dfrac{27}{4}$ m/sec^2.

45. Acceleration $= \dfrac{dv}{dt} = \dfrac{d}{dt}[8(s - t)^{1/2} + 1]$

$\qquad = 4(s - t)^{-1/2}\left(\dfrac{ds}{dt} - 1\right)$

$\qquad = 4(s - t)^{-1/2}(v - 1)$

$\qquad = 4(s - t)^{-1/2}[(8(s - t)^{1/2} + 1) - 1]$

$\qquad = 32(s - t)^{-1/2}(s - t)^{1/2}$

$\qquad = 32$ ft/sec^2

46. $\qquad\qquad y^4 - 4y^2 = x^4 - 9x^2$

$\dfrac{d}{dx}(y^4) - \dfrac{d}{dx}(4y^2) = \dfrac{d}{dx}(x^4) - \dfrac{d}{dx}(9x^2)$

$4y^3\dfrac{dy}{dx} - 8y\dfrac{dy}{dx} = 4x^3 - 18x$

$\qquad\dfrac{dy}{dx} = \dfrac{4x^3 - 18x}{4y^3 - 8y} = \dfrac{2x^3 - 9x}{2y^3 - 4y}$

Slope at $(3, 2)$: $\dfrac{2(3)^3 - 9(3)}{2(2)^3 - 4(2)} = \dfrac{27}{8}$

Slope at $(-3, 2)$: $\dfrac{2(-3)^3 - 9(-3)}{2(2)^3 - 4(2)} = -\dfrac{27}{8}$

Slope at $(-3, -2)$: $\dfrac{2(-3)^3 - 9(-3)}{2(-2)^3 - 4(-2)} = \dfrac{27}{8}$

Slope at $(3, -2)$: $\dfrac{2(3)^3 - 9(3)}{2(-2)^3 - 4(-2)} = -\dfrac{27}{8}$

47. (a) $\qquad\qquad x^3 + y^3 - 9xy = 0$

$\dfrac{d}{dx}(x^3) + \dfrac{d}{dx}(y^3) - 9\dfrac{d}{dx}(xy) = \dfrac{d}{dx}(0)$

$3x^2 + 3y^2\dfrac{dy}{dx} - 9x\dfrac{dy}{dx} - 9(y)(1) = 0$

$\qquad\qquad (3y^2 - 9x)\dfrac{dy}{dx} = 9y - 3x^2$

$\qquad\qquad\qquad \dfrac{dy}{dx} = \dfrac{9y - 3x^2}{3y^2 - 9x} = \dfrac{3y - x^2}{y^2 - 3x}$

Slope at $(4, 2)$: $\dfrac{3(2) - (4)^2}{(2)^2 - 3(4)} = \dfrac{-10}{-8} = \dfrac{5}{4}$

Slope at $(2, 4)$: $\dfrac{3(4) - (2)^2}{(4)^2 - 3(2)} = \dfrac{8}{10} = \dfrac{4}{5}$

(b) The tangent is horizontal when

$\dfrac{dy}{dx} = \dfrac{3y - x^2}{y^2 - 3x} = 0$, or $y = \dfrac{x^2}{3}$.

Substituting $\dfrac{x^2}{3}$ for y in the original equation, we have:

$\qquad\qquad x^3 + y^3 - 9xy = 0$

$x^3 + \left(\dfrac{x^2}{3}\right)^3 - 9x\left(\dfrac{x^2}{3}\right) = 0$

$\qquad\quad x^3 + \dfrac{x^6}{27} - 3x^3 = 0$

$\qquad\qquad \dfrac{x^3}{27}(x^3 - 54) = 0$

$\qquad\qquad x = 0$ or $x = \sqrt[3]{54} = 3\sqrt[3]{2}$

At $x = 0$, we have $y = \dfrac{0^2}{3} = 0$, which gives the

point $(0, 0)$, which is the origin. At $x = 3\sqrt[3]{2}$, we have

$y = \dfrac{1}{3}(3\sqrt[3]{2})^2 = \dfrac{1}{3}(9\sqrt[3]{4}) = 3\sqrt[3]{4}$, so the point other

than the origin is $(3\sqrt[3]{2}, 3\sqrt[3]{4})$ or approximately

$(3.780, 4.762)$.

(c) The equation $x^3 + y^3 - 9xy$ is not affected by

interchanging x and y, so its graph is symmetric about

the line $y = x$ and we may find the desired point by

interchanging the x-value and the y-value in the answer

to part (b). The desired point is $(3\sqrt[3]{4}, 3\sqrt[3]{2})$ or

approximately $(4.762, 3.780)$.

48. $\qquad\qquad x^2 + 2xy - 3y^2 = 0$

$\dfrac{d}{dx}(x^2) + 2\dfrac{d}{dx}(xy) - \dfrac{d}{dx}(3y^2) = \dfrac{d}{dx}(0)$

$2x + 2x\dfrac{dy}{dx} + 2(y)(1) - 6y\dfrac{dy}{dx} = 0$

$\qquad\qquad (2x - 6y)\dfrac{dy}{dx} = -2x - 2y$

$\qquad\qquad\qquad \dfrac{dy}{dx} = \dfrac{-2x - 2y}{2x - 6y} = \dfrac{x + y}{3y - x}$

At $(1, 1)$ the curve has slope $\dfrac{1 + 1}{3(1) - 1} = \dfrac{2}{2} = 1$, so the

normal line is $y = -1(x - 1) + 1$ or $y = -x + 2$.

Substituting $-x + 2$ for y in the original equation, we have:

$\qquad\qquad x^2 + 2xy - 3y^2 = 0$

$\qquad x^2 + 2x(-x + 2) - 3(-x + 2)^2 = 0$

$x^2 - 2x^2 + 4x - 3(x^2 - 4x + 4) = 0$

$\qquad\qquad\qquad -4x^2 + 16x - 12 = 0$

$\qquad\qquad\qquad -4(x - 1)(x - 3) = 0$

$\qquad\qquad\qquad\qquad x = 1$ or $x = 3$

Since the given point $(1, 1)$ had $x = 1$, we choose $x = 3$

and so $y = -(3) + 2 = -1$. The desired point is $(3, -1)$.

49.
$$xy + 2x - y = 0$$

$$\frac{d}{dx}(xy) + \frac{d}{dx}(2x) - \frac{d}{dx}(y) = \frac{d}{dx}(0)$$

$$x\frac{dy}{dx} + (y)(1) + 2 - \frac{dy}{dx} = 0$$

$$(x-1)\frac{dy}{dx} = -2 - y$$

$$\frac{dy}{dx} = \frac{-2-y}{x-1} = \frac{2+y}{1-x}$$

Since the slope of the line $2x + y = 0$ is -2, we wish to find points where the normal has slope -2, that is, where the tangent has slope $\frac{1}{2}$. Thus, we have

$$\frac{2+y}{1-x} = \frac{1}{2}$$

$$2(2+y) = 1 - x$$

$$4 + 2y = 1 - x$$

$$x = -2y - 3$$

Substituting $-2y - 3$ in the original equation, we have:

$$xy + 2x - y = 0$$
$$(-2y-3)y + 2(-2y-3) - y = 0$$
$$-2y^2 - 8y - 6 = 0$$
$$-2(y+1)(y+3) = 0$$
$$y = -1 \text{ or } y = -3$$

At $y = -1$, $x = -2y - 3 = 2 - 3 = -1$.
At $y = -3$: $x = -2y - 3 = 6 - 3 = 3$.
The desired points are $(-1, -1)$ and $(3, -3)$.
Finally, we find the desired normals to the curve, which are the lines of slope -2 passing through each of these points. At $(-1, -1)$, the normal line is $y = -2(x+1) - 1$ or $y = -2x - 3$. At $(3, -3)$, the normal line is $y = -2(x-3) - 3$ or $y = -2x + 3$.

50.
$$x = y^2$$

$$\frac{d}{dx}(x) = \frac{d}{dx}(y^2)$$

$$1 = 2y\frac{dy}{dx}$$

$$\frac{dy}{dx} = \frac{1}{2y}$$

The normal line at (x, y) has slope $-2y$. Thus, the normal line at (b^2, b) is $y = -2b(x - b^2) + b$, or

$y = -2bx + 2b^3 + b$. This line intersects the x-axis at

$x = \frac{2b^3 + b}{2b} = b^2 + \frac{1}{2}$, which is the value of a and must be greater than $\frac{1}{2}$ if $b \neq 0$.

The two normals at $(b^2, \pm b)$ will be perpendicular when they have slopes ± 1, which gives $-2y = \pm 1$ or

$y = \pm\frac{1}{2}\left(\text{or } b = \pm\frac{1}{2}\right)$. The corresponding value of a is

$b^2 + \frac{1}{2} = \left(\frac{1}{2}\right)^2 + \frac{1}{2} = \frac{3}{4}$. Thus, the two nonhorizontal normals are perpendicular when $a = \frac{3}{4}$.

51. (a)
$$\frac{x^2}{a^2} + \frac{y^2}{b^2} = 1$$

$$b^2x^2 + a^2y^2 = a^2b^2$$

$$\frac{d}{dx}(b^2x^2) + \frac{d}{dx}(a^2y^2) = \frac{d}{dx}(a^2b^2)$$

$$2b^2x + 2a^2y\frac{dy}{dx} = 0$$

$$\frac{dy}{dx} = -\frac{2b^2x}{2a^2y} = -\frac{b^2x}{a^2y}$$

The slope at (x_1, y_1) is $-\frac{b^2x_1}{a^2y_1}$.

The tangent line is $y - y_1 = -\frac{b^2x_1}{a^2y_1}(x - x_1)$. This gives:

$$a^2y_1y - a^2y_1^2 = -b^2x_1x + b^2x_1^2$$

$$a^2y_1y + b^2x_1x = a^2y_1^2 + b^2x_1^2.$$

But $a^2y_1^2 + b^2x_1^2 = a^2b^2$ since (x_1, y_1) is on the

ellipse. Therefore, $a^2y_1y + b^2x_1x = a^2b^2$, and

dividing by a^2b^2 gives $\frac{x_1x}{a^2} + \frac{y_1y}{b^2} = 1$.

(b)
$$\frac{x^2}{a^2} - \frac{y^2}{b^2} = 1$$

$$b^2x^2 - a^2y^2 = a^2b^2$$

$$\frac{d}{dx}(b^2x^2) - \frac{d}{dx}(a^2y^2) = \frac{d}{dx}(a^2b^2)$$

$$2b^2x - 2a^2y\frac{dy}{dx} = 0$$

$$\frac{dy}{dx} = \frac{-2b^2x}{-2a^2y} = \frac{b^2x}{a^2y}$$

The slope at (x_1, y_1) is $\frac{b^2x_1}{a^2y_1}$.

The tangent line is $y - y_1 = \frac{b^2x_1}{a^2y_1}(x - x_1)$.

This gives:

$$a^2y_1y - a^2y_1^2 = b^2x_1x - b^2x_1^2$$

$$b^2x_1^2 - a^2y_1^2 = b^2x_1x - a^2y_1y$$

But $b^2x_1^2 - a^2y_1^2 = a^2b^2$ since (x_1, y_1) is on the

hyperbola. Therefore, $b^2x_1x - a^2y_1y = a^2b^2$, and

dividing by a^2b^2 gives $\frac{x_1x}{a^2} - \frac{y_1y}{b^2} = 1$.

52. (a) Solve for y:

$$\frac{x^2}{a^2} - \frac{y^2}{b^2} = 1$$

$$-\frac{y^2}{b^2} = -\frac{x^2}{a^2} + 1$$

$$y^2 = \frac{b^2}{a^2}(x^2 - a^2)$$

$$y = \pm\frac{b}{a}\sqrt{x^2 - a^2}$$

(b) $\displaystyle\lim_{x\to\infty}\frac{f(x)}{g(x)} = \lim_{x\to\infty}\frac{\frac{b}{a}\sqrt{x^2-a^2}}{\frac{b}{a}|x|}$

$\displaystyle = \lim_{x\to\infty}\frac{\sqrt{x^2-a^2}}{\sqrt{x^2}}$

$\displaystyle = \lim_{x\to\infty}\sqrt{1-\frac{a^2}{x^2}} = 1$

(c) $\displaystyle\lim_{x\to\infty}\frac{f(x)}{g(x)} = \lim_{x\to\infty}\frac{-\frac{b}{a}\sqrt{x^2-a^2}}{-\frac{b}{a}|x|}$

$\displaystyle = \lim_{x\to\infty}\frac{\sqrt{x^2-a^2}}{\sqrt{x^2}}$

$\displaystyle = \lim_{x\to\infty}\sqrt{1-\frac{a^2}{x^2}} = 1$

■ Section 3.8 Derivatives of Inverse Trigonometric Functions (pp. 157–163)

Exploration 1   Finding a Derivative on an Inverse Graph Geometrically

1. The graph is shown at the right. It appears to be a one-to-one function

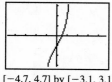

[−4.7, 4.7] by [−3.1, 3.1]

2. $f'(x) = 5x^4 + 2$. The fact that this function is always positive enables us to conclude that f is everywhere increasing, and hence one-to-one.

3. The graph of f^{-1} is shown to the right, along with the graph of f. The graph of f^{-1} is obtained from the graph of f by reflecting it in the line $y = x$.

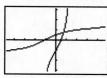

[−4.7, 4.7] by [−3.1, 3.1]

4. The line L is tangent to the graph of f^{-1} at the point (2, 1).

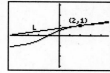

[−4.7, 4.7] by [−3.1, 3.1]

5. The reflection of line L is tangent to the graph of f at the point (1, 2).

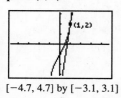

[−4.7, 4.7] by [−3.1, 3.1]

6. The reflection of line L is the tangent line to the graph of $y = x^5 + 2x - 1$ at the point (1, 2). The slope is $\frac{dy}{dx}$ at $x = 1$, which is 7.

7. The slope of L is the reciprocal of the slope of its reflection $\left(\text{since } \frac{\Delta y}{\Delta x} \text{ gets reflected to become } \frac{\Delta x}{\Delta y}\right)$. It is $\frac{1}{7}$.

8. $\frac{1}{7}$

Quick Review 3.8

1. Domain: [−1, 1]
   Range: $\left[-\frac{\pi}{2}, \frac{\pi}{2}\right]$
   At 1: $\frac{\pi}{2}$

2. Domain: [−1, 1]
   Range: [0, π]
   At 1: 0

3. Domain: all reals
   Range: $\left(-\frac{\pi}{2}, \frac{\pi}{2}\right)$
   At 1: $\frac{\pi}{4}$

4. Domain: $(-\infty, -1] \cup [1, \infty)$
   Range: $\left[0, \frac{\pi}{2}\right) \cup \left(\frac{\pi}{2}, \pi\right]$
   At 1: 0

5. Domain: all reals
   Range: all reals
   At 1: 1

6. $f(x) = y = 3x - 8$

   $y + 8 = 3x$

   $x = \dfrac{y+8}{3}$

   Interchange x and y:

   $y = \dfrac{x+8}{3}$

   $f^{-1}(x) = \dfrac{x+8}{3}$

7. $f(x) = y = \sqrt[3]{x+5}$

   $y^3 = x + 5$

   $x = y^3 - 5$

   Interchange x and y:

   $y = x^3 - 5$

   $f^{-1}(x) = x^3 - 5$

8. $f(x) = y = \dfrac{8}{x}$

$x = \dfrac{8}{y}$

Interchange x and y:

$y = \dfrac{8}{x}$

$f^{-1}(x) = \dfrac{8}{x}$

9. $f(x) = y = \dfrac{3x-2}{x}$

$xy = 3x - 2$

$(y-3)x = -2$

$x = \dfrac{-2}{y-3} = \dfrac{2}{3-y}$

Interchange x and y:

$y = \dfrac{2}{3-x}$

$f^{-1}(x) = \dfrac{2}{3-x}$

10. $f(x) = y = \arctan\dfrac{x}{3}$

$\tan y = \dfrac{x}{3}, \; -\dfrac{\pi}{2} < y < \dfrac{\pi}{2}$

$x = 3\tan y, \; -\dfrac{\pi}{2} < y < \dfrac{\pi}{2}$

Interchange x and y:

$y = 3\tan x, \; -\dfrac{\pi}{2} < x < \dfrac{\pi}{2}$

$f^{-1}(x) = 3\tan x, \; -\dfrac{\pi}{2} < x < \dfrac{\pi}{2}$

Section 3.8 Exercises

1. $\dfrac{dy}{dx} = \dfrac{d}{dx}\cos^{-1}(x^2) = -\dfrac{1}{\sqrt{1-(x^2)^2}}\dfrac{d}{dx}(x^2)$

$= -\dfrac{1}{\sqrt{1-x^4}}(2x) = -\dfrac{2x}{\sqrt{1-x^4}}$

2. $\dfrac{dy}{dx} = \dfrac{d}{dx}\cos^{-1}\left(\dfrac{1}{x}\right) = -\dfrac{1}{\sqrt{1-\left(\dfrac{1}{x}\right)^2}}\dfrac{d}{dx}\left(\dfrac{1}{x}\right)$

$= -\dfrac{1}{\sqrt{1-\left(\dfrac{1}{x}\right)^2}}\left(-\dfrac{1}{x^2}\right) = \dfrac{1}{|x|\sqrt{x^2-1}}$

3. $\dfrac{dy}{dt} = \dfrac{d}{dt}\sin^{-1}\sqrt{2}\,t = \dfrac{1}{\sqrt{1-(\sqrt{2}\,t)^2}}\dfrac{d}{dt}(\sqrt{2}\,t) = \dfrac{\sqrt{2}}{\sqrt{1-2t^2}}$

4. $\dfrac{dy}{dt} = \dfrac{d}{dt}\sin^{-1}(1-t) = \dfrac{1}{\sqrt{1-(1-t)^2}}\dfrac{d}{dt}(1-t)$

$= -\dfrac{1}{\sqrt{2t-t^2}}$

5. $\dfrac{dy}{ds} = \dfrac{d}{ds}\sec^{-1}(2s+1)$

$= \dfrac{1}{|2s+1|\sqrt{(2s+1)^2-1}}\dfrac{d}{ds}(2s+1)$

$= \dfrac{1}{|2s+1|\sqrt{4s^2+4s}}(2) = \dfrac{1}{|2s+1|\sqrt{s^2+s}}$

6. $\dfrac{dy}{ds} = \dfrac{d}{ds}\sec^{-1}5s = \dfrac{1}{|5s|\sqrt{(5s)^2-1}}\dfrac{d}{ds}(5s) = \dfrac{1}{|s|\sqrt{25s^2-1}}$

7. $\dfrac{dy}{dx} = \dfrac{d}{dx}\csc^{-1}(x^2+1)$

$= -\dfrac{1}{|x^2+1|\sqrt{(x^2+1)^2-1}}\dfrac{d}{dx}(x^2+1)$

$= -\dfrac{2x}{(x^2+1)\sqrt{x^4+2x^2}} = -\dfrac{2}{(x^2+1)\sqrt{x^2+2}}$

Note that the condition $x > 0$ is required in the last step.

8. $\dfrac{dy}{dx} = \dfrac{d}{dx}\csc^{-1}\left(\dfrac{x}{2}\right) = -\dfrac{1}{\left|\dfrac{x}{2}\right|\sqrt{\left(\dfrac{x}{2}\right)^2-1}}\dfrac{d}{dx}\left(\dfrac{x}{2}\right)$

$= -\dfrac{2}{|x|\sqrt{x^2-4}}$

9. $\dfrac{dy}{dt} = \dfrac{d}{dt}\sec^{-1}\left(\dfrac{1}{t}\right) = \dfrac{1}{\left|\dfrac{1}{t}\right|\sqrt{\left(\dfrac{1}{t}\right)^2-1}}\dfrac{d}{dt}\left(\dfrac{1}{t}\right)$

$= \dfrac{1}{\left|\dfrac{1}{t}\right|\sqrt{\left(\dfrac{1}{t}\right)^2-1}}\left(-\dfrac{1}{t^2}\right) = -\dfrac{1}{\sqrt{1-t^2}}$

Note that the condition $t > 0$ is required in the last step.

10. $\dfrac{dy}{dt} = \dfrac{d}{dt}\sin^{-1}\left(\dfrac{3}{t^2}\right) = \dfrac{1}{\sqrt{1-\left(\dfrac{3}{t^2}\right)^2}}\dfrac{d}{dt}\left(\dfrac{3}{t^2}\right)$

$= \dfrac{1}{\sqrt{1-\dfrac{9}{t^4}}}\left(-\dfrac{6}{t^3}\right) = -\dfrac{6}{t\sqrt{t^4-9}}$

11. $\dfrac{dy}{dt} = \dfrac{d}{dt}\cot^{-1}\sqrt{t} = -\dfrac{1}{1+(\sqrt{t})^2}\dfrac{d}{dt}\sqrt{t}$

$= -\dfrac{1}{2\sqrt{t}(t+1)}$

12. $\dfrac{dy}{dt} = \dfrac{d}{dt}\cot^{-1}\sqrt{t-1} = -\dfrac{1}{1+(\sqrt{t-1})^2}\dfrac{d}{dt}\sqrt{t-1}$

$= -\left(\dfrac{1}{1+t-1}\right)\left(\dfrac{1}{2\sqrt{t-1}}\right) = -\dfrac{1}{2t\sqrt{t-1}}$

13. $\dfrac{dy}{ds} = \dfrac{d}{ds}\left(s\sqrt{1-s^2}\right) + \dfrac{d}{ds}(\cos^{-1}s)$

$= (s)\left(\dfrac{1}{2\sqrt{1-s^2}}\right)(-2s) + (\sqrt{1-s^2})(1) - \dfrac{1}{\sqrt{1-s^2}}$

$= -\dfrac{s^2}{\sqrt{1-s^2}} + \sqrt{1-s^2} - \dfrac{1}{\sqrt{1-s^2}}$

$= \dfrac{-s^2 + (1-s^2) - 1}{\sqrt{1-s^2}}$

$= -\dfrac{2s^2}{\sqrt{1-s^2}}$

14. $\dfrac{dy}{ds} = \dfrac{d}{ds}\sqrt{s^2-1} - \dfrac{d}{ds}\sec^{-1}s$

$= \dfrac{1}{2\sqrt{s^2-1}}(2s) - \dfrac{1}{|s|\sqrt{s^2-1}}$

$= \dfrac{s|s| - 1}{|s|\sqrt{s^2-1}}$

15. $\dfrac{dy}{dx} = \dfrac{d}{dx}(\tan^{-1}\sqrt{x^2-1}) + \dfrac{d}{dx}(\csc^{-1}x)$

$= \dfrac{1}{1+(\sqrt{x^2-1})^2}\dfrac{d}{dx}(\sqrt{x^2-1}) - \dfrac{1}{|x|\sqrt{x^2-1}}$

$= \dfrac{1}{x^2}\dfrac{1}{2\sqrt{x^2-1}}(2x) - \dfrac{1}{|x|\sqrt{x^2-1}}$

$= \dfrac{1}{x\sqrt{x^2-1}} - \dfrac{1}{|x|\sqrt{x^2-1}}$

$= 0$

Note that the condition $x > 1$ is required in the last step.

16. $\dfrac{dy}{dx} = \dfrac{d}{dx}\left(\cot^{-1}\dfrac{1}{x}\right) - \dfrac{d}{dx}(\tan^{-1}x)$

$= -\dfrac{1}{1+\left(\dfrac{1}{x^2}\right)}\dfrac{d}{dx}\left(\dfrac{1}{x}\right) - \dfrac{1}{1+x^2}$

$= \left(-\dfrac{1}{1+\dfrac{1}{x^2}}\right)\left(-\dfrac{1}{x^2}\right) - \dfrac{1}{1+x^2}$

$= \dfrac{1}{x^2+1} - \dfrac{1}{1+x^2}$

$= 0,\ x \neq 0$

The condition $x \neq 0$ is required because the original function was undefined when $x \neq 0$.

17. $\dfrac{dy}{dx} = \dfrac{d}{dx}(x\sin^{-1}x) + \dfrac{d}{dx}(\sqrt{1-x^2})$

$= (x)\left(\dfrac{1}{\sqrt{1-x^2}}\right) + (\sin^{-1}x)(1) + \dfrac{1}{2\sqrt{1-x^2}}(-2x)$

$= \sin^{-1}x$

18. $\dfrac{dy}{dx} = \dfrac{d}{dx}[\sin^{-1}(2x)]^{-1}$

$= -[\sin^{-1}(2x)]^{-2}\dfrac{d}{dx}\sin^{-1}(2x)$

$= -[\sin^{-1}(2x)]^{-2}\dfrac{1}{\sqrt{1-4x^2}}(2)$

$= -\dfrac{2}{[\sin^{-1}(2x)]^2\sqrt{1-4x^2}}$

19. (a) Since $\dfrac{dy}{dx} = \sec^2 x$, the slope at $\left(\dfrac{\pi}{4}, 1\right)$ is $\sec^2\left(\dfrac{\pi}{4}\right) = 2$.
The tangent line is given by $y = 2\left(x - \dfrac{\pi}{4}\right) + 1$, or
$y = 2x - \dfrac{\pi}{2} + 1$.

(b) Since $\dfrac{dy}{dx} = \dfrac{1}{1+x^2}$, the slope at $\left(1, \dfrac{\pi}{4}\right)$ is $\dfrac{1}{1+1^2} = \dfrac{1}{2}$.
The tangent line is given by $y = \dfrac{1}{2}(x - 1) + \dfrac{\pi}{4}$, or
$y = \dfrac{1}{2}x - \dfrac{1}{2} + \dfrac{\pi}{4}$.

20. (a) Note that $f'(x) = 5x^4 + 6x^2 + 1$. Thus $f(1) = 3$ and $f'(1) = 12$.

(b) Since the graph of $y = f(x)$ includes the point $(1, 3)$ and the slope of the graph is 12 at this point, the graph of $y = f^{-1}(x)$ will include $(3, 1)$ and the slope will be $\dfrac{1}{12}$. Thus, $f^{-1}(3) = 1$ and $(f^{-1})'(3) = \dfrac{1}{12}$. (We have assumed that $f^{-1}(x)$ is defined and differentiable at $x = 3$. This is true by Theorem 3, because $f'(x) = 5x^4 + 6x^2 + 1$, which is never zero.)

21. (a) Note that $f'(x) = -\sin x + 3$, which is always between 2 and 4. Thus f is differentiable at every point on the interval $(-\infty, \infty)$ and $f'(x)$ is never zero on this interval, so f has a differentiable inverse by Theorem 3.

(b) $f(0) = \cos 0 + 3(0) = 1$;
$f'(0) = -\sin 0 + 3 = 3$

(c) Since the graph of $y = f(x)$ includes the point $(0, 1)$ and the slope of the graph is 3 at this point, the graph of $y = f^{-1}(x)$ will include $(1, 0)$ and the slope will be $\dfrac{1}{3}$. Thus, $f^{-1}(1) = 0$ and $(f^{-1})'(1) = \dfrac{1}{3}$.

22.

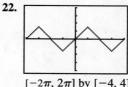

$[-2\pi, 2\pi]$ by $[-4, 4]$

(a) All reals

(b) $\left[-\dfrac{\pi}{2}, \dfrac{\pi}{2}\right]$

22. continued

(c) At the points $x = k\dfrac{\pi}{2}$, where k is an odd integer.

(d)

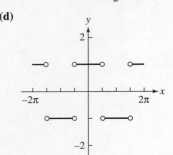

(e) $f'(x) = \dfrac{d}{dx} \sin^{-1}(\sin x)$

$\qquad = \dfrac{1}{\sqrt{1 - \sin^2 x}} \dfrac{d}{dx} \sin x$

$\qquad = \dfrac{\cos x}{\sqrt{1 - \sin^2 x}}$

which is ± 1 depending on whether

$\cos x$ is positive or negative.

23. (a) $v(t) = \dfrac{dx}{dt} = \dfrac{1}{1 + t^2}$ which is always positive.

(b) $a(t) = \dfrac{dv}{dt} = -\dfrac{2t}{(1 + t^2)^2}$ which is always negative.

(c) $\dfrac{\pi}{2}$

24. $\dfrac{d}{dx} \cos^{-1}(x) = \dfrac{d}{dx}\left(\dfrac{\pi}{2} - \sin^{-1} x\right)$

$\qquad = 0 - \dfrac{d}{dx} \sin^{-1}(x)$

$\qquad = -\dfrac{1}{\sqrt{1 - x^2}}$

25. $\dfrac{d}{dx} \cot^{-1} x = \dfrac{d}{dx}\left(\dfrac{\pi}{2} - \tan^{-1}(x)\right)$

$\qquad = 0 - \dfrac{d}{dx} \tan^{-1}(x)$

$\qquad = -\dfrac{1}{1 + x^2}$

26. $\dfrac{d}{dx} \csc^{-1}(x) = \dfrac{d}{dx}\left(\dfrac{\pi}{2} - \sec^{-1}(x)\right)$

$\qquad = 0 - \dfrac{d}{dx} \sec^{-1}(x)$

$\qquad = -\dfrac{1}{|x|\sqrt{x^2 - 1}}$

27. (a) $y = \dfrac{\pi}{2}$

(b) $y = -\dfrac{\pi}{2}$

(c) None, since $\dfrac{d}{dx} \tan^{-1} x = \dfrac{1}{1 + x^2} \neq 0$.

28. (a) $y = 0$

(b) $y = \pi$

(c) None, since $\dfrac{d}{dx} \cot^{-1} x = -\dfrac{1}{1 + x^2} \neq 0$.

29. (a) $y = \dfrac{\pi}{2}$

(b) $y = \dfrac{\pi}{2}$

(c) None, since $\dfrac{d}{dx} \sec^{-1} x = \dfrac{1}{|x|\sqrt{x^2 - 1}} \neq 0$.

30. (a) $y = 0$

(b) $y = 0$

(c) None, since $\dfrac{d}{dx} \csc^{-1} x = -\dfrac{1}{|x|\sqrt{x^2 - 1}} \neq 0$.

31. (a) None, since $\sin^{-1} x$ is undefined for $x > 1$.

(b) None, since $\sin^{-1} x$ is undefined for $x < -1$.

(c) None, since $\dfrac{d}{dx} \sin^{-1} x = \dfrac{1}{\sqrt{1 - x^2}} \neq 0$.

32. (a) None, since $\cos^{-1} x$ is undefined for $x > 1$.

(b) None, since $\cos^{-1} x$ is undefined for $x < -1$.

(c) None, since $\dfrac{d}{dx} \cos^{-1} x = -\dfrac{1}{\sqrt{1 - x^2}} \neq 0$.

33. (a)

$\alpha = \cos^{-1} x, \beta = \sin^{-1} x$

So $\cos^{-1} x + \sin^{-1} x = \alpha + \beta = \dfrac{\pi}{2}$.

(b)

$\alpha = \tan^{-1} x, \beta = \cot^{-1} x$

So $\tan^{-1} x + \cot^{-1} x = \alpha + \beta = \dfrac{\pi}{2}$.

(c)

$\alpha = \sec^{-1} x, \beta = \csc^{-1} x$

So $\sec^{-1} x + \csc^{-1} x = \alpha + \beta = \dfrac{\pi}{2}$.

34.

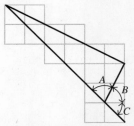

The "straight angle" with the arrows in it is the sum of the three angles A, B, and C.

A is equal to $\tan^{-1} 3$ since the opposite side is 3 times as long as the adjacent side.

B is equal to $\tan^{-1} 2$ since the side opposite it is 2 units and the adjacent side is one unit.

C is equal to $\tan^{-1} 1$ since both the opposite and adjacent sides are one unit long.

But the sum of these three angles is the "straight angle," which has measure π radians.

35.

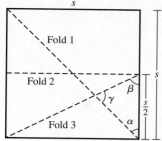

If s is the length of a side of the square, then

$\tan \alpha = \dfrac{s}{s} = 1$, so $\alpha = \tan^{-1} 1$ and

$\tan \beta = \dfrac{s}{\frac{s}{2}} = 2$, so $\beta = \tan^{-1} 2$.

From Exercise 34, we have

$\gamma = \pi - \alpha - \beta = \pi - \tan^{-1} 1 - \tan^{-1} 2 = \tan^{-1} 3$.

■ Section 3.9 Derivatives of Exponential and Logarithmic Functions (pp. 163–171)

Exploration 1   Leaving Milk on the Counter

1. The temperature of the refrigerator is 42°F, the temperature of the milk at time $t = 0$.

2. The temperature of the room is 72°F, the limit to which y tends as t increases.

3. The milk is warming up the fastest at $t = 0$. The second derivative $y'' = -30(\ln(0.98))^2(0.98)^t$ is negative, so y' (the rate at which the milk is warming) is maximized at the lowest value of t.

4. We set $y = 55$ and solve;
$$72 - 30(0.98)^t = 55$$
$$(0.98)^t = \frac{17}{30}$$
$$t \ln (0.98) = \ln \left(\frac{17}{30}\right)$$
$$t = \frac{\ln \left(\dfrac{17}{30}\right)}{\ln (0.98)} \approx 28.114$$

The milk reaches a temperature of 55°F after about 28 minutes.

5. $\dfrac{dy}{dt} = -30 \ln (0.98) \cdot (0.98)^t$. At $t = \dfrac{\ln \left(\frac{17}{30}\right)}{\ln (0.98)}$, $\dfrac{dy}{dt} \approx 0.343$ degrees/minute.

Quick Review 3.9

1. $\log_5 8 = \dfrac{\ln 8}{\ln 5}$

2. $7^x = e^{\ln 7^x} = e^{x \ln 7}$

3. $\ln (e^{\tan x}) = \tan x$

4. $\ln (x^2 - 4) - \ln (x + 2) = \ln \dfrac{x^2 - 4}{x + 2} = \ln \dfrac{(x + 2)(x - 2)}{x + 2}$
$= \ln (x - 2)$

5. $\log_2 (8^{x-5}) = \log_2 (2^3)^{x-5} = \log_2 2^{3x-15} = 3x - 15$

6. $\dfrac{\log_4 x^{15}}{\log_4 x^{12}} = \dfrac{15 \log_4 x}{12 \log_4 x} = \dfrac{15}{12} = \dfrac{5}{4}, x > 0$

7. $3 \ln x - \ln 3x + \ln (12x^2) = \ln x^3 - \ln 3x + \ln (12x^2)$
$= \ln \dfrac{(x^3)(12x^2)}{3x} = \ln (4x^4)$

8.
$$3^x = 19$$
$$\ln 3^x = \ln 19$$
$$x \ln 3 = \ln 19$$
$$x = \frac{\ln 19}{\ln 3} \approx 2.68$$

9.
$$5^t \ln 5 = 18$$
$$5^t = \frac{18}{\ln 5}$$
$$\ln 5^t = \ln \frac{18}{\ln 5}$$
$$t \ln 5 = \ln 18 - \ln (\ln 5)$$
$$t = \frac{\ln 18 - \ln (\ln 5)}{\ln 5} \approx 1.50$$

10.
$$3^{x+1} = 2^x$$
$$\ln 3^{x+1} = \ln 2^x$$
$$(x + 1) \ln 3 = x \ln 2$$
$$x(\ln 3 - \ln 2) = -\ln 3$$
$$x = \frac{\ln 3}{\ln 2 - \ln 3} \approx -2.71$$

Section 3.9 Exercises

1. $\dfrac{dy}{dx} = \dfrac{d}{dx}(2e^x) = 2e^x$

2. $\dfrac{dy}{dx} = \dfrac{d}{dx}(e^{2x}) = e^{2x} \dfrac{d}{dx}(2x) = 2e^{2x}$

3. $\dfrac{dy}{dx} = \dfrac{d}{dx}e^{-x} = e^{-x} \dfrac{d}{dx}(-x) = -e^{-x}$

4. $\dfrac{dy}{dx} = \dfrac{d}{dx}e^{-5x} = e^{-5x} \dfrac{d}{dx}(-5x) = -5e^{-5x}$

5. $\dfrac{dy}{dx} = \dfrac{d}{dx}e^{2x/3} = e^{2x/3} \dfrac{d}{dx}\left(\dfrac{2x}{3}\right) = \dfrac{2}{3}e^{2x/3}$

6. $\dfrac{dy}{dx} = \dfrac{d}{dx}e^{-x/4} = e^{-x/4} \dfrac{d}{dx}\left(-\dfrac{x}{4}\right) = -\dfrac{1}{4}e^{-x/4}$

7. $\dfrac{dy}{dx} = \dfrac{d}{dx}(xe^2) - \dfrac{d}{dx}(e^x) = e^2 - e^x$

8. $\dfrac{dy}{dx} = \dfrac{d}{dx}(x^2e^x) - \dfrac{d}{dx}(xe^x)$
$= (x^2)(e^x) + (e^x)(2x) - [(x)(e^x) + (e^x)(1)]$
$= x^2e^x + xe^x - e^x$

9. $\dfrac{dy}{dx} = \dfrac{d}{dx}e^{\sqrt{x}} = e^{\sqrt{x}} \dfrac{d}{dx}(\sqrt{x}) = \dfrac{e^{\sqrt{x}}}{2\sqrt{x}}$

10. $\dfrac{dy}{dx} = \dfrac{d}{dx}e^{(x^2)} = e^{(x^2)} \dfrac{d}{dx}(x^2) = 2xe^{(x^2)}$

11. $\dfrac{dy}{dx} = \dfrac{d}{dx}(x^\pi) = \pi x^{\pi-1}$

12. $\dfrac{dy}{dx} = \dfrac{d}{dx}(x^{1+\sqrt{2}}) = (1+\sqrt{2})x^{1+\sqrt{2}-1} = (1+\sqrt{2})x^{\sqrt{2}}$

13. $\dfrac{dy}{dx} = \dfrac{d}{dx}x^{-\sqrt{2}} = -\sqrt{2}x^{-\sqrt{2}-1}$

14. $\dfrac{dy}{dx} = \dfrac{d}{dx}x^{1-e} = (1-e)x^{1-e-1} = (1-e)x^{-e}$

15. $\dfrac{dy}{dx} = \dfrac{d}{dx}8^x = 8^x \ln 8$

16. $\dfrac{dy}{dx} = \dfrac{d}{dx}9^{-x} = 9^{-x}(\ln 9)\dfrac{d}{dx}(-x) = -9^{-x}\ln 9$

17. $\begin{aligned}\dfrac{dy}{dx} &= \dfrac{d}{dx}\,3^{\csc x} = 3^{\csc x}(\ln 3)\dfrac{d}{dx}(\csc x)\\ &= 3^{\csc x}(\ln 3)(-\csc x \cot x)\\ &= -3^{\csc x}(\ln 3)(\csc x \cot x)\end{aligned}$

18. $\begin{aligned}\dfrac{dy}{dx} &= \dfrac{d}{dx}\,3^{\cot x} = 3^{\cot x}(\ln 3)\dfrac{d}{dx}(\cot x)\\ &= 3^{\cot x}(\ln 3)(-\csc^2 x)\\ &= -3^{\cot x}(\ln 3)(\csc^2 x)\end{aligned}$

19. Use logarithmic differentiation.

$$y = x^{\ln x}$$
$$\ln y = \ln x^{\ln x}$$
$$\ln y = \ln x \ln x$$
$$\dfrac{d}{dx}(\ln y) = \dfrac{d}{dx}(\ln x)^2$$
$$\dfrac{1}{y}\dfrac{dy}{dx} = (2\ln x)\left(\dfrac{1}{x}\right)$$
$$\dfrac{dy}{dx} = \dfrac{2y\ln x}{x}$$
$$\dfrac{dy}{dx} = \dfrac{2x^{\ln x}\ln x}{x}$$

20. Use logarithmic differentiation.

$$y = x^{1/\ln x}$$
$$\ln y = \ln x^{1/\ln x}$$
$$\ln y = \dfrac{1}{\ln x}\ln x$$
$$\ln y = 1$$
$$y = e$$
$$\dfrac{dy}{dx} = \dfrac{d}{dx}(e) = 0,\ x > 0$$

21. $\dfrac{dy}{dx} = \dfrac{d}{dx}\ln(x^2) = \dfrac{1}{x^2}\dfrac{d}{dx}(x^2) = \dfrac{1}{x^2}(2x) = \dfrac{2}{x}$

22. $\dfrac{dy}{dx} = \dfrac{d}{dx}(\ln x)^2 = 2\ln x \dfrac{d}{dx}(\ln x) = \dfrac{2\ln x}{x}$

23. $\dfrac{dy}{dx} = \dfrac{d}{dx}\ln(x^{-1}) = \dfrac{d}{dx}(-\ln x) = -\dfrac{1}{x},\ x > 0$

24. $\dfrac{dy}{dx} = \dfrac{d}{dx}\ln\dfrac{10}{x} = \dfrac{d}{dx}(\ln 10 - \ln x) = 0 - \dfrac{1}{x} = -\dfrac{1}{x},\ x > 0$

25. $\dfrac{dy}{dx} = \dfrac{d}{dx}\ln(x+2) = \dfrac{1}{x+2}\dfrac{d}{dx}(x+2) = \dfrac{1}{x+2},\ x > -2$

26. $\begin{aligned}\dfrac{dy}{dx} &= \dfrac{d}{dx}\ln(2x+2) = \dfrac{1}{2x+2}\dfrac{d}{dx}(2x+2) = \dfrac{2}{2x+2}\\ &= \dfrac{1}{x+1},\ x > -1\end{aligned}$

27. $\begin{aligned}\dfrac{dy}{dx} &= \dfrac{d}{dx}\ln(2-\cos x) = \dfrac{1}{2-\cos x}\dfrac{d}{dx}(2-\cos x)\\ &= \dfrac{\sin x}{2-\cos x}\end{aligned}$

28. $\dfrac{dy}{dx} = \dfrac{d}{dx}\ln(x^2+1) = \dfrac{1}{x^2+1}\dfrac{d}{dx}(x^2+1) = \dfrac{2x}{x^2+1}$

29. $\dfrac{d}{dx}\ln(\ln x) = \dfrac{1}{\ln x}\dfrac{d}{dx}\ln x = \dfrac{1}{\ln x}\cdot\dfrac{1}{x} = \dfrac{1}{x\ln x}$

30. $\begin{aligned}\dfrac{dy}{dx} &= \dfrac{d}{dx}(x\ln x - x) = (x)\left(\dfrac{1}{x}\right) + (\ln x)(1) - 1\\ &= 1 + \ln x - 1 = \ln x\end{aligned}$

31. $\begin{aligned}\dfrac{dy}{dx} &= \dfrac{d}{dx}(\log_4 x^2) = \dfrac{d}{dx}\dfrac{\ln x^2}{\ln 4} = \dfrac{d}{dx}\left[\left(\dfrac{2}{\ln 4}\right)(\ln x)\right]\\ &= \dfrac{2}{\ln 4}\cdot\dfrac{1}{x} = \dfrac{2}{x\ln 4} = \dfrac{1}{x\ln 2}\end{aligned}$

32. $\begin{aligned}\dfrac{dy}{dx} &= \dfrac{d}{dx}(\log_5 \sqrt{x}) = \dfrac{d}{dx}\dfrac{\ln x^{1/2}}{\ln 5} = \dfrac{d}{dx}\dfrac{\frac{1}{2}\ln x}{\ln 5}\\ &= \dfrac{1}{2\ln 5}\dfrac{d}{dx}(\ln x) = \dfrac{1}{2\ln 5}\cdot\dfrac{1}{x} = \dfrac{1}{2x\ln 5},\ x > 0\end{aligned}$

33. $\begin{aligned}\dfrac{dy}{dx} &= \dfrac{d}{dx}\log_2(3x+1) = \dfrac{1}{(3x+1)\ln 2}\dfrac{d}{dx}(3x+1)\\ &= \dfrac{3}{(3x+1)\ln 2},\ x > -\dfrac{1}{3}\end{aligned}$

34. $\begin{aligned}\dfrac{dy}{dx} &= \dfrac{d}{dx}\log_{10}(x+1)^{1/2} = \dfrac{1}{2}\dfrac{d}{dx}\log_{10}(x+1)\\ &= \dfrac{1}{2}\dfrac{1}{(x+1)\ln 10}\dfrac{d}{dx}(x+1) = \dfrac{1}{2(x+1)\ln 10},\ x > -1\end{aligned}$

35. $\dfrac{dy}{dx} = \dfrac{d}{dx}\log_2\left(\dfrac{1}{x}\right) = \dfrac{d}{dx}(-\log_2 x) = -\dfrac{1}{x\ln 2},\ x > 0$

36. $\begin{aligned}\dfrac{dy}{dx} &= \dfrac{d}{dx}\dfrac{1}{\log_2 x} = -\dfrac{1}{(\log_2 x)^2}\dfrac{d}{dx}(\log_2 x)\\ &= -\dfrac{1}{(\log_2 x)^2}\dfrac{1}{x\ln 2} = -\dfrac{1}{x(\ln 2)(\log_2 x)^2}\ \text{or}\ -\dfrac{\ln 2}{x(\ln x)^2}\end{aligned}$

37. $\begin{aligned}\dfrac{dy}{dx} &= \dfrac{d}{dx}(\ln 2 \cdot \log_2 x) = (\ln 2)\dfrac{d}{dx}(\log_2 x)\\ &= (\ln 2)\left(\dfrac{1}{x\ln 2}\right) = \dfrac{1}{x},\ x > 0\end{aligned}$

38. $\begin{aligned}\dfrac{dy}{dx} &= \dfrac{d}{dx}\log_3(1+x\ln 3) = \dfrac{1}{(1+x\ln 3)\ln 3}\dfrac{d}{dx}(1+x\ln 3)\\ &= \dfrac{\ln 3}{(1+x\ln 3)\ln 3} = \dfrac{1}{1+x\ln 3},\ x > -\dfrac{1}{\ln 3}\end{aligned}$

39. $\begin{aligned}\dfrac{dy}{dx} &= \dfrac{d}{dx}(\log_{10} e^x) = \dfrac{d}{dx}(x\log_{10} e) = \log_{10} e = \dfrac{\ln e}{\ln 10}\\ &= \dfrac{1}{\ln 10}\end{aligned}$

40. $\dfrac{dy}{dx} = \dfrac{d}{dx}\ln 10^x = \dfrac{d}{dx}(x\ln 10) = \ln 10$

41. The line passes through (a, e^a) for some value of a and has slope $m = e^a$. Since the line also passes through the origin, the slope is also given by $m = \dfrac{e^a - 0}{a - 0}$ and we have $e^a = \dfrac{e^a}{a}$, so $a = 1$. Hence, the slope is e and the equation is $y = ex$.

42. For $y = xe^x$, we have $y' = (x)(e^x) + (e^x)(1) = (x + 1)e^x$, so the normal line through the point (a, ae^a) has slope $m = -\dfrac{1}{(a + 1)e^a}$ and its equation is $y = -\dfrac{1}{(a + 1)e^a}(x - a) + ae^a$. The desired normal line includes the point $(0, 0)$, so we have:

$$0 = -\frac{1}{(a + 1)e^a}(0 - a) + ae^a$$

$$0 = \frac{a}{(a + 1)e^a} + ae^a$$

$$0 = a\left(\frac{1}{(a + 1)e^a} + e^a\right)$$

$$a = 0 \text{ or } \frac{1}{(a + 1)e^a} + e^a = 0$$

The equation $\dfrac{1}{(a + 1)e^a} + e^a = 0$ has no solution, so we need to use $a = 0$. The equation of the normal line is

$$y = -\frac{1}{(0 + 1)e^0}(x - 0) + 0e^0, \text{ or } y = -x.$$

43.
$$y = (\sin x)^x$$
$$\ln y = \ln (\sin x)^x$$
$$\ln y = x \ln (\sin x)$$
$$\frac{d}{dx} \ln y = \frac{d}{dx}[x \ln (\sin x)]$$
$$\frac{1}{y}\frac{dy}{dx} = (x)\left(\frac{1}{\sin x}\right)(\cos x) + \ln (\sin x)(1)$$
$$\frac{dy}{dx} = y[x \cot x + \ln (\sin x)]$$
$$\frac{dy}{dx} = (\sin x)^x[x \cot x + \ln (\sin x)]$$

44.
$$y = x^{\tan x}$$
$$\ln y = \ln (x^{\tan x})$$
$$\ln y = (\tan x)(\ln x)$$
$$\frac{d}{dx} \ln y = \frac{d}{dx}[(\tan x)(\ln x)]$$
$$\frac{1}{y}\frac{dy}{dx} = (\tan x)\left(\frac{1}{x}\right) + (\ln x)(\sec^2 x)$$
$$\frac{dy}{dx} = y\left[\frac{\tan x}{x} + (\ln x)(\sec^2 x)\right]$$
$$\frac{dy}{dx} = x^{\tan x}\left[\frac{\tan x}{x} + (\ln x)(\sec^2 x)\right]$$

45.
$$y = \sqrt[5]{\frac{(x - 3)^4(x^2 + 1)}{(2x + 5)^3}} = \left(\frac{(x - 3)^4(x^2 + 1)}{(2x + 5)^3}\right)^{1/5}$$
$$\ln y = \ln \left(\frac{(x - 3)^4(x^2 + 1)}{(2x + 5)^3}\right)^{1/5}$$
$$\ln y = \frac{1}{5} \ln \frac{(x - 3)^4(x^2 + 1)}{(2x + 5)^3}$$
$$\ln y = \frac{1}{5}[4 \ln (x - 3) + \ln (x^2 + 1) - 3 \ln (2x + 5)]$$
$$\frac{d}{dx}(\ln y) = \frac{4}{5}\frac{d}{dx} \ln (x - 3) +$$
$$\frac{1}{5}\frac{d}{dx} \ln (x^2 + 1) - \frac{3}{5}\frac{d}{dx} \ln (2x + 5)$$
$$\frac{1}{y}\frac{dy}{dx} = \frac{4}{5}\frac{1}{x - 3} + \frac{1}{5}\frac{1}{x^2 + 1}(2x) - \frac{3}{5}\frac{1}{2x + 5}(2)$$
$$\frac{dy}{dx} = y\left(\frac{4}{5(x - 3)} + \frac{2x}{5(x^2 + 1)} - \frac{6}{5(2x + 5)}\right)$$
$$\frac{dy}{dx} = \left(\frac{(x - 3)^4(x^2 + 1)}{(2x + 5)^3}\right)^{1/5} \cdot$$
$$\left(\frac{4}{5(x - 3)} + \frac{2x}{5(x^2 + 1)} - \frac{6}{5(2x + 5)}\right)$$

46.
$$y = \frac{x\sqrt{x^2 + 1}}{(x + 1)^{2/3}} = \frac{x(x^2 + 1)^{1/2}}{(x + 1)^{2/3}}$$
$$\ln y = \ln \frac{x(x^2 + 1)^{1/2}}{(x + 1)^{2/3}}$$
$$\ln y = \ln x + \frac{1}{2} \ln (x^2 + 1) - \frac{2}{3} \ln (x + 1)$$
$$\frac{d}{dx} \ln y = \frac{d}{dx} \ln x + \frac{1}{2}\frac{d}{dx} \ln (x^2 + 1) - \frac{2}{3}\frac{d}{dx} \ln (x + 1)$$
$$\frac{1}{y}\frac{dy}{dx} = \frac{1}{x} + \frac{1}{2}\frac{1}{x^2 + 1}(2x) - \frac{2}{3}\frac{1}{x + 1}(1)$$
$$\frac{dy}{dx} = y\left(\frac{1}{x} + \frac{x}{x^2 + 1} - \frac{2}{3(x + 1)}\right)$$
$$\frac{dy}{dx} = \frac{x\sqrt{x^2 + 1}}{(x + 1)^{2/3}}\left(\frac{1}{x} + \frac{x}{x^2 + 1} - \frac{2}{3(x + 1)}\right)$$

47. $\dfrac{dA}{dt} = 20 \dfrac{d}{dt}\left(\dfrac{1}{2}\right)^{t/140}$
$$= 20 \frac{d}{dt} 2^{-t/140}$$
$$= 20 (2^{-t/140})(\ln 2)\frac{d}{dt}\left(-\frac{t}{140}\right)$$
$$= 20(2^{-t/140})(\ln 2)\left(-\frac{1}{140}\right)$$
$$= -\frac{(2^{-t/140})(\ln 2)}{7}$$

At $t = 2$ days, we have
$$\frac{dA}{dt} = -\frac{(2^{-1/70})(\ln 2)}{7} \approx -0.098 \text{ grams/day.}$$

This means that the rate of *decay* is the positive rate of approximately 0.098 grams/day.

48. (a) $\dfrac{d}{dx} \ln (kx) = \dfrac{1}{kx}\dfrac{d}{dx} kx = \dfrac{k}{kx} = \dfrac{1}{x}$

(b) $\dfrac{d}{dx} \ln (kx) = \dfrac{d}{dx} (\ln k + \ln x)$
$$= 0 + \frac{d}{dx} \ln x = \frac{1}{x}$$

49. (a) Since $f'(x) = 2^x \ln 2$, $f'(0) = 2^0 \ln 2 = \ln 2$.

(b) $f'(0) = \lim\limits_{h \to 0} \dfrac{f(h) - f(0)}{h} = \lim\limits_{h \to 0} \dfrac{2^h - 2^0}{h} = \lim\limits_{h \to 0} \dfrac{2^h - 1}{h}$

(c) Since quantities in parts (a) and (b) are equal,

$\lim\limits_{h \to 0} \dfrac{2^h - 1}{h} = \ln 2.$

(d) By following the same procedure as above using

$g(x) = 7^x$, we may see that $\lim\limits_{h \to 0} \dfrac{7^h - 1}{h} = \ln 7.$

50. Recall that a point (a, b) is on the graph of $y = e^x$ if and only if the point (b, a) is on the graph of $y = \ln x$. Since there are points (x, e^x) on the graph of $y = e^x$ with arbitrarily large x-coordinates, there will be points $(x, \ln x)$ on the graph of $y = \ln x$ with arbitrarily large y-coordinates.

51. (a) The graph y_4 is a horizontal line at $y = a$.

(b) The graph of y_3 is always a horizontal line.

a	2	3	4	5
y_3	0.693147	1.098613	1.386295	1.609439
$\ln a$	0.693147	1.098612	1.386294	1.609438

We conclude that the graph of y_3 is a horizontal line at $y = \ln a$.

(c) $\dfrac{d}{dx} a^x = a^x$ if and only if $y_3 = \dfrac{y_2}{y_1} = 1$.

So if $y_3 = \ln a$, then $\dfrac{d}{dx} a^x$ will equal a^x if and only if $\ln a = 1$, or $a = e$.

(d) $y_2 = \dfrac{d}{dx} a^x = a^x \ln a$. This will equal $y_1 = a^x$ if and only if $\ln a = 1$, or $a = e$.

52. $\dfrac{d}{dx}\left(-\dfrac{1}{2}x^2 + k\right) = -x$ and $\dfrac{d}{dx}(\ln x + c) = \dfrac{1}{x}$.

Therefore, at any given value of x, these two curves will have perpendicular tangent lines.

53. (a) Since the line passes through the origin and has slope $\dfrac{1}{e}$, its equation is $y = \dfrac{x}{e}$.

(b) The graph of $y = \ln x$ lies below the graph of the line $y = \dfrac{x}{e}$ for all positive $x \neq e$. Therefore, $\ln x < \dfrac{x}{e}$ for all positive $x \neq e$.

(c) Multiplying by e, $e \ln x < x$ or $\ln x^e < x$.

(d) Exponentiating both sides of $\ln x^e < x$, we have $e^{\ln x^e} < e^x$, or $x^e < e^x$ for all positive $x \neq e$.

(e) Let $x = \pi$ to see that $\pi^e < e^\pi$. Therefore, e^π is bigger.

■ Chapter 3 Review Exercises
(pp. 172–175)

1. $\dfrac{dy}{dx} = \dfrac{d}{dx}\left(x^5 - \dfrac{1}{8}x^2 + \dfrac{1}{4}x\right) = 5x^4 - \dfrac{1}{4}x + \dfrac{1}{4}$

2. $\dfrac{dy}{dx} = \dfrac{d}{dx}(3 - 7x^3 + 3x^7) = -21x^2 + 21x^6$

3. $\dfrac{dy}{dx} = \dfrac{d}{dx}(2 \sin x \cos x)$

$= 2(\sin x)\dfrac{d}{dx}(\cos x) + 2(\cos x)\dfrac{d}{dx}(\sin x)$

$= -2 \sin^2 x + 2 \cos^2 x$

Alternate solution:

$\dfrac{dy}{dx} = \dfrac{d}{dx}(2 \sin x \cos x) = \dfrac{d}{dx} \sin 2x = (\cos 2x)(2)$

$= 2 \cos 2x$

4. $\dfrac{dy}{dx} = \dfrac{d}{dx} \dfrac{2x + 1}{2x - 1} = \dfrac{(2x - 1)(2) - (2x + 1)(2)}{(2x - 1)^2} = -\dfrac{4}{(2x - 1)^2}$

5. $\dfrac{ds}{dt} = \dfrac{d}{dt} \cos (1 - 2t) = -\sin (1 - 2t)(-2) = 2 \sin (1 - 2t)$

6. $\dfrac{ds}{dt} = \dfrac{d}{dt} \cot \left(\dfrac{2}{t}\right) = -\csc^2 \left(\dfrac{2}{t}\right)\dfrac{d}{dt}\left(\dfrac{2}{t}\right) = -\csc^2 \left(\dfrac{2}{t}\right)\left(-\dfrac{2}{t^2}\right)$

$= \dfrac{2}{t^2} \csc^2 \left(\dfrac{2}{t}\right)$

7. $\dfrac{dy}{dx} = \dfrac{d}{dx}\left(\sqrt{x} + 1 + \dfrac{1}{\sqrt{x}}\right) = \dfrac{d}{dx}(x^{1/2} + 1 + x^{-1/2})$

$= \dfrac{1}{2}x^{-1/2} - \dfrac{1}{2}x^{-3/2} = \dfrac{1}{2\sqrt{x}} - \dfrac{1}{2x^{3/2}}$

8. $\dfrac{dy}{dx} = \dfrac{d}{dx}(x\sqrt{2x + 1}) = (x)\left(\dfrac{1}{2\sqrt{2x + 1}}\right)(2) + (\sqrt{2x + 1})(1)$

$= \dfrac{x + (2x + 1)}{\sqrt{2x + 1}} = \dfrac{3x + 1}{\sqrt{2x + 1}}$

9. $\dfrac{dr}{d\theta} = \dfrac{d}{d\theta} \sec (1 + 3\theta) = \sec (1 + 3\theta) \tan (1 + 3\theta)(3)$

$= 3 \sec (1 + 3\theta) \tan (1 + 3\theta)$

10. $\dfrac{dr}{d\theta} = \dfrac{d}{d\theta} \tan^2 (3 - \theta^2)$

$= 2 \tan (3 - \theta^2)\dfrac{d}{d\theta} \tan (3 - \theta^2)$

$= 2 \tan (3 - \theta^2) \sec^2 (3 - \theta^2)(-2\theta)$

$= -4\theta \tan (3 - \theta^2) \sec^2 (3 - \theta^2)$

11. $\dfrac{dy}{dx} = \dfrac{d}{dx}(x^2 \csc 5x)$

$= (x^2)(-\csc 5x \cot 5x)(5) + (\csc 5x)(2x)$

$= -5x^2 \csc 5x \cot 5x + 2x \csc 5x$

12. $\dfrac{dy}{dx} = \dfrac{d}{dx} \ln \sqrt{x} = \dfrac{1}{\sqrt{x}} \dfrac{d}{dx} \sqrt{x} = \dfrac{1}{\sqrt{x}} \cdot \dfrac{1}{2\sqrt{x}} = \dfrac{1}{2x}, x > 0$

13. $\dfrac{dy}{dx} = \dfrac{d}{dx} \ln (1 + e^x) = \dfrac{1}{1 + e^x}\dfrac{d}{dx}(1 + e^x) = \dfrac{e^x}{1 + e^x}$

14. $\dfrac{dy}{dx} = \dfrac{d}{dx}(xe^{-x}) = (x)(e^{-x})(-1) + (e^{-x})(1) = -xe^{-x} + e^{-x}$

15. $\dfrac{dy}{dx} = \dfrac{d}{dx}(e^{1+\ln x}) = \dfrac{d}{dx}(e^{1}e^{\ln x}) = \dfrac{d}{dx}(ex) = e$

16. $\dfrac{dy}{dx} = \dfrac{d}{dx}\ln(\sin x) = \dfrac{1}{\sin x}\dfrac{d}{dx}(\sin x) = \dfrac{\cos x}{\sin x} = \cot x,$ for

values of x in the intervals $(k\pi, (k+1)\pi)$, where k is even.

17. $\dfrac{dr}{dx} = \dfrac{d}{dx}\ln(\cos^{-1} x) = \dfrac{1}{\cos^{-1} x}\dfrac{d}{dx}\cos^{-1} x$

$= \dfrac{1}{\cos^{-1} x}\left(-\dfrac{1}{\sqrt{1-x^2}}\right) = -\dfrac{1}{\cos^{-1} x\sqrt{1-x^2}}$

18. $\dfrac{dr}{d\theta} = \dfrac{d}{d\theta}\log_2(\theta^2) = \dfrac{1}{\theta^2 \ln 2}\dfrac{d}{d\theta}(\theta^2) = \dfrac{2\theta}{\theta^2 \ln 2} = \dfrac{2}{\theta \ln 2}$

19. $\dfrac{ds}{dt} = \dfrac{d}{dt}\log_5(t-7) = \dfrac{1}{(t-7)\ln 5}\dfrac{d}{dt}(t-7) = \dfrac{1}{(t-7)\ln 5},$

$t > 7$

20. $\dfrac{ds}{dt} = \dfrac{d}{dt}(8^{-t}) = 8^{-t}(\ln 8)\dfrac{d}{dt}(-t) = -8^{-t}\ln 8$

21. Use logarithmic differentiation.

$$y = x^{\ln x}$$

$$\ln y = \ln(x^{\ln x})$$

$$\ln y = (\ln x)(\ln x)$$

$$\dfrac{d}{dx}\ln y = \dfrac{d}{dx}(\ln x)^2$$

$$\dfrac{1}{y}\dfrac{dy}{dx} = 2\ln x\dfrac{d}{dx}\ln x$$

$$\dfrac{dy}{dx} = \dfrac{2y\ln x}{x}$$

$$\dfrac{dy}{dx} = \dfrac{2x^{\ln x}\ln x}{x}$$

22. $\dfrac{dy}{dx} = \dfrac{d}{dx}\dfrac{(2x)2^x}{\sqrt{x^2+1}}$

$= \dfrac{\sqrt{x^2+1}\dfrac{d}{dx}[(2x)2^x] - (2x)(2^x)\dfrac{d}{dx}\sqrt{x^2+1}}{x^2+1}$

$= \dfrac{\sqrt{x^2+1}[(2x)(2^x)(\ln 2) + (2^x)(2)] - (2x)(2^x)\dfrac{1}{2\sqrt{x^2+1}}(2x)}{x^2+1}$

$= \dfrac{(x^2+1)(2^x)(2x\ln 2 + 2) - 2x^2(2^x)}{(x^2+1)^{3/2}}$

$= \dfrac{(2\cdot 2^x)[(x^2+1)(x\ln 2 + 1) - x^2]}{(x^2+1)^{3/2}}$

$= \dfrac{(2\cdot 2^x)(x^3\ln 2 + x^2 + x\ln 2 + 1 - x^2)}{(x^2+1)^{3/2}}$

$= \dfrac{(2\cdot 2^x)(x^3\ln 2 + x\ln 2 + 1)}{(x^2+1)^{3/2}}$

Alternate solution, using logarithmic differentiation:

$$y = \dfrac{(2x)2^x}{\sqrt{x^2+1}}$$

$$\ln y = \ln(2x) + \ln(2^x) - \ln\sqrt{x^2+1}$$

$$\ln y = \ln 2 + \ln x + x\ln 2 - \dfrac{1}{2}\ln(x^2+1)$$

$$\dfrac{d}{dx}\ln y = \dfrac{d}{dx}[\ln 2 + \ln x + x\ln 2 - \dfrac{1}{2}\ln(x^2+1)]$$

$$\dfrac{1}{y}\dfrac{dy}{dx} = 0 + \dfrac{1}{x} + \ln 2 - \dfrac{1}{2}\dfrac{1}{x^2+1}(2x)$$

$$\dfrac{dy}{dx} = y\left(\dfrac{1}{x} + \ln 2 - \dfrac{x}{x^2+1}\right)$$

$$\dfrac{dy}{dx} = \dfrac{(2x)2^x}{\sqrt{x^2+1}}\left(\dfrac{1}{x} + \ln 2 - \dfrac{x}{x^2+1}\right)$$

23. $\dfrac{dy}{dx} = \dfrac{d}{dx}e^{\tan^{-1}x} = e^{\tan^{-1}x}\dfrac{d}{dx}\tan^{-1}x = \dfrac{e^{\tan^{-1}x}}{1+x^2}$

24. $\dfrac{dy}{du} = \dfrac{d}{du}\sin^{-1}\sqrt{1-u^2}$

$= \dfrac{1}{\sqrt{1-(\sqrt{1-u^2})^2}}\dfrac{d}{du}\sqrt{1-u^2}$

$= \dfrac{1}{\sqrt{u^2}}\dfrac{1}{2\sqrt{1-u^2}}(-2u) = -\dfrac{u}{|u|\sqrt{1-u^2}}$

25. $\dfrac{dy}{dt} = \dfrac{d}{dt}(t\sec^{-1}t - \dfrac{1}{2}\ln t)$

$= (t)\left(\dfrac{1}{|t|\sqrt{t^2-1}}\right) + (\sec^{-1}t)(1) - \dfrac{1}{2t}$

$= \dfrac{t}{|t|\sqrt{t^2-1}} + \sec^{-1}t - \dfrac{1}{2t}$

26. $\dfrac{dy}{dt} = \dfrac{d}{dt}[(1+t^2)\cot^{-1}2t]$

$= (1+t^2)\left(-\dfrac{1}{1+(2t)^2}\right)(2) + (\cot^{-1}2t)(2t)$

$= -\dfrac{2+2t^2}{1+4t^2} + 2t\cot^{-1}2t$

27. $\dfrac{dy}{dz} = \dfrac{d}{dz}(z\cos^{-1}z - \sqrt{1-z^2})$

$= (z)\left(-\dfrac{1}{\sqrt{1-z^2}}\right) + (\cos^{-1}z)(1) - \dfrac{1}{2\sqrt{1-z^2}}(-2z)$

$= -\dfrac{z}{\sqrt{1-z^2}} + \cos^{-1}z + \dfrac{z}{\sqrt{1-z^2}}$

$= \cos^{-1}z$

28. $\dfrac{dy}{dx} = \dfrac{d}{dx}(2\sqrt{x-1}\csc^{-1}\sqrt{x})$

$= (2\sqrt{x-1})\left(-\dfrac{1}{|\sqrt{x}|\sqrt{(\sqrt{x})^2-1}}\right)\left(\dfrac{1}{2\sqrt{x}}\right)$

$\quad + (2\csc^{-1}\sqrt{x})\left(\dfrac{1}{2\sqrt{x-1}}\right)$

$= -\dfrac{\sqrt{x-1}}{(\sqrt{x})^2\sqrt{x-1}} + \dfrac{\csc^{-1}\sqrt{x}}{\sqrt{x-1}}$

$= -\dfrac{1}{x} + \dfrac{\csc^{-1}\sqrt{x}}{\sqrt{x-1}}$

29. $\dfrac{dy}{dx} = \dfrac{d}{dx}\csc^{-1}(\sec x)$

$= \left(-\dfrac{1}{|\sec x|\sqrt{\sec^2 x - 1}}\right)\dfrac{d}{dx}(\sec x)$

$= -\dfrac{1}{|\sec x|\sqrt{\tan^2 x}}\sec x \tan x$

$= -\dfrac{\sec x \tan x}{|\sec x \tan x|}$

$= -\dfrac{\dfrac{1}{\cos x}\dfrac{\sin x}{\cos x}}{\left|\dfrac{1}{\cos x}\dfrac{\sin x}{\cos x}\right|} = -\dfrac{\sin x}{|\sin x|}$

$= \begin{cases} -1, & 0 \le x < \pi, \quad x \ne \dfrac{\pi}{2} \\ 1, & \pi < x \le 2\pi, \quad x \ne \dfrac{3\pi}{2} \end{cases}$

Alternate method:

On the domain $0 \le x \le 2\pi$, $x \ne \dfrac{\pi}{2}$, $x \ne \dfrac{3\pi}{2}$, we may rewrite the function as follows:

$y = \csc^{-1}(\sec x)$

$= \dfrac{\pi}{2} - \sec^{-1}(\sec x)$

$= \dfrac{\pi}{2} - \cos^{-1}(\cos x)$

$= \begin{cases} \dfrac{\pi}{2} - x, & 0 \le x \le \pi, \quad x \ne \dfrac{\pi}{2} \\ \dfrac{\pi}{2} - (\pi - x), & \pi < x \le 2\pi, \quad x \ne \dfrac{3\pi}{2} \end{cases}$

$= \begin{cases} \dfrac{\pi}{2} - x, & 0 \le x \le \pi, \quad x \ne \dfrac{\pi}{2} \\ -\dfrac{\pi}{2} + x, & \pi < x \le 2\pi, \quad x \ne \dfrac{3\pi}{2} \end{cases}$

Therefore, $\dfrac{dy}{dx} = \begin{cases} -1, & 0 \le x < \pi, \quad x \ne \dfrac{\pi}{2} \\ 1, & \pi < x \le 2\pi, \quad x \ne \dfrac{3\pi}{2} \end{cases}$

Note that the derivative exists at 0 and 2π only because these are the endpoints of the given domain; the two-sided derivative of $y = \csc^{-1}(\sec x)$ does not exist at these points.

30. $\dfrac{dr}{d\theta} = \dfrac{d}{d\theta}\left(\dfrac{1 + \sin\theta}{1 - \cos\theta}\right)^2$

$= 2\left(\dfrac{1 + \sin\theta}{1 - \cos\theta}\right)\left(\dfrac{(1 - \cos\theta)(\cos\theta) - (1 + \sin\theta)(\sin\theta)}{(1 - \cos\theta)^2}\right)$

$= 2\left(\dfrac{1 + \sin\theta}{1 - \cos\theta}\right)\left(\dfrac{\cos\theta - \cos^2\theta - \sin\theta - \sin^2\theta}{(1 - \cos\theta)^2}\right)$

$= 2\left(\dfrac{1 + \sin\theta}{1 - \cos\theta}\right)\left(\dfrac{\cos\theta - \sin\theta - 1}{(1 - \cos\theta)^2}\right)$

31. Since $y = \ln x^2$ is defined for all $x \ne 0$ and

$\dfrac{dy}{dx} = \dfrac{1}{x^2}\dfrac{d}{dx}(x^2) = \dfrac{2x}{x^2} = \dfrac{2}{x}$, the function is differentiable for all $x \ne 0$.

32. Since $y = \sin x - x\cos x$ is defined for all real x and $\dfrac{dy}{dx} = \cos x - (x)(-\sin x) - (\cos x)(1) = x\sin x$, the function is differentiable for all real x.

33. Since $y = \sqrt{\dfrac{1 - x}{1 + x^2}}$ is defined for all $x < 1$ and

$\dfrac{dy}{dx} = \dfrac{1}{2\sqrt{\dfrac{1 - x}{1 + x^2}}}\dfrac{(1 + x^2)(-1) - (1 - x)(2x)}{(1 + x^2)^2}$

$= \dfrac{x^2 - 2x - 1}{2\sqrt{1 - x}\,(1 + x^2)^{3/2}}$, which is defined only for $x < 1$,

the function is differentiable for all $x < 1$.

34. Since $y = (2x - 7)^{-1}(x + 5) = \dfrac{x + 5}{2x - 7}$ is defined for all $x \ne \dfrac{7}{2}$ and $\dfrac{dy}{dx} = \dfrac{(2x - 7)(1) - (x + 5)(2)}{(2x - 7)^2} = -\dfrac{17}{(2x - 7)^2}$, the function is differentiable for all $x \ne \dfrac{7}{2}$.

35. Use implicit differentiation.

$$xy + 2x + 3y = 1$$

$$\dfrac{d}{dx}(xy) + \dfrac{d}{dx}(2x) + \dfrac{d}{dx}(3y) = \dfrac{d}{dx}(1)$$

$$x\dfrac{dy}{dx} + (y)(1) + 2 + 3\dfrac{dy}{dx} = 0$$

$$(x + 3)\dfrac{dy}{dx} = -(y + 2)$$

$$\dfrac{dy}{dx} = -\dfrac{y + 2}{x + 3}$$

36. Use implicit differentiation.

$$5x^{4/5} + 10y^{6/5} = 15$$

$$\dfrac{d}{dx}(5x^{4/5}) + \dfrac{d}{dx}(10y^{6/5}) = \dfrac{d}{dx}(15)$$

$$4x^{-1/5} + 12y^{1/5}\dfrac{dy}{dx} = 0$$

$$\dfrac{dy}{dx} = -\dfrac{4x^{-1/5}}{12y^{1/5}} = -\dfrac{1}{3(xy)^{1/5}}$$

37. Use implicit differentiation.

$$\sqrt{xy} = 1$$

$$\dfrac{d}{dx}\sqrt{xy} = \dfrac{d}{dx}(1)$$

$$\dfrac{1}{2\sqrt{xy}}[x\dfrac{dy}{dx} + (y)(1)] = 0$$

$$x\dfrac{dy}{dx} + y = 0$$

$$\dfrac{dy}{dx} = -\dfrac{y}{x}$$

Alternate method:

38. Use implicit differentiation.

$$y^2 = \frac{x}{x+1}$$

$$\frac{d}{dx}y^2 = \frac{d}{dx}\frac{x}{x+1}$$

$$2y\frac{dy}{dx} = \frac{(x+1)(1) - (x)(1)}{(x+1)^2}$$

$$\frac{dy}{dx} = \frac{1}{2y(x+1)^2}$$

39.
$$x^3 + y^3 = 1$$

$$\frac{d}{dx}(x^3) + \frac{d}{dx}(y^3) = \frac{d}{dx}(1)$$

$$3x^2 + 3y^2y' = 0$$

$$y' = -\frac{x^2}{y^2}$$

$$y'' = \frac{d}{dx}\left(-\frac{x^2}{y^2}\right)$$

$$= -\frac{(y^2)(2x) - (x^2)(2y)(y')}{y^4}$$

$$= -\frac{(y^2)(2x) - (x^2)(2y)\left(-\frac{x^2}{y^2}\right)}{y^4}$$

$$= -\frac{2xy^3 + 2x^4}{y^5}$$

$$= -\frac{2x(x^3 + y^3)}{y^5}$$

$$= -\frac{2x}{y^5}$$

since $x^3 + y^3 = 1$

40.
$$y^2 = 1 - \frac{2}{x}$$

$$\frac{d}{dx}(y^2) = \frac{d}{dx}(1) - \frac{d}{dx}\left(\frac{2}{x}\right)$$

$$2yy' = \frac{2}{x^2}$$

$$y' = \frac{2}{x^2(2y)} = \frac{1}{x^2y}$$

$$y'' = \frac{d}{dx}\left(\frac{1}{x^2y}\right)$$

$$= -\frac{1}{(x^2y)^2}\frac{d}{dx}(x^2y)$$

$$= -\frac{1}{(x^2y)^2}[(x^2)(y') + (y)(2x)]$$

$$= -\frac{1}{(x^2y)^2}\left[(x^2)\left(\frac{1}{x^2y}\right) + 2xy\right]$$

$$= -\frac{1}{x^4y^2}\left(\frac{1}{y} + 2xy\right)$$

$$= -\frac{1 + 2xy^2}{x^4y^3}$$

41.
$$y^3 + y = 2\cos x$$

$$\frac{d}{dx}(y^3) + \frac{d}{dx}(y) = \frac{d}{dx}(2\cos x)$$

$$3y^2y' + y' = -2\sin x$$

$$(3y^2 + 1)y' = -2\sin x$$

$$y' = -\frac{2\sin x}{3y^2 + 1}$$

$$y'' = \frac{d}{dx}\left(-\frac{2\sin x}{3y^2 + 1}\right)$$

$$= -\frac{(3y^2 + 1)(2\cos x) - (2\sin x)(6yy')}{(3y^2 + 1)^2}$$

$$= -\frac{(3y^2 + 1)(2\cos x) - (12y\sin x)\left(-\frac{2\sin x}{3y^2 + 1}\right)}{(3y^2 + 1)^2}$$

$$= -2\frac{(3y^2 + 1)^2\cos x + 12y\sin^2 x}{(3y^2 + 1)^3}$$

42.
$$x^{1/3} + y^{1/3} = 4$$

$$\frac{d}{dx}(x^{1/3}) + \frac{d}{dx}(y^{1/3}) = \frac{d}{dx}(4)$$

$$\frac{1}{3}x^{-2/3} + \frac{1}{3}y^{-2/3}y' = 0$$

$$y' = -\frac{x^{-2/3}}{y^{-2/3}} = -\left(\frac{y}{x}\right)^{2/3}$$

$$y'' = \frac{d}{dx}\left[-\left(\frac{y}{x}\right)^{2/3}\right]$$

$$= -\frac{2}{3}\left(\frac{y}{x}\right)^{-1/3}\left(\frac{xy' - (y)(1)}{x^2}\right)$$

$$= -\frac{2}{3}\left(\frac{y}{x}\right)^{-1/3}\left(\frac{(x)\left[-\left(\frac{y}{x}\right)^{2/3}\right] - y}{x^2}\right)$$

$$= -\frac{2}{3}x^{1/3}y^{-1/3}(-x^{-5/3}y^{2/3} - x^{-2}y)$$

$$= \frac{2}{3}x^{-4/3}y^{1/3} + \frac{2}{3}x^{-5/3}y^{2/3}$$

43. $y' = 2x^3 - 3x - 1$,
$y'' = 6x^2 - 3$,
$y''' = 12x$,
$y^{(4)} = 12$, and the rest are all zero.

44. $y' = \frac{x^4}{24}$,

$y'' = \frac{x^3}{6}$,

$y''' = \frac{x^2}{2}$,

$y^{(4)} = x$,

$y^{(5)} = 1$, and the rest are all zero.

45. $\dfrac{dy}{dx} = \dfrac{d}{dx}\sqrt{x^2 - 2x} = \dfrac{1}{2\sqrt{x^2 - 2x}}(2x - 2) = \dfrac{x - 1}{\sqrt{x^2 - 2x}}$

At $x = 3$, we have $y = \sqrt{3^2 - 2(3)} = \sqrt{3}$

and $\dfrac{dy}{dx} = \dfrac{3 - 1}{\sqrt{3^2 - 2(3)}} = \dfrac{2}{\sqrt{3}}$.

  (a) Tangent: $y = \dfrac{2}{\sqrt{3}}(x - 3) + \sqrt{3}$ or $y = \dfrac{2}{\sqrt{3}}x - \sqrt{3}$

  (b) Normal: $y = -\dfrac{\sqrt{3}}{2}(x - 3) + \sqrt{3}$

      or $y = -\dfrac{\sqrt{3}}{2}x + \dfrac{5\sqrt{3}}{2}$

46. $\dfrac{dy}{dx} = \dfrac{d}{dx}(4 + \cot x - 2\csc x)$

    $= -\csc^2 x + 2\csc x \cot x$

At $x = \dfrac{\pi}{2}$, we have

$y = 4 + \cot\dfrac{\pi}{2} - 2\csc\dfrac{\pi}{2} = 4 + 0 - 2 = 2$ and

$\dfrac{dy}{dx} = -\csc^2\dfrac{\pi}{2} + 2\csc\dfrac{\pi}{2}\cot\dfrac{\pi}{2} = -1 + 2(1)(0) = -1$.

  (a) Tangent: $y = -1\left(x - \dfrac{\pi}{2}\right) + 2$ or $y = -x + \dfrac{\pi}{2} + 2$

  (b) Normal: $y = 1\left(x - \dfrac{\pi}{2}\right) + 2$ or $y = x - \dfrac{\pi}{2} + 2$

47. Use implicit differentiation.

$$x^2 + 2y^2 = 9$$

$$\dfrac{d}{dx}(x^2) + \dfrac{d}{dx}(2y^2) = \dfrac{d}{dx}(9)$$

$$2x + 4y\dfrac{dy}{dx} = 0$$

$$\dfrac{dy}{dx} = -\dfrac{2x}{4y} = -\dfrac{x}{2y}$$

Slope at $(1, 2)$: $-\dfrac{1}{2(2)} = -\dfrac{1}{4}$

  (a) Tangent: $y = -\dfrac{1}{4}(x - 1) + 2$ or $y = -\dfrac{1}{4}x + \dfrac{9}{4}$

  (b) Normal: $y = 4(x - 1) + 2$ or $y = 4x - 2$

48. Use implicit differentiation.

$$x + \sqrt{xy} = 6$$

$$\dfrac{d}{dx}(x) + \dfrac{d}{dx}(\sqrt{xy}) = \dfrac{d}{dx}(6)$$

$$1 + \dfrac{1}{2\sqrt{xy}}\left[(x)\left(\dfrac{dy}{dx}\right) + (y)(1)\right] = 0$$

$$\dfrac{x}{2\sqrt{xy}}\dfrac{dy}{dx} = -1 - \dfrac{y}{2\sqrt{xy}}$$

$$\dfrac{dy}{dx} = \dfrac{2\sqrt{xy}}{x}\left(-1 - \dfrac{y}{2\sqrt{xy}}\right)$$

$$= -2\sqrt{\dfrac{y}{x}} - \dfrac{y}{x}$$

Slope at $(4, 1)$: $-2\sqrt{\dfrac{1}{4}} - \dfrac{1}{4} = -\dfrac{2}{2} - \dfrac{1}{4} = -\dfrac{5}{4}$

  (a) Tangent: $y = -\dfrac{5}{4}(x - 4) + 1$ or $y = -\dfrac{5}{4}x + 6$

  (b) Normal: $y = \dfrac{4}{5}(x - 4) + 1$ or $y = \dfrac{4}{5}x - \dfrac{11}{5}$

49. $\dfrac{dy}{dx} = \dfrac{\frac{dy}{dt}}{\frac{dx}{dt}} = \dfrac{-2\sin t}{2\cos t} = -\tan t$

At $t = \dfrac{3\pi}{4}$, we have $x = 2\sin\dfrac{3\pi}{4} = \sqrt{2}$,

$y = 2\cos\dfrac{3\pi}{4} = -\sqrt{2}$, and $\dfrac{dy}{dx} = -\tan\dfrac{3\pi}{4} = 1$.

The equation of the tangent line is

$$y = 1(x - \sqrt{2}) + (-\sqrt{2}), \text{ or } y = x - 2\sqrt{2}.$$

50. $\dfrac{dy}{dx} = \dfrac{\frac{dy}{dt}}{\frac{dx}{dt}} = \dfrac{4\cos t}{-3\sin t} = -\dfrac{4}{3}\cot t$

At $t = \dfrac{3\pi}{4}$, we have $x = 3\cos\dfrac{3\pi}{4} = -\dfrac{3\sqrt{2}}{2}$,

$y = 4\sin\dfrac{3\pi}{4} = 2\sqrt{2}$, and $\dfrac{dy}{dx} = -\dfrac{4}{3}\cot\dfrac{3\pi}{4} = \dfrac{4}{3}$.

The equation of the tangent line is

$$y = \dfrac{4}{3}\left(x + \dfrac{3\sqrt{2}}{2}\right) + 2\sqrt{2}, \text{ or } y = \dfrac{4}{3}x + 4\sqrt{2}.$$

51. $\dfrac{dy}{dx} = \dfrac{\frac{dy}{dt}}{\frac{dx}{dt}} = \dfrac{5\sec^2 t}{3\sec t\tan t} = \dfrac{5\sec t}{3\tan t} = \dfrac{5}{3\sin t}$

At $t = \dfrac{\pi}{6}$, we have $x = 3\sec\dfrac{\pi}{6} = 2\sqrt{3}$,

$y = 5\tan\dfrac{\pi}{6} = \dfrac{5\sqrt{3}}{3}$, and $\dfrac{dy}{dx} = \dfrac{5}{3\sin\left(\frac{\pi}{6}\right)} = \dfrac{10}{3}$.

The equation of the tangent line is

$$y = \dfrac{10}{3}(x - 2\sqrt{3}) + \dfrac{5\sqrt{3}}{3}, \text{ or } y = \dfrac{10}{3}x - 5\sqrt{3}.$$

52. $\dfrac{dy}{dx} = \dfrac{\frac{dy}{dt}}{\frac{dx}{dt}} = \dfrac{1 + \cos t}{-\sin t}$

At $t = -\dfrac{\pi}{4}$, we have $x = \cos\left(-\dfrac{\pi}{4}\right) = \dfrac{\sqrt{2}}{2}$,

$y = -\dfrac{\pi}{4} + \sin\left(-\dfrac{\pi}{4}\right) = -\dfrac{\pi}{4} - \dfrac{\sqrt{2}}{2}$, and

$\dfrac{dy}{dx} = \dfrac{1 + \cos\left(-\frac{\pi}{4}\right)}{-\sin\left(-\frac{\pi}{4}\right)} = \dfrac{1 + \frac{\sqrt{2}}{2}}{\frac{\sqrt{2}}{2}} = \sqrt{2} + 1.$

The equation of the tangent line is

$y = (\sqrt{2} + 1)\left(x - \dfrac{\sqrt{2}}{2}\right) - \dfrac{\pi}{4} - \dfrac{\sqrt{2}}{2}$, or

$y = (1 + \sqrt{2})x - \sqrt{2} - 1 - \dfrac{\pi}{4}.$

This is approximately $y = 2.414x - 3.200.$

53. (a)

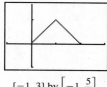

$[-1, 3]$ by $\left[-1, \dfrac{5}{3}\right]$

(b) Yes, because both of the one-sided limits as $x \to 1$ are equal to $f(1) = 1$.

(c) No, because the left-hand derivative at $x = 1$ is $+1$ and the right-hand derivative at $x = 1$ is -1.

54. (a) The function is continuous for all values of m, because the right-hand limit as $x \to 0$ is equal to $f(0) = 0$ for any value of m.

(b) The left-hand derivative at $x = 0$ is $2 \cos (2 \cdot 0) = 2$, and the right-hand derivative at $x = 0$ is m, so in order for the function to be differentiable at $x = 0$, m must be 2.

55. (a) For all $x \neq 0$ **(b)** At $x = 0$

   (c) Nowhere

56. (a) For all x **(b)** Nowhere

   (c) Nowhere

57. Note that $\lim\limits_{x \to 0^-} f(x) = \lim\limits_{x \to 0^-} (2x - 3) = -3$ and

$\lim\limits_{x \to 0^+} f(x) = \lim\limits_{x \to 0^+} (x - 3) = -3$. Since these values agree

with $f(0)$, the function is continuous at $x = 0$. On the other

hand,

$f'(x) = \begin{cases} 2, & -1 \leq x < 0 \\ 1, & 0 < x \leq 4 \end{cases}$, so the derivative is undefined at

$x = 0$.

(a) $[-1, 0) \cup (0, 4]$ **(b)** At $x = 0$

(c) Nowhere in its domain

58. Note that the function is undefined at $x = 0$.

(a) $[-2, 0) \cup (0, 2]$ **(b)** Nowhere

(c) Nowhere in its domain

59.

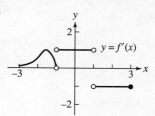

60.

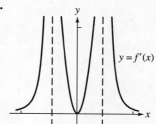

61. (a) iii   **(b)** i

   (c) ii

62. The graph passes through $(0, 5)$ and has slope -2 for $x < 2$ and slope -0.5 for $x > 2$.

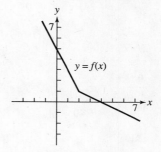

63. The graph passes through $(-1, 2)$ and has slope -2 for $x < 1$, slope 1 for $1 < x < 4$, and slope -1 for $4 < x < 6$.

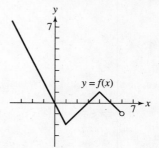

64. i. If $f(x) = \dfrac{9}{28}x^{7/3} + 9$, then $f'(x) = \dfrac{3}{4}x^{4/3}$ and

$f''(x) = x^{1/3}$, which matches the given equation.

ii. If $f'(x) = \dfrac{9}{28}x^{7/3} - 2$, then $f''(x) = \dfrac{3}{4}x^{4/3}$, which

contradicts the given equation $f''(x) = x^{1/3}$.

iii. If $f'(x) = \dfrac{3}{4}x^{4/3} + 6$, then $f''(x) = x^{1/3}$, which matches

the given equation.

64. continued

   iv. If $f(x) = \frac{3}{4}x^{4/3} - 4$, then $f'(x) = x^{1/3}$ and

     $f''(x) = \frac{1}{3}x^{-2/3}$, which contradicts the given equation

     $f''(x) = x^{1/3}$.

   Answer is **D**: **i** and **iii** only could be true. Note,

   however that **i** and **iii** could not simultaneously be true.

65. (a)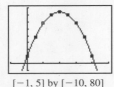

     $[-1, 5]$ by $[-10, 80]$

  (b)

t interval	avg. vel.
$[0, 0.5]$	$\dfrac{38 - 10}{0.5 - 0} = 56$
$[0.5, 1]$	$\dfrac{58 - 38}{1 - 0.5} = 40$
$[1, 1.5]$	$\dfrac{70 - 58}{1.5 - 1} = 24$
$[1.5, 2]$	$\dfrac{74 - 70}{2 - 1.5} = 8$
$[2, 2.5]$	$\dfrac{70 - 74}{2.5 - 2} = -8$
$[2.5, 3]$	$\dfrac{58 - 70}{3 - 2.5} = -24$
$[3, 3.5]$	$\dfrac{38 - 58}{3.5 - 3} = -40$
$[3.5, 4]$	$\dfrac{10 - 38}{4 - 3.5} = -56$

  (c)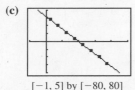

     $[-1, 5]$ by $[-80, 80]$

  (d) Average velocity is a good approximation to velocity.

66. (a) $\dfrac{d}{dx}[\sqrt{x}\,f(x)] = \sqrt{x}\,f'(x) + \dfrac{1}{2\sqrt{x}}f(x)$

     At $x = 1$, the derivative is

     $\sqrt{1}\,f'(1) + \dfrac{1}{2\sqrt{1}}f(1) = 1\left(\dfrac{1}{5}\right) + \left(\dfrac{1}{2}\right)(-3) = -\dfrac{13}{10}$.

  (b) $\dfrac{d}{dx}\sqrt{f(x)} = \dfrac{1}{2\sqrt{f(x)}}f'(x) = \dfrac{f'(x)}{2\sqrt{f(x)}}$

     At $x = 0$, the derivative is $\dfrac{f'(0)}{2\sqrt{f(0)}} = -\dfrac{2}{2\sqrt{9}} = -\dfrac{1}{3}$.

  (c) $\dfrac{d}{dx}f(\sqrt{x}) = f'(\sqrt{x})\dfrac{d}{dx}\sqrt{x} = \dfrac{f'(\sqrt{x})}{2\sqrt{x}}$

     At $x = 1$, the derivative is $\dfrac{f'(\sqrt{1})}{2\sqrt{1}} = \dfrac{f'(1)}{2} = \dfrac{\frac{1}{5}}{2} = \dfrac{1}{10}$.

(d) $\dfrac{d}{dx}f(1 - 5\tan x) = f'(1 - 5\tan x)(-5\sec^2 x)$

    At $x = 0$, the derivative is

    $f'(1 - 5\tan 0)(-5\sec^2 0) = f'(1)(-5) = \left(\dfrac{1}{5}\right)(-5)$

    $= -1.$

(e) $\dfrac{d}{dx}\dfrac{f(x)}{2 + \cos x} = \dfrac{(2 + \cos x)(f'(x)) - (f(x))(-\sin x)}{(2 + \cos x)^2}$

    At $x = 0$, the derivative is

    $\dfrac{(2 + \cos 0)(f'(0)) - (f(0))(-\sin 0)}{(2 + \cos 0)^2} = \dfrac{3f'(0)}{3^2} = -\dfrac{2}{3}.$

(f) $\dfrac{d}{dx}[10\sin\left(\dfrac{\pi x}{2}\right)f^2(x)]$

    $= 10\left(\sin\dfrac{\pi x}{2}\right)(2f(x)f'(x)) + 10f^2(x)\left(\cos\dfrac{\pi x}{2}\right)\left(\dfrac{\pi}{2}\right)$

    $= 20\,f(x)f'(x)\sin\dfrac{\pi x}{2} + 5\pi f^2(x)\cos\dfrac{\pi x}{2}$

    At $x = 1$, the derivative is

    $20\,f(1)f'(1)\sin\dfrac{\pi}{2} + 5\pi f^2(1)\cos\dfrac{\pi}{2}$

    $= 20(-3)\left(\dfrac{1}{5}\right)(1) + 5\pi(-3)^2(0)$

    $= -12.$

67. (a) $\dfrac{d}{dx}[3f(x) - g(x)] = 3f'(x) - g'(x)$

    At $x = -1$, the derivative is

    $3f'(-1) - g'(-1) = 3(2) - 1 = 5.$

  (b) $\dfrac{d}{dx}[f^2(x)g^3(x)]$

    $= f^2(x) \cdot 3g^2(x)g'(x) + g^3(x) \cdot 2f(x)f'(x)$

    $= f(x)g^2(x)[3f(x)g'(x) + 2g(x)f'(x)]$

    At $x = 0$, the derivative is

    $f(0)g^2(0)[3f(0)g'(0) + 2g(0)f'(0)]$

    $= (-1)(-3)^2[3(-1)(4) + 2(-3)(-2)]$

    $= -9[-12 + 12] = 0.$

  (c) $\dfrac{d}{dx}g(f(x)) = g'(f(x))f'(x)$

    At $x = -1$, the derivative is

    $g'(f(-1))f'(-1) = g'(0)f'(-1) = (4)(2) = 8.$

  (d) $\dfrac{d}{dx}f(g(x)) = f'(g(x))g'(x)$

    At $x = -1$, the derivative is

    $f'(g(-1))g'(-1) = f'(-1)g'(-1) = (2)(1) = 2.$

  (e) $\dfrac{d}{dx}\dfrac{f(x)}{g(x) + 2} = \dfrac{(g(x) + 2)f'(x) - f(x)\,g'(x)}{(g(x) + 2)^2}$

    At $x = 0$, the derivative is

    $\dfrac{(g(0) + 2)f'(0) - f(0)g'(0)}{(g(0) + 2)^2} = \dfrac{(-3 + 2)(-2) - (-1)(4)}{(-3 + 2)^2}$

    $= 6.$

(f) $\dfrac{d}{dx} g(x + f(x)) = g'(x + f(x))\dfrac{d}{dx}(x + f(x))$

$= g'(x + f(x))(1 + f'(x))$

At $x = 0$, the derivative is $g'(0 + f(0))[1 + f'(0)]$

$= g'(0 - 1)[1 + (-2)] = (1)(-1) = -1$

68. $\dfrac{dw}{ds} = \dfrac{dw}{dr}\dfrac{dr}{ds} = \dfrac{d}{dr}[\sin(\sqrt{r} - 2)]\dfrac{d}{ds}\left[8 \sin\left(s + \dfrac{\pi}{6}\right)\right]$

$= \left[\cos(\sqrt{r} - 2)\dfrac{1}{2\sqrt{r}}\right]\left[8 \cos\left(s + \dfrac{\pi}{6}\right)\right]$

At $s = 0$, we have $r = 8 \sin\left(0 + \dfrac{\pi}{6}\right) = 4$ and so

$\dfrac{dw}{ds} = \left[\cos(\sqrt{4} - 2)\dfrac{1}{2\sqrt{4}}\right]\left[8 \cos\left(0 + \dfrac{\pi}{6}\right)\right]$

$= \left(\dfrac{\cos 0}{4}\right)\left(8 \cos\dfrac{\pi}{6}\right) = \left(\dfrac{1}{4}\right)\left(\dfrac{8\sqrt{3}}{2}\right) = \sqrt{3}$

69. Solving $\theta^2 t + \theta = 1$ for t, we have

$t = \dfrac{1 - \theta}{\theta^2} = \theta^{-2} - \theta^{-1}$, and we may write:

$$\dfrac{dr}{d\theta} = \dfrac{dr}{dt}\dfrac{dt}{d\theta}$$

$$\dfrac{d}{d\theta}(\theta^2 + 7)^{1/3} = \dfrac{dr}{dt}\dfrac{d}{d\theta}(\theta^{-2} - \theta^{-1})$$

$$\dfrac{1}{3}(\theta^2 + 7)^{-2/3}(2\theta) = \left(\dfrac{dr}{dt}\right)(-2\theta^{-3} + \theta^{-2})$$

$$\dfrac{dr}{dt} = \dfrac{2\theta(\theta^2 + 7)^{-2/3}}{3(-2\theta^{-3} + \theta^{-2})} = \dfrac{2\theta^4(\theta^2 + 7)^{-2/3}}{3(\theta - 2)}$$

At $t = 0$, we may solve $\theta^2 t + \theta = 1$ to obtain $\theta = 1$,

and so $\dfrac{dr}{dt} = \dfrac{2(1)^4(1^2 + 7)^{-2/3}}{3(1 - 2)} = \dfrac{2(8)^{-2/3}}{-3} = -\dfrac{1}{6}$.

70. (a) One possible answer:

$x(t) = 10 \cos\left(t + \dfrac{\pi}{4}\right)$, $y(t) = 1$

(b) $s(0) = 10 \cos\dfrac{\pi}{4} = 5\sqrt{2}$

(c) Farthest left:

When $\cos\left(t + \dfrac{\pi}{4}\right) = -1$, we have $s(t) = -10$.

Farthest right:

When $\cos\left(t + \dfrac{\pi}{4}\right) = 1$, we have $s(t) = 10$.

(d) Since $\cos\dfrac{\pi}{2} = 0$, the particle first reaches the origin at

$t = \dfrac{\pi}{4}$. The velocity is given by

$v(t) = -10 \sin\left(t + \dfrac{\pi}{4}\right)$, so the velocity at

$t = \dfrac{\pi}{4}$ is $-10 \sin\dfrac{\pi}{2} = -10$, and the

speed at $t = \dfrac{\pi}{4}$ is $|-10| = 10$. The acceleration is given

by $a(t) = -10 \cos\left(t + \dfrac{\pi}{4}\right)$, so the acceleration at

$t = \dfrac{\pi}{4}$ is $-10 \cos\dfrac{\pi}{2} = 0$.

71. (a) $\dfrac{ds}{dt} = \dfrac{d}{dt}(64t - 16t^2) = 64 - 32t$

$\dfrac{d^2s}{dt^2} = \dfrac{d}{dt}(64 - 32t) = -32$

(b) The maximum height is reached when $\dfrac{ds}{dt} = 0$, which

occurs at $t = 2$ sec.

(c) When $t = 0$, $\dfrac{ds}{dt} = 64$, so the velocity is 64 ft/sec.

(d) Since $\dfrac{ds}{dt} = \dfrac{d}{dt}(64t - 2.6t^2) = 64 - 5.2t$, the

maximum height is reached at $t = \dfrac{64}{5.2} \approx 12.3$ sec.

The maximum height is $s\left(\dfrac{64}{5.2}\right) \approx 393.8$ ft.

72. (a) Solving $160 = 490t^2$, it takes $\dfrac{4}{7}$ sec.

The average velocity is $\dfrac{160}{\dfrac{4}{7}} = 280$ cm/sec.

(b) Since $v(t) = \dfrac{ds}{dt} = 980t$, the velocity is

$(980)\left(\dfrac{4}{7}\right) = 560$ cm/sec. Since $a(t) = \dfrac{dv}{dt} = 980$, the

acceleration is 980 cm/sec^2.

73. $\dfrac{dV}{dx} = \dfrac{d}{dx}\left[\pi\left(10 - \dfrac{x}{3}\right)x^2\right] = \dfrac{d}{dx}\left[\pi\left(10x^2 - \dfrac{1}{3}x^3\right)\right]$

$= \pi(20x - x^2)$

74. (a) $r(x) = \left(3 - \dfrac{x}{40}\right)^2 x = 9x - \dfrac{3}{20}x^2 + \dfrac{1}{1600}x^3$

(b) The marginal revenue is

$r'(x) = 9 - \dfrac{3}{10}x + \dfrac{3}{1600}x^2$

$= \dfrac{3}{1600}(x^2 - 160x + 4800)$

$= \dfrac{3}{1600}(x - 40)(x - 120),$

which is zero when $x = 40$ or $x = 120$. Since the bus

holds only 60 people, we require $0 \le x \le 60$. The

marginal revenue is 0 when there are 40 people, and the

corresponding fare is $p(40) = \left(3 - \dfrac{40}{40}\right)^2 = \$4.00$.

74. continued

(c) One possible answer:

If the current ridership is less than 40, then the proposed plan may be good. If the current ridership is greater than or equal to 40, then the plan is not a good idea. Look at the graph of $y = r(x)$.

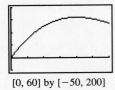

[0, 60] by [−50, 200]

75. (a) Since $x = \tan \theta$, we have

$$\frac{dx}{dt} = (\sec^2 \theta)\frac{d\theta}{dt} = -0.6 \sec^2 \theta.$$ At point A, we have

$\theta = 0$ and $\frac{dx}{dt} = -0.6 \sec^2 0 = -0.6$ km/sec.

(b) $0.6 \dfrac{\text{rad}}{\text{sec}} \cdot \dfrac{1 \text{ revolution}}{2\pi \text{ rad}} \cdot \dfrac{60 \text{ sec}}{1 \text{ min}} = \dfrac{18}{\pi}$ revolutions per

minute or approximately 5.73 revolutions per minute.

76. Let $f(x) = \sin(x - \sin x)$. Then

$$f'(x) = \cos(x - \sin x)\frac{d}{dx}(x - \sin x)$$

$= \cos(x - \sin x)(1 - \cos x)$. This derivative is zero when

$\cos(x - \sin x) = 0$ (which we need not solve) or when

$\cos x = 1$, which occurs at $x = 2k\pi$ for integers k. For each

of these values, $f(x) = f(2k\pi) = \sin(2k\pi - \sin 2k\pi)$

$= \sin(2k\pi - 0) = 0$. Thus, $f(x) = f'(x) = 0$ for $x = 2k\pi$,

which means that the graph has a horizontal tangent at each

of these values of x.

77. $y'(r) = \dfrac{d}{dr}\left(\dfrac{1}{2rl}\sqrt{\dfrac{T}{\pi d}}\right) = \left(\dfrac{1}{2l}\sqrt{\dfrac{T}{\pi d}}\right)\dfrac{d}{dr}\left(\dfrac{1}{r}\right) = -\dfrac{1}{2r^2 l}\sqrt{\dfrac{T}{\pi d}}$

$y'(l) = \dfrac{d}{dl}\left(\dfrac{1}{2rl}\sqrt{\dfrac{T}{\pi d}}\right) = \left(\dfrac{1}{2r}\sqrt{\dfrac{T}{\pi d}}\right)\dfrac{d}{dl}\left(\dfrac{1}{l}\right) = -\dfrac{1}{2rl^2}\sqrt{\dfrac{T}{\pi d}}$

$y'(d) = \dfrac{d}{dd}\left(\dfrac{1}{2rl}\sqrt{\dfrac{T}{\pi d}}\right) = \left(\dfrac{1}{2rl}\sqrt{\dfrac{T}{\pi}}\right)\dfrac{d}{dd}(d^{-1/2})$

$= \dfrac{1}{2rl}\sqrt{\dfrac{T}{\pi}}\left(-\dfrac{1}{2}d^{-3/2}\right) = -\dfrac{1}{4rl}\sqrt{\dfrac{T}{\pi d^3}}$

$y'(T) = \dfrac{d}{dT}\left(\dfrac{1}{2rl}\sqrt{\dfrac{T}{\pi d}}\right) = \left(\dfrac{1}{2rl}\sqrt{\dfrac{1}{\pi d}}\right)\dfrac{d}{dT}(\sqrt{T})$

$= \dfrac{1}{2rl}\sqrt{\dfrac{1}{\pi d}}\left(\dfrac{1}{2\sqrt{T}}\right) = \dfrac{1}{4rl\sqrt{\pi d T}}$

Since $y'(r) < 0$, $y'(l) < 0$, and $y'(d) < 0$, increasing r, l, or

d would decrease the frequency. Since $y'(T) > 0$,

increasing T would increase the frequency.

78. (a) $P(0) = \dfrac{200}{1 + e^5} \approx 1$ student

(b) $\lim\limits_{t\to\infty} P(t) = \lim\limits_{t\to\infty} \dfrac{200}{1 + e^{5-t}} = \dfrac{200}{1} = 200$ students

(c) $P'(t) = \dfrac{d}{dt} 200(1 + e^{5-t})^{-1}$

$= -200(1 + e^{5-t})^{-2}(e^{5-t})(-1)$

$= \dfrac{200e^{5-t}}{(1 + e^{5-t})^2}$

$P''(t) = \dfrac{(1 + e^{5-t})^2(200e^{5-t})(-1) - (200e^{5-t})(2)(1 + e^{5-t})(e^{5-t})(-1)}{(1 + e^{5-t})^4}$

$= \dfrac{(1 + e^{5-t})(-200e^{5-t}) + 400(e^{5-t})^2}{(1 + e^{5-t})^3}$

$= \dfrac{(200e^{5-t})(e^{5-t} - 1)}{(1 + e^{5-t})^3}$

Since $P'' = 0$ when $t = 5$, the critical point of $y = P'(t)$

occurs at $t = 5$. To confirm that this corresponds to the

maximum value of $P'(t)$, note that $P''(t) > 0$ for $t < 5$

and $P''(t) < 0$ for $t > 5$. The maximum rate occurs at

$t = 5$, and this rate is

$P'(5) = \dfrac{200e^0}{(1 + e^0)^2} = \dfrac{200}{2^2} = 50$ students per day.

Note: This problem can also be solved graphically.

79.

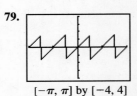

[−π, π] by [−4, 4]

(a) $x \neq k\dfrac{\pi}{4}$, where k is an odd integer

(b) $\left(-\dfrac{\pi}{2}, \dfrac{\pi}{2}\right)$

(c) Where it's not defined, at $x = k\dfrac{\pi}{4}$, k an odd integer

(d) It has period $\dfrac{\pi}{2}$ and continues to repeat the pattern seen

in this window.

80. Use implicit differentiation.

$$x^2 - y^2 = 1$$

$$\frac{d}{dx}(x^2) - \frac{d}{dx}(y^2) = \frac{d}{dx}(1)$$

$$2x - 2yy' = 0$$

$$y' = \frac{2x}{2y} = \frac{x}{y}$$

$$y'' = \frac{d}{dx}\frac{x}{y}$$

$$= \frac{(y)(1) - (x)(y')}{y^2}$$

$$= \frac{y - x\left(\dfrac{x}{y}\right)}{y^2}$$

$$= \frac{y^2 - x^2}{y^3}$$

$$= -\frac{1}{y^3}$$

(since the given equation is $x^2 - y^2 = 1$)

At $(2, \sqrt{3})$, $\dfrac{d^2y}{dx^2} = -\dfrac{1}{y^3} = -\dfrac{1}{(\sqrt{3})^3} = -\dfrac{1}{3\sqrt{3}}$.

Chapter 4
Applications of Derivatives

■ Section 4.1 Extreme Values of Functions
(pp. 177– 185)

Exploration 1   Finding Extreme Values

1. From the graph we can see that there are three critical points: $x = -1, 0, 1$.
   Critical point values: $f(-1) = 0.5, f(0) = 0, f(1) = 0.5$
   Endpoint values: $f(-2) = 0.4, f(2) = 0.4$
   Thus f has absolute maximum value of 0.5 at $x = -1$ and $x = 1$, absolute minimum value of 0 at $x = 0$, and local minimum value of 0.4 at $x = -2$ and $x = 2$.

   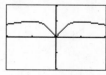

   $[-2, 2]$ by $[-1, 1]$

2. The graph of f' has zeros at $x = -1$ and $x = 1$ where the graph of f has local extreme values. The graph of f' is not defined at $x = 0$, another extreme value of the graph of f.

   $[-2, 2]$ by $[-1, 1]$

3. Using the chain rule and $\dfrac{d}{dx}(|x|) = \dfrac{|x|}{x}$, we find

$$\frac{df}{dx} = \frac{|x|}{x} \cdot \frac{1 - x^2}{(x^2 + 1)^2}.$$

1. $f'(x) = \dfrac{1}{2\sqrt{4 - x}} \cdot \dfrac{d}{dx}(4 - x) = \dfrac{-1}{2\sqrt{4 - x}}$

2. $f'(x) = \dfrac{3}{4}x^{-1/4}$

3. $f'(x) = \dfrac{d}{dx}2(9 - x^2)^{-1/2} = -(9 - x^2)^{-3/2} \cdot \dfrac{d}{dx}(9 - x^2)$
   $= -(9 - x^2)^{-3/2}(-2x) = \dfrac{2x}{(9 - x^2)^{3/2}}$

4. $f'(x) = \dfrac{d}{dx}(x^2 - 1)^{-1/3} = -\dfrac{1}{3}(x^2 - 1)^{-4/3} \cdot \dfrac{d}{dx}(x^2 - 1)$
   $= -\dfrac{1}{3}(x^2 - 1)^{-4/3}(2x) = \dfrac{-2x}{3(x^2 - 1)^{4/3}}$

5. $g'(x) = \dfrac{1}{x^2 + 1} \cdot \dfrac{d}{dx}(x^2 + 1) = \dfrac{2x}{x^2 + 1}$

6. $g'(x) = -\sin(\ln x) \cdot \dfrac{d}{dx}\ln x = -\dfrac{\sin(\ln x)}{x}$

7. $h'(x) = e^{2x} \cdot \dfrac{d}{dx}2x = 2e^{2x}$

8. $h'(x) = \dfrac{d}{dx}e^{\ln x} = \dfrac{d}{dx}x = 1$

9. As $x \to 3^-$, $\sqrt{9 - x^2} \to 0^+$. Therefore, $\lim\limits_{x \to 3^-} f(x) = \infty$.

10. As $x \to -3^+$, $\sqrt{9 - x^2} \to 0^+$. Therefore, $\lim\limits_{x \to -3^+} f(x) = \infty$.

11. **(a)** $\dfrac{d}{dx}(x^3 - 2x) = 3x^2 - 2$

   $f'(1) = 3(1)^2 - 2 = 1$

   (b) $\dfrac{d}{dx}(x + 2) = 1$

   $f'(3) = 1$

   (c) Left-hand derivative:

   $$\lim_{h \to 0^-} \frac{f(2 + h) - f(2)}{h} = \lim_{h \to 0^-} \frac{[(2 + h)^3 - 2(2 + h)] - 4}{h}$$

   $$= \lim_{h \to 0^-} \frac{h^3 + 6h^2 + 10h}{h}$$

   $$= \lim_{h \to 0^-} (h^2 + 6h + 10)$$

   $$= 10$$

   Right-hand derivative:

   $$\lim_{h \to 0^+} \frac{f(2 + h) - f(2)}{h} = \lim_{h \to 0^+} \frac{[(2 + h) + 2] - 4}{h}$$

   $$= \lim_{h \to 0^+} \frac{h}{h}$$

   $$= \lim_{h \to 0^+} 1$$

   $$= 1$$

   Since the left- and right-hand derivatives are not equal,

   $f'(2)$ is undefined.

12. (a) The domain is $x \neq 2$. (See the solution for 11.(c)).

(b) $f'(x) = \begin{cases} 3x^2 - 2, & x < 2 \\ 1, & x > 2 \end{cases}$

Section 4.1 Exercises

1. Maximum at $x = b$, minimum at $x = c_2$;
The Extreme Value Theorem applies because f is continuous on $[a, b]$, so both the maximum and minimum exist.

2. Maximum at $x = c$, minimum at $x = b$;
The Extreme Value Theorem applies because f is continuous on $[a, b]$, so both the maximum and minimum exist.

3. Maximum at $x = c$, no minimum;
The Extreme Value Theorem does not apply, because the function is not defined on a closed interval.

4. No maximum, no minimum;
The Extreme Value Theorem does not apply, because the function is not continuous or defined on a closed interval.

5. Maximum at $x = c$, minimum at $x = a$;
The Extreme Value Theorem does not apply, because the function is not continuous.

6. Maximum at $x = a$, minimum at $x = c$;
The Extreme Value Theorem does not apply since the function is not continuous.

7. Local minimum at $(-1, 0)$, local maximum at $(1, 0)$

8. Minima at $(-2, 0)$ and $(2, 0)$, maximum at $(0, 2)$

9. Maximum at $(0, 5)$ Note that there is no minimum since the endpoint $(2, 0)$ is excluded from the graph.

10. Local maximum at $(-3, 0)$, local minimum at $(2, 0)$, maximum at $(1, 2)$, minimum at $(0, -1)$

11. The first derivative $f'(x) = -\dfrac{1}{x^2} + \dfrac{1}{x}$ has a zero at $x = 1$.

Critical point value: $f(1) = 1 + \ln 1 = 1$

Endpoint values: $f(0.5) = 2 + \ln 0.5 \approx 1.307$

$$f(4) = \frac{1}{4} + \ln 4 \approx 1.636$$

Maximum value is $\dfrac{1}{4} + \ln 4$ at $x = 4$;

minimum value is 1 at $x = 1$;

local maximum at $\left(\dfrac{1}{2}, 2 - \ln 2\right)$

12. The first derivative $g'(x) = -e^{-x}$ has no zeros, so we need only consider the endpoints.

$$g(-1) = e^{-(-1)} = e \qquad g(1) = e^{-1} = \frac{1}{e}$$

Maximum value is e at $x = -1$;

minimum value is $\dfrac{1}{e}$ at $x = 1$.

13. The first derivative $h'(x) = \dfrac{1}{x + 1}$ has no zeros, so we need only consider the endpoints.
$$h(0) = \ln 1 = 0 \qquad h(3) = \ln 4$$
Maximum value is $\ln 4$ at $x = 3$;
minimum value is 0 at $x = 0$.

14. The first derivative $k'(x) = -2xe^{-x^2}$ has a zero at $x = 0$.

Since the domain has no endpoints, any extreme value must

occur at $x = 0$. Since $k(0) = e^{-0^2} = 1$ and $\lim\limits_{x \to \pm\infty} k(x) = 0$,

the maximum value is 1 at $x = 0$.

15. The first derivative $f'(x) = \cos\left(x + \dfrac{\pi}{4}\right)$, has zeros at

$x = \dfrac{\pi}{4}, x = \dfrac{5\pi}{4}$.

Critical point values: $\quad x = \dfrac{\pi}{4} \qquad f(x) = 1$

$$x = \frac{5\pi}{4} \qquad f(x) = -1$$

Endpoint values: $\qquad x = 0 \qquad f(x) = \dfrac{1}{\sqrt{2}}$

$$x = \frac{7\pi}{4} \qquad f(x) = 0$$

Maximum value is 1 at $x = \dfrac{\pi}{4}$;

minimum value is -1 at $x = \dfrac{5\pi}{4}$;

local minimum at $\left(0, \dfrac{1}{\sqrt{2}}\right)$;

local maximum at $\left(\dfrac{7\pi}{4}, 0\right)$

16. The first derivative $g'(x) = \sec x \tan x$ has zeros at $x = 0$

and $x = \pi$ and is undefined at $x = \dfrac{\pi}{2}$. Since $g(x) = \sec x$ is

also undefined at $x = \dfrac{\pi}{2}$, the critical points occur only at

$x = 0$ and $x = \pi$.

Critical point values: $\quad x = 0 \qquad g(x) = 1$
$\qquad\qquad\qquad\qquad\quad x = \pi \qquad g(x) = -1$

Since the range of $g(x)$ is $(-\infty, -1] \cup [1, \infty)$, these values must be a local minimum and local maximum, respectively. Local minimum at $(0, 1)$; local maximum at $(\pi, -1)$

17. The first derivative $f'(x) = \dfrac{2}{5}x^{-3/5}$ is never zero but is

undefined at $x = 0$.

Critical point value: $\quad x = 0 \quad f(x) = 0$
Endpoint value: $\qquad\; x = -3 \;\; f(x) = (-3)^{2/5}$
$$\qquad\qquad\qquad\qquad\qquad = 3^{2/5} \approx 1.552$$

Since $f(x) > 0$ for $x \neq 0$, the critical point at $x = 0$ is a local minimum, and since $f(x) \leq (-3)^{2/5}$ for $-3 \leq x < 1$, the endpoint value at $x = -3$ is a global maximum. Maximum value is $3^{2/5}$ at $x = -3$; minimum value is 0 at $x = 0$.

18. The first derivative $f'(x) = \dfrac{3}{5}x^{-2/5}$ is never zero but is

undefined at $x = 0$.

Critical point value: $x = 0 \qquad f(x) = 0$
Endpoint value: $\qquad x = 3 \qquad f(x) = 3^{3/5} \approx 1.933$
Since $f(x) < 0$ for $x < 0$ and $f(x) > 0$ for $x > 0$, the critical point is not a local minimum or maximum. The maximum value is $3^{3/5}$ at $x = 3$.

19.

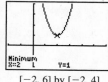

[−2, 6] by [−2, 4]

Minimum value is 1 at $x = 2$.

20.

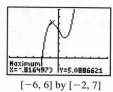

[−6, 6] by [−2, 7]

To find the exact values, note that $y' = 3x^2 - 2$, which is

zero when $x = \pm\sqrt{\dfrac{2}{3}}$. Local maximum at

$\left(-\sqrt{\dfrac{2}{3}}, 4 + \dfrac{4\sqrt{6}}{9}\right) \approx (-0.816, 5.089)$; local minimum at

$\left(\sqrt{\dfrac{2}{3}}, 4 - \dfrac{4\sqrt{6}}{9}\right) \approx (0.816, 2.911)$

21.

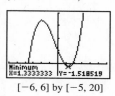

[−6, 6] by [−5, 20]

To find the exact values, note that

$y' = 3x^2 + 2x - 8 = (3x - 4)(x + 2)$, which is zero when

$x = -2$ or $x = \dfrac{4}{3}$. Local maximum at $(-2, 17)$;

local minimum at $\left(\dfrac{4}{3}, -\dfrac{41}{27}\right)$

22.

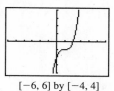

[−6, 6] by [−4, 4]

Note that $y' = 3x^2 - 6x + 3 = 3(x - 1)^2$, which is zero at
$x = 1$. The graph shows that the function assumes lower
values to the left and higher values to the right of this point,
so the function has no local or global extreme values.

23.

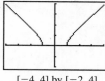

[−4, 4] by [−2, 4]

Minimum value is 0 at $x = -1$ and at $x = 1$.

24.

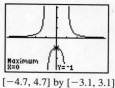

[−4.7, 4.7] by [−3.1, 3.1]

To confirm that there are no "hidden" extrema, note that
$y' = -(x^2 - 1)^{-2}(2x) = \dfrac{-2x}{(x^2 - 1)^2}$ which is zero only at
$x = 0$ and is undefined only where y is undefined. There is
a local maximum at $(0, -1)$.

25.

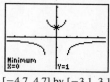

[−1.5, 1.5] by [−0.5, 3]

The minimum value is 1 at $x = 0$.

26.

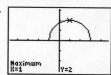

[−4.7, 4.7] by [−3.1, 3.1]

The actual graph of the function has asymptotes at
$x = \pm1$, so there are no extrema near these values. (This is
an example of *grapher failure*.) There is a local
minimum at $(0, 1)$.

27.

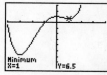

[−4.7, 4.7] by [−3.1, 3.1]

Maximum value is 2 at $x = 1$;
minimum value is 0 at $x = -1$ and at $x = 3$.

28.

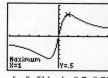

[−4, 4] by [−80, 30]

Minimum value is $-\dfrac{115}{2}$ at $x = -3$;

local maximum at $(0, 10)$;

local minimum at $\left(1, \dfrac{13}{2}\right)$

29.

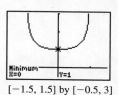

[−5, 5] by [−0.7, 0.7]

Maximum value is $\dfrac{1}{2}$ at $x = 1$;

minimum value is $-\dfrac{1}{2}$ at $x = -1$.

30.

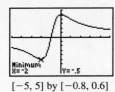

[−5, 5] by [−0.8, 0.6]

Maximum value is $\frac{1}{2}$ at $x = 0$;

minimum value is $-\frac{1}{2}$ at $x = -2$.

31.

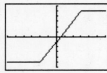

[−6, 6] by [0, 12]

Maximum value is 11 at $x = 5$;
minimum value is 5 on the interval $[−3, 2]$;
local maximum at $(−5, 9)$

32.

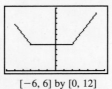

[−3, 8] by [−5, 5]

Maximum value is 4 on the interval $[5, 7]$;
minimum value is −4 on the interval $[−2, 1]$.

33.

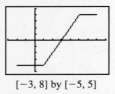

[−6, 6] by [−6, 6]

Maximum value is 5 on the interval $[3, \infty)$;
minimum value is −5 on the interval $(−\infty, −2]$.

34.

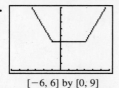

[−6, 6] by [0, 9]

Minimum value is 4 on the interval $[−1, 3]$

35. (a) No, since $f'(x) = \frac{2}{3}(x − 2)^{-1/3}$, which is undefined at
$x = 2$.

(b) The derivative is defined and nonzero for all $x \neq 2$.
Also, $f(2) = 0$ and $f(x) > 0$ for all $x \neq 2$.

(c) No, $f(x)$ need not have a global maximum because its
domain is all real numbers. Any restriction of f to a
closed interval of the form $[a, b]$ would have both a
maximum value and a minimum value on the interval.

(d) The answers are the same as (a) and (b) with 2 replaced
by a.

36. Note that $f(x) = \begin{cases} -x^3 + 9x, & x \leq -3 \text{ or } 0 \leq x < 3 \\ x^3 - 9x, & -3 < x < 0 \text{ or } x \geq 3. \end{cases}$

Therefore, $f'(x) = \begin{cases} -3x^2 + 9, & x < -3 \text{ or } 0 < x < 3 \\ 3x^2 - 9, & -3 < x < 0 \text{ or } x > 3. \end{cases}$

(a) No, since the left- and right-hand derivatives at $x = 0$
are −9 and 9, respectively.

(b) No, since the left- and right-hand derivatives at $x = 3$
are −18 and 18, respectively.

(c) No, since the left- and right-hand derivatives at $x = -3$
are −18 and 18, respectively.

(d) The critical points occur when $f'(x) = 0$
(at $x = \pm\sqrt{3}$) and when $f'(x)$ is undefined (at $x = 0$ or
$x = \pm3$). The minimum value is 0 at $x = -3$, at $x = 0$,
and at $x = 3$; local maxima occur at $(-\sqrt{3}, 6\sqrt{3})$ and
$(\sqrt{3}, 6\sqrt{3})$.

37.

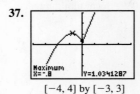

[−4, 4] by [−3, 3]

$y' = x^{2/3}(1) + \frac{2}{3}x^{-1/3}(x + 2) = \frac{5x + 4}{3\sqrt[3]{x}}$

crit. pt.	derivative	extremum	value
$x = -\frac{4}{5}$	0	local max	$\frac{12}{25}10^{1/3} \approx 1.034$
$x = 0$	undefined	local min	0

38.

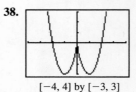

[−4, 4] by [−3, 3]

$y' = x^{2/3}(2x) + \frac{2}{3}x^{-1/3}(x^2 - 4) = \frac{8x^2 - 8}{3\sqrt[3]{x}}$

crit. pt.	derivative	extremum	value
$x = -1$	0	minimum	−3
$x = 0$	undefined	local max	0
$x = 1$	0	minimum	−3

39.

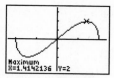

$[-2.35, 2.35]$ by $[-3.5, 3.5]$

$$y' = x \cdot \frac{1}{2\sqrt{4 - x^2}}(-2x) + (1)\sqrt{4 - x^2}$$

$$= \frac{-x^2 + (4 - x^2)}{\sqrt{4 - x^2}} = \frac{4 - 2x^2}{\sqrt{4 - x^2}}$$

crit. pt.	derivative	extremum	value
$x = -2$	undefined	local max	0
$x = -\sqrt{2}$	0	minimum	-2
$x = \sqrt{2}$	0	maximum	2
$x = 2$	undefined	local min	0

40.

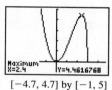

$[-4.7, 4.7]$ by $[-1, 5]$

$$y = x^2 \cdot \frac{1}{2\sqrt{3 - x}}(-1) + 2x\sqrt{3 - x}$$

$$= \frac{-x^2 + 4x(3 - x)}{2\sqrt{3 - x}} = \frac{-5x^2 + 12x}{2\sqrt{3 - x}}$$

crit. pt.	derivative	extremum	value
$x = 0$	0	minimum	0
$x = \frac{12}{5}$	0	local max	$\frac{144}{125}15^{1/2} \approx 4.462$
$x = 3$	undefined	minimum	0

41.

$[-4.7, 4.7]$ by $[0, 6.2]$

$$y' = \begin{cases} -2, & x < 1 \\ 1, & x > 1 \end{cases}$$

crit. pt.	derivative	extremum	value
$x = 1$	undefined	minimum	2

42.

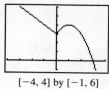

$[-4, 4]$ by $[-1, 6]$

$$y' = \begin{cases} -1, & x < 0 \\ 2 - 2x, & x > 0 \end{cases}$$

crit. pt.	derivative	extremum	value
$x = 0$	undefined	local min	3
$x = 1$	0	local max	4

43.

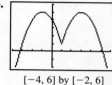

$[-4, 6]$ by $[-2, 6]$

$$y' = \begin{cases} -2x - 2, & x < 1 \\ -2x + 6, & x > 1 \end{cases}$$

crit. pt.	derivative	extremum	value
$x = -1$	0	maximum	5
$x = 1$	undefined	local min	1
$x = 3$	0	maximum	5

44.

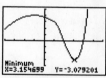

$[-4, 6]$ by $[-5, 5]$

We begin by determining whether $f'(x)$ is defined at $x = 1$, where

$$f(x) = \begin{cases} -\frac{1}{4}x^2 - \frac{1}{2}x + \frac{15}{4}, & x \le 1 \\ x^3 - 6x^2 + 8x, & x > 1 \end{cases}$$

Left-hand derivative:

$$\lim_{h \to 0^-} \frac{f(1 + h) - f(1)}{h} = \lim_{h \to 0^-} \frac{-\frac{1}{4}(1 + h)^2 - \frac{1}{2}(1 + h) + \frac{15}{4} - 3}{h}$$

$$= \lim_{h \to 0^-} \frac{-h^2 - 4h}{4h}$$

$$= \lim_{h \to 0^-} \frac{1}{4}(-h - 4)$$

$$= -1$$

Right-hand derivative:

$$\lim_{h \to 0^+} \frac{f(1 + h) - f(1)}{h}$$

$$= \lim_{h \to 0^+} \frac{(1 + h)^3 - 6(1 + h)^2 + 8(1 + h) - 3}{h}$$

$$= \lim_{h \to 0^+} \frac{h^3 - 3h^2 - h}{h}$$

$$= \lim_{h \to 0^+} (h^2 - 3h - 1)$$

$$= -1$$

Thus $f'(x) = \begin{cases} -\frac{1}{2}x - \frac{1}{2}, & x \le 1 \\ 3x^2 - 12x + 8, & x > 1 \end{cases}$

44. continued

Note that $-\frac{1}{2}x - \frac{1}{2} = 0$ when $x = -1$, and

$3x^2 - 12x + 8 = 0$ when $x = \dfrac{12 \pm \sqrt{12^2 - 4(3)(8)}}{2(3)}$

$= \dfrac{12 \pm \sqrt{48}}{6} = 2 \pm \dfrac{2\sqrt{3}}{3}$.

But $2 - \dfrac{2\sqrt{3}}{3} \approx 0.845 < 1$, so the only critical points

occur at $x = -1$ and $x = 2 + \dfrac{2\sqrt{3}}{3} \approx 3.155$.

crit. pt.	derivative	extremum	value
$x = -1$	0	local max	4
$x \approx 3.155$	0	local max	≈ -3.079

45. Graph (c), since this is the only graph that has positive slope at c.

46. Graph (b), since this is the only graph that represents a differentiable function at a and b and has negative slope at c.

47. Graph (d), since this is the only graph representing a function that is differentiable at b but not at a.

48. Graph (a), since this is the only graph that represents a function that is not differentiable at a or b.

49. (a) $V(x) = 160x - 52x^2 + 4x^3$
$V'(x) = 160 - 104x + 12x^2 = 4(x - 2)(3x - 20)$
The only critical point in the interval $(0, 5)$ is at $x = 2$. The maximum value of $V(x)$ is 144 at $x = 2$.

(b) The largest possible volume of the box is 144 cubic units, and it occurs when $x = 2$.

50. (a) $P'(x) = 2 - 200x^{-2}$
The only critical point in the interval $(0, \infty)$ is at $x = 10$. The minimum value of $P(x)$ is 40 at $x = 10$.

(b) The smallest possible perimeter of the rectangle is 40 units and it occurs at $x = 10$, which makes the rectangle a 10 by 10 square.

51. (a) $f'(x) = 3ax^2 + 2bx + c$ is a quadratic, so it can have 0, 1, or 2 zeros, which would be the critical points of f. Examples:

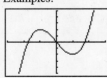

[−3, 3] by [−5, 5]

The function $f(x) = x^3 - 3x$ has two critical points at $x = -1$ and $x = 1$.

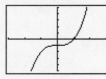

[−3, 3] by [−5, 5]

The function $f(x) = x^3 - 1$ has one critical point at $x = 0$.

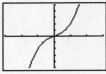

[−3, 3] by [−5, 5]

The function $f(x) = x^3 + x$ has no critical points.

(b) The function can have either two local extreme values or no extreme values. (If there is only one critical point, the cubic function has no extreme values.)

52. (a) By the definition of local maximum value, there is an open interval containing c where $f(x) \leq f(c)$, so $f(x) - f(c) \leq 0$.

(b) Because $x \to c^+$, we have $(x - c) > 0$, and the sign of the quotient must be negative (or zero). This means the limit is nonpositive.

(c) Because $x \to c^-$, we have $(x - c) < 0$, and the sign of the quotient must be positive (or zero). This means the limit is nonnegative.

(d) Assuming that $f'(c)$ exists, the one-sided limits in (b) and (c) above must exist and be equal. Since one is nonpositive and one is nonnegative, the only possible common value is 0.

(e) There will be an open interval containing c where $f(x) - f(c) \geq 0$. The difference quotient for the left-hand derivative will have to be negative (or zero), and the difference quotient for the right-hand derivative will have to be positive (or zero). Taking the limit, the left-hand derivative will be nonpositive, and the right-hand derivative will be nonnegative. Therefore, the only possible value for $f'(c)$ is 0.

53. (a)

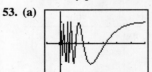

[−0.1, 0.6] by [−1.5, 1.5]

$f(0) = 0$ is not a local extreme value because in any open interval containing $x = 0$, there are infinitely many points where $f(x) = 1$ and where $f(x) = -1$.

(b) One possible answer, on the interval $[0, 1]$:

$$f(x) = \begin{cases} (1 - x) \cos \dfrac{1}{1 - x}, & 0 \leq x < 1 \\ 0, & x = 1 \end{cases}$$

This function has no local extreme value at $x = 1$. Note that it is continuous on $[0, 1]$.

■ Section 4.2 Mean Value Theorem
(pp. 186–194)

Quick Review 4.2

1. $2x^2 - 6 < 0$
$2x^2 < 6$
$x^2 < 3$
$-\sqrt{3} < x < \sqrt{3}$
Interval: $(-\sqrt{3}, \sqrt{3})$

2. $3x^2 - 6 > 0$
$$3x^2 > 6$$
$$x^2 > 2$$
$$x < -\sqrt{2} \text{ or } x > \sqrt{2}$$
Intervals: $(-\infty, -\sqrt{2}) \cup (\sqrt{2}, \infty)$

3. Domain: $8 - 2x^2 \geq 0$
$$8 \geq 2x^2$$
$$4 \geq x^2$$
$$-2 \leq x \leq 2$$
The domain is $[-2, 2]$.

4. f is continuous for all x in the domain, or, in the interval $[-2, 2]$.

5. f is differentiable for all x in the interior of its domain, or, in the interval $(-2, 2)$.

6. We require $x^2 - 1 \neq 0$, so the domain is $x \neq \pm 1$.

7. f is continuous for all x in the domain, or, for all $x \neq \pm 1$.

8. f is differentiable for all x in the domain, or, for all $x \neq \pm 1$.

9. $7 = -2(-2) + C$
$$7 = 4 + C$$
$$C = 3$$

10. $-1 = (1)^2 + 2(1) + C$
$$-1 = 3 + C$$
$$C = -4$$

Section 4.2 Exercises

1. (a) $f'(x) = 5 - 2x$

Since $f'(x) > 0$ on $\left(-\infty, \frac{5}{2}\right)$, $f'(x) = 0$ at $x = \frac{5}{2}$, and $f'(x) < 0$ on $\left(\frac{5}{2}, \infty\right)$, we know that $f(x)$ has a local maximum at $x = \frac{5}{2}$. Since $f\left(\frac{5}{2}\right) = \frac{25}{4}$, the local maximum occurs at the point $\left(\frac{5}{2}, \frac{25}{4}\right)$. (This is also a global maximum.)

(b) Since $f'(x) > 0$ on $\left(-\infty, \frac{5}{2}\right)$, $f(x)$ is increasing on $\left(-\infty, \frac{5}{2}\right]$.

(c) Since $f'(x) < 0$ on $\left(\frac{5}{2}, \infty\right)$, $f(x)$ is decreasing on $\left[\frac{5}{2}, \infty\right)$.

2. (a) $g'(x) = 2x - 1$

Since $g'(x) < 0$ on $\left(-\infty, \frac{1}{2}\right)$, $g'(x) = 0$ at $x = \frac{1}{2}$, and $g'(x) > 0$ on $\left(\frac{1}{2}, \infty\right)$, we know that $g(x)$ has a local minimum at $x = \frac{1}{2}$. Since $g\left(\frac{1}{2}\right) = -\frac{49}{4}$, the local minimum occurs at the point $\left(\frac{1}{2}, -\frac{49}{4}\right)$. (This is also a global minimum.)

(b) Since $g'(x) > 0$ on $\left(\frac{1}{2}, \infty\right)$, $g(x)$ is increasing on $\left[\frac{1}{2}, \infty\right)$.

(c) Since $g'(x) < 0$ on $\left(-\infty, \frac{1}{2}\right)$, $g(x)$ is decreasing on $\left(-\infty, \frac{1}{2}\right]$.

3. (a) $h'(x) = -\dfrac{2}{x^2}$

Since $h'(x)$ is never zero and is undefined only where $h(x)$ is undefined, there are no critical points. Also, the domain $(-\infty, 0) \cup (0, \infty)$ has no endpoints. Therefore, $h(x)$ has no local extrema.

(b) Since $h'(x)$ is never positive, $h(x)$ is not increasing on any interval.

(c) Since $h'(x) < 0$ on $(-\infty, 0) \cup (0, \infty)$, $h(x)$ is decreasing on $(-\infty, 0)$ and on $(0, \infty)$.

4. (a) $k'(x) = -\dfrac{2}{x^3}$

Since $k'(x)$ is never zero and is undefined only where $k(x)$ is undefined, there are no critical points. Also, the domain $(-\infty, 0) \cup (0, \infty)$ has no endpoints. Therefore, $k(x)$ has no local extrema.

(b) Since $k'(x) > 0$ on $(-\infty, 0)$, $k(x)$ is increasing on $(-\infty, 0)$.

(c) Since $k'(x) < 0$ on $(0, \infty)$, $k(x)$ is decreasing on $(0, \infty)$.

5. (a) $f'(x) = 2e^{2x}$

Since $f'(x)$ is never zero or undefined, and the domain of $f(x)$ has no endpoints, $f(x)$ has no extrema.

(b) Since $f'(x)$ is always positive, $f(x)$ is increasing on $(-\infty, \infty)$.

(c) Since $f'(x)$ is never negative, $f(x)$ is not decreasing on any interval.

6. (a) $f'(x) = -0.5e^{-0.5x}$

Since $f'(x)$ is never zero or undefined, and the domain of $f(x)$ has no endpoints, $f(x)$ has no extrema.

(b) Since $f'(x)$ is never positive, $f(x)$ is not increasing on any interval.

(c) Since $f'(x)$ is always negative, $f(x)$ is decreasing on $(-\infty, \infty)$.

7. (a) $y' = -\dfrac{1}{2\sqrt{x+2}}$

In the domain $[-2, \infty)$, y' is never zero and is undefined only at the endpoint $x = -2$. The function y has a local maximum at $(-2, 4)$. (This is also a global maximum.)

(b) Since y' is never positive, y is not increasing on any interval.

(c) Since y' is negative on $(-2, \infty)$, y is decreasing on $[-2, \infty)$.

8. (a) $y' = 4x^3 - 20x = 4x(x + \sqrt{5})(x - \sqrt{5})$

The function has critical points at $x = -\sqrt{5}$, $x = 0$, and $x = \sqrt{5}$. Since $y' < 0$ on $(-\infty, -\sqrt{5})$ and $(0, \sqrt{5})$ and $y' > 0$ on $(-\sqrt{5}, 0)$ and $(\sqrt{5}, \infty)$, the points at $x = \pm\sqrt{5}$ are local minima and the point at $x = 0$ is a local maximum. Thus, the function has a local maximum at $(0, 9)$ and local minima at $(-\sqrt{5}, -16)$ and $(\sqrt{5}, -16)$. (These are also global minima.)

(b) Since $y' > 0$ on $(-\sqrt{5}, 0)$ and $(\sqrt{5}, \infty)$, y is increasing on $[-\sqrt{5}, 0]$ and $[\sqrt{5}, \infty)$.

(c) Since $y' < 0$ on $(-\infty, -\sqrt{5})$ and $(0, \sqrt{5})$, y is decreasing on $(-\infty, -\sqrt{5}]$ and $[0, \sqrt{5}]$.

9.

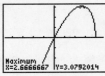

[−4.7, 4.7] by [−3.1, 3.1]

(a) $f'(x) = x \cdot \dfrac{1}{2\sqrt{4-x}}(-1) + \sqrt{4-x}$

$= \dfrac{-3x+8}{2\sqrt{4-x}}$

The local extrema occur at the critical point $x = \dfrac{8}{3}$ and

at the endpoint $x = 4$. There is a local (and absolute)

maximum at $\left(\dfrac{8}{3}, \dfrac{16}{3\sqrt{3}}\right)$ or approximately (2.67, 3.08),

and a local minimum at (4, 0).

(b) Since $f'(x) > 0$ on $\left(-\infty, \dfrac{8}{3}\right)$, $f(x)$ is increasing on

$\left(-\infty, \dfrac{8}{3}\right]$.

(c) Since $f'(x) < 0$ on $\left(\dfrac{8}{3}, 4\right)$, $f(x)$ is decreasing on

$\left[\dfrac{8}{3}, 4\right]$.

10.

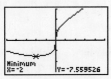

[−5, 5] by [−15, 15]

(a) $g'(x) = x^{1/3}(1) + \dfrac{1}{3}x^{-2/3}(x+8) = \dfrac{4x+8}{3x^{2/3}}$

The local extrema can occur at the critical points

$x = -2$ and $x = 0$, but the graph shows that no extrema

occurs at $x = 0$. There is a local (and absolute)

minimum at $(-2, -6\sqrt[3]{2})$ or approximately

$(-2, -7.56)$.

(b) Since $g'(x) > 0$ on the intervals $(-2, 0)$ and $(0, \infty)$, and

$g(x)$ is continuous at $x = 0$, $g(x)$ is increasing on

$[-2, \infty)$.

(c) Since $g'(x) < 0$ on the interval $(-\infty, -2)$, $g(x)$ is

decreasing on $(-\infty, -2]$.

11.

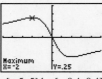

[−5, 5] by [−0.4, 0.4]

(a) $h'(x) = \dfrac{(x^2+4)(-1) - (-x)(2x)}{(x^2+4)^2} = \dfrac{x^2-4}{(x^2+4)^2}$

$= \dfrac{(x+2)(x-2)}{(x^2+4)^2}$

The local extrema occur at the critical points, $x = \pm 2$.

There is a local (and absolute) maximum at $\left(-2, \dfrac{1}{4}\right)$

and a local (and absolute) minimum at $\left(2, -\dfrac{1}{4}\right)$.

(b) Since $h'(x) > 0$ on $(-\infty, -2)$ and $(2, \infty)$, $h(x)$ is

increasing on $(-\infty, -2]$ and $[2, \infty)$.

(c) Since $h'(x) < 0$ on $(-2, 2)$, $h(x)$ is decreasing on

$[-2, 2]$.

12.

[−4.7, 4.7] by [−3.1, 3.1]

(a) $k'(x) = \dfrac{(x^2-4)(1) - x(2x)}{(x^2-4)^2} = -\dfrac{x^2+4}{(x^2-4)^2}$

Since $k'(x)$ is never zero and is undefined only where

$k(x)$ is undefined, there are no critical points. Since

there are no critical points and the domain includes no

endpoints, $k(x)$ has no local extrema.

(b) Since $k'(x)$ is never positive, $k(x)$ is not increasing on

any interval.

(c) Since $k'(x)$ is negative wherever it is defined, $k(x)$ is

decreasing on each interval of its domain: on

$(-\infty, -2)$, $(-2, 2)$, and $(2, \infty)$.

13.

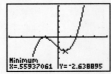

[−4, 4] by [−6, 6]

(a) $f'(x) = 3x^2 - 2 + 2\sin x$

Note that $3x^2 - 2 > 2$ for $|x| \geq 1.2$ and $|2\sin x| \leq 2$ for

all x, so $f'(x) > 0$ for $|x| \geq 1.2$. Therefore, all critical

points occur in the interval $(-1.2, 1.2)$, as suggested by

the graph. Using grapher techniques, there is a local

maximum at approximately $(-1.126, -0.036)$, and a

local minimum at approximately $(0.559, -2.639)$.

(b) $f(x)$ is increasing on the intervals $(-\infty, -1.126]$ and

$[0.559, \infty)$, where the interval endpoints are

approximate.

(c) $f(x)$ is decreasing on the interval $[-1.126, 0.559]$,

where the interval endpoints are approximate.

14.

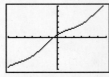

[−6, 6] by [−12, 12]

(a) $g'(x) = 2 - \sin x$

Since $1 \leq g'(x) \leq 3$ for all x, there are no critical

points. Since there are no critical points and the domain

has no endpoints, there are no local extrema.

(b) Since $g'(x) > 0$ for all x, $g(x)$ is increasing on $(-\infty, \infty)$.

(c) Since $g'(x)$ is never negative, $g(x)$ is not decreasing on

any interval.

15. (a) f is continuous on [0, 1] and differentiable on (0, 1).

(b)
$$f'(c) = \frac{f(1) - f(0)}{1 - 0}$$
$$2c + 2 = \frac{2 - (-1)}{1}$$
$$2c = 1$$
$$c = \frac{1}{2}$$

16. (a) f is continuous on [0, 1] and differentiable on (0, 1).

(b)
$$f'(c) = \frac{f(1) - f(0)}{1 - 0}$$
$$\frac{2}{3}c^{-1/3} = \frac{1 - 0}{1}$$
$$c^{-1/3} = \frac{3}{2}$$
$$c = \left(\frac{3}{2}\right)^{-3}$$
$$c = \frac{8}{27}$$

17. (a) f is continuous on [−1, 1] and differentiable on (−1, 1).

(b)
$$f'(c) = \frac{f(1) - f(-1)}{1 - (-1)}$$
$$\frac{1}{\sqrt{1 - c^2}} = \frac{\frac{\pi}{2} - \left(-\frac{\pi}{2}\right)}{2}$$
$$\sqrt{1 - c^2} = \frac{2}{\pi}$$
$$1 - c^2 = \frac{4}{\pi^2}$$
$$c^2 = 1 - \frac{4}{\pi^2}$$
$$c = \pm\sqrt{1 - \frac{4}{\pi^2}} \approx \pm 0.771$$

18. (a) f is continuous on [2, 4] and differentiable on (2, 4).

(b)
$$f'(c) = \frac{f(4) - f(2)}{4 - 2}$$
$$\frac{1}{c - 1} = \frac{\ln 3 - \ln 1}{2}$$
$$c - 1 = \frac{2}{\ln 3}$$
$$c = 1 + \frac{2}{\ln 3} \approx 2.820$$

19. (a) The secant line passes through $(0.5, f(0.5)) = (0.5, 2.5)$ and $(2, f(2)) = (2, 2.5)$, so its equation is $y = 2.5$.

(b) The slope of the secant line is 0, so we need to find c such that $f'(c) = 0$.
$$1 - c^{-2} = 0$$
$$c^{-2} = 1$$
$$c = 1$$
$$f(c) = f(1) = 2$$
The tangent line has slope 0 and passes through (1, 2), so its equation is $y = 2$.

20. (a) The secant line passes through $(1, f(1)) = (1, 0)$ and $(3, f(3)) = (3, \sqrt{2})$, so its slope is
$$\frac{\sqrt{2} - 0}{3 - 1} = \frac{\sqrt{2}}{2} = \frac{1}{\sqrt{2}}.$$
The equation is $y = \frac{1}{\sqrt{2}}(x - 1) + 0$
or $y = \frac{1}{\sqrt{2}}x - \frac{1}{\sqrt{2}}$, or $y \approx 0.707x - 0.707$.

(b) We need to find c such that $f'(c) = \frac{1}{\sqrt{2}}$.
$$\frac{1}{2\sqrt{c - 1}} = \frac{1}{\sqrt{2}}$$
$$2\sqrt{c - 1} = \sqrt{2}$$
$$c - 1 = \frac{1}{2}$$
$$c = \frac{3}{2}$$
$$f(c) = f\left(\frac{3}{2}\right) = \sqrt{\frac{1}{2}} = \frac{1}{\sqrt{2}}$$

The tangent line has slope $\frac{1}{\sqrt{2}}$ and passes through $\left(\frac{3}{2}, \frac{1}{\sqrt{2}}\right)$. Its equation is $y = \frac{1}{\sqrt{2}}\left(x - \frac{3}{2}\right) + \frac{1}{\sqrt{2}}$ or $y = \frac{1}{\sqrt{2}}x - \frac{1}{2\sqrt{2}}$, or $y \approx 0.707x - 0.354$.

21. (a) Since $f'(x) = \frac{1}{3}x^{-2/3}$, f is not differentiable at $x = 0$.

(b)

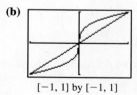

[−1, 1] by [−1, 1]

(c)
$$f'(c) = \frac{f(1) - f(-1)}{1 - (-1)}$$
$$\frac{1}{3}c^{-2/3} = \frac{1 - (-1)}{2}$$
$$\frac{1}{3}c^{-2/3} = 1$$
$$c^{-2/3} = 3$$
$$c = \pm 3^{-3/2} \approx 0.192$$

22. (a) Since $f'(x) = \begin{cases} -1, & 0 \le x < 1 \\ 1, & 3 \ge x > 1 \end{cases}$,

f is not differentiable at $x = 1$. (If f were differentiable at $x = 1$, it would violate the Intermediate Value Theorem for Derivatives.)

(b)

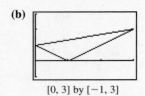

[0, 3] by [−1, 3]

(c) We require $f'(c) = \dfrac{f(3) - f(0)}{3 - 0} = \dfrac{2 - 1}{3} = \dfrac{1}{3}$, but

$f'(x) = \pm 1$ for all x where $f'(x)$ is defined. Therefore,

there is no such value of c.

23. (a) Since $f'(x) = \begin{cases} 1, & -1 \le x < 0 \\ -1, & 1 \ge x > 0 \end{cases}$,

f is not differentiable at $x = 0$. (If f were differentiable at $x = 0$, it would violate the Intermediate Value Theorem for Derivatives.)

(b)

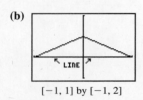

[−1, 1] by [−1, 2]

(c) We require $f'(c) = \dfrac{f(1) - f(-1)}{1 - (-1)} = \dfrac{0 - 0}{2} = 0$, but

$f'(x) = \pm 1$ for all x where $f'(x)$ is defined. Therefore,

there is no such value of c.

24. (a) We test for differentiability at $x = 0$, using the limits given in Section 3.5.

Left-hand derivative:

$$\lim_{h \to 0^-} \frac{f(0 + h) - f(0)}{h} = \lim_{h \to 0^-} \frac{\cos h - 1}{h} = 0$$

Right-hand derivative:

$$\lim_{h \to 0^+} \frac{f(0 + h) - f(0)}{h} = \lim_{h \to 0^+} \frac{(1 + \sin h) - 1}{h}$$
$$= \lim_{h \to 0^+} \frac{\sin h}{h}$$
$$= 1$$

Since the left- and right-hand derivatives are not equal,

f is not differentiable at $x = 0$.

(b)

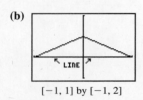

[−π, π] by [−1, 2]

(c) Note that $f'(x) = \begin{cases} -\sin x, & -\pi \le x < 0 \\ \cos x, & 0 < x \le \pi \end{cases}$.

We require $f'(c) = \dfrac{f(\pi) - f(-\pi)}{\pi - (-\pi)} = \dfrac{1 - (-1)}{2\pi} = \dfrac{1}{\pi}$.

For $-\pi < c < 0$, this occurs when $-\sin c = \dfrac{1}{\pi}$, so

$c = -\sin^{-1}\left(\dfrac{1}{\pi}\right) \approx -0.324$ or

$c = -\pi + \sin^{-1}\left(\dfrac{1}{\pi}\right) \approx -2.818$. For $0 < c < \pi$, this

occurs when $\cos c = \dfrac{1}{\pi}$, so $c = \cos^{-1}\left(\dfrac{1}{\pi}\right) \approx 1.247$. The

possible values of c are approximately

$-2.818, -0.324,$ and $1.247.$

25. $f(x) = \dfrac{x^2}{2} + C$

26. $f(x) = 2x + C$

27. $f(x) = x^3 - x^2 + x + C$

28. $f(x) = -\cos x + C$

29. $f(x) = e^x + C$

30. $f(x) = \ln(x - 1) + C$

31. $\quad f(x) = \dfrac{1}{x} + C, x > 0$

$\quad f(2) = 1$

$\quad \dfrac{1}{2} + C = 1$

$\quad\quad C = \dfrac{1}{2}$

$\quad f(x) = \dfrac{1}{x} + \dfrac{1}{2}, x > 0$

32. $\quad f(x) = x^{1/4} + C$

$\quad f(1) = -2$

$1^{1/4} + C = -2$

$\quad 1 + C = -2$

$\quad\quad C = -3$

$\quad f(x) = x^{1/4} - 3$

33. $\quad\quad f(x) = \ln(x + 2) + C$

$\quad\quad f(-1) = 3$

$\ln(-1 + 2) + C = 3$

$\quad\quad 0 + C = 3$

$\quad\quad\quad C = 3$

$\quad\quad f(x) = \ln(x + 2) + 3$

34. $\quad f(x) = x^2 + x - \sin x + C$

$\quad f(0) = 3$

$\quad 0 + C = 3$

$\quad\quad C = 3$

$\quad f(x) = x^2 + x - \sin x + 3$

35. Possible answers:

(a)

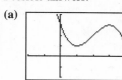

[−2, 4] by [−2, 4]

(b)

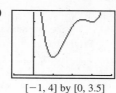

[−1, 4] by [0, 3.5]

(c)

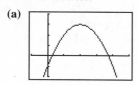

[−1, 4] by [0, 3.5]

36. Possible answers:

(a)

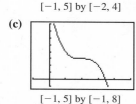

[−1, 5] by [−2, 4]

(b)

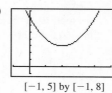

[−1, 5] by [−1, 8]

(c)

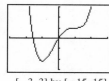

[−1, 5] by [−1, 8]

(d)

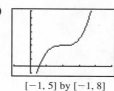

[−1, 5] by [−1, 8]

37. One possible answer:

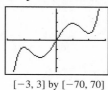

[−3, 3] by [−15, 15]

38. One possible answer:

[−3, 3] by [−70, 70]

39. Because the trucker's average speed was 79.5 mph, and by the Mean Value Theorem, the trucker must have been going that speed at least once during the trip.

40. Let $f(t)$ denote the temperature indicated after t seconds. We assume that $f'(t)$ is defined and continuous for $0 \le t \le 20$. The average rate of change is 10.6°F/sec. Therefore, by the Mean Value Theorem, $f'(c) = 10.6$°F/sec for some value of c in [0, 20]. Since the temperature was constant before $t = 0$, we also know that $f'(0) = 0$°F/min. But f' is continuous, so by the Intermediate Value Theorem, the rate of change $f'(t)$ must have been 10.1°F/sec at some moment during the interval.

41. Because its average speed was approximately 7.667 knots, and by the Mean Value Theorem, it must have been going that speed at least once during the trip.

42. The runner's average speed for the marathon was approximately 11.909 mph. Therefore, by the Mean Value Theorem, the runner must have been going that speed at least once during the marathon. Since the initial speed and final speed are both 0 mph and the runner's speed is continuous, by the Intermediate Value Theorem, the runner's speed must have been 11 mph at least twice.

43. (a) Since $v'(t) = 1.6$, $v(t) = 1.6t + C$. But $v(0) = 0$, so $C = 0$ and $v(t) = 1.6t$. Therefore, $v(30) = 1.6(30) = 48$. The rock will be going 48 m/sec.

(b) Let $s(t)$ represent position.
Since $s'(t) = v(t) = 1.6t$, $s(t) = 0.8t^2 + D$. But $s(0) = 0$, so $D = 0$ and $s(t) = 0.8t^2$. Therefore, $s(30) = 0.8(30)^2 = 720$. The rock travels 720 meters in the 30 seconds it takes to hit bottom, so the bottom of the crevasse is 720 meters below the point of release.

(c) The velocity is now given by $v(t) = 1.6t + C$, where $v(0) = 4$. (Note that the sign of the initial velocity is the same as the sign used for the acceleration, since both act in a downward direction.) Therefore, $v(t) = 1.6t + 4$, and $s(t) = 0.8t^2 + 4t + D$, where $s(0) = 0$ and so $D = 0$. Using $s(t) = 0.8t^2 + 4t$ and the known crevasse depth of 720 meters, we solve $s(t) = 720$ to obtain the positive solution $t \approx 27.604$, and so $v(t) = v(27.604) = 1.6(27.604) + 4 \approx 48.166$. The rock will hit bottom after about 27.604 seconds, and it will be going about 48.166 m/sec.

44. (a) We assume the diving board is located at $s = 0$ and the water at $s = 10$, so that downward velocities are positive. The acceleration due to gravity is 9.8 m/sec^2, so $v'(t) = 9.8$ and $v(t) = 9.8t + C$. Since $v(0) = 0$, we have $v(t) = 9.8t$. Then the position is given by $s(t)$ where $s'(t) = v(t) = 9.8t$, so $s(t) = 4.9t^2 + D$. Since $s(0) = 0$, we have $s(t) = 4.9t^2$. Solving $s(t) = 10$ gives $t^2 = \dfrac{10}{4.9} = \dfrac{100}{49}$, so the positive solution is $t = \dfrac{10}{7}$. The velocity at this time is $v\left(\dfrac{10}{7}\right) = 9.8\left(\dfrac{10}{7}\right) = 14$ m/sec.

(b) Again $v(t) = 9.8t + C$, but this time $v(0) = -2$ and so $v(t) = 9.8t - 2$. Then $s'(t) = 9.8t - 2$, so $s(t) = 4.9t^2 - 2t + D$. Since $s(0) = 0$, we have $s(t) = 4.9t^2 - 2t$. Solving $s(t) = 10$ gives the positive solution $t = \dfrac{2 + 10\sqrt{2}}{9.8} \approx 1.647$ sec.

The velocity at this time is
$$v\left(\frac{2 + 10\sqrt{2}}{9.8}\right) = 9.8\left(\frac{2 + 10\sqrt{2}}{9.8}\right) - 2 = 10\sqrt{2} \text{ m/sec or}$$
about 14.142 m/sec.

45. Because the function is not continuous on [0, 1]. The function does not satisfy the hypotheses of the Mean Value Theorem, and so it need not satisfy the conclusion of the Mean Value Theorem.

46. Because the Mean Value Theorem applies to the function $y = \sin x$ on any interval, and $y = \cos x$ is the derivative of $\sin x$. So, between any two zeros of $\sin x$, its derivative, $\cos x$, must be zero at least once.

47. $f(x)$ must be zero at least once between a and b by the Intermediate Value Theorem. Now suppose that $f(x)$ is zero twice between a and b. Then by the Mean Value Theorem, $f'(x)$ would have to be zero at least once between the two zeros of $f(x)$, but this can't be true since we are given that $f'(x) \neq 0$ on this interval. Therefore, $f(x)$ is zero once and only once between a and b.

48. Let $f(x) = x^4 + 3x + 1$. Then $f(x)$ is continuous and differentiable everywhere. $f'(x) = 4x^3 + 3$, which is never zero between $x = -2$ and $x = -1$. Since $f(-2) = 11$ and $f(-1) = -1$, exercise 47 applies, and $f(x)$ has exactly one zero between $x = -2$ and $x = -1$.

49. Let $f(x) = x + \ln(x + 1)$. Then $f(x)$ is continuous and differentiable everywhere on [0, 3]. $f'(x) = 1 + \dfrac{1}{x + 1}$, which is never zero on [0, 3]. Now $f(0) = 0$, so $x = 0$ is one solution of the equation. If there were a second solution, $f(x)$ would be zero twice in [0, 3], and by the Mean Value Theorem, $f'(x)$ would have to be zero somewhere between the two zeros of $f(x)$. But this can't happen, since $f'(x)$ is never zero on [0, 3]. Therefore, $f(x) = 0$ has exactly one solution in the interval [0, 3].

50. Consider the function $k(x) = f(x) - g(x)$. $k(x)$ is continuous and differentiable on [a, b], and since $k(a) = f(a) - g(a) = 0$ and $k(b) = f(b) - g(b) = 0$, by the Mean Value Theorem, there must be a point c in (a, b) where $k'(c) = 0$. But since $k'(c) = f'(c) - g'(c)$, this means that $f'(c) = g'(c)$, and c is a point where the graphs of f and g have parallel or identical tangent lines.

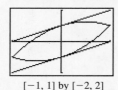

[−1, 1] by [−2, 2]

51. (a) Increasing: [−2, −1.3] and [1.3, 2];
decreasing: [−1.3, 1.3];
local max: $x \approx -1.3$
local min: $x \approx 1.3$

(b) Regression equation: $y = 3x^2 - 5$

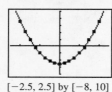

[−2.5, 2.5] by [−8, 10]

(c) Since $f'(x) = 3x^2 - 5$, we have $f(x) = x^3 - 5x + C$. But $f(0) = 0$, so $C = 0$. Then $f(x) = x^3 - 5x$.

52. (a) Toward: $0 < t < 2$ and $5 < t < 8$;
away: $2 < t < 5$

(b) A local extremum in this problem is a time/place where Priya changes the direction of her motion.

(c) Regression equation:
$y = -0.0820x^3 + 0.9163x^2 - 2.5126x + 3.3779$

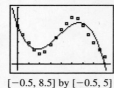

[−0.5, 8.5] by [−0.5, 5]

(d) Using the unrounded values from the regression equation, we obtain
$f'(t) = -0.2459t^2 + 1.8324t - 2.5126$. According to the regression equation, Priya is moving toward the motion detector when $f'(t) < 0$ ($0 < t < 1.81$ and $5.64 < t < 8$), and away from the detector when $f'(t) > 0$ ($1.81 < t < 5.64$).

53. $\dfrac{f(b) - f(a)}{b - a} = \dfrac{\frac{1}{b} - \frac{1}{a}}{b - a} = -\dfrac{1}{ab}$

$f'(c) = -\dfrac{1}{c^2}$, so $-\dfrac{1}{c^2} = -\dfrac{1}{ab}$ and $c^2 = ab$.

Thus, $c = \sqrt{ab}$.

54. $\dfrac{f(b) - f(a)}{b - a} = \dfrac{b^2 - a^2}{b - a} = b + a$

$f'(c) = 2c$, so $2c = b + a$ and $c = \dfrac{a + b}{2}$.

55. By the Mean Value Theorem,
$\sin b - \sin a = (\cos c)(b - a)$ for some c between a and b. Taking the absolute value of both sides and using $|\cos c| \leq 1$ gives the result.

56. Apply the Mean Value Theorem to f on [a, b].

Since $f(b) < f(a)$, $\dfrac{f(b) - f(a)}{b - a}$ is negative, and hence $f'(x)$

must be negative at some point between a and b.

57. Let $f(x)$ be a monotonic function defined on an interval D. For any two values in D, we may let x_1 be the smaller value and let x_2 be the larger value, so $x_1 < x_2$. Then either $f(x_1) < f(x_2)$ (if f is increasing), or $f(x_1) > f(x_2)$ (if f is decreasing), which means $f(x_1) \neq f(x_2)$. Therefore, f is one-to-one.

■ Section 4.3 Connecting f' and f'' with the Graph of f (pp. 194–206)

Exploration 1 Finding f from f'

1. Any function $f(x) = x^4 - 4x^3 + C$ where C is a real number. For example, let $C = 0, 1, 2$. Their graphs are all vertical shifts of each other.

2. Their behavior is the same as the behavior of the function f of Example 8.

Exploration 2   Finding f from f' and f''

1. f has an absolute maximum at $x = 0$ and an absolute minimum of 1 at $x = 4$. We are not given enough information to determine $f(0)$.

2. f has a point of inflection at $x = 2$.

3.

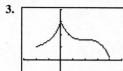

[-3, 5] by [-5, 20]

Quick Review 4.3

1.
$$x^2 - 9 < 0$$
$$(x + 3)(x - 3) < 0$$

Intervals	$x < -3$	$-3 < x < 3$	$3 < x$
Sign of $(x + 3)(x - 3)$	$+$	$-$	$+$

Solution set: $(-3, 3)$

2.
$$x^3 - 4x > 0$$
$$x(x + 2)(x - 2) > 0$$

Intervals	$x < -2$	$-2 < x < 0$	$0 < x < 2$	$2 < x$
Sign of $x(x + 2)(x - 2)$	$-$	$+$	$-$	$+$

Solution set: $(-2, 0) \cup (2, \infty)$

3. f: all reals
f': all reals, since $f'(x) = xe^x + e^x$

4. f: all reals

f': $x \neq 0$, since $f'(x) = \dfrac{3}{5}x^{-2/5}$

5. f: $x \neq 2$

f': $x \neq 2$, since $f'(x) = \dfrac{(x - 2)(1) - (x)(1)}{(x - 2)^2} = \dfrac{-2}{(x - 2)^2}$

6. f: all reals

f': $x \neq 0$, since $f'(x) = \dfrac{2}{5}x^{-3/5}$

7. Left end behavior model: 0
Right end behavior model: $-x^2 e^x$
Horizontal asymptote: $y = 0$

8. Left end behavior model: $x^2 e^{-x}$
Right end behavior model: 0
Horizontal asymptote: $y = 0$

9. Left end behavior model: 0
Right end behavior model: 200
Horizontal asymptotes: $y = 0$, $y = 200$

10. Left end behavior model: 0
Right end behavior model: 375
Horizontal asymptotes: $y = 0$, $y = 375$

Section 4.3 Exercises

1. (a) Zero: $x = \pm 1$;
positive: $(-\infty, -1)$ and $(1, \infty)$;
negative: $(-1, 1)$

(b) Zero: $x = 0$;
positive: $(0, \infty)$;
negative: $(-\infty, 0)$

2. (a) Zero: $x \approx 0, \pm 1.25$;
positive: $(-1.25, 0)$ and $(1.25, \infty)$;
negative: $(-\infty, -1.25)$ and $(0, 1.25)$

(b) Zero: $x \approx \pm 0.7$;
positive: $(-\infty, -0.7)$ and $(0.7, \infty)$;
negative: $(-0.7, 0.7)$

3. (a) $(-\infty, -2]$ and $[0, 2]$

(b) $[-2, 0]$ and $[2, \infty)$

(c) Local maxima: $x = -2$ and $x = 2$;
local minimum: $x = 0$

4. (a) $[-2, 2]$

(b) $(-\infty, -2]$ and $[2, \infty)$

(c) Local maximum: $x = 2$;
local minimum: $x = -2$

5. (a) $[0, 1]$, $[3, 4]$, and $[5.5, 6]$

(b) $[1, 3]$ and $[4, 5.5]$

(c) Local maxima: $x = 1$, $x = 4$
(if f is continuous at $x = 4$), and $x = 6$;
local minima: $x = 0$, $x = 3$, and $x = 5.5$

6. If f is continuous on the interval $[0, 3]$:

(a) $[0, 3]$

(b) Nowhere

(c) Local maximum: $x = 3$;
local minimum: $x = 0$

7. $y' = 2x - 1$

Intervals	$x < \frac{1}{2}$	$x > \frac{1}{2}$
Sign of y'	$-$	$+$
Behavior of y	Decreasing	Increasing

$y'' = 2$ (always positive: concave up)

Graphical support:

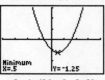

[-4, 4] by [-3, 3]

(a) $\left[\dfrac{1}{2}, \infty\right)$

(b) $\left(-\infty, \dfrac{1}{2}\right]$

(c) $(-\infty, \infty)$

(d) Nowhere

(e) Local (and absolute) minimum at $\left(\dfrac{1}{2}, -\dfrac{5}{4}\right)$

(f) None

8. $y' = -6x^2 + 12x = -6x(x - 2)$

Intervals	$x < 0$	$0 < x < 2$	$2 < x$
Sign of y'	$-$	$+$	$-$
Behavior of y	Decreasing	Increasing	Decreasing

$y'' = -12x + 12 = -12(x - 1)$

Intervals	$x < 1$	$x > 1$
Sign of y''	$+$	$-$
Behavior of y	Concave up	Concave down

Graphical support:

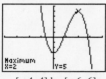

$[-4, 4]$ by $[-6, 6]$

(a) $[0, 2]$

(b) $(-\infty, 0]$ and $[2, \infty)$

(c) $(-\infty, 1)$

(d) $(1, \infty)$

(e) Local maximum: $(2, 5)$;
local minimum: $(0, -3)$

(f) At $(1, 1)$

9. $y' = 8x^3 - 8x = 8x(x - 1)(x + 1)$

Intervals	$x < -1$	$-1 < x < 0$	$0 < x < 1$	$1 < x$
Sign of y'	$-$	$+$	$-$	$+$
Behavior of y	Decreasing	Increasing	Decreasing	Increasing

$y'' = 24x^2 - 8 = 8(\sqrt{3}x - 1)(\sqrt{3}x + 1)$

Intervals	$x < -\dfrac{1}{\sqrt{3}}$	$-\dfrac{1}{\sqrt{3}} < x < \dfrac{1}{\sqrt{3}}$	$\dfrac{1}{\sqrt{3}} < x$
Sign of y''	$+$	$-$	$+$
Behavior of y	Concave up	Concave down	Concave up

Graphical support:

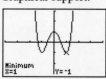

$[-4, 4]$ by $[-3, 3]$

(a) $[-1, 0]$ and $[1, \infty)$

(b) $(-\infty, -1]$ and $[0, 1]$

(c) $\left(-\infty, -\dfrac{1}{\sqrt{3}}\right)$ and $\left(\dfrac{1}{\sqrt{3}}, \infty\right)$

(d) $\left(-\dfrac{1}{\sqrt{3}}, \dfrac{1}{\sqrt{3}}\right)$

(e) Local maximum: $(0, 1)$;
local (and absolute) minima: $(-1, -1)$ and $(1, -1)$

(f) $\left(\pm\dfrac{1}{\sqrt{3}}, -\dfrac{1}{9}\right)$

10. $y' = xe^{1/x}(-x^{-2}) + e^{1/x} = e^{1/x}\left(1 - \dfrac{1}{x}\right)$

Intervals	$x < 0$	$0 < x < 1$	$1 < x$
Sign of y'	$+$	$-$	$+$
Behavior of y	Increasing	Decreasing	Increasing

$y'' = e^{1/x}(x^{-2}) + \left(1 - \dfrac{1}{x}\right)e^{1/x}(-x^{-2}) = \dfrac{e^{1/x}}{x^3}$

Intervals	$x < 0$	$x > 0$
Sign of y''	$-$	$+$
Behavior of y	Concave down	Concave up

Graphical support:

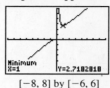

$[-8, 8]$ by $[-6, 6]$

(a) $(-\infty, 0)$ and $[1, \infty)$　　**(b)** $(0, 1]$

(c) $(0, \infty)$　　**(d)** $(-\infty, 0)$

(e) Local minimum: $(1, e)$

(f) None

11. $y' = x\dfrac{1}{2\sqrt{8 - x^2}}(-2x) + (\sqrt{8 - x^2})(1) = \dfrac{8 - 2x^2}{\sqrt{8 - x^2}}$

Intervals	$-\sqrt{8} < x < -2$	$-2 < x < 2$	$2 < x < \sqrt{8}$
Sign of y'	$-$	$+$	$-$
Behavior of y	Decreasing	Increasing	Decreasing

$$y'' = \dfrac{(\sqrt{8 - x^2})(-4x) - (8 - 2x^2)\dfrac{1}{2\sqrt{8 - x^2}}(-2x)}{(\sqrt{8 - x^2})^2}$$

$$= \dfrac{2x^3 - 24x}{(8 - x^2)^{3/2}} = \dfrac{2x(x^2 - 12)}{(8 - x^2)^{3/2}}$$

Intervals	$-\sqrt{8} < x < 0$	$0 < x < \sqrt{8}$
Sign of y''	$+$	$-$
Behavior of y	Concave up	Concave down

Graphical support:

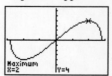

$[-3.02, 3.02]$ by $[-6.5, 6.5]$

(a) $[-2, 2]$

(b) $[-\sqrt{8}, -2]$ and $[2, \sqrt{8}]$

(c) $(-\sqrt{8}, 0)$

(d) $(0, \sqrt{8})$

(e) Local maxima: $(-\sqrt{8}, 0)$ and $(2, 4)$;
local minima: $(-2, -4)$ and $(\sqrt{8}, 0)$
Note that the local extrema at $x = \pm 2$ are also absolute extrema.

(f) $(0, 0)$

12. $y' = \begin{cases} -2x, & x < 0 \\ 2x, & x > 0 \end{cases}$

Intervals	$x < 0$	$x > 0$
Sign of y'	+	+
Behavior of y	Increasing	Increasing

$y'' = \begin{cases} -2, & x < 0 \\ 2, & x > 0 \end{cases}$

Intervals	$x < 0$	$x > 0$
Sign of y''	−	+
Behavior of y	Concave down	Concave up

Graphical support:

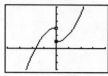

$[-4, 4]$ by $[-3, 6]$

(a) $(-\infty, 0)$ and $[0, \infty)$

(b) None

(c) $(0, \infty)$

(d) $(-\infty, 0)$

(e) Local minimum: $(0, 1)$

(f) Note that $(0, 1)$ is not an inflection point because the graph has no tangent line at this point. There are no inflection points.

13. $y' = 12x^2 + 42x + 36 = 6(x + 2)(2x + 3)$

Intervals	$x < -2$	$-2 < x < -\frac{3}{2}$	$-\frac{3}{2} < x$
Sign of y'	+	−	+
Behavior of y	Increasing	Decreasing	Increasing

$y'' = 24x + 42 = 6(4x + 7)$

Intervals	$x < -\frac{7}{4}$	$-\frac{7}{4} < x$
Sign of y''	−	+
Behavior of y	Concave down	Concave up

Graphical support:

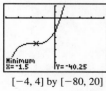

$[-4, 4]$ by $[-80, 20]$

(a) $(-\infty, -2]$ and $\left[-\frac{3}{2}, \infty\right)$

(b) $\left[-2, -\frac{3}{2}\right]$

(c) $\left(-\frac{7}{4}, \infty\right)$

(d) $\left(-\infty, -\frac{7}{4}\right)$

(e) Local maximum: $(-2, -40)$; local minimum: $\left(-\frac{3}{2}, -\frac{161}{4}\right)$

(f) $\left(-\frac{7}{4}, -\frac{321}{8}\right)$

14. $y' = -4x^3 + 12x^2 - 4$

Using grapher techniques, the zeros of y' are $x \approx -0.53$, $x \approx 0.65$, and $x \approx 2.88$.

Intervals	$x < -0.53$	$-0.53 < x < 0.65$	$0.65 < x < 2.88$	$2.88 < x$
Sign of y'	+	−	+	−
Behavior of y	Increasing	Decreasing	Increasing	Decreasing

$y'' = -12x^2 + 24x = -12x(x - 2)$

Intervals	$x < 0$	$0 < x < 2$	$2 < x$
Sign of y''	−	+	−
Behavior of y	Concave down	Concave up	Concave down

Graphical support:

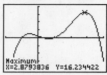

$[-2, 4]$ by $[-20, 20]$

(a) $(-\infty, -0.53]$ and $[0.65, 2.88]$

(b) $[-0.53, 0.65]$ and $[2.88, \infty)$

(c) $(0, 2)$

(d) $(-\infty, 0)$ and $(2, \infty)$

(e) Local maxima: $(-0.53, 2.45)$ and $(2.88, 16.23)$; local minimum: $(0.65, -0.68)$
Note that the local maximum at $x \approx 2.88$ is also an absolute maximum.

(f) $(0,1)$ and $(2, 9)$

15. $y' = \dfrac{2}{5}x^{-4/5}$

Intervals	$x < 0$	$0 < x$
Sign of y'	+	+
Behavior of y	Increasing	Increasing

$y'' = -\dfrac{8}{25}x^{-9/5}$

Intervals	$x < 0$	$0 < x$
Sign of y''	+	−
Behavior of y	Concave up	Concave down

Graphical support:

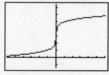

$[-6, 6]$ by $[-1.5, 7.5]$

(a) $(-\infty, \infty)$

(b) None

(c) $(-\infty, 0)$

(d) $(0, \infty)$

(e) None

(f) $(0, 3)$

16. $y' = -\dfrac{1}{3}x^{-2/3}$

Intervals	$x < 0$	$0 < x$
Sign of y'	−	−
Behavior of y	Decreasing	Decreasing

$$y'' = \frac{2}{9}x^{-5/3}$$

Intervals	$x < 0$	$0 < x$
Sign of y''	$-$	$+$
Behavior of y	Concave down	Concave up

Graphical support:

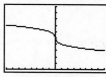

$[-8, 8]$ by $[0, 10]$

(a) None

(b) $(-\infty, \infty)$

(c) $(0, \infty)$

(d) $(-\infty, 0)$

(e) None

(f) $(0, 5)$

17. This problem can be solved using either graphical or analytic methods. For a graphical solution, use NDER to obtain the graphs shown.

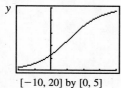

$[-10, 20]$ by $[0, 5]$

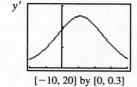

$[-10, 20]$ by $[0, 0.3]$

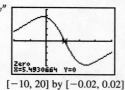

$[-10, 20]$ by $[-0.02, 0.02]$

An analytic solution follows.

$$y' = \frac{(e^x + 3e^{0.8x})(5e^x) - 5e^x(e^x + 2.4e^{0.8x})}{(e^x + 3e^{0.8x})^2}$$

$$= \frac{5e^{2x} + 15e^{1.8x} - 5e^{2x} - 12e^{1.8x}}{(e^x + 3e^{0.8x})^2}$$

$$= \frac{3e^{1.8x}}{(e^x + 3e^{0.8x})^2}$$

Since $y' > 0$ for all x, y is increasing for all x.

$$y'' = \frac{(e^x + 3e^{0.8x})^2(5.4e^{1.8x}) - (3e^{1.8x})(2)(e^x + 3e^{0.8x})(e^x + 2.4e^{0.8x})}{(e^x + 3e^{0.8x})^4}$$

$$= \frac{(e^x + 3e^{0.8x})(5.4e^{1.8x}) - (6e^{1.8x})(e^x + 2.4e^{0.8x})}{(e^x + 3e^{0.8x})^3}$$

$$= \frac{(-0.6e^x + 1.8e^{0.8x})e^{1.8x}}{(e^x + 3e^{0.8x})^3}$$

$$= \frac{0.6(3 - e^{0.2x})e^{2.6x}}{(e^x + 3e^{0.8x})^3}$$

Solve $y'' = 0$: $3 - e^{0.2x} = 0$

$$0.2x = \ln 3$$

$$x = 5 \ln 3$$

Intervals	$x < 5 \ln 3$	$5 \ln 3 < x$
Sign of y''	$+$	$-$
Behavior of y	Concave up	Concave down

17. continued

(a) $(-\infty, \infty)$

(b) None

(c) $(-\infty, 5 \ln 3) \approx (-\infty, 5.49)$

(d) $(5 \ln 3, \infty) \approx (5.49, \infty)$

(e) None

(f) $\left(5 \ln 3, \dfrac{5}{2}\right) \approx (5.49, 2.50)$

18. This problem can be solved using either graphical or analytic methods. For a graphical solution, use NDER to obtain the graphs shown.

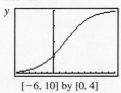

$[-6, 10]$ by $[0, 4]$

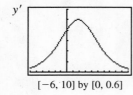

$[-6, 10]$ by $[0, 0.6]$

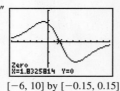

$[-6, 10]$ by $[-0.15, 0.15]$

An analytic solution follows.

$$y = \frac{8e^{-x}}{2e^{-x} + 5e^{-1.5x}} = \frac{8}{2 + 5e^{-0.5x}}$$

$$y' = \frac{(2 + 5e^{-0.5x})(0) - (8)(-2.5e^{-0.5x})}{(2 + 5e^{-0.5x})^2}$$

$$= \frac{20e^{-0.5x}}{(2 + 5e^{-0.5x})^2}$$

Since $y' > 0$ for all x, y is increasing for all x.

$$y'' = \frac{(2 + 5e^{-0.5x})^2(-10e^{-0.5x}) - (20e^{-0.5x})(2)(2 + 5e^{-0.5x})(-2.5e^{-0.5x})}{(2 + 5e^{-0.5x})^4}$$

$$= \frac{(2 + 5e^{-0.5x})(-10e^{-0.5x}) - (40e^{-0.5x})(-2.5e^{-0.5x})}{(2 + 5e^{-0.5x})^3}$$

$$= \frac{10e^{-0.5x}(5e^{-0.5x} - 2)}{(2 + 5e^{-0.5x})^3}$$

Solve $y'' = 0$: $5e^{-0.5x} - 2 = 0$

$$e^{-0.5x} = \frac{2}{5}$$

$$-0.5x = \ln \frac{2}{5}$$

$$x = -2 \ln \frac{2}{5} = 2 \ln \frac{5}{2}$$

Intervals	$x < 2 \ln \dfrac{5}{2}$	$2 \ln \dfrac{5}{2} < x$
Sign of y''	+	−
Behavior of y	Concave up	Concave down

(a) $(-\infty, \infty)$

(b) None

(c) $\left(-\infty, 2 \ln \dfrac{5}{2}\right) \approx (-\infty, 1.83)$

(d) $\left(2 \ln \dfrac{5}{2}, \infty\right) \approx (1.83, \infty)$

(e) None

(f) $\left(2 \ln \dfrac{5}{2}, 2\right) \approx (1.83, 2)$

19. $y' = \begin{cases} 2, & x < 1 \\ -2x, & x > 1 \end{cases}$

Intervals	$x < 1$	$1 < x$
Sign of y'	$+$	$-$
Behavior of y	Increasing	Decreasing

$y'' = \begin{cases} 0, & x < 1 \\ -2, & x > 1 \end{cases}$

Intervals	$x < 1$	$1 < x$
Sign of y''	0	$-$
Behavior of y	Linear	Concave down

Graphical support:

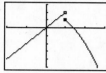

$[-2, 3]$ by $[-5, 3]$

(a) $(-\infty, 1)$

(b) $[1, \infty)$

(c) None

(d) $(1, \infty)$

(e) None

(f) None

20. $y' = e^x$
$y'' = e^x$

Since y' and y'' are both positive on the entire domain, y is increasing and concave up on the entire domain.

Graphical support:

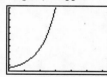

$[0, 2\pi]$ by $[0, 20]$

(a) $[0, 2\pi]$

(b) None

(c) $(0, 2\pi)$

(d) None

(e) Local (and absolute) maximum: $(2\pi, e^{2\pi})$; local (and absolute) minimum: $(0, 1)$

(f) None

21. $y' = xe^{1/x^2}(-2x^{-3}) + (e^{1/x^2})(1)$

$\quad = e^{1/x^2}(1 - 2x^{-2}) = e^{1/x^2}\left(\dfrac{x^2 - 2}{x^2}\right)$

Intervals	$x < -\sqrt{2}$	$-\sqrt{2} < x < 0$	$0 < x < \sqrt{2}$	$\sqrt{2} < x$
Sign of y'	$+$	$-$	$-$	$+$
Behavior of y	Increasing	Decreasing	Decreasing	Increasing

21. continued

$$y'' = (e^{1/x^2})(4x^{-3}) + (1 - 2x^{-2})(e^{1/x^2})(-2x^{-3})$$

$$= (e^{1/x^2})(2x^{-3} + 4x^{-5})$$

$$= 2e^{1/x^2}\left(\frac{x^2 + 2}{x^5}\right)$$

Intervals	$x < 0$	$0 < x$
Sign of y''	$-$	$+$
Behavior of y	Concave down	Concave up

Graphical support:

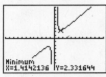

[−12, 12] by [−9, 9]

(a) $(-\infty, -\sqrt{2}]$ and $[\sqrt{2}, \infty)$

(b) $[-\sqrt{2}, 0)$ and $(0, \sqrt{2}]$

(c) $(0, \infty)$

(d) $(-\infty, 0)$

(e) Local maximum: $(-\sqrt{2}, -\sqrt{2e}) \approx (-1.41, -2.33)$; local minimum: $(\sqrt{2}, \sqrt{2e}) \approx (1.41, 2.33)$

(f) None

22. This problem can be solved using either graphical or analytic methods. For a graphical solution, use NDER to obtain the graphs shown.

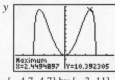

[−4.7, 4.7] by [−3, 11]

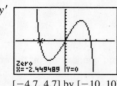

[−4.7, 4.7] by [−10, 10]

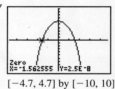

[−4.7, 4.7] by [−10, 10]

An analytic solution follows.

$$y' = x^2 \frac{1}{2\sqrt{9 - x^2}}(-2x) + \sqrt{9 - x^2}(2x)$$

$$= \frac{-3x^3 + 18x}{\sqrt{9 - x^2}} = \frac{-3x(x^2 - 6)}{\sqrt{9 - x^2}}$$

Intervals	$-3 < x < -\sqrt{6}$	$-\sqrt{6} < x < 0$	$0 < x < \sqrt{6}$	$\sqrt{6} < x < 3$
Sign of y'	$+$	$-$	$+$	$-$
Behavior of y	Increasing	Decreasing	Increasing	Decreasing

$$y'' = \frac{(\sqrt{9 - x^2})(-9x^2 + 18) - (-3x^3 + 18x)\dfrac{1}{2\sqrt{9 - x^2}}(-2x)}{(\sqrt{9 - x^2})^2}$$

$$= \frac{(9 - x^2)(-9x^2 + 18) + (-3x^3 + 18x)(x)}{(9 - x^2)^{3/2}}$$

$$= \frac{6x^4 - 81x^2 + 162}{(9 - x^2)^{3/2}}$$

Find the zeros of y'':

$$\frac{3(2x^4 - 27x^2 + 54)}{(9 - x^2)^{3/2}} = 0$$

$$2x^4 - 27x^2 + 54 = 0$$

$$x^2 = \frac{27 \pm \sqrt{27^2 - 4(2)(54)}}{2(2)} = \frac{27 \pm 3\sqrt{33}}{4}$$

$$x = \pm \sqrt{\frac{27 - 3\sqrt{33}}{4}} \approx \pm 1.56$$

Note that we do not use $x = \pm \sqrt{\dfrac{27 + 3\sqrt{33}}{4}} \approx \pm 3.33$, because these values are outside of the domain.

Intervals	$-3 < x < -1.56$	$-1.56 < x < 1.56$	$1.56 < x < 3$
Sign of y''	$-$	$+$	$-$
Behavior of y	Concave down	Concave up	Concave down

(a) $[-3, -\sqrt{6}]$ and $[0, \sqrt{6}]$ or, $\approx[-3, -2.45]$ and $[0, 2.45]$

(b) $[-\sqrt{6}, 0]$ and $[\sqrt{6}, 3]$ or, $\approx[-2.45, 0]$ and $[2.45, 3]$

(c) Approximately $(-1.56, 1.56)$

(d) Approximately $(-3, -1.56)$ and $(1.56, 3)$

(e) Local maxima: $(\pm\sqrt{6}, 6\sqrt{3}) \approx (\pm2.45, 10.39)$; local minima: $(0, 0)$ and $(\pm3, 0)$

(f) $\approx(\pm1.56, 6.25)$

23. $y' = \dfrac{1}{1 + x^2}$

Since $y' > 0$ for all x, y is always increasing.

$$y'' = \frac{d}{dx}(1 + x^2)^{-1} = -(1 + x^2)^{-2}(2x) = \frac{-2x}{(1 + x^2)^2}$$

Intervals	$x < 0$	$0 < x$
Sign of y''	$+$	$-$
Behavior of y	Concave up	Concave down

Graphical support:

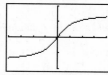

$[-4, 4]$ by $[-2, 2]$

(a) $(-\infty, \infty)$

(b) None

(c) $(-\infty, 0)$

(d) $(0, \infty)$

(e) None

(f) $(0, 0)$

24. $y = x^{3/4}(5 - x) = 5x^{3/4} - x^{7/4}$

$y' = \dfrac{15}{4}x^{-1/4} - \dfrac{7}{4}x^{3/4} = \dfrac{15 - 7x}{4x^{1/4}}$

Intervals	$0 < x < \dfrac{15}{7}$	$\dfrac{15}{7} < x$
Sign of y'	$+$	$-$
Behavior of y	Increasing	Decreasing

$y'' = -\dfrac{15}{16}x^{-5/4} - \dfrac{21}{16}x^{-1/4}$

$= \dfrac{-3(7x + 5)}{16x^{5/4}}$

Since $y'' < 0$ for all $x > 0$, the graph of y is concave down for $x > 0$.

Graphical support:

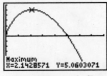

Maximum
X=2.1428571 Y=5.0603071

[0, 8] by [−6, 6]

(a) $\left[0, \dfrac{15}{7}\right]$

(b) $\left[\dfrac{15}{7}, \infty\right)$

(c) None

(d) $(0, \infty)$

(e) Local (and absolute) maximum:

$\left(\dfrac{15}{7}, \left(\dfrac{15}{7}\right)^{3/4} \cdot \dfrac{20}{7}\right) \approx \left(\dfrac{15}{7}, 5.06\right)$;

local minimum: $(0, 0)$

(f) None

25. $y = x^{1/3}(x - 4) = x^{4/3} - 4x^{1/3}$

$y' = \dfrac{4}{3}x^{1/3} - \dfrac{4}{3}x^{-2/3} = \dfrac{4x - 4}{3x^{2/3}}$

Intervals	$x < 0$	$0 < x < 1$	$1 < x$
Sign of y'	$-$	$-$	$+$
Behavior of y	Decreasing	Decreasing	Increasing

$y'' = \dfrac{4}{9}x^{-2/3} + \dfrac{8}{9}x^{-5/3} = \dfrac{4x + 8}{9x^{5/3}}$

Intervals	$x < -2$	$-2 < x < 0$	$0 < x$
Sign of y''	$+$	$-$	$+$
Behavior of y	Concave up	Concave down	Concave up

Graphical support:

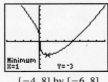

Minimum
X=1   Y=-3

[−4, 8] by [−6, 8]

(a) $[1, \infty)$

(b) $(-\infty, 1]$

(c) $(-\infty, -2)$ and $(0, \infty)$

(d) $(-2, 0)$

(e) Local minimum: $(1, -3)$

(f) $(-2, 6\sqrt[3]{2}) \approx (-2, 7.56)$ and $(0, 0)$

26. $y = x^{1/4}(x + 3) = x^{5/4} + 3x^{1/4}$

$y' = \dfrac{5}{4}x^{1/4} + \dfrac{3}{4}x^{-3/4} = \dfrac{5x + 3}{4x^{3/4}}$

Since $y' > 0$ for all $x > 0$, y is always increasing on its domain $x \geq 0$.

$y'' = \dfrac{5}{16}x^{-3/4} - \dfrac{9}{16}x^{-7/4} = \dfrac{5x - 9}{16x^{7/4}}$

Intervals	$0 < x < \dfrac{9}{5}$	$\dfrac{9}{5} < x$
Sign of y''	$-$	$+$
Behavior of y	Concave down	Concave up

Graphical support:

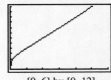

[0, 6] by [0, 12]

(a) $[0, \infty)$

(b) None

(c) $\left(\dfrac{9}{5}, \infty\right)$

(d) $\left(0, \dfrac{9}{5}\right)$

(e) Local (and absolute) minimum: $(0, 0)$

(f) $\left(\dfrac{9}{5}, \dfrac{24}{5} \cdot \sqrt[4]{\dfrac{9}{5}}\right) \approx \left(\dfrac{9}{5}, 5.56\right)$

27. We use a combination of analytic and grapher techniques to solve this problem. Depending on the viewing window chosen, graphs obtained using NDER may exhibit strange behavior near $x = 2$ because, for example, NDER $(y, 2) \approx 1{,}000{,}000$ while y' is actually undefined at $x = 2$. The graph of $y = \dfrac{x^3 - 2x^2 + x - 1}{x - 2}$ is shown below.

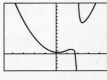

[−4,7, 4.7] by [−5, 15]

$$y' = \frac{(x-2)(3x^2 - 4x + 1) - (x^3 - 2x^2 + x - 1)(1)}{(x-2)^2}$$

$$= \frac{2x^3 - 8x^2 + 8x - 1}{(x-2)^2}$$

The graph of y' is shown below.

[−4,7, 4.7] by [−10, 10]

The zeros of y' are $x \approx 0.15$, $x \approx 1.40$, and $x \approx 2.45$.

Intervals	$x < 0.15$	$0.15 < x < 1.40$	$1.40 < x < 2$	$2 < x < 2.45$	$2.45 < x$
Sign of y'	−	+	−	−	+
Behavior of y	Decreasing	Increasing	Decreasing	Decreasing	Increasing

$$y'' = \frac{(x-2)^2(6x^2 - 16x + 8) - (2x^3 - 8x^2 + 8x - 1)(2)(x-2)}{(x-2)^4}$$

$$= \frac{(x-2)(6x^2 - 16x + 8) - 2(2x^3 - 8x^2 + 8x - 1)}{(x-2)^3}$$

$$= \frac{2x^3 - 12x^2 + 24x - 14}{(x-2)^3}$$

$$= \frac{2(x-1)(x^2 - 5x + 7)}{(x-2)^3}$$

The graph of y'' is shown below.

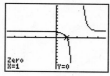

[−4,7, 4.7] by [−10, 10]

Note that the discriminant of $x^2 - 5x + 7$ is $(-5)^2 - 4(1)(7) = -3$, so the only solution of $y'' = 0$ is $x = 1$.

Intervals	$x < 1$	$1 < x < 2$	$2 < x$
Sign of y''	+	−	+
Behavior of y	Concave up	Concave down	Concave up

(a) Approximately $[0.15, 1.40]$ and $[2.45, \infty)$

(b) Approximately $(-\infty, 0.15]$, $[1.40, 2)$, and $(2, 2.45]$

(c) $(-\infty, 1)$ and $(2, \infty)$

(d) $(1, 2)$

(e) Local maximum: $\approx(1.40, 1.29)$; local minima: $\approx(0.15, 0.48)$ and $(2.45, 9.22)$

(f) $(1, 1)$

28. $y' = \dfrac{(x^2 + 1)(1) - x(2x)}{(x^2 + 1)^2} = \dfrac{-x^2 + 1}{(x^2 + 1)^2}$

Intervals	$x < -1$	$-1 < x < 1$	$1 < x$
Sign of y'	$-$	$+$	$-$
Behavior of y	Decreasing	Increasing	Decreasing

$$y'' = \frac{(x^2 + 1)^2(-2x) - (-x^2 + 1)(2)(x^2 + 1)(2x)}{(x^2 + 1)^4}$$

$$= \frac{(x^2 + 1)(-2x) - 4x(-x^2 + 1)}{(x^2 + 1)^3}$$

$$= \frac{2x^3 - 6x}{(x^2 + 1)^3} = \frac{2x(x^2 - 3)}{(x^2 + 1)^3}$$

Intervals	$x < -\sqrt{3}$	$-\sqrt{3} < x < 0$	$0 < x < \sqrt{3}$	$\sqrt{3} < x$
Sign of y''	$-$	$+$	$-$	$+$
Behavior of y	Concave down	Concave up	Concave down	Concave up

Graphical support:

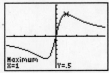

Maximum
X=1   Y=.5

$[-4.7, 4.7]$ by $[-0.7, 0.7]$

(a) $[-1, 1]$

(b) $(-\infty, -1]$ and $[1, \infty)$

(c) $(-\sqrt{3}, 0)$ and $(\sqrt{3}, \infty)$

(d) $(-\infty, -\sqrt{3})$ and $(0, \sqrt{3})$

(e) Local maximum: $\left(1, \dfrac{1}{2}\right)$;

local minimum: $\left(-1, -\dfrac{1}{2}\right)$

(f) $(0, 0)$, $\left(\sqrt{3}, \dfrac{\sqrt{3}}{4}\right)$, and $\left(-\sqrt{3}, -\dfrac{\sqrt{3}}{4}\right)$

29. $y' = (x - 1)^2(x - 2)$

Intervals	$x < 1$	$1 < x < 2$	$2 < x$
Sign of y'	$-$	$-$	$+$
Behavior of y	Decreasing	Decreasing	Increasing

$$y'' = (x - 1)^2(1) + (x - 2)(2)(x - 1)$$
$$= (x - 1)[(x - 1) + 2(x - 2)]$$
$$= (x - 1)(3x - 5)$$

Intervals	$x < 1$	$1 < x < \dfrac{5}{3}$	$\dfrac{5}{3} < x$
Sign of y''	$+$	$-$	$+$
Behavior of y	Concave up	Concave down	Concave up

(a) There are no local maxima.

(b) There is a local (and absolute) minimum at $x = 2$.

(c) There are points of inflection at $x = 1$ and at $x = \dfrac{5}{3}$.

30. $y' = (x - 1)^2(x - 2)(x - 4)$

Intervals	$x < 1$	$1 < x < 2$	$2 < x < 4$	$4 < x$
Sign of y'	$+$	$+$	$-$	$+$
Behavior of y	Increasing	Increasing	Decreasing	Increasing

$$y'' = \frac{d}{dx}[(x - 1)^2(x^2 - 6x + 8)]$$

$$= (x - 1)^2(2x - 6) + (x^2 - 6x + 8)(2)(x - 1)$$

$$= (x - 1)[(x - 1)(2x - 6) + 2(x^2 - 6x + 8)]$$

$$= (x - 1)(4x^2 - 20x + 22)$$

$$= 2(x - 1)(2x^2 - 10x + 11)$$

Note that the zeros of y'' are $x = 1$ and

$$x = \frac{10 \pm \sqrt{10^2 - 4(2)(11)}}{4} = \frac{10 \pm \sqrt{12}}{4} = \frac{5 \pm \sqrt{3}}{2} \approx 1.63 \text{ or } 3.37.$$

The zeros of y'' can also be found graphically, as shown.

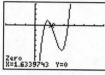

Zero
X=1.6339743 Y=0

$[-3, 7]$ by $[-8, 4]$

Intervals	$x < 1$	$1 < x < 1.63$	$1.63 < x < 3.37$	$3.37 < x$
Sign of y''	$-$	$+$	$-$	$+$
Behavior of y	Concave down	Concave up	Concave down	Concave up

(a) Local maximum at $x = 2$

(b) Local minimum at $x = 4$

(c) Points of inflection at $x = 1$, at $x \approx 1.63$, and at $x \approx 3.37$.

31.

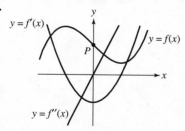

32.

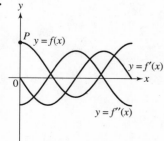

33. (a) Absolute maximum at $(1, 2)$;
absolute minimum at $(3, -2)$

(b) None

(c) One possible answer:

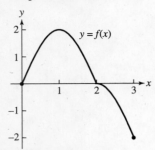

34. (a) Absolute maximum at $(0, 2)$;
absolute minimum at $(2, -1)$ and $(-2, -1)$

(b) At $(1, 0)$ and $(-1, 0)$

(c) One possible answer:

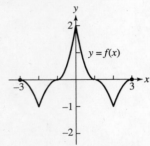

(d) Since f is even, we know $f(3) = f(-3)$. By the
continuity of f, since $f(x) < 0$ when $2 < x < 3$, we
know that $f(3) \leq 0$, and since $f(2) = -1$ and $f'(x) > 0$
when $2 < x < 3$, we know that $f(3) > -1$. In
summary, we know that $f(3) = f(-3)$, $-1 < f(3) \leq 0$,
and $-1 < f(-3) \leq 0$.

35.

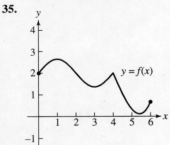

36.

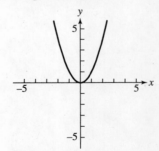

37. (a) $v(t) = s'(t) = 2t - 4$

(b) $a(t) = v'(t) = 2$

(c) It begins at position 3 moving in a negative direction. It
moves to position -1 when $t = 2$, and then changes
direction, moving in a positive direction thereafter.

38. (a) $v(t) = s'(t) = -2 - 2t$

(b) $a(t) = v'(t) = -2$

(c) It begins at position 6 and moves in the negative
direction thereafter.

39. (a) $v(t) = s'(t) = 3t^2 - 3$

(b) $a(t) = v'(t) = 6t$

(c) It begins at position 3 moving in a negative direction. It
moves to position 1 when $t = 1$, and then changes
direction, moving in a positive direction thereafter.

40. (a) $v(t) = s'(t) = 6t - 6t^2$

(b) $a(t) = v'(t) = 6 - 12t$

(c) It begins at position 0. It starts moving in the positive
direction until it reaches position 1 when $t = 1$, and
then it changes direction. It moves in the negative
direction thereafter.

41. (a) The velocity is zero when the tangent line is horizontal,
at approximately $t = 2.2$, $t = 6$, and $t = 9.8$.

(b) The acceleration is zero at the inflection points,
approximately $t = 4$, $t = 8$, and $t = 11$.

42. (a) The velocity is zero when the tangent line is horizontal,
at approximately $t = -0.2$, $t = 4$, and $t = 12$.

(b) The acceleration is zero at the inflection points,
approximately $t = 1.5$, $t = 5.2$, $t = 8$, $t = 11$,
and $t = 13$.

43. No. f must have a horizontal tangent at that point, but f
could be increasing (or decreasing), and there would be no
local extremum. For example, if $f(x) = x^3$,
$f'(0) = 0$ but there is no local extremum at $x = 0$.

44. No. $f''(x)$ could still be positive (or negative) on both sides
of $x = c$, in which case the concavity of the function would
not change at $x = c$. For example, if $f(x) = x^4$, then
$f''(0) = 0$, but f has no inflection point at $x = 0$.

45. One possible answer:

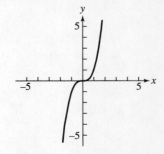

46. One possible answer:

47. One possible answer:

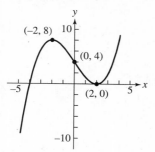

48. One possible answer:

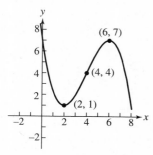

49. (a) Regression equation:

$$y = \frac{2161.4541}{1 + 28.1336e^{-0.8627x}}$$

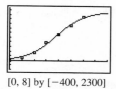

[0, 8] by [−400, 2300]

(b) At approximately $x = 3.868$ (late in 1996), when the sales are about 1081 million dollars/year

(c) 2161.45 million dollars/year

50. (a) In exercise 13, $a = 4$ and $b = 21$, so $-\frac{b}{3a} = -\frac{7}{4}$, which is the x-value where the point of inflection occurs. The local extrema are at $x = -2$ and $x = -\frac{3}{2}$, which are symmetric about $x = -\frac{7}{4}$.

(b) In exercise 8, $a = -2$ and $b = 6$, so $-\frac{b}{3a} = 1$, which is the x-value where the point of inflection occurs. The local extrema are at $x = 0$ and $x = 2$, which are symmetric about $x = 1$.

(c) $f'(x) = 3ax^2 + 2bx + c$ and $f''(x) = 6ax + 2b$.
The point of inflection will occur where $f''(x) = 0$, which is at $x = -\frac{b}{3a}$.
If there are local extrema, they will occur at the zeros of $f'(x)$. Since $f'(x)$ is quadratic, its graph is a parabola and any zeros will be symmetric about the vertex which will also be where $f''(x) = 0$.

51. (a) $f'(x) = \dfrac{(1 + ae^{-bx})(0) - (c)(-abe^{-bx})}{(1 + ae^{-bx})^2}$

$= \dfrac{abce^{-bx}}{(1 + ae^{-bx})^2}$

$= \dfrac{abce^{bx}}{(e^{bx} + a)^2}$,

so the sign of $f'(x)$ is the same as the sign of abc.

(b) $f''(x) = \dfrac{(e^{bx} + a)^2(ab^2ce^{bx}) - (abce^{bx})2(e^{bx} + a)(be^{bx})}{(e^{bx} + a)^4}$

$= \dfrac{(e^{bx} + a)(ab^2ce^{bx}) - (abce^{bx})(2be^{bx})}{(e^{bx} + a)^3}$

$= -\dfrac{ab^2ce^{bx}(e^{bx} - a)}{(e^{bx} + a)^3}$

Since $a > 0$, this changes sign when $x = \dfrac{\ln a}{b}$ due to the $e^{bx} - a$ factor in the numerator, and $f(x)$ has a point of inflection at that location.

52. (a) $f'(x) = 4ax^3 + 3bx^2 + 2cx + d$
$f''(x) = 12ax^2 + 6bx + 2c$
Since $f''(x)$ is quadratic, it must have 0, 1, or 2 zeros. If $f''(x)$ has 0 or 1 zeros, it will not change sign and the concavity of $f(x)$ will not change, so there is no point of inflection. If $f''(x)$ has 2 zeros, it will change sign twice, and $f(x)$ will have 2 points of inflection.

(b) If f has no points of inflection, then $f''(x)$ has 0 or 1 zeros, so the discriminant of $f''(x)$ is ≤ 0. This gives $(6b)^2 - 4(12a)(2c) \leq 0$, or $3b^2 \leq 8ac$. If f has 2 points of inflection, then $f''(x)$ has 2 zeros and the inequality is reversed, so $3b^2 > 8ac$. In summary, f has 2 points of inflection if and only if $3b^2 > 8ac$.

■ Section 4.4 Modeling and Optimization
(pp. 206–220)

Exploration 1   Constructing Cones

1. The circumference of the base of the cone is the circumference of the circle of radius 4 minus x, or $8\pi - x$. Thus, $r = \dfrac{8\pi - x}{2\pi}$. Use the Pythagorean Theorem to find h, and the formula for the volume of a cone to find V.

2. The expression under the radical must be nonnegative, that is, $16 - \left(\dfrac{8\pi - x}{2\pi}\right)^2 \geq 0$.
Solving this inequality for x gives: $0 \leq x \leq 16\pi$.

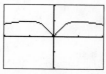

[0, 16π] by [−10, 40]

3. The circumference of the original circle of radius 4 is 8π. Thus, $0 \le x \le 8\pi$.

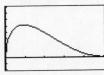

[0, 8π] by [-10, 40]

4. The maximum occurs at about $x = 4.61$. The maximum volume is about $V = 25.80$.

5. Start with $\dfrac{dV}{dx} = \dfrac{2\pi}{3}rh\dfrac{dr}{dx} + \dfrac{\pi}{3}r^2\dfrac{dh}{dx}$. Compute $\dfrac{dr}{dx}$ and $\dfrac{dh}{dx}$, substitute these values in $\dfrac{dV}{dx}$, set $\dfrac{dV}{dx} = 0$, and solve for x to obtain $x = \dfrac{8(3 - \sqrt{6})\pi}{3} \approx 4.61$.

Then $V = \dfrac{128\pi\sqrt{3}}{27} \approx 25.80$.

Quick Review 4.4

1. $y' = 3x^2 - 12x + 12 = 3(x - 2)^2$
Since $y' \ge 0$ for all x (and $y' > 0$ for $x \ne 2$), y is increasing on $(-\infty, \infty)$ and there are no local extrema.

2. $y' = 6x^2 + 6x - 12 = 6(x + 2)(x - 1)$
$y'' = 12x + 6$
The critical points occur at $x = -2$ or $x = 1$, since $y' = 0$ at these points. Since $y''(-2) = -18 < 0$, the graph has a local maximum at $x = -2$. Since $y''(1) = 18 > 0$, the graph has a local minimum at $x = 1$. In summary, there is a local maximum at $(-2, 17)$ and a local minimum at $(1, -10)$.

3. $V = \dfrac{1}{3}\pi r^2 h = \dfrac{1}{3}\pi(5)^2(8) = \dfrac{200\pi}{3}$ cm^3

4. $V = \pi r^2 h = 1000$

$SA = 2\pi rh + 2\pi r^2 = 600$

Solving the volume equation for h gives $h = \dfrac{1000}{\pi r^2}$.

Substituting into the surface area equation gives

$\dfrac{2000}{r} + 2\pi r^2 = 600$. Solving graphically, we have

$r \approx -11.14$, $r \approx 4.01$, or $r \approx 7.13$. Discarding the negative value and using $h = \dfrac{1000}{\pi r^2}$ to find the corresponding values of h, the two possibilities for the dimensions of the cylinder are:

$r \approx 4.01$ cm and $h \approx 19.82$ cm, or,

$r \approx 7.13$ cm and $h \approx 6.26$ cm.

5. Since $y = \sin x$ is an odd function, $\sin(-\alpha) = -\sin\alpha$.

6. Since $y = \cos x$ is an even function, $\cos(-\alpha) = \cos\alpha$.

7. $\sin(\pi - \alpha) = \sin\pi\cos\alpha - \cos\pi\sin\alpha$
$= 0\cos\alpha - (-1)\sin\alpha$
$= \sin\alpha$

8. $\cos(\pi - \alpha) = \cos\pi\cos\alpha + \sin\pi\sin\alpha$
$= (-1)\cos\alpha + 0\sin\alpha$
$= -\cos\alpha$

9. $x^2 + y^2 = 4$ and $y = \sqrt{3}x$
$x^2 + (\sqrt{3}x)^2 = 4$
$x^2 + 3x^2 = 4$
$4x^2 = 4$
$x = \pm 1$
Since $y = \sqrt{3}x$, the solutions are:
$x = 1$ and $y = \sqrt{3}$, or, $x = -1$ and $y = -\sqrt{3}$.
In ordered pair notation, the solutions are $(1, \sqrt{3})$ and $(-1, -\sqrt{3})$.

10. $\dfrac{x^2}{4} + \dfrac{y^2}{9} = 1$ and $y = x + 3$

$\dfrac{x^2}{4} + \dfrac{(x + 3)^2}{9} = 1$

$9x^2 + 4(x + 3)^2 = 36$

$9x^2 + 4x^2 + 24x + 36 = 36$

$13x^2 + 24x = 0$

$x(13x + 24) = 0$

$x = 0$ or $x = -\dfrac{24}{13}$

Since $y = x + 3$, the solutions are:

$x = 0$ and $y = 3$, or, $x = -\dfrac{24}{13}$ and $y = \dfrac{15}{13}$.

In ordered pair notation, the solutions are

$(0, 3)$ and $\left(-\dfrac{24}{13}, \dfrac{15}{13}\right)$.

Section 4.4 Exercises

1. Represent the numbers by x and $20 - x$, where $0 \le x \le 20$.

(a) The sum of the squares is given by
$f(x) = x^2 + (20 - x)^2 = 2x^2 - 40x + 400$. Then
$f'(x) = 4x - 40$. The critical point and endpoints occur at $x = 0$, $x = 10$, and $x = 20$. Then $f(0) = 400$, $f(10) = 200$, and $f(20) = 400$. The sum of the squares is as large as possible for the numbers 0 and 20, and is as small as possible for the numbers 10 and 10.

Graphical support:

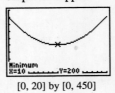

Minimum
X=10   Y=200

[0, 20] by [0, 450]

(b) The sum of one number plus the square root of the other is given by $g(x) = x + \sqrt{20 - x}$. Then

$g'(x) = 1 - \dfrac{1}{2\sqrt{20 - x}}$. The critical point occurs when $2\sqrt{20 - x} = 1$, so $20 - x = \dfrac{1}{4}$ and $x = \dfrac{79}{4}$. Testing the endpoints and critical point, we find

$g(0) = \sqrt{20} \approx 4.47$, $g\left(\dfrac{79}{4}\right) = \dfrac{81}{4} = 20.25$, and

$g(20) = 20$.

The sum is as large as possible when the numbers are

$\frac{79}{4}$ and $\frac{1}{4}$ $\left(\text{summing } \frac{79}{4} + \sqrt{\frac{1}{4}}\right)$, and is as small as

possible when the numbers are 0 and 20

(summing $0 + \sqrt{20}$).

Graphical support:

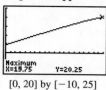

[0, 20] by [−10, 25]

2. Let x and y represent the legs of the triangle, and note that

$0 < x < 5$. Then $x^2 + y^2 = 25$, so $y = \sqrt{25 - x^2}$ (since

$y > 0$). The area is $A = \frac{1}{2}xy = \frac{1}{2}x\sqrt{25 - x^2}$, so

$$\frac{dA}{dx} = \frac{1}{2}x \cdot \frac{1}{2\sqrt{25 - x^2}}(-2x) + \frac{1}{2}\sqrt{25 - x^2}$$

$$= \frac{25 - 2x^2}{2\sqrt{25 - x^2}}.$$

The critical point occurs when $25 - 2x^2 = 0$, which means

$x = \frac{5}{\sqrt{2}}$, (since $x > 0$). This value corresponds to the

largest possible area, since $\frac{dA}{dx} > 0$ for $0 < x < \frac{5}{\sqrt{2}}$ and

$\frac{dA}{dx} < 0$ for $\frac{5}{\sqrt{2}} < x < 5$. When $x = \frac{5}{\sqrt{2}}$, we have

$y = \sqrt{25 - \left(\frac{5}{\sqrt{2}}\right)^2} = \frac{5}{\sqrt{2}}$ and

$A = \frac{1}{2}xy = \frac{1}{2}\left(\frac{5}{\sqrt{2}}\right)^2 = \frac{25}{4}$. Thus, the largest possible area is

$\frac{25}{4}$ cm^2, and the dimensions (legs) are $\frac{5}{\sqrt{2}}$ cm by $\frac{5}{\sqrt{2}}$ cm.

Graphical support:

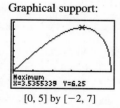

[0, 5] by [−2, 7]

3. Let x represent the length of the rectangle in inches ($x > 0$).

Then the width is $\frac{16}{x}$ and the perimeter is

$P(x) = 2\left(x + \frac{16}{x}\right) = 2x + \frac{32}{x}$.

Since $P'(x) = 2 - 32x^{-2} = \frac{2(x^2 - 16)}{x^2}$ the critical point

occurs at $x = 4$. Since $P'(x) < 0$ for $0 < x < 4$ and

$P'(x) > 0$ for $x > 4$, this critical point corresponds to the

minimum perimeter. The smallest possible perimeter is

$P(4) = 16$ in., and the rectangle's dimensions are

4 in. by 4 in.

Graphical support:

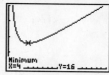

[0, 20] by [0, 40]

4. Let x represent the length of the rectangle in meters

($0 < x < 4$). Then the width is $4 - x$ and the area is

$A(x) = x(4 - x) = 4x - x^2$. Since $A'(x) = 4 - 2x$, the

critical point occurs at $x = 2$. Since $A'(x) > 0$ for

$0 < x < 2$ and $A'(x) < 0$ for $2 < x < 4$, this critical point

corresponds to the maximum area. The rectangle with the

largest area measures 2 m by $4 - 2 = 2$m, so it is a square.

Graphical support:

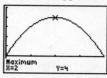

[0, 4] by [−1.5, 5]

5. (a) The equation of line AB is $y = -x + 1$, so the

y-coordinate of P is $-x + 1$.

(b) $A(x) = 2x(1 - x)$

(c) Since $A'(x) = \frac{d}{dx}(2x - 2x^2) = 2 - 4x$, the critical point

occurs at $x = \frac{1}{2}$. Since $A'(x) > 0$ for $0 < x < \frac{1}{2}$ and

$A'(x) < 0$ for $\frac{1}{2} < x < 1$, this critical point corresponds

to the maximum area. The largest possible area is

$A\left(\frac{1}{2}\right) = \frac{1}{2}$ square unit, and the dimensions of the

rectangle are $\frac{1}{2}$ unit by 1 unit.

Graphical support:

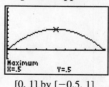

[0, 1] by [−0.5, 1]

6. If the upper right vertex of the rectangle is located at

$(x, 12 - x^2)$ for $0 < x < \sqrt{12}$, then the rectangle's

dimensions are $2x$ by $12 - x^2$ and the area is

$A(x) = 2x(12 - x^2) = 24x - 2x^3$. Then

$A'(x) = 24 - 6x^2 = 6(4 - x^2)$, so the critical point

(for $0 < x < \sqrt{12}$) occurs at $x = 2$. Since $A'(x) > 0$ for

$0 < x < 2$ and $A'(x) < 0$ for $2 < x < \sqrt{12}$, this critical

point corresponds to the maximum area. The largest

possible area is $A(2) = 32$, and the dimensions are 4 by 8.

Graphical support:

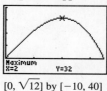

[0, $\sqrt{12}$] by [−10, 40]

7. Let x be the side length of the cut-out square ($0 < x < 4$).

Then the base measures $8 - 2x$ in. by $15 - 2x$ in.,

and the volume is

$V(x) = x(8 - 2x)(15 - 2x) = 4x^3 - 46x^2 + 120x$. Then

$V'(x) = 12x^2 - 92x + 120 = 4(3x - 5)(x - 6)$. Then the

critical point (in $0 < x < 4$) occurs at $x = \dfrac{5}{3}$. Since

$V'(x) > 0$ for $0 < x < \dfrac{5}{3}$ and $V'(x) < 0$ for $\dfrac{5}{3} < x < 4$, the

critical point corresponds to the maximum volume.

The maximum volume is $V\left(\dfrac{5}{3}\right) = \dfrac{2450}{27} \approx 90.74 \text{ in}^3$, and the

dimensions are $\dfrac{5}{3}$ in. by $\dfrac{14}{3}$ in. by $\dfrac{35}{3}$ in.

Graphical support:

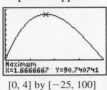

[0, 4] by [−25, 100]

8. Note that the values a and b must satisfy $a^2 + b^2 = 20^2$

and so $b = \sqrt{400 - a^2}$. Then the area is given by

$A = \dfrac{1}{2}ab = \dfrac{1}{2}a\sqrt{400 - a^2}$ for $0 < a < 20$, and

$\dfrac{dA}{da} = \dfrac{1}{2}a\left(\dfrac{1}{2\sqrt{400 - a^2}}\right)(-2a) + \dfrac{1}{2}\sqrt{400 - a^2}$

$= \dfrac{-a^2 + (400 - a^2)}{2\sqrt{400 - a^2}} = \dfrac{200 - a^2}{\sqrt{400 - a^2}}$. The critical point occurs

when $a^2 = 200$. Since $\dfrac{dA}{da} > 0$ for $0 < a < \sqrt{200}$ and

$\dfrac{dA}{da} < 0$ for $\sqrt{200} < a < 20$, this critical point corresponds

to the maximum area. Furthermore, if $a = \sqrt{200}$ then

$b = \sqrt{400 - a^2} = \sqrt{200}$, so the maximum area occurs

when $a = b$.

Graphical support:

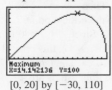

[0, 20] by [−30, 110]

9. Let x be the length in meters of each side that adjoins the river. Then the side parallel to the river measures $800 - 2x$ meters and the area is $A(x) = x(800 - 2x) = 800x - 2x^2$ for $0 < x < 400$. Therefore, $A'(x) = 800 - 4x$ and the critical point occurs at $x = 200$. Since $A'(x) > 0$ for $0 < x < 200$ and $A'(x) < 0$ for $200 < x < 400$, the critical point corresponds to the maximum area. The largest possible area is $A(200) = 80,000 \text{ m}^2$ and the dimensions are 200 m (perpendicular to the river) by 400 m (parallel to the river).

Graphical support:

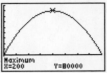

[0, 400] by [−25,000, 90,000]

10. If the subdividing fence measures x meters, then the

pea patch measures x m by $\dfrac{216}{x}$ m and the amount of fence

needed is $f(x) = 3x + 2\dfrac{216}{x} = 3x + 432x^{-1}$. Then

$f'(x) = 3 - 432x^{-2}$ and the critical point (for $x > 0$)

occurs at $x = 12$. Since $f'(x) < 0$ for $0 < x < 12$ and

$f'(x) > 0$ for $x > 12$, the critical point corresponds to the

minimum total length of fence. The pea patch will measure

12 m by 18 m (with a 12-m divider), and the total amount

of fence needed is $f(12) = 72$ m.

Graphical support:

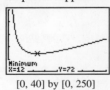

[0, 40] by [0, 250]

11. (a) Let x be the length in feet of each side of the square

base. Then the height is $\dfrac{500}{x^2}$ ft and the surface area

(not including the open top) is

$S(x) = x^2 + 4x\left(\dfrac{500}{x^2}\right) = x^2 + 2000x^{-1}$. Therefore,

$S'(x) = 2x - 2000x^{-2} = \dfrac{2(x^3 - 1000)}{x^2}$ and the critical

point occurs at $x = 10$. Since $S'(x) < 0$ for $0 < x < 10$

and $S'(x) > 0$ for $x > 10$, the critical point corresponds

to the minimum amount of steel used. The dimensions

should be 10 ft by 10 ft by 5 ft, where the height is 5 ft.

(b) Assume that the weight is minimized when the total
area of the bottom and the four sides is minimized.

12. (a) Note that $x^2 y = 1125$, so $y = \dfrac{1125}{x^2}$. Then

$$
\begin{aligned}
c &= 5(x^2 + 4xy) + 10xy \\
&= 5x^2 + 30xy \\
&= 5x^2 + 30x\left(\frac{1125}{x^2}\right) \\
&= 5x^2 + 33{,}750x^{-1}
\end{aligned}
$$

$\dfrac{dc}{dx} = 10x - 33{,}750x^{-2} = \dfrac{10(x^3 - 3375)}{x^2}$.

The critical point occurs at $x = 15$. Since $\dfrac{dc}{dx} < 0$ for

$0 < x < 15$ and $\dfrac{dc}{dx} > 0$ for $x > 15$, the critical point

corresponds to the minimum cost. The values of x and

y are $x = 15$ ft and $y = 5$ ft.

(b) The material for the tank costs 5 dollars/sq ft and the excavation charge is 10 dollars for each square foot of the cross-sectional area of one wall of the hole.

13. Let x be the height in inches of the printed area. Then the

width of the printed area is $\dfrac{50}{x}$ in. and the overall

dimensions are $x + 8$ in. by $\dfrac{50}{x} + 4$ in. The amount of

paper used is

$A(x) = (x + 8)\left(\dfrac{50}{x} + 4\right) = 4x + 82 + \dfrac{400}{x}$ in^2. Then

$A'(x) = 4 - 400x^{-2} = \dfrac{4(x^2 - 100)}{x^2}$ and the critical point

(for $x > 0$) occurs at $x = 10$. Since $A'(x) < 0$ for

$0 < x < 10$ and $A'(x) > 0$ for $x > 10$, the critical point

corresponds to the minimum amount of paper. Using

$x + 8$ and $\dfrac{50}{x} + 4$ for $x = 10$, the overall dimensions are

18 in. high by 9 in. wide.

14. (a) $s(t) = -16t^2 + 96t + 112$
$v(t) = s'(t) = -32t + 96$
At $t = 0$, the velocity is $v(0) = 96$ ft/sec.

(b) The maximum height occurs when $v(t) = 0$, when $t = 3$. The maximum height is $s(3) = 256$ ft and it occurs at $t = 3$ sec.

(c) Note that
$s(t) = -16t^2 + 96t + 112 = -16(t + 1)(t - 7)$,
so $s = 0$ at $t = -1$ or $t = 7$. Choosing the positive value of t, the velocity when $s = 0$ is
$v(7) = -128$ ft/sec.

15. We assume that a and b are held constant. Then

$A(\theta) = \dfrac{1}{2}ab \sin\theta$ and $A'(\theta) = \dfrac{1}{2}ab \cos\theta$. The critical point

(for $0 < \theta < \pi$) occurs at $\theta = \dfrac{\pi}{2}$. Since $A'(\theta) > 0$ for

$0 < \theta < \dfrac{\pi}{2}$ and $A'(\theta) < 0$ for $\dfrac{\pi}{2} < \theta < \pi$, the critical point

corresponds to the maximum area. The angle that

maximizes the triangle's area is $\theta = \dfrac{\pi}{2}$ (or $90°$).

16. Let the can have radius r cm and height h cm. Then

$\pi r^2 h = 1000$, so $h = \dfrac{1000}{\pi r^2}$. The area of material used is

$A = \pi r^2 + 2\pi rh = \pi r^2 + \dfrac{2000}{r}$, so

$\dfrac{dA}{dr} = 2\pi r - 2000r^{-2} = \dfrac{2\pi r^3 - 2000}{r^2}$. The critical point

occurs at $r = \sqrt[3]{\dfrac{1000}{\pi}} = 10\pi^{-1/3}$ cm. Since $\dfrac{dA}{dr} < 0$ for

$0 < r < 10\pi^{-1/3}$ and $\dfrac{dA}{dr} > 0$ for $r > 10\pi^{-1/3}$, the critical

point corresponds to the least amount of material used and

hence the lightest possible can. The dimensions are

$r = 10\pi^{-1/3} \approx 6.83$ cm and $h = 10\pi^{-1/3} \approx 6.83$ cm. In

Example 2, because of the top of the can, the "best" design

is less big around and taller.

17. Note that $\pi r^2 h = 1000$, so $h = \dfrac{1000}{\pi r^2}$. Then

$A = 8r^2 + 2\pi rh = 8r^2 + \dfrac{2000}{r}$, so

$\dfrac{dA}{dr} = 16r - 2000r^{-2} = \dfrac{16(r^3 - 125)}{r^2}$. The critical point

occurs at $r = \sqrt[3]{125} = 5$ cm. Since $\dfrac{dA}{dr} < 0$ for $0 < r < 5$

and $\dfrac{dA}{dr} > 0$ for $r > 5$, the critical point corresponds to the

least amount of aluminum used or wasted and hence the

most economical can. The dimensions are $r = 5$ cm and

$h = \dfrac{40}{\pi}$, so the ratio of h to r is $\dfrac{8}{\pi}$ to 1.

18. (a) The base measures $10 - 2x$ in. by $\dfrac{15 - 2x}{2}$ in., so the volume formula is

$$V(x) = \frac{x(10 - 2x)(15 - 2x)}{2} = 2x^3 - 25x^2 + 75x.$$

(b) We require $x > 0$, $2x < 10$, and $2x < 15$. Combining these requirements, the domain is the interval $(0, 5)$.

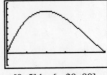

[0, 5] by [−20, 80]

(c)

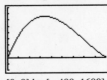

Maximum
X=1.9618739 Y=66.019118

[0, 5] by [−20, 80]

The maximum volume is approximately 66.02 in^3 when $x \approx 1.96$ in.

(d) $V'(x) = 6x^2 - 50x + 75$

The critical point occurs when $V'(x) = 0$, at

$$x = \frac{50 \pm \sqrt{(-50)^2 - 4(6)(75)}}{2(6)} = \frac{50 \pm \sqrt{700}}{12}$$

$$= \frac{25 \pm 5\sqrt{7}}{6}, \text{ that is, } x \approx 1.96 \text{ or } x \approx 6.37. \text{ We discard}$$

the larger value because it is not in the domain. Since $V''(x) = 12x - 50$, which is negative when $x \approx 1.96$, the critical point corresponds to the maximum volume.

The maximum volume occurs when

$$x = \frac{25 - 5\sqrt{7}}{6} \approx 1.96, \text{ which confirms the result in (c).}$$

19. (a) The "sides" of the suitcase will measure $24 - 2x$ in. by $18 - 2x$ in. and will be $2x$ in. apart, so the volume formula is
$$V(x) = 2x(24 - 2x)(18 - 2x) = 8x^3 - 168x^2 + 864x.$$

(b) We require $x > 0$, $2x < 18$, and $2x < 24$. Combining these requirements, the domain is the interval $(0, 9)$.

[0, 9] by [−400, 1600]

(c)

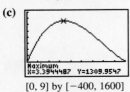

Maximum
X=3.3944487 Y=1309.9547

[0, 9] by [−400, 1600]

The maximum volume is approximately 1309.95 in^3 when $x \approx 3.39$ in.

(d) $V'(x) = 24x^2 - 336x + 864 = 24(x^2 - 14x + 36)$
The critical point is at

$$x = \frac{14 \pm \sqrt{(-14)^2 - 4(1)(36)}}{2(1)} = \frac{14 \pm \sqrt{52}}{2} = 7 \pm \sqrt{13},$$

that is, $x \approx 3.39$ or $x \approx 10.61$. We discard the larger value because it is not in the domain. Since $V''(x) = 24(2x - 14)$, which is negative when $x \approx 3.39$, the critical point corresponds to the maximum volume. The maximum value occurs at $x = 7 - \sqrt{13} \approx 3.39$, which confirms the results in (c).

(e) $8x^3 - 168x^2 + 864x = 1120$
$8(x^3 - 21x^2 + 108x - 140) = 0$
$8(x - 2)(x - 5)(x - 14) = 0$
Since 14 is not in the domain, the possible values of x are $x = 2$ in. or $x = 5$ in.

(f) The dimensions of the resulting box are $2x$ in., $(24 - 2x)$ in., and $(18 - 2x)$ in. Each of these measurements must be positive, so that gives the domain of $(0, 9)$.

20.

6 mi
$\vdash x \dashv$ $6 - x$ Village

2 mi $\sqrt{4 + x^2}$ miles

Jane

Let x be the distance from the point on the shoreline nearest Jane's boat to the point where she lands her boat. Then she needs to row $\sqrt{4 + x^2}$ mi at 2 mph and walk $6 - x$ mi at 5 mph. The total amount of time to reach the village is
$$f(x) = \frac{\sqrt{4 + x^2}}{2} + \frac{6 - x}{5} \text{ hours } (0 \le x \le 6). \text{ Then}$$
$$f'(x) = \frac{1}{2} \frac{1}{2\sqrt{4 + x^2}}(2x) - \frac{1}{5} = \frac{x}{2\sqrt{4 + x^2}} - \frac{1}{5}. \text{ Solving}$$
$f'(x) = 0$, we have:

$$\frac{x}{2\sqrt{4 + x^2}} = \frac{1}{5}$$
$$5x = 2\sqrt{4 + x^2}$$
$$25x^2 = 4(4 + x^2)$$
$$21x^2 = 16$$
$$x = \pm\frac{4}{\sqrt{21}}$$

We discard the negative value of x because it is not in the domain. Checking the endpoints and critical point, we have $f(0) = 2.2, f\left(\dfrac{4}{\sqrt{21}}\right) \approx 2.12$, and $f(6) \approx 3.16$. Jane should land her boat $\dfrac{4}{\sqrt{21}} \approx 0.87$ miles down the shoreline from the point nearest her boat.

21. If the upper right vertex of the rectangle is located at $(x, 4\cos 0.5x)$ for $0 < x < \pi$, then the rectangle has width $2x$ and height $4\cos 0.5x$, so the area is $A(x) = 8x\cos 0.5x$.
Then $A'(x) = 8x(-0.5\sin 0.5x) + 8(\cos 0.5x)(1)$
$\qquad\qquad = -4x\sin 0.5x + 8\cos 0.5x$.
Solving $A'(x)$ graphically for $0 < x < \pi$, we find that $x \approx 1.72$. Evaluating $2x$ and $4\cos 0.5x$ for $x \approx 1.72$, the dimensions of the rectangle are approximately 3.44 (width) by 2.61 (height), and the maximum area is approximately 8.98.

22. Let the radius of the cylinder be r cm, $0 < r < 10$. Then the height is $2\sqrt{100 - r^2}$ and the volume is
$V(r) = 2\pi r^2\sqrt{100 - r^2}$ cm^3. Then

$$V'(r) = 2\pi r^2\left(\frac{1}{2\sqrt{100 - r^2}}\right)(-2r) + (2\pi\sqrt{100 - r^2})(2r)$$
$$= \frac{-2\pi r^3 + 4\pi r(100 - r^2)}{\sqrt{100 - r^2}}$$
$$= \frac{2\pi r(200 - 3r^2)}{\sqrt{100 - r^2}}$$

The critical point for $0 < r < 10$ occurs at $r = \sqrt{\frac{200}{3}} = 10\sqrt{\frac{2}{3}}$. Since $V'(r) > 0$ for $0 < r < 10\sqrt{\frac{2}{3}}$ and $V'(r) < 0$ for $10\sqrt{\frac{2}{3}} < r < 10$, the critical point corresponds to the maximum volume. The dimensions are $r = 10\sqrt{\frac{2}{3}} \approx 8.16$ cm and $h = \frac{20}{\sqrt{3}} \approx 11.55$ cm, and the volume is $\frac{4000\pi}{3\sqrt{3}} \approx 2418.40$ cm^3.

23. (a) $f'(x) = x(-e^{-x}) + e^{-x}(1) = e^{-x}(1 - x)$
The critical point occurs at $x = 1$. Since $f'(x) > 0$ for $0 \le x < 1$ and $f'(x) < 0$ for $x > 1$, the critical point corresponds to the maximum value of f. The absolute maximum of f occurs at $x = 1$.

(b) To find the values of b, use grapher techniques to solve $xe^{-x} = 0.1e^{-0.1}$, $xe^{-x} = 0.2e^{-0.2}$, and so on. To find the values of A, calculate $(b - a)ae^{-a}$, using the unrounded values of b. (Use the *list* features of the grapher in order to keep track of the unrounded values for part (d).)

a	b	A
0.1	3.71	0.33
0.2	2.86	0.44
0.3	2.36	0.46
0.4	2.02	0.43
0.5	1.76	0.38
0.6	1.55	0.31
0.7	1.38	0.23
0.8	1.23	0.15
0.9	1.11	0.08
1.0	1.00	0.00

(c)

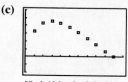

[0, 1.1] by [−0.2, 0.6]

(d) Quadratic:
$A \approx -0.91a^2 + 0.54a + 0.34$

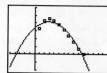

[−0.5, 1.5] by [−0.2, 0.6]

Cubic:
$A \approx 1.74a^3 - 3.78a^2 + 1.86a + 0.19$

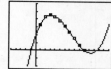

[−0.5, 1.5] by [−0.2, 0.6]

Quartic:
$A \approx -1.92a^4 + 5.96a^3 - 6.87a^2 + 2.71a + 0.12$

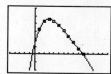

[−0.5, 1.5] by [−0.2, 0.6]

(e) Quadratic:

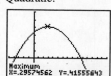

[−0.5, 1.5] by [−0.2, 0.6]

According to the quadratic regression equation, the maximum area occurs at $a \approx 0.30$ and is approximately 0.42.

Cubic:

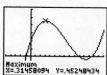

[−0.5, 1.5] by [−0.2, 0.6]

According to the cubic regression equation, the maximum area occurs at $a \approx 0.31$ and is approximately 0.45.

Quartic:

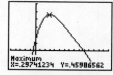

[−0.5, 1.5] by [−0.2, 0.6]

According to the quartic regression equation the maximum area occurs at $a \approx 0.30$ and is approximately 0.46.

24. (a) $f'(x)$ is a quadratic polynomial, and as such it can have 0, 1, or 2 zeros. If it has 0 or 1 zeros, then its sign never changes, so $f(x)$ has no local extrema. If $f'(x)$ has 2 zeros, then its sign changes twice, and $f(x)$ has 2 local extrema at those points.

(b) Possible answers:
No local extrema: $y = x^3$;
2 local extrema: $y = x^3 - 3x$

25. Let x be the length in inches of each edge of the square end, and let y be the length of the box. Then we require $4x + y \le 108$. Since our goal is to maximize volume, we assume $4x + y = 108$ and so $y = 108 - 4x$. The volume is $V(x) = x^2(108 - 4x) = 108x^2 - 4x^3$, where $0 < x < 27$. Then $V' = 216x - 12x^2 = -12x(x - 18)$, so the critical point occurs at $x = 18$ in. Since $V'(x) > 0$ for $0 < x < 18$ and $V'(x) < 0$ for $18 < x < 27$, the critical point corresponds to the maximum volume. The dimensions of the box with the largest possible volume are 18 in. by 18 in. by 36 in.

26. Since $2x + 2y = 36$, we know that $y = 18 - x$. In part (a), the radius is $\dfrac{x}{2\pi}$ and the height is $18 - x$, and so the volume is given by

$\pi r^2 h = \pi\left(\dfrac{x}{2\pi}\right)^2 (18 - x) = \dfrac{1}{4\pi}x^2(18 - x)$. In part (b), the radius is x and the height is $18 - x$, and so the volume is given by $\pi r^2 h = \pi x^2(18 - x)$. Thus, each problem requires us to find the value of x that maximizes $f(x) = x^2(18 - x)$ in the interval $0 < x < 18$, so the two problems have the same answer.

To solve either problem, note that $f(x) = 18x^2 - x^3$ and so $f'(x) = 36x - 3x^2 = -3x(x - 12)$. The critical point occurs at $x = 12$. Since $f'(x) > 0$ for $0 < x < 12$ and $f'(x) < 0$ for $12 < x < 18$, the critical point corresponds to the maximum value of $f(x)$. To maximize the volume in either part (a) or (b), let $x = 12$ cm and $y = 6$ cm.

27. Note that $h^2 + r^2 = 3$ and so $r = \sqrt{3 - h^2}$. Then the volume is given by $V = \dfrac{\pi}{3}r^2 h = \dfrac{\pi}{3}(3 - h^2)h = \pi h - \dfrac{\pi}{3}h^3$ for $0 < h < \sqrt{3}$, and so $\dfrac{dV}{dh} = \pi - \pi h^2 = \pi(1 - h^2)$. The critical point (for $h > 0$) occurs at $h = 1$. Since $\dfrac{dV}{dh} > 0$ for $0 < h < 1$ and $\dfrac{dV}{dh} < 0$ for $1 < h < \sqrt{3}$, the critical point corresponds to the maximum volume. The cone of greatest volume has radius $\sqrt{2}$ m, height 1 m, and volume $\dfrac{2\pi}{3}$ m^3.

28. (a) We require $f(x)$ to have a critical point at $x = 2$. Since $f'(x) = 2x - ax^{-2}$, we have $f'(2) = 4 - \dfrac{a}{4}$ and so our requirement is that $4 - \dfrac{a}{4} = 0$. Therefore, $a = 16$. To verify that the critical point corresponds to a local minimum, note that we now have $f'(x) = 2x - 16x^{-2}$ and so $f''(x) = 2 + 32x^{-3}$, so $f''(2) = 6$, which is positive as expected. So, use $a = 16$.

(b) We require $f''(1) = 0$. Since $f''(x) = 2 + 2ax^{-3}$, we have $f''(1) = 2 + 2a$, so our requirement is that $2 + 2a = 0$. Therefore, $a = -1$. To verify that $x = 1$ is in fact an inflection point, note that we now have $f''(x) = 2 - 2x^{-3}$, which is negative for $0 < x < 1$ and positive for $x > 1$. Therefore, the graph of f is concave down in the interval $(0, 1)$ and concave up in the interval $(1, \infty)$, So, use $a = -1$.

29. $f'(x) = 2x - ax^{-2} = \dfrac{2x^3 - a}{x^2}$, so the only sign change in $f'(x)$ occurs at $x = \left(\dfrac{a}{2}\right)^{1/3}$, where the sign changes from negative to positive. This means there is a local minimum at that point, and there are no local maxima.

30. (a) Note that $f'(x) = 3x^2 + 2ax + b$. We require $f'(-1) = 0$ and $f'(3) = 0$, which give $3 - 2a + b = 0$ and $27 + 6a + b = 0$. Subtracting the first equation from the second, we have $24 + 8a = 0$ and so $a = -3$. Substituting into the first equation, we have $9 + b = 0$, so $b = -9$. Therefore, our equation for $f(x)$ is $f(x) = x^3 - 3x^2 - 9x$. To verify that we have a local maximum at $x = -1$ and a local minimum at $x = 3$, note that $f'(x) = 3x^2 - 6x - 9 = 3(x + 1)(x - 3)$, which is positive for $x < -1$, negative for $-1 < x < 3$, and positive for $x > 3$. So, use $a = -3$ and $b = -9$.

(b) Note that $f'(x) = 3x^2 + 2ax + b$ and $f''(x) = 6x + 2a$. We require $f'(4) = 0$ and $f''(1) = 0$, which give $48 + 8a + b = 0$ and $6 + 2a = 0$. By the second equation, $a = -3$, and so the first equation becomes $48 - 24 + b = 0$. Thus $b = -24$. To verify that we have a local minimum at $x = 4$, and an inflection point at $x = 1$, note that we now have $f''(x) = 6x - 6$. Since f'' changes sign at $x = 1$ and is positive at $x = 4$, the desired conditions are satisfied. So, use $a = -3$ and $b = -24$.

31. Refer to the illustration in the problem statement. Since $x^2 + y^2 = 9$, we have $x = \sqrt{9 - y^2}$. Then the volume of the cone is given by

$$V = \frac{1}{3}\pi r^2 h = \frac{1}{3}\pi x^2(y + 3)$$
$$= \frac{1}{3}\pi(9 - y^2)(y + 3)$$
$$= \frac{\pi}{3}(-y^3 - 3y^2 + 9y + 27),$$

for $-3 < y < 3$.

Thus $\dfrac{dV}{dy} = \dfrac{\pi}{3}(-3y^2 - 6y + 9) = -\pi(y^2 + 2y - 3)$

$$= -\pi(y + 3)(y - 1),$$ so the critical point in

the interval $(-3, 3)$ is $y = 1$. Since $\dfrac{dV}{dy} > 0$ for $-3 < y < 1$ and $\dfrac{dV}{dy} < 0$ for $1 < y < 3$, the critical point does correspond to the maximum value, which is $V(1) = \dfrac{32\pi}{3}$ cubic units.

32. **(a)** Note that $w^2 + d^2 = 12^2$, so $d = \sqrt{144 - w^2}$. Then we may write $S = kwd^2 = kw(144 - w^2) = 144kw - kw^3$ for $0 < w < 12$,

so $\dfrac{dS}{dw} = 144k - 3kw^2 = -3k(w^2 - 48)$. The critical point (for $0 < w < 12$) occurs at $w = \sqrt{48} = 4\sqrt{3}$. Since $\dfrac{dS}{dw} > 0$ for $0 < w < 4\sqrt{3}$ and $\dfrac{dS}{dw} < 0$ for $4\sqrt{3} < w < 12$, the critical point corresponds to the maximum strength. The dimensions are $4\sqrt{3}$ in. wide by $4\sqrt{6}$ in. deep.

(b)

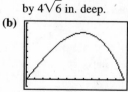

[0, 12] by [−100, 800]

The graph of $S = 144w - w^3$ is shown. The maximum strength shown in the graph occurs at $w = 4\sqrt{3} \approx 6.9$, which agrees with the answer to part (a).

(c)

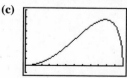

[0, 12] by [−100, 800]

The graph of $S = d^2\sqrt{144 - d^2}$ is shown. The maximum strength shown in the graph occurs at $d = 4\sqrt{6} \approx 9.8$, which agrees with the answer to part (a), and its value is the same as the maximum value found in part (b), as expected.

Changing the value of k changes the maximum strength, but not the dimensions of the strongest beam. The graphs for different values of k look the same except that the vertical scale is different.

33. **(a)** Note that $w^2 + d^2 = 12^2$, so $d = \sqrt{144 - w^2}$. Then we may write $S = kwd^3 = kw(144 - w^2)^{3/2}$, so

$$\frac{dS}{dw} = kw \cdot \frac{3}{2}(144 - w^2)^{1/2}(-2w) + k(144 - w^2)^{3/2}(1)$$
$$= (k\sqrt{144 - w^2})(-3w^2 + 144 - w^2)$$
$$= (-4k\sqrt{144 - w^2})(w^2 - 36)$$

The critical point (for $0 < w < 12$) occurs at $w = 6$. Since $\dfrac{dS}{dw} > 0$ for $0 < w < 6$ and $\dfrac{dS}{dw} < 0$ for $6 < w < 12$, the critical point corresponds to the maximum stiffness. The dimensions are 6 in. wide by $6\sqrt{3}$ in. deep.

(b)

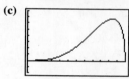

[0, 12] by [−2000, 8000]

The graph of $S = w(144 - w^2)^{3/2}$ is shown. The maximum stiffness shown in the graph occurs at $w = 6$, which agrees with the answer to part (a).

(c)

[0, 12] by [−2000, 8000]

The graph of $S = d^3\sqrt{144 - d^2}$ is shown. The maximum stiffness shown in the graph occurs at $d = 6\sqrt{3} \approx 10.4$ agrees with the answer to part (a), and its value is the same as the maximum value found in part (b), as expected.

Changing the value of k changes the maximum stiffness, but not the dimensions of the stiffest beam. The graphs for different values of k look the same except that the vertical scale is different.

34. **(a)** $v(t) = s'(t) = -10\pi \sin \pi t$

The speed at time t is $10\pi|\sin \pi t|$. The maximum speed is 10π cm/sec and it occurs at $t = \dfrac{1}{2}$, $t = \dfrac{3}{2}$, $t = \dfrac{5}{2}$, and $t = \dfrac{7}{2}$ sec. The position at these times is $s = 0$ cm (rest position), and the acceleration $a(t) = v'(t) = -10\pi^2 \cos \pi t$ is 0 cm/sec^2 at these times.

(b) Since $a(t) = -10\pi^2 \cos \pi t$, the greatest magnitude of the acceleration occurs at $t = 0$, $t = 1$, $t = 2$, $t = 3$, and $t = 4$. At these times, the position of the cart is either $s = -10$ cm or $s = 10$ cm, and the speed of the cart is 0 cm/sec.

35. Since $\dfrac{di}{dt} = -2 \sin t + 2 \cos t$, the largest magnitude of the current occurs when $-2\sin t + 2\cos t = 0$, or

$\sin t = \cos t$. Squaring both sides gives $\sin^2 t = \cos^2 t$, and

we know that $\sin^2 t + \cos^2 t = 1$, so $\sin^2 t = \cos^2 t = \frac{1}{2}$.

Thus the possible values of t are $\frac{\pi}{4}, \frac{3\pi}{4}, \frac{5\pi}{4}$, and so on.

Eliminating extraneous solutions, the solutions of

$\sin t = \cos t$ are $t = \frac{\pi}{4} + k\pi$ for integers k, and at these

times $|i| = |2\cos t + 2\sin t| = 2\sqrt{2}$. The peak current is

$2\sqrt{2}$ amps.

36. The square of the distance is

$$D(x) = \left(x - \frac{3}{2}\right)^2 + (\sqrt{x} + 0)^2 = x^2 - 2x + \frac{9}{4},$$

so $D'(x) = 2x - 2$ and the critical point occurs at $x = 1$.

Since $D'(x) < 0$ for $x < 1$ and $D'(x) > 0$ for $x > 1$, the

critical point corresponds to the minimum distance. The

minimum distance is $\sqrt{D(1)} = \frac{\sqrt{5}}{2}$.

37. Calculus method:

The square of the distance from the point $(1, \sqrt{3})$ to

$(x, \sqrt{16 - x^2})$ is given by

$$D(x) = (x - 1)^2 + (\sqrt{16 - x^2} - \sqrt{3})^2$$

$$= x^2 - 2x + 1 + 16 - x^2 - 2\sqrt{48 - 3x^2} + 3$$

$$= -2x + 20 - 2\sqrt{48 - 3x^2}. \text{ Then}$$

$$D'(x) = -2 - \frac{2}{2\sqrt{48 - 3x^2}}(-6x) = -2 + \frac{6x}{\sqrt{48 - 3x^2}}.$$

Solving $D'(x) = 0$, we have:

$$6x = 2\sqrt{48 - 3x^2}$$
$$36x^2 = 4(48 - 3x^2)$$
$$9x^2 = 48 - 3x^2$$
$$12x^2 = 48$$
$$x = \pm 2$$

We discard $x = -2$ as an extraneous solution, leaving

$x = 2$. Since $D'(x) < 0$ for $-4 < x < 2$ and $D'(x) > 0$ for

$2 < x < 4$, the critical point corresponds to the minimum

distance. The minimum distance is $\sqrt{D(2)} = 2$.

Geometry method:

The semicircle is centered at the origin and has radius 4.

The distance from the origin to $(1, \sqrt{3})$ is

$\sqrt{1^2 + (\sqrt{3})^2} = 2$. The shortest distance from the point to

the semicircle is the distance along the radius containing

the point $(1, \sqrt{3})$. That distance is $4 - 2 = 2$.

38. No. Since $f(x)$ is a quadratic function and the coefficient of

x^2 is positive, it has an absolute minimum at the point

where $f'(x) = 2x - 1 = 0$, and that point is $\left(\frac{1}{2}, \frac{3}{4}\right)$.

39. (a) Because $f(x)$ is periodic with period 2π.

   (b) No. Since $f(x)$ is continuous on $[0, 2\pi]$, its absolute
   minimum occurs at a critical point or endpoint.
   Find the critical points in $[0, 2\pi]$:
   $$f'(x) = -4\sin x - 2\sin 2x = 0$$
   $$-4\sin x - 4\sin x \cos x = 0$$
   $$-4(\sin x)(1 + \cos x) = 0$$
   $$\sin x = 0 \text{ or } \cos x = -1$$
   $$x = 0, \pi, 2\pi$$
   The critical points (and endpoints) are $(0, 8)$, $(\pi, 0)$,
   and $(2\pi, 8)$. Thus, $f(x)$ has an absolute minimum at
   $(\pi, 0)$ and it is never negative.

40. (a)
$$2\sin t = \sin 2t$$
$$2\sin t = 2\sin t \cos t$$
$$2(\sin t)(1 - \cos t) = 0$$
$$\sin t = 0 \text{ or } \cos t = 1$$
$$t = k\pi, \text{ where } k \text{ is an integer}$$
The masses pass each other whenever t is an integer
multiple of π seconds.

   (b) The vertical distance between the objects is the
   absolute value of $f(x) = \sin 2t - 2\sin t$.
   Find the critical points in $[0, 2\pi]$:

   $$f'(x) = 2\cos 2t - 2\cos t = 0$$
   $$2(2\cos^2 t - 1) - 2\cos t = 0$$
   $$2(2\cos^2 t - \cos t - 1) = 0$$
   $$2(2\cos t + 1)(\cos t - 1) = 0$$
   $$\cos t = -\frac{1}{2} \text{ or } \cos t = 1$$
   $$t = \frac{2\pi}{3}, \frac{4\pi}{3}, 0, 2\pi$$

   The critical points (and endpoints) are $(0, 0)$,
   $\left(\frac{2\pi}{3}, -\frac{3\sqrt{3}}{2}\right)$, $\left(\frac{4\pi}{3}, \frac{3\sqrt{3}}{2}\right)$, and $(2\pi, 0)$
   The distance is greatest when $t = \frac{2\pi}{3}$ sec and when
   $t = \frac{4\pi}{3}$ sec. The distance at those times is $\frac{3\sqrt{3}}{2}$ meters.

41. (a)
$$\sin t = \sin\left(t + \frac{\pi}{3}\right)$$
$$\sin t = \sin t \cos \frac{\pi}{3} + \cos t \sin \frac{\pi}{3}$$
$$\sin t = \frac{1}{2}\sin t + \frac{\sqrt{3}}{2}\cos t$$
$$\frac{1}{2}\sin t = \frac{\sqrt{3}}{2}\cos t$$
$$\tan t = \sqrt{3}$$

Solving for t, the particles meet at $t = \frac{\pi}{3}$ sec and at

$t = \frac{4\pi}{3}$ sec.

(b) The distance between the particles is the absolute value

of $f(t) = \sin\left(t + \dfrac{\pi}{3}\right) - \sin t = \dfrac{\sqrt{3}}{2}\cos t - \dfrac{1}{2}\sin t$. Find

the critical points in $[0, 2\pi]$:

$$f'(t) = -\dfrac{\sqrt{3}}{2}\sin t - \dfrac{1}{2}\cos t = 0$$

$$-\dfrac{\sqrt{3}}{2}\sin t = \dfrac{1}{2}\cos t$$

$$\tan t = -\dfrac{1}{\sqrt{3}}$$

The solutions are $t = \dfrac{5\pi}{6}$ and $t = \dfrac{11\pi}{6}$, so the critical

points are at $\left(\dfrac{5\pi}{6}, -1\right)$ and $\left(\dfrac{11\pi}{6}, 1\right)$, and the interval

endpoints are at $\left(0, \dfrac{\sqrt{3}}{2}\right)$, and $\left(2\pi, \dfrac{\sqrt{3}}{2}\right)$. The particles

are farthest apart at $t = \dfrac{5\pi}{6}$ sec and at $t = \dfrac{11\pi}{6}$ sec, and

the maximum distance between the particles is 1 m.

(c) We need to maximize $f'(t)$, so we solve $f''(t) = 0$.

$$f''(t) = -\dfrac{\sqrt{3}}{2}\cos t + \dfrac{1}{2}\sin t = 0$$

$$\dfrac{1}{2}\sin t = \dfrac{\sqrt{3}}{2}\cos t$$

This is the same equation we solved in part (a), so the

solutions are $t = \dfrac{\pi}{3}$ sec and $t = \dfrac{4\pi}{3}$ sec.

For the function $y = f'(t)$, the critical points occur at

$\left(\dfrac{\pi}{3}, -1\right)$ and $\left(\dfrac{4\pi}{3}, 1\right)$, and the interval endpoints are at

$\left(0, -\dfrac{1}{2}\right)$ and $\left(2\pi, -\dfrac{1}{2}\right)$.

Thus, $|f'(t)|$ is maximized at $t = \dfrac{\pi}{3}$ and $t = \dfrac{4\pi}{3}$. But

these are the instants when the particles pass each

other, so the graph of $y = |f(t)|$ has corners at these

points and $\dfrac{d}{dt}|f(t)|$ is undefined at these instants. We

cannot say that the distance is changing the fastest at

any particular instant, but we can say that near $t = \dfrac{\pi}{3}$ or

$t = \dfrac{4\pi}{3}$ the distance is changing faster than at any other

time in the interval.

42. The trapezoid has height $(\cos \theta)$ ft and the trapezoid bases

measure 1 ft and $(1 + 2\sin\theta)$ ft, so the volume is given by

$$V(\theta) = \dfrac{1}{2}(\cos\theta)(1 + 1 + 2\sin\theta)(20)$$

$$= 20(\cos\theta)(1 + \sin\theta).$$

Find the critical points for $0 \le \theta < \dfrac{\pi}{2}$:

$$V'(\theta) = 20(\cos\theta)(\cos\theta) + 20(1 + \sin\theta)(-\sin\theta) = 0$$

$$20\cos^2\theta - 20\sin\theta - 20\sin^2\theta = 0$$

$$20(1 - \sin^2\theta) - 20\sin\theta - 20\sin^2\theta = 0$$

$$-20(2\sin^2\theta + \sin\theta - 1) = 0$$

$$-20(2\sin\theta - 1)(\sin\theta + 1) = 0$$

$$\sin\theta = \dfrac{1}{2} \text{ or } \sin\theta = -1$$

$$\theta = \dfrac{\pi}{6}$$

The critical point is at $\left(\dfrac{\pi}{6}, 15\sqrt{3}\right)$. Since $V'(\theta) > 0$ for

$0 \le \theta < \dfrac{\pi}{6}$ and $V'(\theta) < 0$ for $\dfrac{\pi}{6} < \theta < \dfrac{\pi}{2}$, the critical point

corresponds to the maximum possible trough volume. The

volume is maximized when $\theta = \dfrac{\pi}{6}$.

43. (a)

Sketch segment RS as shown, and let y be the length of

segment QR. Note that $PB = 8.5 - x$, and so

$QB = \sqrt{x^2 - (8.5 - x)^2} = \sqrt{8.5(2x - 8.5)}$.

Also note that triangles QRS and PQB are similar.

$$\dfrac{QR}{RS} = \dfrac{PQ}{QB}$$

$$\dfrac{y}{8.5} = \dfrac{x}{\sqrt{8.5(2x - 8.5)}}$$

$$\dfrac{y^2}{8.5^2} = \dfrac{x^2}{8.5(2x - 8.5)}$$

$$y^2 = \dfrac{8.5x^2}{2x - 8.5}$$

$$L^2 = x^2 + y^2$$

$$L^2 = x^2 + \dfrac{8.5x^2}{2x - 8.5}$$

$$L^2 = \dfrac{x^2(2x - 8.5) + 8.5x^2}{2x - 8.5}$$

$$L^2 = \dfrac{2x^3}{2x - 8.5}$$

43. continued

(b) Note that $x > 4.25$, and let $f(x) = L^2 = \dfrac{2x^3}{2x - 8.5}$. Since $y \le 11$, the approximate domain of f is $5.20 \le x \le 8.5$.

Then

$$f'(x) = \frac{(2x - 8.5)(6x^2) - (2x^3)(2)}{(2x - 8.5)^2} = \frac{x^2(8x - 51)}{(2x - 8.5)^2}$$

For $x > 5.20$, the critical point occurs at

$x = \dfrac{51}{8} = 6.375$ in., and this corresponds to a minimum value of $f(x)$ because $f'(x) < 0$ for $5.20 < x < 6.375$ and $f'(x) > 0$ for $x > 6.375$. Therefore, the value of x that minimizes L^2 is $x = 6.375$ in.

(c) The minimum value of L is

$$\sqrt{\frac{2(6.375)^3}{2(6.375) - 8.5}} \approx 11.04 \text{ in.}$$

44. Since $R = M^2\!\left(\dfrac{C}{2} - \dfrac{M}{3}\right) = \dfrac{C}{2}M^2 - \dfrac{1}{3}M^3$, we have

$\dfrac{dR}{dM} = CM - M^2$. Let $f(M) = CM - M^2$. Then

$f'(M) = C - 2M$, and the critical point for f occurs at

$M = \dfrac{C}{2}$. This value corresponds to a maximum because

$f'(M) > 0$ for $M < \dfrac{C}{2}$ and $f'(M) < 0$ for $M > \dfrac{C}{2}$. The value of M that maximizes $\dfrac{dR}{dM}$ is $M = \dfrac{C}{2}$.

45. The profit is given by

$$P(x) = (n)(x - c) = a + b(100 - x)(x - c)$$
$$= -bx^2 + (100 + c)bx + (a - 100bc).$$

Then $P'(x) = -2bx + (100 + c)b$

$$= b(100 + c - 2x).$$

The critical point occurs at $x = \dfrac{100 + c}{2} = 50 + \dfrac{c}{2}$, and this value corresponds to the maximum profit because

$P'(x) > 0$ for $x < 50 + \dfrac{c}{2}$ and $P'(x) < 0$ for $x > 50 + \dfrac{c}{2}$.

A selling price of $50 + \dfrac{c}{2}$ will bring the maximum profit.

46.

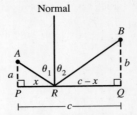

Let P be the foot of the perpendicular from A to the mirror, and Q be the foot of the perpendicular from B to the mirror. Suppose the light strikes the mirror at point R on the way from A to B. Let:

$a = $ distance from A to P

$b = $ distance from B to Q

$c = $ distance from P to Q

$x = $ distance from P to R

To minimize the time is to minimize the total distance the light travels going from A to B. The total distance is

$$D(x) = \sqrt{x^2 + a^2} + \sqrt{(c - x)^2 + b^2}$$

Then

$$D'(x) = \frac{1}{2\sqrt{x^2 + a^2}}(2x) + \frac{1}{2\sqrt{(c - x)^2 + b^2}}[-2(c - x)]$$

$$= \frac{x}{\sqrt{x^2 + a^2}} - \frac{c - x}{\sqrt{(c - x)^2 + b^2}}$$

Solving $D'(x) = 0$ gives the equation

$$\frac{x}{\sqrt{x^2 + a^2}} = \frac{c - x}{\sqrt{(c - x)^2 + b^2}}$$

which we will refer to as Equation 1. Squaring both sides, we have:

$$\frac{x^2}{x^2 + a^2} = \frac{(c - x)^2}{(c - x)^2 + b^2}$$

$$x^2[(c - x)^2 + b^2] = (c - x)^2(x^2 + a^2)$$

$$x^2(c - x)^2 + x^2b^2 = (c - x)^2x^2 + (c - x)^2a^2$$

$$x^2b^2 = (c - x)^2a^2$$

$$x^2b^2 = [c^2 - 2xc + x^2]a^2$$

$$0 = (a^2 - b^2)x^2 - 2a^2cx + a^2c^2$$

$$0 = [(a + b)x - ac][(a - b)x - ac]$$

$$x = \frac{ac}{a + b} \text{ or } x = \frac{ac}{a - b}$$

Note that the value $x = \dfrac{ac}{a - b}$ is an extraneous solution because x and $c - x$ have opposite signs for this value.

The only critical point occurs at $x = \dfrac{ac}{a + b}$.

To verify that this critical point represents the minimum distance, note that

$$D''(x) = \frac{(\sqrt{x^2 + a^2})(1) - (x)\left(\dfrac{x}{\sqrt{x^2 + a^2}}\right)}{x^2 + a^2} -$$

$$\frac{(\sqrt{(c - x)^2 + b^2})(-1) - (c - x)\left(\dfrac{-(c - x)}{\sqrt{(c - x)^2 + b^2}}\right)}{(c - x)^2 + b^2}$$

$$= \frac{(x^2 + a^2) - x^2}{(x^2 + a^2)^{3/2}} - \frac{-[(c - x)^2 + b^2] + (c - x)^2}{[(c - x)^2 + b^2]^{3/2}}$$

$$= \frac{a^2}{(x^2 + a^2)^{3/2}} + \frac{b^2}{[(c - x)^2 + b^2]^{3/2}},$$

which is always positive.

We now know that $D(x)$ is minimized when Equation 1 is true, or, equivalently, $\dfrac{PR}{AR} = \dfrac{QR}{BR}$. This means that the two right triangles APR and BQR are similar, which in turn implies that the two angles must be equal.

47. $\dfrac{dv}{dx} = ka - 2kx$

The critical point occurs at $x = \dfrac{ka}{2k} = \dfrac{a}{2}$, which represents a maximum value

because $\dfrac{d^2v}{dx^2} = -2k$, which is negative for all x. The maximum value of v is

$$kax - kx^2 = ka\left(\frac{a}{2}\right) - k\left(\frac{a}{2}\right)^2 = \frac{ka^2}{4}.$$

48. (a) $v = cr_0 r^2 - cr^3$

$$\frac{dv}{dr} = 2cr_0 r - 3cr^2 = cr(2r_0 - 3r)$$

The critical point occurs at $r = \dfrac{2r_0}{3}$. (Note that $r = 0$ is not in the domain of v.) The critical point represents a maximum because $\dfrac{d^2v}{dr^2} = 2cr_0 - 6cr = 2c(r_0 - 3r)$, which is negative in the domain $\dfrac{r_0}{2} \le r \le r_0$.

(b) We graph $v = (0.5 - r)r^2$, and observe that the

maximum indeed occurs at $v = \left(\dfrac{2}{3}\right)0.5 = \dfrac{1}{3}$.

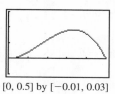

[0, 0.5] by [−0.01, 0.03]

49. Revenue: $r(x) = [200 - 2(x - 50)]x = -2x^2 + 300x$
    Cost: $c(x) = 6000 + 32x$
    Profit: $p(x) = r(x) - c(x)$
                      $= -2x^2 + 268x - 6000,\ 50 \le x \le 80$

Since $p'(x) = -4x + 268 = -4(x - 67)$, the critical point occurs at $x = 67$. This value represents the maximum because $p''(x) = -4$, which is negative for all x in the domain. The maximum profit occurs if 67 people go on the tour.

50. (a) Since $A'(q) = -kmq^{-2} + \dfrac{h}{2}$, the critical point occurs

when $\dfrac{km}{q^2} = \dfrac{h}{2}$, or $q = \sqrt{\dfrac{2km}{h}}$. This corresponds to the

minimum value of $A(q)$ because $A''(q) = 2kmq^{-3}$,

which is positive for $q > 0$.

(b) The new formula for average weekly cost is

$$B(q) = \frac{(k + bq)m}{q} + cm + \frac{hq}{2}$$

$$= \frac{km}{q} + bm + cm + \frac{hq}{2}$$

$$= A(q) + bm$$

Since $B(q)$ differs from $A(q)$ by a constant, the

minimum value of $B(q)$ will occur at the same q-value

as the minimum value of $A(q)$. The most economical

quantity is again $\sqrt{\dfrac{2km}{h}}$.

51. The profit is given by
    $$p(x) = r(x) - c(x)$$
    $$= 6x - (x^3 - 6x^2 + 15x)$$
    $$= -x^3 + 6x^2 - 9x,\ \text{for } x \ge 0.$$
    Then $p'(x) = -3x^2 + 12x - 9 = -3(x - 1)(x - 3)$, so the critical points occur at $x = 1$ and $x = 3$. Since $p'(x) < 0$ for $0 \le x < 1$, $p'(x) > 0$ for $1 < x < 3$, and $p'(x) < 0$ for $x > 3$, the relative maxima occur at the endpoint $x = 0$ and at the critical point $x = 3$. Since $p(0) = p(3) = 0$, this means that for $x \ge 0$, the function $p(x)$ has its absolute maximum value at the points $(0, 0)$ and $(3, 0)$. This result can also be obtained graphically, as shown.

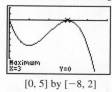

[0, 5] by [−8, 2]

52. The average cost is given by

$a(x) = \dfrac{c(x)}{x} = x^2 - 20x + 20{,}000$. Therefore,

$a'(x) = 2x - 20$ and the critical value is $x = 10$, which

represents the minimum because $a''(x) = 2$, which is

positive for all x. The average cost is minimized at a

production level of 10 items.

53. (a) According to the graph, $y'(0) = 0$.

(b) According to the graph, $y'(-L) = 0$.

(c) $y(0) = 0$, so $d = 0$.

Now $y'(x) = 3ax^2 + 2bx + c$, so $y'(0)$ implies that $c = 0$. Therefore, $y(x) = ax^3 + bx^2$ and $y'(x) = 3ax^2 + 2bx$. Then $y(-L) = -aL^3 + bL^2 = H$ and $y'(-L) = 3aL^2 - 2bL = 0$, so we have two linear equations in the two unknowns a and b. The second equation gives $b = \frac{3aL}{2}$. Substituting into the first equation, we have $-aL^3 + \frac{3aL^3}{2} = H$, or $\frac{aL^3}{2} = H$, so $a = 2\frac{H}{L^3}$. Therefore, $b = 3\frac{H}{L^2}$ and the equation for y is $y(x) = 2\frac{H}{L^3}x^3 + 3\frac{H}{L^2}x^2$, or $y(x) = H\left[2\left(\frac{x}{L}\right)^3 + 3\left(\frac{x}{L}\right)^2\right]$.

54. (a) The base radius of the cone is $r = \frac{2\pi a - x}{2\pi}$ and so the height is $h = \sqrt{a^2 - r^2} = \sqrt{a^2 - \left(\frac{2\pi a - x}{2\pi}\right)^2}$. Therefore,

$$V(x) = \frac{\pi}{3}r^2 h = \frac{\pi}{3}\left(\frac{2\pi a - x}{2\pi}\right)^2 \sqrt{a^2 - \left(\frac{2\pi a - x}{2\pi}\right)^2}.$$

(b) To simplify the calculations, we shall consider the volume as a function of r:

volume $= f(r) = \frac{\pi}{3}r^2\sqrt{a^2 - r^2}$, where $0 < r < a$.

$$f'(r) = \frac{\pi}{3}\frac{d}{dr}(r^2\sqrt{a^2 - r^2})$$

$$= \frac{\pi}{3}\left[r^2 \cdot \frac{1}{2\sqrt{a^2 - r^2}} \cdot (-2r) + (\sqrt{a^2 - r^2})(2r)\right]$$

$$= \frac{\pi}{3}\left[\frac{-r^3 + 2r(a^2 - r^2)}{\sqrt{a^2 - r^2}}\right]$$

$$= \frac{\pi}{3}\left[\frac{2a^2 r - 3r^3}{\sqrt{a^2 - r^2}}\right]$$

$$= \frac{\pi r(2a^2 - 3r^2)}{3\sqrt{a^2 - r^2}}$$

The critical point occurs when $r^2 = \frac{2a^2}{3}$, which gives $r = a\sqrt{\frac{2}{3}} = \frac{a\sqrt{6}}{3}$. Then

$$h = \sqrt{a^2 - r^2} = \sqrt{a^2 - \frac{2a^2}{3}} = \sqrt{\frac{a^2}{3}} = \frac{a\sqrt{3}}{3}. \text{ Using}$$

$r = \frac{a\sqrt{6}}{3}$ and $h = \frac{a\sqrt{3}}{3}$,

we may now find the values of r and h for the given values of a.

When $a = 4$: $r = \frac{4\sqrt{6}}{3}$, $h = \frac{4\sqrt{3}}{3}$;

when $a = 5$: $r = \frac{5\sqrt{6}}{3}$, $h = \frac{5\sqrt{3}}{3}$;

when $a = 6$: $r = 2\sqrt{6}$, $h = 2\sqrt{3}$;

when $a = 8$: $r = \frac{8\sqrt{6}}{3}$, $h = \frac{8\sqrt{3}}{3}$

(c) Since $r = \frac{a\sqrt{6}}{3}$ and $h = \frac{a\sqrt{3}}{3}$, the relationship is $\frac{r}{h} = \sqrt{2}$.

55. (a) Let x_0 represent the fixed value of x at point P, so that P has coordinates (x_0, a), and let $m = f'(x_0)$ be the slope of line RT. Then the equation of line RT is $y = m(x - x_0) + a$. The y-intercept of this line is $m(0 - x_0) + a = a - mx_0$, and the x-intercept is the solution of $m(x - x_0) + a = 0$, or $x = \frac{mx_0 - a}{m}$. Let O designate the origin. Then

(Area of triangle RST)

$\quad = 2$(Area of triangle ORT)

$\quad = 2 \cdot \frac{1}{2}(x\text{-intercept of line } RT)(y\text{-intercept of line } RT)$

$\quad = 2 \cdot \frac{1}{2}\left(\frac{mx_0 - a}{m}\right)(a - mx_0)$

$\quad = -m\left(\frac{mx_0 - a}{m}\right)\left(\frac{mx_0 - a}{m}\right)$

$\quad = -m\left(\frac{mx_0 - a}{m}\right)^2$

$\quad = -m\left(x_0 - \frac{a}{m}\right)^2$

Substituting x for x_0, $f'(x)$ for m, and $f(x)$ for a, we have $A(x) = -f'(x)\left[x - \frac{f(x)}{f'(x)}\right]^2$.

(b) The domain is the open interval $(0, 10)$.

To graph, let $y_1 = f(x) = 5 + 5\sqrt{1 - \frac{x^2}{100}}$,

$y_2 = f'(x) = \text{NDER}(y_1)$, and

$y_3 = A(x) = -y_2\left(x - \frac{y_1}{y_2}\right)^2$.

The graph of the area function $y_3 = A(x)$ is shown below.

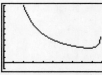

[0, 10] by [−100, 1000]

The vertical asymptotes at $x = 0$ and $x = 10$ correspond to
horizontal or vertical tangent lines, which do not form triangles.

(c) Using our expression for the y-intercept of the tangent line, the height of the triangle is

$$a - mx = f(x) - f'(x) \cdot x$$

$$= 5 + \frac{1}{2}\sqrt{100 - x^2} - \frac{-x}{2\sqrt{100 - x^2}}x$$

$$= 5 + \frac{1}{2}\sqrt{100 - x^2} + \frac{x^2}{2\sqrt{100 - x^2}}$$

We may use graphing methods or the analytic method in part (d) to find that the minimum value of $A(x)$ occurs at $x \approx 8.66$. Substituting this value into the expression above, the height of the triangle is 15. This is 3 times the y-coordinate of the center of the ellipse.

(d) Part (a) remains unchanged. The domain is $(0, C)$. To graph, note that

$$f(x) = B + B\sqrt{1 - \frac{x^2}{C^2}} = B + \frac{B}{C}\sqrt{C^2 - x^2} \text{ and}$$

$$f'(x) = \frac{B}{C}\frac{1}{2\sqrt{C^2 - x^2}}(-2x) = \frac{-Bx}{C\sqrt{C^2 - x^2}}.$$

Therefore, we have

$$A(x) = -f'(x)\left[x - \frac{f(x)}{f'(x)}\right]^2 = \frac{Bx}{C\sqrt{C^2 - x^2}}\left[x - \frac{B + \frac{B}{C}\sqrt{C^2 - x^2}}{\frac{-Bx}{C\sqrt{C^2 - x^2}}}\right]^2$$

$$= \frac{Bx}{C\sqrt{C^2 - x^2}}\left[x - \frac{(BC + B\sqrt{C^2 - x^2})\sqrt{C^2 - x^2}}{-Bx}\right]^2$$

$$= \frac{1}{BCx\sqrt{C^2 - x^2}}[Bx^2 + (BC + B\sqrt{C^2 - x^2})(\sqrt{C^2 - x^2})]^2$$

$$= \frac{1}{BCx\sqrt{C^2 - x^2}}[Bx^2 + BC\sqrt{C^2 - x^2} + B(C^2 - x^2)]^2$$

$$= \frac{1}{BCx\sqrt{C^2 - x^2}}[BC(C + \sqrt{C^2 - x^2})]^2$$

$$= \frac{BC(C + \sqrt{C^2 - x^2})^2}{x\sqrt{C^2 - x^2}}$$

$$A'(x) = BC \cdot \frac{(x\sqrt{C^2 - x^2})(2)(C + \sqrt{C^2 - x^2})\left(\frac{-x}{\sqrt{C^2 - x^2}}\right) - (C + \sqrt{C^2 - x^2})^2\left(x\frac{-x}{\sqrt{C^2 - x^2}} + \sqrt{C^2 - x^2}(1)\right)}{x^2(C^2 - x^2)}$$

$$= \frac{BC(C + \sqrt{C^2 - x^2})}{x^2(C^2 - x^2)}\left[-2x^2 - (C + \sqrt{C^2 - x^2})\left(\frac{-x^2}{\sqrt{C^2 - x^2}} + \sqrt{C^2 - x^2}\right)\right]$$

$$= \frac{BC(C + \sqrt{C^2 - x^2})}{x^2(C^2 - x^2)}\left[-2x^2 + \frac{Cx^2}{\sqrt{C^2 - x^2}} - C\sqrt{C^2 - x^2} + x^2 - (C^2 - x^2)\right]$$

$$= \frac{BC(C + \sqrt{C^2 - x^2})}{x^2(C^2 - x^2)}\left(\frac{Cx^2}{\sqrt{C^2 - x^2}} - C\sqrt{C^2 - x^2} - C^2\right)$$

$$= \frac{BC(C + \sqrt{C^2 - x^2})}{x^2(C^2 - x^2)^{3/2}}[Cx^2 - C(C^2 - x^2) - C^2\sqrt{C^2 - x^2}]$$

$$= \frac{BC^2(C + \sqrt{C^2 - x^2})}{x^2(C^2 - x^2)^{3/2}}(2x^2 - C^2 - C\sqrt{C^2 - x^2})$$

55. continued

To find the critical points for $0 < x < C$, we solve:

$$2x^2 - C^2 = C\sqrt{C^2 - x^2}$$

$$4x^4 - 4C^2x^2 + C^4 = C^4 - C^2x^2$$

$$4x^4 - 3C^2x^2 = 0$$

$$x^2(4x^2 - 3C^2) = 0$$

The minimum value of $A(x)$ for $0 < x < C$ occurs at the critical point $x = \dfrac{C\sqrt{3}}{2}$, or $x^2 = \dfrac{3C^2}{4}$. The corresponding triangle height is

$$a - mx = f(x) - f'(x) \cdot x$$

$$= B + \frac{B}{C}\sqrt{C^2 - x^2} + \frac{Bx^2}{C\sqrt{C^2 - x^2}}$$

$$= B + \frac{B}{C}\sqrt{C^2 - \frac{3C^2}{4}} + \frac{B\left(\frac{3C^2}{4}\right)}{C\sqrt{C^2 - \frac{3C^2}{4}}}$$

$$= B + \frac{B}{C}\left(\frac{C}{2}\right) + \frac{\frac{3BC^2}{4}}{\frac{C^2}{2}}$$

$$= B + \frac{B}{2} + \frac{3B}{2}$$

$$= 3B$$

This shows that the triangle has minimum area when its height is $3B$.

■ Section 4.5 Linearization and Newton's Method (pp. 220–232)

Exploration 1   Approximating with Tangent Lines

1. $f'(x) = 2x$, $f'(1) = 2$, so an equation of the tangent line is $y - 1 = 2(x - 1)$ or $y = 2x - 1$.

3. Since $(y_1 - y_2)(1) = y_1(1) - y_2(1) = 1 - 1 = 0$, this view shifts the action from the point $(1, 1)$ to the point $(1, 0)$. Also $(y_1 - y_2)'(1) = y_1'(1) - y_2'(1) = 2 - 2 = 0$. Thus the tangent line to $y_1 - y_2$ at $x = 1$ is horizontal (the x-axis). The measure of how well y_2 fits y_1 at $(1, 1)$ is the same as the measure of how well the x-axis fits $y_1 - y_2$ at $(1, 0)$.

4. These tables show that the values of $y_1 - y_2$ near $x = 1$ are close to 0 so that y_2 is a good approximation to y_1 near $x = 1$. Here are two tables with Δ Table $= 0.0001$.

X	Y3	
.9994	3.6E-7	
.9995	2.5E-7	
.9996	1.6E-7	
.9997	9E-8	
.9998	4E-8	
.9999	1E-8	
1	0	

Y3 ☐ Y1 − Y2

X	Y3	
1	0	
1.0001	1E-8	
1.0002	4E-8	
1.0003	9E-8	
1.0004	1.6E-7	
1.0005	2.5E-7	
1.0006	3.6E-7	

Y3 ☐ Y1 − Y2

Exploration 2   Using Newton's Method on the Grapher

1–3. Here are the first 11 computations.

4. Answers will vary. Here is what happens for $x_1 = -2$.

Quick Review 4.5

1. $\frac{dy}{dx} = \cos(x^2 + 1) \cdot \frac{d}{dx}(x^2 + 1) = 2x \cos(x^2 + 1)$

2. $\frac{dy}{dx} = \frac{(x + 1)(1 - \sin x) - (x + \cos x)(1)}{(x + 1)^2}$

$= \frac{x - x \sin x + 1 - \sin x - x - \cos x}{(x + 1)^2}$

$= \frac{1 - \cos x - (x + 1)\sin x}{(x + 1)^2}$

3.

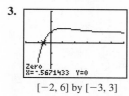

$[-2, 6]$ by $[-3, 3]$

$x \approx -0.567$

4.

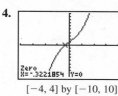

$[-4, 4]$ by $[-10, 10]$

$x \approx -0.322$

5. $f'(x) = (x)(-e^{-x}) + (e^{-x})(1) = e^{-x} - xe^{-x}$
$f'(0) = 1$
The lines passes through $(0, 1)$ and has slope 1. Its equation is $y = x + 1$.

6. $f'(x) = (x)(-e^{-x}) + (e^{-x})(1) = e^{-x} - xe^{-x}$
$f'(-1) = e^1 - (-e^1) = 2e$
The lines passes through $(-1, -e + 1)$ and has slope $2e$.
Its equation is $y = 2e(x + 1) + (-e + 1)$, or
$y = 2ex + e + 1$.

7. (a) $x + 1 = 0$
$x = -1$

(b) $2ex + e + 1 = 0$
$2ex = -(e + 1)$
$x = -\frac{e + 1}{2e} \approx -0.684$

8. $f'(x) = 3x^2 - 4$
$f'(1) = 3(1)^2 - 4 = -1$
Since $f(1) = -2$ and $f'(1) = -1$, the graph of $g(x)$ passes through $(1, -2)$ and has slope -1. Its equation is
$g(x) = -1(x - 1) + (-2)$, or $g(x) = -x - 1$.

x	$f(x)$	$g(x)$
0.7	-1.457	-1.7
0.8	-1.688	-1.8
0.9	-1.871	-1.9
1.0	-2	-2
1.1	-2.069	-2.1
1.2	-2.072	-2.2
1.3	-2.003	-2.3

9. $f'(x) = \cos x$
$f'(1.5) = \cos 1.5$
Since $f(1.5) = \sin 1.5$ and $f'(1.5) = \cos 1.5$, the tangent line passes through $(1.5, \sin 1.5)$ and has slope $\cos 1.5$. Its equation is $y = (\cos 1.5)(x - 1.5) + \sin 1.5$, or approximately $y = 0.071x + 0.891$

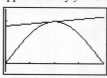

$[0, \pi]$ by $[-0.2, 1.3]$

10. For $x > 3$, $f'(x) = \frac{1}{2\sqrt{x - 3}}$, and so $f'(4) = \frac{1}{2}$. Since
$f(4) = 1$ and $f'(4) = \frac{1}{2}$, the tangent line passes through
$(4, 1)$ and has slope $\frac{1}{2}$. Its equation is $y = \frac{1}{2}(x - 4) + 1$, or
$y = \frac{1}{2}x - 1$.

$[-1, 7]$ by $[-2, 2]$

Section 4.5 Exercises

1. (a) $f'(x) = 3x^2 - 2$
We have $f(2) = 7$ and $f'(2) = 10$.
$L(x) = f(2) + f'(2)(x - 2)$
$= 7 + 10(x - 2)$
$= 10x - 13$

(b) Since $f(2.1) = 8.061$ and $L(2.1) = 8$, the approximation differs from the true value in absolute value by less than 10^{-1}.

2. (a) $f'(x) = \dfrac{1}{2\sqrt{x^2 + 9}}(2x) = \dfrac{x}{\sqrt{x^2 + 9}}$

We have $f(-4) = 5$ and $f'(-4) = -\dfrac{4}{5}$.

$L(x) = f(-4) + f'(-4)(x - (-4))$

$\quad = 5 - \dfrac{4}{5}(x + 4)$

$\quad = -\dfrac{4}{5}x + \dfrac{9}{5}$

(b) Since $f(-3.9) \approx 4.9204$ and $L(-3.9) = 4.92$, the approximation differs from the true value by less than 10^{-3}.

3. (a) $f'(x) = 1 - x^{-2}$

We have $f(1) = 2$ and $f'(1) = 0$.

$L(x) = f(1) + f'(1)(x - 1)$

$\quad = 2 + 0(x - 1)$

$\quad = 2$

(b) Since $f(1.1) \approx 2.009$ and $L(1.1) = 2$, the approximation differs from the true value by less than 10^{-2}.

4. (a) $f'(x) = \dfrac{1}{x + 1}$

We have $f(0) = 0$ and $f'(0) = 1$.

$L(x) = f(0) + f'(0)(x - 0)$

$\quad = 0 + 1x$

$\quad = x$

(b) Since $f(0.1) \approx 0.0953$ and $L(0.1) = 0.1$ the approximation differs from the true value by less than 10^{-2}.

5. (a) $f'(x) = \sec^2 x$

We have $f(\pi) = 0$ and $f'(\pi) = 1$.

$L(x) = f(\pi) + f'(\pi)(x - \pi)$

$\quad = 0 + 1(x - \pi)$

$\quad = x - \pi$

(b) Since $f(\pi + 0.1) \approx 0.10033$ and $L(\pi + 0.1) = 0.1$, the approximation differs from the true value in absolute value by less than 10^{-3}.

6. (a) $f'(x) = -\dfrac{1}{\sqrt{1 - x^2}}$

We have $f(0) = \dfrac{\pi}{2}$ and $f'(0) = -1$.

$L(x) = f(0) + f'(0)(x - 0)$

$\quad = \dfrac{\pi}{2} + (-1)(x - 0)$

$\quad = -x + \dfrac{\pi}{2}$

(b) Since $f(0.1) \approx 1.47063$ and $L(0.1) \approx 1.47080$, the approximation differs from the true value in absolute value by less than 10^{-3}.

7. $f'(x) = k(1 + x)^{k-1}$

We have $f(0) = 1$ and $f'(0) = k$.

$L(x) = f(0) + f'(0)(x - 0)$

$\quad = 1 + k(x - 0)$

$\quad = 1 + kx$

8. (a) $f(x) = (1 - x)^6 = [1 + (-x)]^6 \approx 1 + 6(-x) = 1 - 6x$

(b) $f(x) = \dfrac{2}{1 - x} = 2[1 + (-x)]^{-1} \approx 2[1 + (-1)(-x)]$

$\quad = 2 + 2x$

(c) $f(x) = (1 + x)^{-1/2} \approx 1 + \left(-\dfrac{1}{2}\right)x = 1 - \dfrac{x}{2}$

(d) $f(x) = \sqrt{2 + x^2} = \sqrt{2}\left(1 + \dfrac{x^2}{2}\right)^{1/2}$

$\quad \approx \sqrt{2}\left(1 + \dfrac{1}{2}\dfrac{x^2}{2}\right) = \sqrt{2}\left(1 + \dfrac{x^2}{4}\right)$

(e) $f(x) = (4 + 3x)^{1/3} = 4^{1/3}\left(1 + \dfrac{3x}{4}\right)^{1/3}$

$\quad \approx 4^{1/3}\left(1 + \dfrac{1}{3}\dfrac{3x}{4}\right) = 4^{1/3}\left(1 + \dfrac{x}{4}\right)$

(f) $f(x) = \left(1 - \dfrac{1}{2 + x}\right)^{2/3} = \left[1 + \left(-\dfrac{1}{2 + x}\right)\right]^{2/3}$

$\quad \approx 1 + \dfrac{2}{3}\left(-\dfrac{1}{2 + x}\right) = 1 - \dfrac{2}{6 + 3x}$

9. $f'(x) = \dfrac{1}{2\sqrt{x + 1}} + \cos x$

We have $f(0) = 1$ and $f'(0) = \dfrac{3}{2}$

$L(x) = f(0) + f'(0)(x - 0)$

$\quad = 1 + \dfrac{3}{2}x$

The linearization is the sum of the two individual

linearizations, which are x for $\sin x$ and $1 + \dfrac{1}{2}x$

for $\sqrt{x + 1}$.

10. (a) $(1.002)^{100} = (1 + 0.002)^{100} \approx 1 + (100)(0.002)$

$\quad = 1.2;$

$\left|1.002^{100} - 1.2\right| \approx 0.021 < 10^{-1}$

(b) $\sqrt[3]{1.009} = (1 + 0.009)^{1/3} \approx 1 + \dfrac{1}{3}(0.009) = 1.003;$

$\left|\sqrt[3]{1.009} - 1.003\right| \approx 9 \times 10^{-6} < 10^{-5}$

11. Center $= -1$

$f'(x) = 4x + 4$

We have $f(-1) = -5$ and $f'(-1) = 0$.

$L(x) = f(-1) + f'(-1)(x - (-1)) = -5 + 0(x + 1) = -5$

12. Center $= 8$

$f'(x) = \dfrac{1}{3}x^{-2/3}$

We have $f(8) = 2$ and $f'(8) = \dfrac{1}{12}$.

$L(x) = f(8) + f'(8)(x - 8) = 2 + \dfrac{1}{12}(x - 8) = \dfrac{x}{12} + \dfrac{4}{3}$

13. Center $= 1$

$$f'(x) = \frac{(x+1)(1) - (x)(1)}{(x+1)^2} = \frac{1}{(x+1)^2}$$

We have $f(1) = \frac{1}{2}$ and $f'(1) = \frac{1}{4}$

$$L(x) = f(1) + f'(1)(x - 1) = \frac{1}{2} + \frac{1}{4}(x - 1) = \frac{1}{4}x + \frac{1}{4}$$

Alternate solution:

Using center $= \frac{3}{2}$, we have $f\left(\frac{3}{2}\right) = \frac{3}{5}$ and $f'\left(\frac{3}{2}\right) = \frac{4}{25}$.

$$L(x) = f\left(\frac{3}{2}\right) + f'\left(\frac{3}{2}\right)\left(x - \frac{3}{2}\right) = \frac{3}{5} + \frac{4}{25}\left(x - \frac{3}{2}\right) = \frac{4}{25}x + \frac{9}{25}$$

14. Center $= \frac{\pi}{2}$

$$f'(x) = -\sin x$$

We have $f\left(\frac{\pi}{2}\right) = 0$ and $f'\left(\frac{\pi}{2}\right) = -1$.

$$L(x) = f\left(\frac{\pi}{2}\right) + f'\left(\frac{\pi}{2}\right)\left(x - \frac{\pi}{2}\right) = 0 - 1\left(x - \frac{\pi}{2}\right) = -x + \frac{\pi}{2}$$

15. Let $f(x) = x^3 + x - 1$. Then $f'(x) = 3x^2 + 1$ and

$$x_{n+1} = x_n - \frac{f(x_n)}{f'(x_n)} = x_n - \frac{x_n^3 + x_n - 1}{3x_n^2 + 1}.$$

Note that f is cubic and f' is always positive, so there is exactly one solution. We choose $x_1 = 0$.

$x_1 = 0$
$x_2 = 1$
$x_3 = 0.75$
$x_4 \approx 0.6860465$
$x_5 \approx 0.6823396$
$x_6 \approx 0.6823278$
$x_7 \approx 0.6823278$

Solution: $x \approx 0.682328$

16. Let $f(x) = x^4 + x - 3$. Then $f'(x) = 4x^3 + 1$ and

$$x_{n+1} = x_n - \frac{f(x_n)}{f'(x_n)} = x_n - \frac{x_n^4 + x_n - 3}{4x_n^3 + 1}$$

The graph of $y = f(x)$ shows that $f(x) = 0$ has two solutions.

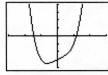

[−3, 3] by [−4, 4]

$x_1 = -1.5$ $x_1 = 1.2$
$x_2 = -1.455$ $x_2 \approx 1.6541962$
$x_3 \approx -1.4526332$ $x_3 \approx 1.1640373$
$x_4 \approx -1.4526269$ $x_4 \approx 1.1640351$
$x_5 \approx -1.4526269$ $x_5 \approx 1.1640351$

Solutions: $x \approx -1.452627, 1.164035$

17. Let $f(x) = x^2 - 2x + 1 - \sin x$.

Then $f'(x) = 2x - 2 - \cos x$ and

$$x_{n+1} = x_n - \frac{f(x_n)}{f'(x_n)} = x_n - \frac{x_n^2 - 2x_n + 1 - \sin x_n}{2x_n - 2 - \cos x_n}$$

The graph of $y = f(x)$ shows that $f(x) = 0$ has two solutions

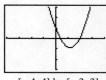

[−4, 4] by [−3, 3]

$x_1 = 0.3$ $x_1 = 2$
$x_2 \approx 0.3825699$ $x_2 \approx 1.9624598$
$x_3 \approx 0.3862295$ $x_3 \approx 1.9615695$
$x_4 \approx 0.3862369$ $x_4 \approx 1.9615690$
$x_5 \approx 0.3862369$ $x_5 \approx 1.9615690$

Solutions: $x \approx 0.386237, 1.961569$

18. Let $f(x) = x^4 - 2$. Then $f'(x) = 4x^3$ and

$$x_{n+1} = x_n - \frac{f(x_n)}{f'(x_n)} = x_n - \frac{x_n^4 - 2}{4x_n^3}.$$

Note that $f(x) = 0$ clearly has two solutions, namely $x = \pm\sqrt[4]{2}$. We use Newton's method to find the decimal equivalents.

$x_1 = 1.5$
$x_2 \approx 1.2731481$
$x_3 \approx 1.1971498$
$x_4 \approx 1.1892858$
$x_5 \approx 1.1892071$
$x_6 \approx 1.1892071$

Solutions: $x \approx \pm 1.189207$

19. (a) Since $\frac{dy}{dx} = 3x^2 - 3$, $dy = (3x^2 - 3)\,dx$.

(b) At the given values,
$dy = (3 \cdot 2^2 - 3)(0.05) = 9(0.05) = 0.45$.

20. (a) Since $\frac{dy}{dx} = \frac{(1 + x^2)(2) - (2x)(2x)}{(1 + x^2)^2} = \frac{2 - 2x^2}{(1 + x^2)^2}$,

$dy = \frac{2 - 2x^2}{(1 + x^2)^2}\,dx$.

(b) At the given values,

$$dy = \frac{2 - 2(-2)^2}{[1 + (-2)^2]^2}(0.1) = \frac{2 - 8}{5^2}(0.1)$$

$= -0.024$.

21. (a) Since $\frac{dy}{dx} = (x^2)\left(\frac{1}{x}\right) + (\ln x)(2x) = 2x \ln x + x$,

$dy = (2x \ln x + x)\,dx$.

(b) At the given values,

$dy = [2(1) \ln (1) + 1](0.01) = 1(0.01) = 0.01$

22. (a) Since $\dfrac{dy}{dx} = (x)\left(\dfrac{1}{2\sqrt{1-x^2}}\right)(-2x) + (\sqrt{1-x^2})(1)$

$= \dfrac{-x^2}{\sqrt{1-x^2}} + \sqrt{1-x^2} = \dfrac{-x^2 + (1-x^2)}{\sqrt{1-x^2}} = \dfrac{1-2x^2}{\sqrt{1-x^2}}$,

$dy = \dfrac{1-2x^2}{\sqrt{1-x^2}}\,dx$.

(b) At the given values, $dy = \dfrac{1-2(0)^2}{\sqrt{1-(0)^2}}(-0.2) = -0.2$.

23. (a) Since $\dfrac{dy}{dx} = e^{\sin x}\cos x$, $dy = (\cos x)e^{\sin x}\,dx$.

(b) At the given values,

$dy = (\cos \pi)(e^{\sin \pi})(-0.1) = (-1)(1)(-0.1) = 0.1$.

24. (a) Since $\dfrac{dy}{dx} = -3\csc\left(1 - \dfrac{x}{3}\right)\cot\left(1 - \dfrac{x}{3}\right)\left(-\dfrac{1}{3}\right)$

$= \csc\left(1 - \dfrac{x}{3}\right)\cot\left(1 - \dfrac{x}{3}\right)$,

$dy = \csc\left(1 - \dfrac{x}{3}\right)\cot\left(1 - \dfrac{x}{3}\right)dx$.

(b) At the given values,

$dy = \csc\left(1 - \dfrac{1}{3}\right)\cot\left(1 - \dfrac{1}{3}\right)(0.1)$

$= 0.1\csc\dfrac{2}{3}\cot\dfrac{2}{3} \approx 0.205525$

25. (a) $\quad y + xy - x = 0$

$y(1 + x) = x$

$y = \dfrac{x}{x+1}$

Since $\dfrac{dy}{dx} = \dfrac{(x+1)(1) - (x)(1)}{(x+1)^2} = \dfrac{1}{(x+1)^2}$,

$dy = \dfrac{dx}{(x+1)^2}$.

(b) At the given values,

$dy = \dfrac{0.01}{(0+1)^2} = 0.01$.

26. (a) Since $\dfrac{dy}{dx} = \sec(x^2 - 1)\tan(x^2 - 1) \cdot (2x)$,

$dy = 2x\sec(x^2 - 1)\tan(x^2 - 1)\,dx$.

(b) At the given values,

$dy = 2(1.5)\sec(1.5^2 - 1)\tan(1.5^2 - 1) \cdot (0.05)$

$= 0.15\sec 1.25\tan 1.25 \approx 1.431663$.

27. (a) $\Delta f = f(0.1) - f(0) = 0.21 - 0 = 0.21$

(b) Since $f'(x) = 2x + 2$, $f'(0) = 2$.
Therefore, $df = 2\,dx = 2(0.1) = 0.2$.

(c) $|\Delta f - df| = |0.21 - 0.2| = 0.01$

28. (a) $\Delta f = f(1.1) - f(1) = 0.231 - 0 = 0.231$

(b) Since $f'(x) = 3x^2 - 1$, $f'(1) = 2$.
Therefore, $df = 2dx = 2(0.1) = 0.2$.

(c) $|\Delta f - df| = |0.231 - 0.2| = 0.031$

29. (a) $\Delta f = f(0.55) - f(0.5) = \dfrac{20}{11} - 2 = -\dfrac{2}{11}$

(b) Since $f'(x) = -x^{-2}$, $f'(0.5) = -4$.

Therefore, $df = -4\,dx = -4(0.05) = -0.2 = -\dfrac{1}{5}$

(c) $|\Delta f - df| = \left|-\dfrac{2}{11} + \dfrac{1}{5}\right| = \dfrac{1}{55}$

30. (a) $\Delta f = f(1.01) - f(1) = 1.04060401 - 1 = 0.04060401$

(b) Since $f'(x) = 4x^3$, $f'(1) = 4$.
Therefore, $df = 4\,dx = 4(0.01) = 0.04$.

(c) $|\Delta f - df| = |0.04060401 - 0.04| = 0.00060401$

31. Note that $\dfrac{dV}{dr} = 4\pi r^2$, $dV = 4\pi r^2\,dr$. When r changes from a to $a + dr$, the change in volume is approximately $4\pi a^2\,dr$.

32. Note that $\dfrac{dS}{dr} = 8\pi r$, so $dS = 8\pi r\,dr$. When r changes from a to $a + dr$, the change in surface area is approximately $8\pi a\,dr$.

33. Note that $\dfrac{dV}{dx} = 3x^2$, so $dV = 3x^2\,dx$. When x changes from a to $a + dx$, the change in volume is approximately $3a^2\,dx$.

34. Note that $\dfrac{dS}{dx} = 12x$, so $dS = 12x\,dx$. When x changes from a to $a + dx$, the change in surface area is approximately $12a\,dx$.

35. Note that $\dfrac{dV}{dr} = 2\pi rh$, so $dV = 2\pi rh\,dr$. When r changes from a to $a + dr$, the change in volume is approximately $2\pi ah\,dr$.

36. Note that $\dfrac{dS}{dh} = 2\pi r$, so $dS = 2\pi r\,dh$. When h changes from a to $a + dh$, the change in lateral surface area is approximately $2\pi r\,dh$.

37. (a) Note that $f'(0) = \cos 0 = 1$.
$L(x) = f(0) + f'(0)(x - 0) = 1 + 1x = x + 1$

(b) $f(0.1) \approx L(0.1) = 1.1$

(c) The actual value is less than 1.1. This is because the derivative is decreasing over the interval $[0, 0.1]$, which means that the graph of $f(x)$ is concave down and lies below its linearization in this interval.

38. (a) Note that $A = \pi r^2$ and $\frac{dA}{dr} = 2\pi r$, so $dA = 2\pi r\, dr$.

When r changes from a to $a + dr$, the change in area is approximately $2\pi a\, dr$. Substituting 2 for a and 0.02 for dr, the change in area is approximately

$$2\pi(2)(0.02) = 0.08\pi \approx 0.2513$$

(b) $\frac{dA}{A} = \frac{0.08\pi}{4\pi} = 0.02 = 2\%$

39. Let A = cross section area, C = circumference, and

D = diameter. Then $D = \frac{C}{\pi}$, so $\frac{dD}{dC} = \frac{1}{\pi}$ and $dD = \frac{1}{\pi}\, dC$.

Also, $A = \pi\left(\frac{D}{2}\right)^2 = \pi\left(\frac{C}{2\pi}\right)^2 = \frac{C^2}{4\pi}$, so $\frac{dA}{dC} = \frac{C}{2\pi}$ and

$dA = \frac{C}{2\pi}\, dC$. When C increases from 10π in. to

$10\pi + 2$ in. the diameter increases by

$dD = \frac{1}{\pi}(2) = \frac{2}{\pi} \approx 0.6366$ in. and the area increases by

approximately $dA = \frac{10\pi}{2\pi}(2) = 10$ in^2.

40. Let x = edge length and V = volume. Then $V = x^3$, and so

$dV = 3x^2\, dx$. With $x = 10$ cm and $dx = 0.01x = 0.1$ cm,

we have $V = 10^3 = 1000$ cm^3 and $dV = 3(10)^2(0.1) = 30$

cm^3, so the percentage error in the volume measurement is

approximately $\frac{dV}{V} = \frac{30}{1000} = 0.03 = 3\%$.

41. Let x = side length and A = area. Then $A = x^2$ and

$\frac{dA}{dx} = 2x$, so $dA = 2x\, dx$. We want $|dA| \le 0.02A$, which

gives $|2x\, dx| \le 0.02x^2$, or $|dx| \le 0.01x$. The side length

should be measured with an error of no more than 1%.

42. The volume of a cylinder is $V = \pi r^2 h$. When h is held

fixed, we have $\frac{dV}{dr} = 2\pi rh$, and so $dV = 2\pi rh\, dr$.

For $h = 30$ in., $r = 6$ in., and $dr = 0.5$ in., the thickness of

the shell is approximately

$$dV = 2\pi rh\, dr = 2\pi(6)(30)(0.5) = 180\pi \approx 565.5 \text{ in}^3.$$

43. Let θ = angle of elevation and h = height of building.

Then $h = 30 \tan \theta$, so $\frac{dh}{d\theta} = 30 \sec^2 \theta$ and $dh = 30 \sec^2 \theta$

$d\theta$. We want $|dh| < 0.04h$, which gives:

$$|30 \sec^2 \theta\, d\theta| < 0.04\,(30 \tan \theta)$$
$$\frac{1}{\cos^2 \theta}|d\theta| < \frac{0.04 \sin \theta}{\cos \theta}$$
$$|d\theta| < 0.04 \sin \theta \cos \theta$$

For $\theta = 75° = \frac{5\pi}{12}$ radians, we have

$|d\theta| < 0.04 \sin \frac{5\pi}{12} \cos \frac{5\pi}{12} = 0.01$ radian. The angle should

be measured with an error of less than 0.01 radian (or

approximately 0.57 degrees), which is a percentage error of

approximately 0.76%.

44. Note that $\frac{dV}{dh} = 3\pi h^2$, so $dV = 3\pi h^2\, dh$. We want

$|dV| \le 0.01V$, which gives $|3\pi h^2\, dh| \le 0.01(\pi h^3)$, or

$|dh| \le \frac{0.01h}{3}$. The height should be measured with an error

of no more than $\frac{1}{3}\%$.

45. (a) Note that $V = \pi r^2 h = 10\pi r^2 = 2.5\pi D^2$, where D is the

interior diameter of the tank. Then $\frac{dV}{dD} = 5\pi D$, so

$dV = 5\pi D\, dD$. We want $|dV| \le 0.01V$, which gives

$|5\pi D\, dD| \le 0.01(2.5\pi D^2)$, or $|dD| \le 0.005D$. The

interior diameter should be measured with an error of

no more than 0.5%.

(b) Now we let D represent the *exterior* diameter of the

tank, and we assume that the paint coverage rate

(number of square feet covered per gallon of paint) is

known precisely. Then, to determine the amount of

paint within 5%, we need to calculate the lateral

surface area S with an error of no more than 5%. Note

that $S = 2\pi rh = 10\pi D$, so $\frac{dS}{dD} = 10\pi$ and

$dS = 10\pi\, dD$. We want $|dS| \le 0.05S$, which gives

$|10\pi\, dD| \le 0.05(10\pi D)$, or $dD \le 0.05D$. The exterior

diameter should be measured with an error of no more

than 5%.

46. Since $V = \pi r^2 h$, we have $\dfrac{dV}{dr} = 2\pi rh$, and $dV = 2\pi rh\, dr$.

We want $|dV| \le 0.001V$, which gives

$|2\pi rh\, dr| \le 0.001\ \pi r^2 h$, or $|dr| \le 0.0005r$. The variation of

the radius should not exceed $\dfrac{1}{2000}$ of the ideal radius, that

is, 0.05% of the ideal radius.

47. We have $\dfrac{dW}{dg} = -bg^{-2}$, so $dW = -bg^{-2}\, dg$.

Then $\dfrac{dW_{moon}}{dW_{earth}} = \dfrac{-b(5.2)^{-2}\, dg}{-b(32)^{-2}\, dg} = \dfrac{32^2}{5.2^2} \approx 37.87$. The ratio is

about 37.87 to 1.

48. (a) Note that $T = 2\pi L^{1/2} g^{-1/2}$, so $\dfrac{dT}{dg} = -\pi L^{1/2} g^{-3/2}$ and

$dT = -\pi L^{1/2} g^{-3/2}\, dg$.

(b) Note that dT and dg have opposite signs. Thus, if g
increases, T decreases and the clock speeds up.

(c) $\qquad -\pi L^{1/2} g^{-3/2}\, dg = dT$

$-\pi(100)^{1/2}(980)^{-3/2}\, dg = 0.001$

$\qquad\qquad\qquad dg \approx -0.9765$

Since $dg \approx -0.9765$, $g \approx 980 - 0.9765 = 979.0235$.

49. If $f'(x) \ne 0$, we have $x_2 = x_1 - \dfrac{f(x_1)}{f'(x_1)} = x_1 - \dfrac{0}{f'(x_1)} = x_1$.

Therefore $x_2 = x_1$, and all later approximations are also

equal to x_1.

50. If $x_1 = h$, then $f'(x_1) = \dfrac{1}{2h^{1/2}}$ and $x_2 = h - \dfrac{h^{1/2}}{\dfrac{1}{2h^{1/2}}}$

$= h - 2h = -h$. If $x_1 = -h$, then

$f'(x_1) = -\dfrac{1}{2\sqrt{h}}$ and $x_2 = -h - \dfrac{h^{1/2}}{-\dfrac{1}{2h^{1/2}}} = -h + 2h = h$

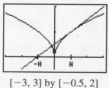

$[-3, 3]$ by $[-0.5, 2]$

51. Note that $f'(x) = \dfrac{1}{3}x^{-2/3}$ and so $x_{n+1} = x_n - \dfrac{f(x_n)}{f'(x_n)}$

$= x_n - \dfrac{x_n^{1/3}}{\dfrac{x_n^{-2/3}}{3}} = x_n - 3x_n = -2x_n$. For $x_1 = 1$, we have

$x_2 = -2$, $x_3 = 4$, $x_4 = -8$, and $x_5 = 16$; $|x_n| = 2^{n-1}$.

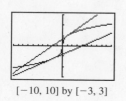

$[-10, 10]$ by $[-3, 3]$

52. (a) i. $Q(a) = f(a)$ implies that $b_0 = f(a)$.

ii. Since $Q'(x) = b_1 + 2b_2(x - a)$, $Q'(a) = f'(a)$
implies that $b_1 = f'(a)$.

iii. Since $Q''(x) = 2b_2$, $Q''(a) = f''(a)$ implies that

$b_2 = \dfrac{f''(a)}{2}$

In summary, $b_0 = f(a)$, $b_1 = f'(a)$, and $b_2 = \dfrac{f''(a)}{2}$.

(b) $f(x) = (1 - x)^{-1}$
$f'(x) = -1(1 - x)^{-2}(-1) = (1 - x)^{-2}$
$f''(x) = -2(1 - x)^{-3}(-1) = 2(1 - x)^{-3}$

Since $f(0) = 1$, $f'(0) = 1$, and $f''(0) = 2$, the

coefficients are $b_0 = 1$, $b_1 = 1$, and $b_2 = \dfrac{2}{2} = 1$. The

quadratic approximation is $Q(x) = 1 + x + x^2$.

(c)

$[-2.35, 2.35]$ by $[-1.25, 3.25]$

As one zooms in, the two graphs quickly become
indistinguishable. They appear to be identical.

(d) $g(x) = x^{-1}$
$g'(x) = -x^{-2}$
$g''(x) = 2x^{-3}$

Since $g(1) = 1$, $g'(1) = -1$, and $g''(1) = 2$, the

coefficients are $b_o = 1$, $b_1 = -1$, and $b_2 = \dfrac{2}{2} = 1$. The

quadratic approximation is

$Q(x) = 1 - (x - 1) + (x - 1)^2$.

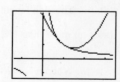

$[-1.35, 3.35]$ by $[-1.25, 3.25]$

As one zooms in, the two graphs quickly become
indistinguishable. They appear to be identical.

(e) $h(x) = (1 + x)^{1/2}$

$$h'(x) = \frac{1}{2}(1 + x)^{-1/2}$$

$$h''(x) = -\frac{1}{4}(1 + x)^{-3/2}$$

Since $h(0) = 1$, $h'(0) = \frac{1}{2}$, and $h''(0) = -\frac{1}{4}$, the

coefficients are $b_0 = 1$, $b_1 = \frac{1}{2}$, and $b_2 = \dfrac{-\frac{1}{4}}{2} = -\frac{1}{8}$.

The quadratic approximation is $Q(x) = 1 + \dfrac{x}{2} - \dfrac{x^2}{8}$.

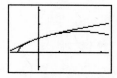

[−1.35, 3.35] by [−1.25, 3.25]

As one zooms in, the two graphs quickly become indistinguishable. They appear to be identical.

(f) The linearization of any differentiable function $u(x)$ at

$x = a$ is $L(x) = u(a) + u'(a)(x - a) = b_0 + b_1(x - a)$,

where b_0 and b_1 are the coefficients of the constant and

linear terms of the quadratic approximation. Thus, the

linearization for $f(x)$ at $x = 0$ is $1 + x$; the linearization

for $g(x)$ at $x = 1$ is $1 - (x - 1)$ or $2 - x$; and the

linearization for $h(x)$ at $x = 0$ is $1 + \dfrac{x}{2}$.

53. Just multiply the corresponding derivative formulas by dx.

(a) Since $\dfrac{d}{dx}(c) = 0$, $d(c) = 0$.

(b) Since $\dfrac{d}{dx}(cu) = c\dfrac{du}{dx}$, $d(cu) = c\,du$.

(c) Since $\dfrac{d}{dx}(u + v) = \dfrac{du}{dx} + \dfrac{dv}{dx}$, $d(u + v) = du + dv$.

(d) Since $\dfrac{d}{dx}(u \cdot v) = u\dfrac{dv}{dx} + v\dfrac{du}{dx}$, $d(u \cdot v) = u\,dv + v\,du$.

(e) Since $\dfrac{d}{dx}\left(\dfrac{u}{v}\right) = \dfrac{v\dfrac{du}{dx} - u\dfrac{dv}{dx}}{v^2}$, $d\left(\dfrac{u}{v}\right) = \dfrac{v\,du - u\,dv}{v^2}$.

(f) Since $\dfrac{d}{dx}u^n = nu^{n-1}\dfrac{du}{dx}$, $d(u^n) = nu^{n-1}\,du$.

54. $\displaystyle\lim_{x \to 0} \frac{\tan x}{x} = \lim_{x \to 0} \frac{\sin x/\cos x}{x}$

$$= \lim_{x \to 0} \left(\frac{1}{\cos x} \cdot \frac{\sin x}{x}\right)$$

$$= \left(\lim_{x \to 0} \frac{1}{\cos x}\right)\left(\lim_{x \to 0} \frac{\sin x}{x}\right)$$

$$= (1)(1) = 1.$$

55. $g(a) = c$, so if $E(a) = 0$, then $g(a) = f(a)$ and $c = f(a)$.

Then $E(x) = f(x) - g(x) = f(x) - f(a) - m(x - a)$.

Thus, $\dfrac{E(x)}{x - a} = \dfrac{f(x) - f(a)}{x - a} - m$.

$\displaystyle\lim_{x \to a} \frac{f(x) - f(a)}{x - a} = f'(a)$, so $\displaystyle\lim_{x \to a} \frac{E(x)}{x - a} = f'(a) - m$.

Therefore, if the limit of $\dfrac{E(x)}{x - a}$ is zero, then $m = f'(a)$ and

$g(x) = L(x)$.

■ Section 4.6 Related Rates (pp. 232–241)

Exploration 1   Sliding Ladder

1. Here the x-axis represents the ground and the y-axis

represents the wall. The curve (x_1, y_1) gives the position of

the bottom of the ladder (distance from the wall) at any

time t in $0 \le t \le \dfrac{13}{3}$. The curve (x_2, y_2) gives the position

of the top of the ladder at any time in $0 \le t \le \dfrac{13}{3}$.

2. $0 \le t \le \dfrac{13}{3}$

3. This is a snapshot at $t \approx 3.1$. The top of the ladder is

moving down the y-axis and the bottom of the ladder is

moving to the right on the x-axis. Both axes are hidden

from view.

[−1, 15] by [−1, 15]

4. $\dfrac{dy}{dt} = y'(t) = -\dfrac{9t}{\sqrt{13^2 - 9t^2}}$

$y'(0.5) \approx -0.348$ ft/sec^2, $y'(1) \approx -0.712$ ft/sec^2,

$y'(1.5) \approx -1.107$ ft/sec^2, $y'(2) \approx -1.561$ ft/sec^2.

Since $\displaystyle\lim_{t \to (13/3)^-} y'(t) = -\infty$, the speed of the top of the ladder

is infinite as it hits the ground.

Quick Review 4.6

1. $D = \sqrt{(7 - 0)^2 + (0 - 5)^2} = \sqrt{49 + 25} = \sqrt{74}$

2. $D = \sqrt{(b - 0)^2 + (0 - a)^2} = \sqrt{a^2 + b^2}$

3. Use implicit differentiation.

$$\frac{d}{dx}(2xy + y^2) = \frac{d}{dx}(x + y)$$

$$2x\frac{dy}{dx} + 2y(1) + 2y\frac{dy}{dx} = (1) + \frac{dy}{dx}$$

$$(2x + 2y - 1)\frac{dy}{dx} = 1 - 2y$$

$$\frac{dy}{dx} = \frac{1 - 2y}{2x + 2y - 1}$$

4. Use implicit differentiation.

$$\frac{d}{dx}(x \sin y) = \frac{d}{dx}(1 - xy)$$
$$(x)(\cos y)\frac{dy}{dx} + (\sin y)(1) = -x\frac{dy}{dx} - y(1)$$
$$(x + x \cos y)\frac{dy}{dx} = -y - \sin y$$
$$\frac{dy}{dx} = \frac{-y - \sin y}{x + x \cos y}$$
$$\frac{dy}{dx} = -\frac{y + \sin y}{x + x \cos y}$$

5. Use implicit differentiation.

$$\frac{d}{dx}x^2 = \frac{d}{dx}\tan y$$
$$2x = \sec^2 y\frac{dy}{dx}$$
$$\frac{dy}{dx} = \frac{2x}{\sec^2 y}$$
$$\frac{dy}{dx} = 2x \cos^2 y$$

6. Use implicit differentiation.

$$\frac{d}{dx}\ln(x + y) = \frac{d}{dx}(2x)$$
$$\frac{1}{x + y}\left(1 + \frac{dy}{dx}\right) = 2$$
$$1 + \frac{dy}{dx} = 2(x + y)$$
$$\frac{dy}{dx} = 2x + 2y - 1$$

7. Using $A(-2, 1)$ we create the parametric equations $x = -2 + at$ and $y = 1 + bt$, which determine a line passing through A at $t = 0$. We determine a and b so that the line passes through $B(4, -3)$ at $t = 1$. Since $4 = -2 + a$, we have $a = 6$, and since $-3 = 1 + b$, we have $b = -4$. Thus, one parametrization for the line segment is $x = -2 + 6t$, $y = 1 - 4t$, $0 \le t \le 1$. (Other answers are possible.)

8. Using $A(0, -4)$, we create the parametric equations $x = 0 + at$ and $y = -4 + bt$, which determine a line passing through A at $t = 0$. We now determine a and b so that the line passes through $B(5, 0)$ at $t = 1$. Since $5 = 0 + a$, we have $a = 5$, and since $0 = -4 + b$, we have $b = 4$. Thus, one parametrization for the line segment is $x = 5t$, $y = -4 + 4t$, $0 \le t \le 1$. (Other answers are possible.)

9. One possible answer: $\frac{\pi}{2} \le t \le \frac{3\pi}{2}$

10. One possible answer: $\frac{3\pi}{2} \le t \le 2\pi$

Section 4.6 Exercises

1. Since $\frac{dA}{dt} = \frac{dA}{dr}\frac{dr}{dt}$, we have $\frac{dA}{dt} = 2\pi r\frac{dr}{dt}$.

2. Since $\frac{dS}{dt} = \frac{dS}{dr}\frac{dr}{dt}$, we have $\frac{dS}{dt} = 8\pi r\frac{dr}{dt}$.

3. (a) Since $\frac{dV}{dt} = \frac{dV}{dh}\frac{dh}{dt}$, we have $\frac{dV}{dt} = \pi r^2\frac{dh}{dt}$.

(b) Since $\frac{dV}{dt} = \frac{dV}{dr}\frac{dr}{dt}$, we have $\frac{dV}{dt} = 2\pi rh\frac{dr}{dt}$.

(c) $\frac{dV}{dt} = \frac{d}{dt}\pi r^2 h = \pi\frac{d}{dt}(r^2 h)$
$$\frac{dV}{dt} = \pi\left(r^2\frac{dh}{dt} + h(2r)\frac{dr}{dt}\right)$$
$$\frac{dV}{dt} = \pi r^2\frac{dh}{dt} + 2\pi rh\frac{dr}{dt}$$

4. (a) $\frac{dP}{dt} = \frac{d}{dt}(RI^2)$
$$\frac{dP}{dt} = R\frac{d}{dt}I^2 + I^2\frac{dR}{dt}$$
$$\frac{dP}{dt} = R\left(2I\frac{dI}{dt}\right) + I^2\frac{dR}{dt}$$
$$\frac{dP}{dt} = 2RI\frac{dI}{dt} + I^2\frac{dR}{dt}$$

(b) If P is constant, we have $\frac{dP}{dt} = 0$, which means $2RI\frac{dI}{dt} + I^2\frac{dR}{dt} = 0$, or $\frac{dR}{dt} = -\frac{2R}{I}\frac{dI}{dt} = -\frac{2P}{I^3}\frac{dI}{dt}$.

5. $\frac{ds}{dt} = \frac{d}{dt}\sqrt{x^2 + y^2 + z^2}$

$$\frac{ds}{dt} = \frac{1}{2\sqrt{x^2 + y^2 + z^2}}\frac{d}{dt}(x^2 + y^2 + z^2)$$

$$\frac{ds}{dt} = \frac{1}{2\sqrt{x^2 + y^2 + z^2}}\left(2x\frac{dx}{dt} + 2y\frac{dy}{dt} + 2z\frac{dz}{dt}\right)$$

$$\frac{ds}{dt} = \frac{x\frac{dx}{dt} + y\frac{dy}{dt} + z\frac{dz}{dt}}{\sqrt{x^2 + y^2 + z^2}}$$

6. $\frac{dA}{dt} = \frac{d}{dt}\left(\frac{1}{2}ab \sin \theta\right)$
$$\frac{dA}{dt} = \frac{1}{2}\left(\frac{da}{dt} \cdot b \cdot \sin \theta + a \cdot \frac{db}{dt} \cdot \sin \theta + ab \cdot \frac{d}{dt}\sin \theta\right)$$
$$\frac{dA}{dt} = \frac{1}{2}\left(b \sin \theta\frac{da}{dt} + a \sin \theta\frac{db}{dt} + ab \cos \theta\frac{d\theta}{dt}\right)$$

7. (a) Since V is increasing at the rate of 1 volt/sec,
$$\frac{dV}{dt} = 1 \text{ volt/sec}.$$

(b) Since I is decreasing at the rate of $\frac{1}{3}$ amp/sec,
$$\frac{dI}{dt} = -\frac{1}{3} \text{ amp/sec}.$$

(c) Differentiating both sides of $V = IR$, we have
$$\frac{dV}{dt} = I\frac{dR}{dt} + R\frac{dI}{dt}.$$

(d) Note that $V = IR$ gives $12 = 2R$, so $R = 6$ ohms. Now substitute the known values into the equation in (c).

$$1 = 2\frac{dR}{dt} + 6\left(-\frac{1}{3}\right)$$
$$3 = 2\frac{dR}{dt}$$
$$\frac{dR}{dt} = \frac{3}{2} \text{ ohms/sec}$$

R is changing at the rate of $\frac{3}{2}$ ohms/sec. Since this value is positive, R is increasing.

8. Step 1:
r = radius of plate
A = area of plate

Step 2:

At the instant in question, $\frac{dr}{dt} = 0.01$ cm/sec, $r = 50$ cm.

Step 3:

We want to find $\frac{dA}{dt}$.

Step 4:

$A = \pi r^2$

Step 5:

$$\frac{dA}{dt} = 2\pi r\frac{dr}{dt}$$

Step 6:

$$\frac{dA}{dt} = 2\pi(50)(0.01) = \pi \text{ cm}^2/\text{sec}$$

At the instant in question, the area is increasing at the rate of π cm^2/sec.

9. Step 1:
l = length of rectangle
w = width of rectangle
A = area of rectangle
P = perimeter of rectangle
D = length of a diagonal of the rectangle

Step 2:

At the instant in question,

$$\frac{dl}{dt} = -2 \text{ cm/sec}, \frac{dw}{dt} = 2 \text{ cm/sec}, l = 12 \text{ cm},$$

and $w = 5$ cm.

Step 3:

We want to find $\frac{dA}{dt}$, $\frac{dP}{dt}$, and $\frac{dD}{dt}$.

Steps 4, 5, and 6:

(a) $A = lw$

$$\frac{dA}{dt} = l\frac{dw}{dt} + w\frac{dl}{dt}$$
$$\frac{dA}{dt} = (12)(2) + (5)(-2) = 14 \text{ cm}^2/\text{sec}$$

The rate of change of the area is 14 cm^2/sec.

(b) $P = 2l + 2w$

$$\frac{dP}{dt} = 2\frac{dl}{dt} + 2\frac{dw}{dt}$$
$$\frac{dP}{dt} = 2(-2) + 2(2) = 0 \text{ cm/sec}$$

The rate of change of the perimeter is 0 cm/sec.

(c) $D = \sqrt{l^2 + w^2}$

$$\frac{dD}{dt} = \frac{1}{2\sqrt{l^2 + w^2}}\left(2l\frac{dl}{dt} + 2w\frac{dw}{dt}\right) = \frac{l\frac{dl}{dt} + w\frac{dw}{dt}}{\sqrt{l^2 + w^2}}$$
$$\frac{dD}{dt} = \frac{(12)(-2) + (5)(2)}{\sqrt{12^2 + 5^2}} = -\frac{14}{13} \text{ cm/sec}$$

The rate of change of the length of the diameter is

$-\frac{14}{13}$ cm/sec.

(d) The area is increasing, because its derivative is positive. The perimeter is not changing, because its derivative is zero. The diagonal length is decreasing, because its derivative is negative.

10. Step 1:
x, y, z = edge lengths of the box
V = volume of the box
S = surface area of the box
s = diagonal length of the box

Step 2:

At the instant in question,

$$\frac{dx}{dt} = 1 \text{ m/sec}, \frac{dy}{dt} = -2 \text{ m/sec}, \frac{dz}{dt} = 1 \text{ m/sec}, x = 4 \text{ m},$$

$y = 3$ m, and $z = 2$ m.

Step 3:

We want to find $\frac{dV}{dt}$, $\frac{dS}{dt}$, and $\frac{ds}{dt}$.

Steps 4, 5, and 6:

(a) $V = xyz$

$$\frac{dV}{dt} = xy\frac{dz}{dt} + xz\frac{dy}{dt} + yz\frac{dx}{dt}$$
$$\frac{dV}{dt} = (4)(3)(1) + (4)(2)(-2) + (3)(2)(1) = 2 \text{ m}^3/\text{sec}$$

The rate of change of the volume is 2 m^3/sec.

(b) $S = 2(xy + xz + yz)$

$$\frac{dS}{dt} = 2\left(x\frac{dy}{dt} + y\frac{dx}{dt} + x\frac{dz}{dt} + z\frac{dx}{dt} + y\frac{dz}{dt} + z\frac{dy}{dt}\right)$$
$$\frac{dS}{dt} = 2[(4)(-2) + (3)(1) + (4)(1) +$$
$$(2)(1) + (3)(1) + (2)(-2)] = 0 \text{ m}^2/\text{sec}$$

The rate of change of the surface area is 0 m^2/sec.

10. continued

(c) $s = \sqrt{x^2 + y^2 + z^2}$

$$\frac{ds}{dt} = \frac{1}{2\sqrt{x^2 + y^2 + z^2}}\left(2x\frac{dx}{dt} + 2y\frac{dy}{dt} + 2z\frac{dz}{dy}\right)$$

$$= \frac{x\frac{dx}{dt} + y\frac{dy}{dt} + z\frac{dz}{dt}}{\sqrt{x^2 + y^2 + z^2}}$$

$$\frac{ds}{dt} = \frac{(4)(1) + (3)(-2) + (2)(1)}{\sqrt{4^2 + 3^2 + 2^2}} = \frac{0}{\sqrt{29}} = 0 \text{ m/sec}$$

The rate of change of the diagonal length is 0 m/sec.

11. Step 1:
$s = $ (diagonal) distance from antenna to airplane
$x = $ horizontal distance from antenna to airplane

Step 2:
At the instant in question,

$s = 10$ mi and $\frac{ds}{dt} = 300$ mph.

Step 3:

We want to find $\frac{dx}{dt}$.

Step 4:
$x^2 + 49 = s^2$ or $x = \sqrt{s^2 - 49}$

Step 5:

$$\frac{dx}{dt} = \frac{1}{2\sqrt{s^2 - 49}}\left(2s\frac{ds}{dt}\right) = \frac{s}{\sqrt{s^2 - 49}}\frac{ds}{dt}$$

Step 6:

$$\frac{dx}{dt} = \frac{10}{\sqrt{10^2 - 49}}(300) = \frac{3000}{\sqrt{51}} \text{ mph} \approx 420.08 \text{ mph}$$

The speed of the airplane is about 420.08 mph.

12. Step 1:
$h = $ height (or depth) of the water in the trough
$V = $ volume of water in the trough

Step 2:

At the instant in question, $\frac{dV}{dt} = 2.5$ ft³/min and $h = 2$ ft.

Step 3:

We want to find $\frac{dh}{dt}$.

Step 4:

The width of the top surface of the water is $\frac{4}{3}h$, so we have

$V = \frac{1}{2}(h)\left(\frac{4}{3}h\right)(15)$, or $V = 10h^2$

Step 5:

$$\frac{dV}{dt} = 20h\frac{dh}{dt}$$

Step 6:

$$2.5 = 20(2)\frac{dh}{dt}$$

$$\frac{dh}{dt} = 0.0625 = \frac{1}{16} \text{ ft/min}$$

The water level is increasing at the rate of $\frac{1}{16}$ ft/min.

13. Step 1:
$x = $ distance from wall to base of ladder
$y = $ height of top of ladder
$A = $ area of triangle formed by the ladder, wall, and ground
$\theta = $ angle between the ladder and the ground

Step 2:

At the instant in question, $x = 12$ ft and $\frac{dx}{dt} = 5$ ft/sec.

Step 3:

We want to find $-\frac{dy}{dt}, \frac{dA}{dt}$, and $\frac{d\theta}{dt}$.

Step 4, 5, and 6:

(a) $x^2 + y^2 = 169$

$$2x\frac{dx}{dt} + 2y\frac{dy}{dt} = 0$$

To evaluate, note that, at the instant in question,

$$y = \sqrt{169 - x^2} = \sqrt{169 - 12^2} = 5.$$

Then $2(12)(5) + 2(5)\frac{dy}{dt} = 0$

$$\frac{dy}{dt} = -12 \text{ ft/sec } \left(\text{or } -\frac{dy}{dt} = 12 \text{ ft/sec}\right)$$

The top of the ladder is sliding down the wall at the

rate of 12 ft/sec. (Note that the *downward* rate of

motion is positive.)

(b) $A = \frac{1}{2}xy$

$$\frac{dA}{dt} = \frac{1}{2}\left(x\frac{dy}{dt} + y\frac{dx}{dt}\right)$$

Using the results from step 2 and from part (a), we

have $\frac{dA}{dt} = \frac{1}{2}[(12)(-12) + (5)(5)] = -\frac{119}{2}$ ft²/sec.

The area of the triangle is changing at the rate of

-59.5 ft²/sec.

(c) $\tan \theta = \frac{y}{x}$

$$\sec^2 \theta \frac{d\theta}{dt} = \frac{x\frac{dy}{dt} - y\frac{dx}{dt}}{x^2}$$

Since $\tan \theta = \frac{5}{12}$, we have $\left(\text{for } 0 \leq \theta < \frac{\pi}{2}\right)$

$\cos \theta = \frac{12}{13}$ and so $\sec^2 \theta = \frac{1}{\left(\frac{12}{13}\right)^2} = \frac{169}{144}$.

Combining this result with the results from step 2 and

from part (a), we have $\frac{169}{144}\frac{d\theta}{dt} = \frac{(12)(-12) - (5)(5)}{12^2}$, so

$\frac{d\theta}{dt} = -1$ radian/sec. The angle is changing at the rate

of -1 radian/sec.

14. Step 1:

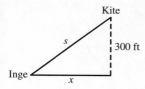

s = length of kite string
x = horizontal distance from Inge to kite

Step 2:

At the instant in question, $\frac{dx}{dt} = 25$ ft/sec and $s = 500$ ft

Step 3:

We want to find $\frac{ds}{dt}$.

Step 4:

$x^2 + 300^2 = s^2$

Step 5:

$2x\frac{dx}{dt} = 2s\frac{ds}{dt}$ or $x\frac{dx}{dt} = s\frac{ds}{dt}$

Step 6:

At the instant in question, since $x^2 + 300^2 = s^2$, we have

$x = \sqrt{s^2 - 300^2} = \sqrt{500^2 - 300^2} = 400$.

Thus $(400)(25) = (500)\frac{ds}{dt}$, so $\frac{ds}{dt} = 20$ ft/sec. Inge must let

the string out at the rate of 20 ft/sec.

15. Step 1:

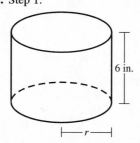

The cylinder shown represents the shape of the hole.
r = radius of cylinder
V = volume of cylinder

Step 2:

At the instant in question, $\frac{dr}{dt} = \frac{0.001\ \text{in.}}{3\ \text{min}} = \frac{1}{3000}$ in./min

and (since the diameter is 3.800 in.), $r = 1.900$ in.

Step 3:

We want to find $\frac{dV}{dt}$.

Step 4:

$V = \pi r^2(6) = 6\pi r^2$

Step 5:

$\frac{dV}{dt} = 12\pi r\frac{dr}{dt}$

Step 6:

$\frac{dV}{dt} = 12\pi(1.900)\left(\frac{1}{3000}\right) = \frac{19\pi}{2500} = 0.0076\pi$

≈ 0.0239 in^3/min

The volume is increasing at the rate of approximately

0.0239 in^3/min.

16. Step 1:

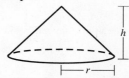

r = base radius of cone
h = height of cone
V = volume of cone

Step 2:

At the instant in question, $h = 4$ m and $\frac{dV}{dt} = 10$ m^3/min.

Step 3:

We want to find $\frac{dh}{dt}$ and $\frac{dr}{dt}$.

Step 4:

Since the height is $\frac{3}{8}$ of the base diameter, we have

$h = \frac{3}{8}(2r)$ or $r = \frac{4}{3}h$.

We also have $V = \frac{1}{3}\pi r^2 h = \frac{1}{3}\pi\left(\frac{4}{3}h\right)^2 h = \frac{16\pi h^3}{27}$. We will

use the equations $V = \frac{16\pi h^3}{27}$ and $r = \frac{4}{3}h$.

Steps 5 and 6:

(a) $\frac{dV}{dt} = \frac{16\pi h^2}{9}\frac{dh}{dt}$

$10 = \frac{16\pi(4)^2}{9}\frac{dh}{dt}$

$\frac{dh}{dt} = \frac{45}{128\pi}$ m/min $= \frac{1125}{32\pi}$ cm/min

The height is changing at the rate of

$\frac{1125}{32\pi} \approx 11.19$ cm/min.

(b) Using the results from Step 4 and part (a), we have

$\frac{dr}{dt} = \frac{4}{3}\frac{dh}{dt} = \frac{4}{3}\left(\frac{1125}{32\pi}\right) = \frac{375}{8\pi}$ cm/min.

The radius is changing at the rate of

$\frac{375}{8\pi} \approx 14.92$ cm/min.

17. Step 1:

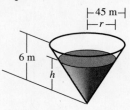

r = radius of top surface of water
h = depth of water in reservoir
V = volume of water in reservoir

Step 2:

At the instant in question, $\frac{dV}{dt} = -50$ m³/min and $h = 5$ m.

Step 3:

We want to find $-\frac{dh}{dt}$ and $\frac{dr}{dt}$.

Step 4:

Note that $\frac{h}{r} = \frac{6}{45}$ by similar cones, so $r = 7.5h$.
Then $V = \frac{1}{3}\pi r^2 h = \frac{1}{3}\pi(7.5h)^2 h = 18.75\pi h^3$

Step 5 and 6:

(a) Since $V = 18.75\pi h^3$, $\frac{dV}{dt} = 56.25\pi h^2 \frac{dh}{dt}$.
Thus $-50 = 56.25\pi(5^2)\frac{dh}{dt}$, and so
$\frac{dh}{dt} = -\frac{8}{225\pi}$ m/min $= -\frac{32}{9\pi}$ cm/min.
The water level is falling by $\frac{32}{9\pi} \approx 1.13$ cm/min.
(Since $\frac{dh}{dt} < 0$, the rate at which the water level is
falling is positive.)

(b) Since $r = 7.5h$, $\frac{dr}{dt} = 7.5\frac{dh}{dt} = -\frac{80}{3\pi}$ cm/min. The rate
of change of the radius of the water's surface is
$-\frac{80}{3\pi} \approx -8.49$ cm/min.

18. (a) Step 1:
y = depth of water in bowl
V = volume of water in bowl

Step 2:

At the instant in question, $\frac{dV}{dt} = -6$ m³/min and
$y = 8$ m.

Step 3:

We want to find the value of $\frac{dy}{dt}$.

Step 4:

$V = \frac{\pi}{3}y^2(39 - y)$ or $V = 13\pi y^2 - \frac{\pi}{3}y^3$

Step 5:

$\frac{dV}{dt} = (26\pi y - \pi y^2)\frac{dy}{dt}$

Step 6:

$-6 = [26\pi(8) - \pi(8^2)]\frac{dy}{dt}$
$-6 = 144\pi\frac{dy}{dt}$
$\frac{dy}{dt} = -\frac{1}{24\pi} \approx -0.01326$ m/min
or $-\frac{25}{6\pi} \approx -1.326$ cm/min

(b) Since $r^2 + (13 - y)^2 = 13^2$,
$r = \sqrt{169 - (13 - y)^2} = \sqrt{26y - y^2}$.

(c) Step 1:
y = depth of water
r = radius of water surface
V = volume of water in bowl

Step 2:

At the instant in question, $\frac{dV}{dt} = -6$ m³/min, $y = 8$ m,
and therefore (from part (a)) $\frac{dy}{dt} = -\frac{1}{24\pi}$ m/min.

Step 3:

We want to find the value of $\frac{dr}{dt}$.

Step 4:

From part (b), $r = \sqrt{26y - y^2}$.

Step 5:

$\frac{dr}{dt} = \frac{1}{2\sqrt{26y - y^2}}(26 - 2y)\frac{dy}{dt} = \frac{13 - y}{\sqrt{26y - y^2}}\frac{dy}{dt}$

Step 6:

$\frac{dr}{dt} = \frac{13 - 8}{\sqrt{26(8) - 8^2}}\left(-\frac{1}{24\pi}\right) = \frac{5}{12}\left(-\frac{1}{24\pi}\right)$
$= -\frac{5}{288\pi} \approx -0.00553$ m/min
or $-\frac{125}{72\pi} \approx -0.553$ cm/min

19. Step 1:
r = radius of spherical droplet
S = surface area of spherical droplet
V = volume of spherical droplet

Step 2:
No numerical information is given.

Step 3:

We want to show that $\frac{dr}{dt}$ is constant.

Step 4:

$S = 4\pi r^2$, $V = \frac{4}{3}\pi r^3$, $\frac{dV}{dt} = kS$ for some constant k

Steps 5 and 6:

Differentiating $V = \frac{4}{3}\pi r^3$, we have $\frac{dV}{dt} = 4\pi r^2\frac{dr}{dt}$.
Substituting kS for $\frac{dV}{dt}$ and S for $4\pi r^2$, we have $kS = S\frac{dr}{dt}$,
or $\frac{dr}{dt} = k$.

20. Step 1:

r = radius of spherical balloon
S = surface area of spherical balloon
V = volume of spherical balloon

Step 2:

At the instant in question, $\dfrac{dV}{dt} = 100\pi$ ft³/min and $r = 5$ ft.

Step 3:

We want to find the values of $\dfrac{dr}{dt}$ and $\dfrac{dS}{dt}$.

Steps 4, 5, and 6:

(a) $V = \dfrac{4}{3}\pi r^3$

$\dfrac{dV}{dt} = 4\pi r^2 \dfrac{dr}{dt}$

$100\pi = 4\pi(5)^2 \dfrac{dr}{dt}$

$\dfrac{dr}{dt} = 1$ ft/min

The radius is increasing at the rate of 1 ft/min.

(b) $S = 4\pi r^2$

$\dfrac{dS}{dt} = 8\pi r \dfrac{dr}{dt}$

$\dfrac{dS}{dt} = 8\pi(5)(1)$

$\dfrac{dS}{dt} = 40\pi$ ft²/min

The surface area is increasing at the rate of

40π ft²/min.

21. Step 1:

l = length of rope
x = horizontal distance from boat to dock
θ = angle between the rope and a vertical line

Step 2:

At the instant in question, $\dfrac{dl}{dt} = -2$ ft/sec and $l = 10$ ft.

Step 3:

We want to find the values of $-\dfrac{dx}{dt}$ and $\dfrac{d\theta}{dt}$.

Step 4, 5, and 6:

(a) $x = \sqrt{l^2 - 36}$

$\dfrac{dx}{dt} = \dfrac{l}{\sqrt{l^2 - 36}}\dfrac{dl}{dt}$

$\dfrac{dx}{dt} = \dfrac{10}{\sqrt{10^2 - 36}}(-2) = -2.5$ ft/sec

The boat is approaching the dock at the rate of

2.5 ft/sec.

(b) $\theta = \cos^{-1}\dfrac{6}{l}$

$\dfrac{d\theta}{dt} = -\dfrac{1}{\sqrt{1 - \left(\dfrac{6}{l}\right)^2}}\left(-\dfrac{6}{l^2}\right)\dfrac{dl}{dt}$

$\dfrac{d\theta}{dt} = -\dfrac{1}{\sqrt{1 - 0.6^2}}\left(-\dfrac{6}{10^2}\right)(-2) = -\dfrac{3}{20}$ radian/sec

The rate of change of angle θ is $-\dfrac{3}{20}$ radian/sec.

22. Step 1:

x = distance from origin to bicycle
y = height of balloon (distance from origin to balloon)
s = distance from balloon to bicycle

Step 2:

We know that $\dfrac{dy}{dt}$ is a constant 1 ft/sec and $\dfrac{dx}{dt}$ is a constant 17 ft/sec. Three seconds before the instant in question, the values of x and y are $x = 0$ ft and $y = 65$ ft. Therefore, at the instant in question $x = 51$ ft and $y = 68$ ft.

Step 3:

We want to find the value of $\dfrac{ds}{dt}$ at the instant in question.

Step 4:

$s = \sqrt{x^2 + y^2}$

Step 5:

$\dfrac{ds}{dt} = \dfrac{1}{2\sqrt{x^2 + y^2}}\left(2x\dfrac{dx}{dt} + 2y\dfrac{dy}{dt}\right) = \dfrac{x\dfrac{dx}{dt} + y\dfrac{dy}{dt}}{\sqrt{x^2 + y^2}}$

Step 6:

$\dfrac{ds}{dt} = \dfrac{(51)(17) + (68)(1)}{\sqrt{51^2 + 68^2}} = 11$ ft/sec

The distance between the balloon and the bicycle is increasing at the rate of 11 ft/sec.

23. (a) $\dfrac{dc}{dt} = \dfrac{d}{dt}(x^3 - 6x^2 + 15x)$

$= (3x^2 - 12x + 15)\dfrac{dx}{dt}$

$= [3(2)^2 - 12(2) + 15](0.1)$

$= 0.3$

$\dfrac{dr}{dt} = \dfrac{d}{dt}(9x) = 9\dfrac{dx}{dt} = 9(0.1) = 0.9$

$\dfrac{dp}{dt} = \dfrac{dr}{dt} - \dfrac{dc}{dt} = 0.9 - 0.3 = 0.6$

(b) $\dfrac{dc}{dt} = \dfrac{d}{dt}\left(x^3 - 6x^2 + \dfrac{45}{x}\right)$

$= \left(3x^2 - 12x - \dfrac{45}{x^2}\right)\dfrac{dx}{dt}$

$= \left[3(1.5)^2 - 12(1.5) - \dfrac{45}{1.5^2}\right](0.05)$

$= -1.5625$

$\dfrac{dr}{dt} = \dfrac{d}{dt}(70x) = 70\dfrac{dx}{dt} = 70(0.05) = 3.5$

$\dfrac{dp}{dt} = \dfrac{dr}{dt} - \dfrac{dc}{dt} = 3.5 - (-1.5625) = 5.0625$

24. (a) Note that the level of the coffee in the cone is not needed until part (b).

Step 1:

V_1 = volume of coffee in pot
y = depth of coffee in pot

Step 2:

$$\frac{dV_1}{dt} = 10 \text{ in}^3/\text{min}$$

Step 3:

We want to find the value of $\frac{dy}{dt}$.

Step 4:

$$V_1 = 9\pi y$$

Step 5:

$$\frac{dV_1}{dt} = 9\pi \frac{dy}{dt}$$

Step 6:

$$10 = 9\pi \frac{dy}{dt}$$

$$\frac{dy}{dt} = \frac{10}{9\pi} \approx 0.354 \text{ in./min}$$

The level in the pot is increasing at the rate of

approximately 0.354 in./min.

(b) Step 1:

V_2 = volume of coffee in filter
r = radius of surface of coffee in filter
h = depth of coffee in filter

Step 2:

At the instant in question, $\frac{dV_2}{dt} = -10 \text{ in}^3/\text{min}$ and

$h = 5$ in.

Step 3:

We want to find $-\frac{dh}{dt}$.

Step 4:

Note that $\frac{r}{h} = \frac{3}{6}$, so $r = \frac{h}{2}$.

Then $V_2 = \frac{1}{3}\pi r^2 h = \frac{\pi h^3}{12}$.

Step 5:

$$\frac{dV_2}{dt} = \frac{\pi h^2}{4} \frac{dh}{dt}$$

Step 6:

$$-10 = \frac{\pi(5)^2}{4} \frac{dh}{dt}$$

$$\frac{dh}{dt} = -\frac{8}{5\pi} \text{ in./min}$$

Note that $\frac{dh}{dt} < 0$, so the rate at which the level is

falling is positive. The level in the cone is falling at the

rate of $\frac{8}{5\pi} \approx 0.509$ in./min.

25. Step 1:

Q = rate of CO_2 exhalation (mL/min)
D = difference between CO_2 concentration in blood pumped to the lungs and CO_2 concentration in blood returning from the lungs (mL/L)
y = cardiac output

Step 2:

At the instant in question, $Q = 233$ mL/min, $D = 41$ mL/L,

$\frac{dD}{dt} = -2$ (mL/L)/min, and $\frac{dQ}{dt} = 0$ mL/min^2.

Step 3:

We want to find the value of $\frac{dy}{dt}$.

Step 4:

$$y = \frac{Q}{D}$$

Step 5:

$$\frac{dy}{dt} = \frac{D\frac{dQ}{dt} - Q\frac{dD}{dt}}{D^2}$$

Step 6:

$$\frac{dy}{dt} = \frac{(41)(0) - (233)(-2)}{(41)^2} = \frac{466}{1681} \approx 0.277 \text{ L/min}^2$$

The cardiac output is increasing at the rate of

approximately 0.277 L/min^2.

26. Step 1:

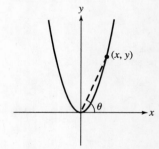

x = x-coordinate of particle's location
y = y-coordinate of particle's location
θ = angle of inclination of line joining the particle to the origin.

Step 2:

At the instant in question,

$$\frac{dx}{dt} = 10 \text{ m/sec and } x = 3 \text{ m.}$$

Step 3:

We want to find $\frac{d\theta}{dt}$.

Step 4:

Since $y = x^2$, we have $\tan \theta = \frac{y}{x} = \frac{x^2}{x} = x$ and so, for

$x > 0$, $\theta = \tan^{-1} x$.

Step 5:

$$\frac{d\theta}{dt} = \frac{1}{1 + x^2}\frac{dx}{dt}$$

Step 6:

$$\frac{d\theta}{dt} = \frac{1}{1 + 3^2}(10) = 1 \text{ radian/sec}$$

The angle of inclination is increasing at the rate of

1 radian/sec.

27. Step 1:

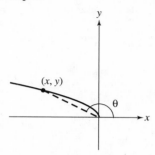

x = x-coordinate of particle's location
y = y-coordinate of particle's location
θ = angle of inclination of line joining the particle to the
origin

Step 2:

At the instant in question, $\frac{dx}{dt} = -8$ m/sec and $x = -4$ m.

Step 3:

We want to find $\frac{d\theta}{dt}$.

Step 4:

Since $y = \sqrt{-x}$, we have $\tan \theta = \frac{y}{x} = \frac{\sqrt{-x}}{x} = -(-x)^{-1/2}$,

and so, for $x < 0$,

$$\theta = \pi + \tan^{-1}[-(-x)^{-1/2}] = \pi - \tan^{-1}(-x)^{-1/2}.$$

Step 5:

$$\frac{d\theta}{dt} = -\frac{1}{1 + [(-x)^{-1/2}]^2}\left(-\frac{1}{2}(-x)^{-3/2}(-1)\right)\frac{dx}{dt}$$

$$= -\frac{1}{1 - \left(\frac{1}{x}\right)}\frac{1}{2(-x)^{3/2}}\frac{dx}{dt}$$

$$= \frac{1}{2\sqrt{-x}(x - 1)}\frac{dx}{dt}$$

Step 6:

$$\frac{d\theta}{dt} = \frac{1}{2\sqrt{4}(-4 - 1)}(-8) = \frac{2}{5} \text{ radian/sec}$$

The angle of inclination is increasing at the rate of

$\frac{2}{5}$ radian/sec.

28. Step 1:

x = x-coordinate of particle
y = y-coordinate of particle
D = distance from origin to particle

Step 2:

At the instant in question, $x = 5$ m, $y = 12$ m,

$\frac{dx}{dt} = -1$ m/sec, and $\frac{dy}{dt} = -5$ m/sec.

Step 3:

We want to find $\frac{dD}{dt}$.

Step 4:

$$D = \sqrt{x^2 + y^2}$$

Step 5:

$$\frac{dD}{dt} = \frac{1}{2\sqrt{x^2 + y^2}}\left(2x\frac{dx}{dt} + 2y\frac{dy}{dt}\right) = \frac{x\frac{dx}{dt} + y\frac{dy}{dt}}{\sqrt{x^2 + y^2}}$$

Step 6:

$$\frac{dD}{dt} = \frac{(5)(-1) + (12)(-5)}{\sqrt{5^2 + 12^2}} = -5 \text{ m/sec}$$

The particle's distance from the origin is changing at the

rate of -5 m/sec.

29. Step 1:

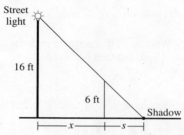

x = distance from streetlight base to man
s = length of shadow

Step 2:

At the instant in question, $\frac{dx}{dt} = -5$ ft/sec and $x = 10$ ft.

Step 3:

We want to find $\frac{ds}{dt}$.

Step 4:

By similar triangles, $\frac{s}{6} = \frac{s + x}{16}$. This is equivalent to

$16s = 6s + 6x$, or $s = \frac{3}{5}x$.

Step 5:

$$\frac{ds}{dt} = \frac{3}{5}\frac{dx}{dt}$$

Step 6:

$$\frac{ds}{dt} = \frac{3}{5}(-5) = -3 \text{ft/sec}$$

The shadow length is changing at the rate of -3 ft/sec.

30. Step 1:

s = distance ball has fallen

x = distance from bottom of pole to shadow

Step 2:

At the instant in question, $s = 16\left(\frac{1}{2}\right)^2 = 4$ ft and

$\frac{ds}{dt} = 32\left(\frac{1}{2}\right) = 16$ ft/sec.

Step 3:

We want to find $\frac{dx}{dt}$.

Step 4:

By similar triangles, $\frac{x - 30}{50 - s} = \frac{x}{50}$. This is equivalent to

$50x - 1500 = 50x - sx$, or $sx = 1500$. We will use

$x = 1500s^{-1}$.

Step 5:

$\frac{dx}{dt} = -1500s^{-2}\frac{ds}{dt}$

Step 6:

$\frac{dx}{dt} = -1500(4)^{-2}(16) = -1500$ ft/sec

The shadow is moving at a velocity of -1500 ft/sec.

31. Step 1:

x = position of car ($x = 0$ when car is right in front of you)

θ = camera angle. (We assume θ is negative until the car passes in front of you, and then positive.)

Step 2:

At the first instant in question, $x = 0$ ft and $\frac{dx}{dt} = 264$ ft/sec.

A half second later, $x = \frac{1}{2}(264) = 132$ ft and

$\frac{dx}{dt} = 264$ ft/sec.

Step 3:

We want to find $\frac{d\theta}{dt}$ at each of the two instants.

Step 4:

$\theta = \tan^{-1}\left(\frac{x}{132}\right)$

Step 5:

$\frac{d\theta}{dt} = \frac{1}{1 + \left(\frac{x}{132}\right)^2} \cdot \frac{1}{132}\frac{dx}{dt}$

Step 6:

When $x = 0$: $\frac{d\theta}{dt} = \frac{1}{1 + \left(\frac{0}{132}\right)^2}\left(\frac{1}{132}\right)(264) = 2$ radians/sec

When $x = 132$: $\frac{d\theta}{dt} = \frac{1}{1 + \left(\frac{132}{132}\right)^2}\left(\frac{1}{132}\right)(264) = 1$ radian/sec

32. Step 1:

r = radius of balls plus ice

S = surface area of ball plus ice

V = volume of ball plus ice

Step 2:

At the instant in question,

$\frac{dV}{dt} = -8$ mL/min $= -8$ cm^3/min and $r = \frac{1}{2}(20) = 10$ cm.

Step 3:

We want to find $-\frac{dS}{dt}$.

Step 4:

We have $V = \frac{4}{3}\pi r^3$ and $S = 4\pi r^2$. These equations can be combined by noting that $r = \left(\frac{3V}{4\pi}\right)^{1/3}$, so $S = 4\pi\left(\frac{3V}{4\pi}\right)^{2/3}$

Step 5:

$\frac{dS}{dt} = 4\pi\left(\frac{2}{3}\right)\left(\frac{3V}{4\pi}\right)^{-1/3}\left(\frac{3}{4\pi}\right)\frac{dV}{dt} = 2\left(\frac{3V}{4\pi}\right)^{-1/3}\frac{dV}{dt}$

Step 6:

Note that $V = \frac{4}{3}\pi(10)^3 = \frac{4000\pi}{3}$.

$\frac{dS}{dt} = 2\left(\frac{3}{4\pi} \cdot \frac{4000\pi}{3}\right)^{-1/3}(-8) = \frac{-16}{\sqrt[3]{1000}} = -1.6$ cm^2/min

Since $\frac{dS}{dt} < 0$, the rate of *decrease* is positive. The surface

area is decreasing at the rate of 1.6 cm^2/min.

33. Step 1:

p = x-coordinate of plane's position

x = x-coordinate of car's position

s = distance from plane to car (line-of-sight)

Step 2:

At the instant in question,

$p = 0$, $\frac{dp}{dt} = 120$ mph, $s = 5$ mi, and $\frac{ds}{dt} = -160$ mph.

Step 3:

We want to find $-\frac{dx}{dt}$.

Step 4:

$(x - p)^2 + 3^2 = s^2$

Step 5:

$2(x - p)\left(\frac{dx}{dt} - \frac{dp}{dt}\right) = 2s\frac{ds}{dt}$

Step 6:

Note that, at the instant in question,

$x = \sqrt{5^2 - 3^2} = 4$ mi.

$2(4 - 0)\left(\frac{dx}{dt} - 120\right) = 2(5)(-160)$

$8\left(\frac{dx}{dt} - 120\right) = -1600$

$\frac{dx}{dt} - 120 = -200$

$\frac{dx}{dt} = -80$ mph

The car's speed is 80 mph.

34. Step 1:

s = shadow length
θ = sun's angle of elevation

Step 2:

At the instant in question,

$s = 60$ ft and $\dfrac{d\theta}{dt} = 0.27°/\text{min} = 0.0015\pi$ radian/min.

Step 3:

We want to find $-\dfrac{ds}{dt}$.

Step 4:

$\tan \theta = \dfrac{80}{s}$ or $s = 80 \cot \theta$

Step 5:

$\dfrac{ds}{dt} = -80 \csc^2 \theta \dfrac{d\theta}{dt}$

Step 6:

Note that, at the moment in question, since $\tan \theta = \dfrac{80}{60}$ and

$0 < \theta < \dfrac{\pi}{2}$, we have $\sin \theta = \dfrac{4}{5}$ and so $\csc \theta = \dfrac{5}{4}$.

$$\dfrac{ds}{dt} = -80\left(\dfrac{5}{4}\right)^2 (0.0015\pi)$$

$$= -0.1875\pi \ \dfrac{\text{ft}}{\text{min}} \cdot \dfrac{12 \text{ in}}{1 \text{ ft}}$$

$$= -2.25\pi \text{ in./min}$$

$$\approx -7.1 \text{ in./min}$$

Since $\dfrac{ds}{dt} < 0$, the rate at which the shadow length is

decreasing is positive. The shadow length is decreasing at

the rate of approximately 7.1 in./min.

35. Step 1:
a = distance from origin to A
b = distance from origin to B
θ = angle shown in problem statement

Step 2:

At the instant in question, $\dfrac{da}{dt} = -2$ m/sec, $\dfrac{db}{dt} = 1$ m/sec,

$a = 10$ m, and $b = 20$ m.

Step 3:

We want to find $\dfrac{d\theta}{dt}$.

Step 4:

$\tan \theta = \dfrac{a}{b}$ or $\theta = \tan^{-1}\left(\dfrac{a}{b}\right)$

Step 5:

$$\dfrac{d\theta}{dt} = \dfrac{1}{1 + \left(\dfrac{a}{b}\right)^2} \dfrac{b\dfrac{da}{dt} - a\dfrac{db}{dt}}{b^2} = \dfrac{b\dfrac{da}{dt} - a\dfrac{db}{dt}}{a^2 + b^2}$$

Step 6:

$$\dfrac{d\theta}{dt} = \dfrac{(20)(-2) - (10)(1)}{10^2 + 20^2} = -0.1 \text{ radian/sec}$$

$$\approx -5.73 \text{ degrees/sec}$$

To the nearest degree, the angle is changing at the rate

of -6 degrees per second.

36. Step 1:

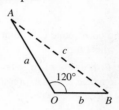

a = distance from O to A
b = distance from O to B
c = distance from A to B

Step 2:

At the instant in question, $a = 5$ nautical miles,

$b = 3$ nautical miles, $\dfrac{da}{dt} = 14$ knots, and $\dfrac{db}{dt} = 21$ knots.

Step 3:

We want to find $\dfrac{dc}{dt}$.

Step 4:
Law of Cosines: $c^2 = a^2 + b^2 - 2ab \cos 120°$
                   $c^2 = a^2 + b^2 + ab$

Step 5:

$$2c\dfrac{dc}{dt} = 2a\dfrac{da}{dt} + 2b\dfrac{db}{dt} + a\dfrac{db}{dt} + b\dfrac{da}{dt}$$

Step 6:

Note that, at the instant in question,

$$c = \sqrt{a^2 + b^2 + ab} = \sqrt{(5)^2 + (3)^2 + (5)(3)} = \sqrt{49} = 7$$

$$2(7)\dfrac{dc}{dt} = 2(5)(14) + 2(3)(21) + (5)(21) + (3)(14)$$

$$14\dfrac{dc}{dt} = 413$$

$$\dfrac{dc}{dt} = 29.5 \text{ knots}$$

The ships are moving apart at a rate of 29.5 knots.

37. $\dfrac{dy}{dt} = \dfrac{dy}{dx}\dfrac{dx}{dt} = -10(1 + x^2)^{-2}(2x)\dfrac{dx}{dt} = -\dfrac{20x}{(1 + x^2)^2}\dfrac{dx}{dt}$

Since $\dfrac{dx}{dt} = 3$ cm/sec, we have

$\dfrac{dy}{dt} = -\dfrac{60x}{(1 + x^2)^2}$ cm/sec.

(a) $\dfrac{dy}{dt} = -\dfrac{60(-2)}{[1 + (-2)^2]^2} = \dfrac{120}{5^2} = \dfrac{24}{5}$ cm/sec

(b) $\dfrac{dy}{dt} = -\dfrac{60(0)}{(1 + 0^2)^2} = 0$ cm/sec

(c) $\dfrac{dy}{dt} = -\dfrac{60(20)}{(1 + 20^2)^2} \approx -0.00746$ cm/sec

38. $\frac{dy}{dt} = \frac{dy}{dx}\frac{dx}{dt} = (3x^2 - 4)\frac{dx}{dt}$

Since $\frac{dx}{dt} = -2$ cm/sec, we have $\frac{dy}{dt} = 8 - 6x^2$ cm/sec.

(a) $\frac{dy}{dt} = 8 - 6(-3)^2 = -46$ cm/sec

(b) $\frac{dy}{dt} = 8 - 6(1)^2 = 2$ cm/sec

(c) $\frac{dy}{dt} = 8 - 6(4)^2 = -88$ cm/sec

39. (a) The point being plotted would correspond to a point on the edge of the wheel as the wheel turns.

(b) One possible answer is $\theta = 16\pi t$, where t is in seconds. (An arbitrary constant may be added to this expression, and we have assumed counterclockwise motion.)

(c) In general, assuming counterclockwise motion:

$\frac{dx}{dt} = -2\sin\theta\frac{d\theta}{dt} = -2(\sin\theta)(16\pi) = -32\pi\sin\theta$

$\frac{dy}{dt} = 2\cos\theta\frac{d\theta}{dt} = 2(\cos\theta)(16\pi) = 32\pi\cos\theta$

At $\theta = \frac{\pi}{4}$:

$\frac{dx}{dt} = -32\pi\sin\frac{\pi}{4} = -16\pi(\sqrt{2}) \approx -71.086$ ft/sec

$\frac{dy}{dt} = 32\pi\cos\frac{\pi}{4} = 16\pi(\sqrt{2}) \approx 71.086$ ft/sec

At $\theta = \frac{\pi}{2}$:

$\frac{dx}{dt} = -32\pi\sin\frac{\pi}{2} = -32\pi \approx -100.531$ ft/sec

$\frac{dy}{dt} = 32\pi\cos\frac{\pi}{2} = 0$ ft/sec

At $\theta = \pi$:

$\frac{dx}{dt} = -32\pi\sin\pi = 0$ ft/sec

$\frac{dy}{dt} = 32\pi\cos\pi = -32\pi \approx -100.531$ ft/sec

40. (a) One possible answer:
$x = 30\cos\theta$, $y = 40 + 30\sin\theta$

(b) Since the ferris wheel makes one revolution every 10 sec, we may let $\theta = 0.2\pi t$ and we may write $x = 30\cos 0.2\pi t$, $y = 40 + 30\sin 0.2\pi t$.
(This assumes that the ferris wheel revolves counterclockwise.)

In general:

$\frac{dx}{dt} = -30(\sin 0.2\pi t)(0.2\pi) = -6\pi\sin 0.2\pi t$

$\frac{dy}{dt} = 30(\cos 0.2\pi t)(0.2\pi) = 6\pi\cos 0.2\pi t$

At $t = 5$:

$\frac{dx}{dt} = -6\pi\sin\pi = 0$ ft/sec

$\frac{dy}{dt} = 6\pi\cos\pi = 6\pi(-1) \approx -18.850$ ft/sec

At $t = 8$:

$\frac{dx}{dt} = -6\pi\sin 1.6\pi \approx 17.927$ ft/sec

$\frac{dy}{dt} = 6\pi\cos 1.6\pi \approx 5.825$ ft/sec

41. (a) $\frac{dy}{dt} = \frac{d}{dt}(uv) = u\frac{dv}{dt} + v\frac{du}{dt}$

$= u(0.05v) + v(0.04u)$

$= 0.09uv$

$= 0.09y$

Since $\frac{dy}{dt} = 0.09y$, the rate of growth of total production is 9% per year.

(b) $\frac{dy}{dt} = \frac{d}{dt}(uv) = u\frac{dv}{dt} + v\frac{du}{dt}$

$= u(0.03v) + v(-0.02u)$

$= 0.01uv$

$= 0.01y$

The total production is increasing at the rate of 1% per year.

■ Chapter 4 Review (pp. 242–245)

1. $y = x\sqrt{2 - x}$

$y' = x\left(\frac{1}{2\sqrt{2 - x}}\right)(-1) + (\sqrt{2 - x})(1)$

$= \frac{-x + 2(2 - x)}{2\sqrt{2 - x}}$

$= \frac{4 - 3x}{2\sqrt{2 - x}}$

The first derivative has a zero at $\frac{4}{3}$.

Critical point value: $x = \frac{4}{3}$ $y = \frac{4\sqrt{6}}{9} \approx 1.09$

Endpoint values: $x = -2$ $y = -4$

                $x = 2$ $y = 0$

The global maximum value is $\frac{4\sqrt{6}}{9}$ at $x = \frac{4}{3}$, and the global minimum value is -4 at $x = -2$.

2. Since y is a cubic function with a positive leading coefficient, we have $\lim\limits_{x\to-\infty} y = -\infty$ and $\lim\limits_{x\to\infty} y = \infty$. There are no global extrema.

3. $y' = (x^2)(e^{1/x^2})(-2x^{-3}) + (e^{1/x^2})(2x)$

$= 2e^{1/x^2}\left(-\frac{1}{x} + x\right)$

$= \frac{2e^{1/x^2}(x - 1)(x + 1)}{x}$

Intervals	$x < -1$	$-1 < x < 0$	$0 < x < 1$	$x > 1$
Sign of y'	$-$	$+$	$-$	$+$
Behavior of y	Decreasing	Increasing	Decreasing	Increasing

$y'' = \frac{d}{dx}[2e^{1/x^2}(-x^{-1} + x)]$

$= (2e^{1/x^2})(x^{-2} + 1) + (-x^{-1} + x)(2e^{1/x^2})(-2x^{-3})$

$= (2e^{1/x^2})(x^{-2} + 1 + 2x^{-4} - 2x^{-2})$

$= \frac{2e^{1/x^2}(x^4 - x^2 + 2)}{x^4}$

$= \frac{2e^{1/x^2}[(x^2 - 0.5)^2 + 1.75]}{x^4}$

The second derivative is always positive (where defined), so the function is concave up for all $x \neq 0$.
Graphical support:

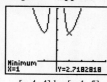

$[-4, 4]$ by $[-1, 5]$

(a) $[-1, 0)$ and $[1, \infty)$

(b) $(-\infty, -1]$ and $(0, 1]$

(c) $(-\infty, 0)$ and $(0, \infty)$

(d) None

(e) Local (and absolute) minima at $(1, e)$ and $(-1, e)$

(f) None

4. Note that the domain of the function is $[-2, 2]$.

$$y' = x\left(\frac{1}{2\sqrt{4 - x^2}}\right)(-2x) + (\sqrt{4 - x^2})(1)$$
$$= \frac{-x^2 + (4 - x^2)}{\sqrt{4 - x^2}}$$
$$= \frac{4 - 2x^2}{\sqrt{4 - x^2}}$$

Intervals	$-2 < x < -\sqrt{2}$	$-\sqrt{2} < x < \sqrt{2}$	$\sqrt{2} < x < 2$
Sign of y'	−	+	−
Behavior of y	Decreasing	Increasing	Decreasing

$$y'' = \frac{(\sqrt{4 - x^2})(-4x) - (4 - 2x^2)\left(\frac{1}{2\sqrt{4 - x^2}}\right)(-2x)}{4 - x^2}$$
$$= \frac{2x(x^2 - 6)}{(4 - x^2)^{3/2}}$$

Note that the values $x = \pm\sqrt{6}$ are not zeros of y'' because they fall outside of the domain.

Intervals	$-2 < x < 0$	$0 < x < 2$
Sign of y''	+	−
Behavior of y	Concave up	Concave down

Graphical support:

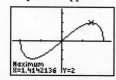

$[-2.35, 2.35]$ by $[-3.5, 3.5]$

(a) $[-\sqrt{2}, \sqrt{2}]$

(b) $[-2, -\sqrt{2}]$ and $[\sqrt{2}, 2]$

(c) $(-2, 0)$

(d) $(0, 2)$

(e) Local maxima: $(-2, 0)$, $(\sqrt{2}, 2)$
Local minima: $(2, 0)$, $(-\sqrt{2}, -2)$
Note that the extrema at $x = \pm\sqrt{2}$ are also absolute extrema.

(f) $(0, 0)$

5. $y' = 1 - 2x - 4x^3$
Using grapher techniques, the zero of y' is $x \approx 0.385$.

Intervals	$x < 0.385$	$0.385 < x$
Sign of y'	+	−
Behavior of y	Increasing	Decreasing

$y'' = -2 - 12x^2 = -2(1 + 6x^2)$
The second derivative is always negative so the function is concave down for all x.

Graphical support:

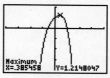

$[-4, 4]$ by $[-4, 2]$

(a) Approximately $(-\infty, 0.385]$

(b) Approximately $[0.385, \infty)$

(c) None

(d) $(-\infty, \infty)$

(e) Local (and absolute) maximum at $\approx (0.385, 1.215)$

(f) None

6. $y' = e^{x-1} - 1$

Intervals	$x < 1$	$1 < x$
Sign of y'	−	+
Behavior of y	Decreasing	Increasing

$y'' = e^{x-1}$

The second derivative is always positive, so the function is concave up for all x.
Graphical support:

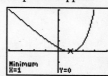

$[-4, 4]$ by $[-2, 4]$

(a) $[1, \infty)$

(b) $(-\infty, 1]$

(c) $(-\infty, \infty)$

(d) None

(e) Local (and absolute) minimum at $(1, 0)$

(f) None

7. Note that the domain is $(-1, 1)$.

$$y = (1 - x^2)^{-1/4}$$

$$y' = -\frac{1}{4}(1 - x^2)^{-5/4}(-2x) = \frac{x}{2(1 - x^2)^{5/4}}$$

Intervals	$-1 < x < 0$	$0 < x < 1$
Sign of y'	$-$	$+$
Behavior of y	Decreasing	Increasing

$$y'' = \frac{2(1 - x^2)^{5/4}(1) - (x)(2)\left(\frac{5}{4}\right)(1 - x^2)^{1/4}(-2x)}{4(1 - x^2)^{5/2}}$$

$$= \frac{(1 - x^2)^{1/4}[2 - 2x^2 + 5x^2]}{4(1 - x^2)^{5/2}}$$

$$= \frac{3x^2 + 2}{4(1 - x^2)^{9/4}}$$

The second derivative is always positive, so the function is concave up on its domain $(-1, 1)$.

Graphical support:

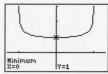

$[-1.3, 1.3]$ by $[-1, 3]$

(a) $[0, 1)$

(b) $(-1, 0]$

(c) $(-1, 1)$

(d) None

(e) Local minimum at $(0, 1)$

(f) None

8. $y' = \dfrac{(x^3 - 1)(1) - (x)(3x^2)}{(x^3 - 1)^2} = -\dfrac{2x^3 + 1}{(x^3 - 1)^2}$

Intervals	$x < -2^{-1/3}$	$-2^{-1/3} < x < 1$	$1 < x$
Sign of y'	$+$	$-$	$-$
Behavior of y	Increasing	Decreasing	Decreasing

$$y'' = -\frac{(x^3 - 1)^2(6x^2) - (2x^3 + 1)(2)(x^3 - 1)(3x^2)}{(x^3 - 1)^4}$$

$$= -\frac{(x^3 - 1)(6x^2) - (2x^3 + 1)(6x^2)}{(x^3 - 1)^3}$$

$$= \frac{6x^2(x^3 + 2)}{(x^3 - 1)^3}$$

Intervals	$x < -2^{1/3}$	$-2^{1/3} < x < 0$	$0 < x < 1$	$1 < x$
Sign of y''	$+$	$-$	$-$	$+$
Behavior of y	Concave up	Concave down	Concave down	Concave up

Graphical support:

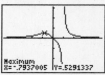

$[-4.7, 4.7]$ by $[-3.1, 3.1]$

(a) $(-\infty, -2^{-1/3}] \approx (-\infty, -0.794]$

(b) $[-2^{-1/3}, 1) \approx [-0.794, 1)$ and $(1, \infty)$

(c) $(-\infty, -2^{1/3}) \approx (-\infty, -1.260)$ and $(1, \infty)$

(d) $(-2^{1/3}, 1) \approx (-1.260, 1)$

(e) Local maximum at

$$\left(-2^{-1/3}, \frac{2}{3} \cdot 2^{-1/3}\right) \approx (-0.794, 0.529)$$

(f) $\left(-2^{1/3}, \dfrac{1}{3} \cdot 2^{1/3}\right) \approx (-1.260, 0.420)$

9. Note that the domain is $[-1, 1]$.

$$y' = -\frac{1}{\sqrt{1 - x^2}}$$

Since y' is negative on $(-1, 1)$ and y is continuous, y is decreasing on its domain $[-1, 1]$.

$$y'' = \frac{d}{dx}[-(1 - x^2)^{-1/2}]$$

$$= \frac{1}{2}(1 - x^2)^{-3/2}(-2x) = -\frac{x}{(1 - x^2)^{3/2}}$$

Intervals	$-1 < x < 0$	$0 < x < 1$
Sign of y''	$+$	$-$
Behavior of y	Concave up	Concave down

Graphical support:

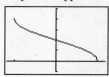

$[-1.175, 1.175]$ by $\left[-\dfrac{\pi}{4}, \dfrac{5\pi}{4}\right]$

(a) None

(b) $[-1, 1]$

(c) $(-1, 0)$

(d) $(0, 1)$

(e) Local (and absolute) maximum at $(-1, \pi)$; local (and absolute) minimum at $(1, 0)$

(f) $\left(0, \dfrac{\pi}{2}\right)$

10. This problem can be solved graphically by using NDER to obtain the graphs shown below.

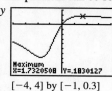

[−4, 4] by [−1, 0.3]

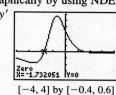

[−4, 4] by [−0.4, 0.6]

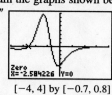

[−4, 4] by [−0.7, 0.8]

An alternative approach using a combination of algebraic and graphical techniques follows.

Note that the denominator of y is always positive because it is equivalent to $(x + 1)^2 + 2$.

$$y' = \frac{(x^2 + 2x + 3)(1) - (x)(2x + 2)}{(x^2 + 2x + 3)^2}$$

$$= \frac{-x^2 + 3}{(x^2 + 2x + 3)^2}$$

Intervals	$x < -\sqrt{3}$	$-\sqrt{3} < x < \sqrt{3}$	$\sqrt{3} < x$
Sign of y'	−	+	−
Behavior of y	Decreasing	Increasing	Decreasing

$$y'' = \frac{(x^2 + 2x + 3)^2(-2x) - (-x^2 + 3)(2)(x^2 + 2x + 3)(2x + 2)}{(x^2 + 2x + 3)^4}$$

$$= \frac{(x^2 + 2x + 3)(-2x) - 2(2x + 2)(-x^2 + 3)}{(x^2 + 2x + 3)^3}$$

$$= \frac{2x^3 - 18x - 12}{(x^2 + 2x + 3)^3}$$

Using graphing techniques, the zeros of $2x^3 - 18x - 12$ (and hence of y'') are at $x \approx -2.584$, $x \approx -0.706$, and $x \approx 3.290$.

Intervals	$(-\infty, -2.584)$	$(-2.584, -0.706)$	$(-0.706, 3.290)$	$(3.290, \infty)$
Sign of y''	−	+	−	+
Behavior of y	Concave down	Concave up	Concave down	Concave up

(a) $[-\sqrt{3}, \sqrt{3}]$

(b) $(-\infty, -\sqrt{3}]$ and $[\sqrt{3}, \infty)$

(c) Approximately $(-2.584, -0.706)$ and $(3.290, \infty)$

(d) Approximately $(-\infty, -2.584)$ and $(-0.706, 3.290)$

(e) Local maximum at $\left(\sqrt{3}, \dfrac{\sqrt{3} - 1}{4}\right)$

$\approx (1.732, 0.183)$;

local minimum at $\left(-\sqrt{3}, \dfrac{-\sqrt{3} - 1}{4}\right)$

$\approx (-1.732, -0.683)$

(f) $\approx (-2.584, -0.573)$, $(-0.706, -0.338)$, and $(3.290, 0.161)$

11. For $x > 0$, $y' = \dfrac{d}{dx} \ln x = \dfrac{1}{x}$

For $x < 0$: $y' = \dfrac{d}{dx} \ln (-x) = \dfrac{1}{-x}(-1) = \dfrac{1}{x}$

Thus $y' = \dfrac{1}{x}$ for all x in the domain.

Intervals	$(-2, 0)$	$(0, 2)$
Sign of y'	$-$	$+$
Behavior of y	Decreasing	Increasing

$y'' = -x^{-2}$

The second derivative is always negative, so the function is concave down on each open interval of its domain.

Graphical support:

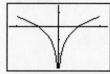

$[-2.35, 2.35]$ by $[-3, 1.5]$

(a) $(0, 2]$

(b) $[-2, 0)$

(c) None

(d) $(-2, 0)$ and $(0, 2)$

(e) Local (and absolute) maxima at $(-2, \ln 2)$ and $(2, \ln 2)$

(f) None

12. $y' = 3 \cos 3x - 4 \sin 4x$

Using graphing techniques, the zeros of y' in the domain

$0 \le x \le 2\pi$ are $x \approx 0.176$, $x \approx 0.994$, $x = \dfrac{\pi}{2} \approx 1.57$,

$x \approx 2.148$, and $x \approx 2.965$, $x \approx 3.834$, $x = \dfrac{3\pi}{2}$, $x \approx 5.591$

Intervals	$0 < x < 0.176$	$0.176 < x < 0.994$	$0.994 < x < \dfrac{\pi}{2}$	$\dfrac{\pi}{2} < x < 2.148$	$2.148 < x < 2.965$
Sign of y'	$+$	$-$	$+$	$-$	$+$
Behavior of y	Increasing	Decreasing	Increasing	Decreasing	Increasing

Intervals	$2.965 < x < 3.834$	$3.834 < x < \dfrac{3\pi}{2}$	$\dfrac{3\pi}{2} < x < 5.591$	$5.591 < x < 2\pi$
Sign of y'	$-$	$+$	$-$	$+$
Behavior of y	Decreasing	Increasing	Decreasing	Increasing

$y'' = -9 \sin 3x - 16 \cos 4x$

Using graphing techniques, the zeros of y'' in the domain
$0 \le x \le 2\pi$ are $x \approx 0.542$, $x \approx 1.266$, $x \approx 1.876$,
$x \approx 2.600$, $x \approx 3.425$, $x \approx 4.281$, $x \approx 5.144$ and $x \approx 6.000$.

Intervals	$0 < x < 0.542$	$0.542 < x < 1.266$	$1.266 < x < 1.876$	$1.876 < x < 2.600$	$2.600 < x < 3.425$
Sign of y''	−	+	−	+	−
Behavior of y	Concave down	Concave up	Concave down	Concave up	Concave down

Intervals	$3.425 < x < 4.281$	$4.281 < x < 5.144$	$5.144 < x < 6.000$	$6.000 < x < 2\pi$
Sign of y''	+	−	+	−
Behavior of y	Concave up	Concave down	Concave up	Concave down

Graphical support:

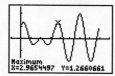

$\left[-\dfrac{\pi}{4}, \dfrac{9\pi}{4}\right]$ by $[-2.5, 2.5]$

(a) Approximately $[0, 0.176]$, $\left[0.994, \dfrac{\pi}{2}\right]$, $[2.148, 2.965]$, $\left[3.834, \dfrac{3\pi}{2}\right]$, and $\left[5.591, 2\pi\right]$

(b) Approximately $[0.176, 0.994]$, $\left[\dfrac{\pi}{2}, 2.148\right]$, $[2.965, 3.834]$, and $\left[\dfrac{3\pi}{2}, 5.591\right]$

(c) Approximately $(0.542, 1.266)$, $(1.876, 2.600)$, $(3.425, 4.281)$, and $(5.144, 6.000)$

(d) Approximately $(0, 0.542)$, $(1.266, 1.876)$, $(2.600, 3.425)$, $(4.281, 5.144)$, and $(6.000, 2\pi)$

(e) Local maxima at $\approx (0.176, 1.266)$, $\left(\dfrac{\pi}{2}, 0\right)$

and $(2.965, 1.266)$, $\left(\dfrac{3\pi}{2}, 2\right)$, and $(2\pi, 1)$;

local minima at $\approx (0, 1)$, $(0.994, -0.513)$,

$(2.148, -0.513)$, $(3.834, -1.806)$,

and $(5.591, -1.806)$

Note that the local extrema at $x \approx 3.834$, $x = \dfrac{3\pi}{2}$,

and $x \approx 5.591$ are also absolute extrema.

(f) $\approx (0.542, 0.437)$, $(1.266, -0.267)$, $(1.876, -0.267)$, $(2.600, 0.437)$, $(3.425, -0.329)$, $(4.281, 0.120)$, $(5.144, 0.120)$, and $(6.000, -0.329)$

13. $y' = \begin{cases} -e^{-x}, & x < 0 \\ 4 - 3x^2, & x > 0 \end{cases}$

Intervals	$x < 0$	$0 < x < \dfrac{2}{\sqrt{3}}$	$\dfrac{2}{\sqrt{3}} < x$
Sign of y'	$-$	$+$	$-$
Behavior of y	Decreasing	Increasing	Decreasing

$y'' = \begin{cases} e^{-x}, & x < 0 \\ -6x, & x > 0 \end{cases}$

Intervals	$x < 0$	$0 < x$
Sign of y''	$+$	$-$
Behavior of y	Concave up	Concave down

Graphical support:

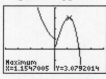

Maximum
X=1.1547005 Y=3.0792014

$[-4, 4]$ by $[-2, 4]$

(a) $\left(0, \dfrac{2}{\sqrt{3}}\right]$

(b) $(-\infty, 0]$ and $\left[\dfrac{2}{\sqrt{3}}, \infty\right)$

(c) $(-\infty, 0)$

(d) $(0, \infty)$

(e) Local maximum at $\left(\dfrac{2}{\sqrt{3}}, \dfrac{16}{3\sqrt{3}}\right) \approx (1.155, 3.079)$

(f) None. Note that there is no point of inflection at $x = 0$ because the derivative is undefined and no tangent line exists at this point.

14. $y' = -5x^4 + 7x^2 + 10x + 4$
Using graphing techniques, the zeros of y' are $x \approx -0.578$ and $x \approx 1.692$.

Intervals	$x < -0.578$	$-0.578 < x < 1.692$	$1.692 < x$
Sign of y'	$-$	$+$	$-$
Behavior of y	Decreasing	Increasing	Decreasing

$y'' = -20x^3 + 14x + 10$
Using graphing techniques, the zero of y'' is $x \approx 1.079$.

Intervals	$x < 1.079$	$1.079 < x$
Sign of y''	$+$	$-$
Behavior of y	Concave up	Concave down

Graphical support:

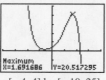

Maximum
X=1.691686 Y=20.517295

$[-4, 4]$ by $[-10, 25]$

(a) Approximately $[-0.578, 1.692]$

(b) Approximately $(-\infty, -0.578]$ and $[1.692, \infty)$

(c) Approximately $(-\infty, 1.079)$

(d) Approximately $(1.079, \infty)$

(e) Local maximum at $\approx (1.692, 20.517)$; local minimum at $\approx (-0.578, 0.972)$

(f) $\approx (1.079, 13.601)$

15. $y = 2x^{4/5} - x^{9/5}$

$y' = \dfrac{8}{5}x^{-1/5} - \dfrac{9}{5}x^{4/5} = \dfrac{8 - 9x}{5\sqrt[5]{x}}$

Intervals	$x < 0$	$0 < x < \dfrac{8}{9}$	$\dfrac{8}{9} < x$
Sign of y'	$-$	$+$	$-$
Behavior of y	Decreasing	Increasing	Decreasing

$y'' = -\dfrac{8}{25}x^{-6/5} - \dfrac{36}{25}x^{-1/5} = -\dfrac{4(2 + 9x)}{25x^{6/5}}$

Intervals	$x < -\dfrac{2}{9}$	$-\dfrac{2}{9} < x < 0$	$0 < x$
Sign of y''	$+$	$-$	$-$
Behavior of y	Concave up	Concave down	Concave down

Graphical support:

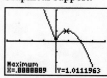

Maximum
X=.8888889   Y=1.0111963

$[-4, 4]$ by $[-3, 3]$

(a) $\left[0, \dfrac{8}{9}\right]$

(b) $(-\infty, 0]$ and $\left[\dfrac{8}{9}, \infty\right)$

(c) $\left(-\infty, -\dfrac{2}{9}\right)$

(d) $\left(-\dfrac{2}{9}, 0\right)$ and $(0, \infty)$

(e) Local maximum at $\left(\dfrac{8}{9}, \dfrac{10}{9} \cdot \left(\dfrac{8}{9}\right)^{4/5}\right) \approx (0.889, 1.011)$;

local minimum at $(0, 0)$

(f) $\left(-\dfrac{2}{9}, \dfrac{20}{9} \cdot \left(-\dfrac{2}{9}\right)^{4/5}\right) \approx \left(-\dfrac{2}{9}, 0.667\right)$

16. We use a combination of analytic and grapher techniques to solve this problem. Depending on the viewing windows chosen, graphs obtained using NDER may exhibit strange behavior near $x = 2$ because, for example, NDER $(y, 2) \approx 5{,}000{,}000$ while y' is actually undefined at $x = 2$. The graph of $y = \dfrac{5 - 4x + 4x^2 - x^3}{x - 2}$ is shown below.

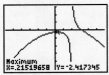

[−5.875, 5.875] by [−50, 30]

$$y' = \frac{(x - 2)(-4 + 8x - 3x^2) - (5 - 4x + 4x^2 - x^3)(1)}{(x - 2)^2}$$

$$= \frac{-2x^3 + 10x^2 - 16x + 3}{(x - 2)^2}$$

The graph of y' is shown below.

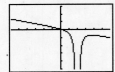

[−5.875, 5.875] by [−50, 30]

The zero of y' is $x \approx 0.215$.

Intervals	$x < 0.215$	$0.215 < x < 2$	$2 < x$
Sign of y'	+	−	−
Behavior of y	Increasing	Decreasing	Decreasing

$$y'' = \frac{(x - 2)^2(-6x^2 + 20x - 16) - (-2x^3 + 10x^2 - 16x + 3)(2)(x - 2)}{(x - 2)^4}$$

$$= \frac{(x - 2)(-6x^2 + 20x - 16) - 2(-2x^3 + 10x^2 - 16x + 3)}{(x - 2)^3}$$

$$= \frac{-2(x^3 - 6x^2 + 12x - 13)}{(x - 2)^3}$$

The graph of y'' is shown below.

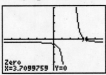

[−5.875, 5.875] by [−20, 20]

The zero of $x^3 - 6x^2 + 12x - 13$
(and hence of y'') is $x \approx 3.710$.

Intervals	$x < 2$	$2 < x < 3.710$	$3.710 < x$
Sign of y''	−	+	−
Behavior of y	Concave down	Concave up	Concave down

(a) Approximately $(-\infty, 0.215]$

(b) Approximately $[0.215, 2)$ and $(2, \infty)$

(c) Approximately $(2, 3.710)$

(d) $(-\infty, 2)$ and approximately $(3.710, \infty)$

(e) Local maximum at $\approx (0.215, -2.417)$

(f) $\approx (3.710, -3.420)$

17. $y' = 6(x + 1)(x - 2)^2$

Intervals	$x < -1$	$-1 < x < 2$	$2 < x$
Sign of y'	$-$	$+$	$+$
Behavior of y	Decreasing	Increasing	Increasing

$$y'' = 6(x + 1)(2)(x - 2) + 6(x - 2)^2(1)$$
$$= 6(x - 2)[(2x + 2) + (x - 2)]$$
$$= 18x(x - 2)$$

Intervals	$x < 0$	$0 < x < 2$	$2 < x$
Sign of y''	$+$	$-$	$+$
Behavior of y	Concave up	Concave down	Concave up

(a) There are no local maxima.

(b) There is a local (and absolute) minimum at $x = -1$.

(c) There are points of inflection at $x = 0$ and at $x = 2$.

18. $y' = 6(x + 1)(x - 2)$

Intervals	$x < -1$	$-1 < x < 2$	$2 < x$
Sign of y'	$+$	$-$	$+$
Behavior of y	Increasing	Decreasing	Increasing

$$y'' = \frac{d}{dx}6(x^2 - x - 2) = 6(2x - 1)$$

Intervals	$x < \frac{1}{2}$	$\frac{1}{2} < x$
Sign of y''	$-$	$+$
Behavior of y	Concave down	Concave up

(a) There is a local maximum at $x = -1$.

(b) There is a local minimum at $x = 2$.

(c) There is a point of inflection at $x = \frac{1}{2}$.

19. Since $\frac{d}{dx}\left(-\frac{1}{4}x^{-4} - e^{-x}\right) = x^{-5} + e^{-x}$,

$f(x) = -\frac{1}{4}x^{-4} - e^{-x} + C.$

20. Since $\frac{d}{dx}\sec x = \sec x \tan x, f(x) = \sec x + C.$

21. Since $\frac{d}{dx}\left(2 \ln x + \frac{1}{3}x^3 + x\right) = \frac{2}{x} + x^2 + 1,$

$f(x) = 2 \ln x + \frac{1}{3}x^3 + x + C.$

22. Since $\frac{d}{dx}\left(\frac{2}{3}x^{3/2} + 2x^{1/2}\right) = \sqrt{x} + \frac{1}{\sqrt{x}},$

$f(x) = \frac{2}{3}x^{3/2} + 2x^{1/2} + C.$

23.
$$f(x) = -\cos x + \sin x + C$$
$$f(\pi) = 3$$
$$1 + 0 + C = 3$$
$$C = 2$$
$$f(x) = -\cos x + \sin x + 2$$

24.
$$f(x) = \frac{3}{4}x^{4/3} + \frac{1}{3}x^3 + \frac{1}{2}x^2 + x + C$$
$$f(1) = 0$$
$$\frac{3}{4} + \frac{1}{3} + \frac{1}{2} + 1 + C = 0$$
$$C = -\frac{31}{12}$$
$$f(x) = \frac{3}{4}x^{4/3} + \frac{1}{3}x^3 + \frac{1}{2}x^2 + x - \frac{31}{12}$$

25. $v(t) = s'(t) = 9.8t + 5$
$s(t) = 4.9t^2 + 5t + C$
$s(0) = 10$
$C = 10$
$s(t) = 4.9t^2 + 5t + 10$

26. $a(t) = v'(t) = 32$
$v(t) = 32t + C_1$
$v(0) = 20$
$C_1 = 20$
$v(t) = s'(t) = 32t + 20$
$s(t) = 16t^2 + 20t + C_2$
$s(0) = 5$
$C_2 = 5$
$s(t) = 16t^2 + 20t + 5$

27. $f(x) = \tan x$

$f'(x) = \sec^2 x$

$$L(x) = f\left(-\frac{\pi}{4}\right) + f'\left(-\frac{\pi}{4}\right)\left[x - \left(-\frac{\pi}{4}\right)\right]$$
$$= \tan\left(-\frac{\pi}{4}\right) + \sec^2\left(-\frac{\pi}{4}\right)\left(x + \frac{\pi}{4}\right)$$
$$= -1 + 2\left(x + \frac{\pi}{4}\right)$$
$$= 2x + \frac{\pi}{2} - 1$$

28. $f(x) = \sec x$

$f'(x) = \sec x \tan x$

$$L(x) = f\left(\frac{\pi}{4}\right) + f'\left(\frac{\pi}{4}\right)\left(x - \frac{\pi}{4}\right)$$
$$= \sec\left(\frac{\pi}{4}\right) + \sec\left(\frac{\pi}{4}\right)\tan\left(\frac{\pi}{4}\right)\left(x - \frac{\pi}{4}\right)$$
$$= \sqrt{2} + \sqrt{2}(1)\left(x - \frac{\pi}{4}\right)$$
$$= \sqrt{2}x - \frac{\pi\sqrt{2}}{4} + \sqrt{2}$$

29. $f(x) = \dfrac{1}{1 + \tan x}$

$f'(x) = -(1 + \tan x)^{-2}(\sec^2 x)$

$$= -\frac{1}{\cos^2 x(1 + \tan x)^2}$$
$$= -\frac{1}{(\cos x + \sin x)^2}$$

$L(x) = f(0) + f'(0)(x - 0)$

$= 1 - 1(x - 0)$

$= -x + 1$

30. $f(x) = e^x + \sin x$
$f'(x) = e^x + \cos x$
$L(x) = f(0) + f'(0)(x - 0)$
$\qquad = 1 + 2(x - 0)$
$\qquad = 2x + 1$

31. The global minimum value of $\frac{1}{2}$ occurs at $x = 2$.

32. (a) The values of y' and y'' are both negative where the graph is decreasing and concave down, at T.

(b) The value of y' is negative and the value of y'' is positive where the graph is decreasing and concave up, at P.

33. (a) The function is increasing on the interval $(0, 2]$.

(b) The function is decreasing on the interval $[-3, 0)$.

(c) The local extreme values occur only at the endpoints of the domain. A local maximum value of 1 occurs at $x = -3$, and a local maximum value of 3 occurs at $x = 2$.

34. The 24th day

35.

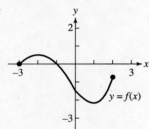

36. (a) We know that f is decreasing on $[0, 1]$ and increasing on $[1, 3]$, the absolute minimum value occurs at $x = 1$ and the absolute maximum value occurs at an endpoint. Since $f(0) = 0$, $f(1) = -2$, and $f(3) = 3$, the absolute minimum value is -2 at $x = 1$ and the absolute maximum value is 3 at $x = 3$.

(b) The concavity of the graph does not change. There are no points of inflection.

(c)

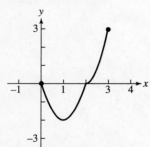

37. (a) $f(x)$ is continuous on $[0.5, 3]$ and differentiable on $(0.5, 3)$.

(b) $f'(x) = (x)\left(\frac{1}{x}\right) + (\ln x)(1) = 1 + \ln x$

Using $a = 0.5$ and $b = 3$, we solve as follows.

$$f'(c) = \frac{f(3) - f(0.5)}{3 - 0.5}$$

$$1 + \ln c = \frac{3 \ln 3 - 0.5 \ln 0.5}{2.5}$$

$$\ln c = \frac{\ln\left(\frac{3^3}{0.5^{0.5}}\right)}{2.5} - 1$$

$$\ln c = 0.4 \ln(27\sqrt{2}) - 1$$

$$c = e^{-1}(27\sqrt{2})^{0.4}$$

$$c = e^{-1}\sqrt[5]{1458} \approx 1.579$$

(c) The slope of the line is

$$m = \frac{f(b) - f(a)}{b - a} = 0.4 \ln (27\sqrt{2}) = 0.2 \ln 1458, \text{ and}$$

the line passes through $(3, 3 \ln 3)$. Its equation is

$y = 0.2(\ln 1458)(x - 3) + 3 \ln 3$, or approximately

$y = 1.457x - 1.075$.

(d) The slope of the line is $m = 0.2 \ln 1458$, and the line passes through
$(c, f(c)) = (e^{-1}\sqrt[5]{1458}, e^{-1}\sqrt[5]{1458}(-1 + 0.2 \ln 1458))$
$\qquad \approx (1.579, 0.722)$.
Its equation is
$y = 0.2(\ln 1458)(x - c) + f(c)$,
$y = 0.2 \ln 1458(x - e^{-1}\sqrt[5]{1458})$
$\qquad + e^{-1}\sqrt[5]{1458}(-1 + 0.2 \ln 1458)$,
$y = 0.2(\ln 1458)x - e^{-1}\sqrt[5]{1458}$,
or approximately $y = 1.457x - 1.579$.

38. (a) $v(t) = s'(t) = 4 - 6t - 3t^2$

(b) $a(t) = v'(t) = -6 - 6t$

(c) The particle starts at position 3 moving in the positive direction, but decelerating. At approximately $t = 0.528$, it reaches position 4.128 and changes direction, beginning to move in the negative direction. After that, it continues to accelerate while moving in the negative direction.

39. (a) $L(x) = f(0) + f'(0)(x - 0)$
$\qquad = -1 + 0(x - 0) = -1$

(b) $f(0.1) \approx L(0.1) = -1$

(c) Greater than the approximation in (b), since $f'(x)$ is actually positive over the interval $(0, 0.1)$ and the estimate is based on the derivative being 0.

40. (a) Since $\frac{dy}{dx} = (x^2)(-e^{-x}) + (e^{-x})(2x) = (2x - x^2)e^{-x}$,

$dy = (2x - x^2)e^{-x} \, dx$.

(b) $dy = [2(1) - (1)^2](e^{-1})(0.01)$
$\qquad = 0.01e^{-1}$
$\qquad \approx 0.00368$

41. (a) Regression equation $y = \dfrac{2701.73}{1 + 17.28e^{-0.36x}}$

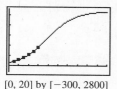

[0, 20] by [−300, 2800]

(b) Note that

$$y' = \frac{d}{dx}2701.73(1 + 17.28e^{-0.36x})^{-1}$$

$$= -2701.73(1 + 17.28e^{-0.36x})^{-2}(17.28)(-0.36e^{-0.36x})$$

$$\approx \frac{16{,}806.9e^{-0.36x}}{(1 + 17.28e^{-0.36x})^2}$$

The graph of y' is shown below.

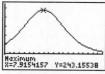

Maximum
X=7.9154157 Y=243.15538

[0, 20] by [−75, 275]

Using graphing techniques, y' has its maximum at $x \approx 7.92$. This corresponds to the year 1998 and represents the inflection point of the logistic curve. The logistic regression equation predicts that the rate of increase in debit card transactions will begin to decrease in 1998, and since $y(7.92) \approx 1351$, there are approximately 1351 million transactions that year.

(c) As x increases, the value of y will increase toward 2701.73. The logistic regression equation predicts a ceiling of approximately 2702 million transactions per year.

42. $f(x) = 2\cos x - \sqrt{1 + x}$

$$f'(x) = -2\sin x - \frac{1}{2\sqrt{1 + x}}$$

$$x_{n+1} = x_n - \frac{f(x_n)}{f'(x_n)}$$

$$= x_n - \frac{2\cos x_n - \sqrt{1 + x_n}}{-2\sin x_n - \dfrac{1}{2\sqrt{1 + x_n}}}$$

The graph of $y = f(x)$ shows that $f(x) = 0$ has one solution, near $x = 1$.

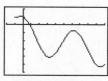

[−2, 10] by [−6, 2]

$x_1 = 1$
$x_2 \approx 0.8361848$
$x_3 \approx 0.8283814$
$x_4 \approx 0.8283608$
$x_5 \approx 0.8283608$

Solution: $x \approx 0.828361$

43. Let t represent time in seconds, where the rocket lifts off at $t = 0$. Since $a(t) = v'(t) = 20$ m/sec^2 and $v(0) = 0$ m/sec, we have $v(t) = 20t$, and so $v(60) = 1200$ m/sec. The speed after 1 minute (60 seconds) will be 1200 m/sec.

44. Let t represent time in seconds, where the rock is blasted upward at $t = 0$. Since $a(t) = v'(t) = -3.72$ m/sec^2 and $v(0) = 93$ m/sec, we have $v(t) = -3.72t + 93$. Since $s'(t) = -3.72t + 93$ and $s(0) = 0$, we have $s(t) = -1.86t^2 + 93t$. Solving $v(t) = 0$, we find that the rock attains its maximum height at $t = 25$ sec and its height at that time is $s(25) = 1162.5$ m.

45. Note that $s = 100 - 2r$ and the sector area is given by

$$A = \pi r^2\left(\frac{s}{2\pi r}\right) = \frac{1}{2}rs = \frac{1}{2}r(100 - 2r) = 50r - r^2.$$ To find

the domain of $A(r) = 50r - r^2$, note that $r > 0$ and

$0 < s < 2\pi r$, which gives $12.1 \approx \dfrac{50}{\pi + 1} < r < 50$. Since

$A'(r) = 50 - 2r$, the critical point occurs at $r = 25$. This

value is in the domain and corresponds to the maximum

area because $A''(r) = -2$, which is negative for all r.

The greatest area is attained when $r = 25$ ft and $s = 50$ ft.

46.

For $0 < x < \sqrt{27}$, the triangle with vertices at $(0, 0)$ and

$(\pm x, 27 - x^2)$ has an area given by

$$A(x) = \frac{1}{2}(2x)(27 - x^2) = 27x - x^3.$$ Since

$A' = 27 - 3x^2 = 3(3 - x)(3 + x)$ and $A'' = -6x$, the

critical point in the interval $(0, \sqrt{27})$ occurs at $x = 3$ and

corresponds to the maximum area because $A''(x)$ is negative

in this interval. The largest possible area is

$A(3) = 54$ square units.

47. If the dimensions are x ft by x ft by h ft, then the total amount of steel used is $x^2 + 4xh$ ft^2. Therefore, $x^2 + 4xh = 108$ and so $h = \dfrac{108 - x^2}{4x}$. The volume is given by $V(x) = x^2h = \dfrac{108x - x^3}{4} = 27x - 0.25x^3$. Then $V'(x) = 27 - 0.75x^2 = 0.75(6 + x)(6 - x)$ and $V''(x) = -1.5x$. The critical point occurs at $x = 6$, and it corresponds to the maximum volume because $V''(x) < 0$ for $x > 0$. The corresponding height is $\dfrac{108 - 6^2}{4(6)} = 3$ ft. The base measures 6 ft by 6 ft, and the height is 3 ft.

48. If the dimensions are x ft by x ft by h ft, then we have $x^2h = 32$ and so $h = \dfrac{32}{x^2}$. Neglecting the quarter-inch thickness of the steel, the area of the steel used is $A(x) = x^2 + 4xh = x^2 + \dfrac{128}{x}$. We can minimize the weight of the vat by minimizing this quantity. Now $A'(x) = 2x - 128x^{-2} = \dfrac{2}{x^2}(x^3 - 4^3)$ and $A''(x) = 2 + 256x^{-3}$. The critical point occurs at $x = 4$ and corresponds to the minimum possible area because $A''(x) > 0$ for $x > 0$. The corresponding height is $\dfrac{32}{4^2} = 2$ ft. The base should measure 4 ft by 4 ft, and the height should be 2 ft.

49. We have $r^2 + \left(\dfrac{h}{2}\right)^2 = 3$, so $r^2 = 3 - \dfrac{h^2}{4}$. We wish to minimize the cylinder's volume
$V = \pi r^2 h = \pi\left(3 - \dfrac{h^2}{4}\right)h = 3\pi h - \dfrac{\pi h^3}{4}$ for $0 < h < 2\sqrt{3}$. Since $\dfrac{dV}{dh} = 3\pi - \dfrac{3\pi h^2}{4} = \dfrac{3\pi}{4}(2 + h)(2 - h)$ and $\dfrac{d^2V}{dh^2} = -\dfrac{3\pi h}{2}$, the critical point occurs at $h = 2$ and it corresponds to the maximum value because $\dfrac{d^2V}{dh^2} < 0$ for $h > 0$. The corresponding value of r is $\sqrt{3 - \dfrac{2^2}{4}} = \sqrt{2}$.
The largest possible cylinder has height 2 and radius $\sqrt{2}$.

50. Note that, from similar cones, $\dfrac{r}{6} = \dfrac{12 - h}{12}$, so $h = 12 - 2r$. The volume of the smaller cone is given by
$V = \dfrac{1}{3}\pi r^2 h = \dfrac{1}{3}\pi r^2(12 - 2r) = 4\pi r^2 - \dfrac{2\pi}{3}r^3$ for $0 < r < 6$. Then $\dfrac{dV}{dr} = 8\pi r - 2\pi r^2 = 2\pi r(4 - r)$, so the critical point occurs at $r = 4$. This critical point corresponds to the maximum volume because $\dfrac{dV}{dr} > 0$ for $0 < r < 4$ and $\dfrac{dV}{dr} < 0$ for $4 < r < 6$. The smaller cone has the largest possible value when $r = 4$ ft and $h = 4$ ft.

51.

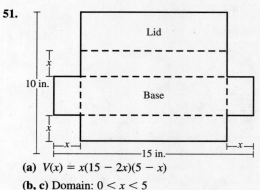

(a) $V(x) = x(15 - 2x)(5 - x)$

(b, c) Domain: $0 < x < 5$

[0, 5] by [−20, 70]

The maximum volume is approximately 66.019 in^3 and it occurs when $x \approx 1.962$ in.

(d) Note that $V(x) = 2x^3 - 25x^2 + 75x$, so $V'(x) = 6x^2 - 50x + 75$. Solving $V'(x) = 0$, we have

$x = \dfrac{50 \pm \sqrt{(-50)^2 - 4(6)(75)}}{2(6)} = \dfrac{50 \pm \sqrt{700}}{12}$

$= \dfrac{50 \pm 10\sqrt{7}}{12} = \dfrac{25 \pm 5\sqrt{7}}{6}$.

These solutions are approximately $x \approx 1.962$ and $x \approx 6.371$, so the critical point in the appropriate domain occurs at

$x = \dfrac{25 - 5\sqrt{7}}{6}$.

52.

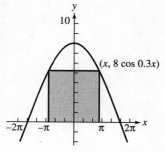

For $0 < x < \dfrac{5\pi}{3}$, the area of the rectangle is given by

$A(x) = (2x)(8\cos 0.3x) = 16x\cos 0.3x$.

Then $A'(x) = 16x(-0.3\sin 0.3x) + 16(\cos 0.3x)(1)$

$\qquad\qquad = 16(\cos 0.3x - 0.3x\sin 0.3x)$

Solving $A'(x) = 0$ graphically, we find that the critical

point occurs at $x \approx 2.868$ and the corresponding area is

approximately 29.925 square units.

53. The cost (in thousands of dollars) is given by

$C(x) = 40x + 30(20 - y) = 40x + 600 - 30\sqrt{x^2 - 144}$.

Then $C'(x) = 40 - \dfrac{30}{2\sqrt{x^2 - 144}}(2x) = 40 - \dfrac{30x}{\sqrt{x^2 - 144}}$.

Solving $C'(x) = 0$, we have:

$\dfrac{30x}{\sqrt{x^2 - 144}} = 40$

$\qquad 3x = 4\sqrt{x^2 - 144}$

$\qquad 9x^2 = 16x^2 - 2304$

$\qquad 2304 = 7x^2$

Choose the positive solution:

$x = +\dfrac{48}{\sqrt{7}} \approx 18.142$ mi

$y = \sqrt{x^2 - 12^2} = \dfrac{36}{\sqrt{7}} \approx 13.607$ mi

54. The length of the track is given by $2x + 2\pi r$, so we have

$2x + 2\pi r = 400$ and therefore $x = 200 - \pi r$. Then the area

of the rectangle is

$\qquad A(r) = 2rx$

$\qquad\qquad = 2r(200 - \pi r)$

$\qquad\qquad = 400r - 2\pi r^2$, for $0 < r < \dfrac{200}{\pi}$.

Therefore, $A'(r) = 400 - 4\pi r$ and $A''(r) = -4\pi$, so the

critical point occurs at $r = \dfrac{100}{\pi}$ m

and this point corresponds to the maximum rectangle area

because $A''(r) < 0$ for all r.

The corresponding value of x is

$x = 200 - \pi\left(\dfrac{100}{\pi}\right) = 100$ m.

The rectangle will have the largest possible area when

$x = 100$ m and $r = \dfrac{100}{\pi}$ m.

55. Assume the profit is k dollars per hundred grade B tires and

$2k$ dollars per hundred grade A tires.

Then the profit is given by

$\qquad P(x) = 2kx + k \cdot \dfrac{40 - 10x}{5 - x}$

$\qquad\qquad = 2k \cdot \dfrac{(20 - 5x) + x(5 - x)}{5 - x}$

$\qquad\qquad = 2k \cdot \dfrac{20 - x^2}{5 - x}$

$\qquad P'(x) = 2k \cdot \dfrac{(5 - x)(-2x) - (20 - x^2)(-1)}{(5 - x)^2}$

$\qquad\qquad = 2k \cdot \dfrac{x^2 - 10x + 20}{(5 - x)^2}$

The solutions of $P'(x) = 0$ are

$x = \dfrac{10 \pm \sqrt{(-10)^2 - 4(1)(20)}}{2(1)} = 5 \pm \sqrt{5}$, so the solution in

the appropriate domain is $x = 5 - \sqrt{5} \approx 2.76$.

Check the profit for the critical point and endpoints:

Critical point: $x \approx 2.76$ $P(x) \approx 11.06k$
Endpoints: $x = 0$ $P(x) = 8k$
    $x = 4$ $P(x) = 8k$

The highest profit is obtained when $x \approx 2.76$ and $y \approx 5.53$,

which corresponds to

276 grade A tires and 553 grade B tires.

56. (a) The distance between the particles is $|f(t)|$ where

$$f(t) = -\cos t + \cos\left(t + \frac{\pi}{4}\right).$$ Then

$$f'(t) = \sin t - \sin\left(t + \frac{\pi}{4}\right)$$

Solving $f'(t) = 0$ graphically, we obtain $t \approx 1.178$, $t \approx 4.230$, and so on.

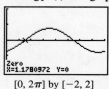

[0, 2π] by [−2, 2]

Alternatively, $f'(t) = 0$ may be solved analytically as follows.

$$f'(t) = \sin\left[\left(t + \frac{\pi}{8}\right) - \frac{\pi}{8}\right] - \sin\left[\left(t + \frac{\pi}{8}\right) + \frac{\pi}{8}\right]$$

$$= \left[\sin\left(t + \frac{\pi}{8}\right)\cos\frac{\pi}{8} - \cos\left(t + \frac{\pi}{8}\right)\sin\frac{\pi}{8}\right] - \left[\sin\left(t + \frac{\pi}{8}\right)\cos\frac{\pi}{8} + \cos\left(t + \frac{\pi}{8}\right)\sin\frac{\pi}{8}\right]$$

$$= -2\sin\frac{\pi}{8}\cos\left(t + \frac{\pi}{8}\right),$$

so the critical points occur when

$$\cos\left(t + \frac{\pi}{8}\right) = 0, \text{ or } t = \frac{3\pi}{8} + k\pi. \text{ At each of these values,}$$

$$f(t) = \pm 2\cos\frac{3\pi}{8} \approx \pm 0.765 \text{ units, so the maximum distance between}$$

the particles is 0.765 units.

(b) Solving $\cos t = \cos\left(t + \frac{\pi}{4}\right)$ graphically, we obtain $t \approx 2.749$, $t \approx 5.890$, and so on.

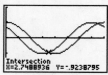

[0, 2π] by [−2, 2]

Alternatively, this problem may be solved analytically as follows.

$$\cos t = \cos\left(t + \frac{\pi}{4}\right)$$

$$\cos\left[\left(t + \frac{\pi}{8}\right) - \frac{\pi}{8}\right] = \cos\left[\left(t + \frac{\pi}{8}\right) + \frac{\pi}{8}\right]$$

$$\cos\left(t + \frac{\pi}{8}\right)\cos\frac{\pi}{8} + \sin\left(t + \frac{\pi}{8}\right)\sin\frac{\pi}{8} = \cos\left(t + \frac{\pi}{8}\right)\cos\frac{\pi}{8} - \sin\left(t + \frac{\pi}{8}\right)\sin\frac{\pi}{8}$$

$$2\sin\left(t + \frac{\pi}{8}\right)\sin\frac{\pi}{8} = 0$$

$$\sin\left(t + \frac{\pi}{8}\right) = 0$$

$$t = \frac{7\pi}{8} + k\pi$$

The particles collide when $t = \frac{7\pi}{8} \approx 2.749$ (plus multiples of π if they keep going.)

57. The dimensions will be x in. by $10 - 2x$ in. by $16 - 2x$ in., so $V(x) = x(10 - 2x)(16 - 2x) = 4x^3 - 52x^2 + 160x$ for $0 < x < 5$.

Then $V'(x) = 12x^2 - 104x + 160 = 4(x - 2)(3x - 20)$, so the critical point in the correct domain is $x = 2$.

This critical point corresponds to the maximum possible volume because $V'(x) > 0$ for $0 < x < 2$ and $V'(x) < 0$ for $2 < x < 5$. The box of largest volume has a height of 2 in. and a base measuring 6 in. by 12 in., and its volume is 144 in^3.

Graphical support:

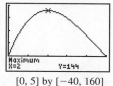

[0, 5] by [−40, 160]

58. Step 1:
r = radius of circle
A = area of circle

Step 2:

At the instant in question, $\dfrac{dr}{dt} = -\dfrac{2}{\pi}$ m/sec and $r = 10$ m.

Step 3:

We want to find $\dfrac{dA}{dt}$.

Step 4:

$A = \pi r^2$

Step 5:

$\dfrac{dA}{dt} = 2\pi r \dfrac{dr}{dt}$

Step 6:

$\dfrac{dA}{dt} = 2\pi(10)\left(-\dfrac{2}{\pi}\right) = -40$

The area is changing at the rate of -40 m^2/sec.

59. Step 1:
x = x-coordinate of particle
y = y-coordinate of particle
D = distance from origin to particle

Step 2:

At the instant in question, $x = 5$ m, $y = 12$ m,

$\dfrac{dx}{dt} = -1$ m/sec, and $\dfrac{dy}{dt} = -5$ m/sec.

Step 3:

We want to find $\dfrac{dD}{dt}$.

Step 4:

$D = \sqrt{x^2 + y^2}$

Step 5:

$\dfrac{dD}{dt} = \dfrac{1}{2\sqrt{x^2 + y^2}}\left(2x\dfrac{dx}{dt} + 2y\dfrac{dy}{dt}\right) = \dfrac{x\dfrac{dx}{dt} + y\dfrac{dy}{dt}}{\sqrt{x^2 + y^2}}$

Step 6:

$\dfrac{dD}{dt} = \dfrac{(5)(-1) + (12)(-5)}{\sqrt{5^2 + 12^2}} = -5$ m/sec

Since $\dfrac{dD}{dt}$ is negative, the particle is *approaching* the origin at the *positive* rate of 5 m/sec.

60. Step 1:
x = edge of length of cube
V = volume of cube

Step 2:

At the instant in question,

$\dfrac{dV}{dt} = 1200$ cm^3/min and $x = 20$ cm.

Step 3:

We want to find $\dfrac{dx}{dt}$.

Step 4:

$V = x^3$

Step 5:

$\dfrac{dV}{dt} = 3x^2\dfrac{dx}{dt}$

Step 6:

$1200 = 3(20)^2\dfrac{dx}{dt}$

$\dfrac{dx}{dt} = 1$ cm/min

The edge length is increasing at the rate of 1 cm/min.

61. Step 1:

x = x-coordinate of point

y = y-coordinate of point

D = distance from origin to point

Step 2:

At the instant in question, $x = 3$ and $\dfrac{dD}{dt} = 11$ units per sec.

Step 3:

We want to find $\dfrac{dx}{dt}$.

Step 4:

Since $D^2 = x^2 + y^2$ and $y = x^{3/2}$, we have

$D = \sqrt{x^2 + x^3}$ for $x \geq 0$.

Step 5:

$$\dfrac{dD}{dt} = \dfrac{1}{2\sqrt{x^2 + x^3}}(2x + 3x^2)\dfrac{dx}{dt}$$

$$= \dfrac{2x + 3x^2}{2x\sqrt{1 + x}}\dfrac{dx}{dt} = \dfrac{3x + 2}{2\sqrt{1 + x}}\dfrac{dx}{dt}$$

Step 6:

$$11 = \dfrac{3(3) + 2}{2\sqrt{4}}\dfrac{dx}{dt}$$

$$\dfrac{dx}{dt} = 4 \text{ units per sec}$$

62. (a) Since $\dfrac{h}{r} = \dfrac{10}{4}$, we may write $h = \dfrac{5r}{2}$ or $r = \dfrac{2h}{5}$.

(b) Step 1:

h = depth of water in tank

r = radius of surface of water

V = volume of water in tank

Step 2:

At the instant in question,

$\dfrac{dV}{dt} = -5$ ft^3/min and $h = 6$ ft.

Step 3:

We want to find $-\dfrac{dh}{dt}$.

Step 4:

$$V = \dfrac{1}{3}\pi r^2 h = \dfrac{4}{75}\pi h^3$$

Step 5:

$$\dfrac{dV}{dt} = \dfrac{4}{25}\pi h^2 \dfrac{dh}{dt}$$

Step 6:

$$-5 = \dfrac{4}{25}\pi(6)^2\dfrac{dh}{dt}$$

$$\dfrac{dh}{dt} = -\dfrac{125}{144\pi} \approx -0.276 \text{ ft/min}$$

Since $\dfrac{dh}{dt}$ is negative, the water level is *dropping* at the

positive rate of ≈ 0.276 ft/min.

63. Step 1:

r = radius of outer layer of cable on the spool

θ = clockwise angle turned by spool

s = length of cable that has been unwound

Step 2:

At the instant in question, $\dfrac{ds}{dt} = 6$ ft/sec and $r = 1.2$ ft

Step 3:

We want to find $\dfrac{d\theta}{dt}$.

Step 4:

$s = r\theta$

Step 5:

Since r is essentially constant, $\dfrac{ds}{dt} = r\dfrac{d\theta}{dt}$.

Step 6:

$$6 = 1.2\dfrac{d\theta}{dt}$$

$$\dfrac{d\theta}{dt} = 5 \text{ radians/sec}$$

The spool is turning at the rate of 5 radians per second.

64. $a(t) = v'(t) = -g = -32$ ft/sec^2

Since $v(0) = 32$ ft/sec, $v(t) = s'(t) = -32t + 32$.

Since $s(0) = -17$ ft, $s(t) = -16t^2 + 32t - 17$.

The shovelful of dirt reaches its maximum height when

$v(t) = 0$, at $t = 1$ sec. Since $s(1) = -1$, the shovelful of dirt

is still below ground level at this time. There was not

enough speed to get the dirt out of the hole. Duck!

65. We have $V = \dfrac{1}{3}\pi r^2 h$, so $\dfrac{dV}{dr} = \dfrac{2}{3}\pi rh$ and $dV = \dfrac{2}{3}\pi rh\, dr$.

When the radius changes from a to $a + dr$, the volume

change is approximately $dV = \dfrac{2}{3}\pi ah\, dr$.

66. (a) Let x = edge of length of cube and S = surface area of

cube. Then $S = 6x^2$, which means $\dfrac{dS}{dx} = 12x$ and

$dS = 12x\, dx$. We want $|dS| \leq 0.02S$, which gives

$|12x\, dx| \leq 0.02(6x^2)$ or $|dx| \leq 0.01x$. The edge should

be measured with an error of no more than 1%.

(b) Let V = volume of cube. Then $V = x^3$, which means

$\dfrac{dV}{dx} = 3x^2$ and $dV = 3x^2\, dx$. We have $|dx| \leq 0.01x$,

which means $|3x^2\, dx| \leq 3x^2(0.01x) = 0.03V$,

so $|dV| \leq 0.03V$. The volume calculation will be

accurate to within approximately 3% of the correct

volume.

67. Let C = circumference, r = radius, S = surface area, and V = volume.

(a) Since $C = 2\pi r$, we have $\dfrac{dC}{dr} = 2\pi$ and so $dC = 2\pi\, dr$.

Therefore, $\left|\dfrac{dC}{C}\right| = \left|\dfrac{2\pi\, dr}{2\pi r}\right| = \left|\dfrac{dr}{r}\right| < \dfrac{0.4\text{ cm}}{10\text{ cm}} = 0.04$ The calculated radius will be within approximately 4% of the correct radius.

(b) Since $S = 4\pi r^2$, we have $\dfrac{dS}{dr} = 8\pi r$ and so

$dS = 8\pi r\, dr$. Therefore, $\left|\dfrac{dS}{S}\right| = \left|\dfrac{8\pi r\, dr}{4\pi r^2}\right|$

$= \left|\dfrac{2\, dr}{r}\right| \le 2(0.04) = 0.08$. The calculated surface area will be within approximately 8% of the correct surface area.

(c) Since $V = \dfrac{4}{3}\pi r^3$, we have $\dfrac{dV}{dr} = 4\pi r^2$ and so

$dV = 4\pi r^2\, dr$. Therefore $\left|\dfrac{dV}{V}\right| = \left|\dfrac{4\pi r^2\, dr}{\frac{4}{3}\pi r^3}\right| = \left|\dfrac{3\, dr}{r}\right| \le 3(0.04) = 0.12$.

The calculated volume will be within approximately 12% of the correct volume.

68. By similar triangles, we have $\dfrac{a}{6} = \dfrac{a+20}{h}$, which gives $ah = 6a + 120$, or $h = 6 + 120a^{-1}$. The height of the lamp post is

approximately $6 + 120(15)^{-1} = 14$ ft. The estimated error in measuring a was $|da| \le 1$ in. $= \dfrac{1}{12}$ ft. Since $\dfrac{dh}{da} = -120a^{-2}$, we

have $|dh| = \left|-120a^{-2}\, da\right| \le 120(15)^{-2}\left(\dfrac{1}{12}\right) = \dfrac{2}{45}$ ft, so the estimated possible error is $\pm\dfrac{2}{45}$ ft or $\pm\dfrac{8}{15}$ in.

69. $\dfrac{dy}{dx} = 2\sin x\cos x - 3$. Since $\sin x$ and $\cos x$ are both between 1 and -1, the value of $2\sin x\cos x$ is never greater than 2.

Therefore, $\dfrac{dy}{dx} \le 2 - 3 = -1$ for all values of x.

Since $\dfrac{dy}{dx}$ is always negative, the function decreases on every interval.

Chapter 5
The Definite Integral

■ Section 5.1 Estimating with Finite Sums
(pp. 247–257)

Exploration 1   Which RAM is the Biggest?

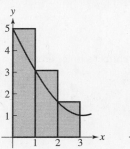 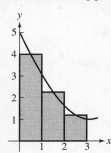 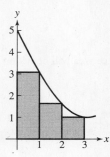

1. LRAM > MRAM > RRAM

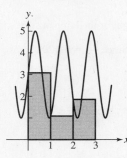 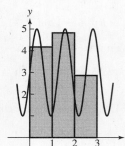 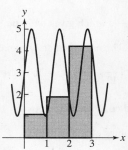

2. MRAM > RRAM > LRAM

3. RRAM > MRAM > LRAM, because the heights of the rectangles increase as you move toward the right under an increasing function.

4. LRAM > MRAM > RRAM, because the heights of the rectangles decrease as you move toward the right under a decreasing function.

Quick Review 5.1

1. 80 mph · 5 hr = 400 mi

2. 48 mph · 3 hr = 144 mi

3. 10 ft/sec^2 · 10 sec = 100 ft/sec

$100 \text{ ft/sec} \cdot \dfrac{1 \text{ mi}}{5280 \text{ ft}} \cdot \dfrac{3600 \text{ sec}}{1 \text{ h}} \approx 68.18 \text{ mph}$

4. $300{,}000 \text{ km/sec} \cdot \dfrac{3600 \text{ sec}}{1 \text{ hr}} \cdot \dfrac{24 \text{ hr}}{1 \text{ day}} \cdot \dfrac{365 \text{ days}}{1 \text{ yr}} \cdot 1 \text{ yr}$
$\approx 9.46 \times 10^{12} \text{ km}$

5. (6 mph)(3 h) + (5 mph)(2 h) = 18 mi + 10 mi = 28 mi

6. $20 \text{ gal/min} \cdot 1 \text{ h} \cdot \dfrac{60 \text{ min}}{1 \text{ h}} = 1200 \text{ gal}$

7. (−1°C/h)(12 h) + (1.5°C)(6 h) = −3°C

8. $300 \text{ ft}^3/\text{sec} \cdot \dfrac{3600 \text{ sec}}{1 \text{ h}} \cdot \dfrac{24 \text{ h}}{1 \text{ day}} \cdot 1 \text{ day} = 25{,}920{,}000 \text{ ft}^3$

9. 350 people/mi^2 · 50 mi^2 = 17,500 people

10. $70 \text{ times/sec} \cdot \dfrac{3600 \text{ sec}}{1 \text{ h}} \cdot 1 \text{ h} \cdot 0.7 = 176{,}400 \text{ times}$

Section 5.1 Exercises

1. (a)

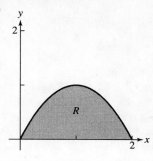

(b)

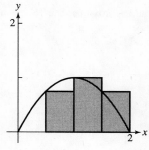

$\Delta x = \dfrac{1}{2}$

LRAM: $[2(0) - (0)^2]\left(\dfrac{1}{2}\right) + \left[2\left(\dfrac{1}{2}\right) - \left(\dfrac{1}{2}\right)^2\right]\left(\dfrac{1}{2}\right) + [2(1) - (1)^2]\left(\dfrac{1}{2}\right) + \left[2\left(\dfrac{3}{2}\right) - \left(\dfrac{3}{2}\right)^2\right]\left(\dfrac{1}{2}\right) = \dfrac{5}{4} = 1.25$

2. (a)

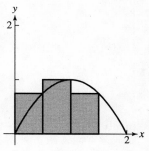

RRAM: $\left[2\left(\dfrac{1}{2}\right) - \left(\dfrac{1}{2}\right)^2\right]\left(\dfrac{1}{2}\right) + [2(1) - (1)^2]\left(\dfrac{1}{2}\right) + \left[2\left(\dfrac{3}{2}\right) - \left(\dfrac{3}{2}\right)^2\right]\left(\dfrac{1}{2}\right) + [2(2) - (2)^2]\left(\dfrac{1}{2}\right) = \dfrac{5}{4} = 1.25$

(b)

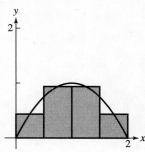

MRAM: $\left[2\left(\dfrac{1}{4}\right) - \left(\dfrac{1}{4}\right)^2\right]\left(\dfrac{1}{2}\right) + \left[2\left(\dfrac{3}{4}\right) - \left(\dfrac{3}{4}\right)^2\right]\left(\dfrac{1}{2}\right) + \left[2\left(\dfrac{5}{4}\right) - \left(\dfrac{5}{4}\right)^2\right]\left(\dfrac{1}{2}\right) + \left[2\left(\dfrac{7}{4}\right) - \left(\dfrac{7}{4}\right)^2\right]\left(\dfrac{1}{2}\right) = \dfrac{11}{8} = 1.375$

3.

n	LRAM_n	MRAM_n	RRAM_n
10	1.32	1.34	1.32
50	1.3328	1.3336	1.3328
100	1.3332	1.3334	1.3332
500	1.333328	1.333336	1.333328

4. The area is $1.\overline{333} = \dfrac{4}{3}$.

5.

n	LRAM_n	MRAM_n	RRAM_n
10	12.645	13.4775	14.445
50	13.3218	13.4991	13.6818
100	13.41045	13.499775	13.59045
500	13.482018	13.499991	13.518018

Estimate the area to be 13.5.

6.

n	LRAM_n	MRAM_n	RRAM_n
10	1.16823	1.09714	1.03490
50	1.11206	1.09855	1.08540
100	1.10531	1.09860	1.09198
500	1.09995	1.09861	1.09728
1000	1.09928	1.09861	1.09795

Estimate the area to be 1.0986.

7.

n	LRAM_n	MRAM_n	RRAM_n
10	0.98001	0.88220	0.78367
50	0.90171	0.88209	0.86244
100	0.89190	0.88208	0.87226
500	0.88404	0.88208	0.88012
1000	0.88306	0.88208	0.88110

Estimate the area to be 0.8821.

8.

n	LRAM_n	MRAM_n	RRAM_n
10	1.98352	2.00825	1.98352
50	1.99934	2.00033	1.99934
100	1.99984	2.00008	1.99984
500	1.99999	2.00000	1.99999

Estimate the area to be 2.

9. LRAM:
Area
$\approx f(2) \cdot 2 + f(4) \cdot 2 + f(6) \cdot 2 + \cdots + f(22) \cdot 2$
$= 2 \cdot (0 + 0.6 + 1.4 + \cdots + 0.5)$
$= 44.8 \ (\text{mg/L}) \cdot \sec$
RRAM:
Area
$\approx f(4) \cdot 2 + f(6) \cdot 2 + f(8) \cdot 2 + \cdots + f(24) \cdot 2$
$= 2(0.6 + 1.4 + 2.7 + \cdots + 0)$
$= 44.8 \ (\text{mg/L}) \cdot \sec$

Patient's cardiac output:

$\dfrac{5 \ \text{mg}}{44.8 \ (\text{mg/L}) \cdot \sec} \cdot \dfrac{60 \ \sec}{1 \ \text{min}} \approx 6.7 \ \text{L/min}$

Note that estimates for the area may vary.

10. (a) LRAM: $1 \cdot (0 + 12 + 22 + 10 + 5 + 13 + 11 + 6 + 2 + 6) = 87 \ \text{in.} = 7.25 \ \text{ft}$

   (b) RRAM: $1 \cdot (12 + 22 + 10 + 5 + 13 + 11 + 6 + 2 + 6 + 0) = 87 \ \text{in.} = 7.25 \ \text{ft}$

11. 5 min = 300 sec

   (a) LRAM: $300 \cdot (1 + 1.2 + 1.7 + \cdots + 1.2) = 5220 \ \text{m}$

   (b) RRAM: $300 \cdot (1.2 + 1.7 + 2.0 + \cdots + 0) = 4920 \ \text{m}$

12. LRAM: $10 \cdot (0 + 44 + 15 + \cdots + 30) = 3490 \ \text{ft}$

   RRAM: $10 \cdot (44 + 15 + 35 + \cdots + 35) = 3840 \ \text{ft}$

   $\text{Average} = \dfrac{3490 \ \text{ft} + 3840 \ \text{ft}}{2} = 3665 \ \text{ft}$

13. (a) LRAM: $0.001(0 + 40 + 62 + \cdots + 137) = 0.898 \ \text{mi}$
   RRAM: $0.001(40 + 62 + 82 + \cdots + 142) = 1.04 \ \text{mi}$
   Average = 0.969 mi

   (b) The halfway point is 0.4845 mi. The average of LRAM and RRAM is 0.4460 at 0.006 h and 0.5665 at 0.007 h. Estimate that it took 0.006 h = 21.6 sec. The car was going 116 mph.

14. Use $f(x) = \sqrt{25 - x^2}$ and approximate the volume using $\pi r^2 h = \pi(\sqrt{25 - n_i^2})^2 \Delta x$, so for the MRAM program, use $\pi(25 - x^2)$ on the interval $[-5, 5]$.

n	MRAM
10	526.21677
20	524.25327
40	523.76240
80	523.63968
160	523.60900

15. $V = \dfrac{4}{3}\pi(5)^3 = \dfrac{500\pi}{3} \approx 523.59878$

n	error	% error
10	2.61799	0.5
20	0.65450	0.125
40	0.16362	0.0312
80	0.04091	0.0078
160	0.01023	0.0020

16. (a) Use LRAM with $\pi(16 - x^2)$.
   $S_8 \approx 146.08406$
   S_8 is an overestimate because each rectangle is above the curve.

   (b) $\dfrac{|V \cdot S_8|}{V} \approx 0.09 = 9\%$

17. (a) Use RRAM with $\pi(16 - x^2)$.
   $S_8 \approx 120.95132$
   S_8 is an underestimate because each rectangle is below the curve.

   (b) $\dfrac{|V - S_8|}{V} \approx 0.10 = 10\%$

18. (a) Use LRAM with $\pi(64 - x^2)$ on the interval $[4, 8]$, $n = 8$.
   $S \approx 372.27873 \ \text{m}^3$

   (b) $\dfrac{|V - S8|}{V} \approx 0.11 = 11\%$

19. (a) $(5)(6.0 + 8.2 + 9.1 + \cdots + 12.7)(30) \approx 15{,}465 \ \text{ft}^3$

   (b) $(5)(8.2 + 9.1 + 9.9 + \cdots + 13.0)(30) \approx 16{,}515 \ \text{ft}^3$

20. Use LRAM with πx on the interval $[0, 5]$, $n = 5$.
   $1(0 + \pi + 2\pi + 3\pi + 4\pi) = 10\pi \approx 31.41593$

21. Use MRAM with πx on the interval $[0, 5]$, $n = 5$.

$$1\left(\frac{1}{2}\pi + \frac{3}{2}\pi + \frac{5}{2}\pi + \frac{7}{2}\pi + \frac{9}{2}\pi\right) = \frac{25}{2}\pi \approx 39.26991$$

22. (a) LRAM$_5$:
   $32.00 + 19.41 + 11.77 + 7.14 + 4.33 = 74.65$ ft/sec

   (b) RRAM$_5$:
   $19.41 + 11.77 + 7.14 + 4.33 + 2.63 = 45.28$ ft/sec

   (c) The upper estimates for speed are 32.00 ft/sec for the first sec, $32.00 + 19.41 = 51.41$ ft/sec for the second sec, and $32.00 + 19.41 + 11.77 = 63.18$ ft/sec for the third sec. Therefore, an upper estimate for the distance fallen is $32.00 + 51.41 + 63.18 = 146.59$ ft.

23. (a) 400 ft/sec $-$ (5 sec)(32 ft/sec^2) $= 240$ ft/sec

   (b) Use RRAM with $400 - 32x$ on $[0, 5]$, $n = 5$.
   $368 + 336 + 304 + 272 + 240 = 1520$ ft

24. (a) Upper $= 70 + 97 + 136 + 190 + 265 = 758$ gal
   Lower $= 50 + 70 + 97 + 136 + 190 = 543$ gal

   (b) Upper $= 70 + 97 + 136 + 190 + 265 + 369 + 516$
   $+ 720 = 2363$ gal
   Lower $= 50 + 70 + 97 + 136 + 190 + 265 + 369$
   $+ 516 = 1693$ gal

   (c) $25{,}000 - 2363 = 22{,}637$ gal

   $\dfrac{22{,}637}{720} \approx 31.44$ h (worst case)

   $25{,}000 - 1693 = 23{,}307$ gal

   $\dfrac{23{,}307}{720} \approx 32.37$ h (best case)

25. (a) Since the release rate of pollutants is increasing, an upper estimate is given by using the data for the end of each month (right rectangles), assuming that new scrubbers were installed before the beginning of January. Upper estimate:
   $30(0.20 + 0.25 + 0.27 + 0.34 + 0.45 + 0.52)$
   ≈ 60.9 tons of pollutants
   A lower estimate is given by using the data for the end of the previous month (left rectangles). We have no data for the beginning of January, but we know that pollutants were released at the new-scrubber rate of 0.05 ton/day, so we may use this value.
   Lower estimate:
   $30(0.05 + 0.20 + 0.25 + 0.27 + 0.34 + 0.45)$
   ≈ 46.8 tons of pollutants

   (b) Using left rectangles, the amount of pollutants released by the end of October is
   $30(0.05 + 0.20 + 0.25 + 0.27 + 0.34 + 0.45$
   $+ 0.52 + 0.63 + 0.70 + 0.81) \approx 126.6$ tons.
   Therefore, a total of 125 tons will have been released into the atmosphere by the end of October.

26. The area of the region is the total number of units sold, in millions, over the 10-year period. The area units are (millions of units per year)(years) = (millions of units).

27. (a) The diagonal of the square has length 2, so the side length is $\sqrt{2}$. Area $= (\sqrt{2})^2 = 2$

   (b) Think of the octagon as a collection of 16 right triangles with a hypotenuse of length 1 and an acute angle measuring $\dfrac{2\pi}{16} = \dfrac{\pi}{8}$.
   Area $= 16\left(\dfrac{1}{2}\right)\left(\sin\dfrac{\pi}{8}\right)\left(\cos\dfrac{\pi}{8}\right)$
   $= 4 \sin\dfrac{\pi}{4}$
   $= 2\sqrt{2} \approx 2.828$

   (c) Think of the 16-gon as a collection of 32 right triangles with a hypotenuse of length 1 and an acute angle measuring $\dfrac{2\pi}{32} = \dfrac{\pi}{16}$.
   Area $= 32\left(\dfrac{1}{2}\right)\left(\sin\dfrac{\pi}{16}\right)\left(\cos\dfrac{\pi}{16}\right)$
   $= 8 \sin\dfrac{\pi}{8} \approx 3.061$

   (d) Each area is less than the area of the circle, π. As n increases, the area approaches π.

28. The statement is false. We disprove it by presenting a counterexample, the function $f(x) = x^2$ over the interval $0 \le x \le 1$, with $n = 1$. MRAM$_1 = 1f(0.5) = 0.25$
   $\dfrac{\text{LRAM}_1 + \text{RRAM}_1}{2} = \dfrac{1f(0) + 1f(1)}{2}$
   $= \dfrac{0 + 1}{2} = 0.5 \ne \text{MRAM}_1$

29. $\text{RRAM}_n f = (\Delta x)[f(x_1) + f(x_2) + \cdots + f(x_{n-1}) + f(x_n)]$
   $= (\Delta x)[f(x_0) + f(x_1) + f(x_2) + \cdots + f(x_{n-1})]$
   $+ (\Delta x)[f(x_n) - f(x_0)]$
   $= \text{LRAM}_n f + (\Delta x)[f(x_n) - f(x_0)]$
   But $f(a) = f(b)$ by symmetry, so $f(x_n) - f(x_0) = 0$. Therefore, $\text{RRAM}_n f = \text{LRAM}_n f$.

30. (a) Each of the isosceles triangles is made up of two right triangles having hypotenuse 1 and an acute angle measuring $\dfrac{2\pi}{2n} = \dfrac{\pi}{n}$. The area of each isosceles triangle is $A_T = 2\left(\dfrac{1}{2}\right)\left(\sin\dfrac{\pi}{n}\right)\left(\cos\dfrac{\pi}{n}\right) = \dfrac{1}{2}\sin\dfrac{2\pi}{n}$.

   (b) The area of the polygon is
   $A_P = nA_T = \dfrac{n}{2}\sin\dfrac{2\pi}{n}$, so
   $\lim_{n\to\infty} A_P = \lim_{n\to\infty} \dfrac{n}{2}\sin\dfrac{2\pi}{n} = \pi$

   (c) Multiply each area by r^2:
   $A_T = \dfrac{1}{2}r^2 \sin\dfrac{2\pi}{n}$
   $A_P = \dfrac{n}{2}r^2 \sin\dfrac{2\pi}{n}$
   $\lim_{n\to\infty} A_P = \pi r^2$

■ Section 5.2 Definite Integrals

(pp. 258–268)

Exploration 1   Finding Integrals by Signed Areas

1. -2. (This is the same area as $\int_0^\pi \sin x \, dx$, but below the x-axis.)

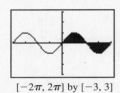

$[-2\pi, 2\pi]$ by $[-3, 3]$

2. 0. (The equal areas above and below the x-axis sum to zero.)

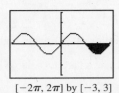

$[-2\pi, 2\pi]$ by $[-3, 3]$

3. 1. (This is half the area of $\int_0^\pi \sin x \, dx$.)

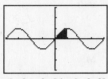

$[-2\pi, 2\pi]$ by $[-3, 3]$

4. $2\pi + 2$. (The same area as $\int_0^\pi \sin x \, dx$ sits above a rectangle of area $\pi \times 2$.)

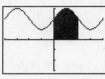

$[-2\pi, 2\pi]$ by $[-3, 3]$

5. 4. (Each rectangle in a typical Riemann sum is twice as tall as in $\int_0^\pi \sin x \, dx$.)

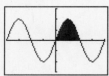

$[-2\pi, 2\pi]$ by $[-3, 3]$

6. 2. (This is the same region as in $\int_0^\pi \sin x \, dx$, translated 2 units to the right.)

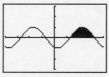

$[-2\pi, 2\pi]$ by $[-3, 3]$

7. 0. (The equal areas above and below the x-axis sum to zero.)

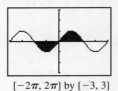

$[-2\pi, 2\pi]$ by $[-3, 3]$

8. 4. (Each rectangle in a typical Riemann sum is twice as wide as in $\int_0^\pi \sin x \, dx$.)

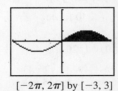

$[-2\pi, 2\pi]$ by $[-3, 3]$

9. 0. (The equal areas above and below the x-axis sum to zero.)

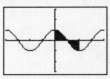

$[-2\pi, 2\pi]$ by $[-3, 3]$

10. 0. (The equal areas above and below the x-axis sum to zero, since $\sin x$ is an odd function.)

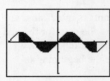

$[-2\pi, 2\pi]$ by $[-3, 3]$

Exploration 2   More Discontinuous Integrands

1. The function has a removable discontinuity at $x = 2$.

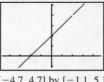

$[-4.7, 4.7]$ by $[-1.1, 5.1]$

2. The thin strip above $x = 2$ has zero area, so the area under the curve is the same as $\int_0^3 (x + 2) \, dx$, which is 10.5.

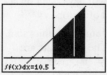

∫f(x)dx=10.5

$[-4.7, 4.7]$ by $[-1.1, 5.1]$

3. The graph has jump discontinuities at all integer values, but the Riemann sums tend to the area of the shaded region shown. The area is the sum of the areas of 5 rectangles (one of them with height 0):

$$\int_0^5 \text{int}(x)\, dx = 0 + 1 + 2 + 3 + 4 = 10.$$

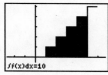

[−2.7, 6.7] by [−1.1, 5.1]

Quick Review 5.2

1. $\sum_{n=1}^{5} n^2 = (1)^2 + (2)^2 + (3)^2 + (4)^2 + (5)^2 = 55$

2. $\sum_{k=0}^{4} (3k - 2) = [3(0) - 2] + [3(1) - 2] + [3(2) - 2]$
$$+ [3(3) - 2] + [3(4) - 2] = 20$$

3. $\sum_{j=0}^{4} 100(j + 1)^2 = 100[(1)^2 + (2)^2 + (3)^2 + (4)^2 + (5)^2]$
$$= 5500$$

4. $\sum_{k=1}^{99} k$

5. $\sum_{k=0}^{25} 2k$

6. $\sum_{k=1}^{500} 3k^2$

7. $2\sum_{x=1}^{50} x^2 + 3\sum_{x=1}^{50} x = \sum_{x=1}^{50} (2x^2 + 3x)$

8. $\sum_{k=0}^{8} x^k + \sum_{k=9}^{20} x^k = \sum_{k=0}^{20} x^k$

9. $\sum_{k=0}^{n} (-1)^k = 0$ if n is odd.

10. $\sum_{k=0}^{n} (-1)^k = 1$ if n is even.

Section 5.2 Exercises

1. $\lim_{\|P\|\to 0} \sum_{k=1}^{n} c_k^2 \Delta x_k = \int_0^2 x^2\, dx$ where P is any partition of [0, 2].

2. $\lim_{\|P\|\to 0} \sum_{k=1}^{n} (c_k^2 - 3c_k)\Delta x_k = \int_{-7}^5 (x^2 - 3x)\, dx$ where P is any partition of [−7, 5].

3. $\lim_{\|P\|\to 0} \sum_{k=1}^{n} \frac{1}{c_k}\Delta x_k = \int_1^4 \frac{1}{x}\, dx$ where P is any partition of [1, 4].

4. $\lim_{\|P\|\to 0} \sum_{k=1}^{n} \frac{1}{1 - c_k}\Delta x_k = \int_2^3 \frac{1}{1 - x}\, dx$ where P is any partition of [2, 3].

5. $\lim_{\|P\|\to 0} \sum_{k=1}^{n} \sqrt{4 - c_k^2}\,\Delta x_k = \int_0^1 \sqrt{4 - x^2}\, dx$ where P is any partition of [0, 1].

6. $\lim_{\|P\|\to 0} \sum_{k=1}^{n} (\sin^3 c_k)\Delta x_k = \int_{-\pi}^{\pi} \sin^3 x\, dx$ where P is any partition of $[-\pi, \pi]$.

7. $\int_{-2}^1 5\, dx = 5[1 - (-2)] = 15$

8. $\int_3^7 (-20)\, dx = (-20)(7 - 3) = -80$

9. $\int_0^3 (-160)\, dt = (-160)(3 - 0) = -480$

10. $\int_{-4}^{-1} \frac{\pi}{2}\, d\theta = \frac{\pi}{2}[-1 - (-4)] = \frac{3\pi}{2}$

11. $\int_{-2.1}^{3.4} 0.5\, ds = 0.5[3.4 - (-2.1)] = 2.75$

12. $\int_{\sqrt{2}}^{\sqrt{18}} \sqrt{2}\, dr = \sqrt{2}(\sqrt{18} - \sqrt{2}) = 4$

13. Graph the region under $y = \frac{x}{2} + 3$ for $-2 \le x \le 4$.

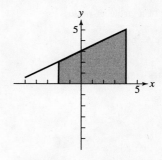

$$\int_{-2}^4 \left(\frac{x}{2} + 3\right) dx = \frac{1}{2}(6)(2 + 5) = 21$$

14. Graph the region under $y = -2x + 4$ for $\frac{1}{2} \le x \le \frac{3}{2}$.

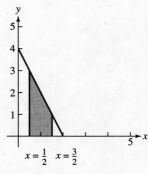

$$\int_{1/2}^{3/2} (-2x + 4)\, dx = \frac{1}{2}(1)(3 + 1) = 2$$

15. Graph the region under $y = \sqrt{9 - x^2}$ for $-3 \le x \le 3$.

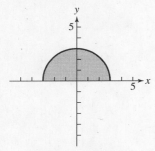

This region is half of a circle of radius 3.

$$\int_{-3}^{3} \sqrt{9 - x^2}\, dx = \frac{1}{2}\pi(3)^2 = \frac{9\pi}{2}$$

16. Graph the region under $y = \sqrt{16 - x^2}$ for $-4 \le x \le 0$.

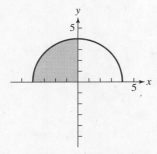

The region is one quarter of a circle of radius 4.

$$\int_{-4}^{0} \sqrt{16 - x^2}\, dx = \frac{1}{4}\pi(4)^2 = 4\pi$$

17. Graph the region under $y = |x|$ for $-2 \le x \le 1$.

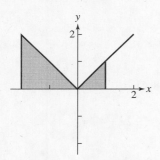

$$\int_{-2}^{1} |x|\, dx = \frac{1}{2}(2)(2) + \frac{1}{2}(1)(1) = \frac{5}{2}$$

18. Graph the region under $y = 1 - |x|$ for $-1 \le x \le 1$.

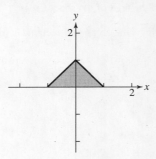

$$\int_{-1}^{1} (1 - |x|)\, dx = \frac{1}{2}(2)(1) = 1$$

19. Graph the region under $y = 2 - |x|$ for $-1 \le x \le 1$.

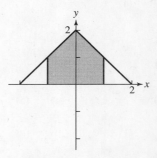

$$\int_{-1}^{1} (2 - |x|)\, dx = \frac{1}{2}(1)(1 + 2) + \frac{1}{2}(1)(1 + 2) = 3$$

20. Graph the region under $y = 1 + \sqrt{1 - x^2}$ for $-1 \le x \le 1$.

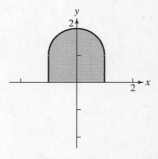

$$\int_{-1}^{1} (1 + \sqrt{1 - x^2})\, dx = (2)(1) + \frac{1}{2}\pi(1)^2 = 2 + \frac{\pi}{2}$$

21. Graph the region under $y = \theta$ for $\pi \le \theta \le 2\pi$

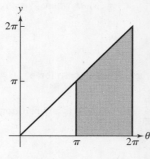

$$\int_{\pi}^{2\pi} \theta\, d\theta = \frac{1}{2}(2\pi - \pi)(2\pi + \pi) = \frac{3\pi^2}{2}$$

22. Graph the region under $y = r$ for $\sqrt{2} \le r \le 5\sqrt{2}$.

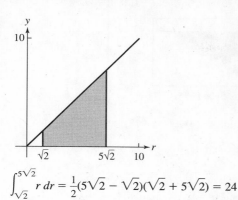

$$\int_{\sqrt{2}}^{5\sqrt{2}} r \, dr = \frac{1}{2}(5\sqrt{2} - \sqrt{2})(\sqrt{2} + 5\sqrt{2}) = 24$$

23. $\int_0^b x \, dx = \frac{1}{2}(b)(b) = \frac{1}{2}b^2$

24. $\int_0^b 4x \, dx = \frac{1}{2}(b)(4b) = 2b^2$

25. $\int_a^b 2s \, ds = \frac{1}{2}(b - a)(2b + 2a) = b^2 - a^2$

26. $\int_a^b 3t \, dt = \frac{1}{2}(b - a)(3b + 3a) = \frac{3}{2}(b^2 - a^2)$

27. $\int_a^{2a} x \, dx = \frac{1}{2}(2a - a)(2a + a) = \frac{3a^2}{2}$

28. $\int_a^{\sqrt{3}a} x \, dx = \frac{1}{2}(\sqrt{3}a - a)(\sqrt{3}a + a) = \frac{1}{2}(3a^2 - a^2) = a^2$

29. Observe that the graph of $f(x) = x^3$ is symmetric with respect to the origin. Hence the area above and below the x-axis is equal for $-1 \le x \le 1$.
$$\int_{-1}^{1} x^3 \, dx = -(\text{area below } x\text{-axis}) + (\text{area above } x\text{-axis}) = 0$$

30. The graph of $f(x) = x^3 + 3$ is three units higher than the graph of $g(x) = x^3$. The extra area is $(3)(1) = 3$.
$$\int_0^1 (x^3 + 3) \, dx = \frac{1}{4} + 3 = \frac{13}{4}$$

31. Observe that the region under the graph of $f(x) = (x - 2)^3$ for $2 \le x \le 3$ is just the region under the graph of $g(x) = x^3$ for $0 \le x \le 1$ translated two units to the right.
$$\int_2^3 (x - 2)^3 \, dx = \int_0^1 x^3 \, dx = \frac{1}{4}$$

32. Observe that the graph of $f(x) = |x|^3$ is symmetric with respect to the y-axis and the right half is the graph of $g(x) = x^3$.
$$\int_{-1}^{1} |x|^3 \, dx = 2\int_0^1 x^3 \, dx = \frac{1}{2}$$

33. Observe from the graph below that the region under the graph of $f(x) = 1 - x^3$ for $0 \le x \le 1$ cuts out a region R from the square identical to the region under the graph of $g(x) = x^3$ for $0 \le x \le 1$.

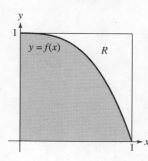

$$\int_0^1 (1 - x^3) \, dx = 1 - \int_0^1 x^3 \, dx = 1 - \frac{1}{4} = \frac{3}{4}$$

34. Observe from the graph of $f(x) = (|x| - 1)^3$ for $-1 \le x \le 2$ that there are two regions below the x-axis and one region above the axis, each of whose area is equal to the area of the region under the graph of $g(x) = x^3$ for $0 \le x \le 1$.

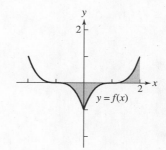

$$\int_{-1}^{2} (|x| - 1)^3 \, dx = 2\left(-\frac{1}{4}\right) + \left(\frac{1}{4}\right) = -\frac{1}{4}$$

35. Observe that the graph of $f(x) = \left(\frac{x}{2}\right)^3$ for $0 \le x \le 2$ is just a horizontal stretch of the graph of $g(x) = x^3$ for $0 \le x \le 1$ by a factor of 2. Thus the area under $f(x) = \left(\frac{x}{2}\right)^3$ for $0 \le x \le 2$ is twice the area under the graph of $g(x) = x^3$ for $0 \le x \le 1$.
$$\int_0^2 \left(\frac{x}{2}\right)^3 \, dx = 2\int_0^1 x^3 \, dx = \frac{1}{2}$$

36. Observe that the graph of $f(x) = x^3$ is symmetric with respect to the origin. Hence the area above and below the x-axis is equal for $-8 \le x \le 8$.
$$\int_{-8}^{8} x^3 \, dx = -(\text{area below } x\text{-axis}) + (\text{area above } x\text{-axis}) = 0$$

37. Observe from the graph below that the region between the graph of $f(x) = x^3 - 1$ and the x-axis for $0 \le x \le 1$ cuts out a region R from the square identical to the region under the graph of $g(x) = x^3$ for $0 \le x \le 1$.

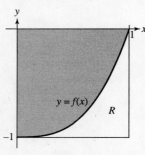

$$\int_0^1 (x^3 - 1)\, dx = -1 + \frac{1}{4} = -\frac{3}{4}$$

38. Observe from the graph below that the region between the graph of $f(x) = \sqrt[3]{x}$ and the x-axis for $0 \le x \le 1$ cuts out a region R from the square identical to the region under the graph of $g(x) = x^3$ for $0 \le x \le 1$.

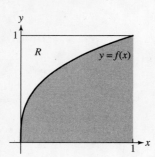

$$\int_0^1 \sqrt[3]{x}\, dx = 1 - \frac{1}{4} = \frac{3}{4}$$

39. $\text{NINT}\!\left(\dfrac{x}{x^2 + 4}, x, 0, 5\right) \approx 0.9905$

40. $3 + 2 \cdot \text{NINT}\!\left(\tan x, x, 0, \dfrac{\pi}{3}\right) \approx 4.3863$

41. $\text{NINT}(4 - x^2, x, -2, 2) \approx 10.6667$

42. $\text{NINT}(x^2 e^{-x}, x, -1, 3) \approx 1.8719$

43. (a) The function has a discontinuity at $x = 0$.

(b)

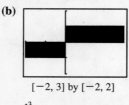

$[-2, 3]$ by $[-2, 2]$

$$\int_{-2}^3 \frac{x}{|x|}\, dx = -2 + 3 = 1$$

44. (a) The function has discontinuities at
$x = -5, -4, -3, -2, -1, 0, 1, 2, 3, 4, 5$.

(b)

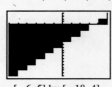

$[-6, 5]$ by $[-18, 4]$

$$\int_{-6}^5 2\,\text{int}(x - 3)\, dx = (-18) + (-16) + (-14)$$
$$+ (-12) + (-10) + (-8) + (-6) + (-4) + (-2)$$
$$+ 0 + 2 = -88$$

45. (a) The function has a discontinuity at $x = -1$.

(b)

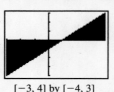

$[-3, 4]$ by $[-4, 3]$

$$\int_{-3}^4 \frac{x^2 - 1}{x + 1}\, dx = -\frac{1}{2}(4)(4) + \frac{1}{2}(3)(3) = -\frac{7}{2}$$

46. (a) The function has a discontinuity at $x = 3$.

(b)

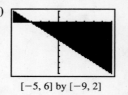

$[-5, 6]$ by $[-9, 2]$

$$\int_{-5}^6 \frac{9 - x^2}{x - 3}\, dx = \frac{1}{2}(2)(2) - \frac{1}{2}(9)(9) = -\frac{77}{2}$$

47. (a) As x approaches 0 from the right, $f(x)$ goes to ∞.

(b) Using right endpoints we have

$$\int_0^1 \frac{1}{x^2}\, dx = \lim_{n \to \infty} \sum_{k=1}^n \left(\frac{1}{\left(\frac{k}{n}\right)^2}\right)\!\left(\frac{1}{n}\right)$$

$$= \lim_{n \to \infty} \sum_{k=1}^n \frac{n}{k^2}$$

$$= \lim_{n \to \infty} n\!\left(1 + \frac{1}{2^2} + \cdots + \frac{1}{n^2}\right).$$

Note that $n\!\left(1 + \dfrac{1}{2^2} + \cdots + \dfrac{1}{n^2}\right) > n$ and $n \to \infty$, so

$$n\!\left(1 + \frac{1}{2^2} + \cdots + \frac{1}{n^2}\right) \to \infty.$$

48. (a) $\Delta x = \dfrac{1}{n},\ x_k = \dfrac{k}{n}$

$$\text{RRAM} = \left(\frac{1}{n}\right)^2 \cdot \frac{1}{n} + \left(\frac{2}{n}\right)^2 \cdot \frac{1}{n} + \cdots + \left(\frac{n}{n}\right)^2 \cdot \frac{1}{n}$$

$$= \sum_{k=1}^n \left(\left(\frac{k}{n}\right)^2 \cdot \frac{1}{n}\right)$$

(b) $\displaystyle\sum_{k=1}^n \left(\left(\frac{k}{n}\right)^2 \cdot \frac{1}{n}\right) = \sum_{k=1}^n \left(\frac{k^2}{n^3}\right) = \frac{1}{n^3} \sum_{k=1}^n k^2$

(c) $\dfrac{1}{n^3} \displaystyle\sum_{k=1}^n k^2 = \dfrac{1}{n^3} \cdot \dfrac{n(n + 1)(2n + 1)}{6} = \dfrac{n(n + 1)(2n + 1)}{6n^3}$

(d) $\displaystyle\lim_{n\to\infty}\sum_{k=1}^{\infty}\left(\left(\frac{k}{n}\right)^2\cdot\frac{1}{n}\right)=\lim_{n\to\infty}\frac{n(n+1)(2n+1)}{6n^3}$

$\displaystyle\qquad\qquad\qquad\qquad = \lim_{n\to\infty}\frac{2n^3+3n^2+n}{6n^3}$

$\displaystyle\qquad\qquad\qquad\qquad = \frac{2}{6}=\frac{1}{3}$

(e) Since $\displaystyle\int_0^1 x^2\,dx$ equals the limit of any Riemann sum over the interval [0, 1] as n approaches ∞, part (d) proves that $\displaystyle\int_0^1 x^2\,dx = \frac{1}{3}$.

■ Section 5.3 Definite Integrals and Antiderivatives (pp. 268–276)

Exploration 1   How Long is the Average Chord of a Circle?

1. The chord is twice as long as the leg of the right triangle in the first quadrant, which has length $\sqrt{r^2-x^2}$ by the Pythagorean Theorem.

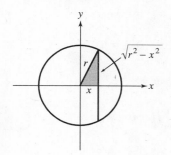

2. Average value $\displaystyle = \frac{1}{r-(-r)}\int_{-r}^{r} 2\sqrt{r^2-x^2}\,dx$.

3. Average value $\displaystyle = \frac{2}{2r}\int_{-r}^{r}\sqrt{r^2-x^2}\,dx$

$\displaystyle\qquad\qquad = \frac{1}{r}\cdot(\text{area of semicircle of radius } r)$

$\displaystyle\qquad\qquad = \frac{1}{r}\cdot\frac{\pi r^2}{2}$

$\displaystyle\qquad\qquad = \frac{\pi r}{2}$

4. Although we only computed the average length of chords perpendicular to a particular diameter, the same computation applies to any diameter. The average length of a chord of a circle of radius r is $\dfrac{\pi r}{2}$.

5. The function $y = 2\sqrt{r^2-x^2}$ is continuous on $[-r, r]$, so the Mean Value Theorem applies and there is a c in $[a, b]$ so that $y(c)$ is the average value $\dfrac{\pi r}{2}$.

Exploration 2   Finding the Derivative of an Integral

Pictures will vary according to the value of x chosen. (Indeed, this is the point of the exploration.) We show a typical solution here.

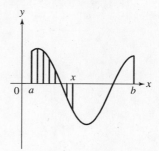

1. We have chosen an arbitrary x between a and b.

2. We have shaded the region using vertical line segments.

3. The shaded region can be written as $\displaystyle\int_a^x f(t)\,dt$ using the definition of the definite integral in Section 5.2. We use t as a dummy variable because x cannot vary between a and itself.

4. The area of the shaded region is our value of $F(x)$.

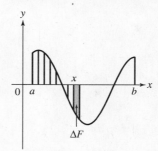

5. We have drawn one more vertical shading segment to represent ΔF.

6. We have moved x a distance of Δx so that it rests above the new shading segment.

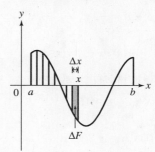

7. Now the (signed) height of the newly-added vertical segment is $f(x)$.

8. The (signed) area of the segment is $\Delta F = \Delta x\cdot f(x)$,

so $\displaystyle F'(x)=\lim_{\Delta x\to 0}\frac{\Delta F}{\Delta x}=f(x)$

Quick Review 5.3

1. $\dfrac{dy}{dx} = \sin x$

2. $\dfrac{dy}{dx} = \cos x$

3. $\dfrac{dy}{dx} = \dfrac{\sec x \tan x}{\sec x} = \tan x$

4. $\dfrac{dy}{dx} = \dfrac{\cos x}{\sin x} = \cot x$

5. $\dfrac{dy}{dx} = \dfrac{\sec x \tan x + \sec^2 x}{\sec x + \tan x} = \sec x$

6. $\dfrac{dy}{dx} = x\left(\dfrac{1}{x}\right) + \ln x - 1 = \ln x$

7. $\dfrac{dy}{dx} = \dfrac{(n+1)x^n}{n+1} = x^n$

8. $\dfrac{dy}{dx} = -\dfrac{1}{(2^x+1)^2} \cdot (\ln 2)2^x = -\dfrac{2^x \ln 2}{(2^x+1)^2}$

9. $\dfrac{dy}{dx} = xe^x + e^x$

10. $\dfrac{dy}{dx} = \dfrac{1}{x^2+1}$

Section 5.3 Exercises

1. (a) $\displaystyle\int_2^2 g(x)\,dx = 0$

(b) $\displaystyle\int_5^1 g(x)\,dx = -\int_1^5 g(x)\,dx = -8$

(c) $\displaystyle\int_1^2 3f(x)\,dx = 3\int_1^2 f(x)\,dx = 3(-4) = -12$

(d) $\displaystyle\int_2^5 f(x)\,dx = \int_2^1 f(x)\,dx + \int_1^5 f(x)\,dx$
$$= -\int_1^2 f(x)\,dx + \int_1^5 f(x)\,dx$$
$$= 4 + 6 = 10$$

(e) $\displaystyle\int_1^5 [f(x) - g(x)]\,dx = \int_1^5 f(x)\,dx - \int_1^5 g(x)\,dx$
$$= 6 - 8 = -2$$

(f) $\displaystyle\int_1^5 [4f(x) - g(x)]\,dx = \int_1^5 4f(x)\,dx - \int_1^5 g(x)\,dx$
$$= 4\int_1^5 f(x)\,dx - \int_1^5 g(x)\,dx$$
$$= 4(6) - 8 = 16$$

2. (a) $\displaystyle\int_1^9 -2f(x)\,dx = -2\int_1^9 f(x)\,dx = -2(-1) = 2$

(b) $\displaystyle\int_7^9 [f(x) + h(x)]\,dx = \int_7^9 f(x)\,dx + \int_7^9 h(x)\,dx$
$$= 5 + 4 = 9$$

(c) $\displaystyle\int_7^9 [2f(x) - 3h(x)]\,dx = \int_7^9 2f(x)\,dx - \int_7^9 3h(x)\,dx$
$$= 2\int_7^9 f(x)\,dx - 3\int_7^9 h(x)\,dx$$
$$= 2(5) - 3(4) = -2$$

(d) $\displaystyle\int_9^1 f(x)\,dx = -\int_1^9 f(x)\,dx = 1$

(e) $\displaystyle\int_1^7 f(x)\,dx = \int_1^9 f(x)\,dx + \int_9^7 f(x)\,dx$
$$= \int_1^9 f(x)\,dx - \int_7^9 f(x)\,dx$$
$$= -1 - 5 = -6$$

(f) $\displaystyle\int_9^7 [h(x) - f(x)]\,dx = \int_9^7 h(x)\,dx - \int_9^7 f(x)\,dx$
$$= -\int_7^9 h(x)\,dx + \int_7^9 f(x)\,dx$$
$$= -4 + 5 = 1$$

3. (a) $\displaystyle\int_1^2 f(u)\,du = 5$

(b) $\displaystyle\int_1^2 \sqrt{3}f(z)\,dz = \sqrt{3}\int_1^2 f(z)\,dz = 5\sqrt{3}$

(c) $\displaystyle\int_2^1 f(t)\,dt = -\int_1^2 f(t)\,dt = -5$

(d) $\displaystyle\int_1^2 [-f(x)]\,dx = -\int_1^2 f(x)\,dx = -5$

4. (a) $\displaystyle\int_0^{-3} g(t)\,dt = -\int_{-3}^0 g(t)\,dt = -\sqrt{2}$

(b) $\displaystyle\int_{-3}^0 g(u)\,du = \sqrt{2}$

(c) $\displaystyle\int_{-3}^0 [-g(x)]\,dx = -\int_{-3}^0 g(x)\,dx = -\sqrt{2}$

(d) $\displaystyle\int_{-3}^0 \dfrac{g(r)}{\sqrt{2}}\,dr = \dfrac{1}{\sqrt{2}}\int_{-3}^0 g(r)\,dr = 1$

5. (a) $\displaystyle\int_3^4 f(z)\,dz = \int_3^0 f(z)\,dz + \int_0^4 f(z)\,dz$
$$= -\int_0^3 f(z)\,dz + \int_0^4 f(z)\,dz$$
$$= -3 + 7 = 4$$

(b) $\displaystyle\int_4^3 f(t)\,dt = \int_4^0 f(t)\,dt + \int_0^3 f(t)\,dt$
$$= -\int_0^4 f(t)\,dt + \int_0^3 f(t)\,dt$$
$$= -7 + 3 = -4$$

6. (a) $\displaystyle\int_1^3 h(r)\,dr = \int_1^{-1} h(r)\,dr + \int_{-1}^3 h(r)\,dr$
$$= -\int_{-1}^1 h(r)\,dr + \int_{-1}^3 h(r)\,dr = 6$$

(b) $\displaystyle-\int_3^1 h(u)\,du = -\int_3^{-1} h(u)\,du - \int_{-1}^1 h(u)\,du$
$$= \int_{-1}^3 h(u)\,du - \int_{-1}^1 h(u)\,du = 6$$

7. An antiderivative of 7 is $F(x) = 7x$.

$$\int_3^1 7 \, dx = F(1) - F(3) = 7 - 21 = -14$$

8. An antiderivative of $5x$ is $F(x) = \frac{5}{2}x^2$.

$$\int_0^2 5x \, dx = F(2) - F(0) = 10 - 0 = 10$$

9. An antiderivative of $\frac{x}{8}$ is $F(x) = \frac{x^2}{16}$.

$$\int_3^5 \frac{x}{8} \, dx = F(5) - F(3) = \frac{25}{16} - \frac{9}{16} = 1$$

10. An antiderivative of $2t - 3$ is $F(t) = t^2 - 3t$.

$$\int_0^2 (2t - 3) \, dt = F(2) - F(0) = -2 - 0 = -2$$

11. An antiderivative of $t - \sqrt{2}$ is $F(t) = \frac{1}{2}t^2 - t\sqrt{2}$.

$$\int_0^{\sqrt{2}} (t - \sqrt{2}) \, dt = F(\sqrt{2}) - F(0) = -1 - 0 = -1$$

12. An antiderivative of $1 + \frac{z}{2}$ is $F(z) = z + \frac{z^2}{4}$.

$$\int_2^1 \left(1 + \frac{z}{2}\right) dz = F(1) - F(2) = \frac{5}{4} - 3 = -\frac{7}{4}$$

13. An antiderivative of $\frac{1}{1 + x^2}$ is $F(x) = \tan^{-1} x$.

$$\int_{-1}^1 \frac{1}{1 + x^2} \, dx = F(1) - F(-1) = \frac{\pi}{4} - \left(-\frac{\pi}{4}\right) = \frac{\pi}{2}$$

14. An antiderivative of $\frac{1}{\sqrt{1 - x^2}}$ is $F(x) = \sin^{-1} x$.

$$\int_{-1/2}^{1/2} \frac{dx}{\sqrt{1 - x^2}} = F\left(\frac{1}{2}\right) - F\left(-\frac{1}{2}\right) = \frac{\pi}{6} - \left(-\frac{\pi}{6}\right) = \frac{\pi}{3}$$

15. An antiderivative of e^x is $F(x) = e^x$.

$$\int_0^2 e^x \, dx = F(2) - F(0) = e^2 - 1 \approx 6.389$$

16. An antiderivative of $\frac{3}{x + 1}$ is $F(x) = 3 \ln |x + 1|$.

$$\int_0^3 \frac{3 \, dx}{x + 1} = F(3) - F(0)$$
$$= 3 \ln 4 - 0$$
$$= 3 \ln 4 \approx 4.159$$

17. Divide the shaded area as follows.

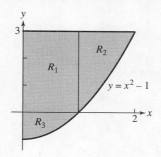

Note that an antiderivative of $x^2 - 1$ is $F(x) = \frac{1}{3}x^3 - x$.

Area of $R_1 = 3(1) = 3$

$$\text{Area of } R_2 = (3)(1) - \int_1^2 (x^2 - 1) \, dx$$
$$= 3 - [F(2) - F(1)]$$
$$= 3 - \left[\left(\frac{2}{3}\right) - \left(-\frac{2}{3}\right)\right] = \frac{5}{3}$$
$$\text{Area of } R_3 = -\int_0^1 (x^2 - 1) \, dx$$
$$= -[F(1) - F(0)]$$
$$= -\left[\left(-\frac{2}{3}\right) - 0\right] = \frac{2}{3}$$

Total shaded area $= 3 + \frac{5}{3} + \frac{2}{3} = \frac{16}{3}$

18. Divide the shaded area as follows.

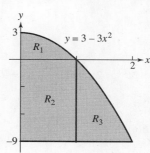

Note that an antiderivative of $3 - 3x^2$ is $F(x) = 3x - x^3$.

$$\text{Area of } R_1 = \int_0^1 (3 - 3x^2) \, dx = F(1) - F(0) = 2$$

Area of $R_2 = (9)(1) = 9$

$$\text{Area of } R_3 = (9)(1) + \int_1^2 (3 - 3x^2) \, dx$$
$$= 9 + [F(2) - F(1)]$$
$$= 9 + (-2 - 2) = 5$$

Total shaded area $= 2 + 9 + 5 = 16$

19. Divide the shaded area as follows.

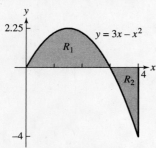

Note that an antiderivative of $3x - x^2$ is $F(x) = \frac{3}{2}x^2 - \frac{1}{3}x^3$.

Area of $R_1 = \int_0^3 (3x - x^2)\, dx = F(3) - F(0) = \frac{9}{2} - 0 = \frac{9}{2}$

Area of $R_2 = -\int_3^4 (3x - x^2)\, dx$

$= -[F(4) - F(3)]$

$= -\left(\frac{8}{3} - \frac{9}{2}\right) = \frac{11}{6}$

Total shaded area $= \frac{9}{2} + \frac{11}{6} = \frac{19}{3}$

20. Divide the shaded area as follows.

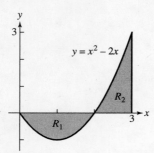

Note that an antiderivative of $x^2 - 2x$ is $F(x) = \frac{1}{3}x^3 - x^2$.

Area of $R_1 = -\int_0^2 (x^2 - 2x)\, dx$

$= -[F(2) - F(0)]$

$= -\left(-\frac{4}{3} - 0\right) = \frac{4}{3}$

Area of $R_2 = \int_2^3 (x^2 - 2x)\, dx$

$= F(3) - F(2)$

$= 0 - \left(-\frac{4}{3}\right) = \frac{4}{3}$

Total shaded area $= \frac{4}{3} + \frac{4}{3} = \frac{8}{3}$

21.

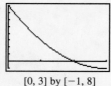

[0, 3] by [−1, 8]

An antiderivative of $x^2 - 6x + 8$ is $F(x) = \frac{1}{3}x^3 - 3x^2 + 8x$.

(a) $\int_0^3 (x^2 - 6x + 8)\, dx = F(3) - F(0) = 6 - 0 = 6$

(b) Area $= \int_0^2 (x^2 - 6x + 8)\, dx - \int_2^3 (x^2 - 6x + 8)\, dx$

$= [F(2) - F(0)] - [F(3) - F(2)]$

$= \left(\frac{20}{3} - 0\right) - \left(6 - \frac{20}{3}\right) = \frac{22}{3}$

22.

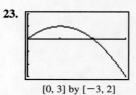

[0, 2] by [−5, 3]

An antiderivative of $-x^2 + 5x - 4$ is

$F(x) = -\frac{1}{3}x^3 + \frac{5}{2}x^2 - 4x.$

(a) $\int_0^2 (-x^2 + 5x - 4)\, dx = F(2) - F(0) = -\frac{2}{3} - 0 = -\frac{2}{3}$

(b) Area $= -\int_0^1 (-x^2 + 5x - 4)\, dx + \int_1^2 (-x^2 + 5x - 4)\, dx$

$= -[F(1) - F(0)] + [F(2) - F(1)]$

$= -\left(-\frac{11}{6} - 0\right) + \left[-\frac{2}{3} - \left(-\frac{11}{6}\right)\right] = 3$

23.

[0, 3] by [−3, 2]

An antiderivative of $2x - x^2$ is $F(x) = x^2 - \frac{1}{3}x^3$.

(a) $\int_0^3 (2x - x^2)\, dx = F(3) - F(0) = 0 - 0 = 0$

(b) Area $= \int_0^2 (2x - x^2)\, dx - \int_2^3 (2x - x^2)\, dx$

$= [F(2) - F(0)] - [F(3) - F(2)]$

$= \left(\frac{4}{3} - 0\right) - \left(0 - \frac{4}{3}\right) = \frac{8}{3}$

24.

[0, 5] by [−5, 5]

An antiderivative of $x^2 - 4x$ is $F(x) = \frac{1}{3}x^3 - 2x^2$.

(a) $\int_0^5 (x^2 - 4x)\, dx = F(5) - F(0) = -\frac{25}{3} - 0 = -\frac{25}{3}$

(b) Area $= -\int_0^4 (x^2 - 4x)\,dx + \int_4^5 (x^2 - 4x)\,dx$

$= -[F(4) - F(0)] + [F(5) - F(4)]$

$= -\left(-\dfrac{32}{3} - 0\right) + \left[-\dfrac{25}{3} - \left(-\dfrac{32}{3}\right)\right] = 13$

25. An antiderivative of $x^2 - 1$ is $F(x) = \dfrac{1}{3}x^3 - x$.

$av = \dfrac{1}{\sqrt{3}}\int_0^{\sqrt{3}} (x^2 - 1)\,dx$

$= \dfrac{1}{\sqrt{3}}\Big[F(\sqrt{3}) - F(0)\Big]$

$= \dfrac{1}{\sqrt{3}}(0 - 0) = 0$

Find $x = c$ in $[0, \sqrt{3}]$ such that $c^2 - 1 = 0$

$c^2 = 1$

$c = \pm 1$

Since 1 is in $[0, \sqrt{3}]$, $x = 1$.

26. An antiderivative of $-\dfrac{x^2}{2}$ is $F(x) = -\dfrac{x^3}{6}$.

$av = \dfrac{1}{3}\int_0^3 \left(-\dfrac{x^2}{2}\right) dx = \dfrac{1}{3}[F(3) - F(0)] = \dfrac{1}{3}\left(-\dfrac{9}{2}\right) = -\dfrac{3}{2}$

Find $x = c$ in $[0, 3]$ such that $-\dfrac{c^2}{2} = -\dfrac{3}{2}$.

$c^2 = 3$

$c = \pm\sqrt{3}$

Since $\sqrt{3}$ is in $[0, 3]$, $x = \sqrt{3}$.

27. An antiderivative of $-3x^2 - 1$ is $F(x) = -x^3 - x$.

$av = \dfrac{1}{1}\int_0^1 (-3x^2 - 1)\,dx = F(1) - F(0) = -2$

Find $x = c$ in $[0, 1]$ such that $-3c^2 - 1 = -2$

$-3c^2 = -1$

$c^2 = \dfrac{1}{3}$

$c = \pm\dfrac{1}{\sqrt{3}}$

Since $\dfrac{1}{\sqrt{3}}$ is in $[0, 1]$. $x = \dfrac{1}{\sqrt{3}}$.

28. An antiderivative of $(x - 1)^2$ is $F(x) = \dfrac{1}{3}(x - 1)^3$.

$av = \dfrac{1}{3}\int_0^3 (x - 1)^2\,dx = \dfrac{1}{3}[F(3) - F(0)] = \dfrac{1}{3}\left(\dfrac{8}{3} + \dfrac{1}{3}\right) = 1$

Find $x = c$ in $[0, 3]$ such that $(c - 1)^2 = 1$.

$c - 1 = \pm 1$

$c = 2$ or $c = 0$.

Since both are in $[0, 3]$, $x = 0$ or $x = 2$.

29. The region between the graph and the x-axis is a triangle of

height 3 and base 6, so the area of the region

is $\dfrac{1}{2}(3)(6) = 9$.

$av(f) = \dfrac{1}{6}\int_{-4}^2 f(x)\,dx = \dfrac{9}{6} = \dfrac{3}{2}$

30. The region between the graph and the x-axis is a rectangle

with a half circle of radius 1 cut out. The area of the region

is $2(1) - \dfrac{1}{2}\pi(1)^2 = \dfrac{4 - \pi}{2}$.

$av(f) = \dfrac{1}{2}\int_{-1}^1 f(t)\,dt = \dfrac{1}{2}\left(\dfrac{4 - \pi}{2}\right) = \dfrac{4 - \pi}{4}$.

31. There are equal areas above and below the x-axis.

$av(f) = \dfrac{1}{2\pi}\int_0^{2\pi} f(t)\,dt = \dfrac{1}{2\pi} \cdot 0 = 0$

32. Since $\tan \theta$ is an odd function, there are equal areas above

and below the x-axis.

$av(f) = \dfrac{1}{\pi/2}\int_{-\pi/4}^{\pi/4} f(\theta)\,d\theta = \dfrac{2}{\pi} \cdot 0 = 0$

33. $\min f = \dfrac{1}{2}$ and $\max f = 1$

$\dfrac{1}{2} \le \int_0^1 \dfrac{1}{1 + x^4}\,dx \le 1$

34. $f(0.5) = \dfrac{16}{17}$

$\left(\dfrac{1}{2}\right)\left(\dfrac{16}{17}\right) \le \int_0^{0.5} \dfrac{1}{1 + x^4}\,dx \le \left(\dfrac{1}{2}\right)(1)$

$\dfrac{8}{17} \le \int_0^{0.5} \dfrac{1}{1 + x^4}\,dx \le \dfrac{1}{2}$

$\left(\dfrac{1}{2}\right)\left(\dfrac{1}{2}\right) \le \int_{0.5}^1 \dfrac{1}{1 + x^4}\,dx \le \left(\dfrac{1}{2}\right)\left(\dfrac{16}{17}\right)$

$\dfrac{1}{4} \le \int_{0.5}^1 \dfrac{1}{1 + x^4}\,dx \le \dfrac{8}{17}$

$\dfrac{8}{17} + \dfrac{1}{4} \le \int_0^1 \dfrac{1}{1 + x^4}\,dx \le \dfrac{1}{2} + \dfrac{8}{17}$

$\dfrac{49}{68} \le \int_0^1 \dfrac{1}{1 + x^4}\,dx \le \dfrac{33}{34}$

35. $\max \sin(x^2) = \sin(1)$ on $[0, 1]$

$\int_0^1 \sin(x^2)\,dx \le \sin(1) < 1$

36. $\max \sqrt{x + 8} = 3$ and $\min \sqrt{x + 8} = 2\sqrt{2}$ on $[0, 1]$

$2\sqrt{2} \le \int_0^1 \sqrt{x + 8}\,dx \le 3$

37. $(b - a)\min f(x) \ge 0$ on $[a, b]$

$0 \le (b - a)\min f(x) \le \int_a^b f(x)\,dx$

38. $(b - a)\max f(x) \le 0$ on $[a, b]$

$\int_a^b f(x)\,dx \le (b - a)\max f(x) \le 0$

39. Yes, $\int_a^b av(f)\,dx = \int_a^b f(x)\,dx$.

This is because $av(f)$ is a constant, so

$$\int_a^b av(f)\,dx = \left[av(f)\cdot x\right]_a^b$$
$$= av(f)\cdot b - av(f)\cdot a$$
$$= (b-a)av(f)$$
$$= (b-a)\left[\frac{1}{b-a}\int_a^b f(x)\,dx\right]$$
$$= \int_a^b f(x)\,dx$$

40. (a) 300 mi

(b) $\dfrac{150\text{ mi}}{30\text{ mph}} + \dfrac{150\text{ mi}}{50\text{ mph}} = 8\text{ h}$

(c) $\dfrac{300\text{ mi}}{8\text{ h}} = 37.5\text{ mph}$

(d) The average speed is the total distance divided by the total time. Algebraically, $\dfrac{d_1+d_2}{t_1+t_2}$. The driver computed $\dfrac{1}{2}\left(\dfrac{d_1}{t_1}+\dfrac{d_2}{t_2}\right)$. The two expressions are not equal.

41. Time for first release $= \dfrac{1000\text{ m}^3}{10\text{ m}^3/\text{min}} = 100\text{ min}$

Time for second release $= \dfrac{1000\text{ m}^3}{20\text{ m}^3/\text{min}} = 50\text{ min}$

Average rate $= \dfrac{\text{total released}}{\text{total time}} = \dfrac{2000\text{ m}^3}{150\text{ min}} = 13\frac{1}{3}\text{ m}^3/\text{min}$

42. $\int_0^1 \sin x\,dx \le \int_0^1 x\,dx = \left[\frac{1}{2}x^2\right]_0^1 = \frac{1}{2}$

43. $\int_0^1 \sec x\,dx \ge \int_0^1\left(1+\frac{x^2}{2}\right)dx = \left[x+\frac{x^3}{6}\right]_0^1 = \frac{7}{6}$

44. (a) Area $= \frac{1}{2}bh$

(b) $\frac{h}{2b}x^2 + C$

(c) $\int_0^b y(x)\,dx = \left[\frac{h}{2b}x^2\right]_0^b = \frac{hb^2}{2b} = \frac{1}{2}bh$

45. $av(x^k) = \dfrac{1}{k}\int_0^k x^k\,dx = \dfrac{1}{k}\left[\dfrac{1}{k+1}x^{k+1}\right]_0^k = \dfrac{k^{k+1}}{k(k+1)}$

Graph $y_1 = \dfrac{x^{x+1}}{x(x+1)}$ and $y_2 = x$ on a graphing calculator and find the point of intersection for $x > 1$.

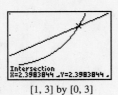
[1, 3] by [0, 3]

Thus, $k \approx 2.39838$

46. An antiderivative of $F'(x)$ is $F(x)$ and an antiderivative of $G'(x)$ is $G(x)$.

$$\int_a^b F'(x)\,dx = F(b) - F(a)$$
$$\int_a^b G'(x)\,dx = G(b) - G(a)$$

Since $F'(x) = G'(x)$, $\int_a^b F'(x)\,dx = \int_a^b G'(x)\,dx$, so

$$F(b) - F(a) = G(b) - G(a).$$

■ Section 5.4 Fundamental Theorem of Calculus (pp. 277–288)

Exploration 1 Graphing NINT f

2. The function $y = \tan x$ has vertical asymptotes at all odd multiples of $\frac{\pi}{2}$. There are six of these between -10 and 10.

3. In attempting to find $F(-10) = \int_3^{-10} \tan(t)\,dt + 5$, the calculator must find a limit of Riemann sums for the integral, using values of $\tan t$ for t between -10 and 3. The large positive and negative values of $\tan t$ found near the asymptotes cause the sums to fluctuate erratically so that no limit is approached. (We will see in Section 8.3 that the "areas" near the asymptotes are infinite, although NINT is not designed to determine this.)

4. $y = \tan x$

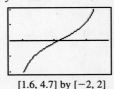
[1.6, 4.7] by [−2, 2]

5. The domain of this continuous function is the open interval $\left(\dfrac{\pi}{2}, \dfrac{3\pi}{2}\right)$.

6. The domain of F is the same as the domain of the continuous function in step 4, namely $\left(\dfrac{\pi}{2}, \dfrac{3\pi}{2}\right)$.

7. We need to choose a closed window narrower than $\left(\dfrac{\pi}{2}, \dfrac{3\pi}{2}\right)$ to avoid the asymptotes.

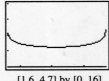
[1.6, 4.7] by [0, 16]

8. The graph of F looks like the graph in step 7. It would be decreasing on $\left(\dfrac{\pi}{2}, \pi\right]$ and increasing on $\left[\pi, \dfrac{3\pi}{2}\right)$, with vertical asymptotes at $x = \dfrac{\pi}{2}$ and $x = \dfrac{3\pi}{2}$.

Exploration 2   The Effect of Changing *a* in
$$\int_a^x f(t)\ dt$$

1.

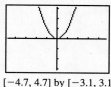

[−4.7, 4.7] by [−3.1, 3.1]

2.

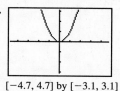

[−4.7, 4.7] by [−3.1, 3.1]

3. Since $\text{NINT}(x^2, x, 0, 0) = 0$, the *x*-intercept is 0.

4. Since $\text{NINT}(x^2, x, 5, 5) = 0$, the *x*-intercept is 5.

5. Changing *a* has no effect on the graph of $y = \dfrac{d}{dx}\displaystyle\int_a^x f(t)\ dt$.

It will always be the same as the graph of $y = f(x)$.

6. Changing *a* shifts the graph of $y = \displaystyle\int_a^x f(t)\ dt$ vertically in

such a way that *a* is always the *x*-intercept. If we change

from a_1 to a_2, the distance of the vertical shift is $\displaystyle\int_{a_2}^{a_1} f(t)\ dt$.

Quick Review 5.4

1. $\dfrac{dy}{dx} = \cos(x^2) \cdot 2x = 2x \cos(x^2)$

2. $\dfrac{dy}{dx} = 2(\sin x)(\cos x) = 2 \sin x \cos x$

3. $\dfrac{dy}{dx} = 2(\sec x)(\sec x \tan x) - 2(\tan x)(\sec^2 x)$

$\qquad = 2 \sec^2 x \tan x - 2 \tan x \sec^2 x = 0$

4. $\dfrac{dy}{dx} = \dfrac{3}{3x} - \dfrac{7}{7x} = 0$

5. $\dfrac{dy}{dx} = 2^x \ln 2$

6. $\dfrac{dy}{dx} = \dfrac{1}{2}x^{-1/2} = \dfrac{1}{2\sqrt{x}}$

7. $\dfrac{dy}{dx} = \dfrac{(-\sin x)(x) - (\cos x)(1)}{x^2} = -\dfrac{x \sin x + \cos x}{x^2}$

8. $\dfrac{dy}{dt} = \cos t, \quad \dfrac{dx}{dt} = -\sin t$

$\dfrac{dy}{dx} = \dfrac{dy/dt}{dx/dt} = \dfrac{\cos t}{-\sin t} = -\cot t$

9. Implicitly differentiate:

$x\dfrac{dy}{dx} + (1)y + 1 = 2y\dfrac{dy}{dx}$

$\dfrac{dy}{dx}(x - 2y) = -(y + 1)$

$\dfrac{dy}{dx} = -\dfrac{y + 1}{x - 2y} = \dfrac{y + 1}{2y - x}$

10. $\dfrac{dy}{dx} = \dfrac{1}{dx/dy} = \dfrac{1}{3x}$

Section 5.4 Exercises

1. $\displaystyle\int_{1/2}^{3}\left(2 - \dfrac{1}{x}\right) dx = \left[2x - \ln|x|\right]_{1/2}^{3}$

$\qquad\qquad = (6 - \ln 3) - \left(1 - \ln \dfrac{1}{2}\right)$

$\qquad\qquad = 5 - \ln 3 + \ln \dfrac{1}{2}$

$\qquad\qquad = 5 - \ln 3 - \ln 2$

$\qquad\qquad = 5 - \ln 6 \approx 3.208$

2. $\displaystyle\int_{2}^{-1} 3^x\ dx = \left[\left(\dfrac{1}{\ln 3}\right)3^x\right]_{2}^{-1}$

$\qquad\qquad = \left(\dfrac{1}{\ln 3}\right)\left(\dfrac{1}{3} - 9\right)$

$\qquad\qquad = -\dfrac{26}{3 \ln 3} \approx -7.889$

3. $\displaystyle\int_{0}^{1} (x^2 + \sqrt{x})\ dx = \left[\dfrac{1}{3}x^3 + \dfrac{2}{3}x^{3/2}\right]_{0}^{1} = \left(\dfrac{1}{3} + \dfrac{2}{3}\right) - (0 + 0) = 1$

4. $\displaystyle\int_{0}^{5} x^{3/2}\ dx = \left[\dfrac{2}{5}x^{5/2}\right]_{0}^{5} = \dfrac{2}{5}(25\sqrt{5} - 0) = 10\sqrt{5} \approx 22.361$

5. $\displaystyle\int_{1}^{32} x^{-6/5}\ dx = \left[-5x^{-1/5}\right]_{1}^{32} = -5\left(\dfrac{1}{2} - 1\right) = \dfrac{5}{2}$

6. $\displaystyle\int_{-2}^{-1} \dfrac{2}{x^2}\ dx = 2\displaystyle\int_{-2}^{-1} x^{-2}\ dx = 2\left[-x^{-1}\right]_{-2}^{-1} = 2\left[1 - \dfrac{1}{2}\right] = 1$

7. $\displaystyle\int_{0}^{\pi} \sin x\ dx = \left[-\cos x\right]_{0}^{\pi} = 1 - (-1) = 2$

8. $\displaystyle\int_{0}^{\pi} (1 + \cos x)\ dx = \left[x + \sin x\right]_{0}^{\pi}$

$\qquad\qquad = (\pi + 0) - (0 + 0)$

$\qquad\qquad = \pi \approx 3.142$

9. $\displaystyle\int_{0}^{\pi/3} 2 \sec^2 \theta\ d\theta = 2\left[\tan \theta\right]_{0}^{\pi/3}$

$\qquad\qquad = 2(\sqrt{3} - 0)$

$\qquad\qquad = 2\sqrt{3} \approx 3.464$

10. $\displaystyle\int_{\pi/6}^{5\pi/6} \csc^2 \theta\ d\theta = \left[-\cot \theta\right]_{\pi/6}^{5\pi/6}$

$\qquad\qquad = \sqrt{3} - (-\sqrt{3})$

$\qquad\qquad = 2\sqrt{3} \approx 3.464$

11. $\displaystyle\int_{\pi/4}^{3\pi/4} \csc x \cot x\ dx = \left[-\csc x\right]_{\pi/4}^{3\pi/4} = (-\sqrt{2}) - (-\sqrt{2}) = 0$

12. $\displaystyle\int_{0}^{\pi/3} 4 \sec x \tan x\ dx = 4\left[\sec x\right]_{0}^{\pi/3} = 4(2 - 1) = 4$

13. $\int_{-1}^{1} (r+1)^2 \, dr = \left[\frac{1}{3}(r+1)^3\right]_{-1}^{1} = \frac{8}{3} - 0 = \frac{8}{3}$

14. $\int_{0}^{4} \frac{1 - \sqrt{u}}{\sqrt{u}} \, du = \int_{0}^{4} (u^{-1/2} - 1) \, du$

$$= \left[2u^{1/2} - u\right]_{0}^{4}$$

$$= (4 - 4) - (0 - 0) = 0$$

15. Graph $y = 2 - x$.

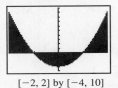

[0, 3] by [−2, 3]

Over [0, 2]: $\int_{0}^{2} (2 - x) \, dx = \left[2x - \frac{1}{2}x^2\right]_{0}^{2} = 2$

Over [2, 3]: $\int_{2}^{3} (2 - x) \, dx = \left[2x - \frac{1}{2}x^2\right]_{2}^{3} = \frac{3}{2} - 2 = -\frac{1}{2}$

Total area $= |2| + \left|-\frac{1}{2}\right| = \frac{5}{2}$

16. Graph $y = 3x^2 - 3$.

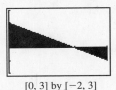

[−2, 2] by [−4, 10]

Over [−2, −1]:

$\int_{-2}^{-1} (3x^2 - 3) \, dx = \left[x^3 - 3x\right]_{-2}^{-1} = 2 - (-2) = 4$

Over [−1, 1]:

$\int_{-1}^{1} (3x^2 - 3) \, dx = \left[x^3 - 3x\right]_{-1}^{1} = -2 - 2 = -4$

Over [1, 2]: $\int_{1}^{2} (3x^2 - 3) \, dx = \left[x^3 - 3x\right]_{1}^{2} = 2 - (-2) = 4$

Total area $= |4| + |-4| + |4| = 12$

17. Graph $y = x^3 - 3x^2 + 2x$.

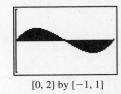

[0, 2] by [−1, 1]

Over [0, 1]:

$\int_{0}^{1} (x^3 - 3x^2 + 2x) \, dx = \left[\frac{1}{4}x^4 - x^3 + x^2\right]_{0}^{1} = \frac{1}{4} - 0 = \frac{1}{4}$

Over [1, 2]:

$\int_{1}^{2} (x^3 - 3x^2 + 2x) \, dx = \left[\frac{1}{4}x^4 - x^3 + x^2\right]_{1}^{2} = 0 - \frac{1}{4} = -\frac{1}{4}$

Total area $= \left|\frac{1}{4}\right| + \left|-\frac{1}{4}\right| = \frac{1}{2}$

18. Graph $y = x^3 - 4x$.

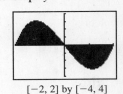

[−2, 2] by [−4, 4]

Over [−2, 0]:

$\int_{-2}^{0} (x^3 - 4x) \, dx = \left[\frac{1}{4}x^4 - 2x^2\right]_{-2}^{0} = 0 - (-4) = 4$

Over [0, 2]:

$\int_{0}^{2} (x^3 - 4x) \, dx = \left[\frac{1}{4}x^4 - 2x^2\right]_{0}^{2} = -4 - 0 = -4$

Total area $= |4| + |-4| = 8$

19. (a) No, $f(x) = \dfrac{x^2 - 1}{x + 1}$ is discontinuous at $x = -1$.

(b) $\dfrac{x^2 - 1}{x + 1} = x - 1, x \neq -1$

The area between the graph of f and the x-axis over

$[-2, 1)$ where f is negative is $\frac{1}{2}(3)(3) = \frac{9}{2}$. The area

between the graph of f and the x-axis over $(1, 3]$ where

f is positive is $\frac{1}{2}(2)(2) = 2$.

$\int_{-2}^{3} \frac{x^2 - 1}{x + 1} \, dx = -\frac{9}{2} + 2 = -\frac{5}{2}$

20. (a) No, $f(x) = \dfrac{9 - x^2}{3x - 9}$ is discontinuous at $x = 3$.

(b) $\dfrac{9 - x^2}{3x - 9} = -\dfrac{3 + x}{3}, x \neq 3$

Note that f is negative for x in [0, 5]. $f(0) = -1$ and

$f(5) = -\frac{8}{3}$. The area between the graph of f and the

x-axis over [0, 5] is $\frac{1}{2}(5 - 0)\left(1 + \frac{8}{3}\right) = \frac{55}{6}$

$\int_{0}^{5} \frac{9 - x^2}{3x - 9} \, dx = -\frac{55}{6}$

21. (a) No, $f(x) = \tan x$ is discontinuous at $x = \dfrac{\pi}{2}$ and $x = \dfrac{3\pi}{2}$.

(b) The integral does not have a value. If $0 < b < \dfrac{\pi}{2}$, then

$$\int_0^b \tan x \, dx = \Big[-\ln |\cos x| \Big]_0^b = -\ln |\cos b| \text{ since the}$$

Fundamental Theorem applies for $[0, b]$. As $b \to \dfrac{\pi^-}{2}$,

$\cos b \to 0^+$ so $-\ln |\cos b| \to \infty$ or $\displaystyle\int_0^b \tan x \, dx \to \infty$.

Hence the integral does not exist over a subinterval of

$[0, 2\pi]$, so it doesn't exist over $[0, 2\pi]$.

22. (a) No, $f(x) = \dfrac{x+1}{x^2 - 1}$ is discontinuous at $x = 1$.

(b) The integral does not have a value. If $0 < b < 1$, then

$$\int_0^b \frac{x+1}{x^2-1} \, dx = \int_0^b \frac{1}{x-1} \, dx = \Big[\ln |x - 1| \Big]_0^b = \ln |b - 1|,$$

since $\dfrac{x+1}{x^2-1} = \dfrac{1}{x-1}$ and the Fundamental Theorem

applies for $[0, b]$. As $b \to 1^-$, $\ln |b - 1| \to -\infty$ or

$\displaystyle\int_0^b \frac{x+1}{x^2-1} \, dx \to -\infty$. Hence the integral does not exist

over a subinterval of $[0, 2]$, so it does not exist over

$[0, 2]$.

23. (a) No, $f(x) = \dfrac{\sin x}{x}$ is discontinuous at $x = 0$.

(b) $\text{NINT}\left(\dfrac{\sin x}{x}, x, -1, 2 \right) \approx 2.55$. The integral exists since

the area is finite because $\dfrac{\sin x}{x}$ is bounded.

24. (a) No, $f(x) = \dfrac{1 - \cos x}{x^2}$ is discontinuous at $x = 0$.

(b) $\text{NINT}\left(\dfrac{1 - \cos x}{x^2}, x, -2, 3 \right) \approx 2.08$. The integral exists

since the area is finite because $\dfrac{1 - \cos x}{x^2}$ is bounded.

25. First, find the area under the graph of $y = x^2$.

$$\int_0^1 x^2 \, dx = \Big[\tfrac{1}{3}x^3 \Big]_0^1 = \frac{1}{3}$$

Next find the area under the graph of $y = 2 - x$.

$$\int_1^2 (2 - x) \, dx = \Big[2x - \tfrac{1}{2}x^2 \Big]_1^2 = 2 - \frac{3}{2} = \frac{1}{2}$$

Area of the shaded region $= \dfrac{1}{3} + \dfrac{1}{2} = \dfrac{5}{6}$

26. First find the area under the graph of $y = \sqrt{x}$.

$$\int_0^1 x^{1/2} \, dx = \Big[\tfrac{2}{3}x^{3/2} \Big]_0^1 = \frac{2}{3}$$

Next find the area under the graph of $y = x^2$.

$$\int_1^2 x^2 \, dx = \Big[\tfrac{1}{3}x^3 \Big]_1^2 = \frac{8}{3} - \frac{1}{3} = \frac{7}{3}$$

Area of the shaded region $= \dfrac{2}{3} + \dfrac{7}{3} = 3$

27. First find the area under the graph of $y = 1 + \cos x$.

$$\int_0^\pi (1 + \cos x) \, dx = \Big[x + \sin x \Big]_0^\pi = \pi$$

The area of the rectangle is 2π.

Area of the shaded region $= 2\pi - \pi = \pi$.

28. First, find the area of the region between $y = \sin x$ and the

x-axis for $\left[\dfrac{\pi}{6}, \dfrac{5\pi}{6} \right]$.

$$\int_{\pi/6}^{5\pi/6} \sin x \, dx = \Big[-\cos x \Big]_{\pi/6}^{5\pi/6} = \frac{\sqrt{3}}{2} - \left(-\frac{\sqrt{3}}{2} \right) = \sqrt{3}$$

The area of the rectangle is $\left(\sin \dfrac{\pi}{6} \right)\left(\dfrac{2\pi}{3} \right) = \dfrac{\pi}{3}$

Area of the shaded region $= \sqrt{3} - \dfrac{\pi}{3}$

29. $\text{NINT}\left(\dfrac{1}{3 + 2\sin x}, x, 0, 10 \right) \approx 3.802$

30. $\text{NINT}\left(\dfrac{2x^4 - 1}{x^4 - 1}, x, -0.8, 0.8 \right) \approx 1.427$

31. $\dfrac{1}{2}\text{NINT}(\sqrt{\cos x}, x, -1, 1) \approx 0.914$

32. $\sqrt{8 - 2x^2} \geq 0$ between $x = -2$ and $x = 2$

$\text{NINT}(\sqrt{8 - 2x^2}, x, -2, 2) \approx 8.886$

33. Plot $y_1 = \text{NINT}(e^{-t^2}, t, 0, x)$, $y_2 = 0.6$ in a $[0, 1]$ by $[0,1]$

window, then use the intersect function to find

$x \approx 0.699$.

34. When $y = 0$, $x = 1$.

$y^3 = 1 - x^3$

$y = \sqrt[3]{1 - x^3}$

$\text{NINT}(\sqrt[3]{1 - x^3}, x, 0, 1) \approx 0.883$

35. $\int_a^x f(t)\, dt + K = \int_b^x f(t)\, dt$

$\quad K = -\int_a^x f(t)\, dt + \int_b^x f(t)\, dt$

$\qquad = \int_x^a f(t)\, dt + \int_b^x f(t)\, dt$

$\qquad = \int_b^a f(t)\, dt$

$\quad K = \int_2^{-1} (t^2 - 3t + 1)\, dt$

$\qquad = \left[\frac{1}{3}t^3 - \frac{3}{2}t^2 + t\right]_2^{-1}$

$\qquad = \left[-\frac{1}{3} - \frac{3}{2} + (-1)\right] - \left[\frac{8}{3} - 6 + 2\right] = -\frac{3}{2}$

36. To find an antiderivative of $\sin^2 x$, recall from trigonometry

that $\cos 2x = 1 - 2\sin^2 x$, so $\sin^2 x = \frac{1}{2} - \frac{1}{2}\cos 2x$.

$\quad K = \int_2^0 \sin^2 t\, dt$

$\qquad = \int_2^0 \left[\frac{1}{2} - \frac{1}{2}\cos(2x)\right] dx$

$\qquad = \left[\frac{1}{2}x - \frac{1}{4}\sin(2x)\right]_2^0$

$\qquad = \left[\frac{1}{2}x - \frac{1}{2}\sin x \cos x\right]_2^0$

$\qquad = 0 - \left(1 - \frac{\sin 2 \cos 2}{2}\right) = \frac{\sin 2 \cos 2 - 2}{2} \approx -1.189$

37. $\frac{dy}{dx} = \sqrt{1 + x^2}$

38. $\frac{dy}{dx} = \frac{d}{dx}\left(\int_x^1 \frac{1}{t}\, dt\right) = \frac{d}{dx}\left(-\int_1^x \frac{1}{t}\, dt\right) = -\frac{1}{x}$

39. $\frac{dy}{dx} = \sin\left[(\sqrt{x})^2\right] \frac{d}{dx}(\sqrt{x}) = (\sin x) \cdot \frac{1}{2}x^{-1/2} = \frac{\sin x}{2\sqrt{x}}$

40. $\frac{dy}{dx} = \cos(2x) \frac{d}{dx}(2x) = 2\cos(2x)$

41. $\frac{dy}{dx} = \frac{d}{dx}\left(\int_0^{x^3} \cos(2t)\, dt - \int_0^{x^2} \cos(2t)\, dt\right)$

$\qquad = \cos(2x^3) \cdot 3x^2 - \cos(2x^2) \cdot 2x$

$\qquad = 3x^2 \cos(2x^3) - 2x \cos(2x^2)$

42. $\frac{dy}{dx} = \frac{d}{dx}\left(\int_{\sin x}^{\cos x} t^2\, dt\right)$

$\qquad = \frac{d}{dx}\left(\int_0^{\cos x} t^2\, dt - \int_0^{\sin x} t^2\, dt\right)$

$\qquad = \cos^2 x \cdot (-\sin x) - \sin^2 x \cdot \cos x$

$\qquad = -\sin x \cos^2 x - \sin^2 x \cos x$

43. Choose (d).

$\quad \frac{dy}{dx} = \frac{d}{dx}\left(\int_\pi^x e^{-t^2}\, dt - 3\right) = e^{-x^2}$

$\quad y(\pi) = \int_\pi^\pi e^{-t^2}\, dt - 3 = 0 - 3 = -3$

44. Choose (c).

$\quad \frac{dy}{dx} = \frac{d}{dx}\left(\int_{-1}^x \sec t\, dt + 4\right) = \sec x$

$\quad y(-1) = \int_{-1}^{-1} \sec t\, dt + 4 = 0 + 4 = 4$

45. Choose (b).

$\quad \frac{dy}{dx} = \frac{d}{dx}\left(\int_0^x \sec t\, dt + 4\right) = \sec x$

$\quad y(0) = \int_0^0 \sec t\, dt + 4 = 0 + 4 = 4$

46. Choose (a).

$\quad \frac{dy}{dx} = \frac{d}{dx}\left(\int_1^x e^{-t^2}\, dt - 3\right) = e^{-x^2}$

$\quad y(1) = \int_1^1 e^{-t^2}\, dt - 3 = 0 - 3 = -3$

47. $x = a$ since $\int_a^a f(t)\, dt = 0$

48. $f(x) = \frac{d}{dx}\left(\int_1^x f(t)\, dt\right) = \frac{d}{dx}(x^2 - 2x + 1) = 2x - 2$

49. $f'(x) = \frac{d}{dx}\left(2 + \int_0^x \frac{10}{1 + t}\, dt\right) = \frac{10}{1 + x}$

$\quad f'(0) = 10$

$\quad f(0) = 2 + \int_0^0 \frac{10}{1 + t}\, dt = 2$

$\quad L(x) = 2 + 10x$

50. $f(x) = \frac{d}{dx}\left(\int_0^x f(t)\, dt\right)$

$\qquad = \frac{d}{dx}(x \cos \pi x)$

$\qquad = x(-\pi \sin \pi x) + 1 \cdot \cos \pi x$

$\qquad = -\pi x \sin \pi x + \cos \pi x$

$\quad f(4) = -4\pi \sin 4\pi + \cos 4\pi = 1$

51. One arch of $\sin kx$ is from $x = 0$ to $x = \frac{\pi}{k}$.

$\quad \text{Area} = \int_0^{\pi/k} \sin kx\, dx = \left[-\frac{1}{k}\cos kx\right]_0^{\pi/k} = \frac{1}{k} - \left(-\frac{1}{k}\right) = \frac{2}{k}$

52. (a) $\int_{-3}^2 (6 - x - x^2)\, dx = \left[6x - \frac{1}{2}x^2 - \frac{1}{3}x^3\right]_{-3}^2$

$\qquad\qquad = \frac{22}{3} - \left(-\frac{27}{2}\right)$

$\qquad\qquad = \frac{125}{6}$

(b) The vertex is at $x = \frac{-(-1)}{2(-1)} = -\frac{1}{2}$. $\left(\text{Recall that the}\right.$

vertex of a parabola $y = ax^2 + bx + c$ is at $x = -\frac{b}{2a}.\left.\right)$

$y\left(-\frac{1}{2}\right) = \frac{25}{4}$, so the height is $\frac{25}{4}$.

(c) The base is $2 - (-3) = 5$.

$\frac{2}{3}$(base)(height) $= \frac{2}{3}(5)\left(\frac{25}{4}\right) = \frac{125}{6}$

53. (a) $H(0) = \int_0^0 f(t)\, dt = 0$

(b) $H'(x) = \frac{d}{dx}\left(\int_0^x f(t)\, dt\right) = f(x)$

$H'(x) > 0$ when $f(x) > 0$.

H is increasing on $[0, 6]$.

(c) H is concave up on the open interval where
$H''(x) = f'(x) > 0$.
$f'(x) > 0$ when $9 < x \le 12$.
H is concave up on $(9, 12)$.

(d) $H(12) = \int_0^{12} f(t)\, dt > 0$ because there is more area

above the x-axis than below the x-axis.

$H(12)$ is positive.

(e) $H'(x) = f(x) = 0$ at $x = 6$ and $x = 12$. Since
$H'(x) = f(x) > 0$ on $[0, 6)$, the values of H are
increasing to the left of $x = 6$, and since
$H'(x) = f(x) < 0$ on $(6, 12]$, the values of H are
decreasing to the right of $x = 6$. H achieves its
maximum value at $x = 6$.

(f) $H(x) > 0$ on $(0, 12]$. Since $H(0) = 0$, H achieves its
minimum value at $x = 0$.

54. (a) $s'(t) = f(t)$. The velocity at $t = 5$ is $f(5) = 2$ units/sec.

(b) $s''(t) = f'(t) < 0$ at $t = 5$ since the graph is decreasing,
so acceleration at $t = 5$ is negative.

(c) $s(3) = \int_0^3 f(x)\, dx = \frac{1}{2}(3)(3) = 4.5$ units

(d) s has its largest value at $t = 6$ sec since
$s'(6) = f(6) = 0$ and $s''(6) = f'(6) < 0$.

(e) The acceleration is zero when $s''(t) = f'(t) = 0$. This
occurs when $t = 4$ sec and $t = 7$ sec.

(f) Since $s(0) = 0$ and $s'(t) = f(t) > 0$ on $(0, 6)$, the
particle moves away from the origin in the positive
direction on $(0, 6)$. The particle then moves in the
negative direction, towards the origin, on $(6, 9)$ since
$s'(t) = f(t) < 0$ on $(6, 9)$ and the area below the x-axis
is smaller than the area above the x-axis.

(g) The particle is on the positive side since

$s(9) = \int_0^9 f(x)\, dx > 0$ (the area below the x-axis is

smaller than the area above the x-axis).

55. (a) $s'(3) = f(3) = 0$ units/sec

(b) $s''(3) = f'(3) > 0$ so acceleration is positive.

(c) $s(3) = \int_0^3 f(x)\, dx = \frac{1}{2}(-6)(3) = -9$ units

(d) $s(6) = \int_0^6 f(x)\, dx = \frac{1}{2}(-6)(3) + \frac{1}{2}(6)(3) = 0$, so the

particle passes through the origin at $t = 6$ sec.

(e) $s''(t) = f'(t) = 0$ at $t = 7$ sec

(f) The particle is moving away from the origin in the
negative direction on $(0, 3)$ since $s(0) = 0$ and
$s'(t) < 0$ on $(0, 3)$. The particle is moving toward the
origin on $(3, 6)$ since $s'(t) > 0$ on $(3, 6)$ and $s(6) = 0$.
The particle moves away from the origin in the positive
direction for $t > 6$ since $s'(t) > 0$.

(g) The particle is on the positive side since

$s(9) = \int_0^9 f(x)\, dx > 0$ (the area below the x-axis is

smaller than the area above the x-axis).

56. (a) $f(t)$ is an even function so $\int_{-x}^0 \frac{\sin(t)}{t}\, dt = \int_0^x \frac{\sin(t)}{t}\, dt$.

$Si(-x) = \int_0^{-x} \frac{\sin(t)}{t}\, dt$

$= -\int_{-x}^0 \frac{\sin(t)}{t}\, dt$

$= -\int_0^x \frac{\sin(t)}{t}\, dt = -Si(x)$

(b) $Si(0) = \int_0^0 \frac{\sin t}{t}\, dt = 0$

(c) $Si'(x) = f(t) = 0$ when $t = \pi k$, k a nonzero integer.

(d)

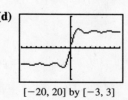

$[-20, 20]$ by $[-3, 3]$

57. (a) $c(100) - c(1) = \int_1^{100} \left(\frac{dc}{dx}\right) dx$

$= \int_1^{100} \frac{1}{2\sqrt{x}}\, dx = \left[\sqrt{x}\right]_1^{100}$

$= 10 - 1 = 9$ or \$9

(b) $c(400) - c(100) = \int_{100}^{400} \left(\frac{dc}{dx}\right) dx$

$= \int_{100}^{400} \frac{1}{2\sqrt{x}}\, dx = \left[\sqrt{x}\right]_{100}^{400}$

$= 20 - 10 = 10$ or \$10

58. $\int_0^3 \left(2 - \frac{2}{(x+1)^2}\right) dx = \left[2x + 2(x+1)^{-1}\right]_0^3$

$\qquad = \left[6 + \frac{1}{2}\right] - 2 = \frac{9}{2}$

$\qquad = 4.5$ thousand

The company should expect \$4500.

59. (a) $\frac{1}{30-0}\int_0^{30}\left(450 - \frac{x^2}{2}\right) dx = \frac{1}{30}\left[450x - \frac{x^3}{6}\right]_0^{30}$

$\qquad = 300$ drums

(b) (300 drums)(\$0.02 per drum) = \$6

60. (a) True, because $h'(x) = f(x)$ and therefore $h''(x) = f'(x)$.

(b) True, because h and h' are both differentiable by part (a).

(c) True, because $h'(1) = f(1) = 0$.

(d) True, because $h'(1) = f(1) = 0$ and $h''(1) = f'(1) < 0$.

(e) False, because $h''(1) = f'(1) < 0$.

(f) False, because $h''(1) = f'(1) \neq 0$

(g) True, because $h'(x) = f(x)$, and f is a decreasing function that includes the point $(1, 0)$.

61. Since $f(t)$ is odd, $\int_{-x}^0 f(t)\, dt = -\int_0^x f(t)\, dt$ because the area between the curve and the x-axis from 0 to x is the opposite of the area between the curve and the x-axis from $-x$ to 0, but it is on the opposite side of the x-axis.

$\int_0^{-x} f(t)\, dt = -\int_{-x}^0 f(t)\, dt = -\left[-\int_0^x f(t)\, dt\right] = \int_0^x f(t)\, dt$

Thus $\int_0^x f(t)\, dt$ is even.

62. Since $f(t)$ is even, $\int_{-x}^0 f(t)\, dt = \int_0^x f(t)\, dt$ because the area between the curve and the x-axis from 0 to x is the same as the area between the curve and the x-axis from $-x$ to 0.

$\int_0^{-x} f(t)\, dt = -\int_{-x}^0 f(t)\, dt = -\int_0^x f(t)\, dt$

Thus $\int_0^x f(t)\, dt$ is odd.

63. If f is an even continuous function, then $\int_0^x f(t)\, dt$ is odd, but $\frac{d}{dx}\int_0^x f(t)\, dt = f(x)$. Therefore, f is the derivative of the odd continuous function $\int_0^x f(t)\, dt$.

Similarly, if f is an odd continuous function, then f is the derivative of the even continuous function $\int_0^x f(t)\, dt$.

64. Solving NINT$\left(\frac{\sin t}{t}, t, 0, x\right) = 1$ graphically, the solution is $x \approx 1.0648397$. We now argue that there are no other solutions, using the functions Si(x) and $f(t)$ as defined in Exercise 56. Since $\frac{d}{dx}$Si$(x) = f(x) = \frac{\sin x}{x}$, Si$(x)$ is increasing on each interval $[2k\pi, (2k + 1)\pi]$ and decreasing on each interval $[(2k + 1)\pi, (2k + 2)\pi]$, where k is a nonnegative integer. Thus, for $x > 0$, Si(x) has its local minima at $x = 2k\pi$, where k is a positive integer. Furthermore, each arch of $y = f(x)$ is smaller in height than the previous one, so $\int_{2k\pi}^{(2k+1)\pi} |f(x)|\, dx > \int_{(2k+1)\pi}^{(2k+2)\pi} |f(x)|\, dx$. This means that

Si$((2k + 2)\pi)$ − Si$(2k\pi) = \int_{2k\pi}^{(2k+2)\pi} f(x)\, dx > 0$, so each successive minimum value is greater than the previous one. Since $f(2\pi) \approx$ NINT$\left(\frac{\sin x}{x}, x, 0, 2\pi\right) \approx 1.42$ and Si(x) is continuous for $x > 0$, this means Si$(x) > 1.42$ (and hence Si$(x) \neq 1$) for $x \geq 2\pi$. Now, Si$(x) = 1$ has exactly one solution in the interval $[0, \pi]$ because Si(x) is increasing on this interval and $x \approx 1.065$ is a solution. Furthermore, Si$(x) = 1$ has no solution on the interval $[\pi, 2\pi]$ because Si(x) is decreasing on this interval and Si$(2\pi) \approx 1.42 > 1$. Thus, Si$(x) = 1$ has exactly one solution in the interval $[0, \infty)$. Also, there is no solution in the interval $(-\infty, 0]$ because Si(x) is odd by Exercise 56 (or 62), which means that Si$(x) \leq 0$ for $x \leq 0$ (since Si$(x) \geq 0$ for $x \geq 0$).

■ Section 5.5 Trapezoidal Rule (pp. 289–297)

Exploration 1　Area Under a Parabolic Arc

1. Let $y = f(x) = Ax^2 + Bx + C$
Then $y_0 = f(-h) = Ah^2 - Bh + C$,
$y_1 = f(0) = A(0)^2 + B(0) + C = C$, and
$y_2 = f(h) = Ah^2 + Bh + C$.

2. $y_0 + 4y_1 + y_2 = Ah^2 - Bh + C + 4C + Ah^2 + Bh + C$
$\qquad = 2Ah^2 + 6C$.

3. $A_p = \int_{-h}^h (Ax^2 + Bx + C)\, dx$

$\qquad = \left[A\frac{x^3}{3} + B\frac{x^2}{2} + Cx\right]_{-h}^h$

$\qquad = A\frac{h^3}{3} + B\frac{h^2}{2} + Ch - \left(-A\frac{h^3}{3} + B\frac{h^2}{2} - Ch\right)$

$\qquad = 2A\frac{h^3}{3} + 2Ch$

$\qquad = \frac{h}{3}(2Ah^2 + 6C)$

4. Substitute the expression in step 2 for the parenthetically enclosed expression in step 3:

$$A_p = \frac{h}{3}(2Ah^2 + 6C)$$
$$= \frac{h}{3}(y_0 + 4y_1 + y_2).$$

Quick Review 5.5

1. $y' = -\sin x$
$y'' = -\cos x$
$y'' < 0$ on $[-1, 1]$, so the curve is concave down on $[-1, 1]$.

2. $y' = 4x^3 - 12$
$y'' = 12x^2$
$y'' > 0$ on $[8, 17]$, so the curve is concave up on $[8, 17]$.

3. $y' = 12x^2 - 6x$
$y'' = 24x - 6$
$y'' < 0$ on $[-8, 0]$, so the curve is concave down on $[-8, 0]$.

4. $y' = \frac{1}{2}\cos\frac{x}{2}$
$y'' = -\frac{1}{4}\sin\frac{x}{2}$
$y'' \leq 0$ on $[48\pi, 50\pi]$, so the curve is concave down on $[48\pi, 50\pi]$.

5. $y' = 2e^{2x}$
$y'' = 4e^{2x}$
$y'' > 0$ on $[-5, 5]$, so the curve is concave up on $[-5, 5]$.

6. $y' = \frac{1}{x}$
$y'' = -\frac{1}{x^2}$
$y'' < 0$ on $[100, 200]$, so the curve is concave down on $[100, 200]$.

7. $y' = -\frac{1}{x^2}$
$y'' = \frac{2}{x^3}$
$y'' > 0$ on $[3, 6]$, so the curve is concave up on $[3, 6]$.

8. $y' = -\csc x \cot x$
$y'' = (-\csc x)(-\csc^2 x) + (\csc x \cot x)(\cot x)$
$= \csc^3 x + \csc x \cot^2 x$
$y'' > 0$ on $[0, \pi]$, so the curve is concave up on $[0, \pi]$.

9. $y' = -100x^9$
$y'' = -900x^8$
$y'' < 0$ on $[10, 10^{10}]$, so the curve is concave down on $[10, 10^{10}]$.

10. $y' = \cos x + \sin x$
$y'' = -\sin x + \cos x$
$y'' < 0$ on $[1, 2]$, so the curve is concave down.

Section 5.5 Exercises

1. (a) $f(x) = x, h = \frac{2-0}{4} = \frac{1}{2}$

x	0	$\frac{1}{2}$	1	$\frac{3}{2}$	2
$f(x)$	0	$\frac{1}{2}$	1	$\frac{3}{2}$	2

$$T = \frac{1}{4}\left(0 + 2\left(\frac{1}{2}\right) + 2(1) + 2\left(\frac{3}{2}\right) + 2\right) = 2$$

(b) $f'(x) = 1, f''(x) = 0$
The approximation is exact.

(c) $\int_0^2 x\, dx = \left[\frac{1}{2}x^2\right]_0^2 = 2$

2. (a) $f(x) = x^2, h = \frac{2-0}{4} = \frac{1}{2}$

x	0	$\frac{1}{2}$	1	$\frac{3}{2}$	2
$f(x)$	0	$\frac{1}{4}$	1	$\frac{9}{4}$	4

$$T = \frac{1}{4}\left(0 + 2\left(\frac{1}{4}\right) + 2(1) + 2\left(\frac{9}{4}\right) + 4\right) = 2.75$$

(b) $f'(x) = 2x, f''(x) = 2 > 0$ on $[0, 2]$
The approximation is an overestimate.

(c) $\int_0^2 x^2\, dx = \left[\frac{1}{3}x^3\right]_0^2 = \frac{8}{3}$

3. (a) $f(x) = x^3, h = \frac{2-0}{4} = \frac{1}{2}$

x	0	$\frac{1}{2}$	1	$\frac{3}{2}$	2
$f(x)$	0	$\frac{1}{8}$	1	$\frac{27}{8}$	8

$$T = \frac{1}{4}\left(0 + 2\left(\frac{1}{8}\right) + 2(1) + 2\left(\frac{27}{8}\right) + 8\right) = 4.25$$

(b) $f'(x) = 3x^2, f''(x) = 6x > 0$ on $[0, 2]$
The approximation is an overestimate.

(c) $\int_0^2 x^3\, dx = \left[\frac{1}{4}x^4\right]_0^2 = 4$

4. (a) $f(x) = \frac{1}{x}, h = \frac{2-1}{4} = \frac{1}{4}$

x	1	$\frac{5}{4}$	$\frac{3}{2}$	$\frac{7}{4}$	2
$f(x)$	1	$\frac{4}{5}$	$\frac{2}{3}$	$\frac{4}{7}$	$\frac{1}{2}$

$$T = \frac{1}{8}\left(1 + 2\left(\frac{4}{5}\right) + 2\left(\frac{2}{3}\right) + 2\left(\frac{4}{7}\right) + \frac{1}{2}\right) \approx 0.697$$

(b) $f'(x) = -\frac{1}{x^2}, f''(x) = \frac{2}{x^3} > 0$ on $[1, 2]$

The approximation is an overestimate.

(c) $\int_1^2 \frac{1}{x}\, dx = \left[\ln|x|\right]_1^2 = \ln 2 \approx 0.693$

5. (a) $f(x) = \sqrt{x}$, $h = \dfrac{4 - 0}{4} = 1$

x	0	1	2	3	4
$f(x)$	0	1	$\sqrt{2}$	$\sqrt{3}$	2

$T = \dfrac{1}{2}(0 + 2(1) + 2(\sqrt{2}) + 2(\sqrt{3}) + 2) \approx 5.146$

(b) $f'(x) = \dfrac{1}{2}x^{-1/2}$, $f''(x) = -\dfrac{1}{4}x^{-3/2} < 0$ on $[0, 4]$

The approximation is an underestimate.

(c) $\displaystyle\int_0^4 \sqrt{x}\, dx = \left[\dfrac{2}{3}x^{3/2}\right]_0^4 = \dfrac{16}{3} \approx 5.333$

6. (a) $f(x) = \sin x$, $h = \dfrac{\pi - 0}{4} = \dfrac{\pi}{4}$

x	0	$\dfrac{\pi}{4}$	$\dfrac{\pi}{2}$	$\dfrac{3\pi}{4}$	π
$f(x)$	0	$\dfrac{\sqrt{2}}{2}$	1	$\dfrac{\sqrt{2}}{2}$	0

$T = \dfrac{\pi}{8}\left(0 + 2\left(\dfrac{\sqrt{2}}{2}\right) + 2(1) + 2\left(\dfrac{\sqrt{2}}{2}\right) + 0\right) \approx 1.896$

(b) $f'(x) = \cos x$, $f''(x) = -\sin x < 0$ on $[0, \pi]$

The approximation is an underestimate.

(c) $\displaystyle\int_0^\pi \sin x\, dx = \Big[-\cos x\Big]_0^\pi = 2$

7. $\dfrac{5}{2}(6.0 + 2(8.2) + 2(9.1) + \cdots + 2(12.7) + 13.0)(30)$

$= 15{,}990 \text{ ft}^3$

8. (a) $\dfrac{200}{2}(0 + 2(520) + 2(800) + 2(1000) + \cdots + 2(860)$

$\qquad\qquad + 0)(20) = 26{,}360{,}000 \text{ ft}^3$

(b) You plan to start with 26,360 fish. You intend to have

$(0.75)(26{,}360) = 19{,}770$ fish to be caught. Since

$\dfrac{19{,}770}{20} = 988.5$, the town can sell at most 988 licenses.

9. Sum the trapezoids and multiply by $\dfrac{1}{3600}$ to change seconds

to hours

$\dfrac{1}{2}(2.2(0 + 30) + (3.2 - 2.2)(30 + 40)$

$\quad + (4.5 - 3.2)(40 + 50) + (5.9 - 4.5)(50 + 60)$

$\quad + (7.8 - 5.9)(60 + 70) + (10.2 - 7.8)(70 + 80)$

$\quad + (12.7 - 10.2)(80 + 90) + (16.0 - 12.7)(90 + 100)$

$\quad + (20.6 - 16.0)(100 + 110)$

$\quad + (26.2 - 20.6)(110 + 120)$

$\quad + (37.1 - 26.2)(120 + 130))\left(\dfrac{1}{3600}\right) \approx 0.9785$ miles

10. (a) $f(x) = x^3 - 2x$, $h = \dfrac{3 - (-1)}{4} = 1$

x	-1	0	1	2	3
$f(x)$	1	0	-1	4	21

$S = \dfrac{1}{3}(1 + 4(0) + 2(-1) + 4(4) + 21) = 12$

(b) $\displaystyle\int_{-1}^3 (x^3 - 2x)\, dx = \left[\dfrac{1}{4}x^4 - x^2\right]_{-1}^3$

$\qquad\qquad = \left(\dfrac{81}{4} - 9\right) - \left(\dfrac{1}{4} - 1\right)$

$\qquad\qquad = 12$

$|E_s| = 0$

(c) For $f(x) = x^3 - 2x$, $M_{f(4)} = 0$ since $f^{(4)} = 0$.

(d) Simpson's Rule for cubic polynomials will always give exact values since $f^{(4)} = 0$ for all cubic polynomials.

11. The average of the 13 discrete temperatures gives equal weight to the low values at the end.

12. (a) $\dfrac{1}{2}(126 + 2 \cdot 65 + 2 \cdot 66 + \cdots + 2 \cdot 58 + 110) = 841$

$av(f) \approx \dfrac{1}{12} \cdot 841 \approx 70.08$

(b) We are approximating the area under the temperature graph. By doubling the endpoints, the error in the first and last trapezoids increases.

13. $S_{50} \approx 3.13791$, $S_{100} \approx 3.14029$

14. $S_{50} \approx 1.08943$, $S_{100} \approx 1.08943$

15. $S_{50} = 1.37066$, $S_{100} = 1.37066$ using $a = 0.0001$ as lower limit

$S_{50} = 1.37076$, $S_{100} = 1.37076$ using $a = 0.000000001$ as lower limit

16. $S_{50} \approx 0.82812$, $S_{100} \approx 0.82812$

17. (a) $T_{10} \approx 1.983523538$

$T_{100} \approx 1.999835504$

$T_{1000} \approx 1.999998355$

(b)

n	$|E_T| = 2 - T_n$
10	$0.016476462 = 1.6476462 \times 10^{-2}$
100	1.64496×10^{-4}
1000	1.645×10^{-6}

(c) $|E_{T_{10n}}| \approx 10^{-2}|E_{T_n}|$

(d) $b - a = \pi$, $h^2 = \dfrac{\pi^2}{n^2}$, $M = 1$

$|E_{T_n}| \le \dfrac{\pi}{12}\left(\dfrac{\pi^2}{n^2}\right) = \dfrac{\pi^3}{12n^2}$

$|E_{T_{10n}}| \le \dfrac{\pi^3}{12(10n)^2} = 10^{-2}|E_{T_n}|$

18. (a) $S_{10} \approx 2.000109517$
$S_{100} \approx 2.000000011$
$S_{1000} \approx 2.000000000$

(b)

n	$|E_S| = 2 - S_n$
10	1.09517×10^{-4}
100	1.1×10^{-8}
1000	0

(c) $\left|E_{S_{10n}}\right| \approx 10^{-4}\left|E_{S_n}\right|$

(d) $b - a = \pi$, $h^4 = \dfrac{\pi^4}{n^4}$, $M = 1$

$\left|E_{S_n}\right| \leq \dfrac{\pi}{180}\left(\dfrac{\pi^4}{n^4}\right) = \dfrac{\pi^5}{180n^4}$

$\left|E_{S_{10n}}\right| \leq \dfrac{\pi^5}{180(10n)^4} = 10^{-4}\left|E_{S_n}\right|$

19. (a) $f'(x) = 2x \cos(x^2)$
$f''(x) = 2x \cdot -2x \sin(x^2) + 2\cos(x^2)$
$\qquad = -4x^2 \sin(x^2) + 2\cos(x^2)$

(b)

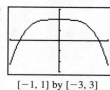

$[-1, 1]$ by $[-3, 3]$

(c) The graph shows that $-3 \leq f''(x) \leq 2$ so $|f''(x)| \leq 3$ for $-1 \leq x \leq 1$.

(d) $|E_T| \leq \dfrac{1 - (-1)}{12}(h^2)(3) = \dfrac{h^2}{2}$

(e) For $0 < h \leq 0.1$, $|E_T| \leq \dfrac{h^2}{2} \leq \dfrac{0.1^2}{2} = 0.005 < 0.01$

(f) $n \geq \dfrac{1 - (-1)}{h} \geq \dfrac{2}{0.1} = 20$

20. (a) $f'''(x) = -4x^2 \cdot 2x \cos(x^2) - 8x \sin(x^2) - 4x \sin(x^2)$
$\qquad = -8x^3 \cos(x^2) - 12x \sin(x^2)$
$f^{(4)}(x) = -8x^3 \cdot -2x \sin(x^2) - 24x^2 \cos(x^2)$
$\qquad\quad - 12x \cdot 2x \cos(x^2) - 12\sin(x^2)$
$\qquad = (16x^4 - 12)\sin(x^2) - 48x^2 \cos(x^2)$

(b)

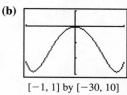

$[-1, 1]$ by $[-30, 10]$

(c) The graph shows that $-30 \leq f^{(4)}(x) \leq 10$ so $|f^{(4)}(x)| \leq 30$ for $-1 \leq x \leq 1$.

(d) $|E_S| \leq \dfrac{1 - (-1)}{180}(h^4)(30) = \dfrac{h^4}{3}$

(e) For $0 < h \leq 0.4$, $|E_S| \leq \dfrac{h^4}{3} \leq \dfrac{0.4^4}{3} \approx 0.00853 < 0.01$

(f) $n \geq \dfrac{1 - (-1)}{h} \geq \dfrac{2}{0.4} = 5$

21. $h = \dfrac{24 \text{ in.}}{6} = 4 \text{ in.}$

Estimate the area to be

$\dfrac{4}{3}[0 + 4(18.75) + 2(24) + 4(26) + 2(24) + 4(18.75) + 0] \approx 466.67 \text{ in}^2$

22. Note that the tank cross-section is represented by the shaded area, not the entire wing cross-section. Using Simpson's Rule, estimate the cross-section area to be

$\dfrac{1}{3}[y_0 + 4y_1 + 2y_2 + 4y_3 + 2y_4 + 4y_5 + y_6]$

$= \dfrac{1}{3}[1.5 + 4(1.6) + 2(1.8) + 4(1.9) + 2(2.0)$

$\qquad + 4(2.1) + 2.1] = 11.2 \text{ ft}^2$

Length $\approx (5000 \text{ lb})\left(\dfrac{1}{42 \text{ lb/ft}^3}\right)\left(\dfrac{1}{11.2 \text{ ft}^2}\right) \approx 10.63 \text{ ft}$

23. $T_n = \dfrac{h}{2}[y_0 + 2y_1 + 2y_2 + \ldots + 2y_{n-1} + y_n]$

$= \dfrac{h[y_0 + y_1 + \ldots + y_{n-1}] + h[y_1 + y_2 + \ldots + y_n]}{2}$

$= \dfrac{\text{LRAM}_n + \text{RRAM}_n}{2}$

24. $S_{2n} = \dfrac{h}{3}(y_0 + 4y_1 + 2y_2 + 4y_3 + \ldots + 2y_{2n-2}$

$\qquad\qquad + 4y_{2n-1} + y_{2n})$

$= \dfrac{1}{3}[h(y_0 + 2y_1 + 2y_2 + \ldots + 2y_{2n-1} + y_{2n})$

$\qquad\quad + (2h)(y_1 + y_3 + y_5 + \ldots + y_{2n-1})]$

$= \dfrac{2T_{2n} + \text{MRAM}_n}{3}$, where $h = \dfrac{b - a}{2n}$.

■ Chapter 5 Review (pp. 298–301)

1.

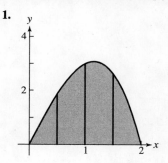

2.

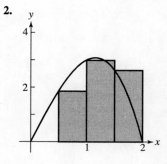

$\text{LRAM}_4: \dfrac{1}{2}\left(0 + \dfrac{15}{8} + 3 + \dfrac{21}{8}\right) = \dfrac{15}{4} = 3.75$

3.

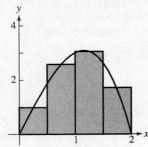

$$\text{MRAM}_4: \frac{1}{2}\left(\frac{63}{64} + \frac{165}{64} + \frac{195}{64} + \frac{105}{64}\right) = 4.125$$

4.

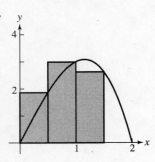

$$\text{RRAM}_4: \frac{1}{2}\left(\frac{15}{8} + 3 + \frac{21}{8} + 0\right) = \frac{15}{4} = 3.75$$

5.

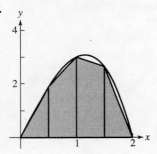

$$T_4 = \frac{1}{2}(\text{LRAM}_4 + \text{RRAM}_4) = \frac{1}{2}\left(\frac{15}{4} + \frac{15}{4}\right) = 3.75$$

6. $\int_0^2 (4x - x^3)\, dx = \left[2x^2 - \frac{1}{4}x^4\right]_0^2 = 8 - 4 = 4$

7.

n	LRAM_n	MRAM_n	RRAM_n
10	1.78204	1.60321	1.46204
20	1.69262	1.60785	1.53262
30	1.66419	1.60873	1.55752
50	1.64195	1.60918	1.57795
100	1.62557	1.60937	1.59357
1000	1.61104	1.60944	1.60784

8. $\int_1^5 \frac{1}{x}\, dx = \left[\ln |x|\right]_1^5 = \ln 5 - \ln 1 = \ln 5 \approx 1.60944$

9. (a) $\int_5^2 f(x)\, dx = -\int_2^5 f(x)\, dx = -3$

The statement is true.

(b) $\int_{-2}^5 [f(x) + g(x)]\, dx$

$$= \int_{-2}^5 f(x)\, dx + \int_{-2}^5 g(x)\, dx$$

$$= \int_{-2}^2 f(x)\, dx + \int_2^5 f(x)\, dx + \int_{-2}^5 g(x)\, dx$$

$$= 4 + 3 + 2 = 9$$

The statement is true.

(c) If $f(x) \le g(x)$ on $[-2, 5]$, then $\int_{-2}^5 f(x)\, dx \le \int_{-2}^5 g(x)\, dx$,

but this is not true since

$$\int_{-2}^5 f(x)\, dx = \int_{-2}^2 f(x) + \int_2^5 f(x) = 4 + 3 = 7 \text{ and}$$

$\int_{-2}^5 g(x)\, dx = 2$. The statement is false.

10. (a) Volume of one cylinder: $\pi r^2 h = \pi \sin^2 (m_i)\, \Delta x$

Total volume: $V = \lim_{n \to \infty} \sum_{i=1}^n \pi \sin^2(m_i)\, \Delta x$

(b) Use $\pi \sin^2 x$ on $[0, \pi]$.

$\text{NINT}(\pi \sin^2 x, x, 0, \pi) \approx 4.9348$

11. (a) Approximations may vary. Using Simpson's Rule, the

area under the curve is approximately

$\frac{1}{3}[0 + 4(0.5) + 2(1) + 4(2) + 2(3.5) + 4(4.5) +$

$2(4.75) + 4(4.5) + 2(3.5) + 4(2) + 0] = 26.5$

The body traveled about 26.5 m.

(b)

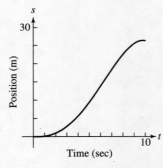

The curve is always increasing because the velocity is always positive, and the graph is steepest when the velocity is highest, at $t = 6$.

12. (a) $\int_0^{10} x^3 \, dx$

(b) $\int_0^{10} x \sin x \, dx$

(c) $\int_0^{10} x(3x - 2)^2 \, dx$

(d) $\int_0^{10} \frac{1}{1 + x^2} \, dx$

(e) $\int_0^{10} \pi\left(9 - \sin^2 \frac{\pi x}{10}\right) dx$

13. The graph is above the x-axis for $0 \le x < 4$ and below the

x-axis for $4 < x \le 6$

Total area $= \int_0^4 (4 - x) \, dx - \int_4^6 (4 - x) \, dx$

$= \left[4x - \frac{1}{2}x^2\right]_0^4 - \left[4x - \frac{1}{2}x^2\right]_4^6$

$= [8 - 0] - [6 - 8] = 10$

14. The graph is above the x-axis for $0 \le x < \frac{\pi}{2}$ and below the

x-axis for $\frac{\pi}{2} < x \le \pi$

Total area $= \int_0^{\pi/2} \cos x \, dx - \int_{\pi/2}^{\pi} \cos x \, dx$

$= \left[\sin x\right]_0^{\pi/2} - \left[\sin x\right]_{\pi/2}^{\pi}$

$= (1 - 0) - (0 - 1) = 2$

15. $\int_{-2}^2 5 \, dx = \left[5x\right]_{-2}^2 = 10 - (-10) = 20$

16. $\int_2^5 4x \, dx = \left[2x^2\right]_2^5 = 50 - 8 = 42$

17. $\int_0^{\pi/4} \cos x \, dx = \left[\sin x\right]_0^{\pi/4} = \frac{\sqrt{2}}{2} - 0 = \frac{\sqrt{2}}{2}$

18. $\int_{-1}^1 (3x^2 - 4x + 7) \, dx = \left[x^3 - 2x^2 + 7x\right]_{-1}^1$

$= 6 - (-10) = 16$

19. $\int_0^1 (8s^3 - 12s^2 + 5) \, ds = \left[2s^4 - 4s^3 + 5s\right]_0^1 = 3 - 0 = 3$

20. $\int_1^2 \frac{4}{x^2} \, dx = \left[-\frac{4}{x}\right]_1^2 = -2 - (-4) = 2$

21. $\int_1^{27} y^{-4/3} \, dy = \left[-3y^{-1/3}\right]_1^{27} = -1 - (-3) = 2$

22. $\int_1^4 \frac{dt}{t\sqrt{t}} = \int_1^4 t^{-3/2} \, dt = \left[-2t^{-1/2}\right]_1^4 = -1 - (-2) = 1$

23. $\int_0^{\pi/3} \sec^2 \theta \, d\theta = \left[\tan \theta\right]_0^{\pi/3} = \sqrt{3} - 0 = \sqrt{3}$

24. $\int_1^e \frac{1}{x} \, dx = \left[\ln |x|\right]_1^e = 1 - 0 = 1$

25. $\int_0^1 \frac{36}{(2x + 1)^3} \, dx = \int_0^1 36(2x + 1)^{-3} \, dx$

$= \left[-9(2x + 1)^{-2}\right]_0^1$

$= -1 - (-9) = 8$

26. $\int_1^2 \left(x + \frac{1}{x^2}\right) dx = \int_1^2 (x + x^{-2}) \, dx$

$= \left[\frac{1}{2}x^2 - x^{-1}\right]_1^2$

$= \frac{3}{2} - \left(-\frac{1}{2}\right) = 2$

27. $\int_{-\pi/3}^0 \sec x \tan x \, dx = \left[\sec x\right]_{-\pi/3}^0 = 1 - 2 = -1$

28. $\int_{-1}^1 2x \sin (1 - x^2) \, dx = \left[\cos (1 - x^2)\right]_{-1}^1 = 1 - 1 = 0$

29. $\int_0^2 \frac{2}{y + 1} \, dy = \left[2 \ln |y + 1|\right]_0^2 = 2 \ln 3 - 0 = 2 \ln 3$

30. Graph $y = \sqrt{4 - x^2}$ on $[0, 2]$.

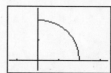

$[-1.35, 3.35]$ by $[-0.5, 2.6]$

The region under the curve is a quarter of a circle of radius 2.

$\int_0^2 \sqrt{4 - x^2} \, dx = \frac{1}{4}\pi(2)^2 = \pi$

31. Graph $y = |x| \, dx$ on $[-4, 8]$.

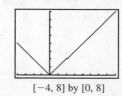

$[-4, 8]$ by $[0, 8]$

The region under the curve consists of two triangles.

$\int_{-4}^8 |x| \, dx = \frac{1}{2}(4)(4) + \frac{1}{2}(8)(8) = 40$

32. Graph $y = \sqrt{64 - x^2}$ on $[-8, 8]$.

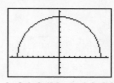

$[-9.4, 9.4]$ by $[-3.2, 9.2]$

The region under the curve $y = \sqrt{64 - x^2}$ is half a circle of radius 8.

$\int_{-8}^8 2\sqrt{64 - x^2} \, dx = 2\int_{-8}^8 \sqrt{64 - x^2} \, dx = 2\left[\frac{1}{2}\pi(8)^2\right] = 64\pi$

33. (a) Note that each interval is 1 day = 24 hours
Upper estimate:
$24(0.020 + 0.021 + 0.023 + 0.025 + 0.028$
$\quad + 0.031 + 0.035) = 4.392$ L
Lower estimate:
$24(0.019 + 0.020 + 0.021 + 0.023 + 0.025$
$\quad + 0.028 + 0.031) = 4.008$ L

(b) $\dfrac{24}{2}[0.019 + 2(0.020) + 2(0.021) + \cdots + 2(0.031)$
$\quad + 0.035] = 4.2$ L

34. (a) Upper estimate:
$3(5.30 + 5.25 + 5.04 + \cdots + 1.11) = 103.05$ ft
Lower estimate:
$3(5.25 + 5.04 + 4.71 + \cdots + 0) = 87.15$ ft

(b) $\dfrac{3}{2}[5.30 + 2(5.25) + 2(5.04) + \cdots + 2(1.11) + 0]$
$\quad = 95.1$ ft

35. One possible answer:
The dx is important because it corresponds to the actual physical quantity Δx in a Riemann sum. Without the Δx, our integral approximations would be way off.

36. $\displaystyle\int_{-4}^{4} f(x)\,dx = \int_{-4}^{0} f(x)\,dx + \int_{0}^{4} f(x)\,dx$

$\qquad = \displaystyle\int_{-4}^{0} (x - 2)\,dx + \int_{0}^{4} x^2\,dx$

$\qquad = \left[\dfrac{1}{2}x^2 - 2x\right]_{-4}^{0} + \left[\dfrac{1}{3}x^3\right]_{0}^{4}$

$\qquad = [0 - 16] + \left[\dfrac{64}{3} - 0\right] = \dfrac{16}{3}$

37. Let $f(x) = \sqrt{1 + \sin^2 x}$

$\max f = \sqrt{2}$ since $\max \sin^2 x = 1$

$\min f = 1$ since $\min \sin^2 x = 0$

$(\min f)(1 - 0) \le \displaystyle\int_{0}^{1} \sqrt{1 + \sin^2 x}\,dx \le (\max f)(1 - 0)$

$0 < 1 \le \displaystyle\int_{0}^{1} \sqrt{1 + \sin^2 x}\,dx \le \sqrt{2}$

38. (a) $av(y) = \dfrac{1}{4 - 0}\displaystyle\int_{0}^{4} \sqrt{x}\,dx = \dfrac{1}{4}\left[\dfrac{2}{3}x^{3/2}\right]_{0}^{4} = \dfrac{1}{4}\left(\dfrac{16}{3} - 0\right) = \dfrac{4}{3}$

(b) $av(y) = \dfrac{1}{a - 0}\displaystyle\int_{0}^{a} \sqrt{x}\,dx = \dfrac{1}{a}\left[\dfrac{2}{3}ax^{3/2}\right]_{0}^{a} = \dfrac{2}{3}a^{3/2}$

39. $\dfrac{dy}{dx} = \sqrt{2 + \cos^3 x}$

40. $\dfrac{dy}{dx} = \sqrt{2 + \cos^3 (7x^2)} \cdot \dfrac{d}{dx}(7x^2) = 14x\sqrt{2 + \cos^3 (7x^2)}$

41. $\dfrac{dy}{dx} = \dfrac{d}{dx}\left(-\displaystyle\int_{1}^{x} \dfrac{6}{3 + t^4}\,dt\right) = -\dfrac{6}{3 + x^4}$

42. $\dfrac{dy}{dx} = \dfrac{d}{dx}\left(\displaystyle\int_{0}^{2x} \dfrac{1}{t^2 + 1}\,dt - \int_{0}^{x} \dfrac{1}{t^2 + 1}\,dt\right)$

$\qquad = \dfrac{1}{(2x)^2 + 1} \cdot 2 - \dfrac{1}{x^2 + 1}$

$\qquad = \dfrac{2}{4x^2 + 1} - \dfrac{1}{x^2 + 1}$

43. $c(x) = \displaystyle\int_{25}^{x} \dfrac{2}{\sqrt{t}}\,dt + 50$

$\qquad = \left[4t^{1/2}\right]_{25}^{x} + 50$

$\qquad = 4\sqrt{x} - 20 + 50$

$\qquad = 4\sqrt{x} + 30$

$c(2500) = 4\sqrt{2500} + 30 = 230$

The total cost for printing 2500 newsletters is \$230.

44. $av(I) = \dfrac{1}{14}\displaystyle\int_{0}^{14} (600 + 600t)\,dt$

$\qquad = \dfrac{1}{14}[600t + 300t^2]_{0}^{14} = 4800$

Rich's average daily inventory is 4800 cases.

$c(t) = 0.04I(t) = 24 + 24t$

$av(c) = \dfrac{1}{14}\displaystyle\int_{0}^{14} (24 + 24t)\,dt = \dfrac{1}{14}\left[24t + 12t^2\right]_{0}^{14} = 192$

Rich's average daily holding cost is \$192.
We could also say $(0.04)4800 = 192$.

45. $\displaystyle\int_{0}^{x} (t^3 - 2t + 3)\,dt = \left[\dfrac{1}{4}t^4 - t^2 + 3t\right]_{0}^{x}$

$\qquad = \dfrac{1}{4}x^4 - x^2 + 3x$

$\dfrac{1}{4}x^4 - x^2 + 3x = 4$

$\dfrac{1}{4}x^4 - x^2 + 3x - 4 = 0$

$x^4 - 4x^2 + 12x - 16 = 0$

Using a graphing calculator, $x \approx -3.09131$

or $x \approx 1.63052$.

46. (a) True, because $g'(x) = f(x)$.

(b) True, because g is differentiable.

(c) True, because $g'(1) = f(1) = 0$.

(d) False, because $g''(1) = f'(1) > 0$.

(e) True, because $g'(1) = f(1) = 0$ and $g''(1) = f'(1) > 0$.

(f) False, because $g''(1) = f'(1) \ne 0$.

(g) True, because $g'(x) = f(x)$, and f is an increasing function which includes the point $(1, 0)$.

47. $\displaystyle\int_{0}^{1} \sqrt{1 + x^4}\,dx = F(1) - F(0)$

48. $y(x) = \displaystyle\int_{5}^{x} \dfrac{\sin t}{t}\,dt + 3$

49. $y' = 2x + \dfrac{1}{x}$

$y'' = 2 - \dfrac{1}{x^2}$

Thus, it satisfies condition **i.**

$y(1) = 1 + \displaystyle\int_1^1 \dfrac{1}{t}\,dt + 1 = 1 + 0 + 1 = 2$

$y'(1) = 2 + \dfrac{1}{1} = 2 + 1 = 3$

Thus, it satisfies condition **ii.**

50. Graph (b).

$y = \displaystyle\int_1^x 2t\,dt + 4 = \left[t^2\right]_1^x + 4 = (x^2 - 1) + 4 = x^2 + 3$

51. (a) Each interval is 5 min $= \dfrac{1}{12}$ h.

$\dfrac{1}{24}[2.5 + 2(2.4) + 2(2.3) + \cdots + 2(2.4) + 2.3]$

$= \dfrac{29}{12} \approx 2.42$ gal

(b) $(60 \text{ mi/h})\!\left(\dfrac{12}{29} \text{ h/gal}\right) \approx 24.83$ mi/gal

52. (a) Using the freefall equation $s = \dfrac{1}{2}gt^2$ from Section 3.4, the distance A falls in 4 seconds is $\dfrac{1}{2}(32)(4^2) = 256$ ft.

When her parachute opens, her altitude is

$6400 - 256 = 6144$ ft.

(b) The distance B falls in 13 seconds is

$\dfrac{1}{2}(32)(13^2) = 2704$ ft. When her parachute opens, her

altitude is $7000 - 2704 = 4296$ ft.

(c) Let t represent the number of seconds after A jumps.

For $t \geq 4$ sec, A's position is given by

$S_A(t) = 6144 - 16(t - 4) = 6208 - 16t$, so A lands at

$t = \dfrac{6208}{16} = 388$ sec. For $t \geq 45 + 13 = 58$ sec, B's

position is given by

$S_B(t) = 4296 - 16(t - 58) = 5224 - 16t$,

so B lands at $t = \dfrac{5224}{16} = 326.5$ sec. B lands first.

53. (a) Area of the trapezoid $= \dfrac{1}{2}(2h)(y_1 + y_3) = h(y_1 + y_3)$

Area of the rectangle $= (2h)y_2 = 2hy_2$

$h(y_1 + y_3) + 2(2hy_2) = h(y_1 + 4y_2 + y_3)$

(b) Let $h = \dfrac{b - a}{2n}$.

$S_{2n} = \dfrac{h}{3}[y_0 + 4y_1 + 2y_2 + 4y_3 + 2y_4 + \cdots + 2y_{2n-2}$

$\qquad\qquad + 4y_{2n-1} + y_{2n}]$

$= \dfrac{1}{3}[h(y_0 + 4y_1 + y_2) + h(y_2 + 4y_3 + y_4) + \cdots$

$\qquad\qquad + h(y_{2n-2} + 4y_{2n-1} + y_{2n})]$

Since each expression of the form

$h(y_{2i-2} + 4y_{2i-1} + y_{2i})$ is equal to twice the area of

the ith of n rectangles plus the area of the ith of n

trapezoids, $S_{2n} = \dfrac{2 \cdot \text{MRAM}_n + T_n}{3}$.

54. (a) $g(1) = \displaystyle\int_1^1 f(t)\,dt = 0$

(b) $g(3) = \displaystyle\int_1^3 f(t)\,dt = -\dfrac{1}{2}(2)(1) = -1$

(c) $g(-1) = \displaystyle\int_1^{-1} f(t)\,dt = -\int_{-1}^1 f(t)\,dt = -\dfrac{1}{4}\pi(2)^2 = -\pi$

(d) $g'(x) = f(x)$; Since $f(x) > 0$ for $-3 < x < 1$ and
$f(x) < 0$ for $1 < x < 3$, $g(x)$ has a relative maximum at
$x = 1$.

(e) $g'(-1) = f(-1) = 2$
The equation of the tangent line is
$y - (-\pi) = 2(x + 1)$ or $y = 2x + 2 - \pi$

(f) $g''(x) = f'(x)$, $f'(x) = 0$ at $x = -1$ and $f'(x)$ is not
defined at $x = 2$. The inflection points are at $x = -1$
and $x = 2$. Note that $g''(x) = f'(x)$ is undefined at
$x = 1$ as well, but since $g''(x) = f'(x)$ is negative on
both sides of $x = 1$, $x = 1$ is not an inflection point.

(g) Note that the absolute maximum is $g(1) = 0$ and the

absolute minimum is

$g(-3) = \displaystyle\int_1^{-3} f(t)\,dt = -\int_{-3}^1 f(t)\,dt = -\dfrac{1}{2}\pi(2)^2 = -2\pi$.

The range of g is $[-2\pi, 0]$.

55. (a) $\text{NINT}(e^{-x^2/2}, x, -10, 10) \approx 2.506628275$

$\text{NINT}(e^{-x^2/2}, x, -20, 20) \approx 2.506628275$

(b) The area is $\sqrt{2\pi}$.

56. First estimate the surface area of the swamp.

$\dfrac{20}{2}[146 + 2(122) + 2(76) + 2(54) + 2(40) + 2(30)$

$\qquad\qquad + 13] = 8030 \text{ ft}^2$

$(5 \text{ ft})(8030 \text{ ft}^2) \cdot \dfrac{1 \text{ yd}^3}{27 \text{ ft}^3} \approx 1500 \text{ yd}^3$

57. (a) $V^2 = (V_{max})^2 \sin^2 (120\pi t)$

Using NINT:

$$av(V^2) = \frac{1}{1} \int_0^1 (V_{max})^2 \sin^2 (120\pi t) \, dt$$

$$= (V_{max})^2 \int_0^1 \sin^2 (120\pi t) \, dt = (V_{max})^2 \frac{1}{2} = \frac{(V_{max})^2}{2}$$

$$V_{rms} = \sqrt{\frac{(V_{max})^2}{2}} = \frac{V_{max}}{\sqrt{2}}$$

(b) $V_{max} = 240\sqrt{2} \approx 339.41$ volts

Chapter 6
Differential Equations and Mathematical Modeling

■ Section 6.1 Antiderivatives and Slope Fields (pp. 303–315)

Exploration 1 Constructing a Slope Field

1. As i and j vary from 1 to 10, 100 ordered pairs are produced. Each ordered pair represents a distinct point in the viewing window.

2. The distance between the points with j fixed and $i = r$ and $i = r + 1$ is the distance between their x-coordinates.

$$\left[\text{Xmin} + \left(2(r+1) - 1 \right)\frac{h}{2} \right] - \left[\text{Xmin} + (2r - 1)\frac{h}{2} \right]$$
$$= (\text{Xmin} - \text{Xmin}) + (2r + 2 - 1 - 2r + 1)\frac{h}{2} = h$$

3. The distance between the points with i fixed and $j = r$ and $j = r + 1$ is the distance between their y-coordinates.

$$\left[\text{Ymin} + \left(2(r+1) - 1 \right)\frac{k}{2} \right] - \left[\text{Ymin} + (2r - 1)\frac{k}{2} \right]$$
$$= (\text{Ymin} - \text{Ymin}) + (2r + 2 - 1 - 2r + 1)\frac{k}{2} = k$$

4. Here $h = k = 1$. Each line segment in the third column has slope $\frac{4}{7}$, because the x-coordinate of the midpoint of each line segment is 2.5. The y-coordinates are $\frac{1}{2}, \frac{3}{2}, \frac{5}{2}, \cdots, \frac{19}{2}$. The 10 graphs are graphs of the functions

$$y = \left(\frac{4}{7} \right)(x - 2.5) + \frac{n}{2}, 2 \le x \le 3, \text{ for } n = 1, 3, 5, \ldots, 19.$$

The length of the line segment can be increased or decreased by adjusting the restriction $2 \le x \le 3$.

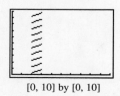

[0, 10] by [0, 10]

5. Again $h = k = 1$. The y-coordinate of the midpoint of each line segment is $\frac{7}{2}$. The x-coordinates of the midpoint of each line segment are $\frac{1}{2}, \frac{3}{2}, \frac{5}{2}, \ldots, \frac{19}{2}$. From left to right the slopes of the line segments are

$$\frac{2}{\frac{1}{2} + 1}, \frac{2}{\frac{3}{2} + 1}, \frac{2}{\frac{5}{2} + 1}, \ldots, \frac{2}{\frac{19}{2} + 1}$$

The 10 graphs are graphs of the functions.

$$y_1 = \left(\frac{2}{\frac{1}{2} + 1} \right)\left(x - \frac{1}{2}\right) + \frac{7}{2}, 0 \le x \le 1,$$

$$y_2 = \left(\frac{3}{\frac{3}{2} + 1} \right)\left(x - \frac{3}{2}\right) + \frac{7}{2}, 1 \le x \le 2,$$

$$y_3 = \left(\frac{2}{\frac{5}{2} + 1} \right)\left(x - \frac{5}{2}\right) + \frac{7}{2}, 2 \le x \le 3,$$

$$\vdots$$

$$y_{10} = \left(\frac{2}{\frac{19}{2} + 1} \right)\left(x - \frac{19}{2}\right) + \frac{7}{2}, 9 \le x \le 10.$$

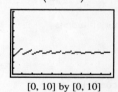

[0, 10] by [0, 10]

6. For each line segment in part (5), make a column of parallel line segments as in part (4).

7. **WL**

Quick Review 6.1

1. $100(1.06) = \$106.00$

2. $100\left(1 + \frac{0.06}{4}\right)^4 \approx \$106.14$

3. $100\left(1 + \frac{0.06}{12}\right)^{12} \approx \$106.17$

4. $100\left(1 + \frac{0.06}{365}\right)^{365} \approx \$106.18$

5. $\frac{dy}{dx} = \frac{d}{dx} \sin 3x = (\cos 3x)(3) = 3\cos 3x$

6. $\frac{dy}{dx} = \frac{d}{dx} \tan \frac{5}{2}x = \left(\sec^2 \frac{5}{2}x\right)\left(\frac{5}{2}\right) = \frac{5}{2}\sec^2 \frac{5}{2}x$

7. $\frac{dy}{dx} = \frac{d}{dx} Ce^{2x} = (Ce^{2x})(2) = 2Ce^{2x}$

8. $\frac{dy}{dx} = \frac{d}{dx} \ln (x + 2) = \frac{1}{x + 2}$

9.

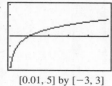

[0.01, 5] by [−3, 3]

By setting the left endpoint at $x = 0.01$ instead of $x = 0$, we avoid an error that occurs when our calculator attempts to calculate $\text{NINT}\left(\frac{1}{x}, x, 0, 1\right)$. The graph appears to be the same as the graph of $y = \ln x$.

10.

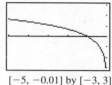

[−5, −0.01] by [−3, 3]

By setting the right endpoint at $x = −0.01$ instead of $x = 0$, we avoid an error that occurs when our calculator attempts to calculate $\text{NINT}\left(\frac{1}{x}, x, -1, 0\right)$. The graph appears to be the same as the graph of $y = \ln(-x)$.

Section 6.1 Exercises

1. $\int (x^2 - 2x + 1)\, dx = \frac{x^3}{3} - x^2 + x + C$

Check:

$\frac{d}{dx}\left(\frac{x^3}{3} - x^2 + x + C\right) = x^2 - 2x + 1$

2. $\int (-3x^{-4})\, dx = x^{-3} + C$

Check:

$\frac{d}{dx}(x^{-3} + C) = -3x^{-4}$

3. $\int (x^2 - 4\sqrt{x})\, dx = \int (x^2 - 4x^{1/2})\, dx = \frac{x^3}{3} - \frac{8}{3}x^{3/2} + C$

Check:

$\frac{d}{dx}\left(\frac{x^3}{3} - \frac{8}{3}x^{3/2} + C\right) = x^2 - 4x^{1/2} = x^2 - 4\sqrt{x}$

4. $\int (8 + \csc x \cot x)\, dx = 8x - \csc x + C$

Check:

$\frac{d}{dx}(8x - \csc x + C) = 8 + \csc x \cot x$

5. $\int e^{4x}\, dx = \frac{1}{4}e^{4x} + C$

Check:

$\frac{d}{dx}\left(\frac{1}{4}e^{4x} + C\right) = e^{4x}$

6. $\int \frac{1}{x+3}\, dx = \ln|x + 3| + C$

Check:

$\frac{d}{dx}[\ln|x + 3| + C] = \frac{1}{x + 3}$

7. $\int (x^5 - 6x + 3)\, dx = \frac{x^6}{6} - 3x^2 + 3x + C$

8. $\int (-x^{-3} + x - 1)\, dx = \frac{x^{-2}}{2} + \frac{x^2}{2} - x + C$

9. $\int \left(e^{t/2} - \frac{5}{t^2}\right)\, dt = \int (e^{t/2} - 5t^{-2})\, dt$

$\qquad = 2e^{t/2} + 5t^{-1} + C$

$\qquad = 2e^{t/2} + \frac{5}{t} + C$

10. $\int \frac{4}{3}\sqrt[3]{t}\, dt = \int \frac{4}{3}t^{1/3}\, dt = t^{4/3} + C$

11. $\int \left(x^3 - \frac{1}{x^3}\right)\, dx = \int (x^3 - x^{-3})\, dx$

$\qquad = \frac{x^4}{4} + \frac{x^{-2}}{2} + C$

$\qquad = \frac{x^4}{4} + \frac{1}{2x^2} + C$

12. $\int \left(\sqrt[3]{x} + \frac{1}{\sqrt[3]{x}}\right)\, dx = \int (x^{1/3} + x^{-1/3})\, dx$

$\qquad = \frac{3}{4}x^{4/3} + \frac{3}{2}x^{2/3} + C$

13. $\int \frac{1}{3}x^{-2/3}\, dx = x^{1/3} + C$

14. $\int (3 \sin x - \sin 3x)\, dx = -3 \cos x + \frac{\cos 3x}{3} + C$

15. $\int \frac{\pi}{2} \cos\left(\frac{\pi}{2}x\right)\, dx = \sin\left(\frac{\pi}{2}x\right) + C$

16. $\int 2 \sec t \tan t\, dt = 2 \sec t + C$

17. $\int \left(\frac{2}{x-1} + \frac{1}{x}\right)\, dx = 2 \ln|x - 1| + \ln|x| + C$

18. $\int \left(\frac{1}{x-2} + \sin 5x - e^{-2x}\right)\, dx$

$\qquad = \ln|x - 2| - \frac{\cos 5x}{5} + \frac{e^{-2x}}{2} + C$

19. $\int 5 \sec^2 5r\, dr = \tan 5r + C$

20. $\int \csc^2 7t\, dt = -\frac{\cot 7t}{7} + C$

21. $\int \cos^2 x\, dx = \int \frac{1 + \cos 2x}{2}\, dx$

$\qquad = \int \left(\frac{1}{2} + \frac{\cos 2x}{2}\right)\, dx$

$\qquad = \frac{x}{2} + \frac{\sin 2x}{4} + C$

22. $\int \sin^2 x\, dx = \int \frac{1 - \cos 2x}{2}\, dx$

$\qquad = \int \left(\frac{1}{2} - \frac{\cos 2x}{2}\right)\, dx = \frac{x}{2} - \frac{\sin 2x}{4} + C$

23. $\int \tan^2 \theta\, d\theta = \int (\sec^2 \theta - 1)\, d\theta = \tan \theta - \theta + C$

24. $\int \cot^2 t \, dt = \int (\csc^2 t - 1) \, dt = -\cot t - t + C$

25. (a) Graph (b)

(b) The slope is always positive, so (a) and (c) can be ruled out.

26. (a) Graph (b)

(b) The solution should have positive slope when x is negative, zero slope when x is zero and negative slope when x is positive since slope $= \dfrac{dy}{dx} = -x$. Graphs (a) and (c) don't show this slope pattern.

27.
$$\frac{dy}{dx} = 2x - 1$$
$$\int \frac{dy}{dx} \, dx = \int (2x - 1) \, dx$$
$$y = x^2 - x + C$$
Initial condition: $y(2) = 0$
$$0 = 2^2 - 2 + C$$
$$0 = 2 + C$$
$$-2 = C$$
Solution: $y = x^2 - x - 2$

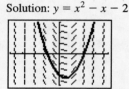

$[-4, 4]$ by $[-3, 3]$

28.
$$\frac{dy}{dx} = \frac{1}{x^2} + x$$
$$\int \frac{dy}{dx} \, dx = \int (x^{-2} + x) \, dx$$
$$y = -x^{-1} + \frac{x^2}{2} + C$$
$$y = \frac{x^2}{2} - \frac{1}{x} + C$$
Initial condition: $y(2) = 1$
$$1 = \frac{2^2}{2} - \frac{1}{2} + C$$
$$1 = \frac{3}{2} + C$$
$$-\frac{1}{2} = C$$
Solution: $y = \dfrac{x^2}{2} - \dfrac{1}{x} - \dfrac{1}{2}$

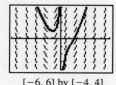

$[-6, 6]$ by $[-4, 4]$

29.
$$\frac{dy}{dx} = \sec^2 x$$
$$\int \frac{dy}{dx} \, dx = \int \sec^2 x \, dx$$
$$y = \tan x + C$$
Initial condition: $y\left(\dfrac{\pi}{4}\right) = -1$
$$-1 = \tan \frac{\pi}{4} + C$$
$$-1 = 1 + C$$
$$-2 = C$$
Solution: $y = \tan x - 2$

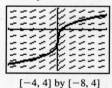

$\left[-\dfrac{\pi}{2}, \dfrac{\pi}{2}\right]$ by $[-8, 8]$

30.
$$\frac{dy}{dx} = x^{-2/3}$$
$$\int \frac{dy}{dx} \, dx = \int x^{-2/3} \, dx$$
$$y = 3x^{1/3} + C$$
Initial condition: $y(-1) = -5$
$$-5 = 3(-1)^{1/3} + C$$
$$-5 = -3 + C$$
$$-2 = C$$
$$y = 3x^{1/3} - 2$$

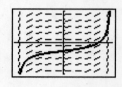

$[-4, 4]$ by $[-8, 4]$

31.
$$\frac{dy}{dx} = 9x^2 - 4x + 5$$
$$\int \frac{dy}{dx} \, dx = \int (9x^2 - 4x + 5) \, dx$$
$$y = 3x^3 - 2x^2 + 5x + C$$
Initial condition: $y(-1) = 0$
$$0 = 3(-1)^3 - 2(-1)^2 + 5(-1) + C$$
$$0 = -10 + C$$
$$10 = C$$
Solution: $y = 3x^3 - 2x^2 + 5x + 10$

32. $\dfrac{dy}{dx} = \cos x + \sin x$

$\displaystyle\int \dfrac{dy}{dx}\, dx = \int (\cos x + \sin x)\, dx$

$y = \sin x - \cos x + C$

Initial condition: $y(\pi) = 1$
$1 = \sin \pi - \cos \pi + C$
$1 = 1 + C$
$0 = C$
Solution: $y = \sin x - \cos x$

33. $\dfrac{dy}{dt} = 2e^{-t}$

$\displaystyle\int \dfrac{dy}{dt}\, dt = \int 2e^{-t}\, dt$

$y = -2e^{-t} + C$

Initial condition: $y(\ln 2) = 0$

$0 = -2e^{-\ln 2} + C$

$0 = -\dfrac{2}{2} + C$

$1 = C$

Solution: $y = -2e^{-t} + 1$

34. $\dfrac{dy}{dx} = \dfrac{1}{x}$

$\displaystyle\int \dfrac{dy}{dx}\, dx = \int \dfrac{1}{x}\, dx$

$y = \ln |x| + C$

Initial condition: $y(e^3) = 0$
$0 = \ln (e^3) + C$
$0 = 3 + C$
$-3 = C$
Solution: $y = \ln |x| - 3$

35. $\dfrac{d^2y}{d\theta^2} = \sin \theta$

$\displaystyle\int \dfrac{d^2y}{d\theta^2}\, d\theta = \int \sin \theta\, d\theta$

$\dfrac{dy}{d\theta} = -\cos \theta + C_1$

Initial condition: $y'(0) = 0$

$0 = -\cos 0 + C_1$

$0 = -1 + C_1$

$1 = C_1$

First derivative: $\dfrac{dy}{d\theta} = -\cos \theta + 1$

$\displaystyle\int \dfrac{dy}{d\theta}\, d\theta = \int (-\cos \theta + 1)\, d\theta$

$y = -\sin \theta + \theta + C_2$

Initial condition: $y(0) = -3$

$-3 = -\sin 0 + 0 + C_2$

$-3 = C_2$

Solution: $y = -\sin \theta + \theta - 3$

36. $\dfrac{d^2y}{dx^2}\, dx = 2 - 6x$

$\displaystyle\int \dfrac{d^2y}{dx^2}\, dx = \int (2 - 6x)\, dx$

$\dfrac{dy}{dx} = 2x - 3x^2 + C_1$

Initial condition: $y'(0) = 4$

$4 = 2(0) - 3(0)^2 + C_1$

$4 = C_1$

First derivative: $\dfrac{dy}{dx} = 2x - 3x^2 + 4$

$\displaystyle\int \dfrac{dy}{dx}\, dx = \int (2x - 3x^2 + 4)\, dx$

$y = x^2 - x^3 + 4x + C_2$

Initial condition: $y(0) = 1$

$1 = 0^2 - 0^3 + 4(0) + C_2$

$1 = C_2$

Solution: $y = x^2 - x^3 + 4x + 1$

or $y = -x^3 + x^2 + 4x + 1$

37. $\dfrac{d^3y}{dt^3} = \dfrac{1}{t^3}$

$\displaystyle\int \dfrac{d^3y}{dt^3}\, dt = \int t^{-3}\, dt$

$\dfrac{d^2y}{dt^2} = -\dfrac{1}{2}t^{-2} + C_1$

Initial condition: $y''(1) = 2$

$2 = -\dfrac{1}{2}(1)^{-2} + C_1$

$2 = -\dfrac{1}{2} + C_1$

$\dfrac{5}{2} = C_1$

Second derivative: $\dfrac{d^2y}{dt^2} = -\dfrac{1}{2}t^{-2} + \dfrac{5}{2}$

$\displaystyle\int \dfrac{d^2y}{dt^2}\, dt = \int \left(-\dfrac{1}{2}t^{-2} + \dfrac{5}{2}\right)\, dt$

$\dfrac{dy}{dt} = \dfrac{1}{2}t^{-1} + \dfrac{5}{2}t + C_2$

Initial condition: $y'(1) = 3$

$3 = \dfrac{1}{2}(1)^{-1} + \dfrac{5}{2}(1) + C_2$

$3 = 3 + C_2$

$0 = C_2$

First derivative: $\dfrac{dy}{dt} = \dfrac{1}{2}t^{-1} + \dfrac{5}{2}t$

$\displaystyle\int \dfrac{dy}{dt}\, dt = \int \left(\dfrac{1}{2}t^{-1} + \dfrac{5}{2}t\right)\, dt$

$y = \dfrac{1}{2}\ln|t| + \dfrac{5}{4}t^2 + C_3$

Initial condition: $y(1) = 1$

$1 = \dfrac{1}{2}\ln 1 + \dfrac{5}{4}(1)^2 + C_3$

$1 = \dfrac{5}{4} + C_3$

$-\dfrac{1}{4} = C_3$

Solution: $y = \dfrac{1}{2}\ln|t| + \dfrac{5}{4}t^2 - \dfrac{1}{4}$

38. $\dfrac{d^4y}{d\theta^4} = \sin\theta + \cos\theta$

$\displaystyle\int \dfrac{d^4y}{d\theta^4}\, d\theta = \int (\sin\theta + \cos\theta)\, d\theta$

$\dfrac{d^3y}{d\theta^3} = -\cos\theta + \sin\theta + C_1$

Initial condition: $y^{(3)}(0) = -3$

$-3 = -\cos 0 + \sin 0 + C_1$

$-3 = -1 + C_1$

$-2 = C_1$

Third derivative: $\dfrac{d^3y}{d\theta^3} = -\cos\theta + \sin\theta - 2$

$\displaystyle\int \dfrac{d^3y}{d\theta^3}\, d\theta = \int (-\cos\theta + \sin\theta - 2)\, d\theta$

$\dfrac{d^2y}{d\theta^2} = -\sin\theta - \cos\theta - 2\theta + C_2$

Initial condition: $y''(0) = -1$

$-1 = -\sin 0 - \cos 0 - 2(0) + C_2$

$-1 = -1 + C_2$

$0 = C_2$

Second derivative: $\dfrac{d^2y}{d\theta^2} = -\sin\theta - \cos\theta - 2\theta$

$\displaystyle\int \dfrac{d^2y}{d\theta^2}\, d\theta = \int (-\sin\theta - \cos\theta - 2\theta)\, d\theta$

$\dfrac{dy}{d\theta} = \cos\theta - \sin\theta - \theta^2 + C_3$

Initial condition: $y'(0) = -1$

$-1 = \cos 0 - \sin 0 - 0^2 + C_3$

$-1 = 1 + C_3$

$-2 = C_3$

First derivative: $\dfrac{dy}{d\theta} = \cos\theta - \sin\theta - \theta^2 - 2$

$\displaystyle\int \dfrac{dy}{d\theta}\, d\theta = \int (\cos\theta - \sin\theta - \theta^2 - 2)\, d\theta$

$y = \sin\theta + \cos\theta - \dfrac{\theta^3}{3} - 2\theta + C_4$

Initial condition: $y(0) = -3$

$-3 = \sin 0 + \cos 0 - \dfrac{0^3}{3} - 2(0) + C_4$

$-3 = 1 + C_4$

$-4 = C_4$

Solution: $y = \sin\theta + \cos\theta - \dfrac{\theta^3}{3} - 2\theta - 4$

39. $\dfrac{ds}{dt} = v = 9.8t + 5$

$\displaystyle\int \dfrac{ds}{dt}\, dt = \int (9.8t + 5)\, dt$

$s = 4.9t^2 + 5t + C$

Initial condition: $s(0) = 10$
$10 = 4.9(0)^2 + 5(0) + C$
$10 = C$
Solution: $s = 4.9t^2 + 5t + 10$

40. $\dfrac{ds}{dt} = v = \sin \pi t$

$\int \dfrac{ds}{dt}\, dt = \int \sin \pi t\, dt$

$s = -\dfrac{1}{\pi}\cos \pi t + C$

Initial condition: $s(1) = 0$

$0 = -\dfrac{1}{\pi}\cos \pi + C$

$0 = \dfrac{1}{\pi} + C$

$-\dfrac{1}{\pi} = C$

Solution: $s = -\dfrac{1}{\pi}\cos \pi t - \dfrac{1}{\pi}$

or $s = -\dfrac{1}{\pi}(1 + \cos \pi t)$

41. $\dfrac{dv}{dt} = a = 32$

$\int \dfrac{dv}{dt}\, dt = \int 32\, dt$

$v = 32t + C_1$

Initial condition: $v(0) = 20$

$20 = 32(0) + C_1$

$20 = C_1$

Velocity: $\dfrac{ds}{dt} = v = 32t + 20$

$\int \dfrac{ds}{dt}\, dt = \int (32t + 20)\, dt$

$s = 16t^2 + 20t + C_2$

Initial condition: $s(0) = 0$

$0 = 16(0)^2 + 20(0) + C_2$

$0 = 0$

Solution: $s = 16t^2 + 20t$

42. $\dfrac{dv}{dt} = a = \cos t$

$\int \dfrac{dv}{dt}\, dt = \int \cos t\, dt$

$v = \sin t + C_1$

Initial condition: $v(0) = -1$

$-1 = \sin 0 + C_1$

$-1 = C_1$

Velocity: $\dfrac{ds}{dt} = v = \sin t - 1$

$\int \dfrac{ds}{dt}\, dt = \int (\sin t - 1)\, dt$

$s = -\cos t - t + C_2$

Initial condition: $s(0) = 1$

$1 = -\cos 0 - 0 + C_2$

$1 = -1 + C_2$

$2 = C_2$

Solution: $s = -\cos t - t + 2$

43.
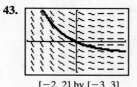
$[-2, 2]$ by $[-3, 3]$

44.
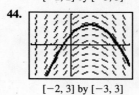
$[-2, 3]$ by $[-3, 3]$

45. $\dfrac{d}{dx}(\tan^{-1} x + C) = \dfrac{1}{1 + x^2}$

46. $\dfrac{d}{dx}(\sin^{-1} x + C) = \dfrac{1}{\sqrt{1 - x^2}}$

47. $\dfrac{d}{dx}(\sec^{-1} x + C) = \dfrac{1}{|x|\sqrt{x^2 - 1}}$

48. $\dfrac{d}{dx}(-\cos^{-1} x + C) = \dfrac{1}{\sqrt{1 - x^2}}$

49. (a) $\dfrac{dy}{dx} = x - \dfrac{1}{x^2}$

$\int \dfrac{dy}{dx}\, dx = \int (x - x^{-2})\, dx$

$y = \dfrac{x^2}{2} + x^{-1} + C = \dfrac{x^2}{2} + \dfrac{1}{x} + C$

Initial condition: $y(1) = 2$

$2 = \dfrac{1^2}{2} + \dfrac{1}{1} + C$

$2 = \dfrac{3}{2} + C$

$\dfrac{1}{2} = C$

Solution: $y = \dfrac{x^2}{2} + \dfrac{1}{x} + \dfrac{1}{2}, \; x > 0$

49. continued

(b) Again, $y = \dfrac{x^2}{2} + \dfrac{1}{x} + C$.

Initial condition: $y(-1) = 1$

$1 = \dfrac{(-1)^2}{2} + \dfrac{1}{(-1)} + C$

$1 = -\dfrac{1}{2} + C$

$\dfrac{3}{2} = C$

Solution: $y = \dfrac{x^2}{2} + \dfrac{1}{x} + \dfrac{3}{2},\ x < 0$

(c) For $x < 0$, $\dfrac{dy}{dx} = \dfrac{d}{dx}\left(\dfrac{1}{x} + \dfrac{x^2}{2} + C_1\right)$

$\quad = -\dfrac{1}{x^2} + x$

$\quad = x - \dfrac{1}{x^2}.$

For $x > 0$, $\dfrac{dy}{dx} = \dfrac{d}{dx}\left(\dfrac{1}{x} + \dfrac{x^2}{2} + C_2\right)$

$\quad = -\dfrac{1}{x^2} + x$

$\quad = x - \dfrac{1}{x^2}.$

And for $x = 0$, $\dfrac{dy}{dx}$ is undefined.

(d) Let C_1 be the value from part (b), and let C_2 be the value from part (a). Thus, $C_1 = \dfrac{3}{2}$ and $C_2 = \dfrac{1}{2}$.

(e) $y(2) = -1 \qquad\qquad y(-2) = 2$

$-1 = \dfrac{1}{2} + \dfrac{2^2}{2} + C_2 \qquad 2 = \dfrac{1}{(-2)} + \dfrac{(-2)^2}{2} + C_1$

$-1 = \dfrac{5}{2} + C_2 \qquad\qquad 2 = \dfrac{3}{2} + C_1$

$-\dfrac{7}{2} = C_2 \qquad\qquad\quad \dfrac{1}{2} = C_1$

Thus, $C_1 = \dfrac{1}{2}$ and $C_2 = -\dfrac{7}{2}$.

50. $\displaystyle\int \dfrac{dr}{dx}\, dx = \int (3x^2 - 6x + 12)\, dx$

$r = x^3 - 3x^2 + 12x + C$

Initial condition: $r(0) = 0$

$0 = 0^3 - 3(0)^2 + 12(0) + C$

$0 = C$

Solution: $r(x) = x^3 - 3x^2 + 12x$

51. $\displaystyle\int \dfrac{dc}{dx}\, dx = \int (3x^2 - 12x + 15)\, dx$

$c = x^3 - 6x^2 + 15x + C$

Initial condition $c(0) = 400$

$400 = 0^3 - 6(0)^2 + 15(0) + C$

$400 = C$

Solution: $c(x) = x^3 - 6x^2 + 15x + 400$

52. (a) $\displaystyle\int f(x)\, dx = \int \dfrac{d}{dx}(x^2 e^x)\, dx = x^2 e^x + C$

(b) $\displaystyle\int g(x)\, dx = \int \dfrac{d}{dx}(x \sin x)\, dx = x \sin x + C$

(c) $\displaystyle\int [-f(x)]\, dx = -\int f(x)\, dx = -x^2 e^x + C$

(d) $\displaystyle\int [-g(x)]\, dx = -\int g(x)\, dx = -x \sin x + C$

(e) $\displaystyle\int [f(x) + g(x)]\, dx = \int f(x)\, dx + \int g(x)\, dx$

$\qquad\qquad = x^2 e^x + x \sin x + C$

(f) $\displaystyle\int [f(x) - g(x)]\, dx = \int f(x)\, dx - \int g(x)\, dx$

$\qquad\qquad = x^2 e^x - x \sin x + C$

(g) $\displaystyle\int [x + f(x)]\, dx = \int x\, dx + \int f(x)\, dx = \dfrac{x^2}{2} + x^2 e^x + C$

(h) $\displaystyle\int [g(x) - 4]\, dx = \int g(x)\, dx - \int 4\, dx = x \sin x - 4x + C$

53. (a) $\displaystyle\int \dfrac{d^2 s}{dt^2}\, dt = \int -k\, dt$

$\dfrac{ds}{dt} = -kt + C_1$

Initial condition: $\dfrac{ds}{dt} = 88$ when $t = 0$

$88 = (-k)(0) + C_1$

$88 = C_1$

Velocity: $\dfrac{ds}{dt} = -kt + 88$

$\displaystyle\int \dfrac{ds}{dt}\, dt = \int (-kt + 88)\, dt$

$s = -\dfrac{k}{2}t^2 + 88t + C_2$

Initial condition: $s = 0$ when $t = 0$

$0 = -\dfrac{k}{2}(0)^2 + 88(0) + C_2$

$0 = C_2$

Solution: $s = -\dfrac{kt^2}{2} + 88t$

(b) $\qquad\qquad \dfrac{ds}{dt} = 0$

$\qquad -kt + 88 = 0$

$\qquad\qquad t = \dfrac{88}{k}$

(c) $\qquad\qquad s\left(\dfrac{88}{k}\right) = 242$

$-\dfrac{k}{2}\left(\dfrac{88}{k}\right)^2 + 88\left(\dfrac{88}{k}\right) = 242$

$\qquad\qquad \dfrac{3872}{k} = 242$

$\qquad\qquad\qquad k = 16 \text{ ft/sec}^2$

54. We first solve $\frac{d^2s}{dt^2} = -k$ with the initial conditions

$s'(0) = 44$ and $s(0) = 0$.

$\int \frac{d^2s}{dt^2} dt = -k$

$\frac{ds}{dt} = -kt + C_1$

Initial condition: $s'(0) = 44$

$44 = (-k)(0) + C_1$

$44 = C_1$

Velocity: $\frac{ds}{dt} = -kt + 44$

$\int \frac{ds}{dt} dt = \int (-kt + 44) \, dt$

$s = -\frac{k}{2}t^2 + 44t + C_2$

Initial condition: $s(0) = 0$

$0 = -\frac{k}{2}(0)^2 + 44(0) + C_2$

$0 = C_2$

Position: $s = -\frac{k}{2}t^2 + 44t$

Now, $\frac{ds}{dt} = -kt + 44 = 0$ when $t = \frac{44}{k}$, so it takes

$\frac{44}{k}$ seconds to stop, and we require:

$$s\left(\frac{44}{k}\right) = 45$$

$$-\frac{k}{2}\left(\frac{44}{k}\right)^2 + 44\left(\frac{44}{k}\right) = 45$$

$$\frac{968}{k} = 45$$

$$k = \frac{968}{45} \approx 21.5$$

It requires a constant deceleration of approximately

21.5 ft/sec^2.

55. $\int \frac{d^2s}{dt^2} dt = \int -5.2 \, dt$

$\frac{ds}{dt} = -5.2t + C_1$

Initial condition: $\frac{ds}{dt} = 0$ when $t = 0$

$0 = -5.2(0) + C_1$

$0 = C_1$

Velocity: $\frac{ds}{dt} = -5.2t$

$\int \frac{ds}{dt} dt = \int -5.2t \, dt$

$s = -2.6t^2 + C_2$

Initial condition: $s = 4$ when $t = 0$

$4 = -2.6(0)^2 + C_2$

$4 = C_2$

Position: $s(t) = -2.6t^2 + 4$

Solving $s(t) = 0$, we have $t^2 = \frac{4}{2.6}$, so the positive

solution is $t \approx 1.240$ sec. They took about 1.240 sec to fall.

56. Solving $\frac{d^2s}{dt^2} = a$, $s(0) = s_0$, and $v(0) = v_0$:

$\int \frac{d^2s}{dt^2} dt = \int a \, dt$

$\frac{ds}{dt} = at + C_1$

Initial condition: $s'(0) = v_0$

$v_0 = (a)(0) + C_1$

$v_0 = C_1$

Velocity: $\frac{ds}{dt} = at + v_0$

$\int \frac{ds}{dt} dt = \int (at + v_0) \, dt$

$s = \frac{a}{2}t^2 + v_0 t + C_2$

Initial condition: $s(0) = s_0$

$s_0 = \frac{a}{2}(0)^2 + (v_0)(0) + C_2$

$s_0 = C_2$

Position: $s = \frac{a}{2}t^2 + v_0 t + s_0$

57. We use the method of Example 7.

$V = \frac{1}{3}\pi r^2 h = \frac{1}{3}\pi\left(\frac{2}{5}h\right)^2 h = \frac{4\pi}{75}h^3$

$\frac{dV}{dt} = \frac{d}{dt}\left(\frac{4\pi}{75}h^3\right)$

$-\frac{1}{6}\sqrt{h} = \frac{4\pi}{25}h^2\frac{dh}{dt}$

$-\frac{25}{24\pi} = h^{3/2}\frac{dh}{dt}$

$-\int \frac{25}{24\pi} dt = \int h^{3/2}\frac{dh}{dt} dt$

$-\frac{25}{24\pi}t = \frac{2}{5}h^{5/2} + C$

Initial condition: $h = 10$ when $t = 0$.

$-\frac{25}{24\pi}(0) = \frac{2}{5}(10)^{5/2} + C$

$C = -\frac{2}{5}(10)^{5/2}$

$-\frac{25}{24\pi}t = \frac{2}{5}h^{5/2} - \frac{2}{5}(10)^{5/2}$

$-\frac{125t}{48\pi} = h^{5/2} - 10^{5/2}$

$h^{5/2} = -\frac{125t}{48\pi} + 10^{5/2}$

$h = \left(-\frac{125t}{48\pi} + 10^{5/2}\right)^{2/5}$

The height is given by $h = \left(-\frac{125t}{48\pi} + 10^{5/2}\right)^{2/5}$ and the

volume is given by

$V = \frac{4\pi}{75}h^3 = \frac{4\pi}{75}\left(-\frac{125t}{48\pi} + 10^{5/2}\right)^{6/5}$.

58. (a) $y = 500e^{0.0475t}$

(b) $1000 = 500e^{0.0475t}$

$2 = e^{0.0475t}$

$\ln 2 = 0.0475t$

$t = \dfrac{\ln 2}{0.0475} \approx 14.6$

It will take approximately 14.6 years.

59. (a) $y = 1200e^{0.0625t}$

(b) $3600 = 1200e^{0.0625t}$

$3 = e^{0.0625t}$

$\ln 3 = 0.0625t$

$t = \dfrac{\ln 3}{0.0625} \approx 17.6$

It will take approximately 17.6 years.

60. (a) $\displaystyle\int x^2 \cos x \, dx = \int_0^x t^2 \cos t \, dt + C$

(b) We require $\displaystyle\int_0^0 t^2 \cos t \, dt + C = 1$, so $C = 1$.

The required antiderivative is $\displaystyle\int_0^x t^2 \cos t \, dt + 1$.

61. (a) $\displaystyle\int xe^x \, dx = \int_0^x te^t \, dt + C$

(b) We require $\displaystyle\int_0^0 te^t \, dt + C = 1$, so $C = 1$.

The required antiderivative is $\displaystyle\int_0^x te^t \, dt + 1$.

62. (a) $\displaystyle\int \frac{d^2y}{dx^2} \, dx = \int 6x \, dx$

$\dfrac{dy}{dx} = 3x^2 + C_1$

Initial condition (horizontal tangent): $y'(0) = 0$

$0 = 3(0)^2 + C_1$

$0 = C_1$

First derivative: $\dfrac{dy}{dx} = 3x^2$

$\displaystyle\int \frac{dy}{dx} \, dx = \int 3x^2 \, dx$

$y = x^3 + C_2$

Initial condition (contains $(0, 1)$): $y(0) = 1$

$1 = (0)^3 + C_2$

$1 = C_2$

Solution: $y = x^3 + 1$

(b) Only one function satisfies the differential equation on $(-\infty, \infty)$ and the initial conditions.

63. Use differential equation graphing mode.
For reference, the equations of the solution curves are as follows.

$(1, 1)$: $y = e^{(x^2-1)/2}$
$(-1, 2)$: $y = 2e^{(x^2-1)/2}$
$(0, -2)$: $y = -2e^{x^2/2}$
$(-2, -1)$: $y = -e^{(x^2-4)/2}$

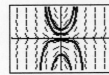

$[-6, 6]$ by $[-4, 4]$

The concavity of each solution curve indicates the sign of y''.

64. Use differential equation graphing mode.
For reference, the equations of the solution curves are as follows.

$(0, 1)$: $y = e^x$
$(0, 2)$: $y = 2e^x$
$(0, -1)$: $y = -e^x$

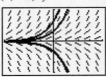

$[-4, 4]$ by $[-3, 3]$

The concavity of each solution curve indicates the sign of y''.

65. Use differential equation graphing mode.
For reference, the equations of the solution curves are as follows.

$(0, 1)$: $y = -3e^{2x} + 4$
$(0, 4)$: $y = 4$
$(0, 5)$: $y = e^{2x} + 4$

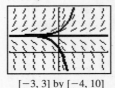

$[-3, 3]$ by $[-4, 10]$

The concavity of each solution curve indicates the sign of y''.

66. Use differential equation graphing mode.

For reference, the equations of the solution curves are as follows.

$(0, 1): y = -\dfrac{1}{x - 1}$

$(0, 2): y = -\dfrac{2}{2x - 1}$

$(0, -1): y = -\dfrac{1}{x + 1}$

$(0, 0): y = 0$

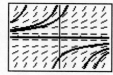

[−2.35, 2.35] by [−1.55, 1.55]

The concavity of each solution curve indicates the sign of y''.

67. (a) $\dfrac{d}{dx}(\ln x + C) = \dfrac{1}{x}$ for $x > 0$

(b) $\dfrac{d}{dx}[\ln(-x) + C] = \dfrac{1}{-x}\dfrac{d}{dx}(-x) = \left(\dfrac{1}{-x}\right)(-1) = \dfrac{1}{x}$
for $x < 0$

(c) For $x > 0$, $\ln|x| + C = \ln x + C$, which is a solution to the differential equation, as we showed in part (a). For $x < 0$, $\ln|x| + C = \ln(-x) + C$, which is a solution to the differential equation, as we showed in part (b). Thus, $\dfrac{d}{dx}\ln|x| = \dfrac{1}{x}$ for all x except 0.

(d) For $x < 0$, we have $y = \ln(-x) + C_1$, which is a solution to the differential equation, as we showed in part (a). For $x > 0$, we have $y = \ln x + C_2$, which is a solution to the differential equation, as we showed part (b). Thus, $\dfrac{dy}{dx} = \dfrac{1}{x}$ for all x except 0.

■ Section 6.2 Integration by Substitution
(pp. 315–323)

Exploration 1 Supporting Indefinite Integrals Graphically

1. $\displaystyle\int \sqrt{1 + x^2} \cdot 2x \, dx = \int \sqrt{u} \, du$
$= \dfrac{2}{3}u^{3/2} + C$
$= \dfrac{2}{3}(1 + x^2)^{3/2} + C$

2. Their derivatives are equal: $\dfrac{dy_1}{dx} = \dfrac{dy_2}{dx} = \sqrt{1 + x^2} \cdot 2x$.

3. $y_1 = y_2 + \dfrac{2}{3}$. By Corollary 3 to the Mean Value Theorem of Section 4.2, y_1 and y_2 must differ by a constant. We find that constant by evaluating the two functions at $x = 0$.

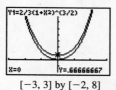

[−3, 3] by [−2, 8]

4.

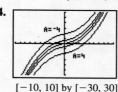

[−10, 10] by [−30, 30]

5. The derivative with respect to x of each function graphed in part (4) is equal to $\sqrt{1 + x^2}$.

Exploration 2 Two Routes to the Integral

1. $\displaystyle\int_{-1}^{1} 3x^2\sqrt{x^3 + 1}\, dx = \int_{0}^{2} \sqrt{u}\, du = \dfrac{2}{3}u^{3/2}\Big]_{0}^{2} = \dfrac{4\sqrt{2}}{3}$

2. $\displaystyle\int 3x^2\sqrt{x^3 + 1}\, dx = \int \sqrt{u}\, du = \dfrac{2}{3}u^{3/2} = \dfrac{2}{3}(x^3 + 1)^{3/2}$ so
$\displaystyle\int_{-1}^{1} 3x^2\sqrt{x^3 + 1}\, dx = \dfrac{2}{3}(x^3 + 1)^{3/2}\Big]_{-1}^{1} = \dfrac{4\sqrt{2}}{3}$.

Quick Review 6.2

1. $\displaystyle\int_{0}^{2} x^4\, dx = \dfrac{1}{5}x^5\Big]_{0}^{2} = \dfrac{1}{5}(2)^5 - \dfrac{1}{5}(0)^5 = \dfrac{32}{5}$

2. $\displaystyle\int_{1}^{5} \sqrt{x - 1}\, dx = \int_{1}^{5} (x - 1)^{1/2}\, dx = \dfrac{2}{3}(x - 1)^{3/2}\Big]_{1}^{5}$
$= \dfrac{2}{3}(4)^{3/2} - \dfrac{2}{3}(0)^{3/2}$
$= \dfrac{2}{3}(8) = \dfrac{16}{3}$

3. $\dfrac{dy}{dx} = 3^x$

4. $\dfrac{dy}{dx} = 3^x$

5. $\dfrac{dy}{dx} = 4(x^3 - 2x^2 + 3)^3(3x^2 - 4x)$

6. $\dfrac{dy}{dx} = 2\sin(4x - 5)\cos(4x - 5) \cdot 4$
$= 8\sin(4x - 5)\cos(4x - 5)$

7. $\dfrac{dy}{dx} = \dfrac{1}{\cos x} \cdot -\sin x = -\tan x$

8. $\dfrac{dy}{dx} = \dfrac{1}{\sin x} \cdot \cos x = \cot x$

9. $\dfrac{dy}{dx} = \dfrac{1}{\sec x + \tan x} \cdot (\sec x \tan x + \sec^2 x)$

$\quad = \dfrac{\sec x \tan x + \sec^2 x}{\sec x + \tan x}$

$\quad = \dfrac{\sec x(\tan x + \sec x)}{\sec x + \tan x}$

$\quad = \sec x$

10. $\dfrac{dy}{dx} = \dfrac{1}{\csc x + \cot x}(-\csc x \cot x - \csc^2 x)$

$\quad = -\dfrac{\csc x \cot x + \csc^2 x}{\csc x + \cot x}$

$\quad = -\dfrac{\csc x(\cot x + \csc x)}{\csc x + \cot x}$

$\quad = -\csc x$

Section 6.2 Exercises

1. $u = 3x$

$du = 3\,dx$

$\dfrac{1}{3}du = dx$

$\displaystyle\int \sin 3x\,dx = \dfrac{1}{3}\int \sin u\,du$

$\quad = -\dfrac{1}{3}\cos u + C$

$\quad = -\dfrac{1}{3}\cos 3x + C$

Check: $\dfrac{d}{dx}\left(-\dfrac{1}{3}\cos 3x + C\right) = -\dfrac{1}{3}(-\sin 3x)(3) = \sin 3x$

2. $u = 2x^2$

$du = 4x\,dx$

$x\,dx = \dfrac{1}{4}du$

$\displaystyle\int x \cos(2x^2)\,dx = \dfrac{1}{4}\int \cos u\,du$

$\quad = \dfrac{1}{4}\sin u + C$

$\quad = \dfrac{1}{4}\sin(2x^2) + C$

Check: $\dfrac{d}{dx}\left(\dfrac{1}{4}\sin(2x^2) + C\right) = \dfrac{1}{4}\cos(2x^2)(4x) = x \cos(2x^2)$

3. $u = 2x$

$du = 2\,dx$

$\dfrac{1}{2}du = dx$

$\displaystyle\int \sec 2x \tan 2x\,dx = \dfrac{1}{2}\int \sec u \tan u\,du$

$\quad = \dfrac{1}{2}\sec u + C$

$\quad = \dfrac{1}{2}\sec 2x + C$

Check: $\dfrac{d}{dx}\left(\dfrac{1}{2}\sec 2x + C\right) = \dfrac{1}{2}\sec 2x \tan 2x \cdot 2 = \sec 2x \tan 2x$

4. $u = 7x - 2$

$du = 7\,dx$

$\dfrac{1}{7}du = dx$

$\displaystyle\int 28(7x - 2)^3\,dx = \dfrac{1}{7}\int 28u^3\,du = u^4 + C = (7x - 2)^4 + C$

Check: $\dfrac{d}{dx}[(7x - 2)^4 + C] = 4(7x - 2)^3(7) = 28(7x - 2)^3$

5. $u = \dfrac{x}{3}$

$du = \dfrac{1}{3}dx$

$3\,du = dx$

$\displaystyle\int \dfrac{dx}{x^2 + 9} = \int \dfrac{3\,du}{9u^2 + 9}$

$\quad = \dfrac{3}{9}\int \dfrac{du}{u^2 + 1}$

$\quad = \dfrac{1}{3}\int \dfrac{du}{u^2 + 1}$

$\quad = \dfrac{1}{3}\tan^{-1} u + C$

$\quad = \dfrac{1}{3}\tan^{-1}\left(\dfrac{x}{3}\right) + C$

Check: $\dfrac{d}{dx}\left(\dfrac{1}{3}\tan^{-1}\dfrac{x}{3} + C\right) = \dfrac{1}{3}\dfrac{1}{1 + \left(\frac{x}{3}\right)^2} \cdot \dfrac{1}{3} = \dfrac{1}{9 + x^2}$

6. $u = 1 - r^3$

$du = -3r^2\,dr$

$-\dfrac{1}{3}du = r^2\,dr$

$\displaystyle\int \dfrac{9r^2\,dr}{\sqrt{1 - r^3}} = 9\left(-\dfrac{1}{3}\right)\int \dfrac{du}{\sqrt{u}}$

$\quad = -3\int u^{-1/2}\,du$

$\quad = -3(2)u^{1/2} + C$

$\quad = -6\sqrt{1 - r^3} + C$

Check: $\dfrac{d}{dx}(-6\sqrt{1 - r^3} + C) = -6\left(\dfrac{1}{2\sqrt{1 - r^3}}\right)(-3r^2)$

$\quad = \dfrac{9r^2}{\sqrt{1 - r^3}}$

7. $u = 1 - \cos\dfrac{t}{2}$

$du = \dfrac{1}{2}\sin\dfrac{t}{2}\,dt$

$2\,du = \sin\dfrac{t}{2}\,dt$

$\displaystyle\int \left(1 - \cos\dfrac{t}{2}\right)^2 \sin\dfrac{t}{2}\,dt = 2\int u^2\,du$

$\quad = \dfrac{2}{3}u^3 + C$

$\quad = \dfrac{2}{3}\left(1 - \cos\dfrac{t}{2}\right)^3 + C$

Check: $\dfrac{d}{dx}\left[\dfrac{2}{3}\left(1 - \cos\dfrac{t}{2}\right)^3 + C\right]$

$\quad = 2\left(1 - \cos\dfrac{t}{2}\right)^2\left(\sin\dfrac{t}{2}\right)\left(\dfrac{1}{2}\right)$

$\quad = \left(1 - \cos\dfrac{t}{2}\right)^2 \sin\dfrac{t}{2}$

8. $u = y^4 + 4y^2 + 1$

$du = (4y^3 + 8y)\, dy$

$du = 4(y^3 + 2y)\, dy$

$\dfrac{1}{4}\, du = (y^3 + 2y)\, dy$

$\displaystyle\int 8(y^4 + 4y^2 + 1)^2 (y^3 + 2y)\, dy = 8\left(\dfrac{1}{4}\right)\int u^2\, du$

$\qquad\qquad = \dfrac{2}{3}u^3 + C$

$\qquad\qquad = \dfrac{2}{3}(y^4 + 4y^2 + 1)^3 + C$

Check: $\dfrac{d}{dx}\left[\dfrac{2}{3}(y^4 + 4y^2 + 1)^3 + C\right]$

$= 2(y^4 + 4y^2 + 1)^2 (4y^3 + 8y)$

$= 8(y^4 + 4y^2 + 1)^2 (y^3 + 2y)$

9. Let $u = 1 - x$

$du = -dx$

$\displaystyle\int \dfrac{dx}{(1-x)^2} = -\int \dfrac{du}{u^2}$

$\qquad = u^{-1} + C$

$\qquad = \dfrac{1}{1-x} + C$

10. Let $u = x + 2$

$du = dx$

$\displaystyle\int \sec^2(x+2)\, dx = \int \sec^2 u\, du$

$\qquad = \tan u + C$

$\qquad = \tan(x+2) + C$

11. Let $u = \tan x$

$du = \sec^2 x\, dx$

$\displaystyle\int \sqrt{\tan x}\, \sec^2 x\, dx = \int u^{1/2}\, du$

$\qquad = \dfrac{2}{3}u^{3/2} + C$

$\qquad = \dfrac{2}{3}(\tan x)^{3/2} + C$

12. Let $u = \theta + \dfrac{\pi}{2}$

$du = d\theta$

$\displaystyle\int \sec\left(\theta + \dfrac{\pi}{2}\right) \tan\left(\theta + \dfrac{\pi}{2}\right) d\theta = \int \sec u \tan u\, du$

$\qquad = \sec u + C$

$\qquad = \sec\left(\theta + \dfrac{\pi}{2}\right) + C$

13. Let $u = \ln x$

$du = \dfrac{1}{x}\, dx$

$\displaystyle\int_e^6 \dfrac{dx}{x \ln x} = \int_1^{\ln 6} \dfrac{du}{u} = \ln|u|\Big]_1^{\ln 6} = \ln(\ln 6)$

14. Let $u = \tan x$

$du = \sec^2 x\, dx$

$\displaystyle\int_{-\pi/4}^{\pi/4} \tan^2 x \sec^2 x\, dx = \int_{-1}^{1} u^2\, du$

$\qquad = \dfrac{1}{3}u^3\Big]_{-1}^{1}$

$\qquad = \dfrac{1}{3}(1) - \dfrac{1}{3}(-1)^3$

$\qquad = \dfrac{1}{3} + \dfrac{1}{3} = \dfrac{2}{3}$

15. Let $u = 3z + 4$

$du = 3\, dz$

$\dfrac{1}{3}\, du = dz$

$\displaystyle\int \cos(3z+4)\, dz = \dfrac{1}{3}\int \cos u\, du$

$\qquad = \dfrac{1}{3}\sin u + C$

$\qquad = \dfrac{1}{3}\sin(3z+4) + C$

16. Let $u = \cot x$

$du = -\csc^2 x\, dx$

$\displaystyle\int \sqrt{\cot x}\, \csc^2 x\, dx = -\int u^{1/2}\, du$

$\qquad = -\dfrac{2}{3}u^{3/2} + C$

$\qquad = -\dfrac{2}{3}(\cot x)^{3/2} + C$

17. Let $u = \ln x$

$du = \dfrac{1}{x}\, dx$

$\displaystyle\int \dfrac{\ln^6 x}{x}\, dx = \int u^6\, du$

$\qquad = \dfrac{1}{7}u^7 + C$

$\qquad = \dfrac{1}{7}(\ln^7 x) + C$

18. Let $u = \tan \dfrac{x}{2}$

$du = \dfrac{1}{2}\sec^2 \dfrac{x}{2}\, dx$

$\displaystyle\int \tan^7 \dfrac{x}{2} \sec^2 \dfrac{x}{2}\, dx = 2\int u^7\, du$

$\qquad = 2 \cdot \dfrac{1}{8}u^8 + C$

$\qquad = \dfrac{1}{4}\tan^8 \dfrac{x}{2} + C$

19. Let $u = s^{4/3} - 8$

$du = \dfrac{4}{3}s^{1/3}\,ds$

$\dfrac{3}{4}du = s^{1/3}\,ds$

$\displaystyle\int s^{1/3}\cos(s^{4/3} - 8)\,ds = \dfrac{3}{4}\int\cos u\,du$

$\qquad\qquad = \dfrac{3}{4}\sin u + C$

$\qquad\qquad = \dfrac{3}{4}\sin(s^{4/3} - 8) + C$

20. $\displaystyle\int\dfrac{dx}{\sin^2 3x} = \int\csc^2 3x\,dx$

Let $u = 3x$

$du = 3\,dx$

$\dfrac{1}{3}du = dx$

$\displaystyle\int\csc^2 3x\,dx = \dfrac{1}{3}\int\csc^2 u\,du$

$\qquad\qquad = -\dfrac{1}{3}\cot u + C$

$\qquad\qquad = -\dfrac{1}{3}\cot(3x) + C$

21. Let $u = \cos(2t + 1)$

$du = -\sin(2t + 1)(2)\,dt$

$-\dfrac{1}{2}du = \sin(2t + 1)\,dt$

$\displaystyle\int\dfrac{\sin(2t + 1)}{\cos^2(2t + 1)}\,dt = -\dfrac{1}{2}\int u^{-2}\,du$

$\qquad\qquad = \dfrac{1}{2}u^{-1} + C$

$\qquad\qquad = \dfrac{1}{2\cos(2t + 1)} + C$

$\qquad\qquad = \dfrac{1}{2}\sec(2t + 1) + C$

22. Let $u = 2 + \sin t$

$du = \cos t\,dt$

$\displaystyle\int\dfrac{6\cos t}{(2 + \sin t)^2}\,dt = 6\int u^{-2}\,du$

$\qquad\qquad = -6u^{-1} + C$

$\qquad\qquad = -\dfrac{6}{2 + \sin t} + C$

23. $\displaystyle\int_{\pi/4}^{3\pi/4}\cot x\,dx = \int_{\pi/4}^{3\pi/4}\dfrac{\cos x}{\sin x}\,dx$

Let $u = \sin x$

$du = \cos x\,dx$

$\displaystyle\int_{\pi/4}^{3\pi/4}\dfrac{\cos x}{\sin x}\,dx = \int_{x = \pi/4}^{x = 3\pi/4}\dfrac{1}{u}\,du$

$\qquad\qquad = \ln|u|\Big]_{x = \pi/4}^{x = 3\pi/4}$

$\qquad\qquad = \ln|\sin x|\Big]_{\pi/4}^{3\pi/4}$

$\qquad\qquad = \ln\left|\dfrac{\sqrt{2}}{2}\right| - \ln\left|\dfrac{\sqrt{2}}{2}\right| = 0$

24. Let $u = x + 2$

$du = dx$

$\displaystyle\int_0^7\dfrac{dx}{x + 2} = \int_2^9\dfrac{1}{u}\,du$

$\qquad\qquad = \ln u\Big]_2^9$

$\qquad\qquad = \ln 9 - \ln 2 \approx 1.504$

25. Let $u = x^2 + 1$

$du = 2x\,dx$

$x\,dx = \dfrac{1}{2}du$

$\displaystyle\int_{-1}^3\dfrac{x\,dx}{x^2 + 1} = \dfrac{1}{2}\int_2^{10}\dfrac{1}{u}\,du$

$\qquad\qquad = \dfrac{1}{2}\ln|u|\Big]_2^{10}$

$\qquad\qquad = \dfrac{1}{2}(\ln 10 - \ln 2) = \dfrac{1}{2}\ln 5 \approx 0.805$

26. $\displaystyle\int_0^5 \frac{40\,dx}{x^2+25} = \int_0^5 \frac{\dfrac{40}{25}}{\left(\dfrac{x}{5}\right)^2 + \left(\dfrac{25}{25}\right)^2}\,dx$

$\displaystyle = \frac{40}{25}\int_0^5 \frac{1}{\left(\dfrac{x}{5}\right)^2 + 1}\,dx$

Let $u = \dfrac{x}{5}$

$du = \dfrac{1}{5}\,dx$

$5\,du = dx$

$\displaystyle\int_0^5 \frac{40\,dx}{x^2+25} = \frac{8}{5}(5)\int_0^1 \frac{1}{u^2+1}\,du$

$\displaystyle = 8\arctan u\Big]_0^1$

$= 8(\arctan 1)$

$\displaystyle = 8\left(\frac{\pi}{4}\right) = 2\pi$

27. $\displaystyle\int \frac{dx}{\cot 3x} = \int \frac{\sin 3x}{\cos 3x}\,dx$

Let $u = \cos 3x$

$du = -3\sin 3x\,dx$

$-\dfrac{1}{3}\,du = \sin 3x\,dx$

$\displaystyle\int \frac{dx}{\cot 3x} = -\frac{1}{3}\int \frac{1}{u}\,du$

$\displaystyle = -\frac{1}{3}\ln|u| + C$

$\displaystyle = -\frac{1}{3}\ln|\cos 3x| + C$

(An equivalent expression is $\dfrac{1}{3}\ln|\sec 3x| + C$.)

28. Let $u = 5x + 8$

$du = 5\,dx$

$\dfrac{1}{5}\,du = dx$

$\displaystyle\int \frac{dx}{\sqrt{5x+8}} = \frac{1}{5}\int u^{-1/2}\,du$

$\displaystyle = \frac{1}{5}\cdot 2u^{1/2} + C$

$\displaystyle = \frac{2}{5}\sqrt{5x+8} + C$

29. $\displaystyle\int \sec x\,dx = \int \sec x\cdot\left(\frac{\sec x + \tan x}{\sec x + \tan x}\right)dx$

$=$

$\displaystyle\int \frac{\sec^2 x + \sec x\tan x}{\sec x + \tan x}\,dx$

Let $u = \sec x + \tan x$

$du = \sec x\tan x + \sec^2 x\,dx$

$\displaystyle\int \sec x\,dx = \int \frac{1}{u}\,du = \ln|u| + C = \ln|\sec x + \tan x| + C$

30. $\displaystyle\int \csc x\,dx = \int \csc x\left(\frac{\csc x + \cot x}{\csc x + \cot x}\right)dx$

$\displaystyle = \int \frac{\csc^2 x + \csc x\cot x}{\csc x + \cot x}\,dx$

Let $u = \csc x + \cot x$

$du = -\csc x\cot x - \csc^2 x\,dx$

$\displaystyle\int \csc x\,dx = -\int \frac{1}{u}\,du$

$= -\ln|u| + C$

$= -\ln|\csc x + \cot x| + C$

31. Let $u = y + 1$

$du = dy$

$\displaystyle\int_0^3 \sqrt{y+1}\,dy = \int_1^4 u^{1/2}\,du$

$\displaystyle = \frac{2}{3}u^{3/2}\Big]_1^4$

$\displaystyle = \frac{2}{3}(4)^{3/2} - \frac{2}{3}(1)^{3/2}$

$\displaystyle = \frac{2}{3}(8) - \frac{2}{3} = \frac{14}{3}$

32. Let $u = 1 - r^2$

$du = -2r\,dr$

$-\dfrac{1}{2}\,du = r\,dr$

$\displaystyle\int_0^1 r\sqrt{1-r^2}\,dr = -\frac{1}{2}\int_1^0 u^{1/2}\,du$

$\displaystyle = -\frac{1}{2}\cdot\frac{2}{3}u^{3/2}\Big]_1^0$

$\displaystyle = -\frac{1}{3}(0) + \frac{1}{3}(1) = \frac{1}{3}$

33. Let $u = \tan x$

$du = \sec^2 x\,dx$

$\displaystyle\int_{-\pi/4}^0 \tan x\sec^2 x\,dx = \int_{-1}^0 u\,du$

$\displaystyle = \frac{1}{2}u^2\Big]_{-1}^0$

$\displaystyle = \frac{1}{2}(0) - \frac{1}{2}(-1)^2$

$\displaystyle = -\frac{1}{2}$

34. Let $u = 4 + r^2$

$du = 2r\,dr$

$\dfrac{1}{2}\,du = r\,dr$

$\displaystyle\int_{-1}^1 \frac{5r}{(4+r^2)^2}\,dr = \frac{5}{2}\int_5^5 u^{-2}\,du = 0$

35. Let $u = 1 + \theta^{3/2}$

$$du = \frac{3}{2}\theta^{1/2}\,d\theta$$

$$\frac{2}{3}\,du = \theta^{1/2}\,d\theta$$

$$\int_0^1 \frac{10\sqrt{\theta}}{(1+\theta^{3/2})^2}\,d\theta = \frac{2}{3}(10)\int_1^2 u^{-2}\,du$$

$$= -\frac{20}{3}u^{-1}\Big]_1^2$$

$$= -\frac{20}{3}\left(\frac{1}{2}-1\right)$$

$$= -\frac{20}{3}\left(-\frac{1}{2}\right) = \frac{10}{3}$$

36. Let $u = 4 + 3\sin x$

$$du = 3\cos x\,dx$$

$$\frac{1}{3}\,du = \cos x\,dx$$

$$\int_{-\pi}^{\pi} \frac{\cos x}{\sqrt{4+3\sin x}}\,dx = \frac{1}{3}\int_4^4 u^{-1/2}\,du = 0$$

37. Let $u = t^5 + 2t$

$$du = (5t^4 + 2)\,dt$$

$$\int_0^1 \sqrt{t^5 + 2t}\,(5t^4+2)\,dt = \int_0^3 u^{1/2}\,du$$

$$= \frac{2}{3}u^{3/2}\Big]_0^3$$

$$= \frac{2}{3}(3)^{3/2}$$

$$= \frac{2}{3}\sqrt{27} = 2\sqrt{3}$$

38. Let $u = \cos 2\theta$

$$du = -2\sin 2\theta\,d\theta$$

$$-\frac{1}{2}\,du = \sin 2\theta\,d\theta$$

$$\int_0^{\pi/6} \cos^{-3} 2\theta \sin 2\theta\,d\theta = -\frac{1}{2}\int_1^{1/2} u^{-3}\,du$$

$$= -\frac{1}{2}\cdot\left(-\frac{1}{2}\right)u^{-2}\Big]_1^{1/2}$$

$$= \frac{1}{4}\left(\left(\frac{1}{2}\right)^{-2} - 1\right)$$

$$= \frac{1}{4}(3) = \frac{3}{4}$$

39. $\dfrac{dy}{dx} = (y+5)(x+2)$

$$\frac{dy}{y+5} = (x+2)dx$$

Integrate both sides.

$$\int \frac{dy}{y+5} = \int (x+2)\,dx$$

On the left,

let $u = y + 5$

$$du = dy$$

$$\int \frac{1}{u}\,du = \frac{1}{2}x^2 + 2x + C$$

$$\ln|u| = \frac{1}{2}x^2 + 2x + C$$

$$\ln|y+5| = \frac{1}{2}x^2 + 2x + C$$

$$|y+5| = e^{(1/2)x^2 + 2x + C}$$

$$|y+5| = e^C e^{(1/2)x^2 + 2x}$$

We now let $C' = e^C$ or $C' = -e^C$, depending on whether $(y+5)$ is positive or negative. Then

$$y + 5 = C'e^{(1/2)x^2 + 2x}$$

$$y = C'e^{(1/2)x^2 + 2x} - 5$$

Since C' represents an arbitrary constant (note that even the value $C' = 0$ gives a solution to the original differential equation), we may write the solution as

$$y = Ce^{(1/2)x^2 + 2x} - 5.$$

40. $\dfrac{dy}{dx} = x\sqrt{y}\cos^2\sqrt{y}$

$$\frac{dy}{\sqrt{y}\cos^2\sqrt{y}} = x\,dx$$

Integrate both sides.

$$\int \frac{dy}{\sqrt{y}\cos^2\sqrt{y}} = \int x\,dx$$

On the left, let $u = \sqrt{y}$

$$du = \frac{1}{2}y^{-1/2}\,dy$$

$$2\,du = y^{-1/2}\,dy$$

$$2\int \frac{du}{\cos^2 u} = \frac{1}{2}x^2 + C$$

$$2\int \sec^2 u\,du = \frac{1}{2}x^2 + C$$

$$2\tan u = \frac{1}{2}x^2 + C$$

$$2\tan\sqrt{y} = \frac{1}{2}x^2 + C$$

$$\tan\sqrt{y} = \frac{1}{4}x^2 + C$$

(Note: technically, C is now $C' = \dfrac{C}{2}$. But C's are generic.)

$$\sqrt{y} = \tan^{-1}\left(\frac{x^2}{4} + C\right)$$

$$y = \left[\tan^{-1}\left(\frac{x^2}{4} + C\right)\right]^2$$

41. $\dfrac{dy}{dx} = (\cos x)e^{y+\sin x}$

$\dfrac{dy}{dx} = (\cos x)(e^y \, e^{\sin x})$

$\dfrac{dy}{e^y} = \cos x \, e^{\sin x} \, dx$

Integrate both sides.

$\displaystyle \int \dfrac{dy}{e^y} = \int \cos x \, e^{\sin x} \, dx$

On the right, let $u = \sin x$

$du = \cos x \, dx$

$-e^{-y} = \displaystyle \int e^u \, du$

$-e^{-y} = e^u + C$

$-e^{-y} = e^{\sin x} + C$

$e^{-y} = -e^{\sin x} + C$

(Note: technically C is now $C' = -C$.)

$-y = \ln\,(C - e^{\sin x})$

$y = -\ln\,(C - e^{\sin x})$

42. $\dfrac{dy}{dx} = e^{x-y}$

$\dfrac{dy}{dx} = e^x e^{-y}$

$\dfrac{dy}{e^{-y}} = e^x \, dx$

Integrate both sides.

$\displaystyle \int \dfrac{dy}{e^{-y}} = \int e^x \, dx$

$\displaystyle \int e^y \, dy = \int e^x \, dx$

$e^y = e^x + C$

$y = \ln\,(e^x + C)$

43. $\dfrac{dy}{dx} = -2xy^2$

$-\dfrac{dy}{y^2} = 2x \, dx$

$-\displaystyle\int \dfrac{dy}{y^2} = \int 2x \, dx$

$y^{-1} = x^2 + C$

$y = \dfrac{1}{x^2 + C}$

$y(1) = \dfrac{1}{1 + C} = 0.25$

$1 + C = 4$

$C = 3$

$y = \dfrac{1}{x^2 + 3}$

44. $\dfrac{dy}{dx} = \dfrac{4\sqrt{y} \ln x}{x}$

$\dfrac{dy}{\sqrt{y}} = 4\,\dfrac{\ln x}{x} \, dx$

Integrate both sides.

$\displaystyle \int \dfrac{dy}{\sqrt{y}} = 4\int \dfrac{\ln x}{x} \, dx$

On the right, let $u = \ln x$

$du = \dfrac{1}{x} \, dx$

$2y^{1/2} = 4\displaystyle\int u \, du$

$2y^{1/2} = 4\left(\dfrac{1}{2}u^2\right) + C$

$2y^{1/2} = 2(\ln x)^2 + C$

$y^{1/2} = (\ln x)^2 + C$

$y = [(\ln x)^2 + C]^2$

$y(e) = [(\ln e)^2 + C]^2 = 1$

$(1 + C)^2 = 1$

$C = 0$

$y = (\ln x)^4$

Note: Absolute value signs are not needed because the original problem involved $\ln x$, so we know that $x > 0$.

45. (a) Let $u = x + 1$

$du = dx$

$\displaystyle \int \sqrt{x + 1} \, dx = \int u^{1/2} \, du$

$\qquad = \dfrac{2}{3}u^{3/2} + C$

$\qquad = \dfrac{2}{3}(x + 1)^{3/2} + C$

Alternatively, $\dfrac{d}{dx}\left(\dfrac{2}{3}(x + 1)^{3/2} + C\right) = \sqrt{x + 1}.$

(b) By Part 1 of the Fundamental Theorem of Calculus, $\dfrac{dy_1}{dx} = \sqrt{x + 1}$ and $\dfrac{dy_2}{dx} = \sqrt{x + 1}$, so both are antiderivatives of $\sqrt{x + 1}$.

(c) Using NINT to find the values of y_1 and y_2, we have:

x	0	1	2	3	4
y_1	0	1.219	2.797	4.667	6.787
y_2	-4.667	-3.448	-1.869	0	2.120
$y_1 - y_2$	4.667	4.667	4.667	4.667	4.667

$C = 4\dfrac{2}{3}$

(d) $C = y_1 - y_2$

$\qquad = \displaystyle\int_0^x \sqrt{x + 1} \, dx - \int_3^x \sqrt{x + 1} \, dx$

$\qquad = \displaystyle\int_0^x \sqrt{x + 1} \, dx + \int_x^3 \sqrt{x + 1} \, dx$

$\qquad = \displaystyle\int_0^3 \sqrt{x + 1} \, dx$

46. (a) $\frac{d}{dx}[F(x) + C]$ should equal $f(x)$.

(b) The slope field should help you visualize the solution curve $y = F(x)$.

(c) The graphs of $y_1 = F(x)$ and $y_2 = \int_0^x f(t)\, dt$ should differ only by a vertical shift C.

(d) A table of values for $y_1 - y_2$ should show that $y_1 - y_2 = C$ for any value of x in the appropriate domain.

(e) The graph of f should be the same as the graph of NDER of $F(x)$.

(f) First, we need to find $F(x)$. Let $u = x^2 + 1$, $du = 2x\, dx$.

$$\int \frac{x}{\sqrt{x^2 + 1}}\, dx = \int \frac{1}{2} u^{-1/2}\, du$$
$$= u^{1/2}$$
$$= \sqrt{x^2 + 1} + C$$

Therefore, we may let $F(x) = \sqrt{x^2 + 1}$.

a) $\frac{d}{dx}(\sqrt{x^2 + 1} + C) = \frac{1}{2\sqrt{x^2 + 1}}(2x)$
$$= \frac{x}{\sqrt{x^2 + 1}} = f(x)$$

b)

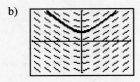

[−4, 4] by [−3, 3]

c)

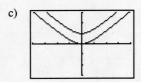

[−4, 4] by [−3, 3]

d)

x	0	1	2	3	4
y_1	1.000	1.414	2.236	3.162	4.123
y_2	0.000	0.414	1.236	2.162	3.123
$y_1 - y_2$	1	1	1	1	1

e)

[−4, 4] by [−3, 3]

47. Let $u = x^4 + 9$, $du = 4x^3\, dx$.

(a) $\int_0^1 \frac{x^3\, dx}{\sqrt{x^4 + 9}} = \int_9^{10} \frac{1}{4} u^{-1/2}\, du = \frac{1}{2} u^{1/2} \Big]_9^{10}$
$$= \frac{1}{2}\sqrt{10} - \frac{1}{2}\sqrt{9}$$
$$= \frac{1}{2}\sqrt{10} - \frac{3}{2} \approx 0.081$$

(b) $\int \frac{x^3}{x^4 + 9}\, dx = \int \frac{1}{4} u^{-1/2}\, du$
$$= \frac{1}{2} u^{1/2} + C$$
$$= \frac{1}{2}\sqrt{x^4 + 9} + C$$

$\int_0^1 \frac{x^3}{x^4 + 9}\, dx = \frac{1}{2}\sqrt{x^4 + 9} \Big]_0^1$
$$= \frac{1}{2}\sqrt{10} - \frac{1}{2}\sqrt{9}$$
$$= \frac{1}{2}\sqrt{10} - \frac{3}{2} \approx 0.081$$

48. Let $u = 1 - \cos 3x$, $du = 3 \sin 3x\, dx$.

(a) $\int_{\pi/6}^{\pi/3} (1 - \cos 3x) \sin 3x\, dx = \int_1^2 \frac{1}{3} u\, du = \frac{1}{6} u^2 \Big]_1^2$
$$= \frac{1}{6}(2)^2 - \frac{1}{6}(1)^2 = \frac{1}{2}$$

(b) $\int (1 - \cos 3x) \sin 3x\, dx = \int \frac{1}{3} u\, du$
$$= \frac{1}{6} u^2 + C$$
$$= \frac{1}{6}(1 - \cos 3x)^2 + C$$

$\int_{\pi/6}^{\pi/3} (1 - \cos 3x) \sin 3x\, dx = \frac{1}{6}(1 - \cos 3x)^2 \Big]_{\pi/6}^{\pi/3}$
$$= \frac{1}{6}(2)^2 - \frac{1}{6}(1)^2 = \frac{1}{2}$$

49. We show that $f'(x) = \tan x$ and $f(3) = 5$, where

$f(x) = \ln \left| \frac{\cos 3}{\cos x} \right| + 5$.

$f'(x) = \frac{d}{dx}\left(\ln \left| \frac{\cos 3}{\cos x} \right| + 5 \right)$
$$= \frac{d}{dx}(\ln |\cos 3| - \ln |\cos x| + 5)$$
$$= -\frac{d}{dx} \ln |\cos x|$$
$$= -\frac{1}{\cos x}(-\sin x) = \tan x$$

$f(3) = \ln \left| \frac{\cos 3}{\cos 3} \right| + 5 = (\ln 1) + 5 = 5$

50. (a) $u = \cot 2\theta, \, du = -2 \csc^2 2\theta \, d\theta$

$$\int \csc^2 2\theta \cot 2\theta \, d\theta = -\frac{1}{2} \int u \, du$$

$$= -\frac{1}{2} \cdot \frac{u^2}{2} + C$$

$$= -\frac{u^2}{4} + C$$

$$= -\frac{1}{4} \cot^2 2\theta + C$$

$$F_1(\theta) = -\frac{1}{4} \cot^2 2\theta$$

(b) $u = \csc 2\theta, \, du = -2 \csc 2\theta \cot 2\theta \, d\theta$

$$\int \csc^2 2\theta \cot 2\theta \, du = -\frac{1}{2} \int u \, du$$

$$= -\frac{1}{2} \cdot \frac{u^2}{2} + C$$

$$= -\frac{u^2}{4} + C$$

$$= -\frac{1}{4} \csc^2 2\theta + C$$

$$F_2(\theta) = -\frac{1}{4} \csc^2 2\theta$$

(c) $F_1{}'(\theta) = \left(-\frac{1}{2} \cot 2\theta\right)(-2 \csc^2 2\theta) = \csc^2 2\theta \cot 2\theta$

$$F_2{}'(\theta) = \left(-\frac{1}{2} \csc 2\theta\right)(-2 \csc 2\theta \cot 2\theta)$$

$$= \csc^2 2\theta \cot 2\theta$$

(d) $F_1(\theta) = F_2(\theta) + b$

$$-\frac{1}{4} \cot^2 2\theta = -\frac{1}{4} \csc^2 2\theta + b$$

$$b = \frac{1}{4}(\csc^2 2\theta - \cot^2 2\theta)$$

$$= \frac{1}{4}\left(\frac{1 - \cos^2 2\theta}{\sin^2 2\theta}\right) = \frac{1}{4}\left(\frac{\sin^2 2\theta}{\sin^2 2\theta}\right) = \frac{1}{4}$$

51. (a) $u = \sin x, \, du = \cos x \, dx$

$$\int 2 \sin x \cos x \, dx = \int 2u \, du = u^2 + C = \sin^2 x + C$$

(b) $u = \cos x, \, du = -\sin x \, dx$

$$\int 2 \sin x \cos x \, dx = \int (-2u) \, du$$

$$= -u^2 + C$$

$$= -\cos^2 x + C$$

(c) $u = 2x, \, du = 2 \, dx$

$$\int 2 \sin x \cos x \, dx = \int \sin 2x \, dx$$

$$= \int \frac{1}{2} \sin u \, du$$

$$= -\frac{1}{2} \cos u + C$$

$$= -\frac{1}{2} \cos 2x + C$$

(d) $\dfrac{d}{dx}(\sin^2 x + C) = 2 \sin x \cos x$

$$\frac{d}{dx}(-\cos^2 x + C) = (-2 \cos x)(-\sin x) = 2 \sin x \cos x$$

$$\frac{d}{dx}\left(-\frac{1}{2} \cos 2x + C\right) = \left(\frac{1}{2} \sin 2x\right)(2)$$

$$= \sin 2x$$

$$= 2 \sin x \cos x$$

■ Section 6.3 Integration by Parts
(pp. 323–329)

Exploration 1   Evaluating and Checking Integrals

1. $u = \ln x \Rightarrow du = \dfrac{dx}{x}$ and $dv = dx \Rightarrow v = x$. Thus,

$$\int \ln x \, dx = \int u \, dv$$

$$= uv - \int v \, du$$

$$= x \ln x - \int dx$$

$$= x \ln x - x + C$$

2. $\dfrac{d}{dx}(x \ln x - x) = \ln x + x\left(\dfrac{1}{x}\right) - 1 = \ln x$

3. The slope field of $\dfrac{dy}{dx} = \ln x$ shows the direction of the curve as it is graphed from left to right across the window.

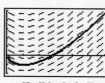

[0, 6] by [−2, 5]

4. The graph of $y_2 = x \ln x - x$ appears to be a vertical shift of the graph of $y_1 = \int_1^x \ln t \, dt$ (down 1 unit). Thus, y_2 appears to be an antiderivative of $\ln x$ which supports $x \ln x - x + C$ as the set of all antiderivatives of $\ln x$.

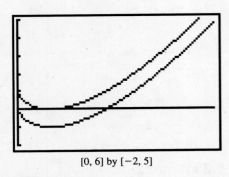

[0, 6] by [−2, 5]

Quick Review 6.3

1. $\dfrac{dy}{dx} = (x^3)(\cos 2x)(2) + (\sin 2x)(3x^2)$

$\quad = 2x^3 \cos 2x + 3x^2 \sin 2x$

2. $\dfrac{dy}{dx} = (e^{2x})\left(\dfrac{3}{3x+1}\right) + \ln(3x+1)(2e^{2x})$

$\quad = \dfrac{3e^{2x}}{3x+1} + 2e^{2x} \ln(3x+1)$

3. $\dfrac{dy}{dx} = \dfrac{1}{1+(2x)^2} \cdot 2$

$\quad = \dfrac{2}{1+4x^2}$

4. $\dfrac{dy}{dx} = \dfrac{1}{\sqrt{1-(x+3)^2}}$

5. $\quad y = \tan^{-1} 3x$

$\quad \tan y = 3x$

$\quad x = \dfrac{1}{3}\tan y$

6. $\quad y = \cos^{-1}(x+1)$

$\quad \cos y = x + 1$

$\quad x = \cos y - 1$

7. $\displaystyle\int_0^1 \sin \pi x \, dx = -\dfrac{1}{\pi}\cos \pi x \Big]_0^1$

$\quad = -\dfrac{1}{\pi}\cos \pi + \dfrac{1}{\pi}\cos 0$

$\quad = -\dfrac{1}{\pi}(-1) + \dfrac{1}{\pi} = \dfrac{2}{\pi}$

8. $\dfrac{dy}{dx} = e^{2x}$

$\quad dy = e^{2x} \, dx$

Integrate both sides.

$\quad \displaystyle\int dy = \int e^{2x} \, dx$

$\quad y = \dfrac{1}{2}e^{2x} + C$

9. $\dfrac{dy}{dx} = x + \sin x$

$\quad dy = (x + \sin x)dx$

Integrate both sides.

$\quad \displaystyle\int dy = \int (x + \sin x) \, dx$

$\quad y = \dfrac{1}{2}x^2 - \cos x + C$

$\quad y(0) = -1 + C = 2$

$\qquad\qquad C = 3$

$\quad y = \dfrac{1}{2}x^2 - \cos x + 3$

10. $\dfrac{d}{dx}\left(\dfrac{1}{2}e^x(\sin x - \cos x)\right)$

$\quad = \dfrac{1}{2}e^x(\cos x + \sin x) + (\sin x - \cos x)\dfrac{1}{2}e^x$

$\quad = \dfrac{1}{2}e^x \cos x + \dfrac{1}{2}e^x \sin x + \dfrac{1}{2}e^x \sin x - \dfrac{1}{2}e^x \cos x$

$\quad = e^x \sin x$

Section 6.3 Exercises

1. Let $u = x$ $\qquad\qquad dv = \sin x \, dx$

$\qquad du = dx$ $\qquad\qquad v = -\cos x$

$\displaystyle\int x \sin x \, dx = -x \cos x + \int \cos x \, dx$

$\qquad\qquad\qquad = -x \cos x + \sin x + C$

Check: $\dfrac{d}{dx}(-x \cos x + \sin x + C)$

$\qquad\qquad = (-x)(-\sin x) + (\cos x)(-1) + \cos x$

$\qquad\qquad = x \sin x$

2. Let $u = x^2$ $\qquad\qquad dv = \cos x \, dx$

$\qquad du = 2x \, dx$ $\qquad\quad v = \sin x$

$\displaystyle\int x^2 \cos x \, dx = x^2 \sin x - 2\int x \sin x \, dx$

Using the result from Exercise 1,

$\quad = x^2 \sin x - 2[-x \cos x + \sin x] + C$

$\quad = 2x \cos x + (x^2 - 2)\sin x + C$

Check: $\dfrac{d}{dx}[2x \cos x + (x^2 - 2)\sin x + C]$

$\quad = (2x)(-\sin x) + (2 \cos x)(1) + (x^2 - 2)(\cos x)$

$\qquad\qquad\qquad + (\sin x)(2x)$

$\quad = x^2 \cos x$

3. Let $u = \ln y$ $\qquad$ $dv = y\,dy$

$\qquad du = \dfrac{1}{y}\,dy$ $\qquad$ $v = \dfrac{1}{2}y^2$

$\int y\ln y\,dy = \dfrac{1}{2}y^2\ln y - \int \dfrac{1}{2}y^2 \cdot \dfrac{1}{y}\,dy$

$\qquad = \dfrac{1}{2}y^2\ln y - \dfrac{1}{2}\int y\,dy$

$\qquad = \dfrac{1}{2}y^2\ln y - \dfrac{1}{4}y^2 + C$

Check: $\dfrac{d}{dy}\left[\dfrac{1}{2}y^2\ln y - \dfrac{1}{4}y^2 + C\right]$

$= \left(\dfrac{1}{2}y^2\right)\left(\dfrac{1}{y}\right) + (\ln y)(y) - \dfrac{1}{2}y$

$= y\ln y$

4. Let $\quad u = \tan^{-1} y$ $\qquad$ $dv = dy$

$\qquad du = \dfrac{1}{1 + y^2}\,dy$ $\qquad$ $v = y$

$\int \tan^{-1} y\,dy = y\tan^{-1} y - \int \dfrac{y}{1 + y^2}\,dy$

Let $w = 1 + y^2$

$\qquad dw = 2y\,dy$

$y\tan^{-1} y - \int \dfrac{y}{1 + y^2}\,dy = y\tan^{-1} y - \dfrac{1}{2}\int \dfrac{1}{w}\,dw$

$\qquad = y\tan^{-1} y - \dfrac{1}{2}\ln|w| + C$

$\qquad = y\tan^{-1} y - \dfrac{1}{2}\ln(1 + y^2) + C$

Check: $\dfrac{d}{dy}\left[y\tan^{-1} y - \dfrac{1}{2}\ln(1 + y^2) + C\right]$

$= \dfrac{y}{1 + y^2} + \tan^{-1} y - \dfrac{1}{2}\left(\dfrac{1}{1 + y^2}\right)(2y) = \tan^{-1} y$

5. Let $u = x$ $\qquad$ $dv = \sec^2 x\,dx$

$\qquad du = dx$ $\qquad$ $v = \tan x$

$\int x\sec^2 x\,dx = x\tan x - \int \tan x\,dx$

$\qquad = x\tan x - \int \dfrac{\sin x}{\cos x}\,dx$

$\qquad = x\tan x + \ln|\cos x| + C$

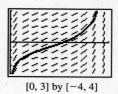

$[-1.5, 1.5]$ by $[-1, 4]$

6. Let $u = \sin^{-1}\theta$ $\qquad$ $dv = d\theta$

$\qquad du = \dfrac{1}{\sqrt{1 - \theta^2}}$ $\qquad$ $v = \theta$

$\int \sin^{-1}\theta\,d\theta = \theta\sin^{-1}\theta - \int \theta \dfrac{1}{\sqrt{1 - \theta^2}}\,d\theta$

Let $w = 1 - \theta^2$

$\qquad dw = -2\theta\,d\theta$

$\theta\sin^{-1}\theta - \int \theta \dfrac{1}{\sqrt{1 - \theta^2}}\,d\theta = \theta\sin^{-1}\theta + \dfrac{1}{2}\int \dfrac{1}{\sqrt{w}}\,dw$

$\qquad = \theta\sin^{-1}\theta + w^{1/2} + C$

$\qquad = \theta\sin^{-1}\theta + \sqrt{1 - \theta^2} + C$

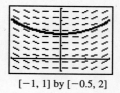

$[-1, 1]$ by $[-0.5, 2]$

7. Let $\quad u = t^2$ $\qquad$ $dv = \sin t\,dt$

$\qquad du = 2t\,dt$ $\qquad$ $v = -\cos t$

$\int t^2\sin t\,dt = -t^2\cos t + 2\int (\cos t)(t)\,dt$

Let $u = t$ $\qquad$ $dv = \cos t\,dt$

$\qquad du = dt$ $\qquad$ $v = \sin t$

$-t^2\cos t + 2\int t\cos t\,dt$

$= -t^2\cos t + 2t\sin t - 2\int \sin t\,dt$

$= -t^2\cos t + 2t\sin t + 2\cos t + C$

$= (2 - t^2)\cos t + 2t\sin t + C$

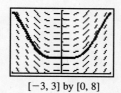

$[-3, 3]$ by $[0, 8]$

8. Let $u = t$ $\qquad$ $dv = \csc^2 t\,dt$

$\qquad du = dt$ $\qquad$ $v = -\cot t$

$\int t\csc^2 t\,dt = -t\cot t + \int \cot t\,dt$

$\qquad = -t\cot t + \int \dfrac{\cos t}{\sin t}\,dt$

$\qquad = -t\cot t + \ln|\sin t| + C$

$[0, 3]$ by $[-4, 4]$

9. Let $u = \ln x$ $\qquad$ $dv = x^3\,dx$

$\qquad du = \dfrac{1}{x}\,dx$ $\qquad$ $v = \dfrac{1}{4}x^4$

$$\int x^3 \ln x\,dx = \frac{1}{4}x^4 \ln x - \frac{1}{4}\int x^4\left(\frac{1}{x}\right) dx$$
$$= \frac{1}{4}x^4 \ln x - \frac{1}{4}\int x^3\,dx$$
$$= \frac{1}{4}x^4 \ln x - \frac{1}{16}x^4 + C$$

10. Use tabular integration with $f(x) = x^4$ and $g(x) = e^{-x}$.

$f(x)$ and its derivatives	$g(x)$ and its integrals
x^4 $\quad$ (+)	e^{-x}
$4x^3$ $\quad$ (−)	$-e^{-x}$
$12x^2$ $\quad$ (+)	e^{-x}
$24x$ $\quad$ (−)	$-e^{-x}$
24 $\quad$ (+)	e^{-x}
0	$-e^{-x}$

$$\int x^4 e^{-x}\,dx$$
$$= -x^4 e^{-x} - 4x^3 e^{-x} - 12x^2 e^{-x} - 24x e^{-x} - 24e^{-x} + C$$
$$= -(x^4 + 4x^3 + 12x^2 + 24x + 24)e^{-x} + C$$

11. Let $u = x^2 - 5x$ $\qquad$ $dv = e^x\,dx$

$\qquad du = (2x - 5)\,dx$ $\qquad$ $v = e^x$

$$\int (x^2 - 5x)e^x\,dx = (x^2 - 5x)e^x - \int e^x(2x - 5)\,dx$$

Let $\quad u = 2x - 5$ $\qquad$ $dv = e^x\,dx$

$\qquad du = 2\,dx$ $\qquad$ $v = e^x$

$$(x^2 - 5x)e^x - \int e^x(2x - 5)\,dx$$
$$= (x^2 - 5x)e^x - (2x - 5)e^x + \int 2e^x\,dx$$
$$= (x^2 - 5x)e^x - (2x - 5)e^x + 2e^x + C$$
$$= (x^2 - 7x + 7)e^x + C$$

12. Use tabular integration with $f(x) = x^3$ and $g(x) = e^{-2x}$.

$f(x)$ and its derivatives	$g(x)$ and its integrals
x^3 $\quad$ (+)	e^{-2x}
$3x^2$ $\quad$ (−)	$-\dfrac{1}{2}e^{-2x}$
$6x$ $\quad$ (+)	$\dfrac{1}{4}e^{-2x}$
6 $\quad$ (−)	$-\dfrac{1}{8}e^{-2x}$
0	$\dfrac{1}{16}e^{-2x}$

$$\int x^3 e^{-2x}\,dx$$
$$= -\frac{1}{2}x^3 e^{-2x} - \frac{3}{4}x^2 e^{-2x} - \frac{3}{4}x e^{-2x} - \frac{3}{8}e^{-2x} + C$$
$$= -\left(\frac{x^3}{2} + \frac{3x^2}{4} + \frac{3x}{4} + \frac{3}{8}\right)e^{-2x} + C$$

13. Let $u = e^y$ $\qquad$ $dv = \sin y\,dy$

$\qquad du = e^y\,dy$ $\qquad$ $v = -\cos y$

$$\int e^y \sin y\,dy = -e^y \cos y + \int \cos y\, e^y\,dy$$

Let $\quad u = e^y$ $\qquad$ $dv = \cos y\,dy$

$\qquad du = e^y\,dy$ $\qquad$ $v = \sin y$

$$\int e^y \sin y\,dy = -e^y \cos y + e^y \sin y - \int \sin y\, e^y\,dy$$
$$2\int e^y \sin y\,dy = -e^y \cos y + e^y \sin y$$
$$\int e^y \sin y\,dy = \frac{1}{2}e^y(\sin y - \cos y) + C$$

14. Let $u = e^{-y}$ $\qquad$ $dv = \cos y\,dy$

$\qquad du = -e^{-y}\,dy$ $\qquad$ $v = \sin y$

$$\int e^{-y}\cos y\,dy = e^{-y}\sin y + \int \sin y\, e^{-y}\,dy$$

Let $u = e^{-y}$ $\qquad$ $dv = \sin y\,dy$

$\qquad du = -e^{-y}\,dy$ $\qquad$ $v = -\cos y$

$$\int e^{-y} \cos y\,dy = e^{-y} \sin y - e^{-y}\cos y - \int e^{-y} \cos y\,dy$$
$$2\int e^{-y} \cos y\,dy = e^{-y} \sin y - e^{-y} \cos y$$
$$\int e^{-y} \cos y\,dy = \frac{1}{2}e^{-y}(\sin y - \cos y) + C$$

15. Use tabular integration with $f(x) = x^2$ and $g(x) = \sin 2x$.

$f(x)$ and its derivatives	$g(x)$ and its integrals
x^2 $\quad$ (+)	$\sin 2x$
$2x$ $\quad$ (−)	$-\dfrac{1}{2}\cos 2x$
2 $\quad$ (+)	$-\dfrac{1}{4}\sin 2x$
0	$\dfrac{1}{8}\cos 2x$

$$\int x^2 \sin 2x\, dx = -\frac{1}{2}x^2\cos 2x + \frac{1}{2}x\sin 2x + \frac{1}{4}\cos 2x + C$$

$$= \left(\frac{1-2x^2}{4}\right)\cos 2x + \frac{x}{2}\sin 2x + C$$

$$\int_0^{\pi/2} x^2 \sin 2x\, dx = \left[\left(\frac{1-2x^2}{4}\right)\cos 2x + \frac{x}{2}\sin 2x\right]_0^{\pi/2}$$

$$= \left(\frac{1-2\left(\frac{\pi}{2}\right)^2}{4}\right)(-1) + 0 - \frac{1}{4}(1) - 0$$

$$= \frac{\pi^2}{8} - \frac{1}{2} \approx 0.734$$

Check: $\text{NINT}\left(x^2\sin 2x, x, 0, \dfrac{\pi}{2}\right) \approx 0.734$

16. Use tabular integration with $f(x) = x^3$ and $g(x) = \cos 2x$.

$f(x)$ and its derivatives	$g(x)$ and its integrals
x^3 $\quad$ (+)	$\cos 2x$
$3x^2$ $\quad$ (−)	$\dfrac{1}{2}\sin 2x$
$6x$ $\quad$ (+)	$-\dfrac{1}{4}\cos 2x$
6 $\quad$ (−)	$-\dfrac{1}{8}\sin 2x$
0	$\dfrac{1}{16}\cos 2x$

$$\int x^3 \cos 2x\, dx = \frac{1}{2}x^3\sin 2x + \frac{3}{4}x^2\cos 2x - \frac{3}{4}x\sin 2x - \frac{3}{8}\cos 2x$$

$$= \left(\frac{x^3}{2} - \frac{3x}{4}\right)\sin 2x + \left(\frac{3x^2}{4} - \frac{3}{8}\right)\cos 2x + C$$

$$\int_0^{\pi/2} x^3\cos 2x\, dx = \left[\left(\frac{x^3}{2} - \frac{3x}{4}\right)\sin 2x + \left(\frac{3x^2}{4} - \frac{3}{8}\right)\cos 2x\right]_0^{\pi/2}$$

$$= 0 + \left(\frac{3\pi^2}{16} - \frac{3}{8}\right)(-1) - 0 - \left(-\frac{3}{8}\right)(1)$$

$$= \frac{3}{4} - \frac{3\pi^2}{16} \approx -1.101$$

Check: $\text{NINT}\left(x^3\cos 2x, x, 0, \dfrac{\pi}{2}\right) \approx -1.101$

17. Let $u = e^{2x}$ $\qquad$ $dv = \cos 3x\, dx$

$\qquad du = 2e^{2x}\, dx$ $\qquad$ $v = \dfrac{1}{3}\sin 3x$

$\displaystyle\int e^{2x}\cos 3x\, dx = (e^{2x})\left(\dfrac{1}{3}\sin 3x\right) - \int\left(\dfrac{1}{3}\sin 3x\right)(2e^{2x}\, dx)$

$\qquad\qquad\qquad = \dfrac{1}{3}e^{2x}\sin 3x - \dfrac{2}{3}\displaystyle\int e^{2x}\sin 3x\, dx$

Let $u = e^{2x}$ $\qquad$ $dv = \sin 3x\, dx$

$\qquad du = 2e^{2x}\, dx$ $\qquad$ $v = -\dfrac{1}{3}\cos 3x$

$\displaystyle\int e^{2x}\cos 3x\, dx = \dfrac{1}{3}e^{2x}\sin 3x - \dfrac{2}{3}\left[(e^{2x})\left(-\dfrac{1}{3}\cos 3x\right) - \int\left(-\dfrac{1}{3}\cos 3x\right)(2e^{2x}\, dx)\right]$

$\qquad\qquad\qquad = \dfrac{1}{9}e^{2x}(3\sin 3x + 2\cos 3x) - \dfrac{4}{9}\displaystyle\int e^{2x}\cos 3x\, dx$

$\dfrac{13}{9}\displaystyle\int e^{2x}\cos 3x\, dx = \dfrac{1}{9}e^{2x}(3\sin 3x + 2\cos 3x)$

$\displaystyle\int e^{2x}\cos 3x\, dx = \dfrac{1}{13}e^{2x}(3\sin 3x + 2\cos 3x)$

$\displaystyle\int_{-2}^{3} e^{2x}\cos 3x\, dx = \left[\dfrac{1}{13}e^{2x}(3\sin 3x + 2\cos 3x)\right]_{-2}^{3}$

$\qquad\qquad\qquad = \dfrac{1}{13}[e^{6}(3\sin 9 + 2\cos 9) - e^{-4}(3\sin(-6) + 2\cos(-6)]$

$\qquad\qquad\qquad = \dfrac{1}{13}[e^{6}(2\cos 9 + 3\sin 9) - e^{-4}(2\cos 6 - 3\sin 6)]$

$\qquad\qquad\qquad \approx -18.186$

Check: NINT$(e^{2x}\cos 3x, x, -2, 3) \approx -18.186$

18. Let $u = e^{-2x}$ $\qquad$ $dv = \sin 2x\, dx$

$\qquad du = -2e^{-2x}\, dx$ $\qquad$ $v = -\dfrac{1}{2}\cos 2x$

$\displaystyle\int e^{-2x}\sin 2x\, dx = (e^{-2x})\left(-\dfrac{1}{2}\cos 2x\right) - \int\left(-\dfrac{1}{2}\cos 2x\right)(-2e^{-2x}\, dx)$

$\qquad\qquad\qquad = -\dfrac{1}{2}e^{-2x}\cos 2x - \displaystyle\int e^{-2x}\cos 2x\, dx$

Let $u = e^{-2x}$ $\qquad$ $dv = \cos 2x\, dx$

$\qquad du = -2e^{-2x}$ $\qquad$ $v = \dfrac{1}{2}\sin 2x$

$\displaystyle\int e^{-2x}\sin 2x\, dx = -\dfrac{1}{2}e^{-2x}\cos 2x - \left[(e^{-2x})\left(\dfrac{1}{2}\sin 2x\right) - \int\left(\dfrac{1}{2}\sin 2x\right)(-2e^{-2x}\, dx)\right]$

$\qquad\qquad\qquad = -\dfrac{1}{2}e^{-2x}(\cos 2x + \sin 2x) - \displaystyle\int e^{-2x}\sin 2x\, dx$

$2\displaystyle\int e^{-2x}\sin 2x\, dx = -\dfrac{1}{2}e^{-2x}(\cos 2x + \sin 2x) + C$

$\displaystyle\int e^{-2x}\sin 2x\, dx = -\dfrac{e^{-2x}}{4}(\cos 2x + \sin 2x) + C$

$\displaystyle\int_{-3}^{2} e^{-2x}\sin 2x\, dx = \left[-\dfrac{e^{-2x}}{4}(\cos 2x + \sin 2x)\right]_{-3}^{2}$

$\qquad\qquad\qquad = -\dfrac{e^{-4}}{4}(\cos 4 + \sin 4) + \dfrac{e^{6}}{4}[\cos(-6) + \sin(-6)]$

$\qquad\qquad\qquad = -\dfrac{e^{-4}}{4}(\cos 4 + \sin 4) + \dfrac{e^{6}}{4}(\cos 6 - \sin 6)$

$\qquad\qquad\qquad \approx 125.028$

Check: NINT$(e^{-2x}\sin 2x, x, -3, 2) \approx 125.028$

19. $y = \int x^2 e^{4x}\, dx$

Let $u = x^2$ ⟨⟩ $dv = e^{4x}dx$

$du = 2x\, dx$ ⟨⟩ $v = \frac{1}{4}e^{4x}$

$y = (x^2)\left(\frac{1}{4}e^{4x}\right) - \int\left(\frac{1}{4}e^{4x}\right)(2x\, dx)$

$= \frac{1}{4}x^2 e^{4x} - \frac{1}{2}\int xe^{4x}dx$

Let $u = x$ ⟨⟩ $dv = e^{4x}\, dx$

$du = dx$ ⟨⟩ $v = \frac{1}{4}e^{4x}$

$y = \frac{1}{4}x^2 e^{4x} - \frac{1}{2}\left[(x)\left(\frac{1}{4}e^{4x}\right) - \int\left(\frac{1}{4}e^{4x}\right)dx\right]$

$y = \frac{1}{4}x^2 e^{4x} - \frac{1}{8}xe^{4x} + \frac{1}{32}e^{4x} + C$

$y = \left(\frac{x^2}{4} - \frac{x}{8} + \frac{1}{32}\right)e^{4x} + C$

20. $y = \int x^2 \ln x\, dx$

Let $u = \ln x$ ⟨⟩ $dv = x^2\, dx$

$du = \frac{1}{x}\, dx$ ⟨⟩ $v = \frac{1}{3}x^3$

$y = (\ln x)\left(\frac{1}{3}x^3\right) - \int\left(\frac{1}{3}x^3\right)\left(\frac{1}{x}\, dx\right)$

$y = \frac{1}{3}x^3\ln x - \frac{1}{3}\int x^2\, dx$

$y = \frac{1}{3}x^3 \ln x - \frac{1}{9}x^3 + C$

21. $y = \int \theta \sec^{-1}\theta\, d\theta$

Let $u = \sec^{-1}\theta$ ⟨⟩ $dv = \theta\, d\theta$

$du = \frac{1}{\theta\sqrt{\theta^2 - 1}}\, du$ ⟨⟩ $v = \frac{1}{2}\theta^2$

Note that we are told $\theta > 1$, so no absolute value is needed

in the expression for du.

$y = (\sec^{-1}\theta)\left(\frac{1}{2}\theta^2\right) - \int\left(\frac{1}{2}\theta^2\right)\left(\frac{1}{\theta\sqrt{\theta^2-1}}\, d\theta\right)$

$y = \frac{\theta^2}{2}\sec^{-1}\theta - \frac{1}{4}\int\frac{2|\theta|\, d\theta}{\sqrt{\theta^2-1}}$

Let $w = \theta^2 - 1$, $dw = 2\theta\, d\theta$

$y = \frac{\theta^2}{2}\sec^{-1}\theta - \frac{1}{4}\int w^{-1/2}\, dw$

$y = \frac{\theta^2}{2}\sec^{-1}\theta - \frac{1}{2}w^{1/2} + C$

$y = \frac{\theta^2}{2}\sec^{-1}\theta - \frac{1}{2}\sqrt{\theta^2 - 1} + C$

22. $y = \int \theta \sec\theta \tan\theta\, d\theta$

Let $u = \theta$ ⟨⟩ $dv = \sec\theta\tan\theta\, d\theta$

$du = d\theta$ ⟨⟩ $v = \sec\theta$

$y = \theta\sec\theta - \int\sec\theta\, d\theta$

$y = \theta\sec\theta - \ln|\sec\theta + \tan\theta| + C$

Note: In the last step, we used the result of Exercise 29 in

Section 6.2.

23. Let $u = x$ ⟨⟩ $dv = \sin x\, dx$

$du = dx$ ⟨⟩ $v = -\cos x$

$\int x \sin x\, dx = -x\cos x + \int\cos x\, dx$

$= -x\cos x + \sin x + C$

(a) $\int_0^\pi |x \sin x|\, dx = \int_0^\pi x \sin x\, dx$

$= \Big[-x\cos x + \sin x\Big]_0^\pi$

$= -\pi(-1) + 0 + 0(1) - 0$

$= \pi$

(b) $\int_\pi^{2\pi} |x \sin x|\, dx = -\int_\pi^{2\pi} x \sin x\, dx$

$= \Big[x\cos x - \sin x\Big]_\pi^{2\pi}$

$= 2\pi(1) - 0 - \pi(-1) + 0$

$= 3\pi$

(c) $\int_0^{2\pi} |x \sin x|\, dx = \int_0^\pi |x \sin x|\, dx + \int_\pi^{2\pi} |x \sin x|\, dx$

$= \pi + 3\pi = 4\pi$

24. We begin by evaluating $\int (x^2 + x + 1)e^{-x}\, dx$.

Let $u = x^2 + x + 1$ ⟨⟩ $dv = e^{-x}\, dx$

$du = (2x + 1)\, dx$ ⟨⟩ $v = -e^{-x}$

$\int (x^2 + x + 1)e^{-x}\, dx$

$= -(x^2 + x + 1)e^{-x} + \int(2x + 1)e^{-x}\, dx$

Let $u = 2x + 1$ ⟨⟩ $dv = e^{-x}\, dx$

$du = 2\, dx$ ⟨⟩ $v = -e^{-x}$

$\int (x^2 + x + 1)e^{-x}\, dx$

$= -(x^2 + x + 1)e^{-x} - (2x + 1)e^{-x} + \int 2e^{-x}\, dx$

$= -(x^2 + x + 1)e^{-x} - (2x + 1)e^{-x} - 2e^{-x} + C$

$= -(x^2 + 3x + 4)e^{-x} + C$

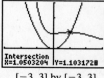

Intersection
X=1.0503204 Y=1.1031728

$[-3, 3]$ by $[-3, 3]$

The graph shows that the two curves intersect at $x = k$,
where $k \approx 1.050$. The area we seek is

$\int_0^k (x^2 + x + 1)e^{-x} - \int_0^k x^2\, dx$

$= \Big[-(x^2 + 3x + 4)e^{-x}\Big]_0^k - \Big[\frac{1}{3}x^3\Big]_0^k$

$\approx (-2.888 + 4) - (0.386 - 0)$

≈ 0.726

25. First, we evaluate $\int e^{-t} \cos t \, dt$.

Let $\quad u = e^{-t} \qquad\qquad dv = \cos t \, dt$

$\qquad du = -e^{-t} \, dt \qquad\quad v = \sin t$

$\int e^{-t} \cos t \, dt = e^{-t} \sin t + \int \sin t \, e^{-t} \, dt$

Let $u = e^{-t} \qquad\qquad dv = \sin t \, dt$

$\qquad du = -e^{-t} \, dt \qquad v = -\cos t$

$\int e^{-t} \cos t \, dt = e^{-t} \sin t - e^{-t} \cos t - \int e^{-t} \cos t \, dt$

$2 \int e^{-t} \cos t \, dt = e^{-t}(\sin t - \cos t) + C$

$\int e^{-t} \cos t \, dt = \frac{1}{2} e^{-t}(\sin t - \cos t) + C$

Now we find the average value of $y = 2e^{-t} \cos t$ for $0 \le t \le 2\pi$.

Average value $= \dfrac{1}{2\pi} \displaystyle\int_0^{2\pi} 2e^{-t} \cos t \, dt$

$= \dfrac{1}{\pi} \displaystyle\int_0^{2\pi} e^{-t} \cos t \, dt$

$= \dfrac{1}{2\pi} e^{-t}(\sin t - \cos t) \Big]_0^{2\pi}$

$= \dfrac{1}{2\pi} [e^{-2\pi}(-1) - e^0(-1)]$

$= \dfrac{1 - e^{-2\pi}}{2\pi} \approx 0.159$

26. (a) Let $u = x \qquad\qquad dv = e^x \, dx$

$\qquad du = dx \qquad\quad v = e^x$

$\int x e^x \, dx = x e^x - \int e^x \, dx$

$\qquad\qquad = x e^x - e^x + C$

$\qquad\qquad = (x - 1)e^x + C$

(b) Using the result from part (a):

Let $\quad u = x^2 \qquad\qquad dv = e^x \, dx$

$\qquad du = 2x \, dx \qquad\quad v = e^x$

$\int x^2 e^x \, dx = x^2 e^x - \int 2x \, e^x \, dx$

$\qquad\qquad = x^2 e^x - 2(x - 1)e^x + C$

$\qquad\qquad = (x^2 - 2x + 2)e^x + C$

(c) Using the result from part (b):

Let $\quad u = x^3 \qquad\qquad dv = e^x \, dx$

$\qquad du = 3x^2 \, dx \qquad\quad v = e^x$

$\int x^3 e^x \, dx = x^3 e^x - \int 3x^2 \, e^x \, dx$

$\qquad\qquad = x^3 e^x - 3(x^2 - 2x + 2)e^x + C$

$\qquad\qquad = (x^3 - 3x^2 + 6x - 6)e^x + C$

(d) $\left[x^n - \dfrac{d}{dx} x^n + \dfrac{d^2}{dx^2} x^n - \cdots + (-1)^n \dfrac{d^n}{dx^n} x^n \right] e^x + C$

or $[x^n - nx^{n-1} + n(n-1)x^{n-2} -$

$\qquad \cdots + (-1)^{n-1}(n)!x + (-1)^n(n!)]e^x + C$

(e) Use mathematical induction or argue based on tabular integration.

Alternately, show that the derivative of the answer to part (d) is $x^n e^x$:

$\dfrac{d}{dx}\Bigg[\left(x^n - nx^{n-1} + n(n-1)x^{n-2} - \right.$

$\qquad \left. \cdots + (-1)^{n-1}(n!)x + (-1)^n n! \right) e^x + C \Bigg]$

$= [x^n - nx^{n-1} + n(n-1)x^{n-2} -$

$\qquad \cdots + (-1)^{n-1}(n!)x + (-1)^n n!]e^x +$

$\qquad e^x \dfrac{d}{dx}[x^n - nx^{n-1} + n(n-1)x^{n-2} -$

$\qquad \cdots + (-1)^{n-1}(n!)x + (-1)^n n!]$

$= [x^n - nx^{n-1} + n(n-1)x^{n-2} -$

$\qquad \cdots + (-1)^{n-1}(n!)x + (-1)^n n!]e^x$

$\qquad + [nx^{n-1} - n(n-1)x^{n-2}$

$\qquad + n(n-1)(n-2)x^{n-3} -$

$\qquad \cdots + (-1)^{n-1}n!]e^x$

$= x^n e^x$

27. Let $w = \sqrt{x}$. Then $dw = \dfrac{dx}{2\sqrt{x}}$, so $dx = 2\sqrt{x} \, dw = 2w \, dw$.

$\int \sin \sqrt{x} \, dx = \int (\sin w)(2w \, dw) = 2 \int w \sin w \, dw$

Let $\quad u = w \qquad\qquad dv = \sin w \, dw$

$\qquad du = dw \qquad\quad v = -\cos w$

$\int w \sin w \, dw = -w \cos w + \int \cos w \, dw$

$\qquad\qquad = -w \cos w + \sin w + C$

$\int \sin \sqrt{x} \, dx = 2 \int w \sin w \, dw$

$\qquad\qquad = -2w \cos w + 2 \sin w + C$

$\qquad\qquad = -2\sqrt{x} \cos \sqrt{x} + 2 \sin \sqrt{x} + C$

28. Let $w = \sqrt{3x + 9}$. Then $dw = \dfrac{1}{2\sqrt{3x+9}}(3)\,dx$, so

$dx = \dfrac{2}{3}\sqrt{3x+9}\,dw = \dfrac{2}{3}w\,dw$.

$\displaystyle\int e^{\sqrt{3x+9}}\,dx = \int (e^w)\left(\dfrac{2}{3}w\,dw\right) = \dfrac{2}{3}\int w\,e^w\,dw$

Let $u = w \quad dv = e^w\,dw$

$du = dw \quad v = e^w$

$\displaystyle\int w\,e^w\,dw = w\,e^w - \int e^w\,dw$

$\qquad\qquad = w\,e^w - e^w$

$\qquad\qquad = (w-1)e^w$

$\displaystyle\int e^{\sqrt{3x+9}}\,dx = \dfrac{2}{3}\int w\,e^w\,dw$

$\qquad\qquad = \dfrac{2}{3}(w-1)e^w$

$\qquad\qquad = \dfrac{2}{3}(\sqrt{3x+9} - 1)e^{\sqrt{3x+9}} + C$

29. Let $w = x^2$. Then $dw = 2x\,dx$.

$\displaystyle\int x^7 e^{x^2}\,dx = \int (x^2)^3 e^{x^2}\,x\,dx = \dfrac{1}{2}\int w^3\,e^w\,dw$.

Use tabular integration with $f(x) = w^3$ and $g(w) = e^w$.

$f(w)$ and its derivatives	$g(w)$ and its integrals
w^3	e^w
$3w^2$	e^w
$6w$	e^w
6	e^w
0	e^w

(+) (−) (+) (−)

$\displaystyle\int w^3\,e^w\,dw = w^3 e^w - 3w^2 e^w + 6w\,e^w - 6e^w + C$

$\qquad\qquad = (w^3 - 3w^2 + 6w - 6)e^w + C$

$\displaystyle\int x^7 e^{x^2}\,dx = \dfrac{1}{2}\int w^3\,e^w\,dw$

$\qquad\qquad = \dfrac{1}{2}(w^3 - 3w^2 + 6w - 6)e^w + C$

$\qquad\qquad = \dfrac{(x^6 - 3x^4 + 6x^2 - 6)e^{x^2}}{2} + C$

30. Let $y = \ln r$. Then $dy = \dfrac{1}{r}\,dr$, and so $dr = r\,dy = e^y\,dy$.

Using the result of Exercise 13, we have:

$\displaystyle\int \sin(\ln r)\,dr = \int (\sin y)e^y\,dy$

$\qquad\qquad = \dfrac{1}{2}e^y(\sin y - \cos y) + C$

$\qquad\qquad = \dfrac{1}{2}e^{\ln r}[\sin(\ln r) - \cos(\ln r)] + C$

$\qquad\qquad = \dfrac{r}{2}[\sin(\ln r) - \cos(\ln r)] + C$

31. Let $u = x^n \qquad dv = \cos x\,dx$

$\quad du = nx^{n-1}dx \qquad v = \sin x$

$\displaystyle\int x^n \cos x\,dx = x^n \sin x - \int (\sin x)(nx^{n-1}dx)$

$\qquad\qquad = x^n \sin x - n\int x^{n-1}\sin x\,dx$

32. Let $u = x^n \qquad dv = \sin x\,dx$

$\quad du = nx^{n-1}\,dx \qquad v = -\cos x$

$\displaystyle\int x^n \sin x\,dx = (x^n)(-\cos x) - \int (-\cos x)(nx^{n-1}\,dx)$

$\qquad\qquad = -x^n\cos x + n\int x^{n-1}\cos x\,dx$

33. Let $u = x^n \qquad dv = e^{ax}\,dx$

$\quad du = nx^{n-1}\,dx \qquad v = \dfrac{1}{a}e^{ax}$

$\displaystyle\int x^n e^{ax}\,dx = (x^n)\left(\dfrac{1}{a}e^{ax}\right) - \int\left(\dfrac{1}{a}e^{ax}\right)(nx^{n-1}\,dx)$

$\qquad\qquad = \dfrac{x^n e^{ax}}{a} - \dfrac{n}{a}\int x^{n-1}e^{ax}\,dx,\ a \neq 0$

34. Let $u = (\ln x)^n \qquad dv = dx$

$\quad du = \dfrac{n(\ln x)^{n-1}}{x}\,dx \quad v = x$

$\displaystyle\int (\ln x)^n\,dx = (\ln x)^n(x) - \int x\left[\dfrac{n(\ln x)^{n-1}}{x}\right]dx$

$\qquad\qquad = x(\ln x)^n - n\int (\ln x)^{n-1}\,dx$

35. (a) Let $y = f^{-1}(x)$. Then $x = f(y)$, so $dx = f'(y)\,dy$.

Hence, $\displaystyle\int f^{-1}(x)\,dx = \int (y)[f'(y)\,dy] = \int y\,f'(y)\,dy$

(b) Let $u = y \qquad dv = f'(y)dy$

$\quad du = dy \qquad v = f(y)$

$\displaystyle\int y\,f'(y)\,dy = y\,f(y) - \int f(y)\,dy$

$\qquad\qquad = f^{-1}(x)(x) - \int f(y)\,dy$

Hence, $\displaystyle\int f^{-1}(x)\,dx = \int y\,f'(y)\,dy$

$\qquad\qquad = x\,f^{-1}(x) - \int f(y)\,dy.$

36. Let $u = f^{-1}(x) \qquad dv = dx$

$\quad du = \left(\dfrac{d}{dx}f^{-1}(x)\right)dx \qquad v = x$

$\displaystyle\int f^{-1}(x)\,dx = xf^{-1}(x) - \int x\left(\dfrac{d}{dx}f^{-1}(x)\right)dx$

37. (a) Using $y = f^{-1}(x) = \sin^{-1}x$ and $f(y) = \sin y$,

$-\dfrac{\pi}{2} \le y \le \dfrac{\pi}{2}$, we have:

$\displaystyle\int \sin^{-1}x\,dx = x\sin^{-1}x - \int \sin y\,dy$

$\qquad\qquad = x\sin^{-1}x + \cos y + C$

$\qquad\qquad = x\sin^{-1}x + \cos(\sin^{-1}x) + C$

37. continued

(b) $\int \sin^{-1} x \, dx = x \sin^{-1} x - \int x\left(\dfrac{d}{dx} \sin^{-1} x\right) dx$

$\qquad = x \sin^{-1} x - \int x \dfrac{1}{\sqrt{1 - x^2}} \, dx$

$u = 1 - x^2, \, du = -2x \, dx$

$\qquad = x \sin^{-1} x + \dfrac{1}{2}\int u^{-1/2} \, du$

$\qquad = x \sin^{-1} x + u^{1/2} + C$

$\qquad = x \sin^{-1} x + \sqrt{1 - x^2} + C$

(c) $\cos(\sin^{-1} x) = \sqrt{1 - x^2}$

38. (a) Using $y = f^{-1}(x) = \tan^{-1} x$ and $f(y) = \tan y$,

$-\dfrac{\pi}{2} < y < \dfrac{\pi}{2}$, we have:

$\int \tan^{-1} x \, dx = x \tan^{-1} x - \int \tan y \, dy$

$\qquad = x \tan^{-1} x - \ln |\sec y| + C$

$\qquad\qquad$ (Section 6.2, Example 5)

$\qquad = x \tan^{-1} x + \ln |\cos y| + C$

$\qquad = x \tan^{-1} x + \ln |\cos(\tan^{-1} x)| + C$

(b) $\int \tan^{-1} x \, dx = x \tan^{-1} x - \int x\left(\dfrac{d}{dx} \tan^{-1} x\right) dx$

$\qquad = x \tan^{-1} x - \int x\left(\dfrac{1}{1 + x^2}\right) dx$

$u = 1 + x^2, \, du = 2x \, dx$

$\qquad = x \tan^{-1} x - \dfrac{1}{2}\int u^{-1} \, du$

$\qquad = x \tan^{-1} x - \dfrac{1}{2}\ln |u| + C$

$\qquad = x \tan^{-1} x - \dfrac{1}{2}\ln (1 + x^2) + C$

(c) $\ln |\cos(\tan^{-1} x)| = \ln \left|\dfrac{1}{\sqrt{1 + x^2}}\right| = -\dfrac{1}{2}\ln (1 + x^2)$

39. (a) Using $y = f^{-1}(x) = \cos^{-1} x$ and

$f(y) = \cos x, \, 0 \leq x \leq \pi$, we have:

$\int \cos^{-1} x \, dx = x \cos^{-1} x - \int \cos y \, dy$

$\qquad = x \cos^{-1} x - \sin y + C$

$\qquad = x \cos^{-1} x - \sin(\cos^{-1} x) + C$

(b) $\int \cos^{-1} x \, dx = x \cos^{-1} x - \int x\left(\dfrac{d}{dx} \cos^{-1} x\right) dx$

$\qquad = x \cos^{-1} x - \int x\left(-\dfrac{1}{\sqrt{1 - x^2}}\right) dx$

$u = 1 - x^2, \, du = -2x \, dx$

$\qquad = x \cos^{-1} x - \dfrac{1}{2}\int u^{-1/2} \, du$

$\qquad = x \cos^{-1} x - u^{1/2} + C$

$\qquad = x \cos^{-1} x - \sqrt{1 - x^2} + C$

(c) $\sin(\cos^{-1} x) = \sqrt{1 - x^2}$

40. (a) Using $y = f^{-1}(x) = \log_2 x$ and $f(y) = 2^y$, we have

$\int \log_2 x \, dx = x \log_2 x - \int 2^y \, dy$

$\qquad = x \log_2 x - \dfrac{2^y}{\ln 2} + C$

$\qquad = x \log_2 x - \dfrac{1}{\ln 2} 2^{\log_2 x}$

(b) $\int \log_2 x \, dx = x \log_2 x - \int x\left(\dfrac{d}{dx} \log_2 x\right) dx$

$\qquad = x \log_2 x - \int x\left(\dfrac{1}{x \ln 2}\right) dx$

$\qquad = x \log_2 x - \int \dfrac{dx}{\ln 2}$

$\qquad = x \log_2 x - \left(\dfrac{1}{\ln 2}\right)x + C$

(c) $2^{\log_2 x} = x$

■ Section 6.4 Exponential Growth and Decay (pp. 330–341)

Exploration 1   Slowing Down More Slowly

1. As m increases the velocity of the object represented by the graph slows down more slowly. That is, the y-coordinates of the graphs decrease to 0 more slowly as m increases.

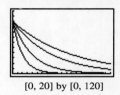

[0, 20] by [0, 120]

2. As we saw in Section 5.1, $s(t) = \displaystyle\int_0^t v(u) \, du$ gives the distance traveled by the object over the time interval $[0, t]$. Since $s(0) = \displaystyle\int_0^0 v(u) \, du = 0$, the integral gives the distance traveled by the object at time t.

3. The total distance traveled is about 200 units for $m = 1$, about 400 units for $m = 2$, about 800 units for $m = 4$, and about 1200 units for $m = 6$.

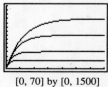

[0, 70] by [0, 1500]

Quick Review 6.4

1. $a = e^b$

2. $c = \ln d$

3. $\ln (x + 3) = 2$

$\qquad x + 3 = e^2$

$\qquad\qquad x = e^2 - 3$

4. $100e^{2x} = 600$

$\qquad e^{2x} = 6$

$\qquad 2x = \ln 6$

$\qquad x = \dfrac{1}{2} \ln 6$

5. $0.85^x = 2.5$

$\ln 0.85^x = \ln 2.5$

$x \ln 0.85 = \ln 2.5$

$x = \dfrac{\ln 2.5}{\ln 0.85} \approx -5.638$

6. $2^{k+1} = 3^k$

$\ln 2^{k+1} = \ln 3^k$

$(k + 1)\ln 2 = k \ln 3$

$\ln 2 = k(\ln 3 - \ln 2)$

$k = \dfrac{\ln 2}{\ln 3 - \ln 2} \approx 1.710$

7. $1.1^t = 10$

$\ln 1.1^t = \ln 10$

$t \ln 1.1 = \ln 10$

$t = \dfrac{\ln 10}{\ln 1.1} = \dfrac{1}{\log 1.1} \approx 24.159$

8. $e^{-2t} = \dfrac{1}{4}$

$-2t = \ln\left(\dfrac{1}{4}\right)$

$t = -\dfrac{1}{2}\ln\left(\dfrac{1}{4}\right) = \dfrac{1}{2}\ln 4 = \ln 2$

9. $\ln(y + 1) = 2x + 3$

$y + 1 = e^{2x+3}$

$y = -1 + e^{2x+3}$

10. $\ln\left|y + 2\right| = 3t - 1$

$\left|y + 2\right| = e^{3t-1}$

$y + 2 = \pm e^{3t-1}$

$y = -2 \pm e^{3t-1}$

Section 6.4 Exercises

1. $y(t) = y_0 e^{kt}$
$y(t) = 100e^{1.5t}$

2. $y(t) = y_0 e^{kt}$
$y(t) = 200e^{-0.5t}$

3. $y(t) = y_0 e^{kt}$
$y(t) = 50e^{kt}$
$y(5) = 100 = 50e^{5k}$
$2 = e^{5k}$
$\ln 2 = 5k$
$k = 0.2 \ln 2$
Solution: $y(t) = 50e^{(0.2 \ln 2)t}$ or $y(t) = 50 \cdot 2^{0.2t}$

4. $y(t) = y_0 e^{kt}$

$y(t) = 60e^{kt}$

$y(10) = 30 = 60e^{10k}$

$\dfrac{1}{2} = e^{10k}$

$\ln \dfrac{1}{2} = 10k$

$k = 0.1 \ln \dfrac{1}{2} = -0.1 \ln 2$

Solution: $y(t) = 60e^{-(0.1 \ln 2)t}$ or $y(t) = 60 \cdot 2^{-t/10}$

5. Doubling time:

$A(t) = A_0 e^{rt}$

$2000 = 1000e^{0.086t}$

$2 = e^{0.086t}$

$\ln 2 = 0.086t$

$t = \dfrac{\ln 2}{0.086} \approx 8.06$ yr

Amount in 30 years:

$A = 1000e^{(0.086)(30)} \approx \$13,197.14$

6. Annual rate:

$A(t) = A_0 e^{rt}$

$4000 = 2000e^{(r)(15)}$

$2 = e^{15r}$

$\ln 2 = 15r$

$r = \dfrac{\ln 2}{15} \approx 0.0462 = 4.62\%$

Amount in 30 years:

$A(t) = A_0 e^{rt}$

$A = 2000e^{[(\ln 2)/15](30)}$

$= 2000e^{2 \ln 2}$

$= 2000 \cdot 2^2$

$= \$8000$

7. Initial deposit:

$A(t) = A_0 e^{rt}$

$2898.44 = A_0 e^{(0.0525)(30)}$

$A_0 = \dfrac{2898.44}{e^{1.575}} \approx \$600.00$

Doubling time:

$A(t) = A_0 e^{rt}$

$1200 = 600e^{0.0525t}$

$2 = e^{0.0525t}$

$\ln 2 = 0.0525t$

$t = \dfrac{\ln 2}{0.0525} \approx 13.2$ years

8. Annual rate:

$A(t) = A_0 e^{rt}$

$10,405.37 = 1200e^{(r)(30)}$

$\dfrac{104.0537}{12} = e^{30r}$

$\ln \dfrac{104.0537}{12} = 30r$

$r = \dfrac{1}{30}\ln \dfrac{104.0537}{12} \approx 0.072 = 7.2\%$

Doubling time:

$A(t) = A_0 e^{rt}$

$2400 = 1200e^{0.072t}$

$2 = e^{0.072t}$

$\ln 2 = 0.072t$

$t = \dfrac{\ln 2}{0.072} \approx 9.63$ years

9. (a) Annually:

$$2 = 1.0475^t$$

$$\ln 2 = t \ln 1.0475$$

$$t = \frac{\ln 2}{\ln 1.0475} \approx 14.94 \text{ years}$$

(b) Monthly:

$$2 = \left(1 + \frac{0.0475}{12}\right)^{12t}$$

$$\ln 2 = 12t \ln\left(1 + \frac{0.0475}{12}\right)$$

$$t = \frac{\ln 2}{12 \ln\left(1 + \frac{0.0475}{12}\right)} \approx 14.62 \text{ years}$$

(c) Quarterly:

$$2 = \left(1 + \frac{0.0475}{4}\right)^{4t}$$

$$\ln 2 = 4t \ln 1.011875$$

$$t = \frac{\ln 2}{4 \ln 1.011875} \approx 14.68 \text{ years}$$

(d) Continuously:

$$2 = e^{0.0475t}$$

$$\ln 2 = 0.0475t$$

$$t = \frac{\ln 2}{0.0475} \approx 14.59 \text{ years}$$

10. (a) Annually:

$$2 = 1.0825^t$$

$$\ln 2 = t \ln 1.0825$$

$$t = \frac{\ln 2}{\ln 1.0825} \approx 8.74 \text{ years}$$

(b) Monthly:

$$2 = \left(1 + \frac{0.0825}{12}\right)^{12t}$$

$$\ln 2 = 12t \ln\left(1 + \frac{0.0825}{12}\right)$$

$$t = \frac{\ln 2}{12 \ln\left(1 + \frac{0.0825}{12}\right)} \approx 8.43 \text{ years}$$

(c) Quarterly:

$$2 = \left(1 + \frac{0.0825}{4}\right)^{4t}$$

$$\ln 2 = 4t \ln 1.020625$$

$$t = \frac{\ln 2}{4 \ln 1.020625} \approx 8.49 \text{ years}$$

(d) Continuously:

$$2 = e^{0.0825t}$$

$$\ln 2 = 0.0825t$$

$$t = \frac{\ln 2}{0.0825} \approx 8.40 \text{ years}$$

11. (a) Since there are 48 half-hour doubling times in 24 hours, there will be $2^{48} \approx 2.8 \times 10^{14}$ bacteria.

(b) The bacteria reproduce fast enough that even if many are destroyed there are still enough left to make the person sick.

12. Using $y = y_0 e^{kt}$, we have

$$10{,}000 = y_0 e^{3k} \text{ and } 40{,}000 = y_0 e^{5k}.$$

Hence $\dfrac{40{,}000}{10{,}000} = \dfrac{y_0 e^{5k}}{y_0 e^{3k}}$, which gives

$e^{2k} = 4$, or $k = \ln 2$. Solving $10{,}000 = y_0 e^{3\ln 2}$, we have

$y_0 = 1250$. There were 1250 bacteria initially.

We could solve this more quickly by noticing that the population increased by a factor of 4, i.e. doubled twice, in 2 hrs, so the doubling time is 1 hr. Thus in 3 hrs the population would have doubled 3 times, so the initial population was $\dfrac{10{,}000}{2^3} = 1250$.

13. $\quad 0.9 = e^{-0.18t}$

$$\ln 0.9 = -0.18t$$

$$t = -\frac{\ln 0.9}{0.18} \approx 0.585 \text{ days}$$

14. (a) Half-life $= \dfrac{\ln 2}{k} = \dfrac{\ln 2}{0.005} \approx 138.6$ days

(b) $\quad 0.05 = e^{-0.005t}$

$$\ln 0.05 = -0.005t$$

$$t = -\frac{\ln 0.05}{0.005} \approx 599.15 \text{ days}$$

The sample will be useful for about 599 days.

15. Since $y_0 = y(0) = 2$, we have:

$$y = 2e^{kt}$$

$$5 = 2e^{(k)(2)}$$

$$\ln 5 = \ln 2 + 2k$$

$$k = \frac{\ln 5 - \ln 2}{2} = 0.5 \ln 2.5$$

Function: $y = 2e^{(0.5 \ln 2.5)t}$ or $y \approx 2e^{0.4581t}$

16. Since $y_0 = y(0) = 1.1$, we have:

$$y = 1.1e^{kt}$$

$$3 = 1.1e^{(k)(-3)}$$

$$\ln 3 = \ln 1.1 - 3k$$

$$k = \frac{1}{3}(\ln 1.1 - \ln 3)$$

Function: $y = 1.1e^{(\ln 1.1 - \ln 3)t/3}$ or $y \approx 1.1e^{-0.3344t}$

17. At time $t = \dfrac{3}{k}$, the amount remaining is

$y_0 e^{-kt} = y_0 e^{-k(3/k)} = y_0 e^{-3} \approx 0.0499 y_0$. This is less than

5% of the original amount, which means that over 95% has

decayed already.

18. $T - T_s = (T_0 - T_s)\, e^{-kt}$

$35 - 65 = (T_0 - 65)e^{-(k)(10)}$

$50 - 65 = (T_0 - 65)e^{-(k)(20)}$

Dividing the first equation by the second, we have:

$2 = e^{10k}$

$k = \dfrac{1}{10} \ln 2$

Substituting back into the first equation, we have:

$-30 = (T_0 - 65)e^{-[(\ln 2)/10](10)}$

$-30 = (T_0 - 65)\left(\dfrac{1}{2}\right)$

$-60 = T_0 - 65$

$5 = T_0$

The beam's initial temperature is 5°F.

19. (a) First, we find the value of k.

$T - T_s = (T_0 - T_s)e^{-kt}$

$60 - 20 = (90 - 20)e^{-(k)(10)}$

$\dfrac{4}{7} = e^{-10k}$

$k = -\dfrac{1}{10}\ln\dfrac{4}{7}$

When the soup cools to 35°, we have:

$35 - 20 = (90 - 20)e^{[(1/10)\ln\,(4/7)]t}$

$15 = 70e^{[(1/10)\ln\,(4/7)]t}$

$\ln\dfrac{3}{14} = \left(\dfrac{1}{10}\ln\dfrac{4}{7}\right)t$

$t = \dfrac{10 \ln\left(\dfrac{3}{14}\right)}{\ln\left(\dfrac{4}{7}\right)} \approx 27.53$ min

It takes a total of about 27.53 minutes, which is an additional 17.53 minutes after the first 10 minutes.

(b) Using the same value of k as in part (a), we have:

$T - T_s = (T_0 - T_s)e^{-kt}$

$35 - (-15) = [90 - (-15)]e^{[(1/10)\ln\,(4/7)]t}$

$50 = 105e^{[(1/10)\ln\,(4/7)]t}$

$\ln\dfrac{10}{21} = \left(\dfrac{1}{10}\ln\dfrac{4}{7}\right)t$

$t = \dfrac{10 \ln\left(\dfrac{10}{21}\right)}{\ln\left(\dfrac{4}{7}\right)} \approx 13.26$

It takes about 13.26 minutes

20. First, we find the value of k.

Taking "right now" as $t = 0$, 60° above room temperature

means $T_0 - T_s = 60$. Thus, we have

$T - T_s = (T_0 - T_s)e^{-kt}$

$70 = 60e^{(-k)(-20)}$

$\dfrac{7}{6} = e^{20k}$

$k = \dfrac{1}{20}\ln\dfrac{7}{6}$

(a) $T - T_s = (T_0 - T_s)e^{-kt} = 60e^{(-(1/20)\ln\,(7/6))(15)} \approx 53.45$

It will be about 53.45°C above room temperature.

(b) $T - T_s = (T_0 - T_s)e^{-kt} = 60e^{(-(1/20)\ln\,(7/6))(120)} \approx 23.79$

It will be about 23.79° above room temperature.

(c) $T - T_s = (T_0 - T_s)e^{-kt}$

$10 = 60e^{(-(1/20)\ln\,(7/6))t}$

$\ln\dfrac{1}{6} = \left(-\dfrac{1}{20}\ln\dfrac{7}{6}\right)t$

$t = -\dfrac{20 \ln (1/6)}{\ln (7/6)} \approx 232.47$ min

It will take about 232.47 min or 3.9 hr.

21. Use $k = \dfrac{\ln 2}{5700}$ (see Example 3).

$e^{-kt} = 0.445$

$-kt = \ln 0.445$

$t = -\dfrac{\ln 0.445}{k} = -\dfrac{5700 \ln 0.445}{\ln 2} \approx 6658$ years

Crater Lake is about 6658 years old.

22. Use $k = \dfrac{\ln 2}{5700}$ (see Example 3).

(a) $e^{-kt} = 0.17$

$-kt = \ln 0.17$

$t = -\dfrac{\ln 0.17}{k} = -\dfrac{5700 \ln 0.17}{\ln 2} \approx 14{,}571$ years

The animal died about 14,571 years before A.D. 2000,

in 12,571 B.C.

(b) $e^{-kt} = 0.18$

$-kt = \ln 0.18$

$t = -\dfrac{\ln 0.18}{k} = -\dfrac{5700 \ln 0.18}{\ln 2} \approx 14{,}101$ years

The animal died about 14,101 years before A.D. 2000,

in 12,101 B.C.

22. continued

(c) $e^{-kt} = 0.16$

$-kt = \ln 0.16$

$t = -\dfrac{\ln 0.16}{k} = -\dfrac{5700 \ln 0.16}{\ln 2} \approx 15{,}070 \text{ years}$

The animal died about 15,070 years before A.D. 2000,

in 13,070 B.C.

23. Note that the total mass is $66 + 7 = 73$ kg.

$v = v_0 e^{-(k/m)t}$

$v = 9e^{-3.9t/73}$

(a) $s(t) = \displaystyle\int 9e^{-3.9t/73}\,dt = -\dfrac{2190}{13}e^{-3.9t/73} + C$

Since $s(0) = 0$ we have $C = \dfrac{2190}{13}$ and

$\displaystyle\lim_{t\to\infty} s(t) = \lim_{t\to\infty} \dfrac{2190}{13}(1 - e^{-3.9t/73}) = \dfrac{2190}{13} \approx 168.5$

The cyclist will coast about 168.5 meters.

(b) $1 = 9e^{-3.9t/73}$

$\dfrac{3.9t}{73} = \ln 9$

$t = \dfrac{73 \ln 9}{3.9} \approx 41.13 \text{ sec}$

It will take about 41.13 seconds.

24. $v = v_0 e^{-(k/m)t}$

$v = 9e^{-(59{,}000/51{,}000{,}000)t}$

$v = 9e^{-59t/51{,}000}$

(a) $s(t) = \displaystyle\int 9e^{-59t/51{,}000}\,dt = -\dfrac{459{,}000}{59}e^{59t/51{,}000} + C$

Since $s(0) = 0$, we have $C = \dfrac{459{,}000}{59}$ and

$\displaystyle\lim_{t\to\infty} s(t) = \lim_{t\to\infty} \dfrac{459{,}000}{59}(1 - e^{-59t/51{,}000})$

$= \dfrac{459{,}000}{59} \approx 7780 \text{ m}$

The ship will coast about 7780 m, or 7.78 km.

(b) $1 = 9e^{-59t/51{,}000}$

$\dfrac{59t}{51{,}000} = \ln 9$

$t = \dfrac{51{,}000 \ln 9}{59} \approx 1899.3 \text{ sec}$

It will take about 31.65 minutes.

25. $y = y_0 e^{-kt}$

$800 = 1000e^{-(k)(10)}$

$0.8 = e^{-10k}$

$k = -\dfrac{\ln 0.8}{10}$

At $t = 10 + 14 = 24$ h:

$y = 1000e^{-(-\ln 0.8/10)24}$

$= 1000e^{2.4 \ln 0.8} \approx 585.4 \text{ kg}$

About 585.4 kg will remain.

26. $0.2 = e^{-0.1t}$

$\ln 0.2 = -0.1t$

$t = -10 \ln 0.2 \approx 16.09 \text{ yr}$

It will take about 16.09 years.

27. (a) $\dfrac{dp}{dh} = kp$

$\dfrac{dp}{p} = k\,dh$

$\displaystyle\int \dfrac{dp}{p} = \int k\,dh$

$\ln |p| = kh + C$

$e^{\ln |p|} = e^{kh + C}$

$|p| = e^C e^{kh}$

$p = Ae^{kh}$

Initial condition: $p = p_0$ when $h = 0$

$p_0 = Ae^0$

$A = p_0$

Solution: $p = p_0 e^{kh}$

Using the given altitude-pressure data, we have

$p_0 = 1013$ millibars, so:

$p = 1013e^{kh}$

$90 = 1013e^{(k)(20)}$

$\dfrac{90}{1013} = e^{20k}$

$k = \dfrac{1}{20} \ln \dfrac{90}{1013} \approx -0.121 \text{ km}^{-1}$

Thus, we have $p \approx 1013e^{-0.121h}$

(b) At 50 km, the pressure is

$1013e^{((1/20)\ln(90/1013))(50)} \approx 2.383$ millibars.

(c) $900 = 1013e^{kh}$

$\dfrac{900}{1013} = e^{kh}$

$h = \dfrac{1}{k} \ln \dfrac{900}{1013} = \dfrac{20 \ln (900/1013)}{\ln (90/1013)} \approx 0.977 \text{ km}$

The pressure is 900 millibars at an altitude of about

0.977 km.

28. By the Law of Exponential Change, $y = 100e^{-0.6t}$. At
$t = 1$ hour, the amount remaining will be
$100e^{-0.6(1)} \approx 54.88$ grams.

29. (a) By the Law of Exponential Change, the solution is
$V = V_0 e^{-(1/40)t}$.

(b) $0.1 = e^{-(1/40)t}$

$\ln 0.1 = -\dfrac{t}{40}$

$t = -40 \ln 0.1 \approx 92.1 \text{ sec}$

It will take about 92.1 seconds.

30. (a) $A(t) = A_0 e^t$

It grows by a factor of e each year.

(b) $3 = e^t$

$\ln 3 = t$

It will take $\ln 3 \approx 1.1$ yr.

(c) In one year your account grows from A_0 to $A_0 e$, so you can earn $A_0 e - A_0$, or $(e - 1)$ times your initial amount. This represents an increase of about 172%.

31. (a) $s(t) = \int v_0 e^{-(k/m)t} \, dt = -\dfrac{v_0 m}{k} e^{-(k/m)t} + C$

Initial condition: $s(0) = 0$

$$0 = -\frac{v_0 m}{k} + C$$

$$\frac{v_0 m}{k} = C$$

$$s(t) = -\frac{v_0 m}{k} e^{-(k/m)t} + \frac{v_0 m}{k}$$

$$= \frac{v_0 m}{k}\left(1 - e^{-(k/m)t}\right)$$

(b) $\displaystyle\lim_{t\to\infty} s(t) = \lim_{t\to\infty} \frac{v_0 m}{k}\left(1 - e^{-(k/m)t}\right) = \frac{v_0 m}{k}$

32. (a) $90 = e^{(r)(100)}$

$\ln 90 = 100r$

$r = \dfrac{\ln 90}{100} \approx 0.045$ or 4.5%

(b) $131 = e^{(r)(100)}$

$\ln 131 = 100r$

$r = \dfrac{\ln 131}{100} \approx 0.049$ or 4.9%

33. $\dfrac{v_0 m}{k} =$ coasting distance

$\dfrac{(0.80)(49.90)}{k} = 1.32$

$k = \dfrac{998}{33}$

We know that $\dfrac{v_0 m}{k} = 1.32$ and $\dfrac{k}{m} = \dfrac{998}{33(49.9)} = \dfrac{20}{33}$.

Using Equation 3, we have:

$s(t) = \dfrac{v_0 m}{k}(1 - e^{-(k/m)t})$

$= 1.32(1 - e^{-20t/33})$

$\approx 1.32(1 - e^{-0.606t})$

A graph of the model is shown superimposed on a graph of the data.

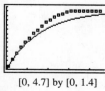

[0, 4.7] by [0, 1.4]

34. (a) $T - T_s = 79.47(0.932)^t$

(b) $T = 10 + 79.47(0.932)^t$

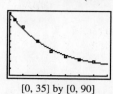

[0, 35] by [0, 90]

(c) Solving $T = 12$ and using the exact values from the regression equation, we obtain $t \approx 52.5$ sec.

(d) Substituting $t = 0$ into the equation we found in part (b), the temperature was approximately 89.47°C.

35. (a) $\dfrac{dT}{dt} = -k(T - T_s)$

$\dfrac{dT}{T - T_s} = -\int k \, dt$

$\displaystyle\int \dfrac{dT}{T - T_s} = -k \, dt$

$\ln |T - T_s| = -kt + C$

$|T - T_s| = e^{-kt + C}$

$T - T_s = \pm e^C e^{-kt}$

$T - T_s = A e^{-kt}$

Initial condition: $T = T_0$ when $t = 0$

$T_0 - T_s = A e^{-(k)(0)}$

$T_0 - T_s = A$

Solution: $T - T_s = (T_0 - T_s)e^{-kt}$

(b) $\displaystyle\lim_{t\to\infty} T = \lim_{t\to\infty} [T_s + (T_0 - T_s)e^{-kt}] = T_s$

Horizontal asymptote: $T = T_s$

36. (a) $2y_0 = y_0 e^{rt}$

$2 = e^{rt}$

$\ln 2 = rt$

$t = \dfrac{\ln 2}{r}$

(b)

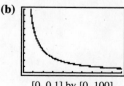

[0, 0.1] by [0, 100]

(c) $\ln 2 \approx 0.69$, so the doubling time is $\dfrac{0.69}{r}$ which is almost the same as the rules.

(d) $\dfrac{70}{5} = 14$ years or $\dfrac{72}{5} = 14.4$ years

36. continued

(e) $3y_0 = y_0 e^{rt}$

$3 = e^{rt}$

$\ln 3 = rt$

$t = \dfrac{\ln 3}{r}$

Since $\ln 3 \approx 1.099$, a suitable rule is $\dfrac{108}{100r}$ or $\dfrac{108}{i}$.

(We choose 108 instead of 110 because 108 has more

factors.)

37. (a)

x	$\left(1 + \dfrac{1}{x}\right)^x$
10	2.5937
100	2.7048
1000	2.7169
10,000	2.7181
100,000	2.7183

$e \approx 2.7183$

Graphical support:

$y_1 = \left(1 + \dfrac{1}{x}\right)^x, y_2 = e$

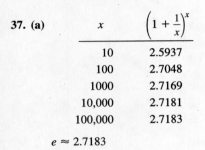

[0, 50] by [0, 4]

(b) $r = 2$

x	$\left(1 + \dfrac{2}{x}\right)^x$
10	6.1917
100	7.2446
1000	7.3743
10,000	7.3876
100,000	7.3889

$e^2 \approx 7.389$

Graphical support:

$y_1 = \left(1 + \dfrac{2}{x}\right)^x, y_2 = e^2$

[0, 500] by [0, 10]

$r = 0.5$

x	$\left(1 + \dfrac{0.5}{x}\right)^x$
10	1.6289
100	1.6467
1000	1.6485
10,000	1.6487
100,000	1.6487

$e^{0.5} \approx 1.6487$

Graphical support:

$y_1 = \left(1 + \dfrac{0.5}{x}\right)^x, y_2 = e^{0.5}$

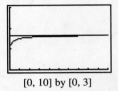

[0, 10] by [0, 3]

(c) As we compound more times, the increment of time between compounding approaches 0. Continuous compounding is based on an instantaneous rate of change which is a limit of average rates as the increment in time approaches 0.

38. (a) To simplify calculations somewhat, we may write:

$$v(t) = \sqrt{\dfrac{mg}{k}} \, \dfrac{e^{at} - e^{-at}}{e^{at} + e^{-at}} \, \dfrac{e^{at}}{e^{at}}$$

$$= \sqrt{\dfrac{mg}{k}} \, \dfrac{e^{2at} - 1}{e^{2at} + 1}$$

$$= \sqrt{\dfrac{mg}{k}} \, \dfrac{(e^{2at} + 1) - 2}{e^{2at} + 1}$$

$$= \sqrt{\dfrac{mg}{k}} \left(1 - \dfrac{2}{e^{2at} + 1}\right)$$

The left side of the differential equation is:

$$m\dfrac{dv}{dt} = m\sqrt{\dfrac{mg}{k}}(2)(e^{2at} + 1)^{-2}(2ae^{2at})$$

$$= 4ma\sqrt{\dfrac{mg}{k}}(e^{2at} + 1)^{-2}(e^{2at})$$

$$= 4m\sqrt{\dfrac{gk}{m}}\sqrt{\dfrac{mg}{k}}(e^{2at} + 1)^{-2}(e^{2at})$$

$$= \dfrac{4mge^{2at}}{(e^{2at} + 1)^2}$$

The right side of the differential equation is:

$$mg - kv^2 = mg - k\left(\frac{mg}{k}\right)\left(1 - \frac{2}{e^{2at} + 1}\right)^2$$

$$= mg\left[1 - \left(1 - \frac{2}{e^{2at} + 1}\right)^2\right]$$

$$= mg\left(1 - 1 + \frac{4}{e^{2at} + 1} - \frac{4}{(e^{2at} + 1)^2}\right)$$

$$= mg\,\frac{4(e^{2at} + 1) - 4}{(e^{2at} + 1)^2}$$

$$= \frac{4\,mg\,e^{2at}}{(e^{2at} + 1)^2}$$

Since the left and right sides are equal, the differential equation is satisfied.

And $v(0) = \sqrt{\dfrac{mg}{k}}\,\dfrac{e^0 - e^0}{e^0 + e^0} = 0$, so the initial condition is also satisfied.

(b) $\displaystyle\lim_{t\to\infty} v(t) = \lim_{t\to\infty}\left(\sqrt{\frac{mg}{k}}\,\frac{e^{at} - e^{-at}}{e^{at} + e^{-at}} \cdot \frac{e^{-at}}{e^{-at}}\right)$

$$= \lim_{t\to\infty}\left(\sqrt{\frac{mg}{k}}\,\frac{1 - e^{-2at}}{1 + e^{-2at}}\right)$$

$$= \sqrt{\frac{mg}{k}}\left(\frac{1 - 0}{1 + 0}\right) = \sqrt{\frac{mg}{k}}$$

The limiting velocity is $\sqrt{\dfrac{mg}{k}}$.

(c) $\sqrt{\dfrac{mg}{k}} = \sqrt{\dfrac{160}{0.005}} \approx 179$ ft/sec

The limiting velocity is about 179 ft/sec,

or about 122 mi/hr.

■ **Section 6.5** Population Growth

(pp. 342–349)

Quick Review 6.5

1. All real numbers

2. $\displaystyle\lim_{x\to\infty} f(x) = \frac{50}{1 + 0} = 50$

  $\displaystyle\lim_{x\to-\infty} f(x) = 0$

3. $y = 0, y = 50$

4. In both f' and f'', the denominator will be a power of
   $1 + 5e^{-0.1x}$, which is never 0. Thus, the domains of both are all real numbers.

5.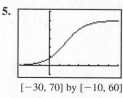

   $[-30, 70]$ by $[-10, 60]$

   $f(x)$ has no zeros.

6. Use NDER $f(x)$, or calculate the derivative as follows.

$$f'(x) = \frac{d}{dx} \frac{50}{1 + 5e^{-0.1x}}$$

$$= \frac{(1 + 5e^{-0.1x})(0) - (50)(5e^{-0.1x})(-0.1)}{(1 + 5e^{-0.1x})^2}$$

$$= \frac{25e^{-0.1x}}{(1 + 5e^{-0.1x})^2}$$

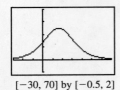

[−30, 70] by [−0.5, 2]

(a) $(-\infty, \infty)$

(b) None

7. Use NDER(NDER $f(x)$), or calculate the second derivatives as follows.

$$f''(x) = \frac{d}{dx} \frac{25e^{-0.1x}}{(1 + 5e^{-0.1x})^2}$$

$$= \frac{(1 + 5e^{-0.1x})^2(25e^{-0.1x})(-0.1) - (25e^{-0.1x})(2)(1 + 5e^{-0.1x})(5e^{-0.1x})(-0.1)}{(1 + 5e^{-0.1x})^4}$$

$$= \frac{-2.5e^{-0.1x}[(1 + 5e^{-0.1x}) - 2(5e^{-0.1x})]}{(1 + 5e^{-0.1x})^3}$$

$$= \frac{12.5e^{-0.2x} - 2.5e^{-0.1x}}{(1 + 5e^{-0.1x})^3}$$

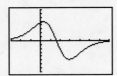

[−30, 70] by [−0.08, 0.08]

Locate the inflection point using graphical methods, or analytically as follows.

$$f''(x) = 0$$

$$\frac{12.5e^{-0.2x} - 2.5e^{-0.1x}}{(1 + 5e^{-0.1x})^3} = 0$$

$$2.5e^{-0.1x}(5e^{-0.1x} - 1) = 0$$

$$e^{-0.1x} = \frac{1}{5}$$

$$-0.1x = -\ln 5$$

$$x = 10 \ln 5 \approx 16.094$$

(a) Since $f''(x) > 0$ for $x < 10 \ln 5$, the graph of f is concave up on the interval $(-\infty, 10 \ln 5)$, or approximately $(-\infty, 16.094)$.

(b) Since $f''(x) < 0$ for $x > 10 \ln 5$, the graph of f is concave down on the interval $(10 \ln 5, \infty)$, or approximately $(16.094, \infty)$.

8. Using the result of the previous exercise, the inflection point occurs at $x = 10 \ln 5$.

Since $f(10 \ln 5) = \dfrac{50}{1 + 5e^{-\ln 5}} = 25$,

the point of inflection is $(10 \ln 5, 25)$, or approximately $(16.094, 25)$.

9. $\dfrac{x - 12}{x^2 - 4x} = \dfrac{A}{x} + \dfrac{B}{x - 4}$

$x - 12 = A(x - 4) + Bx$

$x - 12 = (A + B)x - 4A$

Since $A + B = 1$ and $-4A = -12$, we have $A = 3$ and

$B = -2$.

10. $\dfrac{2x + 16}{x^2 + x - 6} = \dfrac{A}{x + 3} + \dfrac{B}{x - 2}$

$2x + 16 = A(x - 2) + B(x + 3)$

When $x = -3$, the equation becomes $10 = -5A$, and when $x = 2$, the equation becomes $20 = 5B$. Thus, $A = -2$ and $B = 4$.

Section 6.5 Exercises

1. (a) $\dfrac{dP}{dt} = 0.025P$

(b) Using the Law of Exponential Change from Section 6.4, the formula is $P = 75{,}000e^{0.025t}$

(c)

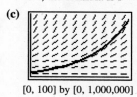

[0, 100] by [0, 1,000,000]

2. (a) $\dfrac{dP}{dt} = 0.019P$

(b) Using the Law of Exponential Change from Section 6.4, the formula is $P = 110{,}000e^{0.019t}$.

(c)

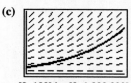

[0, 100] by [0, 1,000,000]

3. (a) $\dfrac{dP}{dt} = \dfrac{k}{M}P(M - P)$

$\dfrac{dP}{dt} = \dfrac{0.05}{200}P(200 - P)$

$\dfrac{dP}{dt} = 0.00025P(200 - P)$

(b) $P = \dfrac{M}{1 + Ae^{-kt}}$

$P = \dfrac{200}{1 + Ae^{-0.05t}}$

Initial condition: $P(0) = 10$

$10 = \dfrac{200}{1 + Ae^0}$

$1 + A = \dfrac{200}{10} = 20$

$A = 19$

Formula: $P = \dfrac{200}{1 + 19e^{-0.05t}}$

(c)

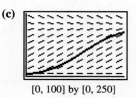

[0, 100] by [0, 250]

4. (a) $\dfrac{dP}{dt} = \dfrac{k}{m}P(M - P)$

$\dfrac{dP}{dt} = \dfrac{0.02}{150}P(150 - P)$

$\dfrac{dP}{dt} = \dfrac{1}{7500}P(150 - P)$

(b) $P = \dfrac{M}{1 + Ae^{-kt}}$

$P = \dfrac{150}{1 + Ae^{-0.02t}}$

Initial condition: $P(0) = 15$

$15 = \dfrac{150}{1 + Ae^0}$

$1 + A = \dfrac{150}{15} = 10$

$A = 9$

Formula: $P = \dfrac{150}{1 + 9e^{-0.02t}}$

(c)

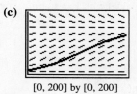

[0, 200] by [0, 200]

5. The growth rate is -0.3 or -30%.

6. The growth rate is 0.075 or 7.5%.

7. $\dfrac{dP}{dt} = 0.04P - 0.0004P^2$

$= 0.0004P(100 - P)$

$= \dfrac{0.04}{100}P(100 - P)$

$= \dfrac{k}{M}P(M - P)$

Thus, $k = 0.04$ and the carrying capacity is $M = 100$.

8. $\dfrac{50}{P}\dfrac{dP}{dt} = 2 - \dfrac{P}{250}$

$\dfrac{1}{P}\dfrac{dP}{dt} = \dfrac{1}{50}\left(2 - \dfrac{P}{250}\right)$

$= \dfrac{1}{25}\left(1 - \dfrac{P}{500}\right)$

$= 0.04\left(1 - \dfrac{P}{500}\right)$

$= k\left(1 - \dfrac{P}{M}\right)$

Thus, $k = 0.04$ and the carrying capacity is $M = 500$.

9. Choose the slope field that shows slopes that increase as y increases. (d)

10. Choose the slope field that matches a logistic differential equation with $M = 100$. (b)

11. Choose the only slope field whose slopes vary with x as well as with y. (c)

12. Choose the slope field that matches a logistic differential equation with $M = 150$. (a)

13. (a) $P(t) = \dfrac{1000}{1 + e^{4.8 - 0.7t}}$

$\qquad = \dfrac{1000}{1 + e^{4.8} e^{-0.7t}}$

$\qquad = \dfrac{M}{1 + Ae^{-kt}}$

This is a logistic growth model with $k = 0.7$ and $M = 1000$.

(b) $P(0) = \dfrac{1000}{1 + e^{4.8}} \approx 8$

Initially there are 8 rabbits.

14. (a) $P(t) = \dfrac{200}{1 + e^{5.3 - t}}$

$\qquad = \dfrac{200}{1 + e^{5.3} e^{-t}}$

$\qquad = \dfrac{M}{1 + Ae^{-kt}}$

This is a logistic growth model with $k = 1$ and $M = 200$.

(b) $P(0) = \dfrac{200}{1 + e^{5.3}} \approx 1$

Initially 1 student has the measles.

15. (a) Note that $\dfrac{dP}{dT} = \dfrac{1 \text{ person}}{14 \text{ sec}} \cdot \dfrac{365 \cdot 24 \cdot 3600 \text{ sec}}{1 \text{ yr}}$

$\qquad \approx 2{,}252{,}571$ people per year.

The relative growth rate is

$\dfrac{\frac{dP}{dT}}{P} \approx \dfrac{2{,}252{,}571}{257{,}313{,}431} \approx 0.00875$ or 0.875%

(b) The population after 8 years will be approximately

$P_0 e^{rt} = 257{,}313{,}431 e^{8r}$

$\qquad \approx 275{,}980{,}017$, where r is the unrounded rate from part (a).

16. (a) Let t be the number of years.

$1000 = 10{,}000(0.8)^t$

$0.1 = 0.8^t$

$\ln 0.1 = t \ln 0.8$

$t = \dfrac{\ln 0.1}{\ln 0.8} \approx 10.32$

It will take about 10.32 years.

(b) Let $f(t) = 10{,}000(0.8)^t$. So that $f(t)$ will round to less

than 1, we actually require $f(t) < 0.5$.

$0.5 = 10{,}000(0.8)^t$

$0.00005 = 0.8^t$

$\ln 0.00005 = t \ln 0.8$

$t = \dfrac{\ln 0.00005}{\ln 0.8} \approx 44.38$

It will take about 44.4 years.

17. (a) $\dfrac{dP}{dt} = 0.0015P(150 - P)$

$\qquad = \dfrac{0.225}{150} P(150 - P)$

$\qquad = \dfrac{k}{M} P(M - P)$

Thus, $k = 0.225$ and $M = 150$.

$P = \dfrac{M}{1 + Ae^{-kt}}$

$\quad = \dfrac{150}{1 + Ae^{-0.225t}}$

Initial condition: $P(0) = 6$

$6 = \dfrac{150}{1 + Ae^0}$

$1 + A = 25$

$A = 24$

Formula: $P = \dfrac{150}{1 + 24e^{-0.225t}}$

(b) $\qquad 100 = \dfrac{150}{1 + 24e^{-0.225t}}$

$1 + 24e^{-0.225t} = \dfrac{3}{2}$

$24e^{-0.225t} = \dfrac{1}{2}$

$e^{-0.225t} = \dfrac{1}{48}$

$-0.225t = -\ln 48$

$t = \dfrac{\ln 48}{0.225} \approx 17.21$ weeks

$125 = \dfrac{150}{1 + 24e^{-0.225t}}$

$1 + 24e^{-0.225t} = \dfrac{6}{5}$

$24e^{-0.225t} = \dfrac{1}{5}$

$e^{-0.225t} = \dfrac{1}{120}$

$-0.225t = -\ln 120$

$t = \dfrac{\ln 120}{0.225} \approx 21.28$

It will take about 17.21 weeks to reach 100 guppies, and about 21.28 weeks to reach 125 guppies.

18. (a) $\dfrac{dP}{dt} = 0.0004P(250 - P)$

$\qquad = \dfrac{0.1}{250}P(250 - P)$

$\qquad = \dfrac{k}{M}P(M - P)$

Thus, $k = 0.1$ and $M = 250$.

$P \;=\; \dfrac{M}{1 + Ae^{-kt}}$

$\quad= \dfrac{250}{1 + Ae^{-0.1t}}$

Initial condition: $P(0) = 28$, where $t = 0$ represents the year 1970.

$28 = \dfrac{250}{1 + Ae^0}$

$28(1 + A) = 250$

$A = \dfrac{250}{28} - 1 = \dfrac{111}{14} \approx 7.9286$

Formula: $P(t) = \dfrac{250}{1 + 111e^{-0.1t}/14}$, or approximately

$\qquad P(t) = \dfrac{250}{1 + 7.9286e^{-0.1t}}$

(b) The population $P(t)$ will round to 250 when

$P(t) \geq 249.5.$

$249.5 = \dfrac{250}{1 + 111e^{-0.1t}/14}$

$249.5\left(1 + \dfrac{111e^{-0.1t}}{14}\right) = 250$

$\dfrac{(249.5)(111e^{-0.1t})}{14} = 0.5$

$e^{-0.1t} = \dfrac{14}{55,389}$

$-0.1t = \ln\dfrac{14}{55,389}$

$t = 10(\ln 55,389 - \ln 14) \approx 82.8$

It will take about 83 years.

19. (a) $y = y_0 e^{-0.01(t/1000)} = y_0 e^{-0.00001t}$

(b) $0.9 = e^{-0.00001t}$

$\ln 0.9 = -0.00001t$

$t = -100,000 \ln 0.9 \approx 10,536$

It will take about 10,536 years.

(c) $y = y_0 e^{-(0.00001)(20,000)} \approx 0.819 y_0$

The tooth size will be about 81.9% of our present tooth size.

20. First find the time to grow from 5000 bees to 10,000 bees.

$\dfrac{dP}{dt} = \dfrac{1}{4}P$

$P(t) = 5000 e^{0.25t}$

$10,000 = 5000 e^{0.25t}$

$2 = e^{0.25t}$

$\ln 2 = 0.25t$

$4 \ln 2 = t$

Now find the time to grow from 10,000 bees to 25,000 bees.

$\dfrac{dP}{dt} = \dfrac{1}{12}P$

$P(t) = 10,000 e^{t/12}$

$25,000 = 10,000 e^{t/12}$

$2.5 = e^{t/12}$

$\ln 2.5 = \dfrac{t}{12}$

$12 \ln 2.5 = t$

The total time required is $4 \ln 2 + 12 \ln 2.5 \approx 13.8$ years.

21. (a) $\dfrac{dx}{dt} = 1000 + 0.10x$

$\displaystyle\int \dfrac{dx}{1000 + 0.1x} = \int dt$

$10 \ln |1000 + 0.1x| = t + C$

$\ln |1000 + 0.1x| = 0.1(t + C)$

$1000 + 0.1x = \pm e^{0.1(t+C)}$

$0.1x = -1000 \pm e^{0.1C}\, e^{0.1t}$

$x = -10,000 \pm 10e^{0.1C}\, e^{0.1t}$

$x = -10,000 + Ae^{0.1t}$

Initial condition: $x(0) = 1000$

$1000 = -10,000 + Ae^0$

$11,000 = A$

Solution: $x = 11,000 e^{0.1t} - 10,000$

(b) $100,000 = 11,000 e^{0.1t} - 10,000$

$10 = e^{0.1t}$

$\ln 10 = 0.1t$

$t = 10 \ln 10 \approx 23$ yr

It will take about 23 years.

22. (a) Using the Law of Exponential Change in Section 6.4, the solution is $p(x) = p_0 e^{-x/100}$, where $p_0 = p(0)$.

Initial condition: $p(100) = 20.09$

$20.09 = p_0 e^{-1}$

$20.09e = p_0$

Solution: $p(x) = (20.09e)e^{-x/100}$

or $p(x) = 20.09 e^{1-0.01x}$

(b) $p(10) = 20.09 e^{0.9} \approx \$49.41$

$p(90) = 20.09 e^{0.1} \approx \$22.20$

(c) $r(x) = xp(x) = 20.09x\, e^{1-0.01x}$

$r'(x) = 20.09[(x)(e^{1-0.01x})(-0.01) + (e^{1-0.01x})(1)]$

$\qquad = 20.09 e^{1-0.01x}(1 - 0.01x)$

The derivative is zero at $x = 100$, positive for $x < 100$, and negative for $x > 100$, so $r(x)$ has its maximum value at $x = 100$.

23. (a) Note that the given years correspond to $x = 0$, $x = 20$, $x = 50$, $x = 70$, and $x = 80$.

$$y = \frac{18.70}{1 + 1.075e^{-0.0422x}}$$

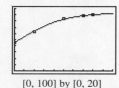

[0, 100] by [0, 20]

(b) Carrying capacity $= \lim_{x \to \infty} y = 18.70$, representing 18.7 million people.

(c) Using NDER twice and solving graphically, we find that $y'' = 0$ when $x \approx 1.7$, corresponding to the year 1912. The population at this time was about $y(1.7) \approx 9.35$ million.

24. (a) $y = \dfrac{24.76}{1 + 7.195e^{-0.0513x}}$

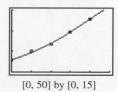

[0, 50] by [0, 15]

(b) Carrying capacity $= \lim_{x \to \infty} y = 24.76$, representing 24.76 million people.

(c) Using NDER twice and solving graphically, we find that $y'' = 0$ when $x \approx 38.44$, corresponding to the year 1988. The population at this time was about $y(38.44) \approx 12.38$ million.

25.
$$\frac{dP}{dt} = \frac{k}{M}P(M - P)$$

$$\frac{M\,dP}{P(M - P)} = k\,dt$$

$$\frac{(M - P) + P}{P(M - P)}\,dP = k\,dt$$

$$\left(\frac{1}{P} + \frac{1}{M - P}\right)dP = k\,dt$$

$$\ln|P| - \ln|M - P| = kt + C$$

$$\ln\left|\frac{P}{M - P}\right| = kt + C$$

$$\ln\left|\frac{M - P}{P}\right| = -kt - C$$

$$\frac{M - P}{P} = \pm e^{-C}e^{-kt}$$

$$\frac{M - P}{P} = Ae^{-kt}$$

$$M - P = APe^{-kt}$$

$$M = P(1 + Ae^{-kt})$$

$$P = \frac{M}{1 + Ae^{-kt}}$$

26. (a) $y = \dfrac{16.90}{1 + 5.132e^{-0.0666x}}$

(b) Carrying capacity $= \lim_{x \to \infty} y = 16.90$ representing 16.9 million people.

27. $\dfrac{dy}{dx} = (\cos x)e^{\sin x}$

$$\int dy = \int (\cos x)e^{\sin x}\,dx$$

$$\int dy = \int e^u\,du$$

$$y = e^u + C$$

$$y = e^{\sin x} + C$$

Initial value: $y(0) = 0$

$$0 = e^{\sin 0} + C$$

$$-1 = C$$

Solution: $y = e^{\sin x} - 1$

28. $\dfrac{dy}{dx} = -2(y - 3)$

$$\int \frac{dy}{y - 3} = -2\int dx$$

$$\ln|y - 3| = -2x + C$$

$$y - 3 = \pm e^{-2x + C}$$

$$y = 3 + Ae^{-2x}$$

Initial condition: $y(0) = 5$

$$5 = 3 + Ae^0$$

$$2 = A$$

Solution: $y = 3 + 2e^{-2x}$

29. $\dfrac{dy}{dx} = \dfrac{x}{y}$

$$\int y\,dy = \int x\,dx$$

$$\frac{y^2}{2} = \frac{x^2}{2} + C$$

Initial condition:

$$y(0) = 2$$

$$\frac{2^2}{2} = \frac{0^2}{2} + C$$

$$2 = C$$

This gives $\dfrac{y^2}{2} = \dfrac{x^2}{2} + 2$, or $y^2 = x^2 + 4$.

But this equation represents two functions, $y = \pm\sqrt{x^2 + 4}$.

The solution of the initial value problem is the function that satisfies the initial condition, namely $y = \sqrt{x^2 + 4}$.

30. $\dfrac{dy}{dx} = y\sqrt{x}$

$\displaystyle\int\dfrac{dy}{y} = \int x^{1/2}\,dx$

$\ln|y| = \dfrac{2}{3}x^{3/2} + C$

$|y| = e^{(2/3)x^{3/2}+C}$

$y = \pm e^{C}e^{(2/3)x^{3/2}}$

$y = Ae^{(2/3)x^{3/2}}$

Initial condition: $y(0) = 1$

$1 = Ae^{0}$

$1 = A$

Solution: $y = e^{(2/3)x^{3/2}}$

31. (a) Note that $k > 0$ and $M > 0$, so the sign of $\dfrac{dP}{dt}$ is the same as the sign of $(M - P)(P - m)$. For $m < P < M$, both $M - P$ and $P - m$ are positive, so the product is positive. For $P < m$ or $P > M$, the expressions $M - P$ and $P - m$ have opposite signs, so the product is negative.

(b) $\dfrac{dP}{dt} = \dfrac{k}{M}(M - P)(P - m)$

$\dfrac{dP}{dt} = \dfrac{k}{1200}(1200 - P)(P - 100)$

$\dfrac{1200}{(1200 - P)(P - 100)}\dfrac{dP}{dt} = k$

$\dfrac{1100}{(1200 - P)(P - 100)}\dfrac{dP}{dt} = \dfrac{11}{12}k$

$\dfrac{(P - 100) + (1200 - P)}{(1200 - P)(P - 100)}\dfrac{dP}{dt} = \dfrac{11}{12}k$

$\left(\dfrac{1}{1200 - P} + \dfrac{1}{P - 100}\right)\dfrac{dP}{dt} = \dfrac{11}{12}k$

$\displaystyle\int\left(\dfrac{1}{1200 - P} + \dfrac{1}{P - 100}\right)dP = \int\dfrac{11}{12}k\,dt$

$-\ln|1200 - P| + \ln|P - 100| = \dfrac{11}{12}kt + C$

$\ln\left|\dfrac{P - 100}{1200 - P}\right| = \dfrac{11}{12}kt + C$

$\dfrac{P - 100}{1200 - P} = \pm e^{C}e^{11kt/12}$

$\dfrac{P - 100}{1200 - P} = Ae^{11kt/12}$

$P - 100 = 1200Ae^{11kt/12} - APe^{11kt/12}$

$P(1 + Ae^{11kt/12}) = 1200Ae^{11kt/12} + 100$

$P = \dfrac{1200Ae^{11kt/12} + 100}{1 + Ae^{11kt/12}}$

(c) $300 = \dfrac{1200Ae^{0} + 100}{1 + Ae^{0}}$

$300(1 + A) = 1200A + 100$

$300 - 100 = 1200A - 300A$

$200 = 900A$

$A = \dfrac{2}{9}$

$P(t) = \dfrac{1200(2/9)e^{11kt/12} + 100}{1 + (2/9)e^{11kt/12}}$

$P(t) = \dfrac{1200(2)e^{11kt/12} + 100(9)}{9 + 2e^{11k/12}}$

$P(t) = \dfrac{300(8e^{11kt/12} + 3)}{9 + 2e^{11kt/12}}$

(d)

[0, 75] by [0, 1500]

Note that the slope field is given by

$\dfrac{dP}{dt} = \dfrac{0.1}{1200}(1200 - P)(P - 100).$

(e) $\dfrac{dP}{dt} = \dfrac{k}{M}(M - P)(P - m)$

$\dfrac{M}{(M - P)(P - m)}\dfrac{dP}{dt} = k$

$\dfrac{M}{M - m}\dfrac{M - m}{(M - P)(P - m)}\dfrac{dP}{dt} = k$

$\dfrac{(P - m) + (M - P)}{(M - P)(P - m)}\dfrac{dP}{dt} = \dfrac{M - m}{M}k$

$\left(\dfrac{1}{M - P} + \dfrac{1}{P - m}\right)\dfrac{dP}{dt} = \dfrac{M - m}{M}k$

$\displaystyle\int\left(\dfrac{1}{M - P} + \dfrac{1}{P - m}\right)dP = \int\dfrac{M - m}{M}k\,dt$

$-\ln|M - P| + \ln|P - m| = \dfrac{M - m}{M}kt + C$

$\ln\left|\dfrac{P - m}{M - P}\right| = \dfrac{M - m}{M}kt + C$

$\dfrac{P - m}{M - P} = \pm e^{C}e^{(M-m)kt/M}$

$\dfrac{P - m}{M - P} = Ae^{(M-m)kt/M}$

$P - m = (M - P)Ae^{(M-m)kt/M}$

$P(1 + Ae^{(M-m)kt/M}) = AMe^{(M-m)kt/M} + m$

$P = \dfrac{AMe^{(M-m)kt/M} + m}{1 + Ae^{(M-m)kt/M}}$

$P(0) = \dfrac{AMe^{0} + m}{1 + Ae^{0}} = \dfrac{AM + m}{1 + A}$

$P(0)(1 + A) = AM + m$

$A(P(0) - M) = m - P(0)$

$A = \dfrac{m - P(0)}{P(0) - M} = \dfrac{P(0) - m}{M - P(0)}$

Therefore, the solution to the differential equation is

$P = \dfrac{AMe^{(M-m)kt/M} + m}{1 + Ae^{(M-m)kt/M}}$ where $A = \dfrac{P(0) - m}{M - P(0)}$.

32. (a) $\dfrac{dp}{dt} = k(t)p$

$$\int \dfrac{dp}{p} = \int k(t)\, dt$$

$$\ln |p| = \int_0^t k(u)\, du + C$$

$$p = \pm e^C e^{\int_0^t k(u)\, du}$$

$$p = A e^{\int_0^t k(u)\, du}$$

Initial condition: $p(0) = p_0$.

$$p_0 = A e^{\int_0^0 k(u)\, du}$$

$$p_0 = A e^0$$

$$p_0 = A$$

Solution: $p(t) = p_0 e^{\int_0^t k(u)\, du}$

(b) $\displaystyle\int_0^9 k(u)\, du = \int_0^9 \dfrac{0.04}{1+u}\, du$

$$= 0.04 \ln (1+u) \Big]_0^9$$

$$= 0.04(\ln 10 - \ln 1)$$

$$= 0.04 \ln 10$$

$$p(9) = p_0 e^{\int_0^9 k(u)\, du}$$

$$= 100 e^{0.04 \ln 10} \approx 109.65$$

After 9 years during which the inflation rate is $\dfrac{0.04}{1+t}$ per year, the price of an item which originally cost \$100 will be increased to \$109.65.

(c) $p(9) = p_0 e^{\int_0^9 0.04\, du} = 100 e^{0.04(9)} \approx 143.33$

The price will be \$143.33.

(d) $\displaystyle\int_0^9 k(u)\, du = \int_0^9 (0.04 + 0.004u)\, du$

$$= \Big[0.04u + 0.002u^2\Big]_0^9 = 0.522$$

$$p(9) = p_0 e^{\int_0^9 k(u)\, du} = 100 e^{0.522} \approx 168.54$$

33. (a) $\dfrac{dP}{dt} = kP^2$

$$\int P^{-2}\, dP = \int k\, dt$$

$$-P^{-1} = kt + C$$

$$P = -\dfrac{1}{kt + C}$$

Initial condition: $P(0) = P_0$

$$P_0 = -\dfrac{1}{C}$$

$$C = -\dfrac{1}{P_0}$$

Solution: $P = -\dfrac{1}{kt - (1/P_0)} = \dfrac{P_0}{1 - kP_0 t}$

(b) There is a vertical asymptote at $t = \dfrac{1}{kP_0}$.

■ Section 6.6 Numerical Methods

(pp. 350–356)

Quick Review 6.6

1. $f'(x) = 3x^2 - 3$
$f'(2) = 3(2)^2 - 3 = 9$

2. $L(x) = f(2) + f'(2)(x - 2)$
$ = 2 + 9(x - 2)$
$ = 9x - 16$

3. $f'(x) = \sec^2 x$
$f'\left(\dfrac{\pi}{4}\right) = \sec^2 \dfrac{\pi}{4} = (\sqrt{2})^2 = 2$

4. $L(x) = f\left(\dfrac{\pi}{4}\right) + f'\left(\dfrac{\pi}{4}\right)\left(x - \dfrac{\pi}{4}\right)$
$ = 1 + 2\left(x - \dfrac{\pi}{4}\right)$
$ = 2x + 1 - \dfrac{\pi}{2}$

5. $f'(x) = 0.2x - 5x^{-2}$
$f'(4) = 0.2(4) - 5(4)^{-2} = 0.4875$

6. $L(x) = f(4) + f'(4)(x - 4)$
$ = 2.85 + 0.4875(x - 4)$
$ = 0.4875x + 0.9$

7. $L(4.1) = 0.4875(4.1) + 0.9 = 2.89875$

$f(4.1) = 0.1(4.1)^2 + \dfrac{5}{4.1} \approx 2.900512$

(a) $|L(4.1) - f(4.1)| \approx 0.001762$

(b) $\dfrac{|L(4.1) - f(4.1)|}{f(4.1)} \approx 0.00061 = 0.061\%$

8. $L(4.2) = 0.4875(4.2) + 0.9 = 2.9475$

$f(4.2) = 0.1(4.2)^2 + \dfrac{5}{4.2} \approx 2.954476$

(a) $|L(4.2) - f(4.2)| \approx 0.006976$

(b) $\dfrac{|L(4.2) - f(4.2)|}{f(4.2)} \approx 0.00236 = 0.236\%$

9. $L(4.5) = 0.4875(4.5) + 0.9 = 3.09375$

$f(4.5) = 0.1(4.5)^2 + \dfrac{5}{4.5} \approx 3.136111$

(a) $|L(4.5) - f(4.5)| \approx 0.042361$

(b) $\dfrac{|L(4.5) - f(4.5)|}{f(4.5)} \approx 0.01351 = 1.351\%$

10. $L(3.5) = 0.4875(3.5) + 0.9 = 2.60625$

$f(3.5) = 0.1(3.5)^2 + \dfrac{5}{3.5} \approx 2.653571$

(a) $|L(3.5) - f(3.5)| \approx 0.047321$

(b) $\dfrac{|L(3.5) - f(3.5)|}{f(3.5)} \approx 0.01783 = 1.783\%$

Section 6.6 Exercises

1. Check the differential equation:

$$y' = \frac{d}{dx}(x - 1 + 2e^{-x}) = 1 + 2e^{-x}(-1) = 1 - 2e^{-x}$$

$$x - y = x - (x - 1 + 2e^{-x}) = 1 - 2e^{-x}$$

Therefore, $y' = x - y$.

Check the initial condition:

$$y(0) = 0 - 1 + 2e^{-(0)} = -1 + 2 = 1$$

2. Check the differential equation:

$$y' = \frac{d}{dx}(x - 1 - e^{-x}) = 1 - e^{-x}(-1) = 1 + e^{-x}$$

$$x - y = x - (x - 1 - e^{-x}) = 1 + e^{-x}$$

Therefore, $y' = x - y$.

Check the initial condition:

$$y(0) = 0 - 1 - e^{-(0)} = -1 - 1 = -2$$

3. Check the differential equation:

$$y' = \frac{d}{dx}\left(\frac{e^{2x} - 2\sin x - \cos x}{5}\right) = \frac{2e^{2x} - 2\cos x + \sin x}{5}$$

$$2y + \sin x = 2\left(\frac{e^{2x} - 2\sin x - \cos x}{5}\right) + \sin x$$

$$= \frac{2e^{2x} - 4\sin x - 2\cos x + 5\sin x}{5}$$

$$= \frac{2e^{2x} - 2\cos x + \sin x}{5}$$

Therefore, $y' = 2y + \sin x$.

Check the initial condition:

$$y(0) = \frac{e^{2(0)} - 2\sin 0 - \cos 0}{5} = \frac{1 - 1}{5} = 0$$

4. Check the differential equation:

$$y' = \frac{d}{dx}(e^x - e^{2x} - 1) = e^x - 2e^{2x}$$

$$y - e^{2x} + 1 = (e^x - e^{2x} - 1) - e^{2x} + 1 = e^x - 2e^{2x}$$

Therefore, $y' = y - e^{2x} + 1$.

Check the initial condition:

$$y(0) = e^0 - e^{2(0)} - 1 = -1$$

5. Note that we are finding an exact solution to the initial value problem discussed in Examples 1–4.

$$\frac{dy}{dx} = 1 + y$$

$$\int \frac{dy}{1 + y} = \int dx$$

$$\ln|1 + y| = x + C$$

$$|1 + y| = e^{x+C}$$

$$1 + y = \pm e^{x+C}$$

$$y = \pm e^C e^x - 1$$

$$y = Ae^x - 1$$

Initial condition: $y(0) = 1$
$$1 = Ae^0 - 1$$
$$2 = A$$
Solution: $y = 2e^x - 1$

6.
$$\frac{dy}{dx} = x(1 - y)$$

$$\int \frac{dy}{1 - y} = \int x\,dx$$

$$-\ln|1 - y| = \frac{1}{2}x^2 + C$$

$$|1 - y| = e^{-(x^2/2) - C}$$

$$1 - y = \pm e^{-(x^2/2) - C}$$

$$y = \pm e^{-C}e^{-x^2/2} + 1$$

$$y = Ae^{-x^2/2} + 1$$

Initial condition: $y(-2) = 0$
$$0 = Ae^{-(-2)^2/2} + 1$$
$$0 = Ae^{-2} + 1$$
$$-e^2 = A$$
Solution: $y = -e^2 e^{-x^2/2} + 1$ or $y = -e^{-(x^2/2)+2} + 1$

7.
$$\frac{dy}{dx} = 2y(x + 1)$$

$$\frac{dy}{y} = 2(x + 1)\,dx$$

$$\int \frac{dy}{y} = \int (2x + 2)\,dx$$

$$\ln|y| = x^2 + 2x + C$$

$$|y| = e^{x^2 + 2x + C}$$

$$y = \pm e^C e^{x^2 + 2x}$$

$$y = A e^{x^2 + 2x}$$

Initial condition: $y(-2) = 2$
$$2 = Ae^{(-2)^2 + 2(-2)}$$
$$2 = A$$
Solution: $y = 2e^{x^2 + 2x}$

8.
$$\frac{dy}{dx} = y^2(1 + 2x)$$

$$\int y^{-2}\,dy = \int (1 + 2x)\,dx$$

$$-y^{-1} = x + x^2 + C$$

$$y = -\frac{1}{x^2 + x + C}$$

Initial condition: $y(-1) = -1$

$$-1 = -\frac{1}{(-1)^2 + (-1) + C}$$

$$-1 = -\frac{1}{C}$$

$$C = 1$$

Solution: $y = -\dfrac{1}{x^2 + x + 1}$

9. To find the approximate values, set $y_1 = 2y + \sin x$ and use EULERT with initial values $x = 0$ and $y = 0$ and step size 0.1 for 10 points. The exact values are given by $y = \frac{1}{5}(e^{2x} - 2\sin x - \cos x)$.

x	y (Euler)	y (exact)	Error
0	0	0	0
0.1	0	0.0053	0.0053
0.2	0.0100	0.0229	0.0129
0.3	0.0318	0.0551	0.0233
0.4	0.0678	0.1051	0.0374
0.5	0.1203	0.1764	0.0561
0.6	0.1923	0.2731	0.0808
0.7	0.2872	0.4004	0.1132
0.8	0.4090	0.5643	0.1553
0.9	0.5626	0.7723	0.2097
1.0	0.7534	1.0332	0.2797

10. To find the approximate values, set $y_1 = x - y$ and use EULERT with initial values $x = 0$ and $y = -2$ and step size 0.1 for 10 points. The exact values are given by $y = x - 1 - e^{-x}$.

x	y (Euler)	y (exact)	Error
0	-2	-2	0
0.1	-1.8000	-1.8048	0.0048
0.2	-1.6100	-1.6187	0.0087
0.3	-1.4290	-1.4408	0.0118
0.4	-1.2561	-1.2703	0.0142
0.5	-1.0905	-1.1065	0.0160
0.6	-0.9314	-0.9488	0.0174
0.7	-0.7783	-0.7966	0.0183
0.8	-0.6305	-0.6493	0.0189
0.9	-0.4874	-0.5066	0.0191
1.0	-0.3487	-0.3679	0.0192

11. To find the approximate values, set $y_1 = 2y(x + 1)$ and use IMPEULT with initial values $x = -2$ and $y = 2$ and step size 0.1 for 20 points. The exact values are given by $y = 2e^{x^2 + 2x}$.

x	$y\left(\begin{array}{c}\text{improved}\\\text{Euler}\end{array}\right)$	y (exact)	Error
-2	2	2	0
-1.9	1.6560	1.6539	0.0021
-1.8	1.3983	1.3954	0.0030
-1.7	1.2042	1.2010	0.0032
-1.6	1.0578	1.0546	0.0032
-1.5	0.9478	0.9447	0.0031
-1.4	0.8663	0.8634	0.0029
-1.3	0.8077	0.8050	0.0027
-1.2	0.7683	0.7658	0.0025
-1.1	0.7456	0.7432	0.0024
-1.0	0.7381	0.7358	0.0023
-0.9	0.7455	0.7432	0.0023
-0.8	0.7682	0.7658	0.0024
-0.7	0.8075	0.8050	0.0024
-0.6	0.8659	0.8634	0.0025
-0.5	0.9473	0.9447	0.0026
-0.4	1.0572	1.0546	0.0026
-0.3	1.2036	1.2010	0.0026
-0.2	1.3976	1.3954	0.0022
-0.1	1.6553	1.6539	0.0014
0	1.9996	2	0.0004

12. To find the approximate values, set $y_1 = x(1 - y)$ and use IMPEULT with initial values $x = -2$ and $y = 0$ and step size 0.1 for 20 points. The exact values are given by $y = -e^{-(x^2/2)+2} + 1$.

x	$y\left(\begin{array}{c}\text{improved}\\\text{Euler}\end{array}\right)$	y (exact)	Error
−2	0	0	0
−1.9	−0.2140	−0.2153	0.0013
−1.8	−0.4593	−0.4623	0.0029
−1.7	−0.7371	−0.7419	0.0049
−1.6	−1.0473	−1.0544	0.0071
−1.5	−1.3892	−1.3989	0.0097
−1.4	−1.7607	−1.7732	0.0125
−1.3	−2.1585	−2.1740	0.0155
−1.2	−2.5780	−2.5966	0.0186
−1.1	−3.0131	−3.0350	0.0219
−1.0	−3.4565	−3.4817	0.0252
−0.9	−3.9000	−3.9283	0.0284
−0.8	−4.3341	−4.3656	0.0315
−0.7	−4.7491	−4.7834	0.0344
−0.6	−5.1348	−5.1719	0.0370
−0.5	−5.4815	−5.5208	0.0394
−0.4	−5.7796	−5.8210	0.0413
−0.3	−6.0210	−6.0639	0.0430
−0.2	−6.1986	−6.2427	0.0441
−0.1	−6.3073	−6.3522	0.0449
0	−6.3438	−6.3891	0.0452

13. To find the approximate values, set $y_1 = x - y$ and use EULERT and IMPEULT with initial values $x = 0$ and $y = 1$ and step size 0.1 for 20 points. The exact values are given by $y = x - 1 + 2e^{-x}$.

x	y (Euler)	$y \left(\begin{array}{c} \text{improved} \\ \text{Euler} \end{array} \right)$	y (exact)	Error (Euler)	Error $\left(\begin{array}{c} \text{improved} \\ \text{Euler} \end{array} \right)$
0	1	1	1	0	0
0.1	0.9000	0.9100	0.9097	0.0097	0.0003
0.2	0.8200	0.8381	0.8375	0.0175	0.0006
0.3	0.7580	0.7824	0.7816	0.0236	0.0008
0.4	0.7122	0.7416	0.7406	0.0284	0.0010
0.5	0.6810	0.7142	0.7131	0.0321	0.0011
0.6	0.6629	0.6988	0.6976	0.0347	0.0012
0.7	0.6566	0.6944	0.6932	0.0366	0.0012
0.8	0.6609	0.7000	0.6987	0.0377	0.0013
0.9	0.6748	0.7145	0.7131	0.0383	0.0013
1.0	0.6974	0.7371	0.7358	0.0384	0.0013
1.1	0.7276	0.7671	0.7657	0.0381	0.0013
1.2	0.7649	0.8037	0.8024	0.0375	0.0013
1.3	0.8084	0.8463	0.8451	0.0367	0.0013
1.4	0.8575	0.8944	0.8932	0.0357	0.0012
1.5	0.9118	0.9475	0.9463	0.0345	0.0012
1.6	0.9706	1.0050	1.0038	0.0332	0.0012
1.7	1.0335	1.0665	1.0654	0.0318	0.0011
1.8	1.1002	1.1317	1.1306	0.0304	0.0011
1.9	1.1702	1.2002	1.1991	0.0290	0.0010
2.0	1.2432	1.2716	1.2707	0.0275	0.0010

14. To find the approximate values, set $y_1 = y - e^{2x} + 1$ and use EULERT and IMPEULT with initial values $x = 0$ and $y = -1$ and step size 0.1 for 20 points. The exact values are given by $y = e^x - e^{2x} - 1$.

x	y (Euler)	$y\left(\dfrac{\text{improved}}{\text{Euler}}\right)$	y (exact)	Error (Euler)	Error $\left(\dfrac{\text{improved}}{\text{Euler}}\right)$
0	−1	−1	−1	0	0
0.1	−1.1000	−1.1161	−1.1162	0.0162	0.0002
0.2	−1.2321	−1.2700	−1.2704	0.0383	0.0004
0.3	−1.4045	−1.4715	−1.4723	0.0677	0.0007
0.4	−1.6272	−1.7325	−1.7337	0.1065	0.0012
0.5	−1.9125	−2.0678	−2.0696	0.1571	0.0018
0.6	−2.2756	−2.4954	−2.4980	0.2224	0.0026
0.7	−2.7351	−3.0378	−3.0414	0.3063	0.0037
0.8	−3.3142	−3.7224	−3.7275	0.4133	0.0050
0.9	−4.0409	−4.5832	−4.5900	0.5492	0.0068
1.0	−4.9499	−5.6616	−5.6708	0.7209	0.0092
1.1	−6.0838	−7.0087	−7.0208	0.9370	0.0121
1.2	−7.4947	−8.6872	−8.7031	1.2084	0.0159
1.3	−9.2465	−10.7738	−10.7944	1.5480	0.0206
1.4	−11.4175	−13.3628	−13.3894	1.9719	0.0267
1.5	−14.1037	−16.5696	−16.6038	2.5001	0.0342
1.6	−17.4227	−20.5358	−20.5795	3.1568	0.0437
1.7	−21.5182	−25.4345	−25.4902	3.9720	0.0556
1.8	−26.5664	−31.4781	−31.5486	4.9822	0.0705
1.9	−32.7829	−38.9262	−39.0153	6.2324	0.0891
2.0	−40.4313	−48.0970	−48.2091	7.7778	0.1121

15. (a)
$$\frac{dy}{dx} = 2y^2(x - 1)$$
$$\frac{dy}{y^2} = 2(x - 1)dx$$
$$\int y^{-2}\, dy = \int (2x - 2)\, dx$$
$$-y^{-1} = x^2 - 2x + C$$

Initial value: $y(2) = -\dfrac{1}{2}$

$2 = 2^2 - 2(2) + C$

$2 = C$

Solution: $-y^{-1} = x^2 - 2x + 2$ or $y = -\dfrac{1}{x^2 - 2x + 2}$

$y(3) = -\dfrac{1}{3^2 - 2(3) + 2} = -\dfrac{1}{5} = -0.2$

(b) To find the approximation, set $y_1 = 2y^2(x - 1)$ and use EULERT with initial values $x = 2$ and $y = -\dfrac{1}{2}$ and step size 0.2 for 5 points. This gives $y(3) \approx -0.1851$; error ≈ 0.0149.

(c) Use step size 0.1 for 10 points. This gives
$y(3) \approx -0.1929$; error ≈ 0.0071.

(d) Use step size 0.05 for 20 points. This gives
$y(3) \approx -0.1965$; error ≈ 0.0035.

16. (a)
$$\frac{dy}{dx} = y - 1$$

$$\int \frac{dy}{y-1} = \int dx$$

$$\ln |y - 1| = x + C$$

$$|y - 1| = e^{x+C}$$

$$y - 1 = \pm e^C e^x$$

$$y = Ae^x + 1$$

Initial condition: $y(0) = 3$

$$3 = Ae^0 + 1$$

$$2 = A$$

Solution: $y = 2e^x + 1$

$$y(1) = 2e + 1 \approx 6.4366$$

(b) To find the approximation, set $y_1 = y - 1$ and use EULERT with initial values $x = 0$ and $y = 3$ and step size 0.2 for 5 points. This gives $y(1) \approx 5.9766$; error ≈ 0.4599.

(c) Use step size 0.1 for 10 points. This gives $y(1) \approx 6.1875$; error ≈ 0.2491.

(d) Use step size 0.05 for 20 points. This gives $y(1) \approx 6.3066$; error ≈ 0.1300.

17. The exact solution is $y = -\dfrac{1}{x^2 - 2x + 2}$, so $y(3) = -0.2$.

(a) To find the approximation, set $y_1 = 2y^2(x - 1)$ and use IMPEULT with initial values $x = 2$ and $y = -\dfrac{1}{2}$ and step size 0.2 for 5 points. This gives $y(3) \approx -0.2024$; error ≈ 0.0024.

(b) Use step size 0.1 for 10 points. This gives $y(3) \approx -0.2005$; error ≈ 0.0005.

(c) Use step size 0.05 for 20 points. This gives $y(3) = -0.2001$; error ≈ 0.0001.

(d) As the step size decreases, the accuracy of the method increases and so the error decreases.

18. The exact solution is $y = 2e^x + 1$, so $y(1) = 2e + 1 \approx 6.4366$.

(a) To find the approximation, set $y_1 = y - 1$ and use IMPEULT with initial values $x = 0$ and $y = 3$ and step size 0.2 for 5 points. This gives $y(1) \approx 6.4054$; error ≈ 0.0311.

(b) Use step size 0.1 for 10 points. This gives $y(1) \approx 6.4282$; error ≈ 0.0084

(c) Use step size 0.05 for 20 points. This gives $y_1 \approx 6.4344$; error ≈ 0.0022.

(d) As the step size decreases, the accuracy of the method increases and so the error decreases.

19. Set $y_1 = 2y + \sin x$ and use EULERG with initial values $x = 0$ and $y = 0$ and step size 0.1. The exact solution is $y = \dfrac{1}{5}(e^{2x} - 2 \sin x - \cos x)$.

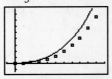

[−0.1, 1.1] by [−0.13, 0.88]

20. Set $y_1 = x - y$ and use EULERG with initial values $x = 0$ and $y = -2$ and step size 0.1. The exact solution is $y = x - 1 - e^{-x}$.

[−0.1, 1.1] by [−2.3, 0.3]

21. Set $y_1 = 2y(x + 1)$ and use IMPEULG with initial values $x = -2$ and $y = 2$ and step size 0.1. The exact solution is $y = 2e^{x^2 + 2x}$.

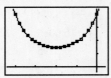

[−2.2, 0.2] by [−0.2, 2.2]

22. Set $y_1 = x(1 - y)$ and use IMPEULG with initial values $x = -2$ and $y = 0$ and step size 0.1. The exact solution is $y = -e^{-(x^2/2)+2} + 1$.

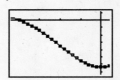

[−2.2, 0.2] by [−7.3, 1.1]

23. To find the approximate values, set $y_1 = x + y$ and use EULERT with initial values $x = 0$ and $y = 1$ and step size -0.1 for 10 points. The exact values are given by $y = 2e^x - x - 1$.

x	y (Euler)	y (exact)	Error
0	1	1.0	0
−0.1	0.9000	0.9097	0.0097
−0.2	0.8200	0.8375	0.0175
−0.3	0.7580	0.7816	0.0236
−0.4	0.7122	0.7406	0.0284
−0.5	0.6810	0.7131	0.0321
−0.6	0.6629	0.6976	0.0347
−0.7	0.6566	0.6932	0.0366
−0.8	0.6609	0.6987	0.0377
−0.9	0.6748	0.7131	0.0383
−1.0	0.6974	0.7358	0.0384

24. To find the approximate values, set $y_1 = x + y$ and use IMPEULT with initial values $x = 0$ and $y = 1$ and step size -0.1 for 10 points. The exact values are given by $y = 2e^x - x - 1$.

x	$y\left(\dfrac{\text{improved}}{\text{Euler}}\right)$	y (exact)	Error
0	1	1.0	0
-0.1	0.9100	0.9097	0.0003
-0.2	0.8381	0.8375	0.0006
-0.3	0.7824	0.7816	0.0008
-0.4	0.7416	0.7406	0.0010
-0.5	0.7142	0.7131	0.0011
-0.6	0.6988	0.6976	0.0012
-0.7	0.6944	0.6932	0.0012
-0.8	0.7000	0.6987	0.0013
-0.9	0.7145	0.7131	0.0013
-1.0	0.7371	0.7358	0.0013

25. Set $y_1 = y + e^x - 2$ and EULERG, with initial values $x = 0$ and $y = 2$ and step sizes 0.1 and 0.05.

(a)

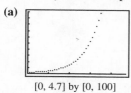

[0, 4.7] by [0, 100]

(b)

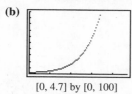

[0, 4.7] by [0, 100]

26. Set $y_1 = \cos(2x - y)$ and use EULERG with initial values $x = 0$ and $y = 2$ and step sizes 0.1 and 0.05.

(a)

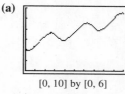

[0, 10] by [0, 6]

(b)

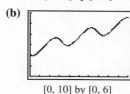

[0, 10] by [0, 6]

27. Set $y_1 = y\left(\dfrac{1}{2} - \ln|y|\right)$ and use IMPEULG with initial values $x = 0$ and $y = \dfrac{1}{3}$ and step size 0.1 and 0.05.

(a)

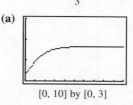

[0, 10] by [0, 3]

(b)

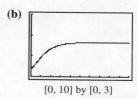

[0, 10] by [0, 3]

28. Set $y = \sin(2x - y)$ and use IMPEULG with initial values $x = 0$ and $y = 1$ and step sizes 0.1 and 0.05.

(a)

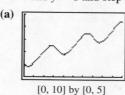

[0, 10] by [0, 5]

(b)

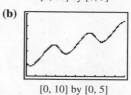

[0, 10] by [0, 5]

29. To find the approximate values, let $y_1 = y$ and use EULERT with initial values $x = 0$ and $y = 1$ and step size 0.05 for 20 points. This gives $y(1) \approx 2.6533$.

Since the exact solution to the initial value problem is $y = e^x$, the exact value of $y(1)$ is e.

30. To find the approximate values, let $y_1 = 3y$ and use IMPEULT with initial values $x = 0$ and $y = 1$ and step size 0.05 for 20 points. This gives $y(1) \approx 19.8845$.

Since the exact solution to the initial value problem is $y = e^{3x}$, the exact value of $y(1)$ is e^3.

31. To find the approximate values, let $y_1 = 1 + y$ and use RUNKUTT with initial values $x = 0$ and $y = 1$ and step size 0.1 for 10 points. The exact values are given by $y = 2e^x - 1$.

x	y (Runge-Kutta)	y (exact)	Error
0	1	1	0
0.1	1.2103	1.2103	0.0000002
0.2	1.4428	1.4428	0.0000004
0.3	1.6997	1.6997	0.0000006
0.4	1.9836	1.9836	0.0000009
0.5	2.2974	2.2974	0.0000013
0.6	2.6442	2.6442	0.0000017
0.7	3.0275	3.0275	0.0000022
0.8	3.4511	3.4511	0.0000027
0.9	3.9192	3.9192	0.0000034
1.0	4.4366	4.4366	0.0000042

32. (a) Set $y_1 = x - y$ and use RUNKUTT with initial values $x = 0$ and $y = 1$ and step size 0.1.

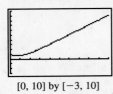

[0, 10] by [−3, 10]

(b) Use RUNKUTT with initial values $x = 0$ and $y = -2$ and step size 0.1.

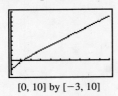

[0, 10] by [−3, 10]

■ Chapter 6 Review Exercises

(pp. 358 – 361)

1. $\displaystyle\int_0^{\pi/3} \sec^2 \theta\, d\theta = \tan \theta \Big]_0^{\pi/3} = \tan \frac{\pi}{3} - \tan 0 = \sqrt{3}$

2. $\displaystyle\int_1^2 \left(x + \frac{1}{x^2}\right) dx = \left[\frac{1}{2}x^2 - x^{-1}\right]_1^2$

$$= \left(\frac{1}{2}(4) - \frac{1}{2}\right) - \left(\frac{1}{2} - 1\right)$$

$$= \frac{3}{2} + \frac{1}{2}$$

$$= \frac{4}{2} = 2$$

3. Let $u = 2x + 1$

$du = 2\, dx$

$\frac{1}{2}\, du = dx$

$\displaystyle\int_0^1 \frac{36}{(2x+1)^3}\, dx = 18\int_1^3 \frac{1}{u^3}\, du$

$$= 18\left(-\frac{1}{2}\right) u^{-2}\Big]_1^3$$

$$= -9\left(\frac{1}{9} - 1\right)$$

$$= -9\left(-\frac{8}{9}\right)$$

$$= 8$$

4. Let $u = 1 - x^2$

$du = -2x\, dx$

$-du = 2x\, dx$

$\displaystyle\int_{-1}^1 2x \sin (1 - x^2)\, dx = -\int_0^0 \sin u\, du = 0$

5. Let $u = \sin x$

$du = \cos x\, dx$

$\displaystyle\int_0^{\pi/2} 5 \sin^{3/2} x \cos x\, dx = \int_0^1 5u^{3/2}\, du$

$$= 5 \cdot \frac{2}{5} u^{5/2}\Big]_0^1$$

$$= 2(1 - 0)$$

$$= 2$$

6. $\displaystyle\int_{1/2}^4 \frac{x^2 + 3x}{x}\, dx = \int_{1/2}^4 (x + 3)\, dx\ (x \neq 0)$

$$= \left(\frac{1}{2}x^2 + 3x\right)\Big]_{1/2}^4$$

$$= \left(\frac{1}{2}(16) + \right.$$

$$\left. 3(4)\right) - \left(\frac{1}{2}\left(\frac{1}{4}\right) + \frac{3}{2}\right)$$

$$= 20 - \left(\frac{1}{8} + \frac{12}{8}\right)$$

$$= 20 - \frac{13}{8}$$

$$= \frac{147}{8}$$

7. Let $u = \tan x$

$du = \sec^2 x\, dx$

$\displaystyle\int_0^{\pi/4} e^{\tan x} \sec^2 x\, dx = \int_0^1 e^u\, du$

$$= e^u\Big]_0^1$$

$$= e^1 - e^0$$

$$= e - 1$$

8. Let $u = \ln r$

$du = \frac{1}{r}\, dr$

$\displaystyle\int_1^e \frac{\sqrt{\ln r}}{r}\, dr = \int_0^1 u^{1/2}\, du$

$$= \frac{2}{3} u^{3/2}\Big]_0^1$$

$$= \frac{2}{3}(1 - 0)$$

$$= \frac{2}{3}$$

9. Let $u = 2 - \sin x$

$du = -\cos x\, dx$

$-du = \cos x\, dx$

$\displaystyle\int \frac{\cos x}{2 - \sin x}\, dx = -\int \frac{1}{u}\, du$

$$= -\ln |u| + C$$

$$= -\ln |2 - \sin x| + C$$

10. Let $u = 3x + 4$

$$du = 3\,dx$$

$$\frac{1}{3}\,du = dx$$

$$\int \frac{dx}{\sqrt[3]{3x+4}} = \frac{1}{3}\int u^{-1/3}\,du$$

$$= \frac{1}{3}\cdot\frac{3}{2}u^{2/3} + C$$

$$= \frac{1}{2}(3x+4)^{2/3} + C$$

11. Let $u = t^2 + 5$

$$du = 2t\,dt$$

$$\frac{1}{2}\,du = t\,dt$$

$$\int \frac{t\,dt}{t^2+5} = \frac{1}{2}\int \frac{1}{u}\,du = \frac{1}{2}\ln|u| + C$$

$$= \frac{1}{2}\ln|t^2+5| + C$$

$$= \frac{1}{2}\ln(t^2+5) + C$$

12. Let $u = \frac{1}{\theta}$

$$du = -\frac{1}{\theta^2}\,d\theta$$

$$\int \frac{1}{\theta^2}\sec\frac{1}{\theta}\tan\frac{1}{\theta}\,d\theta = -\int \sec u \tan u\,du$$

$$= -\sec u + C$$

$$= -\sec\frac{1}{\theta} + C$$

13. Let $u = \ln y$

$$du = \frac{1}{y}\,dy$$

$$\int \frac{\tan(\ln y)}{y}\,dy = \int \tan u\,du$$

$$= \int \frac{\sin u}{\cos u}\,du$$

Let $w = \cos u$

$$dw = -\sin u\,du$$

$$= -\int \frac{1}{w}\,dw$$

$$= -\ln|w| + C$$

$$= -\ln|\cos u| + C$$

$$= -\ln|\cos(\ln y)| + C$$

14. Let $u = e^x$

$$du = e^x\,dx$$

$$\int e^x \sec(e^x)\,dx = \int \sec u\,du$$

$$= \ln|\sec u + \tan u| + C$$

$$= \ln|\sec(e^x) + \tan(e^x)| + C$$

15. Let $u = \ln x$

$$du = \frac{1}{x}\,dx$$

$$\int \frac{dx}{x\ln x} = \int \frac{1}{u}\,du$$

$$= \ln|u| + C$$

$$= \ln|\ln x| + C$$

16. $$\int \frac{dt}{t\sqrt{t}} = \int \frac{dt}{t^{3/2}}$$

$$= \int t^{-3/2}\,dt$$

$$= -2t^{-1/2} + C$$

$$= -\frac{2}{\sqrt{t}} + C$$

17. Use tabular integration with $f(x) = x^3$ and $g(x) = \cos x$.

$f(x)$ and its derivatives		$g(x)$ and its integrals
x^3	(+)	$\cos x$
$3x^2$	(−)	$\sin x$
$6x$	(+)	$-\cos x$
6	(−)	$-\sin x$
0		$\cos x$

$$\int x^3 \cos x\,dx$$

$$= x^3\sin x + 3x^2\cos x - 6x\sin x - 6\cos x + C$$

18. Let $u = \ln x$ $\quad dv = x^4\,dx$

$$du = \frac{1}{x}\,dx \quad v = \frac{1}{5}x^5$$

$$\int x^4 \ln x\,dx = \frac{1}{5}x^5\ln x - \int \frac{1}{5}x^5\left(\frac{1}{x}\right)dx$$

$$= \frac{1}{5}x^5\ln x - \frac{1}{5}\int x^4\,dx$$

$$= \frac{1}{5}x^5\ln x - \frac{1}{25}x^5 + C$$

19. Let $\quad u = e^{3x} \qquad\qquad dv = \sin x\, dx$

$\qquad\qquad du = 3e^{3x}\, dx \qquad\qquad v = -\cos x$

$\int e^{3x} \sin x\, dx = -e^{3x} \cos x + \int 3 \cos x\, e^{3x}\, dx$

Integrate by parts again.

Let $u = 3e^{3x} \qquad\qquad dv = \cos x\, dx$

$\qquad du = 9e^{3x}\, dx \qquad\qquad v = \sin x$

$\int e^{3x} \sin x\, dx = -e^{3x} \cos x + 3e^{3x} \sin x - \int 9e^{3x} \sin x\, dx$

$10 \int e^{3x} \sin x\, dx = -e^{3x} \cos x + 3e^{3x} \sin x + C$

$\int e^{3x} \sin x\, dx = \dfrac{1}{10}[-e^{3x} \cos x + 3e^{3x} \sin x] + C$

$\qquad\qquad = \left(\dfrac{3 \sin x}{10} - \dfrac{\cos x}{10} \right) e^{3x} + C$

20. Let $\quad u = x^2 \qquad\qquad dv = e^{-3x}\, dx$

$\qquad\qquad du = 2x\, dx \qquad\qquad v = -\dfrac{1}{3} e^{-3x}$

$\int x^2 e^{-3x}\, dx = -\dfrac{1}{3} x^2 e^{-3x} + \dfrac{2}{3} \int e^{-3x} x\, dx$

Let $\quad u = x \qquad\qquad dv = e^{-3x}\, dx$

$\qquad\qquad du = dx \qquad\qquad v = -\dfrac{1}{3} e^{-3x}$

$\qquad\qquad = -\dfrac{1}{3} x^2 e^{-3x} + \dfrac{2}{3} \left[-\dfrac{1}{3} x e^{-3x} + \dfrac{1}{3} \int e^{-3x}\, dx \right]$

$\qquad\qquad = -\dfrac{1}{3} x^2 e^{-3x} - \dfrac{2}{9} x e^{-3x} + \dfrac{2}{9} \int e^{-3x}\, dx$

$\qquad\qquad = -\dfrac{1}{3} x^2 e^{-3x} - \dfrac{2}{9} x e^{-3x} - \dfrac{2}{27} e^{-3x} + C$

$\qquad\qquad = \left(-\dfrac{x^2}{3} - \dfrac{2x}{9} - \dfrac{2}{27} \right) e^{-3x} + C$

21. $\dfrac{dy}{dx} = 1 + x + \dfrac{x^2}{2}$

$dy = \left(1 + x + \dfrac{x^2}{2} \right) dx$

$\int dy = \int \left(1 + x + \dfrac{x^2}{2} \right) dx$

$y = x + \dfrac{1}{2} x^2 + \dfrac{1}{6} x^3 + C$

$y(0) = C = 1$

$y = \dfrac{x^3}{6} + \dfrac{x^2}{2} + x + 1$

Graphical support:

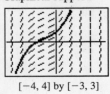

$[-4, 4]$ by $[-3, 3]$

22. $\qquad \dfrac{dy}{dx} = \left(x + \dfrac{1}{x} \right)^2$

$\qquad dy = \left(x + \dfrac{1}{x} \right)^2 dx$

$\qquad \int dy = \int \left(x + \dfrac{1}{x} \right)^2 dx$

$\qquad y = \int \left(x^2 + 2 + \dfrac{1}{x^2} \right) dx$

$\qquad y = \dfrac{1}{3} x^3 + 2x - x^{-1} + C$

$\quad y(1) = \dfrac{1}{3} + 2 - 1 + C = 1$

$\quad \dfrac{4}{3} + C = 1$

$\qquad\qquad C = -\dfrac{1}{3}$

$\qquad\qquad y = \dfrac{x^3}{3} + 2x - \dfrac{1}{x} - \dfrac{1}{3}$

Graphical support:

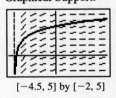

$[-2, 2]$ by $[-10, 10]$

23. $\dfrac{dy}{dt} = \dfrac{1}{t + 4}$

$dy = \dfrac{1}{t + 4}\, dt$

$\int dy = \int \dfrac{1}{t + 4}\, dt$

$y = \ln |t + 4| + C$

$y(-3) = \ln (1) + C = 2$

$C = 2$

$y = \ln (t + 4) + 2$

Graphical Support:

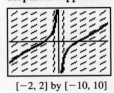

$[-4.5, 5]$ by $[-2, 5]$

24. $\dfrac{dy}{d\theta} = \csc 2\theta \cot 2\theta$

$dy = \csc 2\theta \cot 2\theta\, d\theta$

$\int dy = \int \csc 2\theta \cot 2\theta\, d\theta$

$y = -\dfrac{1}{2} \csc 2\theta + C$

$y \left(\dfrac{\pi}{4} \right) = -\dfrac{1}{2} + C = 1$

$C = \dfrac{3}{2}$

$y = -\dfrac{1}{2} \csc 2\theta + \dfrac{3}{2}$

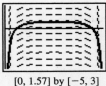

$[0, 1.57]$ by $[-5, 3]$

25. $\dfrac{d(y')}{dx} = 2x - \dfrac{1}{x^2}$

$d(y') = \left(2x - \dfrac{1}{x^2}\right)dx$

$\displaystyle\int d(y') = \int\left(2x - \dfrac{1}{x^2}\right)dx$

$y' = x^2 + x^{-1} + C$

$y'(1) = 2 + C = 1$

$C = -1$

$y' = x^2 + x^{-1} - 1$

$\displaystyle\int dy = \int (x^2 + x^{-1} - 1)\,dx$

$y = \dfrac{1}{3}x^3 + \ln x - x + C$

$y(1) = \dfrac{1}{3} + 0 - 1 + C = 0$

$-\dfrac{2}{3} + C = 0$

$C = \dfrac{2}{3}$

$y = \dfrac{x^3}{3} + \ln x - x + \dfrac{2}{3}$

Graphical support:

Let $f(x) = \dfrac{x^3}{3} + \ln x - x + \dfrac{2}{3}$.

We first show the graph of $y = f'(x) = x^2 + x^{-1} - 1$,

$x > 0$, along with the slope field for $y' = f''(x) = 2x - \dfrac{1}{x^2}$.

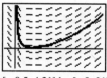

$[-0.5, 4.21]$ by $[-9, 21]$

We now show the graph of $y = f(x)$ along with the slope field

for $y' = f'(x) = x^2 + x^{-1} - 1$.

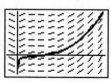

$[-0.5, 4.21]$ by $[-9, 21]$

26. $\dfrac{d(r'')}{dt} = -\cos t$

$d(r'') = -\cos t\,dt$

$\displaystyle\int d(r'') = \int -\cos t\,dt$

$r'' = -\sin t + C$

$r''(0) = C = -1$

$r'' = -\sin t - 1$

$\displaystyle\int d(r') = \int (-\sin t - 1)\,dt$

$r' = \cos t - t + C$

$r'(0) = 1 + C = -1$

$C = -2$

$r' = \cos t - t - 2$

$\displaystyle\int dr = \int (\cos t - t - 2)\,dt$

$r = \sin t - \dfrac{t^2}{2} - 2t + C$

$r(0) = C = -1$

$r = \sin t - \dfrac{t^2}{2} - 2t - 1$

Graphical support:

We first show the graph of $y = r'' = -\sin t - 1$ along

with the slope field for $y' = r''' = -\cos t$.

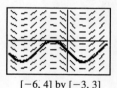

$[-6, 4]$ by $[-3, 3]$

Next, we show the graph of $y = r' = \cos t - t - 2$ along

with the slope field for $y' = r'' = -\sin t - 1$.

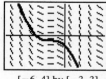

$[-6, 4]$ by $[-3, 3]$

Finally we show the graph of $y = r = \sin t - \dfrac{t^2}{2} - 2t - 1$

along with the slope field for $y' = r' = \cos t - t - 2$.

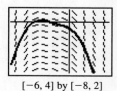

$[-6, 4]$ by $[-8, 2]$

27. $\dfrac{dy}{dx} = y + 2$

$\dfrac{dy}{y + 2} = dx$

$\displaystyle\int \dfrac{dy}{y + 2} = \int dx$

$\ln |y + 2| = x + C$

$y + 2 = Ce^x$

$y = Ce^x - 2$

$y(0) = C - 2 = 2$

$C = 4$

$y = 4e^x - 2$

Graphical support:

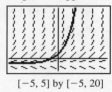

$[-5, 5]$ by $[-5, 20]$

28. $\dfrac{dy}{dx} = (2x + 1)(y + 1)$

$\dfrac{dy}{y + 1} = (2x + 1)\, dx$

$\displaystyle\int \dfrac{dy}{y + 1} = \int (2x + 1)\, dx$

$\ln |y + 1| = x^2 + x + C$

$y + 1 = Ce^{x^2 + x}$

$y = Ce^{x^2 + x} - 1$

$y(-1) = C - 1 = 1$

$C = 2$

$y = 2e^{x^2 + x} - 1$

Graphical support:

$[-3, 3]$ by $[-10, 40]$

29. $\displaystyle\int -f(x)\, dx = -\int f(x)\, dx$

$= -(1 - \sqrt{x}) + C$

$= -1 + \sqrt{x} + C$

Since $-1 + C$ is an arbitrary constant, we may write the indefinite integral as $\sqrt{x} + C$.

30. $\displaystyle\int [x + f(x)]\, dx = \int x\, dx + \int f(x)\, dx$

$= \dfrac{x^2}{2} + (1 - \sqrt{x}) + C$

$= \dfrac{x^2}{2} + 1 - \sqrt{x} + C$

Since $1 + C$ is an arbitrary constant, we may write the indefinite integral as $\dfrac{x^2}{2} - \sqrt{x} + C$.

31. $\displaystyle\int [2f(x) - g(x)]\, dx = 2\int f(x)\, dx - \int g(x)\, dx$

$= 2(1 - \sqrt{x}) - (x + 2) + C$

$= -2\sqrt{x} - x + C$

32. $\displaystyle\int [g(x) - 4]\, dx = \int g(x)\, dx - \int 4\, dx$

$= (x + 2) - 4x + C$

$= 2 - 3x + C$

Since $2 + C$ is an arbitrary constant, we may write the indefinite integral as $-3x + C$.

33. We seek the graph of a function whose derivative is $\dfrac{\sin x}{x}$. Graph (b) is increasing on $[-\pi, \pi]$, where $\dfrac{\sin x}{x}$ is positive, and oscillates slightly outside of this interval. This is the correct choice, and this can be verified by graphing $\text{NINT}\left(\dfrac{\sin x}{x}, x, 0, x\right)$.

34. We seek the graph of a function whose derivative is e^{-x^2}. Since $e^{-x^2} > 0$ for all x, the desired graph is increasing for all x. Thus, the only possibility is graph (d), and we may verify that this is correct by graphing $\text{NINT}(e^{-x^2}, x, 0, x)$.

35. (iv) The given graph looks like the graph of $y = x^2$, which satisfies $\dfrac{dy}{dx} = 2x$ and $y(1) = 1$.

36. Yes, $y = x$ is a solution.

37. (a) $\dfrac{dv}{dt} = 2 + 6t$

$\displaystyle\int dv = \int (2 + 6t)\, dt$

$v = 2t + 3t^2 + C$

Initial condition: $v = 4$ when $t = 0$

$4 = 0 + C$

$4 = C$

$v = 2t + 3t^2 + 4$

(b) $\displaystyle\int_0^1 v(t)\, dt = \int_0^1 (2t + 3t^2 + 4)\, dt$

$= \left[t^2 + t^3 + 4t \right]_0^1$

$= 6 - 0$

$= 6$

The particle moves 6 m.

38.

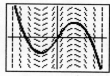

[−10, 10] by [−10, 10]

39. Set $y_1 = y + \cos x$ and use EULERT with initial values $x = 0$ and $y = 0$ and step size 0.1 for 20 points.

x	y
0	0
0.1	0.1000
0.2	0.2095
0.3	0.3285
0.4	0.4568
0.5	0.5946
0.6	0.7418
0.7	0.8986
0.8	1.0649
0.9	1.2411
1.0	1.4273
1.1	1.6241
1.2	1.8319
1.3	2.0513
1.4	2.2832
1.5	2.5285
1.6	2.7884
1.7	3.0643
1.8	3.3579
1.9	3.6709
2.0	4.0057

40. Set $y_1 = (2 - y)(2x + 3)$ and use IMPEULT with intial values $x = -3$ and $y = 1$ and step size 0.1 for 20 points.

x	y
−3	1
−2.9	0.6680
−2.8	0.2599
−2.7	−0.2294
−2.6	−0.8011
−2.5	−1.4509
−2.4	−2.1687
−2.3	−2.9374
−2.2	−3.7333
−2.1	−4.5268
−2.0	−5.2840
−1.9	−5.9686
−1.8	−6.5456
−1.7	−6.9831
−1.6	−7.2562
−1.5	−7.3488
−1.4	−7.2553
−1.3	−6.9813
−1.2	−6.5430
−1.1	−5.9655
−1.0	−5.2805

41. To estimate $y(3)$, set $y_1 = \dfrac{x - 2y}{x + 1}$ and use IMPEULT with initial values $x = 0$ and $y = 1$ and step size 0.05 for 60 points. This gives $y(3) \approx 0.9063$.

42. To estimate $y(4)$, set $y_1 = \dfrac{x^2 - 2y + 1}{x}$ and use EULERT with initial values $x = 1$ and $y = 1$ and step size 0.05 for 60 points. This gives $y(4) \approx 4.4974$.

43. Set $y_1 = e^{-(x+y+2)}$ and use EULERG with initial values $x = 0$ and $y = -2$ and step sizes 0.1 and −0.1.

(a)

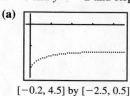

[−0.2, 4.5] by [−2.5, 0.5]

43. continued

(b) Note that we choose a small interval of x-values because the y-values decrease very rapidly and our calculator cannot handle the calculations for $x \leq -1$. (This occurs because the analytic solution is $y = -2 + \ln(2 - e^{-x})$, which has an asymptote at $x = -\ln 2 \approx -0.69$. Obviously, the Euler approximations are misleading for $x \leq -0.7$.)

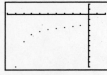

[−1, 0.2] by [−10, 2]

44. Set $y_1 = -\dfrac{x^2 + y}{e^y + x}$ and use IMPEULG with initial

values $x = 0$ and $y = 0$ and step sizes 0.1 and −0.1.

(a)
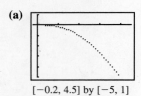

[−0.2, 4.5] by [−5, 1]

(b)
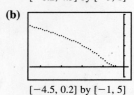

[−4.5, 0.2] by [−1, 5]

45. (a) Half-life $= \dfrac{\ln 2}{k}$

$2.645 = \dfrac{\ln 2}{k}$

$k = \dfrac{\ln 2}{2.645} \approx 0.262059$

(b) Mean life $= \dfrac{1}{k} \approx 3.81593$ years

46. $T - T_s = (T_0 - T_s)e^{-kt}$

$T - 40 = (220 - 40)e^{-kt}$

Use the fact that $T = 180$ and $t = 15$ to find k.

$180 - 40 = (220 - 40)e^{-(k)(15)}$

$e^{15k} = \dfrac{180}{140} = \dfrac{9}{7}$

$k = \dfrac{1}{15}\ln\dfrac{9}{7}$

$T - 40 = (220 - 40)e^{-((1/15)\ln(9/7))t}$

$70 - 40 = (220 - 40)e^{-((1/15)\ln(9/7))t}$

$e^{((1/15)\ln(9/7))t} = \dfrac{180}{30} = 6$

$\left(\dfrac{1}{15}\ln\dfrac{9}{7}\right)t = \ln 6$

$t = \dfrac{15\ln 6}{\ln(9/7)} \approx 107$ min

It took a total of about 107 minutes to cool from 220°F to 70°F. Therefore, the time to cool from 180°F to 70°F was about 92 minutes.

47. $T - T_s = (T_0 - T_s)e^{-kt}$

We have the system:

$$\begin{cases} 39 - T_s = (46 - T_s)e^{-10k} \\ 33 - T_s = (46 - T_s)e^{-20k} \end{cases}$$

Thus, $\dfrac{39 - T_s}{46 - T_s} = e^{-10k}$ and $\dfrac{33 - T_s}{46 - T_s} = e^{-20k}$.

Since $(e^{-10k})^2 = e^{-20k}$, this means:

$$\left(\dfrac{39 - T_s}{46 - T_s}\right)^2 = \dfrac{33 - T_s}{46 - T_s}$$

$$(39 - T_s)^2 = (33 - T_s)(46 - T_s)$$

$$1521 - 78T_s + T_s^2 = 1518 - 79T_s + T_s^2$$

$$T_s = -3$$

The refrigerator temperature was −3°C.

48. Use the method of Example 3 in Section 6.4.

$$e^{-kt} = 0.995$$

$$-kt = \ln 0.995$$

$$t = -\dfrac{1}{k}\ln 0.995 = -\dfrac{5700}{\ln 2}\ln 0.995 \approx 41.2$$

The painting is about 41.2 years old.

49. Use the method of Example 3 in Section 6.4.

Since 90% of the carbon-14 has decayed, 10% remains.

$$e^{-kt} = 0.1$$

$$-kt = \ln 0.1$$

$$t = -\dfrac{1}{k}\ln 0.1 = -\dfrac{5700}{\ln 2}\ln 0.1 \approx 18{,}935$$

The charcoal sample is about 18,935 years old.

50. Use $t = 1988 - 1924 = 64$ years.

$$250\,e^{rt} = 7500$$

$$e^{rt} = 30$$

$$rt = \ln 30$$

$$r = \dfrac{\ln 30}{t} = \dfrac{\ln 30}{64} \approx 0.053$$

The rate of appreciation is about 0.053, or 5.3%.

51. Using the Law of Exponential Change in Section 6.4 with appropriate changes of variables, the solution to the differential equation is $L(x) = L_0 e^{-kx}$, where $L_0 = L(0)$ is the surface intensity. We know $0.5 = e^{-18k}$, so $k = \dfrac{\ln 0.5}{-18}$ and our equation becomes $L(x) = L_0 e^{(\ln 0.5)(x/18)} = L_0\left(\dfrac{1}{2}\right)^{x/18}$. We now find the depth where the intensity is one-tenth of the surface value.

$$0.1 = \left(\frac{1}{2}\right)^{x/18}$$
$$\ln 0.1 = \frac{x}{18}\ln\left(\frac{1}{2}\right)$$
$$x = \frac{18\ln 0.1}{\ln 0.5} \approx 59.8 \text{ ft}$$

You can work without artificial light to a depth of about 59.8 feet.

52. (a)
$$\frac{dy}{dt} = \frac{kA}{V}(c - y)$$
$$\int \frac{dy}{c - y} = \int \frac{kA}{V}\, dt$$
$$-\ln|c - y| = \frac{kA}{V}t + C$$
$$\ln|c - y| = -\frac{kA}{V}t - C$$
$$|c - y| = e^{-(kA/V)t - C}$$
$$c - y = \pm e^{-(kA/V)t - C}$$
$$y = c \pm e^{-(kA/V)t - C}$$
$$y = c + De^{-(kA/V)t}$$

Initial condition $y = y_0$ when $t = 0$
$$y_0 = c + D$$
$$y_0 - c = D$$

Solution: $y = c + (y_0 - c)e^{-(kA/V)t}$

(b) $\displaystyle\lim_{t\to\infty} y(t) = \lim_{t\to\infty}\left[c + (y_0 - c)e^{-(kA/V)t}\right] = c$

53. (a) $P(t) = \dfrac{150}{1 + e^{4.3-t}} = \dfrac{150}{1 + e^{4.3}e^{-t}}$

This is $P = \dfrac{M}{1 + Ae^{-kt}}$ where $M = 150$, $A = e^{4.3}$, and $k = 1$. Therefore, it is a solution of the logistic differential equation.

$\dfrac{dP}{dt} = \dfrac{k}{M}P(M - P)$, or $\dfrac{dP}{dt} = \dfrac{1}{150}P(150 - P)$. The carrying capacity is 150.

(b) $P(0) = \dfrac{150}{1 + e^{4.3}} \approx 2$

Initially there were 2 infected students.

(c) $\dfrac{150}{1 + e^{4.3-t}} = 125$
$$\frac{6}{5} = 1 + e^{4.3-t}$$
$$\frac{1}{5} = e^{4.3-t}$$
$$-\ln 5 = 4.3 - t$$
$$t = 4.3 + \ln 5 \approx 5.9 \text{ days}$$

It took about 6 days.

54. Use the Fundamental Theorem of Calculus.
$$y' = \frac{d}{dx}\left(\int_0^x \sin t^2\, dt\right) + \frac{d}{dx}(x^3 + x + 2)$$
$$= (\sin x^2) + (3x^2 + 1)$$
$$y'' = \frac{d}{dx}(\sin x^2 + 3x^2 + 1)$$
$$= (\cos x^2)(2x) + 6x$$
$$= 2x\cos(x^2) + 6x$$

Thus, the differential equation is satisfied.

Verify the initial conditions:
$$y'(0) = (\sin 0^2) + 3(0)^2 + 1 = 1$$
$$y(0) = \int_0^0 \sin(t^2)\, dt + 0^3 + 0 + 2 = 2$$

55.
$$\frac{dP}{dt} = 0.002P\left(1 - \frac{P}{800}\right)$$
$$\frac{dP}{dt} = 0.002P\left(\frac{800 - P}{800}\right)$$
$$\frac{800}{P(800 - P)}\, dP = 0.002\, dt$$
$$\frac{(800 - P) + P}{P(800 - P)}\, dP = 0.002\, dt$$
$$\int\left(\frac{1}{P} + \frac{1}{800 - P}\right) dP = \int 0.002\, dt$$
$$\ln|P| - \ln|800 - P| = 0.002t + C$$
$$\ln\left|\frac{P}{800 - P}\right| = 0.002t + C$$
$$\ln\left|\frac{800 - P}{P}\right| = -0.002t - C$$
$$\left|\frac{800 - P}{P}\right| = e^{-0.002t - C}$$
$$\frac{800 - P}{P} = \pm e^{-C}e^{-0.002t}$$
$$\frac{800}{P} - 1 = Ae^{-0.002t}$$
$$P = \frac{800}{1 + Ae^{-0.002t}}$$

Initial condition: $P(0) = 50$
$$50 = \frac{800}{1 + Ae^0}$$
$$1 + A = 16$$
$$A = 15$$

Solution: $P = \dfrac{800}{1 + 15e^{-0.002t}}$

56. Method 1–Compare graph of $y_1 = x^2 \ln x$ with

$y_2 = \text{NDER}\left(\dfrac{x^3 \ln x}{3} - \dfrac{x^3}{9}\right)$. The graphs should be the same.

Method 2–Compare graph of $y_1 = \text{NINT}(x^2 \ln x)$ with

$y_2 = \dfrac{x^3 \ln x}{3} - \dfrac{x^3}{9}$. The graphs should be the same or differ

only by a vertical translation.

57. (a) $20{,}000 = 10{,}000(1.063)^t$

$2 = 1.063^t$

$\ln 2 = t \ln 1.063$

$t = \dfrac{\ln 2}{\ln 1.063} \approx 11.345$

It will take about 11.3 years.

(b) $20{,}000 = 10{,}000e^{0.063t}$

$2 = e^{0.063t}$

$\ln 2 = 0.063t$

$t = \dfrac{\ln 2}{0.063} \approx 11.002$

It will take about 11.0 years.

58. (a) $f'(x) = \dfrac{d}{dx}\displaystyle\int_0^x u(t)\,dt = u(x)$

$g'(x) = \dfrac{d}{dx}\displaystyle\int_3^x u(t)\,dt = u(x)$

(b) $C = f(x) - g(x)$

$= \displaystyle\int_0^x u(t)\,dt - \int_3^x u(t)\,dt$

$= \displaystyle\int_0^x u(t)\,dt + \int_x^3 u(t)\,dt$

$= \displaystyle\int_0^3 u(t)\,dt$

59. (a) $y = \dfrac{56.0716}{1 + 5.894e^{-0.0205x}}$

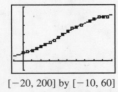

[−20, 200] by [−10, 60]

(b) The carrying capacity is about 56.0716 million people.

(c) Use NDER twice to solve $y'' = 0$. The solution is $x \approx 86.52$, representing (approximately) the year 1887. The population at this time was approximately $P(86.52) \approx 28.0$ million people.

60. (a) $T = 79.961(0.9273)^t$

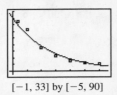

[−1, 33] by [−5, 90]

(b) Solving $T(t) = 40$ graphically, we obtain $t \approx 9.2$ sec. The temperature will reach 40° after about 9.2 seconds.

(c) When the probe was removed, the temperature was about $T(0) \approx 79.96°\text{C}$.

61. $\dfrac{v_0 m}{k} = \text{coasting distance}$

$\dfrac{(0.86)(30.84)}{k} = 0.97$

$k \approx 27.343$

$s(t) = \dfrac{v_0 m}{k}(1 - e^{-(k/m)t})$

$s(t) = 0.97(1 - e^{-(27.343/30.84)t})$

$s(t) = 0.97(1 - e^{-0.8866t})$

A graph of the model is shown superimposed on a graph of the data.

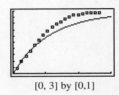

[0, 3] by [0,1]

Chapter 7
Applications of Definite Integrals

■ Section 7.1 Integral as Net Change
(pp. 363–374)

Exploration 1   Revisiting Example 2

1. $s(t) = \displaystyle\int\left(t^2 - \dfrac{8}{(t+1)^2}\right)dt = \dfrac{t^3}{3} + \dfrac{8}{t+1} + C$

$s(0) = \dfrac{0^3}{3} + \dfrac{8}{0+1} + C = 9 \Rightarrow C = 1$

Thus, $s(t) = \dfrac{t^3}{3} + \dfrac{8}{t+1} + 1$.

2. $s(1) = \dfrac{1^3}{3} + \dfrac{8}{1+1} + 1 = \dfrac{16}{3}$. This is the same as the

answer we found in Example 2a.

3. $s(5) = \dfrac{5^3}{3} + \dfrac{8}{5+1} + 1 = 44$. This is the same answer we

found in Example 2b.

Quick Review 7.1

1. On the interval, $\sin 2x = 0$ when $x = -\frac{\pi}{2}$, 0, or $\frac{\pi}{2}$. Test one point on each subinterval: for $x = -\frac{3\pi}{4}$, $\sin 2x = 1$; for $x = -\frac{\pi}{4}$, $\sin 2x = -1$; for $x = \frac{\pi}{4}$, $\sin 2x = 1$; and for $x = \frac{3\pi}{4}$, $\sin 2x = -1$. The function changes sign at $-\frac{\pi}{2}$, 0, and $\frac{\pi}{2}$. The graph is

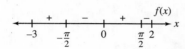

2. $x^2 - 3x + 2 = (x - 1)(x - 2) = 0$ when $x = 1$ or 2. Test one point on each subinterval: for $x = 0$, $x^2 - 3x + 2 = 2$; for $x = \frac{3}{2}$, $x^2 - 3x + 2 = -\frac{1}{4}$; and for $x = 3$, $x^2 - 3x + 2 = 2$. The function changes sign at 1 and 2. The graph is

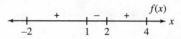

3. $x^2 - 2x + 3 = 0$ has no real solutions, since $b^2 - 4ac = (-2)^2 - 4(1)(3) = -8 < 0$. The function is always positive. The graph is

4. $2x^3 - 3x^2 + 1 = (x - 1)^2(2x + 1) = 0$ when $x = -\frac{1}{2}$ or 1. Test one point on each subinterval: for $x = -1$, $2x^3 - 3x^2 + 1 = -4$; for $x = 0$, $2x^3 - 3x^2 + 1 = 1$; and $x = \frac{3}{2}$, $2x^3 - 3x^2 + 1 = 1$. The function changes sign at $-\frac{1}{2}$. The graph is

5. On the interval, $x \cos 2x = 0$ when $x = 0$, $\frac{\pi}{4}$, $\frac{3\pi}{4}$, or $\frac{5\pi}{4}$. Test one point on each subinterval: for $x = \frac{\pi}{8}$, $x \cos 2x = \frac{\pi\sqrt{2}}{16}$; for $x = \frac{\pi}{2}$, $x \cos 2x = -\frac{\pi}{2}$; for $x = \pi$, $x \cos 2x = \pi$; and for $x = 4$, $x \cos 2x \approx -0.58$. The function changes sign at $\frac{\pi}{4}$, $\frac{3\pi}{4}$, and $\frac{5\pi}{4}$. The graph is

6. $xe^{-x} = 0$ when $x = 0$. On the rest of the interval, xe^{-x} is always positive.

7. $\frac{x}{x^2 + 1} = 0$ when $x = 0$. Test one point on each subinterval: for $x = -1$, $\frac{x}{x^2 + 1} = -\frac{1}{2}$; for $x = 1$, $\frac{x}{x^2 + 1} = \frac{1}{2}$. The function changes sign at 0. The graph is

8. $\frac{x^2 - 2}{x^2 - 4} = 0$ when $x = \pm\sqrt{2}$ and is undefined when $x = \pm 2$. Test one point on each subinterval: for $x = -\frac{5}{2}$, $\frac{x^2 - 2}{x^2 - 4} = \frac{17}{9}$; for $x = -1.9$, $\frac{x^2 - 2}{x^2 - 4} \approx -4.13$; for $x = 0$, $\frac{x^2 - 2}{x^2 - 4} = \frac{1}{2}$; for $x = 1.9$, $\frac{x^2 - 2}{x^2 - 4} \approx -4.13$; and for $x = \frac{5}{2}$, $\frac{x^2 - 2}{x^2 - 4} = \frac{17}{9}$. The function changes sign at -2, $-\sqrt{2}$, $\sqrt{2}$ and 2. The graph is

9. $\sec(1 + \sqrt{1 - \sin^2 x}) = \dfrac{1}{\cos(1 + |\cos x|)}$ is undefined when $x \approx 0.9633 + k\pi$ or $2.1783 + k\pi$ for any integer k. Test for $x = 0$: $\sec(1 + \sqrt{1 - \sin^2 0}) \approx -2.4030$. Test for $x = \pm 1$: $\sec(1 + \sqrt{1 - \sin^2 1}) \approx 32.7984$. The sign alternates over successive subintervals. The function changes sign at $0.9633 + k\pi$ or $2.1783 + k\pi$, where k is an integer. The graph is

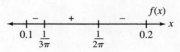

10. On the interval, $\sin\left(\frac{1}{x}\right) = 0$ when $x = \frac{1}{3\pi}$ or $\frac{1}{2\pi}$. Test one point on each subinterval: for $x = 0.1$, $\sin\left(\frac{1}{x}\right) \approx -0.54$; for $x = 0.15$, $\sin\left(\frac{1}{x}\right) \approx 0.37$; and for $x = 0.2$, $\sin\left(\frac{1}{x}\right) \approx -0.96$. The graph changes sign at $\frac{1}{3\pi}$, and $\frac{1}{2\pi}$. The graph is

Section 7.1 Exercises

1. (a) Right when $v(t) > 0$, which is when $\cos t > 0$, i.e., when $0 \le t < \dfrac{\pi}{2}$ or $\dfrac{3\pi}{2} < t \le 2\pi$. Left when $\cos t < 0$, i.e., when $\dfrac{\pi}{2} < t < \dfrac{3\pi}{2}$. Stopped when $\cos t = 0$, i.e., when $t = \dfrac{\pi}{2}$ or $\dfrac{3\pi}{2}$.

(b) Displacement =
$$\int_0^{2\pi} 5 \cos t \, dt = 5\Big[\sin t\Big]_0^{2\pi} = 5[\sin 2\pi - \sin 0] = 0$$

(c) Distance = $\displaystyle\int_0^{2\pi} |5 \cos t| \, dt$
$$= \int_0^{\pi/2} 5 \cos t \, dt + \int_{\pi/2}^{3\pi/2} -5 \cos t \, dt + \int_{3\pi/2}^{2\pi} 5 \cos t \, dt$$
$$= 5 + 10 + 5 = 20$$

2. (a) Right when $v(t) > 0$, which is when $\sin 3t > 0$, i.e., when $0 < t < \dfrac{\pi}{3}$. Left when $\sin 3t < 0$, i.e., when $\dfrac{\pi}{3} < t \le \dfrac{\pi}{2}$. Stopped when $\sin 3t = 0$, i.e., when $t = 0$ or $\dfrac{\pi}{3}$.

(b) Displacement = $\displaystyle\int_0^{\pi/2} 6 \sin 3t \, dt = 6\Big[-\dfrac{1}{3} \cos 3t\Big]_0^{\pi/2}$
$$= -2\Big[\cos \dfrac{3\pi}{2} - \cos 0\Big] = 2$$

(c) Distance = $\displaystyle\int_0^{\pi/2} |6 \sin 3t| \, dt$
$$= \int_0^{\pi/3} 6 \sin 3t \, dt + \int_{\pi/3}^{\pi/2} -6 \sin 3t \, dt = 4 + 2 = 6$$

3. (a) Right when $v(t) = 49 - 9.8t > 0$, i.e., when $0 \le t < 5$. Left when $49 - 9.8t < 0$, i.e., when $5 < t \le 10$. Stopped when $49 - 9.8t = 0$, i.e., when $t = 5$.

(b) Displacement = $\displaystyle\int_0^{10} (49 - 9.8t) \, dt$
$$= \Big[49t - 4.9t^2\Big]_0^{10} = 49[(10 - 10) - 0] = 0$$

(c) Distance = $\displaystyle\int_0^{10} |49 - 9.8t| \, dt$
$$= \int_0^5 (49 - 9.8t) \, dt + \int_5^{10} (-49 + 9.8t) \, dt$$
$$= 122.5 + 122.5 = 245$$

4. (a) Right when
$$v(t) = 6t^2 - 18t + 12 = 6(t - 1)(t - 2) > 0,$$
i.e., when $0 \le t < 1$. Left when $6(t - 1)(t - 2) < 0$, i.e., when $1 < t < 2$. Stopped when
$6(t - 1)(t - 2) = 0$, i.e., when $x = 1$, or 2.

(b) Displacement = $\displaystyle\int_0^2 (6t^2 - 18t + 12) \, dt$
$$= \Big[2t^3 - 9t^2 + 12t\Big]_0^2 = [(16 - 36 + 24) - 0] = 4$$

(c) Distance = $\displaystyle\int_0^2 |6t^2 - 18t + 12| \, dt$
$$= \int_0^1 (6t^2 - 18t + 12) \, dt + \int_1^2 (-6t^2 + 18t - 12) \, dt$$
$$= 5 + 1 = 6$$

5. (a) Right when $v(t) > 0$, which is when $\sin t \ne 0$ and $\cos t > 0$, i.e., when $0 < t < \dfrac{\pi}{2}$ or $\dfrac{3\pi}{2} < t < 2\pi$. Left when $\sin t \ne 0$ and $\cos t < 0$, i.e., when $\dfrac{\pi}{2} < t < \pi$ or $\pi < t < \dfrac{3\pi}{2}$. Stopped when $\sin t = 0$ or $\cos t = 0$, i.e., when $t = 0, \dfrac{\pi}{2}, \pi, \dfrac{3\pi}{2}$, or 2π.

(b) Displacement = $\displaystyle\int_0^{2\pi} 5 \sin^2 t \cos t \, dt = 5\Big[\dfrac{1}{3} \sin^3 t\Big]_0^{2\pi}$
$$= 5[0 - 0] = 0$$

(c) Distance = $\displaystyle\int_0^{2\pi} |5 \sin^2 t \cos t| \, dt$
$$= \int_0^{\pi/2} 5 \sin^2 t \cos t \, dt + \int_{\pi/2}^{3\pi/2} -5 \sin^2 t \cos t \, dt$$
$$+ \int_{3\pi/2}^{2\pi} 5 \sin^2 t \cos t \, dt$$
$$= \dfrac{5}{3} + \dfrac{10}{3} + \dfrac{5}{3} = \dfrac{20}{3}$$

6. (a) Right when $v(t) > 0$, which is when $4 - t > 0$, i.e., when $0 \le t < 4$. Left: never, since $\sqrt{4 - t}$ cannot be negative. Stopped when $4 - t = 0$, i.e., when $t = 4$.

(b) Displacement = $\displaystyle\int_0^4 \sqrt{4 - t} \, dt = \Big[-\dfrac{2}{3}(4 - t)^{3/2}\Big]_0^4$
$$= -\dfrac{2}{3}[0 - 8] = \dfrac{16}{3}$$

(c) Distance = $\displaystyle\int_0^4 \sqrt{4 - t} \, dt = \dfrac{16}{3}$

7. (a) Right when $v(t) > 0$, which is when $\cos t > 0$,

i.e., when $0 \le t < \frac{\pi}{2}$ or $\frac{3\pi}{2} < t \le 2\pi$. Left when

$\cos t < 0$, i.e., when $\frac{\pi}{2} < t < \frac{3\pi}{2}$. Stopped when

$\cos t = 0$, i.e., when $t = \frac{\pi}{2}$ or $\frac{3\pi}{2}$.

(b) Displacement $= \int_0^{2\pi} e^{\sin t} \cos t \, dt = \left[e^{\sin t} \right]_0^{2\pi}$

$= [e^0 - e^0] = 0$

(c) Distance $= \int_0^{2\pi} \left| e^{\sin t} \cos t \right| dt = \int_0^{\pi/2} e^{\sin t} \cos t \, dt +$

$\int_{\pi/2}^{3\pi/2} -e^{\sin t} \cos t \, dt + \int_{3\pi/2}^{2\pi} e^{\sin t} \cos t \, dt$

$= (e - 1) + \left(e - \frac{1}{e} \right) + \left(1 - \frac{1}{e} \right) = 2e - \frac{2}{e} \approx 4.7$

8. (a) Right when $v(t) > 0$, which is when $0 < t \le 3$. Left: never, since $v(t)$ is never negative. Stopped when $t = 0$.

(b) Displacement $= \int_0^3 \frac{t}{1 + t^2} \, dt = \left[\frac{1}{2} \ln (1 + t^2) \right]_0^3$

$= \frac{1}{2}[\ln (10) - \ln (1)] = \frac{\ln 10}{2} \approx 1.15$

(c) Distance $= \int_0^3 \frac{t}{1 + t^2} \, dt = \frac{\ln 10}{2} \approx 1.15$

9. (a) $v(t) = \int a(t) \, dt = t + 2t^{3/2} + C$, and since $v(0) = 0$,

$v(t) = t + 2t^{3/2}$. Then $v(9) = 9 + 2(27) = 63$ mph.

(b) First convert units:

$t + 2t^{3/2}$ mph $= \frac{t}{3600} + \frac{t^{3/2}}{1800}$ mi/sec. Then

Distance $= \int_0^9 \left(\frac{t}{3600} + \frac{t^{3/2}}{1800} \right) dt$

$= \left[\frac{t^2}{7200} + \frac{t^{5/2}}{4500} \right]_0^9 = \left[\left(\frac{9}{800} + \frac{27}{500} \right) - 0 \right] = 0.06525$ mi

$= 344.52$ ft.

10. (a) Displacement $= \int_0^4 (t - 2) \sin t \, dt$

$= \left[\sin t - t \cos t + 2 \cos t \right]_0^4$

$= [(\sin 4 - 4 \cos 4 + 2 \cos 4) - 2] \approx -1.44952$ m

(b) Because the velocity is negative for $0 < t < 2$, positive

for $2 < t < \pi$, and negative for $\pi < t \le 4$,

Distance $= \int_0^2 -(t - 2) \sin t \, dt + \int_2^\pi (t - 2) \sin t \, dt$

$+ \int_\pi^4 -(t - 2) \sin t \, dt$

$= [(2 - \sin 2) + (\pi - \sin 2 - 2)$

$+ (\pi + 2 \cos 4 - \sin 4 - 2)]$

$= 2\pi + 2 \cos 4 - 2 \sin 2 - \sin 4 - 2 \approx 1.91411$ m.

11. (a) $v(t) = \int a(t) \, dt = \int -32 \, dt = -32t + C_1$, where

$C_1 = v(0) = 90$.

Then $v(3) = -32(3) + 90 = -6$ ft/sec.

(b) $s(t) = \int v(t) \, dt = -16t^2 + 90t + C_2$, where

$C_2 = s(0) = 0$. Solve $s(t) = 0$:

$-16t^2 + 90t = 2t(-8t + 45) = 0$

when $t = 0$ or $t = \frac{45}{8} = 5.625$ sec.

The projectile hits the ground at 5.625 sec.

(c) Since starting height = ending height,

Displacement = 0.

(d) Max. Height $= s\left(\frac{5.625}{2} \right)$

$= -16\left(\frac{5.625}{2} \right)^2 + 90\left(\frac{5.625}{2} \right) = 126.5625$, and

Distance = 2(Max. Height) = 253.125 ft.

12. Displacement $= \int_0^c v(t) \, dt = -4 + 5 - 24 = -23$ cm

13. Total distance $= \int_0^c |v(t)| \, dt = 4 + 5 + 24 = 33$ cm

14. At $t = a$, $s = s(0) + \int_0^a v(t) \, dt = 15 - 4 = 11$.

At $t = b$, $s = s(0) + \int_0^b v(t) \, dt = 15 - 4 + 5 = 16$.

At $t = c$, $s = s(0) + \int_0^c v(t) \, dt = 15 - 4 + 5 - 24 = -8$.

15. At $t = a$, where $\frac{dv}{dt}$ is at a maximum (the graph is steepest upward).

16. At $t = c$, where $\frac{dv}{dt}$ is at a maximum (the graph is steepest upward).

17. Distance = Area under curve $= 4\left(\frac{1}{2} \cdot 1 \cdot 2 \right) = 4$

(a) Final position = Initial position + Distance
$= 2 + 4 = 6$; ends at $x = 6$.

(b) 4 meters

18. (a) Positive and negative velocities cancel: the sum of signed areas is zero. Starts and ends at $x = 2$.

(b) Distance = Sum of positive areas $= 4(1 \cdot 1) = 4$ meters

19. (a) Final position $= 2 + \int_0^7 v(t)\, dt$

$$= 2 - \frac{1}{2}(1)(2) + \frac{1}{2}(1)(2) + 1(2)$$
$$\quad + \frac{1}{2}(2)(2) - \frac{1}{2}(2)(1)$$
$$= 5;$$

ends at $x = 5$.

(b) $\int_0^7 |v(t)|\, dt = \frac{1}{2}(1)(2) + \frac{1}{2}(1)(2) + 1(2) + \frac{1}{2}(2)(2)$
$$\quad + \frac{1}{2}(2)(1)$$
$$= 7 \text{ meters}$$

20. (a) Final position $= 2 + \int_0^{10} v(t)\, dt$

$$= 2 + \frac{1}{2}(2)(3) - \frac{1}{2}(1)(3) - (3)(3) - \frac{1}{2}(1)(3)$$
$$\quad + \frac{1}{2}(3)(3)$$
$$= -2.5;$$

ends at $x = -2.5$.

(b) Distance $= \int_0^{10} |v(t)|\, dt$

$$= \frac{1}{2}(2 \cdot 3) + \frac{1}{2}(1)(3) + 3(3) + \frac{1}{2}(1)(3) + \frac{1}{2}(3)(3)$$
$$= 19.5 \text{ meters}$$

21. $\int_0^{10} 27.08 \cdot e^{t/25}\, dt = 27.08\left[25e^{t/25}\right]_0^{10} = 27.08[25e^{0.4} - 25]$

$$\approx 332.965 \text{ billion barrels}$$

22. $\int_0^{24}\left[3.9 - 2.4\sin\left(\frac{\pi t}{12}\right)\right] dt = \left[3.9t + \frac{28.8}{\pi}\cos\left(\frac{\pi t}{12}\right)\right]_0^{24}$

$$= \left[\left(93.6 + \frac{28.8}{\pi}\right) - \frac{28.8}{\pi}\right] = 93.6 \text{ kilowatt-hours}$$

23. (a) Solve $10{,}000(2 - r) = 0$: $r = 2$ miles.

(b) Width $= \Delta r$, Length $= 2\pi r$: Area $= 2\pi r \Delta r$

(c) Population $=$ Population density $\times$ Area

(d) $\int_0^2 10{,}000(2 - r)(2\pi r)\, dr = 20{,}000\pi\int_0^2 (2r - r^2)\, dr$

$$= 20{,}000\pi\left[r^2 - \frac{1}{3}r^3\right]_0^2 = 20{,}000\pi\left[\left(4 - \frac{8}{3}\right) - 0\right]$$

$$= \frac{80{,}000}{3}\pi \approx 83{,}776$$

24. (a) Width $= \Delta r$, Length $= 2\pi r$: Area $= 2\pi r \Delta r$

(b) Volume per second

$$= \text{Inches per second} \times \text{Cross section area}$$
$$8(10 - r^2)\frac{\text{in.}}{\text{sec}} \cdot (2\pi r)\Delta r \text{ in}^2 = \text{flow in } \frac{\text{in}^3}{\text{sec}}$$

(c) $\int_0^3 8(10 - r^2)(2\pi r)\, dr = 16\pi\int_0^3 (10r - r^3)\, dr$

$$= 16\pi\left[5r^2 - \frac{1}{4}r^4\right]_0^3 = 16\pi\left[\left(45 - \frac{81}{4}\right) - 0\right]$$

$$= 396\pi \, \frac{\text{in}^3}{\text{sec}} \approx 1244.07 \, \frac{\text{in}^3}{\text{sec}}$$

25. (Answers may vary.)

Plot the speeds vs. time. Connect the points and find the area under the line graph. The definite integral also gives the area under the curve.

26. (a) Sum of numbers in Sales column $= 797.5$ thousand

(b) Enter the table in a graphing calculator and use QuadReg: $B(x) = 1.6x^2 + 2.3x + 5.0$.

(c) $\int_0^{11} (1.6x^2 + 2.3x + 5.0)\, dx$

$$= \left[\frac{1.6}{3}x^3 + \frac{2.3}{2}x^2 + 5.0x\right]_0^{11}$$

$$\approx 904.02 \text{ thousand}$$

(d) The answer in (a) corresponds to the area of left hand rectangles. These rectangles lie under the curve $B(x)$. The answer in (c) corresponds to the area under the curve. This area is greater than the area of rectangles.

27. (a) $\int_{-0.5}^{10.5} (1.6x^2 + 2.3x + 5.0)\, dx$

$$= \left[\frac{1.6}{3}x^3 + \frac{2.3}{2}x^2 + 5.0x\right]_{-0.5}^{10.5} \approx 798.97 \text{ thousand}$$

(b) The answer in (a) corresponds to the area of rectangles whose heights are the actual sales ("midpoint rectangles"). The curve now gives a better approximation since part of each rectangle is above the curve and part is below.

28. Treat 6 P.M. as 18 o'clock:

$$\frac{b - a}{2n}\left[f(x_0) + \sum_{i=1}^{n-1} 2f(x_i) + f(x_n)\right]$$
$$= \frac{18 - 8}{2(10)}[120 + 2(110) + 2(115) + 2(115) + 2(119)$$
$$\quad + 2(120) + 2(120) + 2(115) + 2(112) + 2(110)$$
$$\quad + 121]$$
$$= 1156.5$$

29. $F(x) = kx$; $6 = k(3)$, so $k = 2$ and $F(x) = 2x$.

(a) $F(9) = 2(9) = 18$N

(b) $W = \int_0^9 F(x)\, dx = \int_0^9 2x\, dx = \left[x^2\right]_0^9 = 81 \text{ N} \cdot \text{cm}$

30. $F(x) = kx$; $10{,}000 = k(1)$, so $k = 10{,}000$.

(a) $W = \int_0^d kx\, dx = \left[\frac{1}{2}kx^2\right]_0^d = \frac{1}{2}kd^2 = \frac{1}{2}(10{,}000)(0.5)^2$

$$= 1250 \text{ inch-pounds}$$

(b) For total distance: $W = \frac{1}{2}(10{,}000)(1)^2 = 5000$

For second half of distance:

$$W = 5000 - 1250 = 3750 \text{ inch-pounds}$$

31. $\frac{(12 - 0)}{2(12)}[0.04 + 2(0.04) + 2(0.05) + 2(0.06) + 2(0.05)$

$$\quad + 2(0.04) + 2(0.04) + 2(0.05) + 2(0.04)$$

$$\quad + 2(0.06) + 2(0.06) + 2(0.05) + 0.05] = 0.585$$

The overall rate, then, is $\frac{0.585}{12} = 0.04875$.

32. $\frac{(12-0)}{2(12)}[3.6 + 2(4.0) + 2(3.1) + 2(2.8) + 2(2.8) + 2(3.2)$

$+ 2(3.3) + 2(3.1) + 2(3.2) + 2(3.4) + 2(3.4)$

$+ 2(3.9) + 4.0] = 40$ thousandths or 0.040

33. (a) $\bar{x} = \frac{M_y}{M} = \frac{\sum m_k x_k}{\sum m_k}$. Taking $dm = \delta dA$ as m_k and letting

$dA \to 0$, $k \to \infty$ yields $\frac{\int x\,dm}{\int dm}$.

(b) $\bar{y} = \frac{M_y}{M} = \frac{\sum m_k y}{\sum m_k}$. Taking $dm = \delta dA$ as m_k and letting

$dA \to 0$, $k \to \infty$ yields $\frac{\int y\,dm}{\int dm}$.

34. By symmetry, $\bar{x} = 0$. For $\bar{y}$, use horizontal strips:

$$\bar{y} = \frac{\int y\,dm}{\int dm} = \frac{\int y\,\delta\,dA}{\int \delta\,dA} = \frac{\int y\,dA}{\int dA}$$

$$= \frac{\int_0^4 y(2\sqrt{y})\,dy}{\int_0^4 2\sqrt{y}\,dy}$$

$$= \frac{2\left[\frac{2}{5}y^{5/2}\right]_0^4}{2\left[\frac{2}{3}y^{3/2}\right]_0^4}$$

$$= \frac{12}{5}$$

35. By symmetry, $\bar{y} = 0$. For $\bar{x}$, use vertical strips:

$$\bar{x} = \frac{\int x\,dm}{\int dm} = \frac{\int x\delta\,dA}{\int \delta\,dA} = \frac{\int x\,dA}{\int dA}$$

$$= \frac{\int_0^2 x(2x)\,dx}{\int_0^2 2x\,dx}$$

$$= \frac{\left[\frac{2}{3}x^3\right]_0^2}{\left[x^2\right]_0^2}$$

$$= \frac{4}{3}$$

■ Section 7.2 Areas in the Plane
(pp. 374–382)

Exploration 1   A Family of Butterflies

1. For $k = 1$:

$$\int_0^\pi [(2 - \sin x) - \sin x]\,dx = \int_0^\pi (2 - 2\sin x)\,dx$$

$$= 2x + 2\cos x \Big]_0^\pi$$

$$= 2\pi - 4$$

For $k = 2$:

$$\int_0^{\pi/2} [(4 - 2\sin 2x) - (2\sin 2x)]\,dx$$

$$= \int_0^{\pi/2} (4 - 4\sin 2x)\,dx$$

$$= 4x + 2\cos 2x \Big]_0^{\pi/2} = 2\pi - 4$$

2. It appears that the areas for $k \geq 3$ will continue to be $2\pi - 4$.

3. $A_k = \int_0^{\pi/k} [(2k - k\sin kx) - k\sin kx]\,dx$

$= \int_0^{\pi/k} (2k - 2k\sin kx)\,dx$

If we make the substitution $u = kx$, then $du = k\,dx$ and the

u-limits become 0 to π. Thus,

$$A_k = \int_0^{\pi/k} (2k - 2k\sin kx)\,dx$$

$$= \int_0^{\pi/k} (2 - 2\sin kx)k\,dx$$

$$= \int_0^\pi (2 - 2\sin u)\,du.$$

4. $2\pi - 4$

5. Because the amplitudes of the sine curves are k, the kth butterfly stands $2k$ units tall. The vertical edges alone have lengths $(2k)$ that increase without bound, so the perimeters are tending to infinity.

Quick Review 7.2

1. $\int_0^\pi \sin x\,dx = \left[-\cos x\right]_0^\pi = -[-1 - 1] = 2$

2. $\int_0^1 e^{2x}\,dx = \left[\frac{1}{2}e^{2x}\right]_0^1 = \frac{1}{2}(e^2 - 1) \approx 3.195$

3. $\int_{-\pi/4}^{\pi/4} \sec^2 x\,dx = \left[\tan x\right]_{-\pi/4}^{\pi/4} = 1 - (-1) = 2$

4. $\int_0^2 (4x - x^3)\,dx = \left[2x^2 - \frac{1}{4}x^4\right]_0^2 = (8 - 4) - 0 = 4$

5. $\int_{-3}^3 \sqrt{9 - x^2}\,dx = \frac{9\pi}{2}$ (This is half the area of a circle of radius 3.)

6. Solve $x^2 - 4x = x + 6$.

$x^2 - 5x - 6 = 0$

$(x - 6)(x + 1) = 0$

$x = 6$ or $x = -1$

$y = 6 + 6 = 12$ or $y = -1 + 6 = 5$

$(6, 12)$ and $(-1, 5)$

7. Solve $e^x = x + 1$. From the graphs, it appears that e^x is always greater than or equal to $x + 1$, so that if they are ever equal, this is when $e^x - (x + 1)$ is at a minimum.

$\frac{d}{dx}[e^x - (x + 1)] = e^x - 1$ is zero when $e^x = 1$, i.e., when $x = 0$. Test: $e^0 = 0 + 1 = 1$. So the solution is $(0, 1)$.

8. Inspection of the graphs shows two intersection points: $(0, 0)$, and $(\pi, 0)$. Check: $0^2 - \pi \cdot 0 = \sin 0 = 0$ and $\pi^2 - \pi^2 = \sin \pi = 0$.

9. Solve $\frac{2x}{x^2 + 1} = x^3$.

$(0, 0)$ is a solution. Now divide by x.

$\frac{2}{x^2 + 1} = x^2$

$2 = x^4 + x^2$

$x^4 + x^2 - 2 = 0$

$x^2 = \frac{-1 \pm \sqrt{1 + 8}}{2} = -2$ or 1

Throw out the negative solution.

$x = \pm 1$

$y = x^3 = \pm 1$

$(0, 0)$, $(-1, -1)$ and $(1, 1)$

10. Use the intersect function on a graphing calculator:

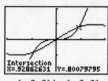

[-2, 2] by [-2, 2]

$(-0.9286, -0.8008)$, $(0, 0)$, and $(0.9286, 0.8008)$

Section 7.2 Exercises

1. $\int_0^{\pi} (1 - \cos^2 x) \, dx = \left[\frac{1}{2}x - \frac{1}{4} \sin 2x\right]_0^{\pi} = \frac{\pi}{2}$

2. Use symmetry:

$2\int_0^{\pi/3} \left(\frac{1}{2} \sec^2 t + 4 \sin^2 t\right) dt = \int_0^{\pi/3} (\sec^2 t + 8 \sin^2 t) \, dt$

$= \left[\tan t + 4t - 2 \sin 2t\right]_0^{\pi/3}$

$= \left(\sqrt{3} + \frac{4\pi}{3} - \sqrt{3}\right) - 0$

$= \frac{4\pi}{3}$

3. $\int_0^1 (y^2 - y^3) \, dy = \left[\frac{1}{3}y^3 - \frac{1}{4}y^4\right]_0^1 = \frac{1}{12}$

4. $\int_0^1 [(12y^2 - 12y^3) - (2y^2 - 2y)] \, dy$

$= \int_0^1 (-12y^3 + 10y^2 + 2y) \, dy$

$= \left[-3y^4 + \frac{10}{3}y^3 + y^2\right]_0^1$

$= -3 + \frac{10}{3} + 1 = \frac{4}{3}$

5. Use the region's symmetry:

$2\int_0^2 [2x^2 - (x^4 - 2x^2)] \, dx = 2\int_0^2 (-x^4 + 4x^2) \, dx$

$= 2\left[-\frac{1}{5}x^5 + \frac{4}{3}x^3\right]_0^2$

$= 2\left[\left(-\frac{32}{5} + \frac{32}{3}\right) - 0\right] = \frac{128}{15}$

6. Use the region's symmetry:

$2\int_0^1 (x^2 + 2x^4) \, dx = 2\left[\frac{1}{3}x^3 + \frac{2}{5}x^5\right]_0^1 = 2\left(\frac{1}{3} + \frac{2}{5}\right) = \frac{22}{15}$

7. Integrate with respect to y:

$\int_0^1 (2\sqrt{y} - y) \, dy = \left[\frac{4}{3}y^{3/2} - \frac{1}{2}y^2\right]_0^1$

$= \left(\frac{4}{3} - \frac{1}{2}\right) - 0 = \frac{5}{6}$

8. Integrate with respect to y:

$\int_0^1 [(2 - y) - \sqrt{y}] \, dy$

$= \left[2y - \frac{1}{2}y^2 - \frac{2}{3}y^{3/2}\right]_0^1 = \left(2 - \frac{1}{2} - \frac{2}{3}\right) - 0 = \frac{5}{6}$

9. Integrate in two parts:

$\int_{-2}^0 [(2x^3 - x^2 - 5x) - (-x^2 + 3x)] \, dx +$

$\int_0^2 [(-x^2 + 3x) - (2x^3 - x^2 - 5x)] \, dx$

$= \int_{-2}^0 (2x^3 - 8x) \, dx + \int_0^2 (-2x^3 + 8x) \, dx$

$= \left[\frac{1}{2}x^4 - 4x^2\right]_{-2}^0 + \left[-\frac{1}{2}x^4 + 4x^2\right]_0^2$

$= [0 - (8 - 16)] + [(-8 + 16) - 0] = 16$

10. Integrate in three parts:

$$\int_{-2}^{-1} [(-x+2) - (4-x^2)] \, dx \; +$$

$$\int_{-1}^{2} [(4-x^2) - (-x+2)] \, dx \; +$$

$$\int_{2}^{3} [(-x+2) - (4-x^2)] \, dx$$

$$= \int_{-2}^{-1} (x^2 - x - 2) \, dx + \int_{-1}^{2} (-x^2 + x + 2) \, dx \; +$$

$$\int_{2}^{3} (x^2 - x - 2) \, dx$$

$$= \left[\frac{1}{3}x^3 - \frac{1}{2}x^2 - 2x \right]_{-2}^{-1} + \left[-\frac{1}{3}x^3 + \frac{1}{2}x^2 + 2x \right]_{-1}^{2} \; +$$

$$\left[\frac{1}{3}x^3 - \frac{1}{2}x^2 - 2x \right]_{2}^{3}$$

$$= \left[\left(-\frac{1}{3} - \frac{1}{2} + 2 \right) - \left(-\frac{8}{3} - 2 + 4 \right) \right] +$$

$$\left[\left(-\frac{8}{3} + 2 + 4 \right) - \left(\frac{1}{3} + \frac{1}{2} - 2 \right) \right] +$$

$$\left[\left(9 - \frac{9}{2} - 6 \right) - \left(\frac{8}{3} - 2 - 4 \right) \right]$$

$$= \frac{49}{6} = 8\frac{1}{6}$$

11. Solve $x^2 - 2 = 2$: $x^2 = 4$, so the curves intersect at

$x = \pm 2$.

$$\int_{-2}^{2} [2 - (x^2 - 2)] \, dx = \int_{-2}^{2} (4 - x^2) \, dx$$

$$= \left[4x - \frac{1}{3}x^3 \right]_{-2}^{2} = \left(8 - \frac{8}{3} \right) - \left(-8 + \frac{8}{3} \right) = \frac{32}{3} = 10\frac{2}{3}$$

12. Solve $2x - x^2 = -3$: $x^2 - 2x - 3 = (x-3)(x+1) = 0$,

so the curves intersect at $x = -1$ and $x = 3$.

$$\int_{-1}^{3} (2x - x^2 + 3) \, dx = \left[x^2 - \frac{1}{3}x^3 + 3x \right]_{-1}^{3}$$

$$= (9 - 9 + 9) - \left(1 + \frac{1}{3} - 3 \right)$$

$$= \frac{32}{3} = 10\frac{2}{3}$$

13. Solve $7 - 2x^2 = x^2 + 4$: $x^2 = 1$, so the curves intersect at

$x = \pm 1$.

$$\int_{-1}^{1} [(7 - 2x^2) - (x^2 + 4)] \, dx = \int_{-1}^{1} (-3x^2 + 3) \, dx$$

$$= 3 \int_{-1}^{1} (1 - x^2) \, dx$$

$$= 3 \left[x - \frac{1}{3}x^3 \right]_{-1}^{1}$$

$$= 3 \left[\frac{2}{3} - \left(-\frac{2}{3} \right) \right] = 4$$

14.

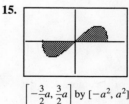

[−3, 3] by [−1, 5]

The curves intersect at $x = \pm 1$ and $x = \pm 2$. Use the

region's symmetry:

$$2 \int_{0}^{1} [(x^4 - 4x^2 + 4) - x^2] \, dx + 2 \int_{1}^{2} [x^2 - (x^4 - 4x^2 + 4)]$$

$$dx \qquad\qquad = 2 \int_{0}^{1} (x^4 - 5x^2 + 4) \, dx \; +$$

$$2 \int_{1}^{2} (-x^4 + 5x^2 - 4) \, dx$$

$$= 2 \left[\frac{1}{5}x^5 - \frac{5}{3}x^3 + 4x \right]_{0}^{1} + 2 \left[-\frac{1}{5}x^5 + \frac{5}{3}x^3 - 4x \right]_{1}^{2}$$

$$= 2 \left[\frac{1}{5} - \frac{5}{3} + 4 \right] + 2 \left[\left(-\frac{32}{5} + \frac{40}{3} - 8 \right) - \left(-\frac{1}{5} + \frac{5}{3} - 4 \right) \right] = 8$$

15.

$$\left[-\frac{3}{2}a, \frac{3}{2}a \right] \text{ by } [-a^2, a^2]$$

The curves intersect at $x = 0$ and $x = \pm a$. Use the region's

symmetry:

$$2 \int_{0}^{a} x\sqrt{a^2 - x^2} \, dx = 2 \left[-\frac{1}{3}(a^2 - x^2)^{3/2} \right]_{0}^{a}$$

$$= 2 \left[0 - \left(-\frac{1}{3}a^3 \right) \right]$$

$$= \frac{2}{3}a^3$$

16.

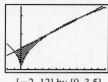

[−2, 12] by [0, 3.5]

The curves intersect at three points:
$x = -1$, $x = 4$ and $x = 9$.
Because of the absolute value sign, break the integral up at
$x = 0$ also:

$$\int_{-1}^{0}\left(\frac{x+6}{5} - \sqrt{-x}\right) dx + \int_{0}^{4}\left(\frac{x+6}{5} - \sqrt{x}\right) dx +$$
$$\int_{4}^{9}\left(\sqrt{x} - \frac{x+6}{5}\right) dx$$

$$= \left[\frac{\frac{1}{2}x^2 + 6x}{5} + \frac{2}{3}(-x)^{3/2}\right]_{-1}^{0} + \left[\frac{\frac{1}{2}x^2 + 6x}{5} - \frac{2}{3}x^{3/2}\right]_{0}^{4} +$$

$$\left[\frac{2}{3}x^{3/2} - \frac{\frac{1}{2}x^2 + 6x}{5}\right]_{4}^{9}$$

$$= \left[0 - \left(-\frac{11}{10} + \frac{2}{3}\right)\right] + \left[\left(\frac{32}{5} - \frac{16}{3}\right) - 0\right] +$$

$$\left[\left(18 - \frac{189}{10}\right) - \left(\frac{16}{3} - \frac{32}{5}\right)\right]$$

$$= \frac{13}{30} + \frac{16}{15} + \frac{1}{6} = \frac{5}{3} = 1\frac{2}{3}$$

17.

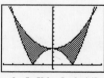

[−5, 5] by [−1, 14]

The curves intersect at $x = 0$ and $x = \pm 4$. Because of the absolute value sign, break the integral up at $x = \pm 2$ also (where $|x^2 - 4|$ turns the corner). Use the graph's symmetry:

$$2\int_{0}^{2}\left[\left(\frac{x^2}{2} + 4\right) - (4 - x^2)\right] dx + 2\int_{2}^{4}\left[\left(\frac{x^2}{2} + 4\right) - (x^2 - 4)\right] dx$$

$$= 2\int_{0}^{2}\frac{3x^2}{2}\, dx + 2\int_{2}^{4}\left(-\frac{x^2}{2} + 8\right) dx$$

$$= 2\left[\frac{x^3}{2}\right]_{0}^{2} + 2\left[-\frac{x^3}{6} + 8x\right]_{2}^{4}$$

$$= 2[4] + 2\left[\left(-\frac{32}{3} + 32\right) - \left(-\frac{4}{3} + 16\right)\right] = \frac{64}{3} = 21\frac{1}{3}$$

18. Solve $y^2 = y + 2$: $y^2 - y - 2 = (y - 2)(y + 1) = 0$, so the curves intersect at $y = -1$ and $y = 2$.

$$\int_{-1}^{2}(y + 2 - y^2)\, dy = \left[\frac{1}{2}y^2 + 2y - \frac{1}{3}y^3\right]_{-1}^{2}$$

$$= \left(2 + 4 - \frac{8}{3}\right) - \left(\frac{1}{2} - 2 + \frac{1}{3}\right)$$

$$= \frac{9}{2} = 4\frac{1}{2}$$

19. Solve for x: $x = \frac{y^2}{4} - 1$ and $x = \frac{y}{4} + 4$.

Now solve $\frac{y^2}{4} - 1 = \frac{y}{4} + 4$: $\frac{y^2}{4} - \frac{y}{4} - 5 = 0$,

$y^2 - y - 20 = (y - 5)(y + 4) = 0$.

The curves intersect at $y = -4$ and $y = 5$.

$$\int_{-4}^{5}\left[\left(\frac{y}{4} + 4\right) - \left(\frac{y^2}{4} - 1\right)\right] dy$$

$$= \int_{-4}^{5}\left(-\frac{y^2}{4} + \frac{y}{4} + 5\right) dy$$

$$= \left[-\frac{y^3}{12} + \frac{y^2}{8} + 5y\right]_{-4}^{5}$$

$$= \left(-\frac{125}{12} + \frac{25}{8} + 25\right) - \left(\frac{16}{3} + 2 - 20\right) = \frac{243}{8} = 30\frac{3}{8}$$

20. Solve for x: $x = y^2$ and $x = 3 - 2y^2$. Now solve

$y^2 = 3 - 2y^2$: $y^2 = 1$, so the curves intersect at $y = \pm 1$.

Use the region's symmetry:

$$2\int_{0}^{1}(3 - 2y^2 - y^2)\, dy = 2\int_{0}^{1}(3 - 3y^2)\, dy$$

$$= 6\int_{0}^{1}(1 - y^2)\, dy$$

$$= 6\left[y - \frac{1}{3}y^3\right]_{0}^{1}$$

$$= 6\left[\left(1 - \frac{1}{3}\right) - 0\right] = 4$$

21. Solve for x: $x = -y^2$ and $x = 2 - 3y^2$.

Now solve $-y^2 = 2 - 3y^2$: $y^2 = 1$, so the curves intersect

at $y = \pm 1$. Use the region's symmetry:

$$2\int_{0}^{1}(2 - 3y^2 + y^2)\, dy = 2\int_{0}^{1}(2 - 2y^2)\, dy$$

$$= 4\int_{0}^{1}(1 - y^2)\, dy = 4\left[y - \frac{1}{3}y^3\right]_{0}^{1} = 4\left[\left(1 - \frac{1}{3}\right) - 0\right] = \frac{8}{3}$$

22. Solve for y: $y = 4 - 4x^2$ and $y = x^4 - 1$.

Now solve $4 - 4x^2 = x^4 - 1$:

$x^4 + 4x^2 - 5 = (x^2 - 1)(x^2 + 5) = 0$.

The curves intersect at $x = \pm 1$.

Use the region's symmetry:

$2\int_0^1 [(4 - 4x^2) - (x^4 - 1)]\, dx$

$= 2\int_0^1 (-x^4 - 4x^2 + 5)\, dx$

$= 2\left[-\frac{1}{5}x^5 - \frac{4}{3}x^3 + 5x\right]_0^1$

$= 2\left[\left(-\frac{1}{5} - \frac{4}{3} + 5\right) - 0\right]$

$= \frac{104}{15} = 6\frac{14}{15}$

23. Solve for x: $x = 3 - y^2$ and $x = -\frac{y^2}{4}$.

Now solve $3 - y^2 = -\frac{y^2}{4}$: $y^2 = 4$,

so the curves intersect at $y = \pm 2$.

Use the region's symmetry:

$2\int_0^2 \left(3 - y^2 + \frac{y^2}{4}\right) dy = 2\int_0^2 \left(3 - \frac{3y^2}{4}\right) dy$

$= 2\left[3y - \frac{y^3}{4}\right]_0^2$

$= 2(6 - 2) - 0 = 8$

24. $\int_0^\pi (2\sin x - \sin 2x)\, dx = \left[-2\cos x + \frac{1}{2}\cos 2x\right]_0^\pi$

$= \left[\left(2 + \frac{1}{2}\right) - \left(-2 + \frac{1}{2}\right)\right] = 4$

25. Use the region's symmetry:

$2\int_0^{\pi/3} (8\cos x - \sec^2 x)\, dx = 2\left[8\sin x - \tan x\right]_0^{\pi/3}$

$= 2[(4\sqrt{3} - \sqrt{3}) - 0] = 6\sqrt{3}$

26.

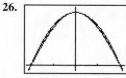

$[-1.1, 1.1]$ by $[-0.1, 1.1]$

The curves intersect at $x = 0$ and $x = \pm 1$, but they do not

cross at $x = 0$.

$2\int_0^1 \left[1 - x^2 - \cos\left(\frac{\pi x}{2}\right)\right] dx$

$= 2\left[x - \frac{1}{3}x^3 - \frac{2}{\pi}\sin\left(\frac{\pi x}{2}\right)\right]_0^1$

$= 2\left[\left(1 - \frac{1}{3} - \frac{2}{\pi}\right) - 0\right] = \frac{4}{3} - \frac{4}{\pi} \approx 0.0601$

27.

$[-1.5, 1.5]$ by $[-1.5, 1.5]$

The curves intersect at $x = 0$ and $x = \pm 1$. Use the area's

symmetry:

$2\int_0^1 \left[\sin\left(\frac{\pi x}{2}\right) - x\right] dx = 2\left[-\frac{2}{\pi}\cos\left(\frac{\pi x}{2}\right) - \frac{1}{2}x^2\right]_0^1$

$= 2\left[-\frac{1}{2} - \left(-\frac{2}{\pi}\right)\right]$

$= \frac{4 - \pi}{\pi} \approx 0.273$

28. Use the region's symmetry, and simplify before integrating:

$2\int_0^{\pi/4} (\sec^2 x - \tan^2 x)\, dx$

$= 2\int_0^{\pi/4} [\sec^2 x - (\sec^2 x - 1)]\, dx$

$= 2\int_0^{\pi/4} dx = 2\left[x\right]_0^{\pi/4} = \frac{\pi}{2}$

29. Use the region's symmetry:

$2\int_0^{\pi/4} (\tan^2 y + \tan^2 y)\, dy = 4\int_0^{\pi/4} \tan^2 y\, dy$

$= 4\left[\tan y - y\right]_0^{\pi/4}$

$= 4\left[\left(1 - \frac{\pi}{4}\right) - 0\right]$

$= 4 - \pi \approx 0.858$

30. $\int_0^{\pi/2} 3\sin y \sqrt{\cos y}\, dy = 3\left[-\frac{2}{3}(\cos y)^{3/2}\right]_0^{\pi/2}$

$= 3\left[0 - \left(-\frac{2}{3}\right)\right] = 2$

31. Solve for x: $x = y^3$ and $x = y$.

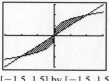

$[-1.5, 1.5]$ by $[-1.5, 1.5]$

The curves intersect at $x = 0$ and $x = \pm 1$. Use the area's

symmetry: $2\int_0^1 (y - y^3)\, dy = 2\left[\frac{1}{2}y^2 - \frac{1}{4}y^4\right]_0^1 = \frac{1}{2}$

32.

[−0.5, 2.5] by [−0.5, 1.5]

$y = x$ and $y = \dfrac{1}{x^2}$ intersect at $x = 1$. Integrate in two parts:

$$\int_0^1 x \, dx + \int_1^2 \frac{1}{x^2} \, dx = \left[\frac{1}{2}x^2\right]_0^1 + \left[-\frac{1}{x}\right]_1^2$$

$$= \frac{1}{2} + \left[-\frac{1}{2} - (-1)\right] = 1$$

33. The curves intersect when $\sin x = \cos x$, i.e., at $x = \dfrac{\pi}{4}$.

$$\int_0^{\pi/4} (\cos x - \sin x) \, dx = \left[\sin x + \cos x\right]_0^{\pi/4}$$

$$= \sqrt{2} - 1 \approx 0.414$$

34.

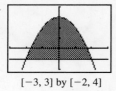

[−3, 3] by [−2, 4]

(a) The curves intersect at $x = \pm 2$.

Use the region's symmetry:

$$2\int_0^2 (3 - x^2 + 1) \, dx = 2\int_0^2 (4 - x^2) \, dx$$

$$= 2\left[4x - \frac{1}{3}x^3\right]_0^2$$

$$= 2\left[\left(8 - \frac{8}{3}\right) - 0\right] = \frac{32}{3}$$

(b) Solve $y = 3 - x^2$ for x: $x = \pm\sqrt{3 - y}$. The

y-intercepts are -1 and 3.

$$\int_{-1}^3 2\sqrt{3 - y} \, dy = 2\left[-\frac{2}{3}(3 - y)^{3/2}\right]_{-1}^3$$

$$= 2\left[0 - \left(-\frac{16}{3}\right)\right] = \frac{32}{3}$$

35. (a)

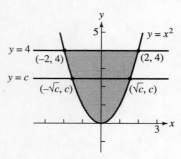

If $y = x^2 = c$, then $x = \pm\sqrt{c}$. So the points are

$(-\sqrt{c}, c)$ and $(\sqrt{c}, c)$.

(b) The two areas in Quadrant I, where $x = \sqrt{y}$, are equal:

$$\int_0^c \sqrt{y} \, dy = \int_c^4 \sqrt{y} \, dy$$

$$\left[\frac{2}{3}y^{3/2}\right]_0^c = \left[\frac{2}{3}y^{3/2}\right]_c^4$$

$$\frac{2}{3}c^{3/2} = \frac{2}{3}4^{3/2} - \frac{2}{3}c^{3/2}$$

$$2c^{3/2} = 8$$

$$c^{3/2} = 4$$

$$c = 4^{2/3} = 2^{4/3}$$

(c) Divide the upper right section into a $(4 - c)$-by-$\sqrt{c}$

rectangle and a leftover portion:

$$\int_0^{\sqrt{c}} (c - x^2) \, dx = (4 - c)\sqrt{c} + \int_{\sqrt{c}}^2 (4 - x^2) \, dx$$

$$\left[cx - \frac{1}{3}x^3\right]_0^{\sqrt{c}} = 4\sqrt{c} - c^{3/2} + \left[4x - \frac{1}{3}x^3\right]_{\sqrt{c}}^2$$

$$c^{3/2} - \frac{1}{3}c^{3/2} = 4\sqrt{c} - c^{3/2}$$

$$+ \left[\left(8 - \frac{8}{3}\right) - \left(4\sqrt{c} - \frac{1}{3}c^{3/2}\right)\right]$$

$$\frac{2}{3}c^{3/2} = 4\sqrt{c} - c^{3/2} + \frac{16}{3} - 4\sqrt{c} + \frac{1}{3}c^{3/2}$$

$$\frac{4}{3}c^{3/2} = \frac{16}{3}$$

$$c^{3/2} = 4$$

$$c = 4^{2/3} = 2^{4/3}$$

36.

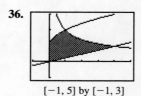

[−1, 5] by [−1, 3]

The key intersection points are at $x = 0$, $x = 1$ and $x = 4$.

Integrate in two parts:

$$\int_0^1 \left(1 + \sqrt{x} - \frac{x}{4}\right) dx + \int_1^4 \left(\frac{2}{\sqrt{x}} - \frac{x}{4}\right) dx$$

$$= \left[x + \frac{2}{3}x^{3/2} - \frac{x^2}{8}\right]_0^1 + \left[4\sqrt{x} - \frac{x^2}{8}\right]_1^4$$

$$= \left(1 + \frac{2}{3} - \frac{1}{8}\right) + \left[(8 - 2) - \left(4 - \frac{1}{8}\right)\right] = \frac{11}{3}$$

37. First find the two areas.

For the triangle, $\frac{1}{2}(2a)(a^2) = a^3$

For the parabola, $2\int_0^a (a^2 - x^2)\, dx = 2\left[a^2x - \frac{1}{3}x^3\right]_0^a = \frac{4}{3}a^3$

The ratio, then, is $\dfrac{a^3}{\frac{4}{3}a^3} = \dfrac{3}{4}$, which remains

constant as a

approaches zero.

38. $\int_a^b [2f(x) - f(x)]\, dx = \int_a^b f(x)\, dx$, which we already know

equals 4.

39. Neither; both integrals come out as zero because the -1-to-0 and 0-to-1 portions of the integrals cancel each other.

40. Sometimes true, namely when $dA = [f(x) - g(x)]\, dx$ is always nonnegative. This happens when $f(x) \geq g(x)$ over the entire interval.

41.

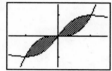

$[-1.5, 1.5]$ by $[-1.5, 1.5]$

The curves intersect at $x = 0$ and $x = \pm 1$. Use the area's symmetry:

$$2\int_0^1 \left(\frac{2x}{x^2+1} - x^3\right) dx = 2\left[\ln\left(x^2+1\right) - \frac{1}{4}x^4\right]_0^1$$
$$= 2\ln 2 - \frac{1}{2}$$
$$= \ln 4 - \frac{1}{2} \approx 0.886$$

42.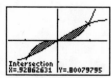

$[-1.5, 1.5]$ by $[-1.5, 1.5]$

The curves intersect at $x = 0$ and $x \approx \pm 0.9286$. Use NINT to find $2\int_0^{0.9286} (\sin x - x^3)\, dx \approx 0.4303$.

43. First graph $y = \cos x$ and $y = x^2$.

$[-1.5, 1.5]$ by $[-0.5, 1.5]$

The curves intersect at $x \approx \pm 0.8241$. Use NINT to find $2\int_0^{0.8241} (\cos x - x^2)\, dx \approx 1.0948$. Multiplying both functions by k will not change the x-value of any intersection point, so the area condition to be met is

$$2 = 2\int_0^{0.8241} (k\cos x - kx^2)\, dx$$
$$\Rightarrow 2 = k \cdot 2\int_0^{0.8241} (\cos x - x^2)\, dx$$
$$\Rightarrow 2 \approx k(1.0948)$$
$$\Rightarrow k \approx 1.8269.$$

44. (a) Solve for y:

$$\frac{x^2}{a^2} + \frac{y^2}{b^2} = 1$$
$$y^2 = b^2\left(1 - \frac{x^2}{a^2}\right)$$
$$y = \pm b\sqrt{1 - \frac{x^2}{a^2}}$$

(b) $\int_{-a}^a \left[b\sqrt{1 - \frac{x^2}{a^2}} - \left(-b\sqrt{1 - \frac{x^2}{a^2}}\right)\right] dx$ or

$2\int_{-a}^a b\sqrt{1 - \frac{x^2}{a^2}}\, dx$ or $4\int_0^a b\sqrt{1 - \frac{x^2}{a^2}}\, dx$

(c) Answers may vary.

(d, e) $2\int_{-a}^a b\sqrt{1 - \frac{x^2}{a^2}}\, dx = 2b\left[\frac{x}{2}\sqrt{1 - \frac{x^2}{a^2}} + \frac{a}{2}\sin^{-1}\frac{x}{a}\right]_{-a}^a$

$$= 2b\left[\frac{a}{2}\sin^{-1}(1) - \frac{a}{2}\sin^{-1}(-1)\right]$$
$$= \pi ab$$

45. By hypothesis, $f(x) - g(x)$ is the same for each region, where $f(x)$ and $g(x)$ represent the upper and lower edges. But then Area $= \int_a^b [f(x) - g(x)]\, dx$ will be the same for each.

46. The curves are shown for $m = \frac{1}{2}$:

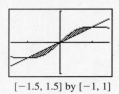

[−1.5, 1.5] by [−1, 1]

In general, the intersection points are where $\frac{x}{x^2 + 1} = mx$,

which is where $x = 0$ or else $x = \pm\sqrt{\frac{1}{m} - 1}$. Then,

because of symmetry, the area is

$$2\int_0^{\sqrt{(1/m)-1}} \left(\frac{x}{x^2 + 1} - mx\right) dx$$

$$= 2\left[\frac{1}{2}\ln(x^2 + 1) - \frac{1}{2}mx^2\right]_0^{\sqrt{(1/m)-1}}$$

$$= \ln\left(\frac{1}{m} - 1 + 1\right) -$$

$$m\left(\frac{1}{m} - 1\right) = m - \ln(m) - 1.$$

■ Section 7.3 Volumes

(pp. 383–394)

Exploration 1   Volume by Cylindrical Shells

1. Its height is $f(x_k) = 3x_k - x_k^2$.

2. Unrolling the cylinder, the circumference becomes one dimension of a rectangle, and the height becomes the other. The thickness Δx is the third dimension of a slab with dimensions $2\pi(x_k + 1)$ by $3x_k - x_k^2$ by Δx. The volume is obtained by multiplying the dimensions together.

3. The limit is the definite integral $\int_0^3 2\pi(x + 1)(3x - x^2)\,dx$.

4. $\frac{45\pi}{2}$

Exploration 2   Surface Area

1. $\int_a^b 2\pi y \sqrt{1 + \left(\frac{dy}{dx}\right)^2}\,dx$

The limit will exist if f and f' are continuous on the interval $[a, b]$.

2. $y = \sin x$, so $\frac{dy}{dx} = \cos x$ and

$$\int_a^b 2\pi y \sqrt{1 + \left(\frac{dy}{dx}\right)^2}\,dx$$

$$= \int_0^{\pi} 2\pi \sin x \sqrt{1 + \cos^2 x}\,dx \approx 14.424.$$

3. $y = \sqrt{x}$, so $\frac{dy}{dx} = \frac{1}{2\sqrt{x}}$ and

$$\int_0^4 2\pi\sqrt{x} \sqrt{1 + \left(\frac{1}{2\sqrt{x}}\right)^2}\,dx \approx 36.177.$$

Quick Review 7.3

1. x^2

2. $s = \frac{x}{\sqrt{2}}$, so Area $= s^2 = \frac{x^2}{2}$.

3. $\frac{1}{2}\pi r^2$ or $\frac{\pi x^2}{2}$

4. $\frac{1}{2}\pi\left(\frac{d}{2}\right)^2$ or $\frac{\pi x^2}{8}$

5. $b = x$ and $h = \frac{\sqrt{3}}{2}x$, so Area $= \frac{1}{2}bh = \frac{\sqrt{3}}{4}x^2$.

6. $b = h = x$, so Area $= \frac{1}{2}bh = \frac{x^2}{2}$.

7. $b = h = \frac{x}{\sqrt{2}}$, so Area $= \frac{1}{2}bh = \frac{x^2}{4}$.

8.

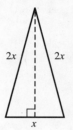

$b = x$ and $h = \sqrt{(2x)^2 - \left(\frac{1}{2}x\right)^2} = \frac{\sqrt{15}}{2}x$, so

Area $= \frac{1}{2}bh = \frac{\sqrt{15}}{4}x^2$.

9. This is a 3-4-5 right triangle. $b = 4x$, $h = 3x$, and

Area $= \frac{1}{2}bh = 6x^2$.

10. The hexagon contains six equilateral triangles with sides of

length x, so from Exercise 5, Area $= 6\left(\frac{\sqrt{3}}{4}x^2\right) = \frac{3\sqrt{3}}{2}x^2$.

Section 7.3 Exercises

1. In each case, the width of the cross section is $w = 2\sqrt{1 - x^2}$.

(a) $A = \pi r^2$, where $r = \frac{w}{2}$, so $A(x) = \pi\left(\frac{w}{2}\right)^2 = \pi(1 - x^2)$.

(b) $A = s^2$, where $s = w$, so $A(x) = w^2 = 4(1 - x^2)$.

(c) $A = s^2$, where $s = \frac{w}{\sqrt{2}}$, so $A(x) = \left(\frac{w}{\sqrt{2}}\right)^2 = 2(1 - x^2)$.

(d) $A = \frac{\sqrt{3}}{4}w^2$ (see Quick Review Exercise 5), so

$A(x) = \frac{\sqrt{3}}{4}(2\sqrt{1 - x^2})^2 = \sqrt{3}(1 - x^2)$.

2. In each case, the width of the cross section is $w = 2\sqrt{x}$.

    (a) $A = \pi r^2$, where $r = \dfrac{w}{2}$, so $A(x) = \pi\left(\dfrac{w}{2}\right)^2 = \pi x$.

    (b) $A = s^2$, where $s = w$, so $A(x) = w^2 = 4x$.

    (c) $A = s^2$, where $s = \dfrac{w}{\sqrt{2}}$, so $A(x) = \left(\dfrac{w}{\sqrt{2}}\right)^2 = 2x$.

    (d) $A = \dfrac{\sqrt{3}}{4}w^2$ (see Quick Review Exercise 5), so
$$A(x) = \dfrac{\sqrt{3}}{4}(2\sqrt{x})^2 = \sqrt{3}x.$$

3. A cross section has width $w = 2\sqrt{x}$ and area
$$A(x) = s^2 = \left(\dfrac{w}{\sqrt{2}}\right)^2 = 2x. \text{ The volume is}$$
$$\int_0^4 2x\,dx = \left[x^2\right]_0^4 = 16.$$

4. A cross section has width $w = (2 - x^2) - x^2 = 2 - 2x^2$
and area $A(x) = \pi r^2 = \pi\left(\dfrac{w}{2}\right)^2 = \pi(1 - x^2)^2$. The volume is
$$\int_{-1}^1 \pi(1 - x^2)^2\,dx = \pi\int_{-1}^1 (x^4 - 2x^2 + 1)\,dx$$
$$= \pi\left[\dfrac{1}{5}x^5 - \dfrac{2}{3}x^3 + x\right]_{-1}^1$$
$$= \dfrac{16}{15}\pi.$$

5. A cross section has width $w = 2\sqrt{1 - x^2}$ and area
$A(x) = s^2 = w^2 = 4(1 - x^2)$. The volume is
$$\int_{-1}^1 4(1 - x^2)\,dx = 4\int_{-1}^1 (1 - x^2)\,dx = 4\left[x - \dfrac{1}{3}x^3\right]_{-1}^1 = \dfrac{16}{3}.$$

6. A cross section has width $w = 2\sqrt{1 - x^2}$ and area
$A(x) = s^2 = \left(\dfrac{w}{\sqrt{2}}\right)^2 = 2(1 - x^2)$. The volume is
$$\int_{-1}^1 2(1 - x^2)\,dx = 2\int_{-1}^1 (1 - x^2)\,dx = 2\left[x - \dfrac{1}{3}x^3\right]_{-1}^1 = \dfrac{8}{3}.$$

7. A cross section has width $w = 2\sqrt{\sin x}$.

    (a) $A(x) = \dfrac{\sqrt{3}}{4}w^2 = \sqrt{3}\sin x$, and
$$V = \int_0^\pi \sqrt{3}\sin x\,dx$$
$$= \sqrt{3}\int_0^\pi \sin x\,dx$$
$$= \sqrt{3}\left[-\cos x\right]_0^\pi$$
$$= 2\sqrt{3}.$$

    (b) $A(x) = s^2 = w^2 = 4\sin x$, and
$$V = \int_0^\pi 4\sin x\,dx = 4\int_0^\pi \sin x\,dx = 4\left[-\cos x\right]_0^\pi = 8.$$

8. A cross section has width $w = \sec x - \tan x$.

    (a) $A(x) = \pi r^2 = \pi\left(\dfrac{w}{2}\right)^2 = \dfrac{\pi}{4}(\sec x - \tan x)^2$, and
$$V = \int_{-\pi/3}^{\pi/3} \dfrac{\pi}{4}(\sec x - \tan x)^2\,dx$$
$$= \dfrac{\pi}{4}\int_{-\pi/3}^{\pi/3} (\sec^2 x - 2\sec x\tan x + \tan^2 x)\,dx$$
$$= \dfrac{\pi}{4}\left[\tan x - 2\sec x + \tan x - x\right]_{-\pi/3}^{\pi/3}$$
$$= \dfrac{\pi}{2}\left[\tan x - \sec x - \dfrac{1}{2}x\right]_{-\pi/3}^{\pi/3}$$
$$= \dfrac{\pi}{2}\left[\left(\sqrt{3} - 2 - \dfrac{\pi}{6}\right) - \left(-\sqrt{3} - 2 + \dfrac{\pi}{6}\right)\right]$$
$$= \pi\sqrt{3} - \dfrac{\pi^2}{6}.$$

    (b) $A(x) = s^2 = w^2 = (\sec x - \tan x)^2$, and
$$V = \int_{-\pi/3}^{\pi/3} (\sec x - \tan x)^2\,dx, \text{ which by same method as}$$
in part (a) equals $4\sqrt{3} - \dfrac{2}{3}\pi$.

9. A cross section has width $w = \sqrt{5}y^2$ and area
$\pi r^2 = \pi\left(\dfrac{w}{2}\right)^2 = \dfrac{5\pi}{4}y^4$. The volume is
$$\int_0^2 \dfrac{5\pi}{4}y^4\,dy = \dfrac{\pi}{4}\left[y^5\right]_0^2 = 8\pi.$$

10. A cross section has width $w = 2\sqrt{1 - y^2}$ and area
$\dfrac{1}{2}s^2 = \dfrac{1}{2}w^2 = 2(1 - y^2)$. The volume is
$$\int_{-1}^1 2(1 - y^2)\,dy = 2\left[y - \dfrac{1}{3}y^3\right]_{-1}^1 = \dfrac{8}{3}.$$

11. (a) The volume is the same as if the square had moved
without twisting: $V = Ah = s^2h$.

    (b) Still s^2h: the lateral distribution of the square cross
sections doesn't affect the volume. That's Cavalieri's
Volume Theorem.

12. Since the diameter of the circular base of the solid extends
from $y = \dfrac{12}{2} = 6$ to $y = 12$, for a diameter of 6 and a radius
of 3, the solid has the same cross sections as the right
circular cone. The volumes are equal by Cavalieri's
Theorem.

13. The solid is a right circular cone of radius 1 and height 2.
$$V = \dfrac{1}{3}Bh = \dfrac{1}{3}(\pi r^2)h = \dfrac{1}{3}(\pi 1^2)2 = \dfrac{2}{3}\pi$$

14. The solid is a right circular cone of radius 3 and height 2.
$$V = \dfrac{1}{3}Bh = \dfrac{1}{3}(\pi r^2)h = \dfrac{1}{3}(\pi 3^2)2 = 6\pi$$

15. A cross section has radius $r = \tan\left(\dfrac{\pi}{4}y\right)$ and area

$A(y) = \pi r^2 = \pi \tan^2\left(\dfrac{\pi}{4}y\right)$. The volume is

$$\int_0^1 \pi \tan^2\left(\dfrac{\pi}{4}y\right) dy = \pi\left[\dfrac{4}{\pi}\tan\left(\dfrac{\pi}{4}y\right) - y\right]_0^1$$
$$= \pi\left(\dfrac{4}{\pi} - 1\right)$$
$$= 4 - \pi.$$

16. A cross section has radius $r = \sin x \cos x$ and area

$A(x) = \pi r^2 = \pi \sin^2 x \cos^2 x$. The shaded region extends

from $x = 0$ to where $\sin x \cos x$ drops back to 0, i.e., where

$x = \dfrac{\pi}{2}$. Now, since $\cos 2x = 2\cos^2 x - 1$, we know

$\cos^2 x = \dfrac{1 + \cos 2x}{2}$ and since $\cos 2x = 1 - 2\sin^2 x$, we

know $\sin^2 x = \dfrac{1 - \cos 2x}{2}$. $\displaystyle\int_0^{\pi/2} \pi \sin^2 x \cos^2 x \, dx$

$$= \pi\int_0^{\pi/2} \dfrac{1 - \cos 2x}{2} \cdot \dfrac{1 + \cos 2x}{2} \, dx$$
$$= \dfrac{\pi}{4}\int_0^{\pi/2} (1 - \cos^2 2x) \, dx = \dfrac{\pi}{4}\int_0^{\pi/2} \sin^2 2x \, dx$$
$$= \dfrac{\pi}{4}\int_0^{\pi/2} \dfrac{1 - \cos 4x}{2} \, dx = \dfrac{\pi}{8}\int_0^{\pi/2} (1 - \cos 4x) \, dx$$
$$= \dfrac{\pi}{8}\left[x - \dfrac{1}{4}\sin 4x\right]_0^{\pi/2} = \dfrac{\pi}{8}\left[\left(\dfrac{\pi}{2} - 0\right) - 0\right] = \dfrac{\pi^2}{16}.$$

17.

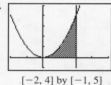

[−2, 4] by [−1, 5]

A cross section has radius $r = x^2$ and area

$A(x) = \pi r^2 = \pi x^4$. The volume is

$$\int_0^2 \pi x^4 \, dx = \pi\left[\dfrac{1}{5}x^5\right]_0^2 = \dfrac{32\pi}{5}.$$

18.

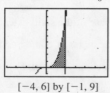

[−4, 6] by [−1, 9]

A cross section has radius $r = x^3$ and area

$A(x) = \pi r^2 = \pi x^6$. The volume is

$$\int_0^2 \pi x^6 \, dx = \pi\left[\dfrac{1}{7}x^7\right]_0^2 = \dfrac{128\pi}{7}.$$

19.

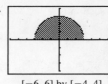

[−6, 6] by [−4, 4]

The solid is a sphere of radius $r = 3$. The volume is

$\dfrac{4}{3}\pi r^3 = 36\pi.$

20.

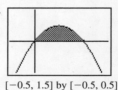

[−0.5, 1.5] by [−0.5, 0.5]

The parabola crosses the line $y = 0$ when

$x - x^2 = x(1 - x) = 0$, i.e., when $x = 0$ or $x = 1$. A cross

section has radius $r = x - x^2$ and area

$A(x) = \pi r^2 = \pi(x - x^2)^2 = \pi(x^2 - 2x^3 + x^4)$.

The volume is

$$\int_0^1 \pi(x^2 - 2x^3 + x^4) \, dx = \pi\left[\dfrac{1}{3}x^3 - \dfrac{1}{2}x^4 + \dfrac{1}{5}x^5\right]_0^1 = \dfrac{\pi}{30}.$$

21.

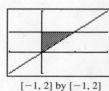

[−1, 2] by [−1, 2]

Use cylindrical shells: A shell has radius y and height y.

The volume is

$$\int_0^1 2\pi(y)(y) \, dy = 2\pi\left[\dfrac{1}{3}y^3\right]_0^1 = \dfrac{2}{3}\pi.$$

22.

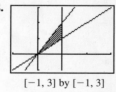

[−1, 3] by [−1, 3]

Use washer cross sections: A washer has inner radius $r = x$,

outer radius $R = 2x$, and area $A(x) = \pi(R^2 - r^2) = 3\pi x^2$.

The volume is $\displaystyle\int_0^1 3\pi x^2 \, dx = 3\pi\left[\dfrac{1}{3}x^3\right]_0^1 = \pi.$

23.

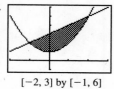

[−2, 3] by [−1, 6]

The curves intersect when $x^2 + 1 = x + 3$, which is when $x^2 - x - 2 = (x - 2)(x + 1) = 0$, i.e., when $x = -1$ or $x = 2$. Use washer cross sections: a washer has inner radius $r = x^2 + 1$, outer radius $R = x + 3$, and area

$$A(x) = \pi(R^2 - r^2)$$
$$= \pi[(x + 3)^2 - (x^2 + 1)^2]$$
$$= \pi(-x^4 - x^2 + 6x + 8). \text{ The volume is}$$

$$\int_{-1}^{2} \pi(-x^4 - x^2 + 6x + 8)\, dx$$

$$= \pi\left[-\frac{1}{5}x^5 - \frac{1}{3}x^3 + 3x^2 + 8x\right]_{-1}^{2}$$

$$= \pi\left[\left(-\frac{32}{5} - \frac{8}{3} + 12 + 16\right) - \left(\frac{1}{5} + \frac{1}{3} + 3 - 8\right)\right] = \frac{117\pi}{5}.$$

24.

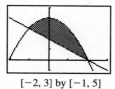

[−2, 3] by [−1, 5]

The curves intersect when $4 - x^2 = 2 - x$, which is when $x^2 - x - 2 = (x - 2)(x + 1) = 0$, i.e., when $x = -1$ or $x = 2$. Use washer cross sections: a washer has inner radius $r = 2 - x$, outer radius $R = 4 - x^2$, and area

$$A(x) = \pi(R^2 - r^2)$$
$$= \pi[(4 - x^2)^2 - (2 - x)^2]$$
$$= \pi(12 + 4x - 9x^2 + x^4).$$

The volume is

$$\int_{-1}^{2} \pi(12 + 4x - 9x^2 + x^4)\, dx$$

$$= \pi\left[12x + 2x^2 - 3x^3 + \frac{1}{5}x^5\right]_{-1}^{2}$$

$$= \pi\left[\left(24 + 8 - 24 + \frac{32}{5}\right) - \left(-12 + 2 + 3 - \frac{1}{5}\right)\right] = \frac{108\pi}{5}.$$

25.

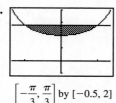

$\left[-\dfrac{\pi}{3}, \dfrac{\pi}{3}\right]$ by [−0.5, 2]

Use washer cross sections: a washer has inner radius $r = \sec x$, outer radius $R = \sqrt{2}$, and area
$A(x) = \pi(R^2 - r^2) = \pi(2 - \sec^2 x).$

The volume is

$$\int_{-\pi/4}^{\pi/4} \pi(2 - \sec^2 x)\, dx = \pi\left[2x - \tan x\right]_{-\pi/4}^{\pi/4}$$

$$= \pi\left[\left(\frac{\pi}{2} - 1\right) - \left(-\frac{\pi}{2} + 1\right)\right]$$

$$= \pi^2 - 2\pi.$$

26.

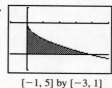

[−1, 5] by [−3, 1]

The curves intersect where $-\sqrt{x} = -2$, which is where $x = 4$. Use washer cross sections: a washer has inner radius $r = \sqrt{x}$, outer radius $R = 2$, and area
$A(x) = \pi(R^2 - r^2) = \pi(4 - x).$

The volume is $\displaystyle\int_0^4 \pi(4 - x)\, dx = \pi\left[4x - \frac{1}{2}x^2\right]_0^4 = 8\pi$

27.

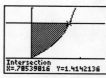

Intersection
X=.78539816   Y=1.4142136

[−0.5, 1.5] by [−0.5, 2]

The curves intersect at $x \approx 0.7854$. A cross section has

radius $r = \sqrt{2} - \sec x \tan x$ and area

$A(x) = \pi r^2 = \pi(\sqrt{2} - \sec x \tan x)^2.$ Use NINT to find

$\displaystyle\int_0^{0.7854} \pi(\sqrt{2} - \sec x \tan x)^2\, dx \approx 2.301.$

28.

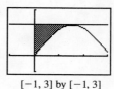

[−1, 3] by [−1, 3]

The curve and horizontal line intersect at $x = \dfrac{\pi}{2}$. A cross

section has radius $2 - 2\sin x$ and area

$A(x) = \pi r^2 = 4\pi(1 - \sin x)^2 = 4\pi(1 - 2\sin x + \sin^2 x).$

The volume is

$$\int_0^{\pi/2} 4\pi(1 - 2\sin x + \sin^2 x)\, dx$$

$$= 4\pi\left[\frac{3}{2}x + 2\cos x - \frac{1}{4}\sin 2x\right]_0^{\pi/2}$$

$$= 4\pi\left(\frac{3\pi}{4} - 2\right) = \pi(3\pi - 8)$$

29.

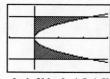

[−1, 3] by [−1.5, 1.5]

A cross section has radius $r = \sqrt{5}y^2$ and area

$A(y) = \pi r^2 = 5\pi y^4.$

The volume is $\displaystyle\int_{-1}^{1} 5\pi y^4\, dy = \pi\left[y^5\right]_{-1}^{1} = 2\pi.$

30.

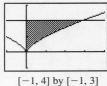

[−1, 4] by [−1, 3]

A cross section has radius $r = y^{3/2}$ and area

$A(y) = \pi r^2 = \pi y^3$. The volume is

$\int_0^2 \pi y^3 \, dy = \pi \left[\frac{1}{4}y^4\right]_0^2 = 4\pi.$

31.

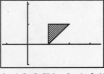

[−1.2, 3.5] by [−1, 2.1]

Use washer cross sections. A washer has inner radius $r = 1$,

outer radius $R = y + 1$, and area

$A(y) = \pi(R^2 - r^2) = \pi[(y + 1)^2 - 1] = \pi(y^2 + 2y)$. The

volume is $\int_0^1 \pi(y^2 + 2y) \, dy = \pi\left[\frac{1}{3}y^3 + y^2\right]_0^1 = \frac{4}{3}\pi.$

32.

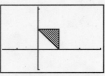

[−1.7, 3] by [−1, 2.1]

Use cylindrical shells: a shell has radius x and height x. The

volume is $\int_0^1 2\pi(x)(x) \, dx = 2\pi\left[\frac{1}{3}x^3\right]_0^1 = \frac{2}{3}\pi.$

33.

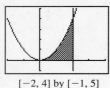

[−2, 4] by [−1, 5]

Use cylindrical shells: A shell has radius x and height x^2.

The volume is $\int_0^2 2\pi(x)(x^2) \, dx = 2\pi\left[\frac{1}{4}x^4\right]_0^2 = 8\pi.$

34.

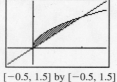

[−0.5, 1.5] by [−0.5, 1.5]

The curves intersect at $x = 0$ and $x = 1$. Use cylindrical

shells: a shell has radius x and height $\sqrt{x} - x$. The volume

is $\int_0^1 2\pi(x)(\sqrt{x} - x) \, dx = 2\pi\left[\frac{2}{5}x^{5/2} - \frac{1}{3}x^3\right]_0^1 = \frac{2\pi}{15}.$

35.

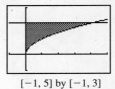

[−1, 5] by [−1, 3]

The curved and horizontal line intersect at (4, 2).

(a) Use washer cross sections: a washer has inner radius

$r = \sqrt{x}$, outer radius $R = 2$, and area

$A(x) = \pi(R^2 - r^2) = \pi(4 - x)$. The volume is

$\int_0^4 \pi(4 - x) \, dx = \pi\left[4x - \frac{1}{2}x^2\right]_0^4 = 8\pi$

(b) A cross section has radius $r = y^2$ and area

$A(y) = \pi r^2 = \pi y^4$.

The volume is $\int_0^2 \pi y^4 \, dy = \pi\left[\frac{1}{5}y^5\right]_0^2 = \frac{32\pi}{5}.$

(c) A cross section has radius $r = 2 - \sqrt{x}$ and area

$A(x) = \pi r^2 = \pi(2 - \sqrt{x})^2 = \pi(4 - 4\sqrt{x} + x).$

The volume is

$\int_0^4 \pi(4 - 4\sqrt{x} + x) \, dx = \pi\left[4x - \frac{8}{3}x^{3/2} + \frac{1}{2}x^2\right]_0^4 = \frac{8\pi}{3}.$

(d) Use washer cross sections: a washer has inner radius

$r = 4 - y^2$, outer radius $R = 4$, and area

$A(y) = \pi(R^2 - r^2) = \pi[16 - (4 - y^2)^2]$

$= \pi(8y^2 - y^4).$

The volume is

$\int_0^2 \pi(8y^2 - y^4) \, dy = \pi\left[\frac{8}{3}y^3 - \frac{1}{5}y^5\right]_0^2 = \frac{224\pi}{15}$

36.

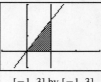

[−1, 3] by [−1, 3]

The slanted and vertical lines intersect at (1, 2)

(a) The solid is a right circular cone of radius 1 and

height 2. The volume is

$\frac{1}{3}Bh = \frac{1}{3}(\pi r^2)h = \frac{1}{3}(\pi 1^2)2 = \frac{2}{3}\pi.$

(b) Use cylindrical shells: a shell has radius $2 - x$ and

height $2x$. The volume is

$\int_0^1 2\pi(2 - x)(2x) \, dx = 4\pi\int_0^1 (2x - x^2) \, dx$

$= 4\pi\left[x^2 - \frac{1}{3}x^3\right]_0^1 = \frac{8\pi}{3}.$

37.

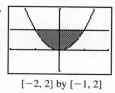

[−2, 2] by [−1, 2]

The curves intersect at $(\pm 1, 1)$.

(a) A cross section has radius $r = 1 - x^2$ and area

$$A(x) = \pi r^2 = \pi(1 - x^2)^2 = \pi(1 - 2x^2 + x^4).$$

The volume is

$$\int_{-1}^{1} \pi(1 - 2x^2 + x^4)\, dx = \pi\left[x - \frac{2}{3}x^3 + \frac{1}{5}x^5\right]_{-1}^{1} = \frac{16\pi}{15}.$$

(b) Use cylindrical shells: a shell has radius $2 - y$ and height $2\sqrt{y}$. The volume is

$$\int_{0}^{1} 2\pi(2 - y)(2\sqrt{y})\, dy = 4\pi\int_{0}^{1}(2\sqrt{y} - y^{3/2})\, dy$$

$$= 4\pi\left[\frac{4}{3}y^{3/2} - \frac{2}{5}y^{5/2}\right]_{0}^{1} = \frac{56\pi}{15}.$$

(c) Use cylindrical shells: a shell has radius $y + 1$ and height $2\sqrt{y}$. The volume is

$$\int_{0}^{1} 2\pi(y + 1)(2\sqrt{y})\, dy = 4\pi\int_{0}^{1}(y^{3/2} + \sqrt{y})\, dy$$

$$= 4\pi\left[\frac{2}{5}y^{5/2} + \frac{2}{3}y^{3/2}\right]_{0}^{1} = \frac{64\pi}{15}.$$

38. (a) A cross section has radius $r = h\left(1 - \frac{x}{b}\right)$ and area

$$A(x) = \pi r^2 = \pi h^2\left(1 - \frac{x}{b}\right)^2. \text{ The volume is}$$

$$\int_{0}^{b} \pi h^2\left(1 - \frac{x}{b}\right)^2 dx = \pi h^2\left[-\frac{b}{3}\left(1 - \frac{x}{b}\right)^3\right]_{0}^{b} = \frac{\pi}{3}bh^2.$$

(b) Use cylindrical shells: a shell has radius x and height $h\left(1 - \frac{x}{b}\right)$. The volume is

$$\int_{0}^{b} 2\pi(x)h\left(1 - \frac{x}{b}\right) dx = 2\pi h\int_{0}^{b}\left(x - \frac{x^2}{b}\right) dx$$

$$= 2\pi h\left[\frac{1}{2}x^2 - \frac{x^3}{3b}\right]_{0}^{b} = \frac{\pi}{3}b^2 h.$$

39.

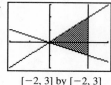

[−2, 3] by [−2, 3]

A shell has radius x and height $x - \left(-\frac{x}{2}\right) = \frac{3}{2}x$.

The volume is $\int_{0}^{2} 2\pi(x)\left(\frac{3}{2}x\right) dx = \pi\left[x^3\right]_{0}^{2} = 8\pi.$

40.

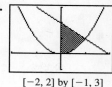

[−2, 2] by [−1, 3]

$x^2 = 2 - x$ at $x = 1$. A shell has radius x and height $2 - x - x^2$. The volume is

$$\int_{0}^{1} 2\pi(x)(2 - x - x^2)\, dx = 2\pi\left[x^2 - \frac{1}{3}x^3 - \frac{1}{4}x^4\right]_{0}^{1} = \frac{5\pi}{6}.$$

41.

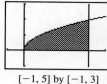

[−1, 5] by [−1, 3]

A shell has radius x and height $\sqrt{x}$. The volume is

$$\int_{0}^{4} 2\pi(x)(\sqrt{x})\, dx = 2\pi\left[\frac{2}{5}x^{5/2}\right]_{0}^{4} = \frac{128\pi}{5}.$$

42.

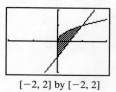

[−2, 2] by [−2, 2]

The functions intersect where $2x - 1 = \sqrt{x}$, i.e., at $x = 1$.

A shell has radius x and height

$\sqrt{x} - (2x - 1) = \sqrt{x} - 2x + 1$. The volume is

$$\int_{0}^{1} 2\pi(x)(\sqrt{x} - 2x + 1)\, dx = 2\pi\int_{0}^{1}(x^{3/2} - 2x^2 + x)\, dx$$

$$= 2\pi\left[\frac{2}{5}x^{5/2} - \frac{2}{3}x^3 + \frac{1}{2}x^2\right]_{0}^{1}$$

$$= \frac{7\pi}{15}.$$

43. A shell has height $12(y^2 - y^3)$.

(a) A shell has radius y. The volume is

$$\int_{0}^{1} 2\pi(y)12(y^2 - y^3)\, dy = 24\pi\int_{0}^{1}(y^3 - y^4)\, dy$$

$$= 24\pi\left[\frac{1}{4}y^4 - \frac{1}{5}y^5\right]_{0}^{1} = \frac{6\pi}{5}.$$

(b) A shell has radius $1 - y$. The volume is

$$\int_{0}^{1} 2\pi(1 - y)12(y^2 - y^3)\, dy$$

$$= 24\pi\int_{0}^{1}(y^4 - 2y^3 + y^2)\, dy$$

$$= 24\pi\left[\frac{1}{5}y^5 - \frac{1}{2}y^4 + \frac{1}{3}y^3\right]_{0}^{1} = \frac{4\pi}{5}.$$

43. continued

(c) A shell has radius $\dfrac{8}{5} - y$. The volume is

$$\int_0^1 2\pi\left(\frac{8}{5} - y\right)12(y^2 - y^3)\,dy$$

$$= 24\pi\int_0^1\left(y^4 - \frac{13}{5}y^3 + \frac{8}{5}y^2\right)dy$$

$$= 24\pi\left[\frac{1}{5}y^5 - \frac{13}{20}y^4 + \frac{8}{15}y^3\right]_0^1 = 2\pi.$$

(d) A shell has radius $y + \dfrac{2}{5}$. The volume is

$$\int_0^1 2\pi\left(y + \frac{2}{5}\right)12(y^2 - y^3)\,dy$$

$$= 24\pi\int_0^1\left(-y^4 + \frac{3}{5}y^3 + \frac{2}{5}y^2\right)dx$$

$$= 24\pi\left[-\frac{1}{5}y^5 + \frac{3}{20}y^4 + \frac{2}{15}y^3\right]_0^1 = 2\pi.$$

44. A shell has height $\dfrac{y^2}{2} - \left(\dfrac{y^4}{4} - \dfrac{y^2}{2}\right) = y^2 - \dfrac{y^4}{4}$.

(a) A shell has radius y. The volume is

$$\int_0^2 2\pi(y)\left(y^2 - \frac{y^4}{4}\right)dy = 2\pi\left[\frac{1}{4}y^4 - \frac{1}{24}y^6\right]_0^2 = \frac{8\pi}{3}.$$

(b) A shell has radius $2 - y$. The volume is

$$\int_0^2 2\pi(2 - y)\left(y^2 - \frac{y^4}{4}\right)dy$$

$$= 2\pi\int_0^2\left(\frac{y^5}{4} - \frac{y^4}{2} - y^3 + 2y^2\right)dy$$

$$= 2\pi\left[\frac{1}{24}y^6 - \frac{1}{10}y^5 - \frac{1}{4}y^4 + \frac{2}{3}y^3\right]_0^2 = \frac{8\pi}{5}.$$

(c) A shell has radius $5 - y$. The volume is

$$\int_0^2 2\pi(5 - y)\left(y^2 - \frac{y^4}{4}\right)dy$$

$$= 2\pi\int_0^2\left(\frac{y^5}{4} - \frac{5y^4}{4} - y^3 + 5y^2\right)dy$$

$$= 2\pi\left[\frac{1}{24}y^6 - \frac{1}{4}y^5 - \frac{1}{4}y^4 + \frac{5}{3}y^3\right]_0^2 = 8\pi.$$

(d) A shell has radius $y + \dfrac{5}{8}$. The volume is

$$\int_0^2 2\pi\left(y + \frac{5}{8}\right)\left(y^2 - \frac{y^4}{4}\right)dy$$

$$= 2\pi\int_0^2\left(-\frac{y^5}{4} - \frac{5y^4}{32} + y^3 + \frac{5y^2}{8}\right)dy$$

$$= 2\pi\left[-\frac{1}{24}y^6 - \frac{1}{32}y^5 + \frac{1}{4}y^4 + \frac{5}{24}y^3\right]_0^2 = 4\pi.$$

45.

[−1, 3] by [−1.4, 9.1]

The functions intersect at (2, 8).

(a) Use washer cross sections: a washer has inner radius $r = x^3$, outer radius $R = 4x$, and area

$A(x) = \pi(R^2 - r^2) = \pi(16x^2 - x^6)$. The volume is

$$\int_0^2 \pi(16x^2 - x^6)\,dx = \pi\left[\frac{16}{3}x^3 - \frac{1}{7}x^7\right]_0^2 = \frac{512\pi}{21}.$$

(b) Use cylindrical shells: a shell has a radius $8 - y$ and height $y^{1/3} - \dfrac{y}{4}$. The volume is

$$\int_0^8 2\pi(8 - y)\left(y^{1/3} - \frac{y}{4}\right)dy$$

$$= 2\pi\int_0^8\left(8y^{1/3} - 2y - y^{4/3} + \frac{y^2}{4}\right)dy$$

$$= 2\pi\left[6y^{4/3} - y^2 - \frac{3}{7}y^{7/3} + \frac{1}{12}y^3\right]_0^8 = \frac{832\pi}{21}.$$

46.

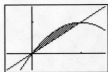

[−0.5, 1.5] by [−0.5, 1.5]

The functions intersect at (0, 0) and (1, 1).

(a) Use cylindrical shells: a shell has radius x and height $2x - x^2 - x = x - x^2$. The volume is

$$\int_0^1 2\pi(x)(x - x^2)\,dx = 2\pi\left[\frac{1}{3}x^3 - \frac{1}{4}x^4\right]_0^1 = \frac{\pi}{6}.$$

(b) Use cylindrical shells: a shell has radius $1 - x$ and height $2x - x^2 - x = x - x^2$. The volume is

$$\int_0^1 2\pi(1 - x)(x - x^2)\,dx = 2\pi\int_0^1 (x^3 - 2x^2 + x)\,dx$$

$$= 2\pi\left[\frac{1}{4}x^4 - \frac{2}{3}x^3 + \frac{1}{2}x^2\right]_0^1$$

$$= \frac{\pi}{6}.$$

47.

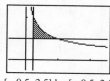

[−0.5, 2.5] by [−0.5, 2.5]

The intersection points are $\left(\frac{1}{4}, 1\right)$, $\left(\frac{1}{4}, 2\right)$, and $(1, 1)$.

(a) A washer has inner radius $r = \frac{1}{4}$, outer radius $R = \frac{1}{y^2}$,

and area $\pi(R^2 - r^2) = \pi\left(\frac{1}{y^4} - \frac{1}{16}\right)$. The volume is

$$\int_1^2 \pi\left(\frac{1}{y^4} - \frac{1}{16}\right) dy = \pi\left[-\frac{1}{3y^3} - \frac{1}{16}y\right]_1^2 = \frac{11\pi}{48}.$$

(b) A shell has radius x and height $\frac{1}{\sqrt{x}} - 1$. The volume is

$$\int_{1/4}^1 2\pi(x)\left(\frac{1}{\sqrt{x}} - 1\right) dx = 2\pi\left[\frac{2}{3}x^{3/2} - \frac{1}{2}x^2\right]_{1/4}^1 = \frac{11\pi}{48}.$$

48. (a) For $0 < x \le \pi$, $xf(x) = \frac{x(\sin x)}{x} = \sin x$.

For $x = 0$, $xf(x) = 0 \cdot 1 = \sin 0 = \sin x$. So

$xf(x) = \sin x$ for $0 \le x \le \pi$.

(b) Use cylindrical shells: a shell has radius x and height y.

The volume is $\int_0^\pi 2\pi xy\, dx$, which from part (a) is

$$\int_0^\pi 2\pi \sin x\, dx = 2\pi\left[-\cos x\right]_0^\pi = 4\pi.$$

49. (a) A cross section has radius $r = \frac{x}{12}\sqrt{36 - x^2}$ and area

$A(x) = \pi r^2 = \frac{\pi}{144}(36x^2 - x^4)$. The volume is

$$\int_0^6 \frac{\pi}{144}(36x^2 - x^4)\, dx = \frac{\pi}{144}\left[12x^3 - \frac{1}{5}x^5\right]_0^6 = \frac{36\pi}{5}\text{ cm}^3.$$

(b) $\left(\frac{36\pi}{5}\text{ cm}^3\right)(8.5\text{ g/cm}^3) \approx 192.3\text{ g}$

50. A cross section has radius $r = |c - \sin x|$ and area

$A(x) = \pi r^2 = \pi(c - \sin x)^2 = \pi(c^2 - 2c\sin x + \sin^2 x)$.

The volume is

$$\int_0^\pi \pi(c^2 - 2c\sin x + \sin^2 x)\, dx$$

$$= \pi\left[c^2 x + 2c\cos x + \frac{1}{2}x - \frac{1}{4}\sin 2x\right]_0^\pi$$

$$= \pi\left[\left(c^2\pi - 2c + \frac{1}{2}\pi\right) - 2c\right]$$

$$= \pi^2 c^2 - 4\pi c + \frac{\pi^2}{2}.$$

(a) Solve

$$\frac{d}{dc}\left[\pi^2 c^2 - 4\pi c + \frac{\pi^2}{2}\right] = 0$$

$$2\pi^2 c - 4\pi = 0$$

$$\pi c - 2 = 0$$

$$c = \frac{2}{\pi}$$

This value of c gives a minimum for V because

$\frac{d^2 V}{dc^2} = 2\pi^2 > 0$.

Then the volume is $\pi^2\left(\frac{2}{\pi}\right)^2 - 4\pi\left(\frac{2}{\pi}\right) + \frac{\pi^2}{2} = \frac{\pi^2}{2} - 4$

(b) Since the derivative with respect to c is not zero

anywhere else besides $c = \frac{2}{\pi}$, the maximum must occur

at $c = 0$ or $c = 1$. The volume for $c = 0$ is $\frac{\pi^2}{2} \approx 4.935$,

and for $c = 1$ it is $\frac{\pi(3\pi - 8)}{2} \approx 2.238$. $c = 0$

maximizes the volume.

(c)

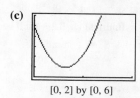

[0, 2] by [0, 6]

The volume gets large without limit. This makes sense, since the curve is sweeping out space in an ever-increasing radius.

51. (a) Using $d = \frac{C}{\pi}$, and $A = \pi\left(\frac{d}{2}\right)^2 = \frac{C^2}{4\pi}$ yields the

following areas (in square inches, rounded to the

nearest tenth): 2.3, 1.6, 1.5, 2.1, 3.2, 4.8, 7.0, 9.3, 10.7,

10.7, 9.3, 6.4, 3.2.

(b) If $C(y)$ is the circumference as a function of y, then the

area of a cross section is

$$A(y) = \pi\left(\frac{C(y)/\pi}{2}\right)^2 = \frac{(C(y))^2}{4\pi},$$

and the volume is $\frac{1}{4\pi}\int_0^6 (C(y))^2\, dy$.

(c) $\frac{1}{4\pi}\int_0^6 A(y)\, dy = \frac{1}{4\pi}\int_0^6 (C(y))^2\, dy$

$$\approx \frac{1}{4\pi}\left(\frac{6 - 0}{24}\right)[5.4^2 + 2(4.5^2 + 4.4^2]$$

$$+ 5.1^2 + 6.3^2 + 7.8^2 + 9.4^2 + 10.8^2 + 11.6^2$$

$$+ 11.6^2 + 10.8^2 + 9.0^2) + 6.3^2] \approx 34.7\text{ in.}^3$$

52. (a) A cross section has radius $r = \sqrt{2y}$ and area

$\pi r^2 = 2\pi y$. The volume is $\int_0^5 2\pi y \, dy = \pi\left[y^2\right]_0^5 = 25\pi$.

(b) $V(h) = \int A(h) \, dh$, so $\dfrac{dV}{dh} = A(h)$.

$\therefore \dfrac{dV}{dt} = \dfrac{dV}{dh} \cdot \dfrac{dh}{dt} = A(h) \cdot \dfrac{dh}{dt}$,

so $\dfrac{dh}{dt} = \dfrac{1}{A(h)} \cdot \dfrac{dV}{dt}$

For $h = 4$, the area is $2\pi(4) = 8\pi$,

so $\dfrac{dh}{dt} = \dfrac{1}{8\pi} \cdot 3 \dfrac{\text{units}^3}{\text{sec}} = \dfrac{3}{8\pi} \cdot \dfrac{\text{units}^3}{\text{sec}}$.

53. (a)

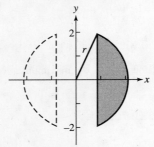

The remaining solid is that swept out by the shaded region in revolution. Use cylindrical shells: a shell has radius x and height $2\sqrt{r^2 - x^2}$. The volume is

$\int_{\sqrt{r^2 - 2^2}}^{r} 2\pi(x)(2\sqrt{r^2 - x^2}) \, dx$

$= 2\pi\left[-\dfrac{2}{3}(r^2 - x^2)^{3/2}\right]_{\sqrt{r^2 - 4}}^{r}$

$= -\dfrac{4}{3}\pi(-8) = \dfrac{32\pi}{3}$.

(b) The answer is independent of r.

54. Partition the appropriate interval in the axis of revolution and measure the radius $r(x)$ of the shadow region at these points. Then use an approximation such as the trapezoidal rule to estimate the integral $\int_a^b \pi r^2(x) \, dx$.

55. Solve $ax - x^2 = 0$: This is true at $x = 0$ and $x = a$. For revolution about the x-axis, a cross section has radius

$r = ax - x^2$ and area

$A(x) = \pi r^2 = \pi(ax - x^2)^2 = \pi(a^2x^2 - 2ax^3 + x^4)$.

The volume is

$\int_0^a \pi(a^2x^2 - 2ax^3 + x^4) \, dx = \pi\left[\dfrac{1}{3}a^2x^3 - \dfrac{1}{2}ax^4 + \dfrac{1}{5}x^5\right]_0^a$

$= \dfrac{1}{30}\pi a^5$.

For revolution about the y-axis, a cylindrical shell has

radius x and height $ax - x^2$. The volume is

$\int_0^a 2\pi(x)(ax - x^2) \, dx = 2\pi\left[\dfrac{1}{3}ax^3 - \dfrac{1}{4}x^4\right]_0^a = \dfrac{1}{6}\pi a^4$.

Setting the two volumes equal,

$\dfrac{1}{30}\pi a^5 = \dfrac{1}{6}\pi a^4$ yields $\dfrac{1}{30}a = \dfrac{1}{6}$, so $a = 5$.

56. The slant height Δs of a tiny horizontal slice can be written as $\Delta s = \sqrt{\Delta x^2 + \Delta y^2} = \sqrt{1 + (g'(y))^2}\Delta y$. So the surface area is approximated by the Riemann sum $\sum_{k=1}^{n} 2\pi g(y_k)\sqrt{1 + (g'(y))^2} \, \Delta y$. The limit of that is the integral.

57. $g'(y) = \dfrac{dx}{dy} = \dfrac{1}{2\sqrt{y}}$, and

$\int_0^2 2\pi\sqrt{y}\sqrt{1 + \left(\dfrac{1}{2\sqrt{y}}\right)^2} \, dy = \int_0^2 \pi\sqrt{4y + 1} \, dy$

$= \left[\dfrac{\pi}{6}(4y + 1)^{3/2}\right]_0^2$

$= \dfrac{13\pi}{3} \approx 13.614$

58. $g'(y) = \dfrac{dx}{dy} = y^2$, and

$\int_0^1 2\pi\left(\dfrac{y^3}{3}\right)\sqrt{1 + (y^2)^2} \, dy = \dfrac{2}{3}\pi\left[\dfrac{1}{6}(1 + y^4)^{3/2}\right]_0^1$

$= \dfrac{\pi}{9}(2\sqrt{2} - 1) \approx 0.638$.

59. $g'(y) = \dfrac{dx}{dy} = \dfrac{1}{2}y^{-1/2}$, and

$\int_1^3 2\pi\left[y^{1/2} - \left(\dfrac{1}{3}\right)^{3/2}\right]\sqrt{1 + \left[\dfrac{1}{2}y^{-1/2}\right]^2} \, dy$

$= 2\pi\int_1^3 \left[y^{1/2} - \left(\dfrac{1}{3}\right)^{3/2}\right]\sqrt{1 + \dfrac{1}{4y}} \, dy$.

Using NINT, this evaluates to ≈ 16.110

60. $g'(y) = \dfrac{dx}{dy} = \dfrac{1}{\sqrt{2y-1}}$, and

$$\int_{5/8}^{1} 2\pi\sqrt{2y-1}\sqrt{1 + \left(\dfrac{1}{\sqrt{2y-1}}\right)^2}\,dy$$

$$= 2\pi\int_{5/8}^{1}\sqrt{2y}\,dy$$

$$= 2\sqrt{2}\pi\left[\dfrac{2}{3}y^{3/2}\right]_{5/8}^{1}$$

$$= \dfrac{4\sqrt{2}}{3}\pi\left(1 - \dfrac{5}{16}\sqrt{\dfrac{5}{2}}\right) \approx 2.997.$$

61. $f'(x) = \dfrac{dy}{dx} = 2x$, and

$$\int_{0}^{2} 2\pi x^2\sqrt{1 + (2x)^2}\,dx = \int_{0}^{2} 2\pi x^2\sqrt{1 + 4x^2}\,dx \text{ evaluates,}$$

using NINT, to ≈ 53.226.

62. $f'(x) = \dfrac{dy}{dx} = 3 - 2x$, and

$$\int_{0}^{3} 2\pi(3x - x^2)\sqrt{1 + (3 - 2x)^2}\,dx \text{ evaluates, using NINT,}$$

to ≈ 44.877.

63. $f'(x) = \dfrac{dy}{dx} = \dfrac{1-x}{\sqrt{2x-x^2}}$, and

$$\int_{0.5}^{1.5} 2\pi\sqrt{2x-x^2}\sqrt{1 + \left(\dfrac{1-x}{\sqrt{2x-x^2}}\right)^2}\,dx = 2\pi\int_{0.5}^{1.5} 1\,dx$$

$$= 2\pi\left[x\right]_{0.5}^{1.5}$$

$$= 2\pi \approx 6.283$$

64. $f'(x) = \dfrac{dy}{dx} = \dfrac{1}{2\sqrt{x+1}}$, and

$$\int_{1}^{5} 2\pi\sqrt{x+1}\sqrt{1 + \left(\dfrac{1}{2\sqrt{x+1}}\right)^2}\,dx$$

$$= 2\pi\int_{1}^{5}\sqrt{x + \dfrac{5}{4}}\,dx$$

$$= 2\pi\left[\dfrac{2}{3}\left(x + \dfrac{5}{4}\right)^{3/2}\right]_{1}^{5}$$

$$= \dfrac{4\pi}{3}\left[\left(\dfrac{25}{4}\right)^{3/2} - \left(\dfrac{9}{4}\right)^{3/2}\right] = \dfrac{49\pi}{3} \approx 51.313$$

65. Hemisphere cross sectional area: $\pi(\sqrt{R^2 - h^2})^2 = A_1$.

Right circular cylinder with cone removed cross sectional

area: $\pi R^2 - \pi h^2 = A_2$

Since $A_1 = A_2$, the two volumes are equal by Cavalieri's

theorem. Thus, volume of hemisphere

= volume of cylinder − volume of cone

$= \pi R^3 - \dfrac{1}{3}\pi R^3 = \dfrac{2}{3}\pi R^3.$

66. Use washer cross sections: a washer has inner radius

$r = b - \sqrt{a^2 - y^2}$, outer radius $R = b + \sqrt{a^2 - y^2}$, and

area $\pi(R^2 - r^2)$

$$= \pi[(b + \sqrt{a^2 - y^2})^2 - (b - \sqrt{a^2 - y^2})^2]$$

$$= 4\pi b\sqrt{a^2 - y^2}. \text{ The volume is}$$

$$\int_{-a}^{a} 4\pi b\sqrt{a^2 - y^2}\,dy = 4\pi b\int_{-a}^{a}\sqrt{a^2 - y^2}\,dy$$

$$= 4\pi b\left(\dfrac{\pi a^2}{2}\right)$$

$$= 2\pi^2 a^2 b$$

67. (a) Put the bottom of the bowl at $(0, -a)$. The area of a

horizontal cross section is $\pi(\sqrt{a^2 - y^2})^2 = \pi(a^2 - y^2)$.

The volume for height h is

$$\int_{-a}^{h-a} \pi(a^2 - y^2)\,dy = \pi\left[a^2 y - \dfrac{1}{3}y^3\right]_{-a}^{h-a} = \dfrac{\pi h^2(3a - h)}{3}.$$

(b) For $h = 4$, $y = -1$ and the area of a cross section is

$\pi(5^2 - 1^2) = 24\pi$. The rate of rise is

$$\dfrac{dh}{dt} = \dfrac{1}{A}\dfrac{dV}{dt} = \dfrac{1}{24\pi}(0.2) = \dfrac{1}{120\pi}\text{ m/sec.}$$

68. (a) A cross section has radius $r = \sqrt{a^2 - x^2}$ and area

$A(x) = \pi r^2 = \pi(\sqrt{a^2 - x^2})^2 = \pi(a^2 - x^2)$. The

volume is

$$\int_{-a}^{a} \pi(a^2 - x^2)\,dx = \pi\left[a^2 x - \dfrac{1}{3}x^3\right]_{-a}^{a}$$

$$= \pi\left[\left(a^3 - \dfrac{1}{3}a^3\right) - \left(-a^3 + \dfrac{1}{3}a^3\right)\right]$$

$$= \dfrac{4}{3}\pi a^3.$$

(b) A cross section has radius $x = r\left(1 - \dfrac{y}{h}\right)$ and area

$A(y) = \pi x^2 = \pi r^2\left(1 - \dfrac{y}{h}\right)^2 = \pi r^2\left(1 - \dfrac{2y}{h} + \dfrac{y^2}{h^2}\right)$. The

volume is

$$\int_{0}^{h} \pi r^2\left(1 - \dfrac{2y}{h} + \dfrac{y^2}{h^2}\right)dy = \pi r^2\left[y - \dfrac{y^2}{h} + \dfrac{y^3}{3h^2}\right]_{0}^{h}$$

$$= \dfrac{1}{3}\pi r^2 h.$$

■ Section 7.4 Lengths of Curves

(pp. 395–401)

Quick Review 7.4

1. $\sqrt{1 + 2x + x^2} = \sqrt{(1 + x)^2}$, which, since $x \geq -1$, equals $1 + x$ or $x + 1$.

2. $\sqrt{1 - x + \dfrac{x^2}{4}} = \sqrt{\left(1 - \dfrac{x}{2}\right)^2}$, which, since $x \leq 2$, equals $1 - \dfrac{x}{2}$ or $\dfrac{2 - x}{2}$.

3. $\sqrt{1 + (\tan x)^2} = \sqrt{(\sec x)^2}$, which, since $0 \leq x < \dfrac{\pi}{2}$, equals $\sec x$.

4. $\sqrt{1 + \left(\dfrac{x}{4} - \dfrac{1}{x}\right)^2} = \sqrt{\dfrac{1}{2} + \dfrac{1}{16}x^2 + \dfrac{1}{x^2}} = \dfrac{1}{4}\sqrt{\dfrac{(x^2 + 4)^2}{x^2}}$ which, since $x > 0$, equals $\dfrac{x^2 + 4}{4x}$.

5. $\sqrt{1 + \cos 2x} = \sqrt{2\cos^2 x}$, which, since $-\dfrac{\pi}{2} \leq x \leq \dfrac{\pi}{2}$, equals $\sqrt{2}\cos x$.

6. $f(x)$ has a corner at $x = 4$.

7. $\dfrac{d}{dx}(5x^{2/3}) = \dfrac{10}{3\sqrt[3]{x}}$ is undefined at $x = 0$. $f(x)$ has a cusp there.

8. $\dfrac{d}{dx}(\sqrt[5]{x+3}) = \dfrac{1}{5(x+3)^{4/5}}$ is undefined for $x = -3$. $f(x)$ has a vertical tangent there.

9. $\sqrt{x^2 - 4x + 4} = |x - 2|$ has a corner at $x = 2$.

10. $\dfrac{d}{dx}\left(1 + \sqrt[3]{\sin x}\right) = \dfrac{\cos x}{3(\sin x)^{2/3}}$ is undefined for $x = k\pi$, where k is any integer. $f(x)$ has vertical tangents at these values of x.

Section 7.4 Exercises

1. **(a)** $y' = 2x$, so
   $$\text{Length} = \int_{-1}^{2} \sqrt{1 + (2x)^2}\, dx = \int_{-1}^{2} \sqrt{1 + 4x^2}\, dx.$$
   (b)
   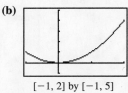
   $[-1, 2]$ by $[-1, 5]$
   (c) Length ≈ 6.126

2. **(a)** $y' = \sec^2 x$, so Length $= \displaystyle\int_{-\pi/3}^{0} \sqrt{1 + \sec^4 x}\, dx.$
   (b)
   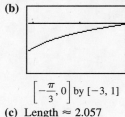
   $\left[-\dfrac{\pi}{3}, 0\right]$ by $[-3, 1]$
   (c) Length ≈ 2.057

3. **(a)** $x' = \cos y$, so Length $= \displaystyle\int_{0}^{\pi} \sqrt{1 + \cos^2 y}\, dy.$
   (b)
   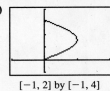
   $[-1, 2]$ by $[-1, 4]$
   (c) Length ≈ 3.820

4. **(a)** $x' = -y(1 - y^2)^{-1/2}$, so
   $$\text{Length} = \int_{-1/2}^{1/2} \sqrt{1 + \dfrac{y^2}{1 - y^2}}\, dy.$$
   (b)
   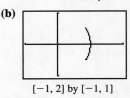
   $[-1, 2]$ by $[-1, 1]$
   (c) Length ≈ 1.047

5. **(a)** $y^2 + 2y = 2x + 1$, so
   $$y^2 + 2y + 1 = (y + 1)^2 = 2x + 2, \text{ and}$$
   $$y = \sqrt{2x + 2} - 1. \text{ Then } y' = \dfrac{1}{\sqrt{2x + 2}}, \text{ and}$$
   $$\text{Length} = \int_{-1}^{7} \sqrt{1 + \dfrac{1}{2x + 2}}\, dx.$$
   (b)
   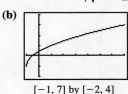
   $[-1, 7]$ by $[-2, 4]$
   (c) Length ≈ 9.294

6. **(a)** $y' = \cos x + x \sin x - \cos x = x \sin x$, so
   $$\text{Length} = \int_{0}^{\pi} \sqrt{1 + x^2 \sin^2 x}\, dx.$$
   (b)
   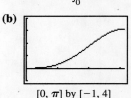
   $[0, \pi]$ by $[-1, 4]$
   (c) Length ≈ 4.698

7. **(a)** $y' = \tan x$, so Length $= \displaystyle\int_{0}^{\pi/6} \sqrt{1 + \tan^2 x}\, dx.$
   (b) $y = \displaystyle\int \tan x\, dx = \ln(|\sec x|)$
   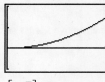
   $\left[0, \dfrac{\pi}{6}\right]$ by $[-0.1, 0.2]$
   (c) Length ≈ 0.549

8. (a) $x' = \sqrt{\sec^2 y - 1}$, so Length $= \int_{-\pi/3}^{\pi/4} \sec y \, dy$.

(b) $x' = \sqrt{\sec^2 y - 1} = |\tan y|$,

so $x = \begin{cases} \ln(\cos y) & -\dfrac{\pi}{3} \le y \le 0 \\ -\ln(\cos y) & 0 < y \le \dfrac{\pi}{4} \end{cases}$

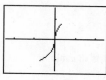

$[-2.4, 2.4]$ by $\left[-\dfrac{\pi}{2}, \dfrac{\pi}{2}\right]$

(c) Length ≈ 2.198

9. (a) $y' = \sec x \tan x$, so

Length $= \int_{-\pi/3}^{\pi/3} \sqrt{1 + \sec^2 x \tan^2 x} \, dx$.

(b)

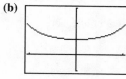

$\left[-\dfrac{\pi}{3}, \dfrac{\pi}{3}\right]$ by $[-1, 3]$

(c) Length ≈ 3.139

10. $y' = \dfrac{(e^x - e^{-x})}{2}$, so Length $= \int_{-3}^{3} \sqrt{1 + \left(\dfrac{e^x - e^{-x}}{2}\right)^2} \, dx$.

(b)

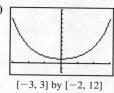

$[-3, 3]$ by $[-2, 12]$

(c) Length ≈ 20.036

11. $y' = \dfrac{1}{2}(x^2 + 2)^{1/2}(2x) = x\sqrt{x^2 + 2}$, so the length is

$\int_0^3 \sqrt{1 + (x\sqrt{x^2 + 2})^2} \, dx = \int_0^3 \sqrt{x^4 + 2x^2 + 1} \, dx$

$= \int_0^3 (x^2 + 1) \, dx = \left[\dfrac{1}{3}x^3 + x\right]_0^3 = 12$.

12. $y' = \dfrac{3}{2}\sqrt{x}$, so the length is

$\int_0^4 \sqrt{1 + \left(\dfrac{3}{2}\sqrt{x}\right)^2} \, dx = \int_0^4 \sqrt{1 + \dfrac{9x}{4}} \, dx$

$= \left[\dfrac{8}{27}\left(1 + \dfrac{9x}{4}\right)^{3/2}\right]_0^4$

$= \dfrac{80\sqrt{10} - 8}{27}$.

13. $x' = y^2 - \dfrac{1}{4y^2}$, so the length is $\int_1^3 \sqrt{1 + \left(y^2 - \dfrac{1}{4y^2}\right)^2} \, dy$

$= \int_1^3 \sqrt{\left(y^2 + \dfrac{1}{4y^2}\right)^2} \, dy = \left[\dfrac{1}{3}y^3 - \dfrac{1}{4y}\right]_1^3 = \dfrac{53}{6}$.

14. $x' = y^3 - \dfrac{1}{4y^3}$, so the length is

$\int_1^2 \sqrt{1 + \left(y^3 - \dfrac{1}{4y^3}\right)^2} \, dy = \int_1^2 \sqrt{\left(y^3 + \dfrac{1}{4y^3}\right)^2} \, dy$

$= \left[\dfrac{1}{4}y^4 - \dfrac{1}{8y^2}\right]_1^2$

$= \dfrac{123}{32}$.

15. $x' = \dfrac{y^2}{2} - \dfrac{1}{2y^2}$, so the length is

$\int_1^2 \sqrt{1 + \left(\dfrac{y^2}{2} - \dfrac{1}{2y^2}\right)^2} \, dy = \int_1^2 \sqrt{\left(\dfrac{y^2}{2} + \dfrac{1}{2y^2}\right)^2} \, dy$

$= \left[\dfrac{1}{6}y^3 - \dfrac{1}{2y}\right]_1^2 = \dfrac{17}{12}$.

16. $y' = x^2 + 2x + 1 - \dfrac{4}{(4x + 4)^2} = (x + 1)^2 - \dfrac{1}{4(x + 1)^2}$

so the length is

$\int_0^2 \sqrt{1 + \left((x + 1)^2 - \dfrac{1}{4(x + 1)^2}\right)^2} \, dx$

$= \int_0^2 \sqrt{\left((x + 1)^2 + \dfrac{1}{4(x + 1)^2}\right)^2} \, dx$

$= \left[\dfrac{1}{3}(x + 1)^3 - \dfrac{1}{4(x + 1)}\right]_0^2 = \dfrac{53}{6}$.

17. $x' = \sqrt{\sec^4 y - 1}$, so the length is

$$\int_{-\pi/4}^{\pi/4} \sqrt{1 + (\sec^4 y - 1)} \, dy = \int_{-\pi/4}^{\pi/4} \sec^2 y \, dy$$
$$= \left[\tan y \right]_{-\pi/4}^{\pi/4} = 2.$$

18. $y' = \sqrt{3x^4 - 1}$, so the length is

$$\int_{-2}^{-1} \sqrt{1 + (3x^4 - 1)} \, dx = \int_{-2}^{-1} \sqrt{3} x^2 \, dx$$
$$= \sqrt{3} \left[\frac{1}{3} x^3 \right]_{-2}^{-1} = \frac{7\sqrt{3}}{3}.$$

19. (a) $\left(\dfrac{dy}{dx} \right)^2$ corresponds to $\dfrac{1}{4x}$ here, so take $\dfrac{dy}{dx}$ as $\dfrac{1}{2\sqrt{x}}$. Then
$y = \sqrt{x} + C$, and, since $(1, 1)$ lies on the curve, $C = 0$.
So $y = \sqrt{x}$.

(b) Only one. We know the derivative of the function and the value of the function at one value of x.

20. (a) $\left(\dfrac{dx}{dy} \right)^2$ corresponds to $\dfrac{1}{y^4}$ here, so take $\dfrac{dx}{dy}$ as $\dfrac{1}{y^2}$.
Then $x = -\dfrac{1}{y} + C$ and, since $(0, 1)$ lies on the curve,
$C = 1$. So $y = \dfrac{1}{1 - x}$.

(b) Only one. We know the derivative of the function and the value of the function at one value of x.

21. $y' = \sqrt{\cos 2x}$, so the length is
$$\int_0^{\pi/4} \sqrt{1 + \cos 2x} \, dx = \int_0^{\pi/4} \sqrt{2 \cos^2 x} \, dx$$
$$= \sqrt{2} \left[\sin x \right]_0^{\pi/4} = 1.$$

22. $y' = -(1 - x^{2/3})^{1/2} x^{-1/3}$, so the length is

$$8 \int_{\sqrt{2}/4}^1 \sqrt{1 + (1 - x^{2/3}) x^{-2/3}} \, dx$$

$$= 8 \int_{\sqrt{2}/4}^1 \sqrt{x^{-2/3}} \, dx$$

$$= 8 \int_{\sqrt{2}/4}^1 x^{-1/3} \, dx$$

$$= 8 \left[\frac{3}{2} x^{2/3} \right]_{\sqrt{2}/4}^1$$

$$= 8 \left[\frac{3}{2} - \frac{3}{2} \left(\frac{1}{2} \right) \right] = 6.$$

23. Find the length of the curve $y = \sin \dfrac{3\pi}{20} x$ for $0 \le x \le 20$.

$y' = \dfrac{3\pi}{20} \cos \dfrac{3\pi}{20} x$, so the length is
$$\int_0^{20} \sqrt{1 + \left(\frac{3\pi}{20} \cos \frac{3\pi}{20} x \right)^2} \, dx,$$ which evaluates, using NINT,

to ≈ 21.07 inches.

24. The area is 300 times the length of the arch.

$y' = -\left(\dfrac{\pi}{2} \right) \sin \left(\dfrac{\pi x}{50} \right)$, so the length is
$$\int_{-25}^{25} \sqrt{1 + \left(\frac{\pi}{2} \right)^2 \sin^2 \left(\frac{\pi x}{50} \right)} \, dx,$$ which evaluates, using NINT,

to ≈ 73.185. Multiply that by 300, then by \$1.75 to obtain

the cost (rounded to the nearest dollar): \$38,422.

25. For track 1: $y_1 = 0$ at $x = \pm 10\sqrt{5} \approx \pm 22.3607$, and

$y_1' = \dfrac{-0.2x}{\sqrt{100 - 0.2x^2}}$. NINT fails to evaluate
$$\int_{-10\sqrt{5}}^{10\sqrt{5}} \sqrt{1 + (y_1')^2} \, dx$$ because of the undefined slope at

the limits, so use the track's symmetry, and "back away"

from the upper limit a little, and find

$2 \displaystyle\int_0^{22.36} \sqrt{1 + (y_1')^2} \, dx \approx 52.548$. Then, pretending the last

little stretch at each end is a straight line, add

$2\sqrt{100 - 0.2(22.36)^2} \approx 0.156$ to get the total length of

track 1 as ≈ 52.704. Using a similar strategy, find the

length of the *right half* of track 2 to be ≈ 32.274. Now

enter $Y_1 = 52.704$ and

$Y_2 = 32.274 + \text{NINT}\left(\sqrt{1 + \left(\dfrac{-0.2t}{\sqrt{150 - 0.2t^2}} \right)^2}, t, x, 0 \right)$ and

graph in a $[-30, 0]$ by $[0, 60]$ window to see the effect of

the x-coordinate of the lane-2 starting position on the length

of lane 2. (Be patient!) Solve graphically to find the

intersection at $x \approx -19.909$, which leads to starting point

coordinates $(-19.909, 8.410)$.

26. $f'(x) = \dfrac{1}{3} x^{-2/3} + \dfrac{2}{3} x^{-1/3}$, but NINT fails on
$$\int_0^2 \sqrt{1 + (f'(x))^2} \, dx$$ because of the undefined slope at

$x = 0$. So, instead solve for x in terms of y using the

quadratic formula. $(x^{1/3})^2 + x^{1/3} - y = 0$, and

$x^{1/3} = \dfrac{-1 \pm \sqrt{1 + 4y}}{2}$. Using the positive values,

$x = \dfrac{1}{8} (\sqrt{1 + 4y} - 1)^3$. Then,

$x' = \dfrac{3}{8} (\sqrt{1 + 4y} - 1)^2 \left(\dfrac{2}{\sqrt{1 + 4y}} \right)$, and
$$\int_0^{2^{1/3} + 2^{2/3}} \sqrt{1 + (x')^2} \, dy \approx 3.6142.$$

27. $f'(x) = \dfrac{(4x^2 + 1) - (8x^2 - 8x)}{(4x^2 + 1)^2} = -\dfrac{4x^2 - 8x - 1}{(4x + 1)^2}$, so the

length is $\displaystyle\int_{-1/2}^{1} \sqrt{1 + \left(\dfrac{4x^2 - 8x - 1}{(4x^2 + 1)^2}\right)^2}\, dx$ which evaluates,

using NINT, to ≈ 2.1089.

28. There is a corner at $x = 0$:

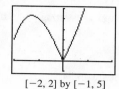

$[-2, 2]$ by $[-1, 5]$

Break the function into two smooth segments:

$$y = \begin{cases} x^3 - 5x & -2 \le x \le 0 \\ x^3 + 5x & 0 < x \le 1 \end{cases} \text{ and}$$

$$y' = \begin{cases} 3x^2 - 5 & -2 \le x < 0 \\ 3x^2 + 5 & 0 < x \le 1 \end{cases}.$$

The length is $\displaystyle\int_{-2}^{1} \sqrt{1 + (y')^2}\, dy$

$= \displaystyle\int_{-2}^{0} \sqrt{1 + (3x^2 - 5)^2}\, dx + \int_{0}^{1} \sqrt{1 + (3x^2 + 5)^2}\, dx$,

which evaluates, using NINT for each part, to ≈ 13.132.

29. $y = (1 - \sqrt{x})^2$, $0 \le x \le 1$

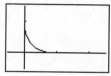

$[-0.5, 2.5]$ by $[-0.5, 1.5]$

$y' = \dfrac{\sqrt{x} - 1}{\sqrt{x}}$, but NINT may fail using y' over the entire

interval because y' is undefined at $x = 0$. So, split the curve

into two equal segments by solving $\sqrt{x} + \sqrt{y} = 1$ with

$y = x$: $x = \dfrac{1}{4}$. The total length is $2\displaystyle\int_{1/4}^{1} \sqrt{1 + \left(\dfrac{\sqrt{x} - 1}{\sqrt{x}}\right)^2}\, dx$,

which evaluates, using NINT, to ≈ 1.623.

30.

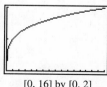

$[0, 16]$ by $[0, 2]$

$y' = \dfrac{1}{4}x^{-3/4}$, but NINT may fail using y' over the entire

interval, because y' is undefined at $x = 0$. So, use

$x = y^4$, $0 \le y \le 2$: $x' = 4y^3$ and the length is

$\displaystyle\int_{0}^{2} \sqrt{1 + (4y^3)^2}\, dy$, which evaluates,

using NINT, to ≈ 16.647.

31. Because the limit of the sum $\sum \Delta x_k$ as the norm of the

partition goes to zero will always be the length $(b - a)$ of

the interval (a, b).

32. No; the curve can be indefinitely long. Consider, for

example, the curve $\dfrac{1}{3}\sin\left(\dfrac{1}{x}\right) + 0.5$ for $0 < x < 1$.

33. (a) The fin is the hypotenuse of a right triangle with leg

lengths Δx_k and $\dfrac{df}{dx}\bigg|_{x = x_{k-1}} \Delta x_k = f'(x_{k-1}) \Delta x_k$.

(b) $\displaystyle\lim_{n \to \infty} \sum_{k=1}^{n} \sqrt{(\Delta x_k)^2 + (f'(x_{k-1}) \Delta x_k)^2}$

$= \displaystyle\lim_{n \to \infty} \sum_{k=1}^{n} \Delta x_k \sqrt{1 + (f'(x_{k-1}))^2}$

$= \displaystyle\int_{a}^{b} \sqrt{1 + (f'(x))^2}\, dx$

34. Yes. Any curve of the form $y = \pm x + c$, where c is a

constant, has constant slope ± 1, so that

$\displaystyle\int_{0}^{a} \sqrt{1 + (y')^2}\, dx = \int_{0}^{a} \sqrt{2}\, dx = a\sqrt{2}$.

■ Section 7.5 Applications from Science and Statistics
(pp. 401–411)

Quick Review 7.5

1. (a) $\displaystyle\int_{0}^{1} e^{-x}\, dx = \left[-e^{-x}\right]_{0}^{1} = 1 - \dfrac{1}{e}$

   (b) ≈ 0.632

2. (a) $\displaystyle\int_{0}^{1} e^{x}\, dx = \left[e^{x}\right]_{0}^{1} = e - 1$

   (b) ≈ 1.718

3. (a) $\displaystyle\int_{\pi/4}^{\pi/2} \sin x\, dx = \left[-\cos x\right]_{\pi/4}^{\pi/2} = \dfrac{\sqrt{2}}{2}$

   (b) ≈ 0.707

4. (a) $\displaystyle\int_{0}^{3} (x^2 + 2)\, dx = \left[\dfrac{1}{3}x^3 + 2x\right]_{0}^{3} = 15$

   (b) 15

5. (a) $\displaystyle\int_{1}^{2} \dfrac{x^2}{x^3 + 1}\, dx = \left[\dfrac{1}{3}\ln (x^3 + 1)\right]_{1}^{2}$

$= \dfrac{1}{3}[\ln 9 - \ln 2]$

$= \dfrac{1}{3}\ln\left(\dfrac{9}{2}\right)$

   (b) ≈ 0.501

6. $\displaystyle\int_{0}^{7} 2\pi(x + 2) \sin x\, dx$

7. $\displaystyle\int_{0}^{7} (1 - x^2)(2\pi x)\, dx$

8. $\int_0^7 \pi \cos^2 x \, dx$

9. $\int_0^7 \pi \left(\frac{y}{2}\right)^2 (10 - y) \, dy$

10. $\int_0^7 \frac{\sqrt{3}}{4} \sin^2 x \, dx$

Section 7.5 Exercises

1. $\int_0^5 xe^{-x/3} \, dx = \left[-3e^{-x/3}(3 + x)\right]_0^5 = -\frac{24}{e^{5/3}} + 9 \approx 4.4670 \text{ J}$

2. $\int_0^3 x \sin\left(\frac{\pi x}{4}\right) dx = \frac{4}{\pi}\left[\frac{4}{\pi}\sin\left(\frac{\pi x}{4}\right) - x\cos\left(\frac{\pi x}{4}\right)\right]_0^3$

$$= \frac{4\sqrt{2}}{\pi}\left(\frac{2}{\pi} + \frac{3}{2}\right)$$

$$\approx 3.8473 \text{ J}$$

3. $\int_0^3 x\sqrt{9 - x^2} \, dx = \left[-\frac{1}{3}(9 - x^2)^{3/2}\right]_0^3 = 9 \text{ J}$

4. $\int_0^{10} (e^{\sin x}\cos x + 2) \, dx = \left[e^{\sin x} + 2x\right]_0^{10}$

$$= e^{\sin 10} + 19 \approx 19.5804 \text{ J}$$

5. When the bucket is x m off the ground, the water weighs

$$F(x) = 490\left(\frac{20 - x}{20}\right) = 490\left(1 - \frac{x}{20}\right) = 490 - 24.5x \text{ N}.$$

Then

$$W = \int_0^{20} (490 - 24.5x) \, dx = \left[490x - 12.25x^2\right]_0^{20} = 4900 \text{ J}.$$

6. When the bucket is x m off the ground, the water weighs

$$F(x) = 490\left(\frac{20 - 4x/5}{20}\right) = 490\left(1 - \frac{x}{25}\right) = 490 - 19.6x \text{ N}.$$

Then

$$W = \int_0^{20} (490 - 19.6x) \, dx = \left[490x - 9.8x^2\right]_0^{20} = 5880 \text{ J}.$$

7. When the bag is x ft off the ground, the sand weighs

$$F(x) = 144\left(\frac{18 - x/2}{18}\right) = 144\left(1 - \frac{x}{36}\right) = 144 - 4x \text{ lb}.$$

Then

$$W = \int_0^{18} (144 - 4x) \, dx = \left[144x - 2x^2\right]_0^{18} = 1944 \text{ ft-lb}$$

8. (a) $F = ks$, so $800 = k(14 - 10)$ and $k = 200$ lb/in.

(b) $F(x) = 200x$, and $\int_0^2 200x \, dx = \left[100x^2\right]_0^2 = 400$ in.-lb.

(c) $F = 200s$, so $s = \frac{1600}{200} = 8$ in.

9. (a) $F = ks$, so $21{,}714 = k(8 - 5)$ and $k = 7238$ lb/in.

(b) $F(x) = 7238x$. $W = \int_0^{1/2} 7238x \, dx = \left[3619x^2\right]_0^{1/2}$

$$= 904.75 \approx 905 \text{ in.-lb, and } W = \int_{1/2}^1 7238x \, dx$$

$$= \left[3619x^2\right]_{1/2}^1 = 2714.25 \approx 2714 \text{ in.-lb.}$$

10. (a) $F = ks$, so $150 = k\left(\frac{1}{16}\right)$ and $k = 2400$ lb/in. Then for

$s = \frac{1}{8}$, $F = 2400\left(\frac{1}{8}\right) = 300$ lb.

(b) $\int_0^{1/8} 2400x \, dx = \left[1200x^2\right]_0^{1/8} = 18.75$ in.-lb

11. When the end of the rope is x m from its starting point, the

$(50 - x)$ m of rope still to go weigh

$F(x) = (0.624)(50 - x)$ N. The total work is

$$\int_0^{50} (0.624)(50 - x) \, dx = 0.624\left[50x - \frac{1}{2}x^2\right]_0^{50} = 780 \text{ J}.$$

12. (a) Work $= \int_{(p_1, V_1)}^{(p_2, V_2)} F(x) \, dx = \int_{(p_1, V_1)}^{(p_2, V_2)} pA \, dx = \int_{(p_1, V_1)}^{(p_2, V_2)} p \, dV$

(b) $p_1 V_1^{1.4} = (50)(243)^{1.4} = 109{,}350$, so $p = \frac{109{,}350}{V^{1.4}}$ and

Work $= \int_{(p_1, V_1)}^{(p_2, V_2)} \frac{109{,}350}{V^{1.4}} \, dV$

$$= 109{,}350\left[-2.5V^{-0.4}\right]_{V = 243}^{V = 32}$$

$$= -37{,}968.75 \text{ in.-lb}$$

13. (a) From the equation $x^2 + y^2 = 3^2$, it follows that a thin

horizontal rectangle has area $2\sqrt{9 - y^2} \, \Delta y$, where y is

distance from the top, and pressure $62.4y$. The total

force is approximately $\sum_{k=1}^n (62.4y_k)(2\sqrt{9 - y_k^2}) \, \Delta y$

$$= \sum_{k=1}^n 124.8y_k\sqrt{9 - y_k^2} \, \Delta y.$$

(b) $\int_0^3 124.8y\sqrt{9 - y^2} \, dy = \left[-41.6(9 - y^2)^{3/2}\right]_0^3$

$$= 1123.2 \text{ lb}$$

14. (a) From the equation $\frac{x^2}{3^2} + \frac{y^2}{8^2} = 1$, it follows that a thin

horizontal rectangle has area $6\sqrt{1 - \frac{y^2}{64}} \, \Delta y$, where y is

distance from the top, and pressure $62.4y$. The total

force is approximately

$$\sum_{k=1}^n (62.4y_k)\left(6\sqrt{1 - \frac{y_k^2}{64}}\right) \Delta y = \sum_{k=1}^n 374.4y_k\sqrt{1 - \frac{y_k^2}{64}} \, \Delta y.$$

(b) $\int_0^8 374.4y\sqrt{1 - \frac{y^2}{64}} \, dy = \left[-7987.2\left(1 - \frac{y^2}{64}\right)^{3/2}\right]_0^8$

$$= 7987.2 \text{ lb}$$

15. (a) From the equation $x = \frac{3}{8}y$, it follows that a thin horizontal rectangle has area $\frac{3}{4}y\Delta y$, where y is the distance from the top of the triangle, the pressure is $62.4(y - 3)$. The total force is approximately

$$\sum_{k=1}^{n} 62.4(y_k - 3)\left(\frac{3}{4}y_k\right)\Delta y = \sum_{k=1}^{n} 46.8(y_k^2 - 3y_k)\,\Delta y.$$

(b) $\displaystyle\int_3^8 46.8(y_2^2 - 3y)\,dy = \left[15.6y^3 - 70.2y^2\right]_3^8$

$= 3494.4 - (-210.6) = 3705$ lb

16. (a) From the equation $y = \frac{x^2}{2}$, it follows that a thin horizontal rectangle has area $2\sqrt{2y}\Delta y$, where y is distance from the bottom, and pressure $62.4(4 - y)$. The total force is approximately

$$\sum_{k=1}^{n} 62.4(4 - y_k)(2\sqrt{2y_k})\Delta y$$
$$= \sum_{k=1}^{n} 124.8\sqrt{2}(4\sqrt{y_k} - y_k^{3/2})\Delta y.$$

(b) $\displaystyle\int_0^4 124.8\sqrt{2}(4\sqrt{y} - y^{3/2})\,dy$

$= 124.8\sqrt{2}\left[\frac{8}{3}y^{3/2} - \frac{2}{5}y^{5/2}\right]_0^4$

$= 1064.96\sqrt{2} \approx 1506.1$ lb

17. (a) Work to raise a thin slice $= 62.4(10 \times 12)(\Delta y)y$.

Total work $= \displaystyle\int_0^{20} 62.4(120)y\,dy = 62.4\left[60y^2\right]_0^{20}$

$= 1,497,600$ ft-lb

(b) $(1,497,600 \text{ ft-lb}) \div (250 \text{ ft-lb/sec}) = 5990.4$ sec ≈ 100 min

(c) Work to empty half the tank $= \displaystyle\int_0^{10} 62.4(120)y\,dy$

$= 62.4\left[60y^2\right]_0^{10} = 374,400$ ft-lb, and

$374,400 \div 250 = 1497.6$ sec ≈ 25 min

(d) The weight per ft³ of water is a simple multiplicative factor in the answers. So divide by 62.4 and multiply by the appropriate weight-density

For 62.26:

$1,497,600\left(\dfrac{62.26}{62.4}\right) = 1,494,240$ ft-lb and

$5990.4\left(\dfrac{62.26}{62.4}\right) = 5976.96$ sec ≈ 100 min.

For 62.5:

$1,497,600\left(\dfrac{62.5}{62.4}\right) = 1,500,000$ ft-lb and

$5990.4\left(\dfrac{62.5}{62.4}\right) = 6000$ sec $= 100$ min.

18. The work needed to raise a thin disk is $\pi(10)^2(51.2)y\Delta y$, where y is height up from the bottom. The total work is

$$\int_0^{30} 100\pi(51.2)y\,dy = 5120\pi\left[\frac{1}{2}y^2\right]_0^{30} \approx 7,238,229 \text{ ft-lb}$$

19. Work to pump through the valve is $\pi(2)^2(62.4)(y + 15)\Delta y$ for a thin disk and

$$\int_0^6 4\pi(62.4)(y + 15)\,dy = 249.6\pi\left[\frac{1}{2}y^2 + 15y\right]_0^6$$
$$\approx 84,687.3 \text{ ft-lb}$$

for the whole tank. Work to pump over the rim is $\pi(2)^2(62.4)(6 + 15)\Delta y$ for a thin disk and

$$\int_0^6 4\pi(62.4)(21)\,dy = 4\pi(62.4)(21)(6) \approx 98,801.8 \text{ ft-lb for}$$

the whole tank. Through a hose attached to a valve in the bottom is faster, because it takes more time for a pump with a given power output to do more work.

20. The work is the same as if the straw were initially an inch long and just touched the surface, and lengthened as the liquid level dropped. For a thin disk, the volume is $\pi\left(\dfrac{y + 17.5}{14}\right)^2\Delta y$ and the work to raise it is $\pi\left(\dfrac{y + 17.5}{14}\right)^2\left(\dfrac{4}{9}\right)(8 - y)\Delta y$. The total work is $\displaystyle\int_0^7 \pi\left(\dfrac{y + 17.5}{14}\right)^2\left(\dfrac{4}{9}\right)(8 - y)\,dy$, which using NINT evaluates to ≈ 91.3244 in.-oz.

21. The work is that already calculated (to pump the oil to the rim) plus the work needed to raise the entire amount 3 ft higher. The latter comes to $\left(\dfrac{1}{3}\pi r^2 h\right)(57)(3) = 57\pi(4)^2(8) = 22,921.06$ ft-lb, and the total is $22,921.06 + 30,561.41 \approx 53,482.5$ ft-lb.

22. The weight density is a simple multiplicative factor: Divide by 57 and multiply by 64.5.

$30,561.41\left(\dfrac{64.5}{57}\right) \approx 34,582.65$ ft-lb.

23. The work to raise a thin disk is

$\pi r^2(56)h = \pi(\sqrt{10^2 - y^2})^2(56)(10 + 2 - y)\Delta y$

$= 56\pi(12 - y)(100 - y^2)\Delta y$. The total work is

$\int_0^{10} 56\pi(12 - y)(100 - y^2)\,dy$, which evaluates using NINT

to $\approx 967,611$ ft-lb. This will come to

$(967,611)(\$0.005) \approx \$4838$, so yes, there's enough money

to hire the firm.

24. Pipe radius $= \frac{1}{6}$ ft;

Work to fill pipe $= \int_0^{360} \pi\left(\frac{1}{6}\right)^2(62.4)y\,dy = 112,320\pi$ ft-lb.

Work to fill tank $= \int_{360}^{385} \pi(10)^2(62.4)y\,dy$

$= 58,110,000\pi$ ft-lb.

Total work $= 58,222,320\pi$ ft-lb, which will take

$58,222,320\pi \div 1650 \approx 110,855$ sec ≈ 31 hr.

25. (a) The pressure at depth y is $62.4y$, and the area of a thin

horizontal strip is $2\Delta y$. The depth of water is $\frac{11}{6}$ ft, so

the total force on an end is

$\int_0^{11/6} (62.4y)(2\,dy) \approx 209.73$ lb.

(b) On the sides, which are twice as long as the ends, the

initial total force is doubled to ≈ 419.47 lb. When the

tank is upended, the depth is doubled to $\frac{11}{3}$ ft, and the

force on a side becomes $\int_0^{11/3} (62.4y)(2\,dy) \approx 838.93$ lb,

which means that the fluid force doubles.

26. 3.75 in. $= \frac{5}{16}$ ft, and 7.75 in. $= \frac{31}{48}$ ft.

Force on a side $= \int p\,dA = \int_0^{31/48} (64.5y)\left(\frac{5}{16}\,dy\right) \approx 4.2$ lb.

27. (a) 0.5 (50%), since half of a normal distribution lies
below the mean.

(b) Use NINT to find $\int_{63}^{65} f(x)\,dx$, where

$f(x) = \dfrac{1}{3.2\sqrt{2\pi}}e^{-(x-63.4)^2/(2 \cdot 3.2^2)}$. The result is

≈ 0.24 (24%).

(c) 6 ft = 72 in. Pick 82 in. as a conveniently high upper

limit and with NINT, find $\int_{72}^{82} f(x)\,dx$. The result is

≈ 0.0036 (0.36%).

(d) 0 if we assume a continuous distribution. Between

59.5 in. and 60.5 in., the proportion is

$\int_{59.5}^{60.5} f(x)\,dx \approx 0.071$ (7.1%)

28. Use $f(x) = \dfrac{1}{100\sqrt{2\pi}}e^{-(x-498)^2/(2 \cdot 100^2)}$

(a) $\int_{400}^{500} f(x)\,dx \approx 0.34$ (34%)

(b) Take 1000 as a conveniently high upper limit:

$\int_{700}^{1000} f(x)\,dx \approx 0.0217$, which means about

$0.0217(300) \approx 6.5$ people

29. Integration is a good approximation to the area (which
represents the probability), since the area is a kind of
Riemann sum.

30. The proportion of lightbulbs that last between 100 and 800
hours.

31. $\int_{6,370,000}^{35,780,000} \dfrac{1000MG}{r^2}\,dr = 1000\,MG\left[-\dfrac{1}{r}\right]_{6,370,000}^{35,780,000}$, which for

$M = 5.975 \times 10^{24}$, $G = 6.6726 \times 10^{-11}$ evaluates to

$\approx 5.1446 \times 10^{10}$ J.

32. (a) The distance goes from 2 m to 1 m. The work by an

external force equals the work done by repulsion in

moving the electrons from a 1-m distance to a 2-m

distance:

$\text{Work} = \int_1^2 \dfrac{23 \times 10^{-29}}{r^2}\,dr$

$= 23 \times 10^{-29}\left[-\dfrac{1}{r}\right]_1^2$

$= 1.15 \times 10^{-28}$ J

(b) Again, find the work done by the fixed electrons in
pushing the third one away. The total work is the sum
of the work by each fixed electron. The changes in
distance are 4 m to 6 m and 2 m to 4 m, respectively.

$\text{Work} = \int_4^6 \dfrac{23 \times 10^{-29}}{r^2}\,dr + \int_2^4 \dfrac{23 \times 10^{-29}}{r^2}\,dr$

$= 23 \times 10^{-29}\left(\left[-\dfrac{1}{r}\right]_4^6 + \left[-\dfrac{1}{r}\right]_2^4\right)$

$\approx 7.6667 \times 10^{-29}$ J.

33. $F = m\left(\dfrac{dv}{dt}\right) = mv\left(\dfrac{dv}{dx}\right)$, so

$$W = \int_{x_1}^{x_2} F(x)\,dx$$

$$= \int_{x_1}^{x_2} mv\left(\frac{dv}{dx}\right) dx$$

$$= \int_{v_1}^{v_2} mv\,dv$$

$$= \frac{1}{2}mv_2{}^2 - \frac{1}{2}mv_1{}^2$$

34. Work = Change in kinetic energy = $\frac{1}{2}mv^2$.

$$m = \frac{2\ \text{oz}}{32\ \text{ft/sec}^2} = \frac{1/8\ \text{lb}}{32\ \text{ft/sec}^2} = \frac{1}{256}\ \text{slug, so}$$

Work $= \dfrac{1}{2}\left(\dfrac{1}{256}\right)(160)^2 = 50$ ft-lb.

35. $0.3125\ \text{lb} = \dfrac{0.3125\ \text{lb}}{32\ \text{ft/sec}^2} = 0.009765625$ slug, and

$90\ \text{mph} = 90\left(\dfrac{5280\ \text{ft}}{1\ \text{mi}}\right)\left(\dfrac{1\ \text{hr}}{3600\ \text{sec}}\right) = 132$ ft/sec, so

Work = change in kinetic energy $= \dfrac{1}{2}(0.009765625)(132)^2$

≈ 85.1 ft-lb.

36. $1.6\ \text{oz} = 1.6\ \text{oz}\left(\dfrac{1\ \text{lb}}{16\ \text{oz}}\right)/(32\ \text{ft/sec}^2) = 0.003125$ slug, so

Work $= \dfrac{1}{2}(0.003125)(280)^2 = 122.5$ ft-lb.

37. $2\ \text{oz} = 2\ \text{oz}\left(\dfrac{1\ \text{lb}}{16\ \text{oz}}\right)/(32\ \text{ft/sec}^2) = \dfrac{1}{256}$ slug, and

$124\ \text{mph} = 124\ \text{mph}\left(\dfrac{5280\ \text{ft}}{1\ \text{mi}}\right)\left(\dfrac{1\ \text{hr}}{3600\ \text{sec}}\right) = 181.867$ ft/sec,

so Work $= \dfrac{1}{2}\left(\dfrac{1}{256}\right)(181.867)^2 \approx 64.6$ ft-lb.

38. $14.5\ \text{oz} = 14.5\ \text{oz}\left(\dfrac{1\ \text{lb}}{16\ \text{oz}}\right)/(32\ \text{ft/sec}^2) \approx 0.02832$ slug, so

Work $= \dfrac{1}{2}(0.02832)(88)^2 \approx 109.7$ ft-lb.

39. $6.5\ \text{oz} = 6.5\ \text{oz}\left(\dfrac{1\ \text{lb}}{16\ \text{oz}}\right)/(32\ \text{ft/sec}^2) \approx 0.01270$ slug, so

Work $= \dfrac{1}{2}(0.01270)(132)^2 \approx 110.6$ ft-lb.

40. $2\ \text{oz} = \dfrac{1}{8}\ \text{lb} = \dfrac{1}{256}$ slug. Compression energy of spring

$= \dfrac{1}{2}ks^2 = \dfrac{1}{2}(18)\left(\dfrac{1}{4}\right)^2 = 0.5625$ ft-lb, and final height is

given by $mgh = 0.5625$ ft-lb, so $h = \dfrac{0.5625}{(1/256)(32)} = 4.5$ ft.

■ Chapter 7 Review Exercises
(pp. 413–415)

1. $\displaystyle\int_0^5 v(t)\,dt = \int_0^5 (t^2 - 0.2t^3)\,dt$

$$= \left[\frac{1}{3}t^3 - 0.05t^4\right]_0^5 \approx 10.417\ \text{ft}$$

2. $\displaystyle\int_0^7 c(t)\,dt = \int_0^7 (4 + 0.001t^4)\,dt$

$$= \left[4t + 0.0002t^5\right]_0^7 \approx 31.361\ \text{gal}$$

3. $\displaystyle\int_0^{100} B(x)\,dx = \int_0^{100} (21 - e^{0.03x})\,dx$

$$\approx \left[21x - 33.333e^{0.03x}\right]_0^{100} \approx 1464$$

4. $\displaystyle\int_0^2 \rho(x)\,dx = \int_0^2 (11 - 4x)\,dx = \left[11x - 2x^2\right]_0^2 = 14\ \text{g}$

5. $\displaystyle\int_0^{24} E(t)\,dt = \int_0^{24} 300\left(2 - \cos\left(\frac{\pi t}{12}\right)\right)dt$

$$= 300\left[2t - \frac{12}{\pi}\sin\left(\frac{\pi t}{12}\right)\right]_0^{24} = 14{,}400$$

6.

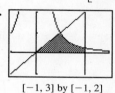

[−1, 3] by [−1, 2]

The curves intersect at $x = 1$. The area is

$$\int_0^1 x\,dx + \int_1^2 \frac{1}{x^2}\,dx = \left[\frac{1}{2}x^2\right]_0^1 + \left[-\frac{1}{x}\right]_1^2$$

$$= \frac{1}{2} + \left(-\frac{1}{2} + 1\right) = 1.$$

7.

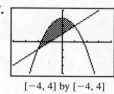

[−4, 4] by [−4, 4]

The curves intersect at $x = -2$ and $x = 1$. The area is

$$\int_{-2}^1 [3 - x^2 - (x + 1)]\,dx = \int_{-2}^1 (-x^2 - x + 2)\,dx$$

$$= \left[-\frac{1}{3}x^3 - \frac{1}{2}x^2 + 2x\right]_{-2}^1$$

$$= \left(-\frac{1}{3} - \frac{1}{2} + 2\right) - \left(\frac{8}{3} - 2 - 4\right)$$

$$= \frac{9}{2}.$$

8. $\sqrt{x} + \sqrt{y} = 1$ implies $y = (1 - \sqrt{x})^2 = 1 - 2\sqrt{x} + x$.

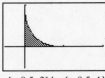

$[-0.5, 2]$ by $[-0.5, 1]$

The area is $\int_0^1 (1 - 2\sqrt{x} + x)\, dx = \left[x - \frac{4}{3}x^{3/2} + \frac{1}{2}x^2 \right]_0^1$

$= \frac{1}{6}.$

9. $x = 2y^2$ implies $y = \sqrt{\frac{x}{2}}$.

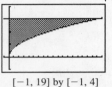

$[-1, 19]$ by $[-1, 4]$

The curves intersect at $x = 18$. The area is

$\int_0^{18} \left(3 - \sqrt{\frac{x}{2}} \right) dx = \left[3x - \frac{4}{3}\left(\frac{x}{2}\right)^{3/2} \right]_0^{18} = 18,$

or $\int_0^3 2y^2\, dy = \left[\frac{2}{3}y^3 \right]_0^3 = 18.$

10. $4x = y^2 - 4$ implies $x = \frac{1}{4}y^2 - 1$, and $4x = y + 16$ implies $x = \frac{1}{4}y + 4$.

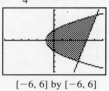

$[-6, 6]$ by $[-6, 6]$

The curves intersect at $(3, -4)$ and $(5.25, 5)$. The area is

$\int_{-4}^5 \left[\left(\frac{1}{4}y + 4 \right) - \left(\frac{1}{4}y^2 - 1 \right) \right] dy$

$= \int_{-4}^5 \left(-\frac{1}{4}y^2 + \frac{1}{4}y + 5 \right) dy$

$= \left[-\frac{1}{12}y^3 + \frac{1}{8}y^2 + 5y \right]_{-4}^5$

$= \frac{425}{24} - \left(-\frac{38}{3} \right) = \frac{243}{8} = 30.375.$

11.

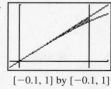

$[-0.1, 1]$ by $[-0.1, 1]$

The area is $\int_0^{\pi/4} (x - \sin x)\, dx = \left[\frac{1}{2}x^2 + \cos x \right]_0^{\pi/4}$

$= \frac{\pi^2}{32} + \frac{\sqrt{2}}{2} - 1$

$\approx 0.0155.$

12.

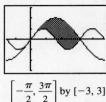

$\left[-\frac{\pi}{2}, \frac{3\pi}{2} \right]$ by $[-3, 3]$

The area is

$\int_0^\pi (2 \sin x - \sin 2x)\, dx = \left[-2 \cos x + \frac{1}{2} \cos 2x \right]_0^\pi = 4.$

13.

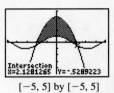

$[-5, 5]$ by $[-5, 5]$

The curves intersect at $x \approx \pm 2.1281$. The area is

$\int_{-2.1281}^{2.1281} (4 - x^2 - \cos x)\, dx,$

which using NINT evaluates to ≈ 8.9023.

14.

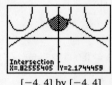

$[-4, 4]$ by $[-4, 4]$

The curves intersect at $x \approx \pm 0.8256$. The area is

$\int_{-0.8256}^{0.8256} (3 - |x| - \sec^2 x)\, dx,$

which using NINT evaluates to ≈ 2.1043.

15. Solve $1 + \cos x = 2 - \cos x$ for the x-values at the two ends of the region: $x = 2\pi \pm \frac{\pi}{3}$, i.e., $\frac{5\pi}{3}$ or $\frac{7\pi}{3}$. Use the symmetry of the area:

$2\int_{2\pi}^{7\pi/3} [(1 + \cos x) - (2 - \cos x)]\, dx$

$= 2\int_{2\pi}^{7\pi/3} (2 \cos x - 1)\, dx$

$= 2\left[2 \sin x - x \right]_{2\pi}^{7\pi/3}$

$= 2\sqrt{3} - \frac{2}{3}\pi \approx 1.370.$

16. $\int_{\pi/3}^{5\pi/3} [(2 - \cos x) - (1 + \cos x)]\, dx$

$= \int_{\pi/3}^{5\pi/3} (1 - 2 \cos x)\, dx$

$= \left[x - 2 \sin x \right]_{\pi/3}^{5\pi/3}$

$= 2\sqrt{3} + \frac{4}{3}\pi \approx 7.653$

17. Solve $x^3 - x = \dfrac{x}{x^2 + 1}$ to find the intersection points at

$x = 0$ and $x = \pm 2^{1/4}$. Then use the area's symmetry:

the area is

$$2\int_0^{2^{1/4}} \left[\frac{x}{x^2 + 1} - (x^3 - x) \right] dx$$

$$= 2\left[\frac{1}{2} \ln (x^2 + 1) - \frac{1}{4}x^4 + \frac{1}{2}x^2 \right]_0^{2^{1/4}}$$

$$= \ln (\sqrt{2} + 1) + \sqrt{2} - 1 \approx 1.2956.$$

18. Use the intersect function on a graphing calculator to determine that the curves intersect at $x \approx \pm 1.8933$.

The area is

$$\int_{-1.8933}^{1.8933} \left(3^{1-x^2} - \frac{x^2 - 3}{10} \right) dx,$$

which using NINT evaluates to ≈ 5.7312.

19. Use the x- and y-axis symmetries of the area:

$$4\int_0^{\pi} x \sin x \, dx = 4\left[\sin x - x \cos x \right]_0^{\pi} = 4\pi.$$

20. A cross section has radius $r = 3x^4$ and area

$$A(x) = \pi r^2 = 9\pi x^8.$$

$$V = \int_{-1}^{1} 9\pi x^8 \, dx = \pi \left[x^9 \right]_{-1}^{1} = 2\pi.$$

21.

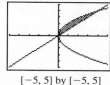

$[-5, 5]$ by $[-5, 5]$

The graphs intersect at $(0, 0)$ and $(4, 4)$.

(a) Use cylindrical shells. A shell has radius y and height

$y - \dfrac{y^2}{4}$. The total volume is

$$\int_0^4 2\pi(y)\left(y - \frac{y^2}{4} \right) dy = 2\pi\int_0^4 \left(y^2 - \frac{y^3}{4} \right) dy$$

$$= 2\pi\left[\frac{1}{3}y^3 - \frac{1}{16}y^4 \right]_0^4$$

$$= \frac{32\pi}{3}.$$

(b) Use cylindrical shells. A shell has radius x and height

$2\sqrt{x} - x$. The total volume is

$$\int_0^4 2\pi(x)(2\sqrt{x} - x) \, dx = 2\pi\int_0^4 (2x^{3/2} - x^2) \, dx$$

$$= 2\pi\left[\frac{4}{5}x^{5/2} - \frac{1}{3}x^3 \right]_0^4$$

$$= \frac{128\pi}{15}.$$

(c) Use cylindrical shells. A shell has radius $4 - x$ and

height $2\sqrt{x} - x$. The total volume is

$$\int_0^4 2\pi(4 - x)(2\sqrt{x} - x) \, dx$$

$$= 2\pi\int_0^4 (8\sqrt{x} - 4x - 2x^{3/2} + x^2) \, dx$$

$$= 2\pi\left[\frac{16}{3}x^{3/2} - 2x^2 - \frac{4}{5}x^{5/2} + \frac{1}{3}x^3 \right]_0^4 = \frac{64\pi}{5}.$$

(d) Use cylindrical shells. A shell has radius $4 - y$ and

height $y - \dfrac{y^2}{4}$. The total volume is

$$\int_0^4 2\pi(4 - y)\left(y - \frac{y^2}{4} \right) dy$$

$$= 2\pi\int_0^4 \left(4y - 2y^2 + \frac{y^3}{4} \right) dy$$

$$= 2\pi\left[2y^2 - \frac{2}{3}y^3 + \frac{1}{16}y^4 \right]_0^4 = \frac{32\pi}{3}.$$

22. (a) Use disks. The volume is

$$\pi\int_0^2 (\sqrt{2y})^2 \, dy = \pi\int_0^2 2y \, dy = \pi y^2 \Big|_0^2 = 4\pi.$$

(b) $\pi\int_0^k 2y \, dy = \pi y^2 \Big|_0^k = \pi k^2$

(c) Since $V = \pi k^2$, $\dfrac{dV}{dt} = 2\pi k\dfrac{dk}{dt}$.

When $k = 1$, $\dfrac{dk}{dt} = \dfrac{1}{2\pi k}\dfrac{dV}{dt} = \left(\dfrac{1}{2\pi} \right)(2) = \dfrac{1}{\pi}$,

so the depth is increasing at the rate of $\dfrac{1}{\pi}$ unit per

second.

23. The football is a solid of revolution about the x-axis. A

cross section has radius $\sqrt{12\left(1 - \dfrac{4x^2}{121} \right)}$ and area

$\pi r^2 = 12\pi\left(1 - \dfrac{4x^2}{121} \right)$. The volume is, given the symmetry,

$$2\int_0^{11/2} 12\pi\left(1 - \frac{4x^2}{121} \right) dx = 24\pi\int_0^{11/2} \left(1 - \frac{4x^2}{121} \right) dx$$

$$= 24\pi\left[x - \left(\frac{2}{11} \right)^2 \left(\frac{1}{3} \right)x^3 \right]_0^{11/2}$$

$$= 24\pi\left[\frac{11}{2} - \frac{11}{6} \right]$$

$$= 88\pi \approx 276 \text{ in}^3.$$

24. The width of a cross section is $2 \sin x$, and the area is

$\dfrac{1}{2}\pi r^2 = \dfrac{1}{2}\pi \sin^2 x$. The volume is

$$\int_0^{\pi} \frac{1}{2}\pi \sin^2 x \, dx = \frac{\pi}{2}\left[\frac{1}{2}x - \frac{1}{4}\sin 2x \right]_0^{\pi} = \frac{\pi^2}{4}.$$

25.

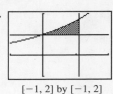

[−1, 2] by [−1, 2]

Use washer cross sections. A washer has inner radius $r = 1$,

outer radius $R = e^{x/2}$, and area $\pi(R^2 - r^2) = \pi(e^x - 1)$.

The volume is

$$\int_0^{\ln 3} \pi(e^x - 1)\, dx = \pi\left[e^x - x\right]_0^{\ln 3}$$
$$= \pi(3 - \ln 3 - 1)$$
$$= \pi(2 - \ln 3).$$

26. Use cylindrical shells. Taking the hole to be vertical, a shell

has radius x and height $2\sqrt{2^2 - x^2}$. The volume of the

piece cut out is

$$\int_0^{\sqrt{3}} 2\pi(x)(2\sqrt{2^2 - x^2})\, dx = 2\pi\int_0^{\sqrt{3}} 2x\sqrt{4 - x^2}\, dx$$
$$= 2\pi\left[-\frac{2}{3}(4 - x^2)^{3/2}\right]_0^{\sqrt{3}}$$
$$= -\frac{4}{3}\pi(1 - 8)$$
$$= \frac{28\pi}{3} \approx 29.3215 \text{ ft}^3.$$

27. The curve crosses the x-axis at $x = \pm 3$. $y' = -2x$, so the

length is $\int_{-3}^{3} \sqrt{1 + (-2x)^2}\, dx = \int_{-3}^{3} \sqrt{1 + 4x^2}\, dx$, which

using NINT evaluates to ≈ 19.4942.

28.

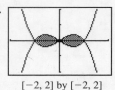

[−2, 2] by [−2, 2]

The curves intersect at $x = 0$ and $x = \pm 1$. Use the graphs'

x- and y-axis symmetry:

$\dfrac{d}{dx}(x^3 - x) = 3x^2 - 1$, and the total perimeter is

$4\int_0^1 \sqrt{1 + (3x^2 - 1)^2}\, dx$, which using NINT evaluates to

$\approx 5.2454.$

29.

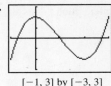

[−1, 3] by [−3, 3]

$y' = 3x^2 - 6x$ equals zero when $x = 0$ or 2. The maximum

is at $x = 0$, the minimum at $x = 2$. The distance between

them along the curve is $\int_0^2 \sqrt{1 + (3x^2 - 6x)^2}\, dx$, which

using NINT evaluates to ≈ 4.5920. The time taken is about

$\dfrac{4.5920}{2} = 2.296$ sec.

30. If (b) were true, then the curve $y = k \sin x$ would have to
get vanishingly short as k approached zero. Since in fact the
curve's length approaches 2π instead, (b) is false and (a) is
true.

31. $F'(x) = \sqrt{x^4 - 1}$, so

$$\int_2^5 \sqrt{1 + (F'(x))^2}\, dx = \int_2^5 \sqrt{x^4}\, dx$$
$$= \int_2^5 x^2\, dx$$
$$= \left[\frac{1}{3}x^3\right]_2^5 = 39.$$

32. (a) $(100 \text{ N})(40 \text{ m}) = 4000$ J

(b) When the end has traveled a distance y, the weight of

the remaining portion is $(40 - y)(0.8) = 32 - 0.8y$.

The total work to lift the rope is

$$\int_0^{40} (32 - 0.8y)\, dy = \left[32y - 0.4y^2\right]_0^{40} = 640 \text{ J}.$$

(c) $4000 + 640 = 4640$ J

33. The weight of the water at elevation x (starting from $x = 0$)

is $(800)(8)\left(\dfrac{4750 - x/2}{4750}\right) = \dfrac{128}{95}\left(4750 - \dfrac{1}{2}x\right)$. The total work

is $\displaystyle\int_0^{4750} \dfrac{128}{95}\left(4750 - \dfrac{1}{2}x\right) dx = \dfrac{128}{95}\left[4750x - \dfrac{1}{4}x^2\right]_0^{4750}$
$$= 22{,}800{,}000 \text{ ft-lb}.$$

34. $F = ks$, so $k = \dfrac{F}{s} = \dfrac{80}{0.3} = \dfrac{800}{3}$ N/m. Then

$$\text{Work} = \int_0^{0.3} \dfrac{800}{3}x\, dx = \left[\dfrac{800}{6}x^2\right]_0^{0.3} = 12 \text{ J}.$$

To stretch the additional meter,

$$\text{Work} = \int_{0.3}^{1.3} \dfrac{800}{3}x\, dx = \left[\dfrac{800}{6}x^2\right]_{0.3}^{1.3} \approx 213.3 \text{ J}.$$

35. The work is positive going uphill, since the force pushes in
the direction of travel. The work is negative going downhill.

36. The radius of a horizontal cross section is $\sqrt{8^2 - y^2}$, where y is distance below the rim. The area is $\pi(64 - y^2)$, the weight is $0.04\pi(64 - y^2)\,\Delta y$, and the work to lift it over the rim is $0.04\pi(64 - y^2)(y)\,\Delta y$. The total work is

$$\int_2^8 0.04\pi y(64 - y^2)\,dy = 0.04\pi\int_2^8 (64y - y^3)\,dy$$
$$= 0.04\pi\left[32y^2 - \frac{1}{4}y^4\right]_2^8$$
$$= 36\pi \approx 113.097 \text{ in.-lb.}$$

37. The width of a thin horizontal strip is $2(2y) = 4y$, and the force against it is $80(2 - y)4y\,\Delta y$. The total force is

$$\int_0^2 320y(2 - y)\,dy = 320\int_0^2 (-y^2 + 2y)\,dy$$
$$= 320\left[-\frac{1}{3}y^3 + y^2\right]_0^2$$
$$= \frac{1280}{3} \approx 426.67 \text{ lb.}$$

38. $5.75 \text{ in.} = \frac{23}{48}$ ft, $3.5 \text{ in.} = \frac{7}{24}$ ft, and $10 \text{ in.} = \frac{5}{6}$ ft.

For the base,
$$\text{Force} = 57\left(\frac{23}{48} \times \frac{7}{24} \times \frac{5}{6}\right) \approx 6.6385 \text{ lb.}$$
For the front and back,
$$\text{Force} = \int_0^{5/6} 57\left(\frac{7}{24}\right)y\,dy = \frac{399}{24}\left[\frac{1}{2}y^2\right]_0^{5/6} \approx 5.7726 \text{ lb.}$$
For the sides,
$$\text{Force} = \int_0^{5/6} 57\left(\frac{23}{48}\right)y\,dy = \frac{1311}{48}\left[\frac{1}{2}y^2\right]_0^{5/6} \approx 9.4835 \text{ lb.}$$

39. A square's height is $y = (\sqrt{6} - \sqrt{x})^2$, and its area is $y^2 = (\sqrt{6} - \sqrt{x})^4$. The volume is $\int_0^6 (\sqrt{6} - \sqrt{x})^4\,dx$, which using NINT evaluates to exactly 14.4.

40. Choose 50 cm as a conveniently large upper limit.
$$\int_{20}^{50} \frac{1}{3.4\sqrt{2\pi}} e^{-(x-17.2)^2/(2\cdot 3.4^2)}\,dx, \text{ evaluates,}$$
using NINT to ≈ 0.2051 (20.5%).

41. Answers will vary. Find μ, then use the fact that 68% of the class is within σ of μ to find σ, and then choose a conveniently large number b and calculate
$$\int_{10}^{b} \frac{1}{\sigma\sqrt{2\pi}} e^{-(x-\mu)^2/(2\sigma^2)}\,dx.$$

42. Use $f(x) = \frac{1}{\sqrt{2\pi}} e^{-x^2/2}$.

(a) $\int_{-1}^{1} f(x)\,dx$ evaluates, using NINT, to ≈ 0.6827 (68.27%).

(b) $\int_{-2}^{2} f(x)\,dx \approx 0.9545$ (95.45%)

(c) $\int_{-3}^{3} f(x)\,dx \approx 0.9973$ (99.73%)

43. Because $f(x) \geq 0$ and $\int_{-\infty}^{\infty} f(x)\,dx = 1$

44.
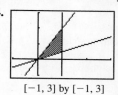
$[-1, 3]$ by $[-1, 3]$

A shell has radius x and height $2x - \frac{x}{2} = \frac{3}{2}x$. The total volume is $\int_0^1 2\pi(x)\left(\frac{3}{2}x\right)dx = \pi\left[x^3\right]_0^1 = \pi$.

45.
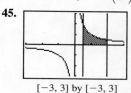
$[-3, 3]$ by $[-3, 3]$

A shell has radius x and height $\frac{1}{x}$. The total volume is
$$\int_{1/2}^{2} 2\pi(x)\left(\frac{1}{x}\right)dx = \int_{1/2}^{2} 2\pi\,dx = \left[2\pi x\right]_{1/2}^{2} = 3\pi.$$

46.
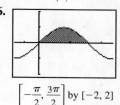
$\left[-\frac{\pi}{2}, \frac{3\pi}{2}\right]$ by $[-2, 2]$

A shell has radius x and height $\sin x$. The total volume is
$$\int_0^{\pi} 2\pi(x)(\sin x)\,dx = 2\pi\left[\sin x - x\cos x\right]_0^{\pi} = 2\pi^2.$$

47.
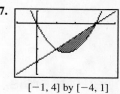
$[-1, 4]$ by $[-4, 1]$

The curves intersect at $x = 1$ and $x = 3$. A shell has radius x and height $x - 3 - (x^2 - 3x) = -x^2 + 4x - 3$. The total volume is

$$\int_1^3 2\pi(x)(-x^2 + 4x - 3)\,dx = 2\pi\int_1^3 (-x^3 + 4x^2 - 3x)\,dx$$
$$= 2\pi\left[-\frac{1}{4}x^4 + \frac{4}{3}x^3 - \frac{3}{2}x^2\right]_1^3$$
$$= \frac{16\pi}{3}.$$

48. Use the intersect function on a graphing calculator to determine that the curves intersect at $x = \pm 1.8933$. A shell has radius x and height $3^{1-x^2} - \dfrac{x^2 - 3}{10}$. The volume, which is calculated using the *right half* of the area, is

$$\int_0^{1.8933} 2\pi(x)\left(3^{1-x^2} - \frac{x^2-3}{10}\right) dx,$$ which using NINT evaluates to ≈ 9.7717.

49. (a) $y = -\dfrac{5}{4}(x+2)(x-2) = 5 - \dfrac{5}{4}x^2$

(b) Revolve about the line $x = 4$, using cylindrical shells. A shell has radius $4 - x$ and height $5 - \dfrac{5}{4}x^2$. The total volume is

$$\int_{-2}^{2} 2\pi(4-x)\left(5 - \frac{5}{4}x^2\right) dx$$
$$= 10\pi\int_{-2}^{2}\left(\frac{1}{4}x^3 - x^2 - x + 4\right) dx$$
$$= 10\pi\left[\frac{1}{16}x^4 - \frac{1}{3}x^3 - \frac{1}{2}x^2 + 4x\right]_{-2}^{2}$$
$$= \frac{320}{3}\pi \approx 335.1032 \text{ in}^3.$$

50. Since $\dfrac{dL}{dx} = \dfrac{1}{x} + f'(x)$ must equal $\sqrt{1 + (f'(x))^2}$,

$1 + (f'(x))^2 = \dfrac{1}{x^2} + \dfrac{2}{x}f'(x) + (f'(x))^2$, and

$f'(x) = \dfrac{1}{2}x - \dfrac{1}{2x}$. Then $f(x) = \dfrac{1}{4}x^2 - \dfrac{1}{2}\ln x + C$, and the requirement to pass through $(1, 1)$ means that $C = \dfrac{3}{4}$. The function is $f(x) = \dfrac{1}{4}x^2 - \dfrac{1}{2}\ln x + \dfrac{3}{4} = \dfrac{x^2 - 2\ln x + 3}{4}$.

51. $y' = \sec^2 x$, so the area is $\displaystyle\int_0^{\pi/4} 2\pi(\tan x)\sqrt{1 + (\sec^2 x)^2}\, dx$, which using NINT evaluates to ≈ 3.84.

52. $x = \dfrac{1}{y}$ and $x' = -\dfrac{1}{y^2}$, so the area is

$$\int_1^2 2\pi\left(\frac{1}{y}\right)\sqrt{1 + \left(-\frac{1}{y^2}\right)^2}\, dy,$$

which using NINT evaluates to ≈ 5.02.

Chapter 8
L'Hôpital's Rule, Improper Integrals, and Partial Fractions

■ Section 8.1 L'Hôpital's Rule (pp. 417–425)

Exploration 1 Exploring L'Hôpital's Rule Graphically

1. $\displaystyle\lim_{x\to 0}\frac{\sin x}{x} = \lim_{x\to 0}\frac{\cos x}{1} = 1$

2. The two graphs suggest that $\displaystyle\lim_{x\to 0}\frac{y_1}{y_2} = \lim_{x\to 0}\frac{y_1'}{y_2'}$.

3. $y_5 = \dfrac{x\cos x - \sin x}{x^2}$. The graphs of y_3 and y_5 clearly show that l'Hôpital's Rule does not say that $\displaystyle\lim_{x\to 0}\frac{y_1}{y_2}$ is equal to $\displaystyle\lim_{x\to 0}\left(\frac{y_1}{y_2}\right)'$.

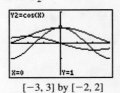

$[-3, 3]$ by $[-2, 2]$

Quick Review 8.1

1.

x	$\left(1 + \dfrac{0.1}{x}\right)^x$
1	1.1000
10	1.1046
100	1.1051
1000	1.1052
10,000	1.1052
1,000,000	1.1052

As $x\to\infty$, $\left(1 + \dfrac{0.1}{x}\right)^x$ approaches 1.1052.

2.

x	$x^{1/(\ln x)}$
0.1	2.7183
0.01	2.7183
0.001	2.7183
0.0001	2.7183
0.00001	2.7183

As $x\to 0^+$, $x^{1/(\ln x)}$ approaches 2.7183.

3.

x	$\left(1 - \dfrac{1}{x}\right)^x$
-1	0.5
-0.1	0.78679
-0.01	0.95490
-0.001	0.99312
-0.0001	0.99908
-0.00001	0.99988
-0.000001	0.99999

As $x\to 0^-$, $\left(1 - \dfrac{1}{x}\right)^x$ approaches 1.

4.

x	$\left(1 + \dfrac{1}{x}\right)^x$
-1.1	13.981
-1.01	105.77
-1.001	1007.9
-1.0001	10010

As $x\to -1^-$, $\left(1 + \dfrac{1}{x}\right)^x$ goes to ∞.

5.

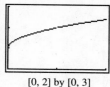

[0, 2] by [0, 3]

As $t \to 1$, $\dfrac{t-1}{\sqrt{t}-1}$ approaches 2.

6.

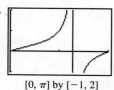

[0, 500] by [0, 3]

As $x \to \infty$, $\dfrac{\sqrt{4x^2+1}}{x+1}$ approaches 2.

7.

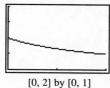

[−5, 5] by [−1, 4]

As $x \to 0$, $\dfrac{\sin 3x}{x}$ approaches 3.

8.

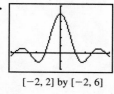

[0, π] by [−1, 2]

As $\theta \to \dfrac{\pi}{2}$, $\dfrac{\tan \theta}{2 + \tan \theta}$ approaches 1.

9. $y = \dfrac{1}{h} \sin h$

10. $y = (1 + h)^{1/h}$

Section 8.1 Exercises

1.

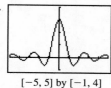

[0, 2] by [0, 1]

From the graph, the limit appears to be $\dfrac{1}{4}$.

$$\lim_{x \to 2} \frac{x-2}{x^2-4} = \lim_{x \to 2} \frac{1}{2x} = \frac{1}{4}$$

2.

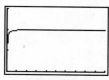

[−2, 2] by [−2, 6]

From the graph, the limit appears to be 5.

$$\lim_{x \to 0} \frac{\sin 5x}{x} = \lim_{x \to 0} \frac{5 \cos 5x}{1} = 5$$

3.

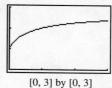

[0, 3] by [0, 3]

From the graph, the limit appears to be 1. The limit leads to the indeterminate form ∞^0.

$$\ln \left(1 + \frac{1}{x}\right)^x = x \ln \left(1 + \frac{1}{x}\right) = \frac{\ln \left(1 + \frac{1}{x}\right)}{\frac{1}{x}}$$

$$\lim_{x \to 0^+} \frac{\ln \left(1 + \frac{1}{x}\right)}{\frac{1}{x}} = \lim_{x \to 0^+} \frac{\frac{1}{1 + 1/x}\left(-\frac{1}{x^2}\right)}{-\frac{1}{x^2}}$$

$$= \lim_{x \to 0^+} \frac{1}{1 + \frac{1}{x}}$$

$$= \lim_{x \to 0^+} \frac{x}{x+1} = 0$$

Therefore,

$$\lim_{x \to 0^+} \left(1 + \frac{1}{x}\right)^x = \lim_{x \to 0^+} f(x) = \lim_{x \to 0^+} e^{\ln f(x)} = e^0 = 1.$$

4.

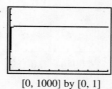

[0, 1000] by [0, 1]

From the graph, the limit appears to be about 0.714.

$$\lim_{x \to \infty} \frac{5x^2 - 3x}{7x^2 + 1} = \lim_{x \to \infty} \frac{10x - 3}{14x} = \lim_{x \to \infty} \frac{10}{14} = \frac{5}{7} \approx 0.71429$$

5. $\displaystyle \lim_{x \to 1} \frac{x^3 - 1}{4x^3 - x - 3} = \lim_{x \to 1} \frac{3x^2}{12x^2 - 1} = \frac{3}{11}$

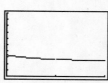

[0, 2] by [0, 1]

The graph supports the answer.

6. $\displaystyle \lim_{x \to 0} \frac{1 - \cos x}{x^2} = \lim_{x \to 0} \frac{\sin x}{2x} = \lim_{x \to 0} \frac{\cos x}{2} = \frac{1}{2}$

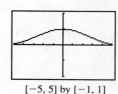

[−5, 5] by [−1, 1]

The graph supports the answer.

7. The limit leads to the indeterminate form 1^∞.

Let $\ln f(x) = \ln(e^x + x)^{1/x} = \dfrac{\ln(e^x + x)}{x}$.

$$\lim_{x \to 0^+} \frac{\ln(e^x + x)}{x} = \lim_{x \to 0^+} \frac{\dfrac{e^x + 1}{e^x + x}}{1} = \lim_{x \to 0^+} \frac{e^x + 1}{e^x + x} = \frac{2}{1} = 2$$

$$\lim_{x \to 0^+} (e^x + x)^{1/x} = \lim_{x \to 0^+} f(x) = \lim_{x \to 0^+} e^{\ln f(x)} = e^2$$

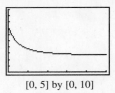

[0, 5] by [0, 10]

The graph supports the answer.

8. $\lim\limits_{x \to \infty} \dfrac{2x^2 + 3x}{x^3 + x + 1} = \lim\limits_{x \to \infty} \dfrac{4x + 3}{3x^2 + 1} = \lim\limits_{x \to \infty} \dfrac{4}{6x} = 0$

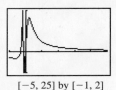

[−5, 25] by [−1, 2]

The graph supports the answer.

9. (a)

x	10	10^2	10^3	10^4	10^5
$f(x)$	1.1513	0.2303	0.0345	0.00461	0.00058

Estimate the limit to be 0.

(b) $\lim\limits_{x \to \infty} \dfrac{\ln x^5}{x} = \lim\limits_{x \to \infty} \dfrac{5 \ln x}{x} = \lim\limits_{x \to \infty} \dfrac{5/x}{1} = \dfrac{0}{1} = 0$

10. (a)

x	10^0	10^{-1}	10^{-2}	10^{-3}	10^{-4}
$f(x)$	0.1585	0.1666	0.1667	0.1667	0.1667

Estimate the limit to be $\dfrac{1}{6}$.

(b) $\lim\limits_{x \to 0^+} \dfrac{x - \sin x}{x^3} = \lim\limits_{x \to 0^+} \dfrac{1 - \cos x}{3x^2}$

$$= \lim_{x \to 0^+} \frac{\sin x}{6x}$$

$$= \lim_{x \to 0^+} \frac{\cos x}{6}$$

$$= \frac{1}{6}$$

11. Let $f(\theta) = \dfrac{\sin 3\theta}{\sin 4\theta}$.

θ	$\pm 10^0$	$\pm 10^{-1}$	$\pm 10^{-2}$	$\pm 10^{-3}$	$\pm 10^{-4}$
$f(\theta)$	−0.1865	0.7589	0.7501	0.7500	0.7500

Estimate the limit to be $\dfrac{3}{4}$.

$$\lim_{\theta \to 0} \frac{\sin 3\theta}{\sin 4\theta} = \lim_{\theta \to 0} \frac{3 \cos 3\theta}{4 \cos 4\theta} = \frac{3}{4}$$

12. Let $f(t) = \dfrac{1}{\sin t} - \dfrac{1}{t} = \dfrac{t - \sin t}{t \sin t}$.

t	$\pm 10^0$	$\pm 10^{-1}$	$\pm 10^{-2}$	$\pm 10^{-3}$
$f(t)$	±0.1884	±0.0167	±0.0017	±0.00017

Estimate the limit to be 0.

$$\lim_{t \to 0} \left(\frac{1}{\sin t} - \frac{1}{t} \right) = \lim_{t \to 0} \frac{t - \sin t}{t \sin t}$$

$$= \lim_{t \to 0} \frac{1 - \cos t}{t \cos t + \sin t}$$

$$= \lim_{t \to 0} \frac{\sin t}{-t \sin t + \cos t + \cos t} = 0$$

13. Let $f(x) = (1 + x)^{1/x}$.

x	10	10^2	10^3	10^4	10^5
$f(x)$	1.2710	1.0472	1.0069	1.0009	1.0001

Estimate the limit to be 1.

$$\ln f(x) = \frac{\ln(1 + x)}{x}$$

$$\lim_{x \to \infty} \frac{\ln(1 + x)}{x} = \lim_{x \to \infty} \frac{\dfrac{1}{1 + x}}{1} = \frac{0}{1} = 0$$

$$\lim_{x \to \infty} (1 + x)^{1/x} = \lim_{x \to \infty} f(x) = \lim_{x \to \infty} e^{\ln f(x)} = e^0 = 1$$

14. Let $f(x) = \dfrac{x - 2x^2}{3x^2 + 5x}$.

x	10	10^2	10^3	10^4	10^5
$f(x)$	−0.5429	−0.6525	−0.6652	−0.6665	−0.6667

Estimate the limit to be $-\dfrac{2}{3}$.

$$\lim_{x \to \infty} \frac{x - 2x^2}{3x^2 + 5x} = \lim_{x \to \infty} \frac{1 - 4x}{6x + 5} = \lim_{x \to \infty} -\frac{4}{6} = -\frac{2}{3}$$

15. $\lim\limits_{\theta \to 0} \dfrac{\sin \theta^2}{\theta} = \lim\limits_{\theta \to 0} \dfrac{2\theta \cos \theta^2}{1} = (2)(0) \cos(0)^2 = 0$

16. $\lim\limits_{\theta \to \pi/2} \dfrac{1 - \sin \theta}{1 + \cos 2\theta} = \lim\limits_{\theta \to \pi/2} \dfrac{-\cos \theta}{-2 \sin 2\theta}$

$$= \lim_{\theta \to \pi/2} \frac{\sin \theta}{-4 \cos 2\theta}$$

$$= \frac{\sin \pi/2}{-4 \cos \pi}$$

$$= \frac{1}{4}$$

17. $\lim\limits_{t \to 0} \dfrac{\cos t - 1}{e^t - t - 1} = \lim\limits_{t \to 0} \dfrac{-\sin t}{e^t - 1} = \lim\limits_{t \to 0} \dfrac{-\cos t}{e^t} = -1$

18. $\displaystyle\lim_{t\to 1}\frac{t-1}{\ln t-\sin\pi t}=\lim_{t\to 1}\frac{1}{\frac{1}{t}-\pi\cos\pi t}$

$\displaystyle=\frac{1}{1-\pi(-1)}$

$\displaystyle=\frac{1}{\pi+1}$

19. $\displaystyle\lim_{x\to\infty}\frac{\ln(x+1)}{\log_2 x}=\lim_{x\to\infty}\frac{\frac{1}{x+1}}{\frac{1}{x\ln 2}}$

$\displaystyle=\lim_{x\to\infty}\frac{x\ln 2}{x+1}$

$\displaystyle=\lim_{x\to\infty}\ln 2$

$=\ln 2$

20. $\displaystyle\lim_{x\to\infty}\frac{\log_2 x}{\log_3(x+3)}=\lim_{x\to\infty}\frac{\frac{1}{x\ln 2}}{\frac{1}{(x+3)\ln 3}}$

$\displaystyle=\lim_{x\to\infty}\frac{(x+3)\ln 3}{x\ln 2}$

$\displaystyle=\lim_{x\to\infty}\frac{x\ln 3+3\ln 3}{x\ln 2}$

$\displaystyle=\lim_{x\to\infty}\frac{\ln 3}{\ln 2}$

$\displaystyle=\frac{\ln 3}{\ln 2}$

21. $\displaystyle\lim_{y\to 0^+}\frac{\ln(y^2+2y)}{\ln y}=\lim_{y\to 0^+}\frac{\frac{2y+2}{y^2+2y}}{\frac{1}{y}}$

$\displaystyle=\lim_{y\to 0^+}\frac{y(2y+2)}{y^2+2y}$

$\displaystyle=\lim_{y\to 0^+}\frac{2y^2+2y}{y^2+2y}$

$\displaystyle=\lim_{y\to 0^+}\frac{4y+2}{2y+2}$

$\displaystyle=\frac{4(0)+2}{2(0)+2}=\frac{2}{2}=1$

22. $\displaystyle\lim_{y\to\pi/2}\left(\frac{\pi}{2}-y\right)\tan y=\lim_{y\to\pi/2}\frac{\left(\frac{\pi}{2}-y\right)\sin y}{\cos y}$

$\displaystyle=\lim_{y\to\pi/2}\frac{\left(\frac{\pi}{2}-y\right)\cos y+(-1)\sin y}{-\sin y}$

$\displaystyle=\frac{\left(\frac{\pi}{2}-\frac{\pi}{2}\right)\cos\frac{\pi}{2}+(-1)\sin\frac{\pi}{2}}{-\sin\frac{\pi}{2}}$

$\displaystyle=\frac{(-1)(1)}{-(1)}=1$

23. $\displaystyle\lim_{x\to 0^+}x\ln x=\lim_{x\to 0^+}\frac{\ln x}{\frac{1}{x}}$

$\displaystyle=\lim_{x\to 0^+}\frac{\frac{1}{x}}{-\frac{1}{x^2}}$

$\displaystyle=\lim_{x\to 0^+}\frac{-x^2}{x}$

$\displaystyle=\lim_{x\to 0^+}-x=0$

24. $\displaystyle\lim_{x\to\infty}x\tan\frac{1}{x}=\lim_{x\to\infty}\frac{\tan\frac{1}{x}}{\frac{1}{x}}$

$\displaystyle=\lim_{x\to\infty}\frac{-\frac{1}{x^2}\sec^2\frac{1}{x}}{-\frac{1}{x^2}}$

$\displaystyle=\lim_{x\to\infty}\sec^2\frac{1}{x}$

$=\sec^2 0=1$

25. $\displaystyle\lim_{x\to 0^+}(\csc x-\cot x+\cos x)$

$\displaystyle=\lim_{x\to 0^+}\left(\frac{1}{\sin x}-\frac{\cos x}{\sin x}+\cos x\right)$

$\displaystyle=\lim_{x\to 0^+}\frac{1-\cos x+\cos x\sin x}{\sin x}$

$\displaystyle=\lim_{x\to 0^+}\frac{\sin x+\cos x\cos x-\sin x\sin x}{\cos x}=1$

26. $\lim\limits_{x\to\infty} (\ln 2x - \ln (x + 1)) = \lim\limits_{x\to\infty} \ln \left(\dfrac{2x}{x + 1} \right)$

Let $f(x) = \dfrac{2x}{x + 1}$.

$\lim\limits_{x\to\infty} \dfrac{2x}{x + 1} = \lim\limits_{x\to\infty} \dfrac{2}{1} = 2$

Therefore,

$\lim\limits_{x\to\infty} (\ln 2x - \ln (x + 1)) = \lim\limits_{x\to\infty} \ln f(x) = \ln 2$

27. $\lim\limits_{x\to 0^+} (\ln x - \ln \sin x) = \lim\limits_{x\to 0^+} \ln \dfrac{x}{\sin x}$

Let $f(x) = \dfrac{x}{\sin x}$.

$\lim\limits_{x\to 0^+} \dfrac{x}{\sin x} = \lim\limits_{x\to 0^+} \dfrac{1}{\cos x} = 1$

Therefore,

$\lim\limits_{x\to 0^+} (\ln x - \ln \sin x) = \lim\limits_{x\to 0^+} \ln f(x) = \ln 1 = 0$

28. $\lim\limits_{x\to 0^+} \left(\dfrac{1}{x} - \dfrac{1}{\sqrt{x}} \right) = \lim\limits_{x\to 0^+} \dfrac{1 - \sqrt{x}}{x} = \infty$

29. The limit leads to the indeterminate form 1^∞.

Let $f(x) = (e^x + x)^{1/x}$.

$\ln (e^x + x)^{1/x} = \dfrac{\ln (e^x + x)}{x}$

$\lim\limits_{x\to 0} \dfrac{\ln (e^x + x)}{x} = \lim\limits_{x\to 0} \dfrac{\dfrac{e^x + 1}{e^x + x}}{1} = 2$

$\lim\limits_{x\to 0} (e^x + x)^{1/x} = \lim\limits_{x\to 0} e^{\ln f(x)} = e^2$

30. The limit leads to the indeterminate form ∞^0.

Let $f(x) = \left(\dfrac{1}{x^2} \right)^x$.

$\ln \left(\dfrac{1}{x^2} \right)^x = x \ln \left(\dfrac{1}{x^2} \right) = \dfrac{\ln \left(\dfrac{1}{x^2} \right)}{\dfrac{1}{x}}$

$\lim\limits_{x\to 0} \dfrac{\ln \left(\dfrac{1}{x^2} \right)}{\dfrac{1}{x}} = \lim\limits_{x\to 0} \dfrac{\dfrac{-2/x^3}{1/x^2}}{-1/x^2} = \lim\limits_{x\to 0} 2x = 0$

$\lim\limits_{x\to 0} \left(\dfrac{1}{x^2} \right)^x = \lim\limits_{x\to 0} e^{\ln f(x)} = e^0 = 1$

31. $\lim\limits_{x\to \pm\infty} \dfrac{3x - 5}{2x^2 - x + 2} = \lim\limits_{x\to \pm\infty} \dfrac{3}{4x - 1} = 0$

32. $\lim\limits_{x\to 0} \dfrac{\sin 7x}{\tan 11x} = \lim\limits_{x\to 0} \dfrac{7 \cos 7x}{11 \sec^2 11x} = \dfrac{7}{11}$

33. The limit leads to the indeterminate form ∞^0.

Let $f(x) = (\ln x)^{1/x}$.

$\ln (\ln x)^{1/x} = \dfrac{\ln (\ln x)}{x}$

$\lim\limits_{x\to\infty} \dfrac{\ln (\ln x)}{x} = \lim\limits_{x\to\infty} \dfrac{\dfrac{1/x}{\ln x}}{1} = \lim\limits_{x\to\infty} \dfrac{1}{x \ln x} = 0$

$\lim\limits_{x\to\infty} (\ln x)^{1/x} = \lim\limits_{x\to\infty} e^{\ln f(x)} = e^0 = 1$

34. The limit leads to the indeterminate form ∞^0.

Let $f(x) = (1 + 2x)^{1/(2 \ln x)}$.

$\ln (1 + 2x)^{1/(2 \ln x)} = \dfrac{\ln (1 + 2x)}{2 \ln x}$

$\lim\limits_{x\to\infty} \dfrac{\ln (1 + 2x)}{2 \ln x} = \lim\limits_{x\to\infty} \dfrac{\dfrac{2}{1 + 2x}}{\dfrac{2}{x}} = \lim\limits_{x\to\infty} \dfrac{x}{1 + 2x} = \lim\limits_{x\to\infty} \dfrac{1}{2} = \dfrac{1}{2}$

$\lim\limits_{x\to\infty} (1 + 2x)^{1/(2 \ln x)} = \lim\limits_{x\to\infty} e^{\ln f(x)} = e^{1/2} = \sqrt{e}$

35. The limit leads to the indeterminate form 0^0.

Let $f(x) = (x^2 - 2x + 1)^{x-1}$

$\ln (x^2 - 2x + 1)^{x-1} = (x - 1) \ln (x^2 - 2x + 1)$

$= \dfrac{\ln (x^2 - 2x + 1)}{\dfrac{1}{x - 1}}$

$\lim\limits_{x\to 1} \dfrac{\ln (x^2 - 2x + 1)}{\dfrac{1}{x - 1}} = \lim\limits_{x\to 1} \dfrac{\dfrac{2x - 2}{x^2 - 2x + 1}}{-\dfrac{1}{(x - 1)^2}}$

$= \lim\limits_{x\to 1} \dfrac{\dfrac{2(x - 1)}{(x - 1)^2}}{-\dfrac{1}{(x - 1)^2}}$

$= \lim\limits_{x\to 1} -2(x - 1) = 0$

$\lim\limits_{x\to 1} (x^2 - 2x + 1)^{x-1} = \lim\limits_{x\to 1} e^{\ln f(x)} = e^0 = 1$

36. The limit leads to the indeterminate form 0^0.

Let $f(x) = (\cos x)^{\cos x}$.

$\ln (\cos x)^{\cos x} = (\cos x) \ln (\cos x) = \dfrac{\ln (\cos x)}{\sec x}$

$\lim\limits_{x\to \pi/2^-} \dfrac{\ln (\cos x)}{\sec x} = \lim\limits_{x\to \pi/2^-} \dfrac{\dfrac{-\sin x}{\cos x}}{\sec x \tan x}$

$= \lim\limits_{x\to \pi/2^-} \dfrac{-\tan x}{\sec x \tan x}$

$= \lim\limits_{x\to \pi/2^-} -\cos x = 0$

$\lim\limits_{x\to \pi/2^-} (\cos x)^{\cos x} = \lim\limits_{x\to \pi/2^-} e^{\ln f(x)} = e^0 = 1$

37. The limit leads to the indeterminate form 1^∞.

Let $f(x) = (1 + x)^{1/x}$.

$$\ln (1 + x)^{1/x} = \frac{\ln (1 + x)}{x}$$

$$\lim_{x \to 0^+} \frac{\ln (1 + x)}{x} = \lim_{x \to 0^+} \frac{\frac{1}{1 + x}}{1} = 1$$

$$\lim_{x \to 0^+} (1 + x)^{1/x} = \lim_{x \to 0^+} e^{\ln f(x)} = e^1 = e$$

38. The limit leads to the indeterminate form 1^∞.

Let $f(x) = x^{1/(x-1)}$.

$$\ln x^{1/(x-1)} = \frac{\ln x}{x - 1}$$

$$\lim_{x \to 1} \frac{\ln x}{x - 1} = \lim_{x \to 1} \frac{1/x}{1} = 1$$

$$\lim_{x \to 1} x^{1/(x-1)} = \lim_{x \to 1} e^{\ln f(x)} = e^1 = e$$

39. The limit leads to the indeterminate form 0^0.

Let $f(x) = (\sin x)^x$.

$$\ln (\sin x)^x = x \ln (\sin x) = \frac{\ln (\sin x)}{\frac{1}{x}}$$

$$\lim_{x \to 0^+} \frac{\ln (\sin x)}{\frac{1}{x}} = \lim_{x \to 0^+} \frac{\frac{\cos x}{\sin x}}{-\frac{1}{x^2}}$$

$$= \lim_{x \to 0^+} \frac{-x^2 \cos x}{\sin x}$$

$$= \lim_{x \to 0^+} \frac{x^2 \sin x - 2x \cos x}{\cos x} = 0$$

$$\lim_{x \to 0^+} (\sin x)^x = \lim_{x \to 0^+} e^{\ln f(x)} = e^0 = 1$$

40. The limit leads to the indeterminate form 0^0.

Let $f(x) = (\sin x)^{\tan x}$

$$\ln (\sin x)^{\tan x} = \tan x \ln (\sin x) = \frac{\ln (\sin x)}{\cot x}$$

$$\lim_{x \to 0^+} \frac{\ln (\sin x)}{\cot x} = \lim_{x \to 0^+} \frac{\frac{\cos x}{\sin x}}{-\csc^2 x} = \lim_{x \to 0^+} (-\sin x \cos x) = 0$$

$$\lim_{x \to 0^+} (\sin x)^{\tan x} = \lim_{x \to 0^+} e^{\ln f(x)} = e^0 = 1$$

41. The limit leads to the indeterminate form $1^{-\infty}$.

Let $f(x) = x^{1/(1-x)}$.

$$\ln x^{1/(1-x)} = \frac{\ln x}{1 - x}$$

$$\lim_{x \to 1^+} \frac{\ln x}{1 - x} = \lim_{x \to 1^+} \frac{\frac{1}{x}}{-1} = -1$$

$$\lim_{x \to 1^+} x^{1/(1-x)} = \lim_{x \to 1^+} e^{\ln f(x)} = e^{-1} = \frac{1}{e}$$

42. $\displaystyle\int_x^{2x} \frac{dt}{t} = \Big[\ln |t|\Big]_x^{2x} = \ln |2x| - \ln |x| = \ln \left|\frac{2x}{x}\right|$

$$\lim_{x \to \infty} \int_x^{2x} \frac{dt}{t} = \lim_{x \to \infty} \ln \left|\frac{2x}{x}\right| = \lim_{x \to \infty} \ln 2 = \ln 2$$

43. (a) L'Hôpital's Rule does not help because applying L'Hôpital's Rule to this quotient essentially "inverts" the problem by interchanging the numerator and denominator (see below). It is still essentially the same problem and one is no closer to a solution. Applying L'Hôpital's Rule a second time returns to the original problem.

$$\lim_{x \to \infty} \frac{\sqrt{9x + 1}}{\sqrt{x + 1}} = \lim_{x \to \infty} \frac{(9/2)(9x + 1)^{-1/2}}{(1/2)(x + 1)^{-1/2}} = \lim_{x \to \infty} \frac{9\sqrt{x + 1}}{\sqrt{9x + 1}}$$

(b)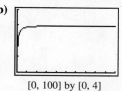

[0, 100] by [0, 4]

The limit appears to be 3.

(c) $\displaystyle\lim_{x \to \infty} \frac{\sqrt{9x + 1}}{\sqrt{x + 1}} = \lim_{x \to \infty} \frac{\sqrt{9 + \dfrac{1}{x}}}{\sqrt{1 + \dfrac{1}{x}}} = \frac{\sqrt{9}}{\sqrt{1}} = 3$

44. (a) L'Hôpital's Rule does not help because applying L'Hôpital's Rule to this quotient essentially "inverts" the problem by interchanging the numerator and denominator (see below). It is still essentially the same problem and one is no closer to a solution. Applying L'Hôpital's Rule a second time returns to the original problem.

$$\lim_{x \to \pi/2} \frac{\sec x}{\tan x} = \lim_{x \to \pi/2} \frac{\sec x \tan x}{\sec^2 x} = \lim_{x \to \pi/2} \frac{\tan x}{\sec x}$$

(b)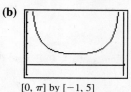

[0, π] by [-1, 5]

The limit appears to be 1.

(c) $\displaystyle\lim_{x \to \pi/2} \frac{\sec x}{\tan x} = \lim_{x \to \pi/2} \frac{\frac{1}{\cos x}}{\frac{\sin x}{\cos x}} = \lim_{x \to \pi/2} \frac{1}{\sin x} = 1$

45. Possible answers:

(a) $f(x) = 7(x - 3); g(x) = x - 3$

$$\lim_{x \to 3} \frac{f(x)}{g(x)} = \lim_{x \to 3} \frac{7(x - 3)}{x - 3} = \lim_{x \to 3} \frac{7}{1} = 7$$

(b) $f(x) = (x - 3)^2; g(x) = x - 3$

$$\lim_{x \to 3} \frac{f(x)}{g(x)} = \lim_{x \to 3} \frac{(x - 3)^2}{x - 3} = \lim_{x \to 3} \frac{2(x - 3)}{1} = 0$$

(c) $f(x) = x - 3; g(x) = (x - 3)^3$

$$\lim_{x \to 3} \frac{f(x)}{g(x)} = \lim_{x \to 3} \frac{x - 3}{(x - 3)^3} = \lim_{x \to 3} \frac{1}{3(x - 3)^2} = \infty$$

46. Answers may vary.

(a) $f(x) = 3x + 1$; $g(x) = x$

$$\lim_{x\to\infty}\frac{f(x)}{g(x)} = \lim_{x\to\infty}\frac{3x+1}{x} = \lim_{x\to\infty}\frac{3}{1} = 3$$

(b) $f(x) = x + 1$; $g(x) = x^2$

$$\lim_{x\to\infty}\frac{f(x)}{g(x)} = \lim_{x\to\infty}\frac{x+1}{x^2} = \lim_{x\to\infty}\frac{1}{2x} = 0$$

(c) $f(x) = x^2$; $g(x) = x + 1$

$$\lim_{x\to\infty}\frac{f(x)}{g(x)} = \lim_{x\to\infty}\frac{x^2}{x+1} = \lim_{x\to\infty}\frac{2x}{1} = \infty$$

47. Find c such that $\lim\limits_{x\to 0} f(x) = c$.

$$\begin{aligned}
\lim_{x\to 0} f(x) &= \lim_{x\to 0}\frac{9x - 3\sin 3x}{5x^3}\\
&= \lim_{x\to 0}\frac{9 - 9\cos 3x}{15x^2}\\
&= \lim_{x\to 0}\frac{27\sin 3x}{30x}\\
&= \lim_{x\to 0}\frac{81\cos 3x}{30} = \frac{81}{30} = \frac{27}{10}
\end{aligned}$$

Thus, $c = \dfrac{27}{10}$. This works since $\lim\limits_{x\to 0} f(x) = c = f(0)$, so f is continuous.

48. $f(x)$ is defined at $x \ne 0$. $\lim\limits_{x\to 0} f(x)$ leads to the indeterminate form 0^0.

$$\ln |x|^x = x\ln|x| = \frac{\ln|x|}{\dfrac{1}{x}}$$

$$\lim_{x\to 0}\frac{\ln|x|}{\dfrac{1}{x}} = \lim_{x\to 0}\frac{\dfrac{1}{x}}{-\dfrac{1}{x^2}} = \lim_{x\to 0} -x = 0$$

$$\lim_{x\to 0} |x|^x = \lim_{x\to 0} e^{x\ln|x|} = e^0 = 1$$

Thus, f has a removable discontinuity at $x = 0$. Extend the definition of f by letting $f(0) = 1$.

49. (a) The limit leads to the indeterminate form 1^∞.

Let $f(k) = \left(1 + \dfrac{r}{k}\right)^{kt}$.

$$\ln f(k) = kt\ln\left(1 + \frac{r}{k}\right) = \frac{t\ln\left(1 + \dfrac{r}{k}\right)}{\dfrac{1}{k}}$$

$$\lim_{k\to\infty}\frac{t\ln\left(1 + \dfrac{r}{k}\right)}{\dfrac{1}{k}} = \lim_{k\to\infty}\frac{t\left(-\dfrac{r}{k^2}\right)\left(1 + \dfrac{r}{k}\right)^{-1}}{-\dfrac{1}{k^2}}$$

$$= \lim_{k\to\infty}\frac{rt}{1 + \dfrac{r}{k}} = \frac{rt}{1} = rt$$

$$\lim_{k\to\infty} A_0\left(1 + \frac{r}{k}\right)^{kt} = A_0\lim_{k\to\infty}\left(1 + \frac{r}{k}\right)^{kt}$$

$$= A_0\lim_{k\to\infty} e^{\ln f(k)}$$

$$= A_0 e^{rt}$$

(b) Part (a) shows that as the number of compoundings per year increases toward infinity, the limit of interest compounded k times per year is interest compounded continuously.

50. (a) For $x \ne 0$, $\dfrac{f'(x)}{g'(x)} = \dfrac{1}{1} = 1$.

$$\lim_{x\to 0}\frac{f'(x)}{g'(x)} = 1$$
$$\lim_{x\to 0}\frac{f(x)}{g(x)} = \frac{2}{1} = 2$$

(b) This does not contradict L'Hôpital's Rule since $\lim\limits_{x\to 0} f(x) = 2$ and $\lim\limits_{x\to 0} g(x) = 1$.

51. (a) $A(t) = \displaystyle\int_0^t e^{-x}\,dx = \left[-e^{-x}\right]_0^t = -e^{-t} + 1$

$$\lim_{t\to\infty} A(t) = \lim_{t\to\infty}(-e^{-t} + 1) = \lim_{t\to\infty}\left(-\frac{1}{e^t} + 1\right) = 1$$

(b) $V(t) = \pi\displaystyle\int_0^t (e^{-x})^2\,dx$

$$= \pi\int_0^t e^{-2x}\,dx$$

$$= \pi\left[-\frac{1}{2}e^{-2x}\right]_0^t$$

$$= \pi\left(-\frac{1}{2}e^{-2t} + \frac{1}{2}\right)$$

$$= \frac{\pi}{2}(-e^{-2t} + 1)$$

$$\lim_{t\to\infty}\frac{V(t)}{A(t)} = \lim_{t\to\infty}\frac{\dfrac{\pi}{2}(-e^{-2t} + 1)}{-e^{-t} + 1} = \frac{\dfrac{\pi}{2}(1)}{1} = \frac{\pi}{2}$$

(c) $\displaystyle\lim_{t\to 0^+}\frac{V(t)}{A(t)} = \lim_{t\to 0^+}\frac{\dfrac{\pi}{2}(-e^{-2t} + 1)}{-e^{-t} + 1}$

$$= \lim_{t\to 0^+}\frac{\dfrac{\pi}{2}(2e^{-2t})}{e^{-t}}$$

$$= \frac{\dfrac{\pi}{2}(2)}{1} = \pi$$

52. (a)

x	$f(x)$
0.1	0.04542
0.01	0.00495
0.001	0.00050
0.0001	0.00005

The limit appears to be 0.

(b) $\displaystyle\lim_{x\to 0}\frac{\sin x}{1 + 2x} = \frac{0}{1} = 0$

L'Hôpital's Rule is not applied here because the limit is not of the form $\dfrac{0}{0}$ or $\dfrac{\infty}{\infty}$, since the denominator has limit 1.

53. (a) $f(x) = e^{x \ln (1 + 1/x)}$

$1 + \dfrac{1}{x} > 0$ when $x < -1$ or $x > 0$

Domain: $(-\infty, -1) \cup (0, \infty)$

(b) The form is 0^{-1}, so $\lim\limits_{x \to -1^{-}} f(x) = \infty$

(c) $\lim\limits_{x \to -\infty} x \ln \left(1 + \dfrac{1}{x}\right) = \lim\limits_{x \to -\infty} \dfrac{\ln \left(1 + \dfrac{1}{x}\right)}{\dfrac{1}{x}}$

$= \lim\limits_{x \to -\infty} \dfrac{\left(-\dfrac{1}{x^2}\right)\left(1 + \dfrac{1}{x}\right)^{-1}}{-\dfrac{1}{x^2}}$

$= \lim\limits_{x \to -\infty} \dfrac{1}{1 + \dfrac{1}{x}} = 1$

$\lim\limits_{x \to -\infty} f(x) = \lim\limits_{x \to -\infty} e^{x \ln (1 + 1/x)} = e$

54. (a) Because the difference in the numerator is so small compared to the values being subtracted, any calculator or computer with limited precision will give the incorrect result that $1 - \cos x^6$ is 0 for even moderately small values of x. For example, at $x = 0.1$, $\cos x^6 \approx 0.9999999999995$ (13 places), so on a 10-place calculator, $\cos x^6 = 1$ and $1 - \cos x^6 = 0$.

(b) Same reason as in part (a) applies.

(c) $\lim\limits_{x \to 0} \dfrac{1 - \cos x^6}{x^{12}} = \lim\limits_{x \to 0} \dfrac{6x^5 \sin x^6}{12x^{11}}$

$= \lim\limits_{x \to 0} \dfrac{\sin x^6}{2x^6}$

$= \lim\limits_{x \to 0} \dfrac{6x^5 \cos x^6}{12x^5}$

$= \lim\limits_{x \to 0} \dfrac{\cos x^6}{2} = \dfrac{1}{2}$

(d) The graph and/or table on a grapher show the value of the function to be 0 for x-values moderately close to 0, but the limit is 1/2. The calculator is giving unreliable information because there is significant round-off error in computing values of this function on a limited precision device.

55. (a) $f'(x) = 3x^2$, $g'(x) = 2x - 1$

$f(1) - f(-1) = 2$, $g(1) - g(-1) = -2$

$\dfrac{3c^2}{2c - 1} = \dfrac{2}{-2}$

$3c^2 = -2c + 1$

$3c^2 + 2c - 1 = 0$

$(3c - 1)(c + 1) = 0$

$c = \dfrac{1}{3}$ or $c = -1$

The value of c that satisfies the property is $c = \dfrac{1}{3}$.

(b) $f'(x) = -\sin x$, $g'(x) = \cos x$

$f\left(\dfrac{\pi}{2}\right) - f(0) = -1$, $g\left(\dfrac{\pi}{2}\right) - g(0) = 1$

$\dfrac{-\sin c}{\cos c} = \dfrac{-1}{1}$

$\tan c = 1$

$c = \tan^{-1} 1 = \dfrac{\pi}{4}$ on $\left(0, \dfrac{\pi}{2}\right)$

56. (a) $\ln f(x)^{g(x)} = g(x) \ln f(x)$

$\lim\limits_{x \to c} (g(x) \ln f(x)) = \left(\lim\limits_{x \to c} g(x)\right)\left(\lim\limits_{x \to c} \ln f(x)\right)$

$= \infty(-\infty) = -\infty$

$\lim\limits_{x \to c} f(x)^{g(x)} = \lim\limits_{x \to c} e^{\ln f(x)^{g(x)}} = e^{-\infty} = 0$

(b) $\lim\limits_{x \to c} (g(x) \ln f(x)) = \left(\lim\limits_{x \to c} g(x)\right)\left(\lim\limits_{x \to c} \ln f(x)\right)$

$= (-\infty)(-\infty) = \infty$

$\lim\limits_{x \to c} f(x)^{g(x)} = \lim\limits_{x \to c} e^{\ln f(x)^{g(x)}} = e^{\infty} = \infty$

■ Section 8.2 Relative Rates of Growth

(pp. 425–433)

Exploration 1   Comparing Rates of Growth as $x \to \infty$

1. $\lim\limits_{x \to \infty} \dfrac{a^x}{x^2} = \lim\limits_{x \to \infty} \dfrac{(\ln a)(a^x)}{2x} = \lim\limits_{x \to \infty} \dfrac{(\ln a)^2 a^x}{2} = \infty$, so a^x grows faster than x^2 as $x \to \infty$.

2. $\lim\limits_{x \to \infty} \dfrac{3^x}{2^x} = \lim\limits_{x \to \infty} 1.5^x = \infty$

3. $\lim\limits_{x \to \infty} \dfrac{a^x}{b^x} = \lim\limits_{x \to \infty} \left(\dfrac{a}{b}\right)^x = \infty$ because $\dfrac{a}{b} > 1$.

Quick Review 8.2

1. $\lim\limits_{x \to \infty} \dfrac{\ln x}{e^x} = \lim\limits_{x \to \infty} \dfrac{\frac{1}{x}}{e^x} = 0$

2. $\lim\limits_{x \to \infty} \dfrac{e^x}{x^3} = \lim\limits_{x \to \infty} \dfrac{e^x}{3x^2} = \lim\limits_{x \to \infty} \dfrac{e^x}{6x} = \lim\limits_{x \to \infty} \dfrac{e^x}{6} = \infty$

3. $\lim\limits_{x \to -\infty} \dfrac{x^2}{e^{2x}} = \infty$

4. $\lim\limits_{x \to \infty} \dfrac{x^2}{e^{2x}} = \lim\limits_{x \to \infty} \dfrac{2x}{2e^{2x}} = \lim\limits_{x \to \infty} \dfrac{2}{4e^{2x}} = 0$

5. $-3x^4$

6. $\dfrac{2x^3}{x} = 2x^2$

7. $\lim\limits_{x \to \infty} \dfrac{f(x)}{g(x)} = \lim\limits_{x \to \infty} \dfrac{x + \ln x}{x} = \lim\limits_{x \to \infty} \dfrac{1 + \dfrac{1}{x}}{1} = 1$

8. $\lim\limits_{x \to \infty} \dfrac{f(x)}{g(x)} = \lim\limits_{x \to \infty} \dfrac{\sqrt{4x^2 + 5x}}{2x} = \lim\limits_{x \to \infty} \sqrt{1 + \dfrac{5}{4x}} = 1$

9. (a) $f(x) = \dfrac{e^x + x^2}{e^x} = 1 + \dfrac{x^2}{e^x}$

$f'(x) = \dfrac{2xe^x - x^2e^x}{e^{2x}} = \dfrac{2x - x^2}{e^x}$

$\dfrac{2x - x^2}{e^x} = 0$

$x(2 - x) = 0$

$x = 0 \text{ or } x = 2$

$f'(x) < 0$ for $x < 0$ or $x > 2$

The graph decreases, increases, and then decreases.

$f(0) = 1; f(2) = 1 + \dfrac{4}{e^2} \approx 1.541$

f has a local maximum at $\approx (2, 1.541)$ and has a local

minimum at $(0, 1)$.

(b) f is increasing on $[0, 2]$

(c) f is decreasing on $(-\infty, 0]$ and $[2, \infty)$.

10. $f(x) = \dfrac{x + \sin x}{x} = 1 + \dfrac{\sin x}{x}, x \neq 0$

Observe that $\left|\dfrac{\sin x}{x}\right| < 1$ since $|\sin x| < |x|$ for $x \neq 0$.

$\lim\limits_{x \to 0} f(x) = 1 + \lim\limits_{x \to 0} \dfrac{\sin x}{x} = 1 + 1 = 2$

Thus the values of f get close to 2 as x gets close to 0, so f

doesn't have an absolute maximum value. f is not defined at

0.

Section 8.2 Exercises

1. $\lim\limits_{x \to \infty} \dfrac{x^3 - 3x + 1}{e^x} = \lim\limits_{x \to \infty} \dfrac{3x^2 - 3}{e^x} = \lim\limits_{x \to \infty} \dfrac{6x}{e^x} = \lim\limits_{x \to \infty} \dfrac{6}{e^x} = 0$

$x^3 - 3x + 1$ grows slower than e^x as $x \to \infty$.

2. First observe that $\sqrt{1 + x^4}$ grows at the same rate as x^2.

$\lim\limits_{x \to \infty} \dfrac{\sqrt{1 + x^4}}{x^2} = \lim\limits_{x \to \infty} \sqrt{\dfrac{1 + x^4}{x^4}} = \lim\limits_{x \to \infty} \sqrt{\dfrac{1}{x^4} + 1} = 1$

Next compare x^2 with e^x.

$\lim\limits_{x \to \infty} \dfrac{x^2}{e^x} = \lim\limits_{x \to \infty} \dfrac{2x}{e^x} = \lim\limits_{x \to \infty} \dfrac{2}{e^x} = 0$

x^2 grows slower than e^x as $x \to \infty$, so $\sqrt{1 + x^4}$ grows slower

than e^x as $x \to \infty$.

3. $\lim\limits_{x \to \infty} \dfrac{4^x}{e^x} = \lim\limits_{x \to \infty} \left(\dfrac{4}{e}\right)^x = \infty$ since $\dfrac{4}{e} > 1$.

4^x grows faster than e^x as $x \to \infty$.

4. $\lim\limits_{x \to \infty} \dfrac{(5/2)^x}{e^x} = \lim\limits_{x \to \infty} \left(\dfrac{5}{2e}\right)^x = 0$ since $\dfrac{5}{2e} < 1$.

$\left(\dfrac{5}{2}\right)^x$ grows slower than e^x as $x \to \infty$.

5. $\lim\limits_{x \to \infty} \dfrac{e^{x+1}}{e^x} = \lim\limits_{x \to \infty} e = e$

e^{x+1} grows at the same rate as e^x as $x \to \infty$.

6. $\lim\limits_{x \to \infty} \dfrac{x \ln x - x}{e^x} = \lim\limits_{x \to \infty} \dfrac{x\left(\dfrac{1}{x}\right) + \ln x - 1}{e^x}$

$= \lim\limits_{x \to \infty} \dfrac{\ln x}{e^x}$

$= \lim\limits_{x \to \infty} \dfrac{1/x}{e^x} = 0$

$x \ln x - x$ grows slower than e^x as $x \to \infty$.

7. $\lim\limits_{x \to \infty} \dfrac{e^{\cos x}}{e^x} = 0$ since $e^{\cos x} \leq e$ for all x.

$e^{\cos x}$ grows slower than e^x as $x \to \infty$.

8. $\lim\limits_{x \to \infty} \dfrac{xe^x}{e^x} = \lim\limits_{x \to \infty} x = \infty$

xe^x grows faster than e^x as $x \to \infty$.

9. $\lim\limits_{x \to \infty} \dfrac{x^{1000}}{e^x} = 0$ $\left(\text{Repeated application of L'Hôpital's Rule}\right.$

gets $\lim\limits_{x \to \infty} \dfrac{1000!}{e^x} = 0.\Big)$ x^{1000} grows slower than e^x as $x \to \infty$.

10. $\lim\limits_{x \to \infty} \dfrac{(e^x + e^{-x})/2}{e^x} = \lim\limits_{x \to \infty} \left(\dfrac{1}{2} + \dfrac{1}{2e^{2x}}\right) = \dfrac{1}{2}$

$\dfrac{e^x + e^{-x}}{2}$ grows at the same rate as e^x as $x \to \infty$.

11. $\lim\limits_{x \to \infty} \dfrac{x^2 + 4x}{x^2} = \lim\limits_{x \to \infty} \left(1 + \dfrac{4}{x}\right) = 1$

$x^2 + 4x$ grows at the same rate as x^2 as $x \to \infty$.

12. $\lim\limits_{x \to \infty} \dfrac{x^3 + 3}{x^2} = \lim\limits_{x \to \infty} \left(x + \dfrac{3}{x^2}\right) = \infty$

$x^3 + 3$ grows faster than x^2 as $x \to \infty$.

13. $\lim\limits_{x \to \infty} \dfrac{15x + 3}{x^2} = \lim\limits_{x \to \infty} \left(\dfrac{15}{x} + \dfrac{3}{x^2}\right) = 0$

$15x + 3$ grows slower than x^2 as $x \to \infty$.

14. $\lim\limits_{x \to \infty} \dfrac{\sqrt{x^4 + 5x}}{x^2} = \lim\limits_{x \to \infty} \sqrt{\dfrac{x^4 + 5x}{x^4}} = \lim\limits_{x \to \infty} \sqrt{1 + \dfrac{5}{x^3}} = 1$

$\sqrt{x^4 + 5x}$ grows at the same rate as x^2 as $x \to \infty$.

15. $\lim\limits_{x \to \infty} \dfrac{\ln x}{x^2} = \lim\limits_{x \to \infty} \dfrac{1/x}{2x} = \lim\limits_{x \to \infty} \dfrac{1}{2x^2} = 0$

$\ln x$ grows slower than x^2 as $x \to \infty$.

16. $\lim\limits_{x \to \infty} \dfrac{2^x}{x^2} = \lim\limits_{x \to \infty} \dfrac{(\ln 2)2^x}{2x} = \lim\limits_{x \to \infty} \dfrac{(\ln 2)^2 \, 2^x}{2} = \infty$.

2^x grows faster than x^2 as $x \to \infty$.

17. $\lim\limits_{x \to \infty} \dfrac{\log_2 x^2}{\ln x} = \lim\limits_{x \to \infty} \dfrac{2 \log_2 x}{\ln x} = \lim\limits_{x \to \infty} \dfrac{2(\ln x)/(\ln 2)}{\ln x} = \dfrac{2}{\ln 2}$

$\log_2 x^2$ grows at the same rate as $\ln x$ as $x \to \infty$.

18. $\lim\limits_{x \to \infty} \dfrac{\log \sqrt{x}}{\ln x} = \lim\limits_{x \to \infty} \dfrac{\log x}{2 \ln x} = \lim\limits_{x \to \infty} \dfrac{(\ln x)/(\ln 10)}{2 \ln x} = \dfrac{1}{2 \ln 10}$

$\log \sqrt{x}$ grows at the same rate as $\ln x$ as $x \to \infty$.

19. $\lim\limits_{x\to\infty} \dfrac{1/\sqrt{x}}{\ln x} = \lim\limits_{x\to\infty} \dfrac{1}{\sqrt{x}\,\ln x} = 0$

$\dfrac{1}{\sqrt{x}}$ grows slower than $\ln x$ as $x\to\infty$.

20. $\lim\limits_{x\to\infty} \dfrac{e^{-x}}{\ln x} = \lim\limits_{x\to\infty} \dfrac{1}{e^x \ln x} = 0$

e^{-x} grows slower than $\ln x$ as $x\to\infty$.

21. $\lim\limits_{x\to\infty} \dfrac{x - 2\ln x}{\ln x} = \lim\limits_{x\to\infty}\left(\dfrac{x}{\ln x} - 2\right) = \lim\limits_{x\to\infty}\left(\dfrac{1}{1/x} - 2\right)$

$\quad = \lim\limits_{x\to\infty}(x - 2) = \infty$

$x - 2\ln x$ grows faster than $\ln x$ as $x\to\infty$.

22. $\lim\limits_{x\to\infty} \dfrac{5\ln x}{\ln x} = 5$

$5\ln x$ grows at the same rate as $\ln x$ as $x\to\infty$.

23. Compare e^x to x^x.

$\lim\limits_{x\to\infty} \dfrac{e^x}{x^x} = \lim\limits_{x\to\infty}\left(\dfrac{e}{x}\right)^x = 0$

e^x grows slower than x^x.

Compare e^x to $(\ln x)^x$.

$\lim\limits_{x\to\infty} \dfrac{e^x}{(\ln x)^x} = \lim\limits_{x\to\infty}\left(\dfrac{e}{\ln x}\right)^x = 0$

e^x grows slower than $(\ln x)^x$.

Compare e^x to $e^{x/2}$.

$\lim\limits_{x\to\infty} \dfrac{e^x}{e^{x/2}} = \lim\limits_{x\to\infty} e^{x/2} = \infty$

e^x grows faster than $e^{x/2}$.

Compare x^x to $(\ln x)^x$.

$\lim\limits_{x\to\infty} \dfrac{x^x}{(\ln x)^x} = \lim\limits_{x\to\infty}\left(\dfrac{x}{\ln x}\right)^x = \infty$ since $\lim\limits_{x\to\infty}\dfrac{x}{\ln x} = \lim\limits_{x\to\infty}\dfrac{1}{1/x} = \infty$.

x^x grows faster than $(\ln x)^x$.

Thus, in order from slowest-growing to fastest-growing, we get $e^{x/2}$, e^x, $(\ln x)^x$, x^x.

24. Compare 2^x to x^2.

$\lim\limits_{x\to\infty} \dfrac{2^x}{x^2} = \lim\limits_{x\to\infty} \dfrac{(\ln 2)2^x}{2x} = \lim\limits_{x\to\infty} \dfrac{(\ln 2)^2\, 2^x}{2} = \infty$

2^x grows faster than x^2.

Compare 2^x to $(\ln 2)^x$.

$\lim\limits_{x\to\infty} \dfrac{2^x}{(\ln 2)^x} = \lim\limits_{x\to\infty}\left(\dfrac{2}{\ln 2}\right)^x = \infty$ since $\dfrac{2}{\ln 2} > 1$.

2^x grows faster than $(\ln 2)^x$.

Compare 2^x to e^x.

$\lim\limits_{x\to\infty} \dfrac{2^x}{e^x} = \lim\limits_{x\to\infty}\left(\dfrac{2}{e}\right)^x = 0$ since $\dfrac{2}{e} < 1$.

2^x grows slower than e^x.

Compare x^2 to $(\ln 2)^x$.

$\lim\limits_{x\to\infty} \dfrac{x^2}{(\ln 2)^x} = \infty$ since $\lim\limits_{x\to\infty} x^2 = \infty$ and $\lim\limits_{x\to\infty} (\ln 2)^x = 0$.

x^2 grows faster than $(\ln 2)^x$.

Thus, in order from slowest-growing to fastest-growing, we get $(\ln 2)^x$, x^2, 2^x, e^x.

25. Compare f_1 to f_2.

$\lim\limits_{x\to\infty} \dfrac{f_2(x)}{f_1(x)} = \lim\limits_{x\to\infty} \dfrac{\sqrt{10x + 1}}{\sqrt{x}} = \lim\limits_{x\to\infty} \sqrt{10 + \dfrac{1}{x}} = \sqrt{10}$

Thus f_1 and f_2 grow at the same rate.

Compare f_1 to f_3.

$\lim\limits_{x\to\infty} \dfrac{f_3(x)}{f_1(x)} = \lim\limits_{x\to\infty} \dfrac{\sqrt{x + 1}}{\sqrt{x}} = \lim\limits_{x\to\infty} \sqrt{1 + \dfrac{1}{x}} = 1$

Thus f_1 and f_3 grow at the same rate.

By transitivity, f_2 and f_3 grow at the same rate, so all three functions grow at the same rate as $x\to\infty$.

26. Compare f_1 to f_2.

$\lim\limits_{x\to\infty} \dfrac{f_2(x)}{f_1(x)} = \lim\limits_{x\to\infty} \dfrac{\sqrt{x^4 + x}}{x^2} = \lim\limits_{x\to\infty} \sqrt{1 + \dfrac{1}{x^3}} = 1$

Thus f_1 and f_2 grow at the same rate.

Compare f_1 to f_3.

$\lim\limits_{x\to\infty} \dfrac{f_3(x)}{f_1(x)} = \lim\limits_{x\to\infty} \dfrac{\sqrt{x^4 - x^3}}{x^2} = \lim\limits_{x\to\infty} \sqrt{1 - \dfrac{1}{x}} = 1$

Thus f_1 and f_3 grow at the same rate.

By transitivity, f_2 and f_3 grow at the same rate, so all three functions grow at the same rate as $x\to\infty$.

27. Compare f_1 to f_2.

$\lim\limits_{x\to\infty} \dfrac{f_2(x)}{f_1(x)} = \lim\limits_{x\to\infty} \dfrac{\sqrt{9^x + 2^x}}{3^x}$

$\quad = \lim\limits_{x\to\infty} \dfrac{\sqrt{9^x + 2^x}}{\sqrt{9^x}}$

$\quad = \lim\limits_{x\to\infty} \sqrt{1 + \left(\dfrac{2}{9}\right)^x} = 1$

Thus f_1 and f_2 grow at the same rate.

Compare f_1 to f_3.

$\lim\limits_{x\to\infty} \dfrac{f_3(x)}{f_1(x)} = \lim\limits_{x\to\infty} \dfrac{\sqrt{9^x - 4^x}}{3^x}$

$\quad = \lim\limits_{x\to\infty} \dfrac{\sqrt{9^x - 4^x}}{\sqrt{9^x}}$

$\quad = \lim\limits_{x\to\infty} \sqrt{1 - \left(\dfrac{4}{9}\right)^x} = 1$

Thus f_1 and f_3 grow at the same rate.

By transitivity, f_2 and f_3 grow at the same rate, so all three functions grow at the same rate as $x\to\infty$.

28. Compare f_1 to f_2.

$$\lim_{x \to \infty} \frac{f_2(x)}{f_1(x)} = \lim_{x \to \infty} \frac{\dfrac{x^4 + 2x^2 - 1}{x + 1}}{x^3}$$

$$= \lim_{x \to \infty} \frac{x^4 + 2x^2 - 1}{x^4 + x^3}$$

$$= \lim_{x \to \infty} \frac{1 + \dfrac{2}{x^2} - \dfrac{1}{x^4}}{1 + \dfrac{1}{x}} = 1$$

Thus f_1 and f_2 grow at the same rate.

Compare f_1 and f_3.

$$\lim_{x \to \infty} \frac{f_3(x)}{f_1(x)} = \lim_{x \to \infty} \frac{\dfrac{2x^5 - 1}{x^2 + 1}}{x^3}$$

$$= \lim_{x \to \infty} \frac{2x^5 - 1}{x^5 + x^3}$$

$$= \lim_{x \to \infty} \frac{2 - \dfrac{1}{x^5}}{1 + \dfrac{1}{x^2}} = 2$$

Thus f_1 and f_3 grow at the same rate.
By transitivity, f_2 and f_3 grow at the same rate, so all three functions grow at the same rate.

29. (a) False, since $\lim\limits_{x \to \infty} \dfrac{x}{x} = 1 \neq 0$.

(b) False, since $\lim\limits_{x \to \infty} \dfrac{x}{x + 5} = 1 \neq 0$.

(c) True, since $\lim\limits_{x \to \infty} \dfrac{x}{x + 5} = 1 \leq 1$.

(d) True, since $\lim\limits_{x \to \infty} \dfrac{x}{2x} = \dfrac{1}{2} \leq 1$.

(e) True, since $\lim\limits_{x \to \infty} \dfrac{e^x}{e^{2x}} = \lim\limits_{x \to \infty} \dfrac{1}{e^x} = 0$.

(f) True, since $\lim\limits_{x \to \infty} \dfrac{x + \ln x}{x} = \lim\limits_{x \to \infty} \dfrac{1 + \dfrac{1}{x}}{1} = 1 \leq 1$.

(g) False, since $\lim\limits_{x \to \infty} \dfrac{\ln x}{\ln 2x} = \lim\limits_{x \to \infty} \dfrac{1/x}{1/x} = 1 \neq 0$.

(h) True, since $\lim\limits_{x \to \infty} \dfrac{\sqrt{x^2 + 5}}{x} = \lim\limits_{x \to \infty} \sqrt{1 + \dfrac{5}{x^2}} = 1 \leq 1$.

30. (a) True, since $\lim\limits_{x \to \infty} \dfrac{\dfrac{1}{x + 3}}{\dfrac{1}{x}} = \lim\limits_{x \to \infty} \dfrac{x}{x + 3} = 1 \leq 1$.

(b) True, since $\lim\limits_{x \to \infty} \dfrac{\dfrac{1}{x} + \dfrac{1}{x^2}}{\dfrac{1}{x}} = \lim\limits_{x \to \infty} \dfrac{1 + \dfrac{1}{x}}{1} = 1 \leq 1$.

(c) False, since $\lim\limits_{x \to \infty} \dfrac{\dfrac{1}{x} - \dfrac{1}{x^2}}{\dfrac{1}{x}} = \lim\limits_{x \to \infty} \dfrac{1 - \dfrac{1}{x}}{1} = 1 \neq 0$.

(d) True, since $\lim\limits_{x \to \infty} \dfrac{2 + \cos x}{2} \leq \lim\limits_{x \to \infty} \dfrac{3}{2} = \dfrac{3}{2}$.

(e) True, since $\lim\limits_{x \to \infty} \dfrac{e^x + x}{e^x} = \lim\limits_{x \to \infty} \dfrac{e^x + 1}{e^x}$

$$= \lim_{x \to \infty} \frac{1 + \dfrac{1}{e^x}}{1} = 1 \leq 1.$$

(f) True, since $\lim\limits_{x \to \infty} \dfrac{x \ln x}{x^2} = \lim\limits_{x \to \infty} \dfrac{\ln x}{x} = \lim\limits_{x \to \infty} \dfrac{1/x}{1} = 0$.

(g) True, since $\lim\limits_{x \to \infty} \dfrac{\ln (\ln x)}{\ln x} = \lim\limits_{x \to \infty} \dfrac{\dfrac{1}{x \ln x}}{\dfrac{1}{x}}$

$$= \lim_{x \to \infty} \frac{1}{\ln x} = 0 \leq 1.$$

(h) False, since $\lim\limits_{x \to \infty} \dfrac{\ln x}{\ln (x^2 + 1)} = \lim\limits_{x \to \infty} \dfrac{1/x}{\dfrac{2x}{x^2 + 1}}$

$$= \lim_{x \to \infty} \frac{x^2 + 1}{2x^2} = \frac{1}{2} \neq 0.$$

31. From the graph, $\lim\limits_{x \to \infty} \dfrac{f(x)}{g(x)} = \infty$, so $\lim\limits_{x \to \infty} \dfrac{g(x)}{f(x)} = 0$.
Thus $g = o(f)$, so **ii** is true.

32. From the graph, $\lim\limits_{x \to \infty} \dfrac{f(x)}{g(x)} = 0$. Thus $f = o(g)$, so **i** is true.

33. From the graph, $\lim\limits_{x \to \infty} \dfrac{f(x)}{g(x)} \leq 1$ and not equal to zero. Thus, f and g grow at the same rate, so **iii** is true.

34. From the graph, $\lim\limits_{x \to \infty} \dfrac{f(x)}{g(x)} \leq 3$ and not equal to zero. Thus, f and g grow at the same rate, so **iii** is true.

35. (a) The nth derivative of x^n is $n!$, a constant. We can apply L'Hôpital's Rule n times to find $\lim\limits_{x \to \infty} \dfrac{e^x}{x^n}$.

$$\lim_{x \to \infty} \frac{e^x}{x^n} = \cdots = \lim_{x \to \infty} \frac{e^x}{n!} = \infty$$

Thus e^x grows faster than x^n as $x \to \infty$ for any positive integer n.

(b) The nth derivative of a^x, $a > 1$, is $(\ln a)^n a^x$. We can apply L'Hôpital's Rule n times to find $\lim\limits_{x \to \infty} \dfrac{a^x}{x^n}$.

$$\lim_{x \to \infty} \frac{a^x}{x^n} = \cdots = \lim_{x \to \infty} \frac{(\ln a)^n a^x}{n!} = \infty$$

Thus a^x grows faster than x^n as $x \to \infty$ for any positive integer n.

36. (a) Apply L'Hôpital's Rule n times to find

$$\lim_{x \to \infty} \frac{e^x}{a_n x^n + a_{n-1} x^{n-1} + \cdots + a_1 x + a_0}.$$

$$\lim_{x \to \infty} \frac{e^x}{a_n x^n + a_{n-1} x^{n-1} + \cdots + a_1 x + a_0} = \lim_{x \to \infty} \frac{e^x}{a_n n!} = \infty$$

Thus e^x grows faster than

$$a_n x^n + a_{n-1} x^{n-1} + \cdots + a_1 x + a_0 \text{ as } x \to \infty.$$

(b) Apply L'Hôpital's Rule n times to find

$$\lim_{x \to \infty} \frac{a^x}{a_n x^n + a_{n-1} x^{n-1} + \cdots + a_1 x + a_0}.$$

$$\lim_{x \to \infty} \frac{a^x}{a_n x^n + a_{n-1} x^{n-1} + \cdots + a_1 x + a_0} = \cdots$$

$$= \lim_{x \to \infty} \frac{(\ln a)^n a^x}{a_n n!} = \infty$$

Thus a_x grows faster than

$$a_n x^n + a_{n-1} x^{n-1} + \cdots + a_1 x + a_0 \text{ as } x \to \infty.$$

37. (a) $\displaystyle \lim_{x \to \infty} \frac{\ln x}{x^{1/n}} = \lim_{x \to \infty} \frac{\frac{1}{x}}{\frac{1}{n} x^{(1/n)-1}} = \lim_{x \to \infty} \frac{n}{x^{1/n}} = 0$

Thus $\ln x$ grows slower than $x^{1/n}$ as $x \to \infty$ for any

positive integer n.

(b) $\displaystyle \lim_{x \to \infty} \frac{\ln x}{x^a} = \lim_{x \to \infty} \frac{\frac{1}{x}}{a x^{a-1}} = \lim_{x \to \infty} \frac{1}{a x^a} = 0$

Thus $\ln x$ grows slower than x^a as $x \to \infty$ for any number

$a > 0$.

38. $\displaystyle \lim_{x \to \infty} \frac{\ln x}{a_n x^n + a_{n-1} x^{n-1} + \cdots + a_1 x + a_0}$

$$= \lim_{x \to \infty} \frac{\frac{1}{x}}{n a_n x^{n-1} + (n-1) a_{n-1} x^{n-2} + \cdots + a_1}$$

$$= \lim_{x \to \infty} \frac{1}{n a_n x^n + (n-1) a_{n-1} x^{n-1} + \cdots + a_1 x} = 0$$

Thus $\ln x$ grows slower than any nonconstant

polynomial as $x \to \infty$.

39. Compare $n \log_2 n$ to $n^{3/2}$ as $n \to \infty$.

$$\lim_{n \to \infty} \frac{n \log_2 n}{n^{3/2}} = \lim_{n \to \infty} \frac{\log_2 n}{n^{1/2}}$$

$$= \lim_{n \to \infty} \frac{\frac{(\ln n)}{(\ln 2)}}{n^{1/2}}$$

$$= \lim_{n \to \infty} \frac{\frac{1}{n \ln 2}}{\frac{1}{2 n^{1/2}}}$$

$$= \lim_{n \to \infty} \frac{2}{n^{1/2} (\ln 2)} = 0$$

Thus $n \log_2 n$ grows slower than $n^{3/2}$ as $n \to \infty$.

Compare $n \log_2 n$ to $n(\log_2 n)^2$

$$\lim_{n \to \infty} \frac{n \log_2 n}{n(\log_2 n)^2} = \lim_{n \to \infty} \frac{1}{\log_2 n} = 0$$

Thus $n \log_2 n$ grows slower than $n(\log_2 n)^2$ as $n \to \infty$.
The algorithm of order of $n \log_2 n$ is likely the most
efficient because of the three functions, it grows the most
slowly as $n \to \infty$.

40. (a) It might take 1,000,000 searches if it is the last item in
the search.

(b) $\log_2 1{,}000{,}000 \approx 19.9$; it might take 20 binary
searches.

41. Since f and g grow at the same rate, there exists a nonzero

number L such that $\displaystyle \lim_{x \to \infty} \frac{f(x)}{g(x)} = L$. Then for sufficiently

large x, $\dfrac{f(x)}{g(x)} < L + 1 \le M$ for some integer M.

Similarly, for sufficiently large x, $\dfrac{g(x)}{f(x)} < \dfrac{1}{L} + 1 \le N$ for

some integer N.

42. (a) The limit will be the ratio of the leading coefficients of
the polynomials since the polynomials must have the
same degree.

(b) By the same reason as in (a), the limit will be the ratio
of the leading coefficients of the polynomial.

43. (a) $\displaystyle \lim_{x \to \infty} \frac{x^5}{x^2} = \lim_{x \to \infty} x^3 = \infty$

x^5 grows faster than x^2.

(b) $\displaystyle \lim_{x \to \infty} \frac{5x^3}{2x^3} = \lim_{x \to \infty} \frac{5}{2} = \frac{5}{2}$

$5x^3$ and $2x^3$ have the same rate of growth.

(c) $m > n$ since $\displaystyle \lim_{x \to \infty} \frac{x^m}{x^n} = \lim_{x \to \infty} x^{m-n} = \infty$.

(d) $m = n$ since $\displaystyle \lim_{x \to \infty} \frac{x^m}{x^n} = \lim_{x \to \infty} x^{m-n}$ is nonzero and finite.

(e) Degree of $g >$ degree of f ($m > n$) since $\displaystyle \lim_{x \to \infty} \frac{g(x)}{f(x)} = \infty$.

(f) Degree of $g =$ degree of f ($m = n$) since $\displaystyle \lim_{x \to \infty} \frac{g(x)}{f(x)}$ is

nonzero and finite.

44. **(a)** $f = o(g)$ as $x \to a$ if $\lim\limits_{x \to a} \dfrac{f(x)}{g(x)} = 0$

Suppose f and g are both positive in some open interval

containing a. Then $f = O(g)$ as $x \to a$ if there is a

positive integer M for which $\dfrac{f(x)}{g(x)} \le M$ for x sufficiently

close to a.

(b) From Section 5.5, we know that $\left|E_S\right| \le \dfrac{b-a}{180} h^4 M$

where M is a bound for the absolute value of $f^{(4)}$ on

$[a, b]$. Thus, $\dfrac{\left|E_S\right|}{h^4} \le (b - a)\dfrac{M}{180} \le \text{int}\left[(b - a)\dfrac{M}{180}\right] + 1$

as $h \to 0$, so $\left|E_S\right| = O(h^4)$. Thus as $h \to 0$, $E_S \to 0$.

(c) From Section 5.5, we know that $\left|E_T\right| \le \dfrac{b-a}{12} h^2 M$

where M is a bound for the absolute value of f'' on

$[a, b]$. Thus $\dfrac{\left|E_T\right|}{h^2} \le (b - a)\dfrac{M}{12} \le \text{int}\left[(b - a)\dfrac{M}{12}\right] + 1$ as

$h \to 0$, so $\left|E_T\right| = O(h^2)$. Thus as $h \to 0$, $E_T \to 0$.

45. **(a)** $\lim\limits_{x \to \infty} \dfrac{|f(x)|}{|g(x)|} = \lim\limits_{x \to \infty} \dfrac{-f(x)}{-g(x)} = \lim\limits_{x \to \infty} \dfrac{f(x)}{g(x)} = \infty$

Thus $|f|$ grows faster than $|g|$ as $x \to \infty$ by definition.

(b) $\lim\limits_{x \to \infty} \dfrac{|f(x)|}{|g(x)|} = \lim\limits_{x \to \infty} \dfrac{-f(x)}{-g(x)} = \lim\limits_{x \to \infty} \dfrac{f(x)}{g(x)} = L$

Thus $|f|$ grows at the same rate as $|g|$ as $x \to \infty$ by

definition.

46. **(a)** $\lim\limits_{x \to \infty} \dfrac{f(-x)}{g(-x)} = \lim\limits_{x \to -\infty} \dfrac{f(x)}{g(x)} = \infty$

Thus $f(-x)$ grows faster than $g(-x)$ by definition.

(b) $\lim\limits_{x \to \infty} \dfrac{f(-x)}{g(-x)} = \lim\limits_{x \to -\infty} \dfrac{f(x)}{g(x)} = L$

Thus $f(-x)$ grows at the same rate as $g(-x)$ by

definition.

■ Section 8.3 Improper Integrals

(pp. 433–444)

Exploration 1 Investigating $\int_0^1 \dfrac{dx}{x^p}$

1. Because $\dfrac{1}{x^p}$ has an infinite discontinuity at $x = 0$.

2. $\int_0^1 \dfrac{dx}{x} = \lim\limits_{c \to 0^+} \int_c^1 \dfrac{dx}{x} = \lim\limits_{c \to 0^+} \left[\ln x\right]_c^1 = \lim\limits_{c \to 0^+} (-\ln c) = \infty$

3. If $p > 1$, then

$$\int_0^1 \dfrac{dx}{x^p} = \lim\limits_{c \to 0^+} \int_c^1 \dfrac{dx}{x^p}$$

$$= \lim\limits_{c \to 0^+} \dfrac{x^{-p+1}}{-p+1}\Big]_c^1$$

$$= \lim\limits_{c \to 0^+} \left(\dfrac{1 - c^{-p+1}}{-p+1}\right) = \infty \text{ because } (-p+1) < 0.$$

4. If $0 < p < 1$, then

$$\int_0^1 \dfrac{dx}{x^p} = \lim\limits_{c \to 0^+} \int_c^1 \dfrac{dx}{x^p}$$

$$= \lim\limits_{c \to 0^+} \dfrac{x^{-p+1}}{-p+1}\Big]_c^1$$

$$= \lim\limits_{c \to 0^+} \left(\dfrac{1 - c^{-p+1}}{-p+1}\right) = \dfrac{1}{1-p}$$

Quick Review 8.3

1. $\int_0^3 \dfrac{dx}{x+3} = \left[\ln|x+3|\right]_0^3 = \ln 6 - \ln 3 = \ln 2$

2. $\int_{-1}^1 \dfrac{x\,dx}{x^2+1} = \left[\dfrac{1}{2}\ln|x^2+1|\right]_{-1}^1 = \dfrac{1}{2}\ln 2 - \dfrac{1}{2}\ln 2 = 0$

3. $\int \dfrac{dx}{x^2+4} = \dfrac{1}{4}\int \dfrac{dx}{\left(\frac{x}{2}\right)^2 + 1}$

$$= \dfrac{1}{4}\left(2\tan^{-1}\dfrac{x}{2}\right) + C$$

$$= \dfrac{1}{2}\tan^{-1}\dfrac{x}{2} + C$$

4. $\int \dfrac{dx}{x^4} = \int x^{-4}\,dx = -\dfrac{1}{3}x^{-3} + C$

5. $9 - x^2 > 0$ for $-3 < x < 3$
The domain is $(-3, 3)$.

6. $x - 1 > 0$ for $x > 1$
The domain is $(1, \infty)$.

7. $-1 \le \cos x \le 1$, so $\left|\cos x\right| \le 1$.

$$\left|\dfrac{\cos x}{x^2}\right| = \dfrac{|\cos x|}{|x^2|} \le \dfrac{1}{x^2}$$

8. $x^2 - 1 \le x^2$ so $\sqrt{x^2 - 1} \le \sqrt{x^2} = x$ for $x > 1$

$$\dfrac{1}{\sqrt{x^2 - 1}} \ge \dfrac{1}{x}$$

9. $\lim\limits_{x \to \infty} \dfrac{f(x)}{g(x)} = \lim\limits_{x \to \infty} \dfrac{4e^x - 5}{3e^x + 7} = \lim\limits_{x \to \infty} \dfrac{4e^x}{3e^x} = \lim\limits_{x \to \infty} \dfrac{4}{3} = \dfrac{4}{3}$

Thus f and g grow at the same rate as $x \to \infty$.

10. $\lim\limits_{x \to \infty} \dfrac{f(x)}{g(x)} = \lim\limits_{x \to \infty} \dfrac{\sqrt{2x-1}}{\sqrt{x+3}}$

$$= \lim\limits_{x \to \infty} \sqrt{\dfrac{2x-1}{x+3}}$$

$$= \lim\limits_{x \to \infty} \sqrt{\dfrac{2 - \frac{1}{x}}{1 + \frac{3}{x}}} = \sqrt{2}$$

Section 8.3 Exercises

1. (a) The integral is improper because of an infinite limit of integration.

(b) $\int_0^\infty \frac{dx}{x^2+1} = \lim_{b\to\infty} \int_0^b \frac{dx}{x^2+1}$

$= \lim_{b\to\infty} \left[\tan^{-1}x\right]_0^b$

$= \lim_{b\to\infty} (\tan^{-1}b - 0)$

$= \frac{\pi}{2}$

The integral converges.

(c) $\frac{\pi}{2}$

2. (a) The integral is improper because the integrand has an infinite discontinuity at $x = 0$.

(b) $\int_0^1 \frac{dx}{\sqrt{x}} = \lim_{b\to 0^+} \int_b^1 \frac{dx}{\sqrt{x}}$

$= \lim_{b\to 0^+} \left[2\sqrt{x}\right]_b^1$

$= \lim_{b\to 0^+} (2 - 2\sqrt{b}) = 2$

The integral converges.

(c) 2

3. (a) The integral involves improper integrals because the integrand has an infinite discontinuity at $x = 0$.

(b) $\int_{-8}^1 \frac{dx}{x^{1/3}} = \int_{-8}^0 \frac{dx}{x^{1/3}} + \int_0^1 \frac{dx}{x^{1/3}}$

$\int_{-8}^0 \frac{dx}{x^{1/3}} = \lim_{b\to 0^-} \int_{-8}^b \frac{dx}{x^{1/3}}$

$= \lim_{b\to 0^-} \left[\frac{3}{2}x^{2/3}\right]_{-8}^b$

$= \lim_{b\to 0^-} \left(\frac{3}{2}b^{2/3} - 6\right) = -6$

$\int_0^1 \frac{dx}{x^{1/3}} = \lim_{b\to 0^+} \int_b^1 \frac{dx}{x^{1/3}}$

$= \lim_{b\to 0^+} \left[\frac{3}{2}x^{2/3}\right]_b^1$

$= \lim_{b\to 0^+} \left(\frac{3}{2} - \frac{3}{2}b^{2/3}\right)$

$= \frac{3}{2}$

$\int_{-8}^1 \frac{dx}{x^{1/3}} = -6 + \frac{3}{2} = -\frac{9}{2}$

The integral converges.

(c) $-\frac{9}{2}$

4. (a) The integral is improper because of two infinite limits of integration.

(b) $\int_{-\infty}^\infty \frac{2x\,dx}{(x^2+1)^2} = \int_{-\infty}^0 \frac{2x\,dx}{(x^2+1)^2} + \int_0^\infty \frac{2x\,dx}{(x^2+1)^2}$

$\int_{-\infty}^0 \frac{2x\,dx}{(x^2+1)^2} = \lim_{b\to -\infty} \int_b^0 \frac{2x\,dx}{(x^2+1)^2}$

$= \lim_{b\to -\infty} \left[-(x^2+1)^{-1}\right]_b^0$

$= \lim_{b\to -\infty} [-1 + (b^2+1)^{-1}] = -1$

$\int_0^\infty \frac{2x\,dx}{(x^2+1)^2} = \lim_{b\to\infty} \int_0^b \frac{2x\,dx}{(x^2+1)^2}$

$= \lim_{b\to\infty} \left[-(x^2+1)^{-1}\right]_0^b$

$= \lim_{b\to\infty} [-(b^2+1)^{-1} + 1] = 1$

$\int_{-\infty}^\infty \frac{2x\,dx}{(x^2+1)^2} = -1 + 1 = 0$

The integral converges.

(c) 0

5. (a) The integral is improper because the integrand has an infinite discontinuity at 0.

(b) $\int_0^{\ln 2} x^{-2} e^{1/x}\,dx = \lim_{b\to 0^+} \int_b^{\ln 2} x^{-2} e^{1/x}\,dx$

$= \lim_{b\to 0^+} \left[-e^{1/x}\right]_b^{\ln 2}$

$= \lim_{b\to 0^+} [-e^{1/\ln 2} + e^{1/b}] = \infty$

The integral diverges.

(c) No value

6. (a) The integral is improper because the integrand has an infinite discontinuity at $x = 0$.

(b) $\int_0^{\pi/2} \cot\theta\,d\theta = \lim_{b\to 0^+} \int_b^{\pi/2} \cot\theta\,d\theta$

$= \lim_{b\to 0^+} \int_b^{\pi/2} \frac{\cos\theta\,d\theta}{\sin\theta}$

$= \lim_{b\to 0^+} \left[\ln|\sin\theta|\right]_b^{\pi/2}$

$= \lim_{b\to 0^+} (0 - \ln|\sin b|) = \infty$

The integral diverges.

(c) No value

7. $\int_1^\infty \frac{dx}{x^{1.001}} = \lim_{b\to\infty} \int_1^b \frac{dx}{x^{1.001}}$

$= \lim_{b\to\infty} \left[-1000\,x^{-0.001}\right]_1^b$

$= \lim_{b\to\infty} (-1000b^{-0.001} + 1000) = 1000$

8. $\int_{-1}^{1} \frac{dx}{x^{2/3}} = \int_{-1}^{0} \frac{dx}{x^{2/3}} + \int_{0}^{1} \frac{dx}{x^{2/3}}$

$\int_{-1}^{0} \frac{dx}{x^{2/3}} = \lim_{b \to 0^-} \int_{-1}^{b} \frac{dx}{x^{2/3}}$

$\qquad = \lim_{b \to 0^-} \left[3x^{1/3} \right]_{-1}^{b}$

$\qquad = \lim_{b \to 0^-} (3b^{1/3} + 3) = 3$

$\int_{0}^{1} \frac{dx}{x^{2/3}} = \lim_{b \to 0^+} \int_{b}^{1} \frac{dx}{x^{2/3}}$

$\qquad = \lim_{b \to 0^+} \left[3x^{1/3} \right]_{b}^{1}$

$\qquad = \lim_{b \to 0^+} (3 - 3b^{1/3}) = 3$

$\int_{-1}^{1} \frac{dx}{x^{2/3}} = 3 + 3 = 6$

9. $\int_{0}^{4} \frac{dr}{\sqrt{4-r}} = \lim_{b \to 4^-} \int_{0}^{b} \frac{dr}{\sqrt{4-r}}$

$\qquad = \lim_{b \to 4^-} \left[-2\sqrt{4-r} \right]_{0}^{b}$

$\qquad = \lim_{b \to 4^-} (-2\sqrt{4-b} + 4) = 4$

10. $\int_{0}^{1} \frac{dr}{r^{0.999}} = \lim_{b \to 0^+} \int_{b}^{1} \frac{dr}{r^{0.999}}$

$\qquad = \lim_{b \to 0^+} \left[1000r^{0.001} \right]_{b}^{1}$

$\qquad = \lim_{b \to 0^+} (1000 - 1000b^{0.001}) = 1000$

11. $\int_{0}^{1} \frac{dx}{\sqrt{1-x^2}} = \lim_{b \to 1^-} \int_{0}^{b} \frac{dx}{\sqrt{1-x^2}}$

$\qquad = \lim_{b \to 1^-} \left[\sin^{-1} x \right]_{0}^{b}$

$\qquad = \lim_{b \to 1^-} (\sin^{-1} b - 0) = \frac{\pi}{2}$

12. $\int_{-\infty}^{2} \frac{2\,dx}{x^2+4} = \lim_{b \to -\infty} \int_{b}^{2} \frac{(1/2)\,dx}{(x/2)^2+1}$

$\qquad = \lim_{b \to -\infty} \left[\tan^{-1} \frac{x}{2} \right]_{b}^{2}$

$\qquad = \lim_{b \to -\infty} \left(\frac{\pi}{4} - \tan^{-1} \frac{b}{2} \right)$

$\qquad = \frac{\pi}{4} + \frac{\pi}{2} = \frac{3\pi}{4}$

13. $\int_{-\infty}^{-2} \frac{2\,dx}{x^2-1} = \lim_{b \to -\infty} \int_{b}^{-2} \frac{[(x+1)-(x-1)]\,dx}{(x+1)(x-1)}$

$\qquad = \lim_{b \to -\infty} \int_{b}^{-2} \left(\frac{1}{x-1} - \frac{1}{x+1} \right) dx$

$\qquad = \lim_{b \to -\infty} \left[\ln|x-1| - \ln|x+1| \right]_{b}^{-2}$

$\qquad = \lim_{b \to -\infty} \left[\ln \left| \frac{x-1}{x+1} \right| \right]_{b}^{-2}$

$\qquad = \lim_{b \to -\infty} \left(\ln 3 - \ln \left| \frac{b-1}{b+1} \right| \right)$

$\qquad = \ln 3 - \ln 1 = \ln 3$

14. $\int_{2}^{\infty} \frac{3\,dt}{t^2-t} = \lim_{b \to \infty} \int_{2}^{\infty} \frac{3[t-(t-1)]\,dt}{t(t-1)}$

$\qquad = \lim_{b \to \infty} \int_{2}^{\infty} \left(\frac{3}{t-1} - \frac{3}{t} \right) dt$

$\qquad = \lim_{b \to \infty} \left[3\ln|t-1| - 3\ln|t| \right]_{2}^{b}$

$\qquad = \lim_{b \to \infty} \left[3\ln \left| \frac{t-1}{t} \right| \right]_{2}^{b}$

$\qquad = \lim_{b \to \infty} \left(3\ln \left| \frac{b-1}{b} \right| - 3\ln \frac{1}{2} \right)$

$\qquad = 3\ln 1 + 3\ln 2 = 3\ln 2$

15. $\int_{0}^{1} \frac{\theta+1}{\sqrt{\theta^2+2\theta}} = \lim_{b \to 0^+} \int_{b}^{1} \frac{1}{2} \frac{(2\theta+2)\,d\theta}{\sqrt{\theta^2+2\theta}}$

$\qquad = \lim_{b \to 0^+} \left[\sqrt{\theta^2+2\theta} \right]_{b}^{1}$

$\qquad = \lim_{b \to 0^+} (\sqrt{3} - \sqrt{b^2+2b}) = \sqrt{3}$

16. $\int_{0}^{2} \frac{s+1}{\sqrt{4-s^2}}\,ds = \lim_{b \to 2^-} \int_{0}^{b} \left(\frac{s}{\sqrt{4-s^2}} + \frac{1}{\sqrt{4-s^2}} \right) ds$

$\lim_{b \to 2^-} \int_{0}^{b} \left(\frac{s}{\sqrt{4-s^2}} + \frac{1}{2\sqrt{1-(s/2)^2}} \right) ds$

$\qquad = \lim_{b \to 2^-} \left[-\sqrt{4-s^2} + \sin^{-1} \frac{s}{2} \right]_{0}^{b}$

$\qquad = \lim_{b \to 2^-} \left(-\sqrt{4-b^2} + \sin^{-1} \frac{b}{2} + 2 \right)$

$\qquad = \sin^{-1} 1 + 2 = \frac{\pi}{2} + 2$

17. First integrate $\displaystyle\int \frac{dx}{(1+x)\sqrt{x}}$ by letting

$u = \sqrt{x}$, so $du = \dfrac{1}{2\sqrt{x}}\,dx$.

$$\int \frac{dx}{(1+x)\sqrt{x}} = \int \frac{2\,du}{1+u^2}$$

$$= 2\tan^{-1} u + C$$

$$= 2\tan^{-1}\sqrt{x} + C$$

Now evaluate the improper integral. Note that the integrand is infinite at $x = 0$.

$$\int_0^\infty \frac{dx}{(1+x)\sqrt{x}} = \int_0^1 \frac{dx}{(1+x)\sqrt{x}} + \int_1^\infty \frac{dx}{(1+x)\sqrt{x}}$$

$$= \lim_{b\to 0^+} \int_b^1 \frac{dx}{(1+x)\sqrt{x}} + \lim_{c\to\infty} \int_1^c \frac{dx}{(1+x)\sqrt{x}}$$

$$= \lim_{b\to 0^+} \left[2\tan^{-1}\sqrt{x}\right]_b^1 + \lim_{c\to\infty}\left[2\tan^{-1}\sqrt{x}\right]_1^c$$

$$= \lim_{b\to 0^+}\left(2\tan^{-1}1 - 2\tan^{-1}\sqrt{b}\right) +$$

$$\lim_{c\to\infty}\left(2\tan^{-1}\sqrt{c} - 2\tan^{-1}1\right)$$

$$= \left(\frac{\pi}{2} - 0\right) + \left(\pi - \frac{\pi}{2}\right) = \pi$$

18. $\displaystyle\int_1^\infty \frac{dx}{x\sqrt{x^2-1}} = \int_1^2 \frac{dx}{x\sqrt{x^2-1}} + \int_2^\infty \frac{dx}{x\sqrt{x^2-1}}$

$$\int_1^2 \frac{dx}{x\sqrt{x^2-1}} = \lim_{b\to 1^+} \int_b^2 \frac{dx}{x\sqrt{x^2-1}}$$

$$= \lim_{b\to 1^+} \left[\sec^{-1} x\right]_b^2$$

$$= \lim_{b\to 1^+}\left(\sec^{-1}2 - \sec^{-1}b\right)$$

$$= \sec^{-1}2 - \sec^{-1}1 = \frac{\pi}{3}$$

$$\int_2^\infty \frac{dx}{x\sqrt{x^2-1}} = \lim_{b\to\infty} \int_2^b \frac{dx}{x\sqrt{x^2-1}}$$

$$= \lim_{b\to\infty}\left[\sec^{-1}x\right]_2^b$$

$$= \lim_{b\to\infty}\left(\sec^{-1}b - \sec^{-1}2\right)$$

$$= \frac{\pi}{2} - \frac{\pi}{3} = \frac{\pi}{6}$$

$$\int_1^\infty \frac{dx}{x\sqrt{x^2-1}} = \frac{\pi}{3} + \frac{\pi}{6} = \frac{\pi}{2}$$

19. $\displaystyle\int_1^2 \frac{ds}{s\sqrt{s^2-1}} = \lim_{b\to 1^+} \int_b^2 \frac{ds}{s\sqrt{s^2-1}}$

$$= \lim_{b\to 1^+}\left[\sec^{-1}s\right]_b^2$$

$$= \lim_{b\to 1^+}\left(\sec^{-1}2 - \sec^{-1}b\right)$$

$$= \sec^{-1}2 - \sec^{-1}1 = \frac{\pi}{3}$$

20. $\displaystyle\int_{-1}^\infty \frac{d\theta}{\theta^2+5\theta+6} = \lim_{b\to\infty} \int_{-1}^b \frac{(\theta+3)-(\theta+2)}{(\theta+3)(\theta+2)}\,d\theta$

$$= \lim_{b\to\infty} \int_{-1}^b \left(\frac{1}{\theta+2} - \frac{1}{\theta+3}\right) d\theta$$

$$= \lim_{b\to\infty}\left[\ln|\theta+2| - \ln|\theta+3|\right]_{-1}^b$$

$$= \lim_{b\to\infty}\left[\ln\left|\frac{\theta+2}{\theta+3}\right|\right]_{-1}^b$$

$$= \lim_{b\to\infty}\left(\ln\left|\frac{b+2}{b+3}\right| - \ln\frac{1}{2}\right) = \ln 2$$

21. Integrate $\displaystyle\int \frac{16\tan^{-1}x}{1+x^2}\,dx$ by letting $u = \tan^{-1}x$, so

$$du = \frac{dx}{1+x^2}.$$

$$\int \frac{16\tan^{-1}x}{1+x^2}\,dx = \int 16u\,du = 8u^2 + C$$

$$= 8(\tan^{-1}x)^2 + C$$

$$\int_0^\infty \frac{16\tan^{-1}x}{1+x^2}\,dx = \lim_{b\to\infty} \int_0^b \frac{16\tan^{-1}x}{1+x^2}\,dx$$

$$= \lim_{b\to\infty}\left[8(\tan^{-1}x)^2\right]_0^b$$

$$= \lim_{b\to\infty}\left[8(\tan^{-1}b)^2 - 0\right]$$

$$= 8\left(\frac{\pi}{2}\right)^2 = 2\pi^2$$

22. $\displaystyle\int_{-1}^4 \frac{dx}{\sqrt{|x|}} = \int_{-1}^0 \frac{dx}{\sqrt{-x}} + \int_0^4 \frac{dx}{\sqrt{x}}$

$$\int_{-1}^0 \frac{dx}{\sqrt{-x}} = \lim_{b\to 0^-} \int_{-1}^b \frac{dx}{\sqrt{-x}}$$

$$= \lim_{b\to 0^-}\left[-2\sqrt{-x}\right]_{-1}^b$$

$$= \lim_{b\to 0^-}\left(-2\sqrt{-b} + 2\right) = 2$$

$$\int_0^4 \frac{dx}{\sqrt{x}} = \lim_{b\to 0^+} \int_b^4 \frac{dx}{\sqrt{x}}$$

$$= \lim_{b\to 0^+}\left[2\sqrt{x}\right]_b^4$$

$$= \lim_{b\to 0^+}\left(4 - 2\sqrt{b}\right) = 4$$

$$\int_{-1}^4 \frac{dx}{\sqrt{|x|}} = 2 + 4 = 6$$

23. Integrate $\int \theta e^{\theta} \, d\theta$ by parts.

$u = \theta \qquad dv = e^{\theta} \, d\theta$

$du = d\theta \quad v = e^{\theta}$

$\int \theta e^{\theta} \, d\theta = \theta e^{\theta} - \int e^{\theta} \, d\theta = \theta e^{\theta} - e^{\theta} + C$

$\int_{-\infty}^{0} \theta e^{\theta} \, d\theta = \lim_{b \to -\infty} \int_{b}^{0} \theta e^{\theta} \, d\theta$

$\qquad = \lim_{b \to -\infty} \left[\theta e^{\theta} - e^{\theta} \right]_{b}^{0}$

$\qquad = \lim_{b \to -\infty} (-1 - be^{b} + e^{b}) = -1$

$\left(\text{Note that } \lim_{b \to -\infty} be^{b} = \lim_{c \to \infty} -ce^{-c} = \lim_{c \to \infty} -\frac{c}{e^{c}} \right.$

$\left. = \lim_{c \to \infty} -\frac{1}{e^{c}} = 0 \text{ and } \lim_{b \to -\infty} e^{b} = \lim_{c \to \infty} e^{-c} = 0. \right)$

24. Integrate $\int 2e^{-\theta} \sin \theta \, d\theta$ by parts.

$u = 2 \sin \theta \qquad dv = e^{-\theta} \, d\theta$

$du = 2 \cos \theta \, d\theta \quad v = -e^{-\theta}$

$\int 2e^{-\theta} \sin \theta \, d\theta = -2e^{-\theta} \sin \theta + \int 2e^{-\theta} \cos \theta \, d\theta$

Integrate $\int 2e^{-\theta} \cos \theta \, d\theta$ by parts.

$u = 2 \cos \theta \qquad dv = e^{-\theta} \, d\theta$

$du = -2 \sin \theta \, d\theta \quad v = -e^{-\theta}$

$\int 2e^{-\theta} \cos \theta \, d\theta = -2e^{-\theta} \cos \theta - \int 2e^{-\theta} \sin \theta \, d\theta$

Thus,

$\int 2e^{-\theta} \sin \theta \, d\theta$

$\qquad = -2e^{-\theta} \sin \theta - 2e^{-\theta} \cos \theta - \int 2e^{-\theta} \sin \theta \, d\theta$

$2\int 2e^{-\theta} \sin \theta \, d\theta = -2e^{-\theta} \sin \theta - 2e^{-\theta} \cos \theta + C_1$

$\int 2e^{-\theta} \sin \theta \, d\theta = -e^{-\theta} \sin \theta - e^{-\theta} \cos \theta + C$

$\int_{0}^{\infty} 2e^{-\theta} \sin \theta \, d\theta = \lim_{b \to \infty} \int_{0}^{b} 2e^{-\theta} \sin \theta \, d\theta$

$\qquad = \lim_{b \to \infty} \left[-e^{-\theta} \sin \theta - e^{-\theta} \cos \theta \right]_{0}^{b}$

$\qquad = \lim_{b \to \infty} (-e^{-b} \sin b - e^{-b} \cos b + 1) = 1$

25. $\int_{-\infty}^{\infty} e^{-|x|} \, dx = \int_{-\infty}^{0} e^{x} \, dx + \int_{0}^{\infty} e^{-x} \, dx$

$\int_{-\infty}^{0} e^{x} \, dx = \lim_{b \to -\infty} \int_{b}^{0} e^{x} \, dx = \lim_{b \to -\infty} \left[e^{x} \right]_{b}^{0} = \lim_{b \to -\infty} (1 - e^{b}) = 1$

$\int_{0}^{\infty} e^{-x} \, dx = \lim_{b \to \infty} \int_{0}^{b} e^{-x} \, dx = \lim_{b \to \infty} \left[-e^{-x} \right]_{0}^{b}$

$\qquad = \lim_{b \to \infty} (-e^{-b} + 1) = 1$

$\int_{-\infty}^{\infty} e^{-|x|} \, dx = 1 + 1 = 2$

26. Integrate $\int x \ln x \, dx$ by parts.

$u = \ln x \qquad\qquad dv = x \, dx$

$du = \frac{1}{x} \, dx \qquad\quad v = \frac{1}{2}x^2$

$\int x \ln x \, dx = \frac{1}{2}x^2 \ln x - \int \frac{1}{2}x \, dx = \frac{1}{2}x^2 \ln x - \frac{1}{4}x^2 + C$

$\int_{0}^{1} x \ln x = \lim_{b \to 0^+} \int_{b}^{1} x \ln x \, dx$

$\qquad = \lim_{b \to 0^+} \left[\frac{1}{2}x^2 \ln x - \frac{1}{4}x^2 \right]_{b}^{1}$

$\qquad = \lim_{b \to 0^+} \left(-\frac{1}{4} - \frac{1}{2}b^2 \ln b + \frac{1}{4}b^2 \right)$

$\qquad = -\frac{1}{4}$

$\left(\text{Note that } \lim_{b \to 0^+} b^2 \ln b = \lim_{b \to 0^+} \frac{\ln b}{1/b^2} = \lim_{b \to 0^+} \frac{1/b}{-2/b^3} \right.$

$\left. = \lim_{b \to 0^+} -\frac{b^2}{2} = 0. \right)$

27. $\int_{0}^{\pi/2} \tan \theta \, d\theta = \lim_{b \to \pi/2} \int_{0}^{b} \frac{\sin \theta}{\cos \theta} \, d\theta$

$\qquad = \lim_{b \to \pi/2} \left[-\ln |\cos \theta| \right]_{0}^{b}$

$\qquad = \lim_{b \to \pi/2} [-\ln |\cos b| + 0] = \infty$

The integral diverges.

28. On $[0, \pi]$, $0 \le \dfrac{\sin \theta}{\sqrt{\pi - \theta}} \le \dfrac{1}{\sqrt{\pi - \theta}}$, so

$$\int_0^\pi \frac{\sin \theta}{\sqrt{\pi - \theta}} \, d\theta \le \int_0^\pi \frac{1}{\sqrt{\pi - \theta}} \, d\theta$$

$$\int_0^\pi \frac{1}{\sqrt{\pi - \theta}} \, d\theta = \lim_{b \to \pi^-} \int_0^b \frac{1}{\sqrt{\pi - \theta}} \, d\theta$$

$$= \lim_{b \to \pi^-} \left[-2\sqrt{\pi - \theta} \right]_0^b$$

$$= \lim_{b \to \pi^-} (-2\sqrt{\pi - b} + 2\sqrt{\pi})$$

$$= -2\sqrt{0} + 2\sqrt{\pi}$$

$$= 2\sqrt{\pi}$$

Since this integral converges, the given integral converges.

29. $\displaystyle\int_{-\infty}^\infty 2xe^{-x^2} \, dx = \int_0^\infty 2xe^{-x^2} \, dx + \int_{-\infty}^0 2xe^{-x^2} \, dx$

$$\int_0^\infty 2xe^{-x^2} \, dx = \lim_{b \to \infty} \int_0^b 2xe^{-x^2} \, dx$$

$$= \lim_{b \to \infty} \left[-e^{-x^2} \right]_0^b$$

$$= \lim_{b \to \infty} [-e^{-b^2} + 1] = 1$$

$$\int_{-\infty}^0 2xe^{-x^2} \, dx = \lim_{b \to -\infty} \int_b^0 2xe^{-x^2} \, dx$$

$$= \lim_{b \to -\infty} \left[-e^{-x^2} \right]_b^0$$

$$= \lim_{b \to -\infty} [-1 + e^{-b^2}] = -1$$

The integral converges.

30. $\displaystyle\int_0^4 \frac{e^{-\sqrt{x}}}{\sqrt{x}} \, dx = \lim_{b \to 0^+} \int_b^4 \frac{e^{-\sqrt{x}}}{\sqrt{x}} \, dx$

$$= \lim_{b \to 0^+} \left[-2e^{-\sqrt{x}} \right]_b^4$$

$$= \lim_{b \to 0^+} [-2e^{-2} + 2e^{-\sqrt{b}}]$$

$$= -2e^{-2} + 2$$

The integral converges.

31. $0 \le \dfrac{1}{\sqrt{t} + \sin t} \le \dfrac{1}{\sqrt{t}}$ on $(0, \pi]$ since $\sin t \ge 0$ on $[0, \pi]$.

$$\int_0^\pi \frac{dt}{\sqrt{t}} = \lim_{b \to 0^+} \int_b^\pi \frac{dt}{\sqrt{t}}$$

$$= \lim_{b \to 0^+} \left[2\sqrt{t} \right]_b^\pi$$

$$= \lim_{b \to 0^+} [2\sqrt{\pi} - 2\sqrt{b}]$$

$$= 2\sqrt{\pi}$$

Since this integral converges, the given integral converges.

32. $0 \le \dfrac{1}{\sqrt{x}} \le \dfrac{1}{\sqrt{x - 1}}$ on $[4, \infty)$

$$\int_4^\infty \frac{dx}{\sqrt{x}} = \lim_{b \to \infty} \int_4^b \frac{dx}{\sqrt{x}} = \lim_{b \to \infty} \left[2\sqrt{x} \right]_4^b = \lim_{b \to \infty} [2\sqrt{b} - 4] = \infty$$

Since this integral diverges, the given integral diverges.

33. $0 \le \dfrac{1}{x^3 + 1} \le \dfrac{1}{x^3}$ on $[1, \infty)$

$$\int_1^\infty \frac{dx}{x^3} = \lim_{b \to \infty} \int_1^b \frac{dx}{x^3}$$

$$= \lim_{b \to \infty} \left[-\frac{1}{2}x^{-2} \right]_1^b$$

$$= \lim_{b \to \infty} \left[-\frac{1}{2}b^{-2} + \frac{1}{2} \right] = \frac{1}{2}$$

Since this integral converges, the given integral converges.

34. $\displaystyle\int_0^2 \frac{dx}{1 - x^2} = \int_0^1 \frac{dx}{1 - x^2} + \int_1^2 \frac{dx}{1 - x^2}$

$$\int_0^1 \frac{dx}{1 - x^2} = \lim_{b \to 1^-} \int_0^b \frac{1/2[(1 - x) + (1 + x)]}{(1 - x)(1 + x)} \, dx$$

$$= \lim_{b \to 1^-} \int_0^b \left[\frac{1}{2(1 + x)} + \frac{1}{2(1 - x)} \right] dx$$

$$= \lim_{b \to 1^-} \left[\frac{1}{2} \ln |1 + x| - \frac{1}{2} \ln |1 - x| \right]_0^b$$

$$= \lim_{b \to 1^-} \left[\frac{1}{2} \ln \left| \frac{1 + x}{1 - x} \right| \right]_0^b$$

$$= \lim_{b \to 1^-} \left[\frac{1}{2} \ln \left| \frac{1 + b}{1 - b} \right| - 0 \right] = \infty$$

Since this integral diverges, the given integral diverges.

35. $\displaystyle\int_0^2 \frac{dx}{1 - x} = \int_0^1 \frac{dx}{1 - x} + \int_1^2 \frac{dx}{1 - x}$

$$\int_0^1 \frac{dx}{1 - x} = \lim_{b \to 1^-} \int_0^b \frac{dx}{1 - x}$$

$$= \lim_{b \to 1^-} \left[-\ln |1 - x| \right]_0^b$$

$$= \lim_{b \to 1^-} (-\ln |1 - b| + 0) = \infty$$

Since this integral diverges, the given integral diverges.

36. $\int_{-1}^{1} \ln |x| \, dx = 2\int_{0}^{1} \ln x \, dx$ by symmetry of $\ln |x|$ about the y-axis. Integrate $\int \ln x \, dx$ by parts.

$$u = \ln x \qquad\qquad dv = dx$$

$$du = \frac{1}{x} \, dx \qquad\qquad v = x$$

$$\int \ln x \, dx = x \ln x - \int dx = x \ln x - x + C$$

$$2\int_{0}^{1} \ln x \, dx = 2 \lim_{b \to 0^+} \int_{b}^{1} \ln x \, dx$$

$$= 2 \lim_{b \to 0^+} \left[x \ln x - x \right]_{b}^{1}$$

$$= 2 \lim_{b \to 0^+} [-1 - b \ln b + b] = -2$$

$$\left(\text{Note that } \lim_{b \to 0^+} b \ln b = \lim_{b \to 0^+} \frac{\ln b}{1/b} = \lim_{b \to 0^+} \frac{1/b}{-1/b^2} \right.$$

$$\left. = \lim_{b \to 0^+} -b = 0. \right)$$

The integral converges.

37. $0 \le \dfrac{1}{1 + e^\theta} \le \dfrac{1}{e^\theta}$ on $[1, \infty)$

$$\int_{1}^{\infty} \frac{1}{e^\theta} \, d\theta = \lim_{b \to \infty} \int_{1}^{b} e^{-\theta} \, d\theta$$

$$= \lim_{b \to \infty} \left[-e^{-\theta} \right]_{1}^{b}$$

$$= \lim_{b \to \infty} [-e^{-b} + e^{-1}]$$

$$= \frac{1}{e}$$

Since this integral converges, the given integral converges.

38. $0 \le \dfrac{1}{x} \le \dfrac{1}{\sqrt{x^2 - 1}}$ on $[2, \infty)$

$$\int_{2}^{\infty} \frac{dx}{x} = \lim_{b \to \infty} \int_{2}^{b} \frac{dx}{x} = \lim_{b \to \infty} \left[\ln x \right]_{2}^{b} = \lim_{b \to \infty} (\ln b - \ln 2) = \infty$$

Since this integral diverges, the given integral diverges.

39. Let $f(x) = \dfrac{\sqrt{x + 1}}{x^2}$ and $g(x) = \dfrac{1}{x^{3/2}}$. Both are continuous on

$[1, \infty)$.

$$\lim_{x \to \infty} \frac{f(x)}{g(x)} = \lim_{x \to \infty} \frac{\sqrt{x + 1}}{\sqrt{x}} = \lim_{x \to \infty} \sqrt{1 + \frac{1}{x}} = 1$$

$$\int_{1}^{\infty} \frac{1}{x^{3/2}} \, dx = \lim_{b \to \infty} \int_{1}^{b} x^{-3/2} \, dx$$

$$= \lim_{b \to \infty} \left[-2x^{-1/2} \right]_{1}^{b}$$

$$= \lim_{b \to \infty} (-2b^{-1/2} + 2) = 2$$

Since this integral converges, the given integral converges.

40. $\int_{0}^{\infty} \dfrac{dx}{\sqrt{x}} = \int_{0}^{1} \dfrac{dx}{\sqrt{x}} + \int_{1}^{\infty} \dfrac{dx}{\sqrt{x}}$

$$\int_{1}^{\infty} \frac{dx}{\sqrt{x}} = \lim_{b \to \infty} \int_{1}^{b} \frac{dx}{\sqrt{x}}$$

$$= \lim_{b \to \infty} \left[2\sqrt{x} \right]_{1}^{b}$$

$$= \lim_{b \to \infty} (2\sqrt{b} - 2) = \infty$$

Since this integral diverges, the given integral diverges.

41. $0 \le \dfrac{1}{x} \le \dfrac{2 + \cos x}{x}$ on $[\pi, \infty)$

$$\int_{\pi}^{\infty} \frac{dx}{x} = \lim_{b \to \infty} \int_{\pi}^{b} \frac{dx}{x} = \lim_{b \to \infty} \left[\ln x \right]_{\pi}^{b} = \lim_{b \to \infty} (\ln b - \ln \pi) = \infty$$

Since this integral diverges, the given integral diverges.

42. $0 \le \dfrac{1 + \sin x}{x^2} \le \dfrac{2}{x^2}$ on $[\pi, \infty)$

$$\int_{\pi}^{\infty} \frac{2 \, dx}{x^2} = \lim_{b \to \infty} \int_{\pi}^{b} 2x^{-2} \, dx$$

$$= \lim_{b \to \infty} \left[-2x^{-1} \right]_{\pi}^{b}$$

$$= \lim_{b \to \infty} \left(-2b^{-1} + \frac{2}{\pi} \right) = \frac{2}{\pi}$$

Since this integral converges, the given integral converges.

43. First rewrite $\dfrac{1}{e^x + e^{-x}}$.

$$\frac{1}{e^x + e^{-x}} = \frac{1}{e^{-x}(e^{2x} + 1)} = \frac{e^x}{1 + (e^x)^2}$$

Integrate $\int \dfrac{e^x \, dx}{1 + (e^x)^2}$ by letting $u = e^x$ so $du = e^x \, dx$.

$$\int \frac{dx}{e^x + e^{-x}} = \int \frac{e^x \, dx}{1 + (e^x)^2}$$

$$= \int \frac{du}{1 + u^2}$$

$$= \tan^{-1} u + C$$

$$= \tan^{-1} e^x + C$$

$$\int_{-\infty}^{\infty} \frac{dx}{e^x + e^{-x}} = \int_{-\infty}^{0} \frac{dx}{e^x + e^{-x}} + \int_{0}^{\infty} \frac{dx}{e^x + e^{-x}}$$

$$\int_{-\infty}^{0} \frac{dx}{e^x + e^{-x}} = \lim_{b \to -\infty} \int_{b}^{0} \frac{dx}{e^x + e^{-x}}$$

$$= \lim_{b \to -\infty} \left[\tan^{-1} e^x \right]_{b}^{0}$$

$$= \lim_{b \to -\infty} [\tan^{-1} 1 - \tan^{-1} e^b]$$

$$= \frac{\pi}{4} - 0 = \frac{\pi}{4}$$

$$\int_{0}^{\infty} \frac{dx}{e^x + e^{-x}} = \lim_{b \to \infty} \int_{0}^{b} \frac{dx}{e^x + e^{-x}}$$

$$= \lim_{b \to \infty} \left[\tan^{-1} e^x \right]_{0}^{b}$$

$$= \lim_{b \to \infty} [\tan^{-1} e^b - \tan^{-1} 1]$$

$$= \frac{\pi}{2} - \frac{\pi}{4} = \frac{\pi}{4}$$

Thus, the given integral converges.

44. $\int_{-\infty}^{\infty} \dfrac{dx}{\sqrt{x^4+1}} = 2\int_{0}^{\infty} \dfrac{dx}{\sqrt{x^4+1}}$ by symmetry about the y-axis

$\int_{0}^{\infty} \dfrac{dx}{\sqrt{x^4+1}} = \int_{0}^{1} \dfrac{dx}{\sqrt{x^4+1}} + \int_{1}^{\infty} \dfrac{dx}{\sqrt{x^4+1}}$

$\int_{0}^{1} \dfrac{dx}{\sqrt{x^4+1}}$ exists because $\dfrac{1}{\sqrt{x^4+1}}$ exists on $[0, 1]$.

$0 \le \dfrac{1}{\sqrt{x^4+1}} \le \dfrac{1}{x^2}$ on $[1, \infty)$.

$\int_{1}^{\infty} \dfrac{1}{x^2}\,dx = \lim_{b\to\infty} \int_{1}^{b} x^{-2}\,dx$

$= \lim_{b\to\infty} \left[-x^{-1}\right]_{1}^{b}$

$= \lim_{b\to\infty} \left[-\dfrac{1}{b} + 1\right] = 1$

Since this integral converges, the given integral converges.

45. Integrate $\int \dfrac{dy}{(1+y^2)(1+\tan^{-1} y)}$ by letting $u = \tan^{-1} y$ so

$du = \dfrac{dy}{1+y^2}$

$\int \dfrac{dy}{(1+y^2)(1+\tan^{-1} y)} = \int \dfrac{du}{1+u}$

$= \ln|1 + u| + C$

$= \ln|1 + \tan^{-1} y| + C$

$\int_{0}^{\infty} \dfrac{dy}{(1+y^2)(1+\tan^{-1} y)} = \lim_{b\to\infty} \int_{0}^{b} \dfrac{dy}{(1+y^2)(1+\tan^{-1} y)}$

$= \lim_{b\to\infty} \left[\ln|1 + \tan^{-1} y|\right]_{0}^{b}$

$= \lim_{b\to\infty} (\ln|1 + \tan^{-1} b| - 0)$

$= \ln\left(1 + \dfrac{\pi}{2}\right)$

The integral converges.

46. $\int_{-\infty}^{\infty} \dfrac{e^{-y}\,dy}{y^2+1} = \int_{-\infty}^{0} \dfrac{e^{-y}\,dy}{y^2+1} + \int_{0}^{\infty} \dfrac{e^{-y}\,dy}{y^2+1}$

$\int_{-\infty}^{0} \dfrac{e^{-y}\,dy}{y^2+1}$ diverges since

$\lim_{y\to-\infty} \dfrac{e^{-y}}{y^2+1} = \lim_{y\to\infty} \dfrac{e^{y}}{y^2+1} = \lim_{y\to\infty} \dfrac{e^{y}}{2y} = \lim_{y\to\infty} \dfrac{e^{y}}{2} = \infty$

Thus the given integral diverges.

47. For $x \ge 0$, $y \ge 0$ on $[1, \infty)$.

Area $= \int_{1}^{\infty} \dfrac{\ln x}{x^2}\,dx = \lim_{b\to\infty} \int_{1}^{b} \dfrac{\ln x}{x^2}\,dx$

Integrate $\int \dfrac{\ln x}{x^2}\,dx$ by parts.

$u = \ln x \qquad\qquad dv = \dfrac{dx}{x^2}$

$du = \dfrac{1}{x}\,dx \qquad\qquad v = -\dfrac{1}{x}$

$\int \dfrac{\ln x}{x^2} = -\dfrac{\ln x}{x} + \int \dfrac{dx}{x^2} = -\dfrac{\ln x}{x} - \dfrac{1}{x} + C$

Area $= \lim_{b\to\infty} \left[-\dfrac{\ln x}{x} - \dfrac{1}{x}\right]_{1}^{b} = \lim_{b\to\infty} \left[-\dfrac{\ln b}{b} - \dfrac{1}{b} + 1\right] = 1$

$\left(\text{Note that } \lim_{b\to\infty} \dfrac{\ln b}{b} = \lim_{b\to\infty} \dfrac{1/b}{1} = 0.\right)$

48. For $x \ge 0$, $y \ge 0$ on $[1, \infty)$.

Area $= \int_{1}^{\infty} \dfrac{\ln x}{x}\,dx = \lim_{b\to\infty} \int_{1}^{b} \dfrac{\ln x}{x}\,dx$

Integrate $\int \dfrac{\ln x}{x}\,dx$ by letting $u = \ln x$ so $du = \dfrac{dx}{x}$.

$\int \dfrac{\ln x}{x}\,dx = \int u\,du = \dfrac{1}{2}u^2 + C = \dfrac{1}{2}(\ln x)^2 + C$

Area $= \lim_{b\to\infty} \left[\dfrac{1}{2}(\ln x)^2\right]_{1}^{b} = \lim_{b\to\infty} \dfrac{1}{2}(\ln b)^2 = \infty$

49. (a) The integral in Example 1 gives the area of region R.

Area $= \int_{1}^{\infty} \dfrac{dx}{x} = \lim_{b\to\infty} \ln x \Big]_{1}^{b} = \infty$

(b) Refer to Exploration 2 of Section 7.3.

$y' = -\dfrac{1}{x^2}$

The surface area of the solid is given by the following integral.

$\int_{1}^{\infty} 2\pi\left(\dfrac{1}{x}\right)\sqrt{1 + \left(-\dfrac{1}{x^2}\right)^2}\,dx = 2\pi \int_{1}^{\infty} \dfrac{1}{x}\sqrt{\dfrac{x^4+1}{x^4}}\,dx$

$= 2\pi \int_{1}^{\infty} \dfrac{\sqrt{x^4+1}}{x^3}\,dx$

Since $0 \le \dfrac{1}{x} \le \dfrac{\sqrt{x^4+1}}{x^3}$ on $[1, \infty)$, the direct comparison test shows that the integral for the surface area diverges. The surface area is ∞.

(c) Volume $= \int_{1}^{\infty} \pi\left(\dfrac{1}{x}\right)^2\,dx = \pi \int_{1}^{\infty} \dfrac{1}{x^2}\,dx$

$= \pi \lim_{b\to\infty} \int_{1}^{b} \dfrac{1}{x^2}\,dx$

$= \pi \lim_{b\to\infty} \left[-\dfrac{1}{x}\right]_{1}^{b}$

$= \pi \lim_{b\to\infty} \left(-\dfrac{1}{b} + 1\right) = \pi$

(d) Gabriel's horn has finite volume so it could only hold a finite amount of paint, but it has infinite surface area so it would require an infinite amount of paint to cover itself.

50. (a) $f(x) = \dfrac{1}{\sqrt{2\pi}}\, e^{-x^2/2}$

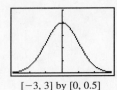

[−3, 3] by [0, 0.5]

f is increasing on $(-\infty, 0]$. f is decreasing on $[0, \infty)$.

f has a local maximum at $\left(0, f(0)\right) = \left(0, \dfrac{1}{\sqrt{2\pi}}\right)$

(b) $\text{NINT}\left(\dfrac{1}{\sqrt{2\pi}}\, e^{-x^2/2}, x, -1, 1\right) \approx 0.683$

$\text{NINT}\left(\dfrac{1}{\sqrt{2\pi}}\, e^{-x^2/2}, x, -2, 2\right) \approx 0.954$

$\text{NINT}\left(\dfrac{1}{\sqrt{2\pi}}\, e^{-x^2/2}, x, -3, 3\right) \approx 0.997$

(c) Part (b) suggests that as b increases, the integral approaches 1. We can make $\displaystyle\int_{-b}^{b} f(x)\,dx$ as close to 1 as we want by choosing $b > 1$ large enough. Also, we can make $\displaystyle\int_{b}^{\infty} f(x)\,dx$ and $\displaystyle\int_{-\infty}^{-b} f(x)\,dx$ as small as we want by choosing b large enough. This is because $0 < f(x) < e^{-x/2}$ for $x > 1$. (Likewise, $0 < f(x) < e^{x/2}$ for $x < -1$) Thus,

$\displaystyle\int_{b}^{\infty} f(x)\,dx < \int_{b}^{\infty} e^{-x/2}\,dx$

$\displaystyle\int_{b}^{\infty} e^{-x/2}\,dx = \lim_{c\to\infty} \int_{b}^{c} e^{-x/2}\,dx$

$\displaystyle = \lim_{c\to\infty} \left[-2e^{-x/2}\right]_{b}^{c}$

$\displaystyle = \lim_{c\to\infty} \left[-2e^{-c/2} + 2e^{-b/2}\right]$

$\displaystyle = 2e^{-b/2}$

As $b \to \infty$, $2e^{-b/2} \to 0$, so for large enough b, $\displaystyle\int_{b}^{\infty} f(x)\,dx$ is as small as we want. Likewise, for large enough b, $\displaystyle\int_{-\infty}^{-b} f(x)\,dx$ is as small as we want.

51. (a) For $x \geq 6$, $x^2 \geq 6x$, so $e^{-x^2} \leq e^{-6x}$

$\displaystyle\int_{6}^{\infty} e^{-x^2}\,dx \leq \int_{6}^{\infty} e^{-6x}\,dx$

$\displaystyle = \lim_{b\to\infty} \int_{6}^{b} e^{-6x}\,dx$

$\displaystyle = \lim_{b\to\infty} \left[-\frac{1}{6}e^{-6x}\right]_{6}^{b}$

$\displaystyle = \lim_{b\to\infty} \left(-\frac{1}{6}e^{-6b} + \frac{1}{6}e^{-36}\right)$

$\displaystyle = \frac{1}{6}e^{-36} < 4 \times 10^{-17}$

(b) $\displaystyle\int_{1}^{\infty} e^{-x^2}\,dx = \int_{1}^{6} e^{-x^2}\,dx + \int_{6}^{\infty} e^{-x^2}\,dx$

$\displaystyle \leq \int_{1}^{6} e^{-x^2}\,dx + 4 \times 10^{-17}$

Thus, from part (a) we have shown that the error is bounded by 4×10^{-17}.

(c) $\displaystyle\int_{1}^{\infty} e^{-x^2}\,dx \approx \text{NINT}(e^{-x^2}, x, 1, 6) \approx 0.1394027926$

(This agrees with Figure 8.16.)

(d) $\displaystyle\int_{0}^{\infty} e^{-x^2}\,dx = \int_{0}^{3} e^{-x^2}\,dx + \int_{3}^{\infty} e^{-x^2}\,dx$

$\displaystyle \leq \int_{0}^{3} e^{-x^2}\,dx + \int_{3}^{\infty} e^{-3x}\,dx$

since $x^2 \geq 3x$ for $x > 3$.

$\displaystyle\int_{3}^{\infty} e^{-3x}\,dx = \lim_{b\to\infty} \int_{3}^{b} e^{-3x}\,dx$

$\displaystyle = \lim_{b\to\infty} \left[-\frac{1}{3}e^{-3x}\right]_{3}^{b}$

$\displaystyle = \lim_{b\to\infty} \left(-\frac{1}{3}e^{-3b} + \frac{1}{3}e^{-9}\right)$

$\displaystyle = \frac{1}{3}e^{-9} \approx 0.000041 < 0.000042$

52. (a) Since f is even, $f(-x) = f(x)$. Let $u = -x$, $du = -dx$.

$\displaystyle\int_{-\infty}^{\infty} f(x)\,dx = \int_{-\infty}^{0} f(x)\,dx + \int_{0}^{\infty} f(x)\,dx$

$\displaystyle = \int_{\infty}^{0} f(-u)(-1)\,du + \int_{0}^{\infty} f(x)\,dx$

$\displaystyle = \int_{0}^{\infty} f(u)\,du + \int_{0}^{\infty} f(x)\,dx$

$\displaystyle = 2\int_{0}^{\infty} f(x)\,dx$

(b) Since f is odd, $f(-x) = -f(x)$. Let $u = -x$, $du = -dx$

$\displaystyle\int_{-\infty}^{\infty} f(x)\,dx = \int_{-\infty}^{0} f(x)\,dx + \int_{0}^{\infty} f(x)\,dx$

$\displaystyle = \int_{\infty}^{0} f(-u)(-1)\,du + \int_{0}^{\infty} f(x)\,dx$

$\displaystyle = -\int_{0}^{\infty} f(u)\,du + \int_{0}^{\infty} f(x)\,dx = 0$

53. (a) $\displaystyle\int_0^\infty \frac{2x\,dx}{x^2+1} = \lim_{b\to\infty}\int_0^b \frac{2x\,dx}{x^2+1}$

$\displaystyle\phantom{\int_0^\infty \frac{2x\,dx}{x^2+1}} = \lim_{b\to\infty}\left[\ln(x^2+1)\right]_0^b$

$\displaystyle\phantom{\int_0^\infty \frac{2x\,dx}{x^2+1}} = \lim_{b\to\infty}\ln(b^2+1) = \infty$

Thus the integral diverges.

(b) Both $\displaystyle\int_0^\infty \frac{2x\,dx}{x^2+1}$ and $\displaystyle\int_{-\infty}^0 \frac{2x\,dx}{x^2+1}$ must converge in order

for $\displaystyle\int_{-\infty}^\infty \frac{2x\,dx}{x^2+1}$ to converge.

(c) $\displaystyle\lim_{b\to\infty}\int_{-b}^b \frac{2x\,dx}{x^2+1} = \lim_{b\to\infty}\left[\ln(x^2+1)\right]_{-b}^b$

$\displaystyle\phantom{\lim_{b\to\infty}\int_{-b}^b} = \lim_{b\to\infty}[\ln(b^2+1) - \ln(b^2+1)]$

$\displaystyle\phantom{\lim_{b\to\infty}\int_{-b}^b} = \lim_{b\to\infty} 0 = 0.$

Note that $\dfrac{2x}{x^2+1}$ is an odd function so $\displaystyle\int_{-b}^b \frac{2x\,dx}{x^2+1} = 0$.

(d) Because the determination of convergence is not made using the method in part (c). In order for the integral to converge, there must be finite areas in both directions (toward ∞ and toward $-\infty$). In this case, there are infinite areas in both directions, but when one computes the integral over an interval $[-b, b]$, there is cancellation which gives 0 as the result.

54. By symmetry, find the perimeter of one side, say for

$0 \le x \le 1,\ y \ge 0.$

$y^{2/3} = 1 - x^{2/3}$

$y = (1 - x^{2/3})^{3/2}$

$\dfrac{dy}{dx} = \dfrac{3}{2}(1-x^{2/3})^{1/2}\left(-\dfrac{2}{3}x^{-1/3}\right) = -x^{-1/3}(1-x^{2/3})^{1/2}$

$\left(\dfrac{dy}{dx}\right)^2 = x^{-2/3}(1 - x^{2/3}) = (x^{-2/3} - 1)$

$\sqrt{1 + \left(\dfrac{dy}{dx}\right)^2} = \sqrt{x^{-2/3}} = x^{-1/3}$

$\displaystyle\int_0^1 x^{-1/3}\,dx = \lim_{b\to 0^+}\int_b^1 x^{-1/3}\,dx$

$\displaystyle\phantom{\int_0^1 x^{-1/3}\,dx} = \lim_{b\to 0^+}\left[\dfrac{3}{2}x^{2/3}\right]_b^1$

$\displaystyle\phantom{\int_0^1 x^{-1/3}\,dx} = \lim_{b\to 0^+}\left[\dfrac{3}{2} - \dfrac{3}{2}b^{2/3}\right] = \dfrac{3}{2}$

Thus, the perimeter is $4\left(\dfrac{3}{2}\right) = 6$.

55. Suppose $0 \le f(x) \le g(x)$ for all $x \ge a$.

From the properties of integrals, for any $b > a$,

$\displaystyle\int_a^b f(x) \le \int_a^b g(x)\,dx.$

If the infinite integral of g converges, then taking the limit in the above inequality as $b\to\infty$ shows that the infinite integral of f is bounded above by the infinite integral of g. Therefore, the infinite integral of f must be finite and it converges. If the infinite integral of f diverges, it must grow to infinity. So taking the limit in the above inequality as $b\to\infty$ shows that the infinite integral of g must also diverge to infinity.

56. (a) For $n = 0$:

$\displaystyle\int_0^\infty e^{-x}\,dx = \lim_{b\to\infty}\int_0^b e^{-x}\,dx$

$\displaystyle\phantom{\int_0^\infty e^{-x}\,dx} = \lim_{b\to\infty}\left[-e^{-x}\right]_0^b$

$\displaystyle\phantom{\int_0^\infty e^{-x}\,dx} = \lim_{b\to\infty}[-e^{-b} + 1] = 1$

For $n = 1$:

$u = x \qquad\qquad dv = e^{-x}\,dx$

$du = dx \qquad\qquad v = -e^{-x}$

$\displaystyle\int_0^\infty xe^{-x}\,dx = \lim_{b\to\infty}\int_0^b xe^{-x}\,dx$

$\displaystyle\phantom{\int_0^\infty xe^{-x}\,dx} = \lim_{b\to\infty}\left(\left[-xe^{-x}\right]_0^b + \int_0^b e^{-x}\,dx\right)$

$\displaystyle\phantom{\int_0^\infty xe^{-x}\,dx} = \lim_{b\to\infty}\left(-\dfrac{b}{e^b}\right) + \lim_{b\to\infty}\int_0^b e^{-x}\,dx$

$\displaystyle\phantom{\int_0^\infty xe^{-x}\,dx} = \lim_{b\to\infty}\left(-\dfrac{1}{e^b}\right) + 1 = 1$

For $n = 2$:

$u = x^2 \qquad\qquad dv = e^{-x}\,dx$

$du = 2x\,dx \qquad\qquad v = -e^{-x}$

$\displaystyle\int_0^\infty x^2 e^{-x}\,dx = \lim_{b\to\infty}\int_0^b x^2 e^{-x}\,dx$

$\displaystyle\phantom{\int_0^\infty x^2 e^{-x}\,dx} = \lim_{b\to\infty}\left(\left[-x^2 e^{-x}\right]_0^b + \int_0^b 2x e^{-x}\,dx\right)$

$\displaystyle\phantom{\int_0^\infty x^2 e^{-x}\,dx} = \lim_{b\to\infty}\left(-\dfrac{b^2}{e^b}\right) + 2\lim_{b\to\infty}\int_0^b xe^{-x}\,dx$

$\displaystyle\phantom{\int_0^\infty x^2 e^{-x}\,dx} = \lim_{b\to\infty}\left(-\dfrac{2b}{e^b}\right) + 2(1)$

$\displaystyle\phantom{\int_0^\infty x^2 e^{-x}\,dx} = \lim_{b\to\infty}\left(-\dfrac{2}{e^b}\right) + 2 = 2$

56. continued

(b) Evaluate $\int x^n e^{-x} \, dx$ using integration by parts

$u = x^n$ $dv = e^{-x} \, dx$

$du = nx^{n-1}$ $v = -e^{-x}$

$\int x^n e^{-x} \, dx = -x^n e^{-x} + \int nx^{n-1} e^{-x} \, dx$

$f(n+1) = \int_0^\infty x^n e^{-x} \, dx$

$\qquad = \lim_{b \to \infty} \left[-x^n e^{-x} \right]_0^b + \int_0^\infty nx^{n-1} e^{-x} \, dx$

$\qquad = \lim_{b \to \infty} \left(-\dfrac{b^n}{e^b} \right) + n \int_0^\infty x^{n-1} e^{-x} \, dx$

$\qquad = nf(n)$

$\left(\text{Note: apply L'Hôpital's Rule } n \text{ times to show that} \right.$

$\left. \lim_{b \to \infty} \left(-\dfrac{b^n}{e^b} \right) = 0. \right)$

(c) Since $f(n+1) = nf(n)$,

$f(n+1) = n(n-1) \cdots f(1) = n!$; thus

$\int_0^\infty x^n e^{-x} \, dx$ converges for all integers $n \geq 0$.

57. (a) On a grapher, plot $\text{NINT} \left(\dfrac{\sin x}{x}, x, 0, x \right)$ or create a table

of values. For large values of x, $f(x)$ appears to

approach approximately 1.57.

(b) Yes, the integral appears to converge.

58. (a) $\displaystyle\int_{-\infty}^1 \dfrac{dx}{1 + x^2} = \lim_{b \to -\infty} \int_b^1 \dfrac{dx}{1 + x^2}$

$\qquad = \lim_{b \to -\infty} \left[\tan^{-1} x \right]_b^1$

$\qquad = \lim_{b \to -\infty} (\tan^{-1} 1 - \tan^{-1} b)$

$\qquad = \dfrac{\pi}{4} + \dfrac{\pi}{2} = \dfrac{3\pi}{4}$

$\displaystyle\int_1^\infty \dfrac{dx}{1 + x^2} = \lim_{b \to \infty} \int_1^b \dfrac{dx}{1 + x^2}$

$\qquad = \lim_{b \to \infty} \left[\tan^{-1} x \right]_1^b$

$\qquad = \lim_{b \to \infty} [\tan^{-1} b - \tan^{-1} 1]$

$\qquad = \dfrac{\pi}{2} - \dfrac{\pi}{4} = \dfrac{\pi}{4}$

$\displaystyle\int_{-\infty}^\infty \dfrac{dx}{1 + x^2} = \dfrac{3\pi}{4} + \dfrac{\pi}{4} = \pi$

(b) $\displaystyle\int_{-\infty}^c f(x) \, dx = \int_{-\infty}^0 f(x) \, dx + \int_0^c f(x) \, dx$

$\displaystyle\int_c^\infty f(x) \, dx = \int_c^0 f(x) \, dx + \int_0^\infty f(x) \, dx$

Thus,

$\displaystyle\int_{-\infty}^c f(x) \, dx + \int_c^\infty f(x) \, dx$

$\displaystyle = \int_{-\infty}^0 f(x) \, dx + \int_0^c f(x) \, dx + \int_c^0 f(x) \, dx + \int_0^\infty f(x) \, dx$

$\displaystyle = \int_{-\infty}^0 f(x) \, dx + \int_0^\infty f(x) \, dx, \text{ because}$

$\displaystyle\int_0^c f(x) \, dx + \int_c^0 f(x) \, dx = \int_0^c f(x) \, dx - \int_0^c f(x) \, dx = 0.$

■ Section 8.4 Partial Fractions and Integral Tables (pp. 444–453)

Quick Review 8.4

1. Solving the first equation for B yields $B = -3A - 5$.
Substitute into the second equation.

$-2A + 3(-3A - 5) = 7$

$\quad -2A - 9A - 15 = 7$

$\qquad\qquad -11A = 22$

$\qquad\qquad\qquad A = -2$

Substituting $A = -2$ into $B = -3A - 5$ gives $B = 1$. The
solution is $A = -2$, $B = 1$.

2. Solve by Gaussian elimination. Multiply first equation by
-3 and add to second equation. Multiply first equation by
-1 and add to third equation.

$A + 2B - C = 0$

$\quad -7B + 5C = 1$

$\quad -B + 2C = 4$

Multiply third equation by -7 and add to second equation.

$A + 2B - C = 0$

$\qquad -9C = -27$

$\quad -B + 2C = 4$

Solve the second equation for C to get $C = 3$. Solve for B
by substituting $C = 3$ into the third equation.

$-B + 2(3) = 4$

$\qquad -B = -2$

$\qquad\quad B = 2$

Solve for A by substituting $B = 2$ and $C = 3$ into the first
equation.

$A + 2(2) - 3 = 0$

$\quad A + 1 = 0$

$\qquad A = -1$

The solution is $A = -1$, $B = 2$, $C = 3$.

3.
$$x^2 - 3x - 4 \overline{\smash{\big)}\ 2x^3 - 5x^2 - 10x - 7}$$

$$\begin{array}{r} 2x + 1 \\ 2x^3 - 6x^2 \quad - 8x \\ \hline x^2 - 2x - 7 \\ x^2 - 3x - 4 \\ \hline \end{array}$$

$2x + 1 + \dfrac{x - 3}{x^2 - 3x - 4}$

4. $x^2 + 4x + 5 \overline{)2x^2 + 11x + \ 6}$
$$\underline{2x^2 + \ 8x + 10}$$
$$3x - \ 4$$

$$2 + \frac{3x - 4}{x^2 + 4x + 5}$$

5. $x^3 - 3x^2 + x - 3 = x^2(x - 3) + (x - 3)$
$$= (x - 3)(x^2 + 1)$$

6. $y^4 - 5y^2 + 4 = (y^2 - 4)(y^2 - 1)$
$$= (y - 2)(y + 2)(y - 1)(y + 1)$$

7. $\dfrac{2}{x + 3} - \dfrac{3}{x - 2} = \dfrac{2(x - 2)}{(x - 2)(x + 3)} - \dfrac{3(x + 3)}{(x - 2)(x + 3)}$
$$= \frac{2x - 4 - 3x - 9}{(x - 2)(x + 3)}$$
$$= \frac{-x - 13}{(x - 2)(x + 3)}$$
$$= -\frac{x + 13}{x^2 + x - 6}$$

8. $\dfrac{x - 1}{x^2 - 4x + 5} - \dfrac{2}{x + 5}$
$$= \frac{(x - 1)(x + 5)}{(x + 5)(x^2 - 4x + 5)} - \frac{2(x^2 - 4x + 5)}{(x + 5)(x^2 - 4x + 5)}$$
$$= \frac{x^2 + 4x - 5 - 2x^2 + 8x - 10}{(x + 5)(x^2 - 4x + 5)}$$
$$= \frac{-x^2 + 12x - 15}{(x + 5)(x^2 - 4x + 5)}$$

9. $\dfrac{t - 1}{t^2 + 2} - \dfrac{3t + 4}{t^2 + 1} = \dfrac{(t - 1)(t^2 + 1)}{(t^2 + 2)(t^2 + 1)} - \dfrac{(3t + 4)(t^2 + 2)}{(t^2 + 2)(t^2 + 1)}$
$$= \frac{t^3 - t^2 + t - 1 - 3t^3 - 4t^2 - 6t - 8}{(t^2 + 2)(t^2 + 1)}$$
$$= \frac{-2t^3 - 5t^2 - 5t - 9}{(t^2 + 2)(t^2 + 1)}$$
$$= -\frac{2t^3 + 5t^2 + 5t + 9}{(t^2 + 2)(t^2 + 1)}$$

10. $\dfrac{2}{x - 1} - \dfrac{3}{(x - 1)^2} + \dfrac{1}{(x - 1)^3}$
$$= \frac{2(x - 1)^2}{(x - 1)^3} - \frac{3(x - 1)}{(x - 1)^3} + \frac{1}{(x - 1)^3}$$
$$= \frac{2x^2 - 4x + 2 - 3x + 3 + 1}{(x - 1)^3}$$
$$= \frac{2x^2 - 7x + 6}{(x - 1)^3}$$

Section 8.4 Exercises

1. $x^2 - 3x + 2 = (x - 2)(x - 1)$
$$\frac{5x - 7}{x^2 - 3x + 2} = \frac{A}{x - 2} + \frac{B}{x - 1}$$
$$5x - 7 = A(x - 1) + B(x - 2)$$
$$= (A + B)x - (A + 2B)$$

Equating coefficients of like terms gives

$A + B = 5$ and $A + 2B = 7$.

Solving the system simultaneously yields $A = 3$, $B = 2$.
$$\frac{5x - 7}{x^2 - 3x + 2} = \frac{3}{x - 2} + \frac{2}{x - 1}$$

2. $x^2 - 2x + 1 = (x - 1)^2$
$$\frac{2x + 2}{x^2 - 2x + 1} = \frac{A}{x - 1} + \frac{B}{(x - 1)^2}$$
$$2x + 2 = A(x - 1) + B$$
$$= Ax + (-A + B)$$

Equating coefficients of like terms gives

$A = 2$ and $-A + B = 2$.

Solving the system simultaneously yields $A = 2$, $B = 4$.
$$\frac{2x + 2}{x^2 - 2x + 1} = \frac{2}{x - 1} + \frac{4}{(x - 1)^2}$$

3. $\dfrac{t + 1}{t^2(t - 1)} = \dfrac{A}{t - 1} + \dfrac{B}{t} + \dfrac{C}{t^2}$
$$t + 1 = At^2 + Bt(t - 1) + C(t - 1)$$
$$= (A + B)t^2 + (-B + C)t - C$$

Equating coefficients of like terms gives

$A + B = 0$, $-B + C = 1$, and $-C = 1$.

Solving the system simultaneously yields

$A = 2$, $B = -2$, $C = -1$.
$$\frac{t + 1}{t^2(t - 1)} = \frac{2}{t - 1} - \frac{2}{t} - \frac{1}{t^2}$$

4. $s^3 - s^2 - 6s = s(s^2 - s - 6) = s(s - 3)(s + 2)$
$$\frac{4}{s^3 - s^2 - 6s} = \frac{A}{s} + \frac{B}{s - 3} + \frac{C}{s + 2}$$
$$4 = A(s - 3)(s + 2) + B(s)(s + 2) + C(s)(s - 3)$$
$$= A(s^2 - s - 6) + B(s^2 + 2s) + C(s^2 - 3s)$$
$$= (A + B + C)s^2 + (-A + 2B - 3C)s - 6A$$

Equating coefficients of like terms gives

$A + B + C = 0$, $-A + 2B - 3C = 0$, $-6A = 4$

Solving the system simultaneously yields

$A = -\dfrac{2}{3}$, $B = \dfrac{4}{15}$, $C = \dfrac{2}{5}$.
$$\frac{4}{s^3 - s^2 - 6s} = -\frac{2}{3s} + \frac{4}{15(s - 3)} + \frac{2}{5(s + 2)}$$

5.
$$x^2 - 5x + 6 \overline{\smash{\big)}\ x^2 \qquad + 8} \atop {1}$$
$$\underline{x^2 - 5x + 6}$$
$$5x + 2$$

$$\frac{x^2 + 8}{x^2 - 5x + 6} = 1 + \frac{5x + 2}{x^2 - 5x + 6}$$
$$x^2 - 5x + 6 = (x - 3)(x - 2)$$

$$\frac{5x + 2}{x^2 - 5x + 6} = \frac{A}{x - 3} + \frac{B}{x - 2}$$
$$5x + 2 = A(x - 2) + B(x - 3)$$
$$= (A + B)x + (-2A - 3B)$$

Equating coefficients of like terms gives

$$A + B = 5 \text{ and } -2A - 3B = 2$$

Solving the system simultaneously yields

$$A = 17, B = -12.$$
$$\frac{x^2 + 8}{x^2 - 5x + 6} = 1 + \frac{17}{x - 3} - \frac{12}{x - 2}$$

6.
$$y^2 + 4 \overline{\smash{\big)}\ y^3 \qquad + 1} \atop {y}$$
$$\underline{y^3 \qquad + 4y + 0}$$
$$-4y + 1$$

$$\frac{y^3 + 1}{y^2 + 4} = y + \frac{-4y + 1}{y^2 + 4}$$

The rational function cannot be decomposed any further.

7. $1 - x^2 = (1 - x)(1 + x)$

$$\frac{1}{1 - x^2} = \frac{A}{1 - x} + \frac{B}{1 + x}$$
$$1 = A(1 + x) + B(1 - x)$$
$$= (A - B)x + (A + B)$$

Equating coefficients of like terms gives

$$A - B = 0 \text{ and } A + B = 1.$$

Solving the system simultaneously yields

$$A = \frac{1}{2}, B = \frac{1}{2}.$$
$$\int \frac{dx}{1 - x^2} = \int \frac{1/2}{1 - x} dx + \int \frac{1/2}{1 + x} dx$$
$$= -\frac{1}{2} \ln |1 - x| + \frac{1}{2} \ln |1 + x| + C$$
$$= \frac{1}{2} \ln \left| \frac{1 + x}{1 - x} \right| + C$$

8. $x^2 + 2x = x(x + 2)$

$$\frac{1}{x^2 + 2x} = \frac{A}{x} + \frac{B}{x + 2}$$
$$1 = A(x + 2) + Bx$$
$$= (A + B)x + 2A$$

Equating coefficients of like terms gives

$$A + B = 0 \text{ and } 2A = 1$$

Solving the system simultaneously yields $A = \frac{1}{2}, B = -\frac{1}{2}$.

$$\int \frac{dx}{x^2 + 2x} = \int \frac{1/2}{x} dx + \int \frac{-1/2}{x + 2} dx$$
$$= \frac{1}{2} \ln |x| - \frac{1}{2} \ln |x + 2| + C$$
$$= \frac{1}{2} \ln \left| \frac{x}{x + 2} \right| + C$$

9. $y^2 - 2y - 3 = (y - 3)(y + 1)$

$$\frac{y}{y^2 - 2y - 3} = \frac{A}{y - 3} + \frac{B}{y + 1}$$
$$y = A(y + 1) + B(y - 3)$$
$$= (A + B)y + (A - 3B)$$

Equating coefficients of like terms gives

$$A + B = 1 \text{ and } A - 3B = 0.$$

Solving the system simultaneously yields $A = \frac{3}{4}, B = \frac{1}{4}$.

$$\int \frac{y \, dy}{y^2 - 2y - 3} = \int \frac{3/4}{y - 3} dy + \int \frac{1/4}{y + 1} dy$$
$$= \frac{3}{4} \ln |y - 3| + \frac{1}{4} \ln |y + 1| + C$$

10. $y^2 + y = y(y + 1)$

$$\frac{y + 4}{y^2 + y} = \frac{A}{y} + \frac{B}{y + 1}$$
$$y + 4 = A(y + 1) + By$$
$$= (A + B)y + A$$

Equating coefficients of like terms gives

$$A + B = 1 \text{ and } A = 4.$$

Solving the system simultaneously yields $A = 4, B = -3$.

$$\int \frac{y + 4}{y^2 + y} dy = \int \frac{4}{y} dy + \int \frac{-3}{y + 1} dy$$
$$= 4 \ln |y| - 3 \ln |y + 1| + C$$

11. $t^3 + t^2 - 2t = t(t^2 + t - 2) = t(t + 2)(t - 1)$

$$\frac{1}{t^3 + t^2 - 2t} = \frac{A}{t} + \frac{B}{t + 2} + \frac{C}{t - 1}$$

$1 = A(t + 2)(t - 1) + B(t)(t - 1) + C(t)(t + 2)$

$\quad = A(t^2 + t - 2) + B(t^2 - t) + C(t^2 + 2t)$

$\quad = (A + B + C)t^2 + (A - B + 2C)t - 2A$

Equating coefficients of like terms gives

$A + B + C = 0, A - B + 2C = 0,$ and $-2A = 1.$

Solving the system simultaneously yields

$A = -\dfrac{1}{2}, B = \dfrac{1}{6}, C = \dfrac{1}{3}.$

$$\int \frac{dt}{t^3 + t^2 - 2t} = \int \frac{-1/2}{t} \, dt + \int \frac{1/6}{t + 2} \, dt + \int \frac{1/3}{t - 1} \, dt$$

$$= -\frac{1}{2} \ln |t| + \frac{1}{6} \ln |t + 2| + \frac{1}{3} \ln |t - 1| + C$$

12. $2t^3 - 8t = 2t(t^2 - 4) = 2t(t - 2)(t + 2)$

$$\frac{t + 3}{2t^3 - 8t} = \frac{A}{t} + \frac{B}{t - 2} + \frac{C}{t + 2}$$

$t + 3 = 2A(t - 2)(t + 2) + 2B(t)(t + 2) + 2C(t)(t - 2)$

$\quad = 2A(t^2 - 4) + 2B(t^2 + 2t) + 2C(t^2 - 2t)$

$\quad = (2A + 2B + 2C)t^2 + (4B - 4C)t - 8A$

Equating coefficients of like terms gives

$2A + 2B + 2C = 0, 4B - 4C = 1, -8A = 3$

Solving the system simultaneously yields

$A = -\dfrac{3}{8}, B = \dfrac{5}{16}, C = \dfrac{1}{16}.$

$$\int \frac{t + 3}{2t^3 - 8t} \, dt = \int \frac{-3/8}{t} \, dt + \int \frac{5/16}{t - 2} \, dt + \int \frac{1/16}{t + 2} \, dt$$

$$= -\frac{3}{8} \ln |t| + \frac{5}{16} \ln |t - 2| + \frac{1}{16} \ln |t + 2| + C$$

13. $s^2 + 4 \overline{) s^3 }$ with quotient s

$\qquad \quad \underline{s^3 + 4s}$

$\qquad \qquad \quad -4s$

$$\frac{s^3}{s^2 + 4} = s + \frac{-4s}{s^2 + 4}$$

$$\int \frac{s^3}{s^2 + 4} \, ds = \int s \, ds - \int \frac{4s}{s^2 + 4} \, ds$$

$$= \frac{1}{2}s^2 - 2 \ln (s^2 + 4) + C$$

14. $s^2 + 1 \overline{) s^4 }$ with quotient $s^2 - 1$

$\qquad \qquad \underline{ + 2s}$

$\qquad \quad \underline{s^4 + s^2}$

$\qquad \qquad \quad -s^2 + 2s$

$\qquad \qquad \quad \underline{-s^2 - 1}$

$\qquad \qquad \qquad \quad 2s + 1$

$$\frac{s^4 + 2s}{s^2 + 1} = s^2 - 1 + \frac{2s + 1}{s^2 + 1} = s^2 - 1 + \frac{2s}{s^2 + 1} + \frac{1}{s^2 + 1}$$

$$\int \frac{s^4 + 2s}{s^2 + 1} \, ds = \int (s^2 - 1) \, ds + \int \frac{2s \, ds}{s^2 + 1} + \int \frac{ds}{s^2 + 1}$$

$$= \frac{1}{3}s^3 - s + \ln (s^2 + 1) + \tan^{-1} s + C$$

15. $x^2 + x + 1 \overline{) 5x^2 }$ with quotient 5

$\qquad \qquad \quad \underline{5x^2 + 5x + 5}$

$\qquad \qquad \qquad \quad -5x - 5$

$$\frac{5x^2}{x^2 + x + 1} = 5 - \frac{5x + 5}{x^2 + x + 1}$$

$$\int \frac{5x^2 \, dx}{x^2 + x + 1} = \int 5 \, dx - 5\int \frac{x + 1}{x^2 + x + 1} \, dx$$

$$= 5x - 5\int \frac{x + 1}{x^2 + x + 1} \, dx$$

To evaluate the second integral, complete the square in the denominator.

$$x^2 + x + 1 = x^2 + x + \frac{1}{4} + \frac{3}{4} = \left(x + \frac{1}{2}\right)^2 + \frac{3}{4}$$

$$\int \frac{x + 1}{x^2 + x + 1} \, dx$$

$$= \int \frac{x + 1}{(x + 1/2)^2 + 3/4} \, dx$$

$$= \int \frac{x + 1/2}{(x + 1/2)^2 + 3/4} \, dx + \int \frac{1/2}{(x + 1/2)^2 + 3/4} \, dx$$

$$= \frac{1}{2} \ln\left[\left(x + \frac{1}{2}\right)^2 + \frac{3}{4}\right] + \frac{1}{2}\int \frac{dx}{(x + 1/2)^2 + (\sqrt{3}/2)^2}$$

$$= \frac{1}{2} \ln (x^2 + x + 1) + \frac{1}{2}\left(\frac{2}{\sqrt{3}}\right) \tan^{-1}\left(\frac{x + 1/2}{\sqrt{3}/2}\right)$$

$$= \frac{1}{2} \ln (x^2 + x + 1) + \frac{1}{\sqrt{3}} \tan^{-1}\left(\frac{2x + 1}{\sqrt{3}}\right)$$

The second integral was evaluated by using Formula 16 from the Brief Table of Integrals.

$$\int \frac{5x^2 \, dx}{x^2 + x + 1}$$

$$= 5x - \frac{5}{2} \ln (x^2 + x + 1) - \frac{5}{\sqrt{3}} \tan^{-1}\left(\frac{2x + 1}{\sqrt{3}}\right) + C$$

16. $(x - 1)(x^2 + 2x + 1) = (x - 1)(x + 1)^2$

$$\frac{x^2}{(x - 1)(x^2 + 2x + 1)} = \frac{A}{x - 1} + \frac{B}{x + 1} + \frac{C}{(x + 1)^2}$$

$x^2 = A(x + 1)^2 + B(x - 1)(x + 1) + C(x - 1)$

$\quad = A(x^2 + 2x + 1) + B(x^2 - 1) + C(x - 1)$

$\quad = (A + B)x^2 + (2A + C)x + A - B - C$

Equating coefficients of like terms gives

$A + B = 1, 2A + C = 0,$ and $A - B - C = 0.$

Solving the system simultaneously yields

$A = \dfrac{1}{4}, B = \dfrac{3}{4}, C = -\dfrac{1}{2}.$

$$\int \frac{x^2 \, dx}{(x - 1)(x^2 + 2x + 1)}$$

$$= \int \frac{1/4}{x - 1} \, dx + \int \frac{3/4}{x + 1} \, dx + \int \frac{-1/2}{(x + 1)^2} \, dx$$

$$= \frac{1}{4} \ln |x - 1| + \frac{3}{4} \ln |x + 1| + \frac{1}{2(x + 1)} + C$$

17. $(x^2 - 1)^2 = (x + 1)^2(x - 1)^2$

$$\frac{1}{(x^2 - 1)^2} = \frac{A}{x + 1} + \frac{B}{(x + 1)^2} + \frac{C}{x - 1} + \frac{D}{(x - 1)^2}$$

$$1 = A(x + 1)(x - 1)^2 + B(x - 1)^2 + C(x + 1)^2(x - 1)$$

$$+ D(x + 1)^2$$

$$= A(x^3 - x^2 - x + 1) + B(x^2 - 2x + 1)$$

$$+ C(x^3 + x^2 - x - 1) + D(x^2 + 2x + 1)$$

$$= (A + C)x^3 + (-A + B + C + D)x^2$$

$$+ (-A - 2B - C + 2D)x + (A + B - C + D)$$

Equating coefficients of like terms gives

$A + C = 0, -A + B + C + D = 0,$

$-A - 2B - C + 2D = 0,$ and $A + B - C + D = 1$

Solving the system simultaneously yields

$$A = \frac{1}{4}, B = \frac{1}{4}, C = -\frac{1}{4}, D = \frac{1}{4}.$$

$$\int \frac{dx}{(x^2 - 1)^2}$$

$$= \int \frac{1/4}{x + 1}\, dx + \int \frac{1/4}{(x + 1)^2}\, dx + \int \frac{-1/4}{x - 1}\, dx + \int \frac{1/4}{(x - 1)^2}\, dx$$

$$= \frac{1}{4} \ln |x + 1| - \frac{1}{4(x + 1)} - \frac{1}{4} \ln |x - 1| - \frac{1}{4(x - 1)} + C$$

18. $x^2 + 5x - 6 = (x + 6)(x - 1)$

$$\frac{x + 4}{x^2 + 5x - 6} = \frac{A}{x + 6} + \frac{B}{x - 1}$$

$$x + 4 = A(x - 1) + B(x + 6)$$

$$= (A + B)x + (-A + 6B)$$

Equating coefficients of like terms gives

$A + B = 1$ and $-A + 6B = 4.$

Solving the system simultaneously yields

$$A = \frac{2}{7}, B = \frac{5}{7}.$$

$$\int \frac{x + 4}{x^2 + 5x - 6}\, dx = \int \frac{2/7}{x + 6}\, dx + \int \frac{5/7}{x - 1}\, dx$$

$$= \frac{2}{7} \ln |x + 6| + \frac{5}{7} \ln |x - 1| + C$$

19. Complete the square in the denominator.

$$r^2 - 2r + 2 = r^2 - 2r + 1 + 1 = (r - 1)^2 + 1$$

$$\int \frac{2\, dr}{r^2 - 2r + 2} = \int \frac{2\, dr}{(r - 1)^2 + 1} = 2 \tan^{-1} (r - 1) + C$$

20. Complete the square in the denominator.

$$r^2 - 4r + 5 = r^2 - 4r + 4 + 1 = (r - 2)^2 + 1$$

$$\int \frac{3\, dr}{r^2 - 4r + 5} = \int \frac{3\, dr}{(r - 2)^2 + 1} = 3 \tan^{-1} (r - 2) + C$$

21. $x^3 - 1 = (x - 1)(x^2 + x + 1)$

$$\frac{x^2 - 2x - 2}{x^3 - 1} = \frac{A}{x - 1} + \frac{Bx + C}{x^2 + x + 1}$$

$$x^2 - 2x - 2 = A(x^2 + x + 1) + (Bx + C)(x - 1)$$

$$= (A + B)x^2 + (A - B + C)x + (A - C)$$

Equating coefficients of like terms gives

$A + B = 1, A - B + C = -2,$ and $A - C = -2.$

Solving the system simultaneously yields

$A = -1, B = 2, C = 1.$

$$\int \frac{x^2 - 2x - 2}{x^3 - 1}\, dx = \int \frac{-1}{x - 1}\, dx + \int \frac{2x + 1}{x^2 + x + 1}\, dx$$

$$= -\ln |x - 1| + \ln (x^2 + x + 1) + C$$

22. $x^3 + 1 = (x + 1)(x^2 - x + 1)$

$$\frac{x^2 - 4x + 4}{x^3 + 1} = \frac{A}{x + 1} + \frac{Bx + C}{x^2 - x + 1}$$

$$x^2 - 4x + 4 = A(x^2 - x + 1) + (Bx + C)(x + 1)$$

$$= (A + B)x^2 + (-A + B + C)x + (A + C)$$

Equating coefficients of like terms gives

$A + B = 1, -A + B + C = -4,$ and $A + C = 4.$

Solving the system simultaneously yields

$A = 3, B = -2, C = 1.$

$$\int \frac{x^2 - 4x + 4}{x^3 + 1}\, dx = \int \frac{3}{x + 1}\, dx + \int \frac{-2x + 1}{x^2 - x + 1}\, dx$$

$$= 3 \ln |x + 1| - \ln (x^2 - x + 1) + C$$

23. $\dfrac{3x^2 - 2x + 12}{(x^2 + 4)^2} = \dfrac{Ax + B}{x^2 + 4} + \dfrac{Cx + D}{(x^2 + 4)^2}$

$$3x^2 - 2x + 12 = (Ax + B)(x^2 + 4) + (Cx + D)$$

$$= Ax^3 + Bx^2 + (4A + C)x + 4B + D$$

Equating coefficients of like terms gives

$A = 0, B = 3, 4A + C = -2,$ and $4B + D = 12$

Solving the system simultaneously yields

$A = 0, B = 3, C = -2, D = 0.$

$$\int \frac{3x^2 - 2x + 12}{(x^2 + 4)^2}\, dx = \int \frac{3}{x^2 + 4}\, dx + \int \frac{-2x}{(x^2 + 4)^2}\, dx$$

$$= \frac{3}{2} \tan^{-1} \frac{x}{2} + \frac{1}{x^2 + 4} + C$$

The first integral was evaluated by using Formula 16 from the Brief Table of Integrals.

24. $\dfrac{x^3 + 2x^2 + 2}{(x^2 + 1)^2} = \dfrac{Ax + B}{(x^2 + 1)} + \dfrac{Cx + D}{(x^2 + 1)^2}$

$x^3 + 2x^2 + 2 = (Ax + B)(x^2 + 1) + (Cx + D)$

$\qquad\qquad = Ax^3 + Bx^2 + (A + C)x + (B + D)$

Equating coefficients of like terms gives

$A = 1, B = 2, A + C = 0, B + D = 2$

Solving the system simultaneously yields

$A = 1, B = 2, C = -1, D = 0.$

$\displaystyle\int \dfrac{x^3 + 2x^2 + 2}{(x^2 + 1)^2}\, dx$

$\displaystyle = \int \dfrac{x + 2}{x^2 + 1}\, dx + \int \dfrac{-x}{(x^2 + 1)^2}\, dx$

$\displaystyle = \int \dfrac{x}{x^2 + 1}\, dx + \int \dfrac{2}{x^2 + 1}\, dx - \int \dfrac{x}{(x^2 + 1)^2}\, dx$

$\displaystyle = \dfrac{1}{2} \ln (x^2 + 1) + 2 \tan^{-1} x + \dfrac{1}{2(x^2 + 1)} + C$

25. $\theta + 1 \overline{)\theta}$
$\qquad \dfrac{\theta + 1}{-1}$

$\dfrac{\theta}{\theta + 1} = 1 - \dfrac{1}{\theta + 1}$

$\displaystyle\int_0^1 \dfrac{\theta}{\theta + 1}\, d\theta = \int_0^1 d\theta - \int_0^1 \dfrac{1}{\theta + 1}\, d\theta$

$\displaystyle\qquad = \Big[\theta\Big]_0^1 - \Big[\ln |\theta + 1|\Big]_0^1$

$\displaystyle\qquad = 1 - \ln 2$

26. $\theta^2 + 1 \overline{)\theta^2}$
$\qquad \dfrac{\theta^2 + 1}{-1}$

$\dfrac{\theta^2}{\theta^2 + 1} = 1 - \dfrac{1}{\theta^2 + 1}$

$\displaystyle\int_0^2 \dfrac{\theta^2}{\theta^2 + 1}\, d\theta = \int_0^2 d\theta - \int_0^2 \dfrac{1}{\theta^2 + 1}\, d\theta$

$\displaystyle\qquad = \Big[\theta\Big]_0^2 - \Big[\tan^{-1} \theta\Big]_0^2$

$\displaystyle\qquad = 2 - \tan^{-1} 2$

27. $\dfrac{1}{y^2 - y}\, dy = e^x\, dx$

$\displaystyle\int \dfrac{1}{y(y - 1)}\, dy = \int e^x\, dx = e^x + C_1$

$\dfrac{1}{y(y - 1)} = \dfrac{A}{y} + \dfrac{B}{y - 1}$

$1 = A(y - 1) + B(y)$

$\qquad = (A + B)y - A$

Equating coefficients of like terms gives

$A + B = 0$ and $-A = 1$

Solving the system simultaneously yields $A = -1, B = 1.$

$\displaystyle\int \dfrac{1}{y(y - 1)}\, dy = \int -\dfrac{1}{y}\, dy + \int \dfrac{1}{y - 1}\, dy$

$\displaystyle\qquad = -\ln |y| + \ln |y - 1| + C_2$

$-\ln |y| + \ln |y - 1| = e^x + C$

Substitute $x = 0, y = 2.$

$-\ln 2 + 0 = 1 + C$ or $C = -1 - \ln 2$

The solution to the initial value problem is

$-\ln |y| + \ln |y - 1| = e^x - 1 - \ln 2.$

28. $\dfrac{1}{(y + 1)^2}\, dy = \sin \theta\, d\theta$

$\displaystyle\int \dfrac{1}{(y + 1)^2}\, dy = \int \sin \theta\, d\theta$

$-\dfrac{1}{y + 1} = -\cos \theta + C$

Substitute $x = \dfrac{\pi}{2}, y = 0.$

$-1 = 0 + C$ or $C = -1$

The solution to the initial value problem is

$-\dfrac{1}{y + 1} = -\cos \theta - 1$

$y + 1 = \dfrac{1}{\cos \theta + 1}$

$y = \dfrac{1}{\cos \theta + 1} - 1$

29. $dy = \dfrac{dx}{x^2 - 3x + 2}$

$x^2 - 3x + 2 = (x - 2)(x - 1)$

$\dfrac{1}{x^2 - 3x + 2} = \dfrac{A}{x - 2} + \dfrac{B}{x - 1}$

$1 = A(x - 1) + B(x - 2)$

$1 = (A + B)x - A - 2B$

Equating coefficients of like terms gives

$A + B = 0, -A - 2B = 1$

Solving the system simultaneously yields $A = 1, B = -1.$

$\displaystyle\int dy = \int \dfrac{dx}{x^2 - 3x + 2} = \int \dfrac{dx}{x - 2} - \int \dfrac{dx}{x - 1}$

$y = \ln |x - 2| - \ln |x - 1| + C$

Substitute $x = 3, y = 0.$

$0 = 0 - \ln 2 + C$ or $C = \ln 2$

The solution to the initial value problem is

$y = \ln |x - 2| - \ln |x - 1| + \ln 2$

30.

$$\frac{ds}{2s+2} = \frac{dt}{t^2+2t}$$

$$\int \frac{ds}{2s+2} = \frac{1}{2}\int \frac{ds}{s+1} = \frac{1}{2}\ln|s+1| + C_1$$

$$t^2 + 2t = t(t+2)$$

$$\frac{1}{t^2+2t} = \frac{A}{t} + \frac{B}{t+2}$$

$$1 = A(t+2) + Bt$$

$$1 = (A+B)t + 2A$$

Equating coefficients of like terms gives

$$A + B = 0 \text{ and } 2A = 1$$

Solving the system simultaneously yields $A = \frac{1}{2}$, $B = -\frac{1}{2}$.

$$\int \frac{dt}{t^2+2t} = \int \frac{1/2}{t} dt - \int \frac{1/2}{t+2} dt$$

$$= \frac{1}{2}\ln|t| - \frac{1}{2}\ln|t+2| + C_2$$

$$\frac{1}{2}\ln|s+1| = \frac{1}{2}\ln|t| - \frac{1}{2}\ln|t+2| + C_3$$

$$\ln|s+1| = \ln|t| - \ln|t+2| + C$$

Substitute $t = 1$, $s = 1$.

$$\ln 2 = 0 - \ln 3 + C \text{ or } C = \ln 2 + \ln 3 = \ln 6$$

The solution to the initial value problem is

$$\ln|s+1| = \ln|t| - \ln|t+2| + \ln 6$$

$$\ln|s+1| = \ln\left|\frac{6t}{t+2}\right|$$

$$|s+1| = \left|\frac{6t}{t+2}\right|.$$

31. (a) Complete the square in the denominator.

$$5 + 4x - x^2 = 5 - (x^2 - 4x)$$

$$= 9 - (x^2 - 4x + 4)$$

$$= 9 - (x-2)^2$$

Let $u = x - 2$ so $du = dx$, and then use Formula 18

with $x = u$ and $a = 3$.

$$\int \frac{dx}{5+4x-x^2} = \int \frac{du}{9-u^2}$$

$$= \frac{1}{6}\ln\left|\frac{u+3}{u-3}\right| + C$$

$$= \frac{1}{6}\ln\left|\frac{x+1}{x-5}\right| + C$$

(b) $\dfrac{d}{dx}\left(\dfrac{1}{2a}\ln\left|\dfrac{x+a}{x-a}\right| + C\right)$

$$= \frac{1}{2a}\frac{d}{dx}\left(\ln|x+a| - \ln|x-a|\right)$$

$$= \frac{1}{2a}\left(\frac{1}{x+a} - \frac{1}{x-a}\right)$$

$$= \frac{1}{2a}\left[\frac{x-a}{(x+a)(x-a)} - \frac{x+a}{(x+a)(x-a)}\right]$$

$$= -\frac{1}{x^2-a^2} = \frac{1}{a^2-x^2}$$

32. (a) Complete the square in the denominator.

$$x^2 - 2x + 2 = (x^2 - 2x + 1) + 1$$

$$= (x-1)^2 + 1$$

$$= 1 + (x-1)^2$$

Let $u = x - 1$ so $du = dx$ and then use Formula 17

with $x = u$ and $a = 1$.

$$\int \frac{dx}{(x^2-2x+2)^2} = \int \frac{du}{(1+u^2)^2}$$

$$= \frac{u}{2(1+u^2)} + \frac{1}{2}\tan^{-1}u + C$$

$$= \frac{x-1}{2(x^2-2x+2)} + \frac{1}{2}\tan^{-1}(x-1) + C$$

(b) $\dfrac{d}{dx}\left[\dfrac{x}{2a^2(a^2+x^2)} + \dfrac{1}{2a^3}\tan^{-1}\dfrac{x}{a} + C\right]$

$$= \frac{1}{2a^2}\left[\frac{(a^2+x^2) - x(2x)]}{(a^2+x^2)^2}\right] + \frac{1}{2a^3}\left[\frac{1/a}{1+(x/a)^2}\right]$$

$$= \frac{a^2-x^2}{2a^2(a^2+x^2)^2} + \frac{1}{2a^4}\left(\frac{a^2}{a^2+x^2}\right)$$

$$= \frac{1}{2a^2}\left[\frac{a^2-x^2}{(a^2+x^2)^2} + \frac{1}{a^2+x^2}\right]$$

$$= \frac{1}{2a^2}\left[\frac{2a^2}{(a^2+x^2)^2}\right] = \frac{1}{(a^2+x^2)^2}$$

33. Volume $= \displaystyle\int_{0.5}^{2.5} \pi\left(\frac{9}{3x-x^2}\right)dx = 9\pi\int_{0.5}^{2.5}\frac{dx}{3x-x^2}$

$$3x - x^2 = x(3-x)$$

$$\frac{1}{3x-x^2} = \frac{A}{x} + \frac{B}{3-x}$$

$$1 = A(3-x) + Bx$$

$$= (-A+B)x + 3A$$

Equating coefficients of like terms gives

$$-A + B = 0 \text{ and } 3A = 1$$

Solving the system simultaneously yields $A = \frac{1}{3}$, $B = \frac{1}{3}$.

$$9\pi\int_{0.5}^{2.5}\frac{dx}{3x-x^2} = 3\pi\left(\int_{0.5}^{2.5}\frac{dx}{x} + \int_{0.5}^{2.5}\frac{dx}{3-x}\right)$$

$$= 3\pi\left(\left[\ln|x|\right]_{0.5}^{2.5} + \left[-\ln|3-x|\right]_{0.5}^{2.5}\right)$$

$$= 3\pi(\ln 2.5 - \ln 0.5 - \ln 0.5 + \ln 2.5)$$

$$= 3\pi \ln 25 = 6\pi \ln 5$$

34. Volume $= \int_0^1 2\pi x \left[\dfrac{2}{(x+1)(2-x)} \right] dx$

$$= 4\pi \int_0^1 \frac{x\,dx}{(x+1)(2-x)}$$

$$\frac{x}{(x+1)(2-x)} = \frac{A}{x+1} + \frac{B}{2-x}$$

$$x = A(2-x) + B(x+1)$$

$$= (-A+B)x + (2A+B)$$

Equating coefficients of like terms gives

$$-A+B = 1 \text{ and } 2A+B = 0$$

Solving the system simultaneously yields $A = -\dfrac{1}{3}, B = \dfrac{2}{3}$.

$$4\pi \int_0^1 \frac{x\,dx}{(x+1)(2-x)}$$

$$= \frac{4\pi}{3}\left(\int_0^1 \frac{-dx}{x+1} + \int_0^1 \frac{2\,dx}{2-x} \right)$$

$$= \frac{4\pi}{3}\left(\Big[-\ln|x+1| \Big]_0^1 + \Big[-2\ln|2-x| \Big]_0^1 \right)$$

$$= \frac{4\pi}{3}(-\ln 2 + 2\ln 2) = \frac{4\pi \ln 2}{3}$$

35. $y = 3\tan\theta,\ dy = 3\sec^2\theta\,d\theta,\ -\dfrac{\pi}{2} < \theta < \dfrac{\pi}{2}$

$$9 + y^2 = 9 + 9\tan^2\theta = 9\sec^2\theta$$

$$\int \frac{dy}{\sqrt{9+y^2}} = \int \frac{3\sec^2\theta}{|3\sec\theta|}\,d\theta$$

$$= \int \sec\theta\,d\theta$$

$$= \ln|\sec\theta + \tan\theta| + C_1$$

$$= \ln\left| \frac{\sqrt{9+y^2}}{3} + \frac{y}{3} \right| + C_1$$

$$= \ln\left| \sqrt{9+y^2} + y \right| - \ln 3 + C_1$$

$$= \ln\left| \sqrt{9+y^2} + y \right| + C$$

Use Formula 88 for $\int \sec\theta\,d\theta$ with $x = \theta$ and $a = 1$. Use Figure 8.18(a) from the text with $a = 3$ to get

$$\sqrt{9+y^2} = 3|\sec\theta|.$$

36. $t = 5\sin\theta,\ dt = 5\cos\theta\,d\theta,\ -\dfrac{\pi}{2} \le \theta \le \dfrac{\pi}{2}$

$$25 - t^2 = 25 - 25\sin^2\theta = 25\cos^2\theta$$

$$\int \sqrt{25-t^2}\,dt = \int 5|\cos\theta|(5\cos\theta)\,d\theta$$

$$= 25\int \cos^2\theta\,d\theta$$

$$= 25\int \frac{1+\cos 2\theta}{2}\,d\theta$$

$$= \frac{25\theta}{2} + \frac{25\sin 2\theta}{4} + C$$

$$= \frac{25}{2}\theta + \frac{25}{2}\sin\theta\cos\theta + C$$

$$= \frac{25}{2}\sin^{-1}\frac{t}{5} + \frac{25}{2}\left(\frac{t}{5}\right)\frac{\sqrt{25-t^2}}{5} + C$$

$$= \frac{25}{2}\sin^{-1}\frac{t}{5} + \frac{t\sqrt{25-t^2}}{2} + C$$

Use Figure 8.18(b) from the text with $a = 5$ and $x = t$ to get $\sqrt{25-t^2} = 5|\cos\theta|$.

37. $x = \dfrac{7}{2}\sec\theta,\ dx = \dfrac{7}{2}\sec\theta\tan\theta\,d\theta,\ 0 \le \theta < \dfrac{\pi}{2}$

$$4x^2 - 49 = 49\sec^2\theta - 49 = 49\tan^2\theta$$

$$\int \frac{dx}{\sqrt{4x^2-49}} = \int \frac{7/2\sec\theta\tan\theta\,d\theta}{|7\tan\theta|}$$

$$= \int \frac{1}{2}\sec\theta\,d\theta$$

$$= \frac{1}{2}\ln|\sec\theta + \tan\theta| + C_1$$

$$= \frac{1}{2}\ln\left| \frac{2x}{7} + \frac{\sqrt{4x^2-49}}{7} \right| + C_1$$

$$= \frac{1}{2}\ln\left| 2x + \sqrt{4x^2-49} \right| - \frac{1}{2}\ln 7 + C_1$$

$$= \frac{1}{2}\ln\left| 2x + \sqrt{4x^2-49} \right| + C$$

Use Figure 8.18(c) from the text with $a = \dfrac{7}{2}$ to get

$$\sqrt{x^2 - \frac{49}{4}} = \frac{7}{2}\tan\theta.$$

38. $x = \tan\theta$, $dx = \sec^2\theta\,d\theta$, $-\dfrac{\pi}{2} < \theta < \dfrac{\pi}{2}$

$x^2 + 1 = \tan^2\theta + 1 = \sec^2\theta$

$\displaystyle\int \frac{dx}{x^2\sqrt{x^2+1}} = \int \frac{\sec^2\theta\,d\theta}{\tan^2\theta\,|\sec\theta|}$

$\displaystyle = \int \frac{\sec\theta\,d\theta}{\tan^2\theta}$

$\displaystyle = \int \frac{\cos\theta}{\sin^2\theta}\,d\theta$

$\displaystyle = \int (\sin\theta)^{-2}\cos\theta\,d\theta$

$= -(\sin\theta)^{-1} + C$

$= -\csc\theta + C$

$= -\dfrac{\sqrt{1+x^2}}{x} + C$

Use Figure 8.18(a) from the text with $a = 1$ to get

$\csc\theta = \dfrac{\sqrt{1+x^2}}{x}$.

39. $x = \sin\theta$, $dx = \cos\theta\,d\theta$, $-\dfrac{\pi}{2} < \theta < \dfrac{\pi}{2}$

$1 - x^2 = 1 - \sin^2\theta = \cos^2\theta$

$\displaystyle\int \frac{x^3\,dx}{\sqrt{1-x^2}} = \int \frac{\sin^3\theta\cos\theta\,d\theta}{|\cos\theta|}$

$\displaystyle = \int \sin^3\theta\,d\theta$

$\displaystyle = \int (1 - \cos^2\theta)\sin\theta\,d\theta$

$= -\cos\theta + \dfrac{1}{3}\cos^3\theta + C$

$= \cos\theta\left(-1 + \dfrac{1}{3}\cos^2\theta\right) + C$

$= \sqrt{1-x^2}\left[-1 + \dfrac{1}{3}(1-x^2)\right] + C$

$= -\dfrac{x^2\sqrt{1-x^2}}{3} - \dfrac{2\sqrt{1-x^2}}{3} + C$

Use Figure 18.8(b) from the text with $a = 1$

to get $\sqrt{1-x^2} = \cos\theta$.

40. $x = \sec\theta$, $dx = \sec\theta\tan\theta\,d\theta$, $0 \le \theta < \dfrac{\pi}{2}$

$x^2 - 1 = \sec^2\theta - 1 = \tan^2\theta$

$\displaystyle\int \frac{2\,dx}{x^3\sqrt{x^2-1}} = \int \frac{2\sec\theta\tan\theta\,d\theta}{\sec^3\theta\,|\tan\theta|}$

$\displaystyle = \int \frac{2\,d\theta}{\sec^2\theta}$

$\displaystyle = \int 2\cos^2\theta\,d\theta$

$\displaystyle = \int \left(1 + \cos 2\theta\right)d\theta$

$= \theta + \dfrac{1}{2}\sin 2\theta + C$

$= \theta + \sin\theta\cos\theta + C$

$= \sec^{-1}x + \dfrac{\sqrt{x^2-1}}{x}\left(\dfrac{1}{x}\right) + C$

$= \sec^{-1}x + \dfrac{\sqrt{x^2-1}}{x^2} + C$

41. $z = 4\sin\theta$, $dz = 4\cos\theta\,d\theta$, $0 < \theta < \dfrac{\pi}{2}$

$16 - z^2 = 16 - 16\sin^2\theta = 16\cos^2\theta$

$\displaystyle\int \frac{\sqrt{16-z^2}}{z}\,dz$

$\displaystyle = \int \frac{|4\cos\theta|\,(4\cos\theta)}{}\,d\theta$

$\displaystyle = \int \frac{4\cos^2\theta}{\sin\theta}\,d\theta$

$\displaystyle = \int \frac{4 - 4\sin^2\theta}{\sin\theta}\,d\theta$

$\displaystyle = \int (4\csc\theta - 4\sin\theta)\,d\theta$

$= -4\ln|\csc\theta + \cot\theta| + 4\cos\theta + C$

$= -4\ln\left|\dfrac{4}{z} + \dfrac{\sqrt{16-z^2}}{z}\right| + 4\left(\dfrac{\sqrt{16-z^2}}{4}\right) + C$

$= -4\ln\left|\dfrac{4 + \sqrt{16-z^2}}{z}\right| + \sqrt{16-z^2} + C$

Use Formula 89 with $a = 1$ and $x = \theta$. Use Figure 8.18(b) from the text with $a = 4$ to get

$\csc\theta = \dfrac{4}{|z|}$, $\cot\theta = \dfrac{\sqrt{16-z^2}}{|z|}$ and $\cos\theta = \dfrac{\sqrt{16-z^2}}{4}$.

42. $w = 2\sin\theta$, $dw = 2\cos\theta\,d\theta$, $-\dfrac{\pi}{2} < \theta < \dfrac{\pi}{2}$

$4 - w^2 = 4 - 4\sin^2\theta = 4\cos^2\theta$

$\displaystyle\int \frac{8\,dw}{w^2\sqrt{4-w^2}} = \int \frac{8(2\cos\theta)\,d\theta}{4\sin^2\theta\,|2\cos\theta|}$

$\displaystyle = \int 2\csc^2\theta\,d\theta$

$= -2\cot\theta + C$

$= \dfrac{-2\sqrt{4-w^2}}{w} + C$

Use Figure 8.18(b) from the text with $a = 2$ and $x = w$ to get $\cot\theta = \dfrac{\sqrt{4-w^2}}{w}$.

43. $dy = \dfrac{dx}{\sqrt{x^2 - 9}}$

$x = 3 \sec \theta, \; dx = 3 \sec \theta \tan \theta \, d\theta, \; 0 < \theta < \dfrac{\pi}{2}$

$x^2 - 9 = 9 \sec^2 \theta - 9 = 9 \tan^2 \theta$

$\begin{aligned} y &= \int \dfrac{dx}{\sqrt{x^2 - 9}} \\ &= \int \dfrac{3 \sec \theta \tan \theta \, d\theta}{|3 \tan \theta|} \\ &= \int \sec \theta \, d\theta \\ &= \ln |\sec \theta + \tan \theta| + C \\ &= \ln \left| \dfrac{x}{3} + \dfrac{\sqrt{x^2 - 9}}{3} \right| + C \end{aligned}$

Substitute $x = 5, \; y = \ln 3$.

$\ln 3 = \ln \left(\dfrac{5}{3} + \dfrac{4}{3} \right) + C$ or $C = 0$

The solution to the initial value problem is

$y = \ln \left| \dfrac{x}{3} + \dfrac{\sqrt{x^2 - 9}}{3} \right|.$

44. $(x^2 + 1)^2 \dfrac{dy}{dx} = \sqrt{x^2 + 1}$

$dy = \dfrac{dx}{(x^2 + 1)^{3/2}}$

$x = \tan \theta, \; dx = \sec^2 \theta \, d\theta, \; -\dfrac{\pi}{2} < \theta < \dfrac{\pi}{2}$

$x^2 + 1 = \tan^2 \theta + 1 = \sec^2 \theta$

$\begin{aligned} y &= \int \dfrac{dx}{(x^2 + 1)^{3/2}} \\ &= \int \dfrac{\sec^2 \theta \, d\theta}{|\sec^3 \theta|} \\ &= \int \cos \theta \, d\theta \\ &= \sin \theta + C \\ &= \dfrac{x}{\sqrt{x^2 + 1}} + C \end{aligned}$

Substitute $x = 0, \; y = 1$.

$1 = C$

The solution to the initial value problem is

$y = \dfrac{x}{\sqrt{x^2 + 1}} + 1.$

45. For $x \geq 0, \; y \geq 0$ on $[0, 3]$

Area $= \displaystyle\int_0^3 \dfrac{\sqrt{9 - x^2}}{3} \, dx$

$x = 3 \sin \theta, \; dx = 3 \cos \theta \, d\theta, \; 0 \leq \theta \leq \dfrac{\pi}{2}$

$9 - x^2 = 9 - 9 \sin^2 \theta = 9 \cos^2 \theta$

When $x = 0, \; \theta = 0$ and when $x = 3, \; \theta = \dfrac{\pi}{2}$.

$\begin{aligned} \int_0^3 \dfrac{\sqrt{9 - x^2}}{3} \, dx &= \int_0^{\pi/2} \dfrac{3 \, |\cos \theta|}{3} \, 3 \cos \theta \, d\theta \\ &= \int_0^{\pi/2} 3 \cos^2 \theta \, d\theta \\ &= 3 \int_0^{\pi/2} \dfrac{1 + \cos 2\theta}{2} \, d\theta \\ &= 3 \left[\dfrac{\theta}{2} + \dfrac{\sin 2\theta}{4} \right]_0^{\pi/2} \\ &= \dfrac{3\pi}{4} \approx 2.356 \end{aligned}$

46. Volume $= \displaystyle\int_0^1 \pi \left(\dfrac{2}{1 + x^2} \right)^2 dx = 4\pi \int_0^1 \dfrac{dx}{(1 + x^2)^2}$

$x = \tan \theta, \; dx = \sec^2 \theta \, d\theta, \; 0 \leq \theta \leq \dfrac{\pi}{4}$ (since $0 < x < 1$)

$1 + x^2 = 1 + \tan^2 \theta = \sec^2 \theta$

When $x = 0, \; \theta = 0$ and when $x = 1, \; \theta = \dfrac{\pi}{4}$.

$\begin{aligned} \int_0^1 \dfrac{dx}{(1 + x^2)^2} &= \int_0^{\pi/4} \dfrac{\sec^2 \theta}{\sec^4 \theta} \, d\theta \\ &= \int_0^{\pi/4} \cos^2 \theta \, d\theta \\ &= \int_0^{\pi/4} \dfrac{1 + \cos 2\theta}{2} \, d\theta \\ &= \left[\dfrac{1}{2} \theta + \dfrac{\sin 2\theta}{4} \right]_0^{\pi/4} \\ &= \dfrac{\pi}{8} + \dfrac{1}{4} \end{aligned}$

Volume $= 4\pi \left(\dfrac{\pi}{8} + \dfrac{1}{4} \right) = \pi \left(\dfrac{\pi}{2} + 1 \right) \approx 8.076$

47. (a) $\dfrac{dx}{x(1000 - x)} = \dfrac{1}{250} \, dt$

$\dfrac{1}{x(1000 - x)} = \dfrac{A}{x} + \dfrac{B}{1000 - x}$

$1 = A(1000 - x) + Bx$

$\quad = (-A + B)x + 1000A$

Equating the coefficients and solving for A and B gives

$A = \dfrac{1}{1000}, \; B = \dfrac{1}{1000}$

$\begin{aligned} \int \dfrac{dx}{x(1000 - x)} &= \int \dfrac{(1/1000) \, dx}{x} + \int \dfrac{(1/1000) \, dx}{1000 - x} \\ &= \dfrac{1}{1000} \ln x - \dfrac{1}{1000} \ln (1000 - x) + C_1 \\ &= \dfrac{1}{1000} \ln \dfrac{x}{1000 - x} + C_1 \end{aligned}$

$\dfrac{1}{1000} \ln \dfrac{x}{1000 - x} = \dfrac{t}{250} + C_2$

$\ln \dfrac{x}{1000 - x} = 4t + C$

$\dfrac{x}{1000 - x} = e^{4t + C} = Ae^{4t}$

47. continued

When $t = 0$, $x = 2$.

$$\frac{2}{998} = A \text{ or } A = \frac{1}{499}$$

$$\frac{x}{1000 - x} = \frac{1}{499}e^{4t}$$

$$x = \frac{1000}{499}e^{4t} - \frac{x}{499}e^{4t}$$

$$x\left(1 + \frac{e^{4t}}{499}\right) = \frac{1000e^{4t}}{499}$$

$$x = \frac{1000e^{4t}}{499 + e^{4t}}$$

$$\text{or } x = \frac{1000}{1 + 499e^{-4t}}$$

(b) $500 = \dfrac{1000}{1 + 499e^{-4t}}$

$1 + 499e^{-4t} = 2$

$e^{-4t} = \dfrac{1}{499}$

$t = -\dfrac{1}{4}\ln\dfrac{1}{499} \approx 1.553$

Half the population will have heard the rumor in about 1.553 days.

(c) $\dfrac{dx}{dt} = \dfrac{1}{250}x(1000 - x)$

$\dfrac{dx}{dt}$ will be greatest when $y = x(1000 - x)$ is greatest.

This occurs when $x = 500$ which occurs when

$t \approx 1.553$ as shown in part (b).

48. $\dfrac{dy}{dx} = -\dfrac{2x}{1 - x^2}$

$ds = \sqrt{1 + \left(\dfrac{-2x}{1 - x^2}\right)^2}\, dx$

$= \sqrt{\dfrac{x^4 + 2x^2 + 1}{(1 - x^2)^2}}$

$= \left|\dfrac{x^2 + 1}{1 - x^2}\right| dx$

$= -\dfrac{x^2 + 1}{x^2 - 1}\, dx \text{ for } 0 \le x \le \dfrac{1}{2}$

Arc length $= \displaystyle\int_0^{1/2}\left(-\dfrac{x^2 + 1}{x^2 - 1}\right) dx$

$$\begin{array}{r} 1 \\ x^2 - 1 \overline{)\, x^2 + 1} \\ \underline{x^2 - 1} \\ 2 \end{array}$$

$-\dfrac{x^2 + 1}{x^2 - 1} = -1 - \dfrac{2}{x^2 - 1}$

$\dfrac{2}{x^2 - 1} = \dfrac{A}{x - 1} + \dfrac{B}{x + 1}$

where $A = 1$ and $B = -1$

$\displaystyle\int_0^{1/2}\left(-\dfrac{x^2 + 1}{x^2 - 1}\right) dx = \int_0^{1/2}\left(-1 - \dfrac{1}{x - 1} + \dfrac{1}{x + 1}\right) dx$

$= \Big[-x - \ln|x - 1| + \ln|x + 1|\Big]_0^{1/2}$

$= -\dfrac{1}{2} - \ln\dfrac{1}{2} + \ln\dfrac{3}{2}$

$= \ln 3 - \dfrac{1}{2}$

49. (a) From the figure, $\tan\dfrac{x}{2} = \dfrac{\sin x}{1 + \cos x}$.

(b) From part (a), $z = \dfrac{\sin x}{1 + \cos x}$

$z(1 + \cos x) = \sin x$

$z^2(1 + \cos x)^2 = \sin^2 x$

$z^2(1 + \cos x)^2 = 1 - \cos^2 x$

$z^2(1 + \cos x)^2 - (1 - \cos x)(1 + \cos x) = 0$

$(1 + \cos x)(z^2 + z^2\cos x - 1 + \cos x) = 0$

$1 + \cos x = 0 \quad \text{or} \quad (z^2 + 1)\cos x = 1 - z^2$

$\cos x = -1 \qquad \cos x = \dfrac{1 - z^2}{1 + z^2}$

$\cos x = -1$ does not make sense in this case.

(c) From part (b), $\cos x = \dfrac{1 - z^2}{1 + z^2}$

$\sin^2 x = 1 - \cos^2 x$

$= 1 - \dfrac{(1 - z^2)^2}{(1 + z^2)^2}$

$= \dfrac{(1 + z^2)^2 - (1 - z^2)^2}{(1 + z^2)^2}$

$= \dfrac{1 + 2z^2 + z^4 - 1 + 2z^2 - z^4}{(1 + z^2)^2}$

$= \dfrac{4z^2}{(1 + z^2)^2}$

$\sin x = \pm\dfrac{2z}{1 + z^2}$

Only $\sin x = \dfrac{2z}{1 + z^2}$ makes sense in this case.

(d) $z = \tan\dfrac{x}{2}$

$dz = \left(\dfrac{1}{2}\sec^2\dfrac{x}{2}\right) dx$

$dz = \dfrac{1}{2}\left(1 + \tan^2\dfrac{x}{2}\right) dx$

$dz = \dfrac{1}{2}(1 + z^2)\, dx$

$dx = \dfrac{2\, dz}{1 + z^2}$

50. $\displaystyle\int \frac{dx}{1 + \sin x} = \int \frac{\dfrac{2\,dz}{1 + z^2}}{1 + \dfrac{2z}{1 + z^2}}$

$\displaystyle = \int \frac{2\,dz}{z^2 + 2z + 1}$

$\displaystyle = \int \frac{2\,dz}{(z + 1)^2} = -\frac{2}{z + 1} + C$

$\displaystyle = -\frac{2}{\tan \dfrac{x}{2} + 1} + C$

51. $\displaystyle\int \frac{dx}{1 - \cos x} = \int \frac{\dfrac{2\,dz}{1 + z^2}}{1 - \dfrac{1 - z^2}{1 + z^2}}$

$\displaystyle = \int \frac{dz}{z^2}$

$\displaystyle = -\frac{1}{z} + C = -\frac{1}{\tan \dfrac{x}{2}} + C$

52. $\displaystyle\int \frac{d\theta}{1 - \sin \theta} = \int \frac{\dfrac{2\,dz}{1 + z^2}}{1 - \dfrac{2z}{1 + z^2}}$

$\displaystyle = \int \frac{2\,dz}{z^2 - 2z + 1}$

$\displaystyle = \int \frac{2\,dz}{(z - 1)^2}$

$\displaystyle = -\frac{2}{z - 1} + C$

$\displaystyle = -\frac{2}{\tan \dfrac{\theta}{2} - 1} + C$

$\displaystyle = \frac{2}{1 - \tan \dfrac{\theta}{2}} + C$

53. $\displaystyle\int \frac{dt}{1 + \sin t + \cos t} = \int \frac{\dfrac{2\,dz}{1 + z^2}}{1 + \dfrac{2z}{1 + z^2} + \dfrac{1 - z^2}{1 + z^2}}$

$\displaystyle = \int \frac{dz}{z + 1}$

$\displaystyle = \ln |z + 1| + C$

$\displaystyle = \ln \left| \tan \frac{t}{2} + 1 \right| + C$

■ Chapter 8 Review Exercises
(pp. 454–455)

1. $\displaystyle\lim_{t \to 0} \frac{t - \ln(1 + 2t)}{t^2} = \lim_{t \to 0} \frac{1 - \dfrac{2}{1 + 2t}}{2t} = \infty$ for $t \to 0^-$ and

$-\infty$ for $t \to 0^+$

The limit does not exist.

2. $\displaystyle\lim_{t \to 0} \frac{\tan 3t}{\tan 5t} = \lim_{t \to 0} \frac{3 \sec^2 3t}{5 \sec^2 5t} = \frac{3}{5}$

3. $\displaystyle\lim_{x \to 0} \frac{x \sin x}{1 - \cos x} = \lim_{x \to 0} \frac{x \cos x + \sin x}{\sin x}$

$\displaystyle = \lim_{x \to 0} \frac{-x \sin x + \cos x + \cos x}{\cos x} = 2$

4. The limit leads to the indeterminate form 1^∞.

$$f(x) = x^{1/(1-x)}$$

$$\ln f(x) = \frac{\ln x}{1 - x}$$

$$\lim_{x \to 1} \frac{\ln x}{1 - x} = \lim_{x \to 1} \frac{1/x}{-1} = -1$$

$$\lim_{x \to 1} x^{1/(1-x)} = \lim_{x \to 1} e^{\ln f(x)} = e^{-1} = \frac{1}{e}$$

5. The limit leads to the indeterminate form ∞^0.

$$f(x) = x^{1/x}$$

$$\ln f(x) = \frac{\ln x}{x}$$

$$\lim_{x \to \infty} \frac{\ln x}{x} = \lim_{x \to \infty} \frac{1/x}{1} = 0$$

$$\lim_{x \to \infty} x^{1/x} = \lim_{x \to \infty} e^{\ln f(x)} = e^0 = 1$$

6. The limit leads to the indeterminate form 1^∞.

$$f(x) = \left(1 + \frac{3}{x}\right)^x$$

$$\ln f(x) = x \ln\left(1 + \frac{3}{x}\right) = \frac{\ln\left(1 + \dfrac{3}{x}\right)}{\dfrac{1}{x}}$$

$$\lim_{x \to \infty} \frac{\ln\left(1 + \dfrac{3}{x}\right)}{\dfrac{1}{x}} = \lim_{x \to \infty} \frac{\dfrac{-3/x^2}{1 + 3/x}}{-\dfrac{1}{x^2}} = \lim_{x \to \infty} \frac{3x}{x + 3} = 3$$

$$\lim_{x \to \infty} \left(1 + \frac{3}{x}\right)^x = \lim_{x \to \infty} e^{\ln f(x)} = e^3$$

7. $\displaystyle\lim_{r \to \infty} \frac{\cos r}{\ln r} = 0$ since $|\cos r| \le 1$ and $\ln r \to \infty$ as $r \to \infty$.

8. $\displaystyle\lim_{\theta \to \pi/2} \left(\theta - \frac{\pi}{2}\right) \sec \theta = \lim_{\theta \to \pi/2} \frac{\theta - \dfrac{\pi}{2}}{\cos \theta} = \lim_{\theta \to \pi/2} \frac{1}{-\sin \theta} = -1$

9. $\lim\limits_{x \to 1} \left(\dfrac{1}{x-1} - \dfrac{1}{\ln x} \right) = \lim\limits_{x \to 1} \left[\dfrac{\ln x - x + 1}{(x-1)\ln x} \right]$

$\qquad\qquad = \lim\limits_{x \to 1} \dfrac{\dfrac{1}{x} - 1}{\dfrac{x-1}{x} + \ln x}$

$\qquad\qquad = \lim\limits_{x \to 1} \dfrac{1-x}{x - 1 + x\ln x}$

$\qquad\qquad = \lim\limits_{x \to 1} \dfrac{-1}{1 + x/x + \ln x} = -\dfrac{1}{2}$

10. The limit leads to the indeterminate form ∞^0.

$f(x) = \left(1 + \dfrac{1}{x}\right)^x$

$\ln f(x) = x \ln\left(1 + \dfrac{1}{x}\right) = \dfrac{\ln(1 + 1/x)}{1/x}$

$\lim\limits_{x \to 0^+} \dfrac{\ln(1 + 1/x)}{1/x} = \lim\limits_{x \to 0^+} \dfrac{\dfrac{-1/x^2}{1 + 1/x}}{-1/x^2} = \lim\limits_{x \to 0^+} \dfrac{x}{x+1} = 0$

$\lim\limits_{x \to 0^+} \left(1 + \dfrac{1}{x}\right)^x = \lim\limits_{x \to 0^+} e^{\ln f(x)} = e^0 = 1$

11. The limit leads to the indeterminate form 0^0.

$f(\theta) = (\tan\theta)^\theta$

$\ln f(\theta) = \theta \ln(\tan\theta) = \dfrac{\ln(\tan\theta)}{1/\theta}$

$\lim\limits_{x \to 0^+} \dfrac{\ln(\tan\theta)}{1/\theta} = \lim\limits_{x \to 0^+} \dfrac{\dfrac{\sec^2\theta}{\tan\theta}}{-\dfrac{1}{\theta^2}}$

$\qquad\qquad = \lim\limits_{x \to 0^+} -\dfrac{\theta^2}{\sin\theta\cos\theta}$

$\qquad\qquad = \lim\limits_{x \to 0^+} \dfrac{-2\theta}{-\sin^2\theta + \cos^2\theta} = 0$

$\lim\limits_{x \to 0^+} (\tan\theta)^\theta = \lim\limits_{x \to 0^+} e^{\ln f(\theta)} = e^0 = 1$

12. $\lim\limits_{\theta \to \infty} \theta^2 \sin\left(\dfrac{1}{\theta}\right) = \lim\limits_{t \to 0^+} \dfrac{\sin t}{t^2} = \lim\limits_{t \to 0^+} \dfrac{\cos t}{2t} = \infty$

13. $\lim\limits_{x \to \infty} \dfrac{x^3 - 3x^2 + 1}{2x^2 + x - 3} = \lim\limits_{x \to \infty} \dfrac{3x^2 - 6x}{4x + 1} = \lim\limits_{x \to \infty} \dfrac{6x - 6}{4} = \infty$

14. $\lim\limits_{x \to \infty} \dfrac{3x^2 - x + 1}{x^4 - x^3 + 2} = \lim\limits_{x \to \infty} \dfrac{6x - 1}{4x^3 - 3x^2} = \lim\limits_{x \to \infty} \dfrac{6}{12x^2 - 6x} = 0$

15. $\lim\limits_{x \to \infty} \dfrac{f(x)}{g(x)} = \lim\limits_{x \to \infty} \dfrac{x}{5x} = \dfrac{1}{5}$

f grows at the same rate as g.

16. $\lim\limits_{x \to \infty} \dfrac{f(x)}{g(x)} = \lim\limits_{x \to \infty} \dfrac{\log_2 x}{\log_3 x} = \lim\limits_{x \to \infty} \dfrac{(\ln x)/(\ln 2)}{(\ln x)/(\ln 3)} = \dfrac{\ln 3}{\ln 2}$

f grows at the same rate as g.

17. $\lim\limits_{x \to \infty} \dfrac{f(x)}{g(x)} = \lim\limits_{x \to \infty} \dfrac{x}{x + 1/x} = \lim\limits_{x \to \infty} \dfrac{1}{1 - 1/x^2} = 1$

f grows at the same rate as g.

18. $\lim\limits_{x \to \infty} \dfrac{f(x)}{g(x)} = \lim\limits_{x \to \infty} \dfrac{x/100}{xe^{-x}} = \lim\limits_{x \to \infty} \dfrac{e^x}{100} = \infty$

f grows faster than g.

19. $\lim\limits_{x \to \infty} \dfrac{f(x)}{g(x)} = \lim\limits_{x \to \infty} \dfrac{x}{\tan^{-1} x} = \infty$ since

$\lim\limits_{x \to \infty} \tan^{-1} x = \dfrac{\pi}{2}$ and $\lim\limits_{x \to \infty} x = \infty$

f grows faster than g.

20. $\lim\limits_{x \to \infty} \dfrac{f(x)}{g(x)} = \lim\limits_{x \to \infty} \dfrac{\csc^{-1} x}{1/x}$

$\qquad\qquad = \lim\limits_{x \to \infty} \dfrac{-\dfrac{1}{x\sqrt{x^2 - 1}}}{-\dfrac{1}{x^2}}$

$\qquad\qquad = \lim\limits_{x \to \infty} \dfrac{x}{\sqrt{x^2 - 1}}$

$\qquad\qquad = \lim\limits_{x \to \infty} \sqrt{\dfrac{x^2}{x^2 - 1}}$

$\qquad\qquad = \lim\limits_{x \to \infty} \sqrt{\dfrac{1}{1 - 1/x^2}} = 1$

f grows at the same rate as g.

21. $\lim\limits_{x \to \infty} \dfrac{f(x)}{g(x)} = \lim\limits_{x \to \infty} \dfrac{x^{\ln x}}{x^{\log_2 x}}$

$\qquad\qquad = \lim\limits_{x \to \infty} x^{\ln x - \log_2 x}$

$\qquad\qquad = \lim\limits_{x \to \infty} x^{\ln x - (\ln x)/\ln 2}$

$\qquad\qquad = \lim\limits_{x \to \infty} x^{(\ln x)(1 - 1/\ln 2)}$

$\qquad\qquad = \lim\limits_{x \to \infty} \left(\dfrac{1}{x}\right)^{(\ln x)(1/\ln 2 - 1)} = 0$

Note that $1 - \dfrac{1}{\ln 2} < 0$ since $\ln 2 < 1$.

f grows slower than g.

22. $\lim\limits_{x \to \infty} \dfrac{f(x)}{g(x)} = \lim\limits_{x \to \infty} \dfrac{3^{-x}}{2^{-x}} = \lim\limits_{x \to \infty} \dfrac{2^x}{3^x} = \lim\limits_{x \to \infty} \left(\dfrac{2}{3}\right)^x = 0$ since $\dfrac{2}{3} < 1$.

f grows slower than g.

23. $\lim\limits_{x \to \infty} \dfrac{f(x)}{g(x)} = \lim\limits_{x \to \infty} \dfrac{\ln 2x}{\ln x^2} = \lim\limits_{x \to \infty} \dfrac{\ln x + \ln 2}{2\ln x} = \lim\limits_{x \to \infty} \dfrac{1/x}{2/x} = \dfrac{1}{2}$

f grows at the same rate as g.

24. $\lim\limits_{x \to \infty} \dfrac{f(x)}{g(x)} = \lim\limits_{x \to \infty} \dfrac{10x^3 + 2x^2}{e^x}$

$\qquad\qquad = \lim\limits_{x \to \infty} \dfrac{30x^2 + 4x}{e^x}$

$\qquad\qquad = \lim\limits_{x \to \infty} \dfrac{60x + 4}{e^x}$

$\qquad\qquad = \lim\limits_{x \to \infty} \dfrac{60}{e^x} = 0$

f grows slower than g.

25. $\displaystyle\lim_{x\to\infty}\frac{f(x)}{g(x)}=\lim_{x\to\infty}\frac{\tan^{-1}(1/x)}{1/x}$

$\displaystyle\qquad\qquad=\lim_{x\to\infty}\frac{\dfrac{1}{1+(1/x)^2}(-x^{-2})}{-x^{-2}}$

$\displaystyle\qquad\qquad=\lim_{x\to\infty}\frac{1}{1+(1/x)^2}=1$

f grows at the same rate as g.

26. $\displaystyle\lim_{x\to\infty}\frac{f(x)}{g(x)}=\lim_{x\to\infty}\frac{\sin^{-1}(1/x)}{(1/x^2)}$

$\displaystyle\qquad\qquad=\lim_{x\to\infty}\frac{\dfrac{1}{\sqrt{1-(1/x^2)}}(-x^{-2})}{-2x^{-3}}$

$\displaystyle\qquad\qquad=\lim_{x\to\infty}\frac{x}{2\sqrt{1-(1/x)^2}}=\infty$

f grows faster than g.

27. (a) $\displaystyle\lim_{x\to0}f(x)=\lim_{x\to0}\frac{2^{\sin x}-1}{e^x-1}=\lim_{x\to0}\frac{(\ln 2)(\cos x)2^{\sin x}}{e^x}=\ln 2$

(b) Define $f(0)=\ln 2$.

28. (a) $\displaystyle\lim_{x\to0^+}f(x)=\lim_{x\to0^+}x\ln x$

$\displaystyle\qquad\qquad=\lim_{x\to0^+}\frac{\ln x}{1/x}$

$\displaystyle\qquad\qquad=\lim_{x\to0^+}\frac{1/x}{-1/x^2}$

$\displaystyle\qquad\qquad=\lim_{x\to0^+}(-x)=0$

(b) Define $f(0)=0$.

29. $\displaystyle\lim_{x\to\infty}\frac{\dfrac{1}{x^2}+\dfrac{1}{x^4}}{\dfrac{1}{x^2}}=\lim_{x\to\infty}\left(1+\frac{1}{x^2}\right)=1\le1$

True

30. $\displaystyle\lim_{x\to\infty}\frac{\dfrac{1}{x^2}+\dfrac{1}{x^4}}{\dfrac{1}{x^4}}=\lim_{x\to\infty}(x^2+1)=\infty$

False

31. $\displaystyle\lim_{x\to\infty}\frac{x}{x+\ln x}=\lim_{x\to\infty}\frac{1}{1+\dfrac{1}{x}}=1\ne0$

False

32. $\displaystyle\lim_{x\to\infty}\frac{\ln(\ln x)}{\ln x}=\lim_{x\to\infty}\frac{\dfrac{1}{x\ln x}}{\dfrac{1}{x}}=\lim_{x\to\infty}\frac{1}{\ln x}=0$

True

33. $\displaystyle\lim_{x\to\infty}\frac{\tan^{-1}x}{1}=\frac{\pi}{2}\le\frac{\pi}{2}$

True

34. $\displaystyle\lim_{x\to\infty}\frac{\dfrac{1}{x^4}}{\dfrac{1}{x^2}+\dfrac{1}{x^4}}=\lim_{x\to\infty}\frac{1}{x^2+1}=0\le1$

True

35. $\displaystyle\lim_{x\to\infty}\frac{\dfrac{1}{x^4}}{\dfrac{1}{x^2}+\dfrac{1}{x^4}}=\lim_{x\to\infty}\frac{1}{x^2+1}=0$

True

36. $\displaystyle\lim_{x\to\infty}\frac{\ln x}{x+1}=\lim_{x\to\infty}\frac{\dfrac{1}{x}}{1}=0$

True

37. $\displaystyle\lim_{x\to\infty}\frac{\ln 2x}{\ln x}=\lim_{x\to\infty}\frac{\dfrac{1}{x}}{\dfrac{1}{x}}=1\le1$

True

38. $\displaystyle\lim_{x\to\infty}\frac{\sec^{-1}x}{1}=\frac{\pi}{2}\le\frac{\pi}{2}$

True

39. $x=3\sin\theta,\;dx=3\cos\theta\,d\theta,\;-\dfrac{\pi}{2}\le\theta\le\dfrac{\pi}{2}$

$\displaystyle\int\frac{dx}{\sqrt{9-x^2}}=\int\frac{3\cos\theta\,d\theta}{|3\cos\theta|}$

$\displaystyle\qquad\qquad=\int d\theta$

$\displaystyle\qquad\qquad=\theta+C$

$\displaystyle\qquad\qquad=\sin^{-1}\frac{x}{3}+C$

$\displaystyle\int_0^3\frac{dx}{\sqrt{9-x^2}}=\lim_{b\to3^-}\int_0^b\frac{dx}{\sqrt{9-x^2}}$

$\displaystyle\qquad\qquad=\lim_{b\to3^-}\left[\sin^{-1}\frac{x}{3}\right]_0^b$

$\displaystyle\qquad\qquad=\lim_{b\to3^-}\left(\sin^{-1}\frac{b}{3}\right)=\frac{\pi}{2}$

40. $u = \ln x$ $\qquad$ $dv = dx$

$du = \dfrac{1}{x}\,dx$ $\qquad$ $v = x$

$\displaystyle\int \ln x\,dx = x \ln x - \int dx = x \ln x - x + C$

$\displaystyle\int_0^1 \ln x\,dx = \lim_{b\to 0^+} \int_b^1 \ln x\,dx$

$\qquad = \displaystyle\lim_{b\to 0^+} \left[x \ln x - x \right]_b^1$

$\qquad = \displaystyle\lim_{b\to 0^+} (-1 - b \ln b + b)$

$\qquad = -1 - \displaystyle\lim_{b\to 0^+} \dfrac{\ln b}{1/b}$

$\qquad = -1 - \displaystyle\lim_{b\to 0^+} \dfrac{1/b}{-1/b^2}$

$\qquad = -1 - \displaystyle\lim_{b\to 0^+} (-b) = -1$

41. $\displaystyle\int_{-1}^1 \dfrac{dy}{y^{2/3}} = \int_{-1}^0 \dfrac{dy}{y^{2/3}} + \int_0^1 \dfrac{dy}{y^{2/3}}$

$\displaystyle\int_{-1}^0 \dfrac{dy}{y^{2/3}} = \lim_{b\to 0^-} \int_{-1}^b y^{-2/3}\,dy$

$\qquad = \displaystyle\lim_{b\to 0^-} \left[3 y^{1/3} \right]_{-1}^b$

$\qquad = \displaystyle\lim_{b\to 0^-} [3 b^{1/3} + 3] = 3$

$\displaystyle\int_0^1 \dfrac{dy}{y^{2/3}} = \lim_{b\to 0^+} \int_b^1 y^{-2/3}\,dy$

$\qquad = \displaystyle\lim_{b\to 0^+} \left[3 y^{1/3} \right]_b^1$

$\qquad = \displaystyle\lim_{b\to 0^+} [3 - 3 b^{1/3}] = 3$

$\displaystyle\int_{-1}^1 \dfrac{dy}{y^{2/3}} = 3 + 3 = 6$

42. $\displaystyle\int_{-2}^0 \dfrac{d\theta}{(\theta+1)^{3/5}} = \int_{-2}^{-1} \dfrac{d\theta}{(\theta+1)^{3/5}} + \int_{-1}^0 \dfrac{d\theta}{(\theta+1)^{3/5}}$

$\displaystyle\int_{-2}^{-1} \dfrac{d\theta}{(\theta+1)^{3/5}} = \lim_{b\to -1^-} \int_{-2}^b \dfrac{d\theta}{(\theta+1)^{3/5}}$

$\qquad = \displaystyle\lim_{b\to -1^-} \left[\dfrac{5}{2}(\theta+1)^{2/5} \right]_{-2}^b$

$\qquad = \displaystyle\lim_{b\to -1^-} \left[\dfrac{5}{2}(b+1)^{2/5} - \dfrac{5}{2} \right] = -\dfrac{5}{2}$

$\displaystyle\int_{-1}^0 \dfrac{d\theta}{(\theta+1)^{3/5}} = \lim_{b\to -1^+} \int_b^0 \dfrac{d\theta}{(\theta+1)^{3/5}}$

$\qquad = \displaystyle\lim_{b\to -1^+} \left[\dfrac{5}{2}(\theta+1)^{2/5} \right]_b^0$

$\qquad = \displaystyle\lim_{b\to -1^+} \left[\dfrac{5}{2} - \dfrac{5}{2}(b+1)^{2/5} \right] = \dfrac{5}{2}$

$\displaystyle\int_{-2}^0 \dfrac{d\theta}{(\theta+1)^{3/5}} = -\dfrac{5}{2} + \dfrac{5}{2} = 0$

43. $\displaystyle\int_3^\infty \dfrac{2\,dx}{x^2 - 2x} = \lim_{b\to\infty} \int_3^b \dfrac{2\,dx}{x(x-2)}$

$\dfrac{2}{x(x-2)} = \dfrac{A}{x} + \dfrac{B}{x-2}$

$2 = A(x-2) + Bx = (A+B)x - 2A$

where $A = -1$, $B = 1$.

$\displaystyle\int_3^\infty \dfrac{2\,dx}{x(x-2)} = \lim_{b\to\infty} \int_3^b \left(-\dfrac{1}{x} + \dfrac{1}{x-2} \right) dx$

$\qquad = \displaystyle\lim_{b\to\infty} \left[-\ln|x| + \ln|x-2| \right]_3^b$

$\qquad = \displaystyle\lim_{b\to\infty} \left[\ln \dfrac{x-2}{x} \right]_3^b$

$\qquad = \displaystyle\lim_{b\to\infty} \left(\ln \dfrac{b-2}{b} - \ln \dfrac{1}{3} \right) = \ln 3$

44. $\displaystyle\int_1^\infty \dfrac{3x-1}{4x^3 - x^2}\,dx = \lim_{b\to\infty} \int_1^b \dfrac{3x-1}{x^2(4x-1)}\,dx$

$\dfrac{3x-1}{x^2(4x-1)} = \dfrac{A}{4x-1} + \dfrac{B}{x} + \dfrac{C}{x^2}$

$3x - 1 = Ax^2 + Bx(4x-1) + C(4x-1)$

$\qquad = (A + 4B)x^2 + (-B + 4C)x - C$

where $A = -4$, $B = 1$, $C = 1$

$\displaystyle\int_1^\infty \dfrac{3x-1}{4x^3 - x^2}\,dx = \lim_{b\to\infty} \int_1^b \left(-\dfrac{4}{4x-1} + \dfrac{1}{x} + \dfrac{1}{x^2} \right) dx$

$\qquad = \displaystyle\lim_{b\to\infty} \left[-\ln|4x-1| + \ln|x| - \dfrac{1}{x} \right]_1^b$

$\qquad = \displaystyle\lim_{b\to\infty} \left(\ln \dfrac{b}{4b-1} - \dfrac{1}{b} + \ln 3 + 1 \right)$

$\qquad = \ln \dfrac{1}{4} + \ln 3 + 1 = \ln \dfrac{3}{4} + 1$

45. $u = x^2$ $\qquad$ $dv = e^{-x}\,dx$

$du = 2x\,dx$ $\qquad$ $v = -e^{-x}$

$\displaystyle\int x^2 e^{-x}\,dx = -x^2 e^{-x} + \int 2x\,e^{-x}\,dx$

$u = 2x$ $\qquad$ $dv = e^{-x}\,dx$

$du = 2\,dx$ $\qquad$ $v = -e^{-x}$

$\displaystyle\int x^2 e^{-x}\,dx = -x^2 e^{-x} - 2x\,e^{-x} + \int 2e^{-x}\,dx$

$\qquad = -x^2 e^{-x} - 2x\,e^{-x} - 2\,e^{-x} + C$

$\displaystyle\int_0^\infty x^2 e^{-x}\,dx = \lim_{b\to\infty} \int_0^b x^2 e^{-x}\,dx$

$\qquad = \displaystyle\lim_{b\to\infty} \left[-x^2 e^{-x} - 2x\,e^{-x} - 2\,e^{-x} \right]_0^b$

$\qquad = \displaystyle\lim_{b\to\infty} \left[-\dfrac{b^2}{e^b} - \dfrac{2b}{e^b} - \dfrac{2}{e^b} + 2 \right] = 2$

46. $u = x \qquad\qquad dv = e^{3x}\, dx$

$du = dx \qquad\qquad v = \frac{1}{3}e^{3x}$

$\displaystyle \int x\, e^{3x}\, dx = \frac{1}{3}x\, e^{3x} - \int \frac{1}{3}\, e^{3x}\, dx$

$\qquad\qquad = \frac{1}{3}x\, e^{3x} - \frac{1}{9}\, e^{3x} + C$

$\displaystyle \int_{-\infty}^{0} x\, e^{3x}\, dx = \lim_{b\to -\infty} \int_{b}^{0} x\, e^{3x}\, dx$

$\qquad\qquad = \lim_{b\to -\infty}\left[\frac{1}{3}x\, e^{3x} - \frac{1}{9}\, e^{3x}\right]_{b}^{0}$

$\qquad\qquad = \lim_{b\to -\infty}\left[-\frac{1}{9} - \frac{1}{3}b\, e^{3b} + \frac{1}{9}\, e^{3b}\right] = -\frac{1}{9}$

47. $\dfrac{4t^3 + t - 1}{t^2(t-1)(t^2+1)} = \dfrac{A}{t} + \dfrac{B}{t^2} + \dfrac{C}{t-1} + \dfrac{Dt+E}{t^2+1}$

$4t^3 + t - 1 = At(t-1)(t^2+1) + B(t-1)(t^2+1)$

$\qquad\qquad\qquad + Ct^2(t^2+1) + (Dt+E)t^2(t-1)$

$\qquad\qquad = (A+C+D)t^4 + (-A+B-D+E)t^3$

$\qquad\qquad\qquad + (A-B+C-E)t^2 + (-A+B)t - B$

Equating coefficients of like terms gives

$A + C + D = 0,\ -A + B - D + E = 4,$

$A - B + C - E = 0,\ -A + B = 1$ and $-B = -1$.

Solving the system simultaneously yields

$A = 0,\ B = 1,\ C = 2,\ D = -2,\ E = 1.$

$\displaystyle \int \frac{4t^3 + t - 1}{t^2(t-1)(t^2+1)}\, dt$

$\displaystyle = \int \frac{dt}{t^2} + \int \frac{2\, dt}{t-1} + \int \frac{-2t+1}{t^2+1}\, dt$

$\displaystyle = \int \frac{dt}{t^2} + \int \frac{2\, dt}{t-1} - \int \frac{2t\, dt}{t^2+1} + \int \frac{1\, dt}{t^2+1}$

$\displaystyle = -\frac{1}{t} + 2\ln|t-1| - \ln|t^2+1| + \tan^{-1} t + C$

$\displaystyle = -\frac{1}{t} + \ln \frac{(t-1)^2}{t^2+1} + \tan^{-1} t + C$

$\displaystyle \int_{-\infty}^{\infty} \frac{4t^3 + t - 1}{t^2(t-1)(t^2+1)}\, dt$

$\displaystyle = \int_{-\infty}^{-1} \frac{4t^3 + t - 1}{t^2(t-1)(t^2+1)}\, dt + \int_{-1}^{0} \frac{4t^3 + t - 1}{t^2(t-1)(t^2+1)}\, dt$

$\displaystyle + \int_{0}^{1/2} \frac{4t^3 + t - 1}{t^2(t-1)(t^2+1)}\, dt + \int_{1/2}^{1} \frac{4t^3 + t - 1}{t^2(t-1)(t^2+1)}\, dt$

$\displaystyle + \int_{1}^{2} \frac{4t^3 + t - 1}{t^2(t-1)(t^2+1)}\, dt + \int_{2}^{\infty} \frac{4t^3 + t - 1}{t^2(t-1)(t^2+1)}\, dt$

Note that the integral must be broken up since the integrand has infinite discontinuities at $t = 0$ and $t = 1$.

$\displaystyle \int_{-1}^{0} \frac{4t^3 + t - 1}{t^2(t-1)(t^2+1)}\, dt$

$\displaystyle = \lim_{b\to 0^-} \int_{-1}^{b} \frac{4t^3 + t - 1}{t^2(t-1)(t^2+1)}\, dt$

$\displaystyle = \lim_{b\to 0^-}\left[-\frac{1}{t} + \ln \frac{(t-1)^2}{t^2+1} + \tan^{-1} t\right]_{-1}^{b}$

$\displaystyle = \lim_{b\to 0^-}\left[-\frac{1}{b} + \ln \frac{(b-1)^2}{b^2+1} + \tan^{-1} b - 1 - \ln 2 + \frac{\pi}{4}\right]$

$= \infty$

Since this limit diverges, the given integral diverges.

48. $\displaystyle \int_{-\infty}^{\infty} \frac{4\, dx}{x^2 + 16} = \int_{-\infty}^{0} \frac{4\, dx}{x^2 + 16} + \int_{0}^{\infty} \frac{4\, dx}{x^2 + 16}$

$\displaystyle \int \frac{4\, dx}{x^2 + 16} = \tan^{-1} \frac{x}{4} + C$ using Formula 16 with $a = 4$

$\displaystyle \int_{-\infty}^{0} \frac{4\, dx}{x^2 + 16} = \lim_{b\to -\infty} \int_{b}^{0} \frac{4\, dx}{x^2 + 16}$

$\displaystyle = \lim_{b\to -\infty}\left[\tan^{-1} \frac{x}{4}\right]_{b}^{0}$

$\displaystyle = \lim_{b\to -\infty}\left(-\tan^{-1} \frac{b}{4}\right) = \frac{\pi}{2}$

$\displaystyle \int_{0}^{\infty} \frac{4\, dx}{x^2 + 16} = \lim_{b\to \infty} \int_{0}^{b} \frac{4\, dx}{x^2 + 16}$

$\displaystyle = \lim_{b\to \infty}\left[\tan^{-1} \frac{x}{4}\right]_{0}^{b}$

$\displaystyle = \lim_{b\to \infty}\left(\tan^{-1} \frac{b}{4}\right) = \frac{\pi}{2}$

$\displaystyle \int_{-\infty}^{\infty} \frac{4\, dx}{x^2 + 16} = \frac{\pi}{2} + \frac{\pi}{2} = \pi$

49. Use the limit comparison test with $f(\theta) = \dfrac{1}{\sqrt{\theta^2 + 1}}$ and

$g(\theta) = \dfrac{1}{\theta}$. Both are positive continuous functions on $[1, \infty)$.

$\displaystyle \lim_{\theta\to\infty} \frac{f(\theta)}{g(\theta)} = \lim_{\theta\to\infty} \frac{\sqrt{\theta^2 + 1}}{\theta} = \lim_{\theta\to\infty} \sqrt{1 + \frac{1}{\theta^2}} = 1$

Since $\displaystyle \int_{1}^{\infty} g(\theta)\, d\theta = \int_{1}^{\infty} \frac{1}{\theta}\, d\theta$

$\displaystyle = \lim_{b\to\infty} \int_{1}^{b} \frac{1}{\theta}\, d\theta$

$\displaystyle = \lim_{b\to\infty} \left[\ln \theta\right]_{1}^{b}$

$\displaystyle = \lim_{b\to\infty} \ln b$

$= \infty,$

we know that $\displaystyle \int_{1}^{\infty} g(\theta)\, d\theta$ diverges and so $\displaystyle \int_{1}^{\infty} f(\theta)\, d\theta$

diverges. This means that the given integral diverges.

50. Evaluate $\int e^{-x} \cos x \, dx$ using integration by parts.

$u = \cos x$ $\qquad$ $dv = e^{-x} \, dx$

$du = -\sin x \, dx$ $\qquad$ $v = -e^{-x}$

$\int e^{-x} \cos x \, dx = -e^{-x} \cos x - \int \sin x \, e^{-x} \, dx$

Evaluate $\int \sin x \, e^{-x} \, dx$ using integration by parts.

$u = \sin x$ $\qquad$ $dv = e^{-x} \, dx$

$du = \cos x \, dx$ $\qquad$ $v = -e^{-x}$

$\int \sin x \, e^{-x} \, dx = -e^{-x} \sin x + \int e^{-x} \cos x \, dx$

$\int e^{-x} \cos x \, dx = -e^{-x} \cos x + e^{-x} \sin x - \int e^{-x} \cos x \, dx$

$2 \int e^{-x} \cos x \, dx = e^{-x} \sin x - e^{-x} \cos x + C_1$

$\int e^{-x} \cos x \, dx = \dfrac{e^{-x} \sin x - e^{-x} \cos x}{2} + C$

$\displaystyle\int_0^\infty e^{-u} \cos u \, du = \lim_{b \to \infty} \int_0^b e^{-x} \cos x \, dx$

$\qquad = \displaystyle\lim_{b \to \infty} \left[\dfrac{e^{-x} \sin x - e^{-x} \cos x}{2} \right]_0^b$

$\qquad = \displaystyle\lim_{b \to \infty} \left[\dfrac{e^{-b} \sin b - e^{-b} \cos b}{2} + \dfrac{1}{2} \right]$

$\qquad = \dfrac{1}{2}$

Hence the integral converges.

Note that we cannot use a comparison test since $e^{-x} \cos x < 0$ for some values on $[0, \infty)$.

51. $0 \le \dfrac{1}{z} \le \dfrac{\ln z}{z}$ on $[e, \infty)$

$\displaystyle\int_e^\infty \dfrac{dz}{z} = \lim_{b \to \infty} \int_e^b \dfrac{dz}{z} = \lim_{b \to \infty} \left[\ln |z| \right]_e^b = \lim_{b \to \infty} (\ln b - 1) = \infty$

Since this integral diverges, $\displaystyle\int_e^\infty \dfrac{1}{z} \, dz$ diverges, so the given

integral diverges.

52. $0 \le \dfrac{e^{-t}}{\sqrt{t}} \le e^{-t}$ on $[1, \infty)$

$\displaystyle\int_1^\infty e^{-t} \, dt = \lim_{b \to \infty} \int_1^b e^{-t} \, dt$

$\qquad = \displaystyle\lim_{b \to \infty} \left[-e^{-t} \right]_1^b$

$\qquad = \displaystyle\lim_{b \to \infty} \left(-e^{-b} + \dfrac{1}{e} \right) = \dfrac{1}{e}$

Since this integral converges, the given integral converges.

53. $\displaystyle\int \dfrac{dx}{e^x + e^{-x}} = \int \dfrac{dx}{e^{-x}(e^{2x} + 1)} = \int \dfrac{e^x \, dx}{(e^x)^2 + 1}$

Let $u = e^x$, $du = e^x \, dx$

$\displaystyle\int \dfrac{dx}{e^x + e^{-x}} = \int \dfrac{du}{u^2 + 1} = \tan^{-1} u + C = \tan^{-1} e^x + C$

$\displaystyle\int_{-\infty}^\infty \dfrac{dx}{e^x + e^{-x}} = \int_{-\infty}^0 \dfrac{dx}{e^x + e^{-x}} + \int_0^\infty \dfrac{dx}{e^x + e^{-x}}$

$\displaystyle\int_{-\infty}^0 \dfrac{dx}{e^x + e^{-x}} = \lim_{b \to -\infty} \int_b^0 \dfrac{dx}{e^x + e^{-x}}$

$\qquad = \displaystyle\lim_{b \to -\infty} \left[\tan^{-1} e^x \right]_b^0$

$\qquad = \displaystyle\lim_{b \to -\infty} \left(\dfrac{\pi}{4} - \tan^{-1} e^b \right) = \dfrac{\pi}{4}$

$\displaystyle\int_0^\infty \dfrac{dx}{e^x + e^{-x}} = \lim_{b \to \infty} \int_0^b \dfrac{dx}{e^x + e^{-x}}$

$\qquad = \displaystyle\lim_{b \to \infty} \left[\tan^{-1} e^x \right]_0^b$

$\qquad = \displaystyle\lim_{b \to \infty} \left(\tan^{-1} e^b - \dfrac{\pi}{4} \right)$

$\qquad = \dfrac{\pi}{2} - \dfrac{\pi}{4} = \dfrac{\pi}{4}$

Since these two integrals converge, the given integral converges.

54. The integral has an infinite discontinuity at $x = 0$.

$\displaystyle\int_{-\infty}^\infty \dfrac{dx}{x^2(1 + e^x)} = \int_{-\infty}^{-1} \dfrac{dx}{x^2(1 + e^x)} + \int_{-1}^0 \dfrac{dx}{x^2(1 + e^x)}$

$\qquad\qquad + \displaystyle\int_0^1 \dfrac{dx}{x^2(1 + e^x)} + \int_1^\infty \dfrac{dx}{x^2(1 + e^x)}$

$0 \le \dfrac{1}{4x^2} \le \dfrac{1}{x^2(1 + e^x)}$ on $(0, 1]$ since $1 + e^x \le 4$ on $(0, 1]$.

$\displaystyle\int_0^1 \dfrac{dx}{4x^2} = \lim_{b \to 0^+} \int_b^1 \dfrac{dx}{4x^2} = \lim_{b \to 0^+} \left[-\dfrac{1}{4x} \right]_b^1 = \lim_{b \to 0^+} \left[-\dfrac{1}{4} + \dfrac{1}{4b} \right] = \infty$

Since this integral diverges, $\displaystyle\int_0^1 \dfrac{dx}{x^2(1 + e^x)}$ diverges, so the

given integral diverges.

55. $x^2 - 7x + 12 = (x - 4)(x - 3)$

$\dfrac{2x + 1}{x^2 - 7x + 12} = \dfrac{A}{x - 4} + \dfrac{B}{x - 3}$

$2x + 1 = A(x - 3) + B(x - 4)$

$\qquad = (A + B)x - 3A - 4B$

Equating coefficients of like terms gives

$A + B = 2$ and $-3A - 4B = 1$.

Solving the system simultaneously yields $A = 9$, $B = -7$.

$\displaystyle\int \dfrac{2x + 1}{x^2 - 7x + 12} \, dx = \int \dfrac{9 \, dx}{x - 4} + \int \dfrac{-7 \, dx}{x - 3}$

$\qquad = 9 \ln |x - 4| - 7 \ln |x - 3| + C$

56. $\dfrac{8}{x^3(x+2)} = \dfrac{A}{x+2} + \dfrac{B}{x} + \dfrac{C}{x^2} + \dfrac{D}{x^3}$

$8 = Ax^3 + Bx^2(x+2) + Cx(x+2) + D(x+2)$

$\qquad = (A+B)x^3 + (2B+C)x^2 + (2C+D)x + 2D$

Equating coefficients of like terms gives

$A+B = 0,\ 2B+C = 0,\ 2C+D = 0,\ \text{and}\ 2D = 8$

Solving the system simultaneously yields

$A = -1,\ B = 1,\ C = -2,\ D = 4$

$\displaystyle\int \dfrac{8\,dx}{x^3(x+2)} = \int \dfrac{-dx}{x+2} + \int \dfrac{dx}{x} + \int \dfrac{-2\,dx}{x^2} + \int \dfrac{4\,dx}{x^3}$

$\qquad = -\ln|x+2| + \ln|x| + \dfrac{2}{x} - \dfrac{2}{x^2} + C$

57. $t^3 + t = t(t^2+1)$

$\dfrac{3t^2 + 4t + 4}{t^3 + t} = \dfrac{A}{t} + \dfrac{Bt+C}{t^2+1}$

$3t^2 + 4t + 4 = A(t^2+1) + (Bt+C)t$

$\qquad = (A+B)t^2 + Ct + A$

Equating coefficients of like terms gives

$A+B = 3,\ C = 4\ \text{and}\ A = 4.$

Solving the system simultaneously yields

$A = 4,\ B = -1,\ C = 4$

$\displaystyle\int \dfrac{3t^2+4t+4}{t^3+t}\,dt = \int \dfrac{4\,dt}{t} + \int \dfrac{-t+4}{t^2+1}\,dt$

$\qquad = \int \dfrac{4\,dt}{t} - \int \dfrac{t\,dt}{t^2+1} + \int \dfrac{4\,dt}{t^2+1}$

$\qquad = 4\ln|t| - \dfrac{1}{2}\ln(t^2+1) + 4\tan^{-1} t + C$

58. $t^4 + 4t^2 + 3 = (t^2+3)(t^2+1)$

$\dfrac{1}{(t^2+1)(t^2+3)} = \dfrac{At+B}{t^2+1} + \dfrac{Ct+D}{t^2+3}$

$1 = (At+B)(t^2+3) + (Ct+D)(t^2+1)$

$\qquad = (A+C)t^3 + (B+D)t^2 + (3A+C)t + 3B+D$

Equating coefficients of like terms gives

$A+C = 0,\ B+D = 0,\ 3A+C = 0,\ \text{and}\ 3B+D = 1$

Solving the system simultaneously yields

$A = 0,\ B = \dfrac{1}{2},\ C = 0,\ D = -\dfrac{1}{2}$

$\displaystyle\int \dfrac{dt}{(t^2+3)(t^2+1)} = \int \dfrac{1/2}{t^2+1}\,dt - \int \dfrac{1/2}{t^2+3}\,dt$

$\qquad = \dfrac{1}{2}\tan^{-1} t - \dfrac{1}{2\sqrt{3}}\tan^{-1}\dfrac{t}{\sqrt{3}} + C$

Evaluate the integrals using Formula 16, with $x = t$, $a = 1$

in the first integral and $a = \sqrt{3}$ in the second.

59.

$$x^3 - x\,\overline{)x^3 + 1}$$
$$\underline{x^3 - x}$$
$$x + 1$$

$\dfrac{x^3+1}{x^3-x} = 1 + \dfrac{x+1}{x^3-x} = 1 + \dfrac{x+1}{x(x^2-1)} = 1 + \dfrac{x+1}{x(x-1)(x+1)}$

$\dfrac{x+1}{x(x-1)(x+1)} = \dfrac{A}{x} + \dfrac{B}{x-1} + \dfrac{C}{x+1}$

$x+1 = A(x-1)(x+1) + Bx(x+1) + Cx(x-1)$

$\qquad = (A+B+C)x^2 + (B-C)x - A$

Equating coefficients of like terms gives

$A+B+C = 0,\ B-C = 1,\ \text{and}\ -A = 1.$

Solving the system simultaneously yields

$A = -1,\ B = 1,\ C = 0$

$\displaystyle\int \dfrac{x^3+1}{x^3-x}\,dx = \int dx - \int \dfrac{dx}{x} + \int \dfrac{dx}{x-1}$

$\qquad = x - \ln|x| + \ln|x-1| + C$

60.

$$x^2 + 4x + 3\,\overline{)x^3 + 4x^2 }$$
$$\underline{x^3 + 4x^2 + 3x}$$
$$-3x$$

$\dfrac{x^3+4x^2}{x^2+4x+3} = x + \dfrac{-3x}{x^2+4x+3} = x + \dfrac{-3x}{(x+1)(x+3)}$

$\dfrac{-3x}{(x+1)(x+3)} = \dfrac{A}{x+1} + \dfrac{B}{x+3}$

$-3x = A(x+3) + B(x+1)$

$-3x = (A+B)x + 3A + B$

Equating coefficients of like terms gives

$A+B = -3,\ 3A+B = 0$

Solving the system simultaneously yields $A = \dfrac{3}{2},\ B = -\dfrac{9}{2}.$

$\displaystyle\int \dfrac{x^3+4x^2}{x^2+4x+3}\,dx = \int x\,dx + \int \dfrac{3/2}{x+1}\,dx - \int \dfrac{9/2}{x+3}\,dx$

$\qquad = \dfrac{x^2}{2} + \dfrac{3}{2}\ln|x+1| - \dfrac{9}{2}\ln|x+3| + C$

61. $\dfrac{dy}{y(500-y)} = 0.002\, dx$

$\dfrac{1}{y(500-y)} = \dfrac{A}{y} + \dfrac{B}{500-y}$

$1 = A(500-y) + By$

$\quad = (B-A)y + 500A$

where $A = \dfrac{1}{500}$, $B = \dfrac{1}{500}$.

$\displaystyle\int \dfrac{dy}{y(500-y)} = \int \dfrac{1/500}{y}\,dy + \int \dfrac{1/500}{500-y}\,dy$

$\quad = \dfrac{1}{500}\ln|y| - \dfrac{1}{500}\ln|500-y| + C_1$

$\quad = \dfrac{1}{500}\ln\left|\dfrac{y}{500-y}\right| + C_1$

$\dfrac{1}{500}\ln\left|\dfrac{y}{500-y}\right| + C_1 = 0.002x + C_2$

$\ln\left|\dfrac{y}{500-y}\right| = x + C$

$\dfrac{y}{500-y} = ke^x$

Substitute $x=0$, $y=20$.

$\dfrac{20}{480} = ke^0$ or $k = \dfrac{1}{24}$

$\dfrac{y}{500-y} = \dfrac{1}{24}e^x$

$24y = 500e^x - ye^x$

$(e^x + 24)y = 500e^x$

$y = \dfrac{500\,e^x}{e^x + 24}$

$y = \dfrac{500}{1 + 24\,e^{-x}}$

62. $\dfrac{dy}{y^2+1} = \dfrac{dx}{x+1}$

$\displaystyle\int \dfrac{dy}{y^2+1} = \int \dfrac{dx}{x+1}$

$\tan^{-1}y + C_1 = \ln|x+1| + C_2$

$\tan^{-1}y = \ln|x+1| + C$

Substitute $x=0$, $y=\dfrac{\pi}{4}$

$\tan^{-1}\dfrac{\pi}{4} = C$

$\tan^{-1}y = \ln|x+1| + \tan^{-1}\dfrac{\pi}{4}$

$y = \tan\left(\ln|x+1| + \tan^{-1}\dfrac{\pi}{4}\right)$

63. $y = \dfrac{1}{3}\tan\theta$, $dy = \dfrac{1}{3}\sec^2\theta\,d\theta$, $-\dfrac{\pi}{2} < \theta < \dfrac{\pi}{2}$

$1 + 9y^2 = 1 + \tan^2\theta = \sec^2\theta$

$\displaystyle\int \dfrac{3\,dy}{\sqrt{1+9y^2}} = \int \dfrac{\sec^2\theta\,d\theta}{|\sec\theta|}$

$\quad = \displaystyle\int \sec\theta\,d\theta$

$\quad = \ln|\sec\theta + \tan\theta| + C$

$\quad = \ln\left|\sqrt{1+9y^2} + 3y\right| + C$

Integrate by using Formula 88 with $a=1$ and $x=\theta$.

Use Figure 8.18(a) from the text with $a=\dfrac{1}{3}$ and $x=y$.

64. $t = \dfrac{1}{3}\sin\theta$, $dt = \dfrac{1}{3}\cos\theta\,d\theta$, $-\dfrac{\pi}{2} \le \theta \le \dfrac{\pi}{2}$

$1 - 9t^2 = 1 - \sin^2\theta = \cos^2\theta$

$\displaystyle\int \sqrt{1-9t^2}\,dt = \int |\cos\theta|\left(\dfrac{1}{3}\cos\theta\right)d\theta$

$\quad = \displaystyle\int \dfrac{1}{3}\cos^2\theta\,d\theta$

$\quad = \displaystyle\int \dfrac{1+\cos 2\theta}{6}\,d\theta$

$\quad = \dfrac{\theta}{6} + \dfrac{\sin 2\theta}{12} + C$

$\quad = \dfrac{\theta}{6} + \dfrac{\sin\theta\cos\theta}{6} + C$

$\quad = \dfrac{\sin^{-1}3t}{6} + \dfrac{3t\sqrt{1-9t^2}}{6} + C$

$\quad = \dfrac{1}{6}\sin^{-1}3t + \dfrac{1}{2}t\sqrt{1-9t^2} + C$

Use Figure 8.18(b) with $a=\dfrac{1}{3}$ and $x=t$.

65. $x = \dfrac{3}{5}\sec\theta$, $dx = \dfrac{3}{5}\sec\theta\tan\theta\,d\theta$, $0 \le \theta < \dfrac{\pi}{2}$

$25x^2 - 9 = 9\sec^2\theta - 9 = 9\tan^2\theta$

$\displaystyle\int \dfrac{5\,dx}{\sqrt{25x^2-9}} = \int \dfrac{3\sec\theta\tan\theta\,d\theta}{3|\tan\theta|}$

$\quad = \displaystyle\int \sec\theta\,d\theta$

$\quad = \ln|\sec\theta + \tan\theta| + C_1$

$\quad = \ln\left|\dfrac{5x}{3} + \dfrac{\sqrt{25x^2-9}}{3}\right| + C_1$

$\quad = \ln\left(5x + \sqrt{25x^2-9}\right) + C$

Integrate by using Formula 88 with $a=1$ and $x=\theta$.

Use Figure 8.18(c) with $a=\dfrac{3}{5}$.

66. $x = \sin\theta,\ dx = \cos\theta\ d\theta,\ -\dfrac{\pi}{2} \le \theta \le \dfrac{\pi}{2}$

$$1 - x^2 = \cos^2\theta$$

$$\int \frac{4x^2\ dx}{(1 - x^2)^{3/2}} = \int \frac{4\sin^2\theta\cos\theta}{|\cos^3\theta|}\ d\theta$$

$$= \int \frac{4(1 - \cos^2\theta)}{\cos^2\theta}\ d\theta$$

$$= \int (4\sec^2\theta - 4)\ d\theta$$

$$= 4\tan\theta - 4\theta + C$$

$$= \frac{4x}{\sqrt{1 - x^2}} - 4\sin^{-1}x + C$$

Use Figure 8.18(b) with $a = 1$.

67. For $x \ge 0$, $y \ge 0$ on $(0, 1]$.

$$\text{Volume} = \int_0^1 \pi(-\ln x)^2\ dx$$

$$= \pi \int_0^1 (\ln x)^2\ dx$$

$$= \pi \lim_{b \to 0^+} \int_b^1 (\ln x)^2\ dx$$

Evaluate $\int (\ln x)^2\ dx$ by using integration by parts.

$u = (\ln x)^2 \qquad\qquad dv = dx$

$du = \dfrac{2\ln x}{x}\ dx \qquad v = x$

$\int (\ln x)^2\ dx = x\,(\ln x)^2 - \int 2\ln x\ dx$

Evaluate $\int 2\ln x\ dx$ by using integration by parts.

$u = 2\ln x \qquad\qquad dv = dx$

$du = \dfrac{2}{x}\ dx \qquad v = x$

$\int 2\ln x\ dx = 2x\ln x - \int 2\ dx = 2x\ln x - 2x + C$

$\int (\ln x)^2\ dx = x\,(\ln x)^2 - 2x\ln x + 2x + C$

$\text{Area} = \pi \lim_{b \to 0^+} \left[x(\ln x)^2 - 2x\ln x + 2x \right]_b^1$

$= \pi \lim_{b \to 0^+} [2 - b(\ln b)^2 + 2b\ln b - 2b]$

$= 2\pi - \lim_{b \to 0^+} \dfrac{\pi(\ln b)^2}{1/b} + 2\lim_{b \to 0^+} \dfrac{\pi\ln b}{1/b}$

$= 2\pi - \lim_{b \to 0^+} \dfrac{2\pi(\ln b)(1/b)}{-1/b^2} + 2\lim_{b \to 0^+} \dfrac{\pi/b}{-1/b^2}$

$= 2\pi - \lim_{b \to 0^+} \dfrac{2\pi(\ln b)}{-1/b} + 2\lim_{b \to 0^+} (-\pi b)$

$= 2\pi - \lim_{b \to 0^+} \dfrac{2\pi/b}{1/b^2} - \lim_{b \to 0^+} 2\pi b = 2\pi$

68. For $x \ge 0$, $y \ge 0$ on $[0, \infty)$.

$$\text{Area} = \int_0^\infty xe^{-x}\ dx = \lim_{b \to \infty} \int_0^b xe^{-x}\ dx$$

Evaluate $\int xe^{-x}\ dx$ by using integration by parts.

$u = x \qquad\qquad dv = e^{-x}\ dx$

$du = dx \qquad\qquad v = -e^{-x}$

$\int xe^{-x}\ dx = -xe^{-x} + \int e^{-x}\ dx = -xe^{-x} - e^{-x} + C$

$\text{Area} = \lim_{b \to \infty} \left[-xe^{-x} - e^{-x} \right]_0^b$

$= \lim_{b \to \infty} [-be^{-b} - e^{-b} + 1]$

$= -\lim_{b \to \infty} \dfrac{b}{e^b} + 1$

$= -\lim_{b \to \infty} \dfrac{1}{e^b} + 1 = 1$

69. (a) $\dfrac{dx}{dt} = k(a - x)^2$

$$\frac{dx}{(a - x)^2} = k\ dt$$

$$\int \frac{dx}{(a - x)^2} = \int k\ dt = kt + C_1$$

$$\frac{1}{a - x} + C_2 = kt + C_1$$

$$\frac{1}{a - x} = kt + C$$

Substitute $x = 0$, $t = 0$

$$\frac{1}{a} = C$$

$$\frac{1}{a - x} = kt + \frac{1}{a}$$

$$\frac{1}{kt + 1/a} = a - x$$

$$x = a - \frac{1}{kt + 1/a}$$

69. continued

(b) $\dfrac{dx}{(a-x)(b-x)} = k\,dt$

$\displaystyle\int \dfrac{dx}{(a-x)(b-x)} = \int k\,dt = kt + C_1$

$\dfrac{1}{(a-x)(b-x)} = \dfrac{A}{a-x} + \dfrac{B}{b-x}$

$1 = A(b-x) + B(a-x)$

$\quad = (-A - B)x + bA + aB$

Equating coefficients of like terms gives

$-A - B = 0$ and $bA + aB = 1$

Solving the system simultaneously yields

$A = -\dfrac{1}{a-b},\ B = \dfrac{1}{a-b}$

$\displaystyle\int \dfrac{dx}{(a-x)(b-x)} = \int \dfrac{-1/(a-b)}{a-x}\,dx + \int \dfrac{1/(a-b)}{b-x}\,dx$

$\qquad = \dfrac{\ln|a-x|}{a-b} - \dfrac{\ln|b-x|}{a-b} + C_2$

$\qquad = \dfrac{1}{a-b}\ln\left|\dfrac{a-x}{b-x}\right| + C_2$

$\dfrac{1}{a-b}\ln\left|\dfrac{a-x}{b-x}\right| + C_2 = kt + C_1$

$\ln\left|\dfrac{a-x}{b-x}\right| = (a-b)kt + C$

$\dfrac{a-x}{b-x} = De^{(a-b)kt}$

Substitute $t = 0$, $x = 0$.

$\dfrac{a}{b} = D$

$\dfrac{a-x}{b-x} = \dfrac{a}{b}e^{(a-b)kt}$

$ab - bx = abe^{(a-b)kt} - axe^{(a-b)kt}$

$x(ae^{(a-b)kt} - b) = ab(e^{(a-b)kt} - 1)$

$x = \dfrac{ab(e^{(a-b)kt} - 1)}{ae^{(a-b)kt} - b}$

Multiply the rational expression by $\dfrac{e^{bkt}}{e^{bkt}}$.

$x = \dfrac{ab(e^{akt} - e^{bkt})}{ae^{akt} - be^{bkt}}$

Chapter 9
Infinite Series

■ Section 9.1 Power Series (pp. 457–468)

Exploration 1   Power Series for Other Functions

1. $1 - x + x^2 - x^3 + \cdots + (-x)^n + \cdots$.

2. $x - x^2 + x^3 - x^4 + \cdots + (-1)^n x^{n+1} + \cdots$.

3. $1 + 2x + 4x^2 + 8x^3 + \cdots + (2x)^n + \cdots$.

4. $1 - (x-1) + (x-1)^2 - (x-1)^3 + \cdots$
$\quad + (-1)^n(x-1)^n + \cdots$.

This geometric series converges for $-1 < x - 1 < 1$, which is equivalent to $0 < x < 2$. The interval of convergence is $(0, 2)$.

5. $\dfrac{1}{3} - \dfrac{1}{3}(x-1) + \dfrac{1}{3}(x-1)^2 - \dfrac{1}{3}(x-1)^3 + \cdots$
$\quad + \left(-\dfrac{1}{3}\right)^n (x-1)^n + \cdots$.

This geometric series converges for $-1 < x - 1 < 1$, which is equivalent to $0 < x < 2$. The interval of convergence is $(0, 2)$.

Exploration 2   A Power Series for $\tan^{-1} x$

1. $1 - x^2 + x^4 - x^6 + \cdots + (-1)^n x^{2n} + \cdots$.

2. $\tan^{-1} x = \displaystyle\int_0^x \dfrac{1}{1+t^2}\,dt$

$\qquad = \displaystyle\int_0^x (1 - t^2 + t^4 - t^6 + \cdots + (-1)^n t^{2n} + \cdots)\,dt$

$\qquad = \left[t - \dfrac{t^3}{3} + \dfrac{t^5}{5} - \dfrac{t^7}{7} + \cdots + (-1)^n \dfrac{t^{2n+1}}{2n+1} + \cdots\right]_0^x$

$\qquad = x - \dfrac{x^3}{3} + \dfrac{x^5}{5} - \dfrac{x^7}{7} + \cdots + (-1)^n \dfrac{x^{2n+1}}{2n+1} \cdots$.

3. The graphs of the first four partial sums appear to be converging on the interval $(-1, 1)$.

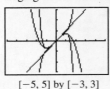

$[-5, 5]$ by $[-3, 3]$

4. When $x = 1$, the series becomes

$1 - \dfrac{1}{3} + \dfrac{1}{5} - \dfrac{1}{7} + \cdots + \dfrac{(-1)^n}{2n+1} + \cdots$.

This series does appear to converge. The terms are getting smaller, and because they alternate in sign they cause the partial sums to oscillate above and below a limit. The two calculator statements shown below will cause the successive partial sums to appear on the calculator each time the ENTER button is pushed. The partial sums will appear to be approaching a limit of $\pi/4$ (which is $\tan^{-1}(1)$), although very slowly.

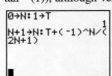

Exploration 3   A Series with a Curious Property

1. $f'(x) = 1 + x + \dfrac{x^2}{2!} + \dfrac{x^3}{3!} + \cdots + \dfrac{x^n}{n!} + \cdots$.

2. $f(0) = 1 + 0 + 0 + \cdots = 1$.

3. Since this function is its own derivative and takes on the value 1 at $x = 0$, we suspect that it must be e^x.

4. If $y = f(x)$, then $\dfrac{dy}{dx} = y$ and $y = 1$ when $x = 0$.

5. The differential equation is separable.

$$\frac{dy}{y} = dx$$

$$\int \frac{dy}{y} = \int dx$$

$$\ln|y| = x + C$$

$$y = Ke^k$$

$$1 = Ke^0 \Rightarrow K = 1$$

$$\therefore y = e^x.$$

6. The first three partial sums are shown in the graph below. It is risky to draw any conclusions about the interval of convergence from just three partial sums, but so far the convergence to the graph of $y = e^x$ only looks good on $(-1, 1)$. Your answer might differ.

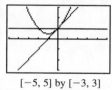

$[-5, 5]$ by $[-3, 3]$

7. The next three partial sums show that the convergence extends outside the interval $(-1, 1)$ in both directions, so $(-1, 1)$ was apparently an underestimate. Your answer in #6 might have been better, but unless you guessed "all real numbers," you still underestimated! (See Example 4 in Section 9.3.)

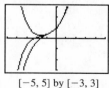

$[-5, 5]$ by $[-3, 3]$

Quick Review 9.1

1. $u_1 = \dfrac{4}{1 + 2} = \dfrac{4}{3}$

$u_2 = \dfrac{4}{2 + 2} = \dfrac{4}{4} = 1$

$u_3 = \dfrac{4}{3 + 2} = \dfrac{4}{5}$

$u_4 = \dfrac{4}{4 + 2} = \dfrac{4}{6} = \dfrac{2}{3}$

$u_{30} = \dfrac{4}{30 + 2} = \dfrac{4}{32} = \dfrac{1}{8}$

2. $u_1 = \dfrac{(-1)^1}{1} = -1$

$u_2 = \dfrac{(-1)^2}{2} = \dfrac{1}{2}$

$u_3 = \dfrac{(-1)^3}{3} = -\dfrac{1}{3}$

$u_4 = \dfrac{(-1)^4}{4} = \dfrac{1}{4}$

$u_{30} = \dfrac{(-1)^{30}}{30} = \dfrac{1}{30}$

3. (a) Since $\dfrac{6}{2} = \dfrac{18}{6} = \dfrac{54}{18} = 3$, the common ratio is 3.

(b) $2(3^9) = 39,366$

(c) $a_n = 2(3^{n-1})$

4. (a) Since $\dfrac{-4}{8} = \dfrac{2}{-4} = \dfrac{-1}{2} = -\dfrac{1}{2}$, the common ratio is $-\dfrac{1}{2}$.

(b) $8\left(-\dfrac{1}{2}\right)^9 = -\dfrac{1}{64}$

(c) $a_n = 8\left(-\dfrac{1}{2}\right)^{n-1} = 8(-0.5)^{n-1}$

5. (a) We graph the points $\left(n, \dfrac{1 - n}{n^2}\right)$ for $n = 1, 2, 3, \ldots$. (Note that there is a point at $(1, 0)$ that does not show in the graph.)

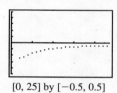

$[0, 25]$ by $[-0.5, 0.5]$

(b) $\displaystyle\lim_{n\to\infty} a_n = \lim_{n\to\infty} \dfrac{1 - n}{n^2} = 0$

6. (a) We graph the points $\left(n, \left(1 + \dfrac{1}{n}\right)^n\right)$ for $n = 1, 2, 3, \ldots$.

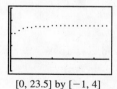

$[0, 23.5]$ by $[-1, 4]$

(b) $\displaystyle\lim_{n\to\infty} a_n = \lim_{n\to\infty} \left(1 + \dfrac{1}{n}\right)^n = e$

7. (a) We graph the points $(n, (-1)^n)$ for $n = 1, 2, 3, \ldots$.

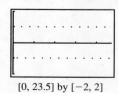

$[0, 23.5]$ by $[-2, 2]$

(b) $\displaystyle\lim_{n\to\infty} a_n$ does not exist because the values of a_n oscillate between -1 and 1.

8. (a) We graph the points $\left(n, \dfrac{1-2n}{1+2n}\right)$ for $n = 1, 2, 3, \dots$.

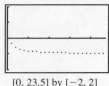

[0, 23.5] by [−2, 2]

(b) $\displaystyle\lim_{n\to\infty} a_n = \lim_{n\to\infty} \frac{1-2n}{1+2n} = -\frac{2}{2} = -1$

9. (a) We graph the points $\left(n, 2 - \dfrac{1}{n}\right)$ for $n = 1, 2, 3, \dots$.

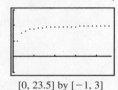

[0, 23.5] by [−1, 3]

(b) $\displaystyle\lim_{n\to\infty} a_n = \lim_{n\to\infty}\left(2 - \frac{1}{n}\right) = 2$

10. (a) We graph the points $\left(n, \dfrac{\ln(n+1)}{n}\right)$ for $n = 1, 2, 3, \dots$.

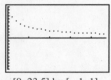

[0, 23.5] by [−1, 1]

(b) $\displaystyle\lim_{n\to\infty} a_n = \lim_{n\to\infty} \frac{\ln(n+1)}{n} = \lim_{n\to\infty} \frac{\frac{1}{(n+1)}}{1} = 0$

Section 9.1 Exercises

1. (a) Let u_n represent the value of * in the nth term, starting with $n = 1$. Then $\dfrac{1}{u_1} = 1$, $-\dfrac{1}{u_2} = -\dfrac{1}{4}$, $\dfrac{1}{u_3} = \dfrac{1}{9}$, and $-\dfrac{1}{u_4} = -\dfrac{1}{16}$, so $u_1 = 1$, $u_2 = 4$, $u_3 = 9$, and $u_4 = 16$. We may write $u_n = n^2$, or * $= n^2$.

(b) Let u_n represent the value of * in the nth term, starting with $n = 0$. Then $\dfrac{1}{u_0} = 1$, $-\dfrac{1}{u_1} = -\dfrac{1}{4}$, $\dfrac{1}{u_2} = \dfrac{1}{9}$, and $-\dfrac{1}{u_3} = -\dfrac{1}{16}$, so $u_0 = 1$, $u_1 = 4$, $u_2 = 9$, and $u_3 = 16$. We may write $u_n = (n+1)^2$, or * $= (n+1)^2$.

(c) If * $= 3$, the series is
$$(-1)^3\left(\frac{-1}{1^2}\right) + (-1)^4\left(\frac{-1}{2^2}\right) + (-1)^5\left(\frac{-1}{3^2}\right) +$$
$$(-1)^6\left(\frac{-1}{4^2}\right) + \cdots,$$ which is the same as the desired series. Thus let * $= 3$.

2. (a) Note that $a_0 = 1$, $a_1 = \dfrac{1}{3}$, $a_2 = \dfrac{1}{9}$, and so on. Thus
$$a_n = \left(\frac{1}{3}\right)^n.$$

(b) Note that $a_1 = 1$, $a_2 = -\dfrac{1}{2}$, $a_3 = \dfrac{1}{3}$, and so on. Thus
$$a_n = \frac{(-1)^{n-1}}{n}.$$

(c) Note that $a_0 = 5$, $a_1 = 0.5$, $a_2 = 0.05$, and so on. Thus
$$a_n = 5(0.1)^n = \frac{5}{10^n}.$$

3. Different, since the terms of $\displaystyle\sum_{n=1}^{\infty}\left(-\frac{1}{2}\right)^{n-1}$ alternate between positive and negative, while the terms of $\displaystyle\sum_{n=1}^{\infty} -\left(\frac{1}{2}\right)^{n-1}$ are all negative.

4. The same, since both series can be represented as
$$1 - \frac{1}{2} + \frac{1}{4} - \frac{1}{8} + \cdots.$$

5. The same, since both series can be represented as
$$1 - \frac{1}{2} + \frac{1}{4} - \frac{1}{8} + \cdots.$$

6. Different, since $\displaystyle\sum_{n=1}^{\infty}\left(-\frac{1}{2}\right)^{n-1} = 1 - \frac{1}{2} + \frac{1}{4} - \frac{1}{8} + \cdots$ but
$$\sum_{n=1}^{\infty} \frac{(-1)^n}{2^{n-1}} = -1 + \frac{1}{2} - \frac{1}{4} + \frac{1}{8} - \cdots.$$

7. Converges; $\displaystyle\sum_{n=0}^{\infty}\left(\frac{2}{3}\right)^n = \frac{1}{1 - \frac{2}{3}} = 3$

8. Diverges, because the terms do not approach zero.

9. Converges; $\displaystyle\sum_{n=0}^{\infty}\left(\frac{5}{4}\right)\left(\frac{2}{3}\right)^n = \frac{\frac{5}{4}}{1 - \frac{2}{3}} = 3\left(\frac{5}{4}\right) = \frac{15}{4}$

10. Diverges, because the common ratio is ≥ 1 and the terms do not approach zero.

11. Diverges, because the terms alternate between 1 and -1 and do not approach zero.

12. Converges; $\displaystyle\sum_{n=0}^{\infty} 3(-0.1)^n = \frac{3}{1 - (-0.1)} = \frac{30}{11}$

13. Converges; $\displaystyle\sum_{n=0}^{\infty} \sin^n\left(\frac{\pi}{4} + n\pi\right)$

$$= 1 + \left(-\frac{1}{\sqrt{2}}\right)^1 + \left(\frac{1}{\sqrt{2}}\right)^2 + \left(-\frac{1}{\sqrt{2}}\right)^3 + \cdots$$

$$= \sum_{n=0}^{\infty}\left(-\frac{1}{\sqrt{2}}\right)^n = \frac{1}{1 - \left(-\frac{1}{\sqrt{2}}\right)} = \frac{\sqrt{2}}{\sqrt{2}+1}$$

$$= \frac{\sqrt{2}(\sqrt{2}-1)}{(\sqrt{2}+1)(\sqrt{2}-1)} = \frac{2-\sqrt{2}}{2-1} = 2 - \sqrt{2}$$

14. Diverges, because the terms do not approach zero.

15. Converges; since $\dfrac{e}{\pi} \approx 0.865 < 1$, $\displaystyle\sum_{n=1}^{\infty} \left(\dfrac{e}{\pi}\right)^n = \dfrac{\dfrac{e}{\pi}}{1 - \left(\dfrac{e}{\pi}\right)}$

$= \dfrac{e}{\pi - e}$

16. Converges; $\displaystyle\sum_{n=0}^{\infty} \dfrac{5^n}{6^{n+1}} = \sum_{n=0}^{\infty} \dfrac{1}{6}\left(\dfrac{5}{6}\right)^n = \dfrac{\dfrac{1}{6}}{1 - \left(\dfrac{5}{6}\right)} = 1$

17. Since $\displaystyle\sum_{n=0}^{\infty} 2^n x^n = \sum_{n=0}^{\infty} (2x)^n$, the series converges when $|2x| < 1$ and the interval of convergence is $\left(-\dfrac{1}{2}, \dfrac{1}{2}\right)$. Since the sum of the series is $\dfrac{1}{1 - 2x}$, the series represents the function $f(x) = \dfrac{1}{1 - 2x}$, $-\dfrac{1}{2} < x < \dfrac{1}{2}$.

18. Since $\displaystyle\sum_{n=0}^{\infty} (-1)^n (x + 1)^n = \sum_{n=0}^{\infty} [-(x + 1)]^n$, the series converges when $|-(x + 1)| < 1$ and the interval of convergence is $(-2, 0)$. Since the sum of the series is $\dfrac{1}{1 - [-(x + 1)]} = \dfrac{1}{x + 2}$, the series represents the function $f(x) = \dfrac{1}{x + 2}$, $-2 < x < 0$.

19. Since $\displaystyle\sum_{n=0}^{\infty} \left(-\dfrac{1}{2}\right)^n (x - 3)^n = \sum_{n=0}^{\infty} \left(\dfrac{3 - x}{2}\right)^n$, the series converges when $\left|\dfrac{3 - x}{2}\right| < 1$ and the interval of convergence is $(1, 5)$. Since the sum of the series is $\dfrac{1}{1 - \dfrac{(3 - x)}{2}} = \dfrac{2}{x - 1}$. the series represents the function $f(x) = \dfrac{2}{x - 1}$, $1 < x < 5$.

20. For $\displaystyle\sum_{n=0}^{\infty} 3\left(\dfrac{x - 1}{2}\right)^n$, the series converges when $\left|\dfrac{x - 1}{2}\right| < 1$ and the interval of convergence is $(-1, 3)$.

Since the sum of the series is $\dfrac{3}{1 - \dfrac{(x - 1)}{2}} = \dfrac{6}{3 - x}$, the series represents the function $f(x) = \dfrac{6}{3 - x}$, $-1 < x < 3$.

21. Since $\displaystyle\sum_{n=0}^{\infty} \sin^n x = \sum_{n=0}^{\infty} (\sin x)^n$, the series converges when $|\sin x| < 1$. Thus, the series converges for all values of x except odd integer multiples of $\dfrac{\pi}{2}$, that is, $x \neq (2k + 1)\dfrac{\pi}{2}$ for integers k. Since the sum of the series is $\dfrac{1}{1 - \sin x}$, the series represents the function $f(x) = \dfrac{1}{1 - \sin x}$, $x \neq (2k + 1)\dfrac{\pi}{2}$.

22. Since $\displaystyle\sum_{n=0}^{\infty} \tan^n x = \sum_{n=0}^{\infty} (\tan x)^n$, the series converges when $|\tan x| < 1$. Thus, the series converges for $-\dfrac{\pi}{4} + k\pi < x < \dfrac{\pi}{4} + k\pi$, where k is any integer. Since the sum of the series is $\dfrac{1}{1 - \tan x}$, the series represents the function $f(x) = \dfrac{1}{1 - \tan x}$, $-\dfrac{\pi}{4} + k\pi < x < \dfrac{\pi}{4} + k\pi$.

23. **(a)** Since the terms are all positive and do not approach zero, the partial sums tend toward infinity.

(b) The partial sums are alternately 1 and 0.

(c) The partial sums alternate between positive and negative while their magnitude increases toward infinity.

24. Since $\displaystyle\sum_{n=0}^{\infty} \dfrac{e^{n\pi}}{\pi^{ne}} = \sum_{n=0}^{\infty} \left(\dfrac{e^{\pi}}{\pi^e}\right)^n$, this is a geometric series with common ratio $r = \dfrac{e^{\pi}}{\pi^e} \approx 1.03$, which is greater than one.

25. $\displaystyle\sum_{n=0}^{\infty} x^n = 20$

$\dfrac{1}{1 - x} = 20, |x| < 1$

$1 = 20 - 20x$

$20x = 19$

$x = \dfrac{19}{20}$

26. One possible answer:

For any real number $a \neq 0$,

use $\dfrac{a}{2} + \dfrac{a}{4} + \dfrac{a}{8} + \dfrac{a}{16} + \dfrac{a}{32} + \cdots$. To get 0,

use $1 - \dfrac{1}{2} - \dfrac{1}{4} - \dfrac{1}{8} - \dfrac{1}{16} - \dfrac{1}{32} \cdots$.

27. Assuming the series begins at $n = 1$:

(a) $\displaystyle\sum_{n=1}^{\infty} 2r^{n-1} = \dfrac{2}{1 - r} = 5, |r| < 1$

$2 = 5 - 5r$

$5r = 3$

$r = \dfrac{3}{5}$

Series: $\displaystyle\sum_{n=1}^{\infty} 2\left(\dfrac{3}{5}\right)^{n-1}$

(b) $\displaystyle\sum_{n=1}^{\infty} \dfrac{13}{2} r^{n-1} = \dfrac{\dfrac{13}{2}}{1 - r} = 5, |r| < 1$

$\dfrac{13}{2} = 5 - 5r$

$5r = -\dfrac{3}{2}$

$r = -\dfrac{3}{10}$

Series: $\displaystyle\sum_{n=1}^{\infty} \dfrac{13}{2}\left(-\dfrac{3}{10}\right)^{n-1}$

28. Let $a = \dfrac{21}{100}$ and $r = \dfrac{1}{100}$, giving

$$0.\overline{21} = 0.21 + 0.21(0.01) + 0.21(0.01)^2$$
$$+ 0.21(0.01)^3 + \cdots$$
$$= \sum_{n=0}^{\infty} 0.21(0.01)^n$$
$$= \frac{0.21}{1 - 0.01}$$
$$= \frac{0.21}{0.99}$$
$$= \frac{7}{33}$$

29. Let $a = \dfrac{234}{1000}$ and $r = \dfrac{1}{1000}$, giving

$$0.\overline{234} = 0.234 + 0.234(0.001) + 0.234(0.001)^2$$
$$+ 0.234(0.001)^3 + \cdots$$
$$= \sum_{n=0}^{\infty} 0.234(0.001)^n$$
$$= \frac{0.234}{1 - 0.001}$$
$$= \frac{0.234}{0.999}$$
$$= \frac{26}{111}$$

30. $0.\overline{7} = 0.7 + 0.7(0.1) + 0.7(0.1)^2 + 0.7(0.1)^3 + \cdots$

$$= \sum_{n=0}^{\infty} 0.7(0.1)^n$$
$$= \frac{0.7}{1 - 0.1}$$
$$= \frac{0.7}{0.9}$$
$$= \frac{7}{9}$$

31. $0.\overline{d} = \dfrac{d}{10}[1 + 0.1 + 0.1^2 + 0.1^3 + \cdots]$

$$= \frac{d}{10} \sum_{n=0}^{\infty} (0.1)^n$$
$$= \frac{d}{10} \frac{1}{1 - 0.1}$$
$$= \frac{d}{10} \frac{1}{0.9}$$
$$= \frac{d}{9}$$

32. $0.0\overline{6} = 0.06 + 0.06(0.1) + 0.06(0.1)^2 + 0.06(0.1)^3 + \cdots$

$$= \sum_{n=0}^{\infty} 0.06(.1)^n$$
$$= \frac{0.06}{1 - 0.1}$$
$$= \frac{0.06}{0.9}$$
$$= \frac{1}{15}$$

33. $1.\overline{414} = 1 + 0.414 + 0.414(0.001) + 0.414(0.001)^2$

$$= 1 + \sum_{n=0}^{\infty} 0.414(0.001)^n$$
$$= 1 + \frac{0.414}{1 - 0.001}$$
$$= 1 + \frac{46}{111}$$
$$= \frac{157}{111}$$

34. $1.24\overline{123} = 1.24 + 0.00123 + 0.00123(0.001)$

$$+ 0.00123(0.001)^2 + \cdots$$
$$= 1.24 + \sum_{n=1}^{\infty} 0.00123(0.001)^n$$
$$= 1.24 + \frac{0.00123}{0.999}$$
$$= \frac{124}{100} + \frac{41}{33,300}$$
$$= \frac{41,333}{33,300}$$

35. $3.\overline{142857} = 3 + 0.142857(1 + 0.000001$

$$+ 0.000001^2 + \cdots)$$
$$= 3 + 0.142857 \sum_{n=0}^{\infty} 0.000001^n$$
$$= 3 + (0.142857)\left(\frac{1}{1 - 0.000001}\right)$$
$$= 3 + \frac{0.142857}{0.999999}$$
$$= 3 + \frac{1}{7}$$
$$= \frac{22}{7}$$

36. Total distance $= 4 + 2[4(0.6) + 4(0.6)^2 + 4(0.6)^3 + \cdots]$

$$= 4 + 2 \sum_{n=0}^{\infty} 2.4(0.6)^n$$
$$= 4 + 2 \cdot \frac{2.4}{1 - 0.6}$$
$$= 4 + 2 \cdot 6$$
$$= 16\text{m}$$

37. Total time $= \sqrt{\dfrac{4}{4.9}} + 2\left[\sqrt{\dfrac{4(0.6)}{4.9}} + \sqrt{\dfrac{4(0.6)^2}{4.9}}\right.$

$$\left. + \sqrt{\frac{4(0.6)^3}{4.9}} + \cdots \right]$$
$$= \sqrt{\frac{4}{4.9}} + 2\sqrt{\frac{4(0.6)}{4.9}}[1 + \sqrt{0.6} + (\sqrt{0.6})^2 + \cdots]$$
$$= \sqrt{\frac{4}{4.9}} + 2\sqrt{\frac{4(0.6)}{4.9}} \cdot \frac{1}{1 - \sqrt{0.6}}$$
$$\approx 7.113 \text{ sec}$$

38. The area of each square is half of the area of the preceding

square, so the total of all the areas is $\sum\limits_{n=0}^{\infty} 4\left(\dfrac{1}{2}\right)^n$

$= \dfrac{4}{1 - \left(\dfrac{1}{2}\right)} = 8 \text{ m}^2.$

39. Total area $= \sum\limits_{n=1}^{\infty} 2^n \cdot \dfrac{1}{2} \cdot \pi\left(\dfrac{1}{2^n}\right)^2$

$= \sum\limits_{n=1}^{\infty} \dfrac{\pi}{2} \cdot \left(\dfrac{1}{2}\right)^n$

$= \sum\limits_{n=0}^{\infty} \dfrac{\pi}{4}\left(\dfrac{1}{2}\right)^n$

$= \dfrac{\dfrac{\pi}{4}}{1 - \left(\dfrac{1}{2}\right)}$

$= \dfrac{\pi}{2}$

40. (a) $S - rS = (a + ar + ar^2 + ar^3 + \cdots + ar^{n-2} + ar^{n-1})$
$ -(ar + ar^2 + ar^3 + ar^4 + \cdots + ar^{n-1} + ar^n)$
$ = a - ar^n$

(b) Just factor and divide by $1 - r$:

$S - rS = a - ar^n$

$S(1 - r) = a - ar^n$

$S = \dfrac{a - ar^n}{1 - r}$

41. Using the notation $S_n = a + ar + ar^2 + ar^3 + \ldots + ar^{n-1}$,

the formula from Exercise 40 is $S_n = \dfrac{a - ar^n}{1 - r}$.

If $|r| < 1$, then $\lim\limits_{n \to \infty} r^n = 0$ and so $\sum\limits_{n=1}^{\infty} ar^{n-1}$

$= \lim\limits_{n \to \infty} S_n = \lim\limits_{n \to \infty} \dfrac{a - ar^n}{1 - r} = \dfrac{a}{1 - r}.$

If $|r| > 1$ or $r = -1$, then r^n has no finite limit as $n \to \infty$,

so the expression $\dfrac{a - ar^n}{1 - r}$ has no finite limit and $\sum\limits_{n=1}^{\infty} ar^{n-1}$

diverges.

If $r = 1$, then the nth partial sum is na, which goes to $\pm\infty$.

42. Comparing $\dfrac{1}{1 + 3x}$ with $\dfrac{a}{1 - r}$, the leading term is $a = 1$ and

the common ratio is $r = -3x$.

Series: $1 - 3x + 9x^2 - \cdots + (-3x)^n + \cdots$

Interval: The series converges when $|-3x| < 1$, so the

interval of convergence is $\left(-\dfrac{1}{3}, \dfrac{1}{3}\right)$.

43. Comparing $\dfrac{x}{1 - 2x}$ with $\dfrac{a}{1 - r}$, the first term is $a = x$ and

the common ratio is $r = 2x$.

Series: $x + 2x^2 + 4x^3 + \cdots + 2^{n-1}x^n + \cdots$

Interval: The series converges when $|2x| < 1$, so the interval

of convergence is $\left(-\dfrac{1}{2}, \dfrac{1}{2}\right)$.

44. Comparing $\dfrac{3}{1 - x^3}$ with $\dfrac{a}{1 - r}$, the first term is $a = 3$ and

the common ratio is $r = x^3$.

Series: $3 + 3x^3 + 3x^6 + \cdots + 3x^{3n} + \cdots$

Interval: The series converges when $|x^3| < 1$, so the interval

of convergence is $(-1, 1)$.

45. Comparing $\dfrac{1}{1 + (x - 4)}$ with $\dfrac{a}{1 - r}$, the first term is $a = 1$

and the common ratio is $r = -(x - 4)$.

Series: $1 - (x - 4) + (x - 4)^2 - \cdots + (-1)^n(x - 4)^n + \cdots$

Interval: The series converges when $|x - 4| < 1$, so the

interval of convergence is $(3, 5)$.

46. Comparing $\dfrac{1}{4}\left(\dfrac{1}{1 + (x - 1)}\right)$ with $\dfrac{a}{1 - r}$, the first term is

$a = \dfrac{1}{4}$ and the common ratio is $r = -(x - 1) = 1 - x$.

Series:

$\dfrac{1}{4} - \dfrac{1}{4}(x - 1) + \dfrac{1}{4}(x - 1)^2 - \cdots + \dfrac{1}{4}(-1)^n(x - 1)^n + \cdots$

Interval: The series converges when $|x - 1| < 1$, so the

interval of convergence is $(0, 2)$.

47. Rewriting $\dfrac{1}{2 - x}$ as $\dfrac{1}{1 - (x - 1)}$ and comparing with $\dfrac{a}{1 - r}$,

The first term is $a = 1$ and the common ratio is $r = x - 1$.

Series: $1 + (x - 1) + (x - 1)^2 + \cdots + (x - 1)^n + \cdots$

Interval: The series converges when $|x - 1| < 1$, so the

interval of convergence is $(0, 2)$.

Alternate solution:

Rewriting $\dfrac{1}{2 - x}$ as $\dfrac{1}{2}\left(\dfrac{1}{1 - \left(\dfrac{x}{2}\right)}\right)$ and comparing with $\dfrac{a}{1 - r}$,

the first is $a = \dfrac{1}{2}$ and the common ratio is $r = \dfrac{x}{2}$.

Series: $\dfrac{1}{2} + \dfrac{1}{4}x + \dfrac{1}{8}x^2 + \cdots + \dfrac{1}{2^{n+1}}x^n + \cdots$

Interval: The series converges when $\left|\dfrac{x}{2}\right| < 1$, so the interval

of convergence is $(-2, 2)$.

48. $1 + e^b + e^{2b} + e^{3b} + \cdots = \sum\limits_{n=0}^{\infty} (e^b)^n$

$\phantom{1 + e^b + e^{2b} + e^{3b} + \cdots} = \dfrac{1}{1 - e^b} = 9$

$1 = 9 - 9e^b$

$9e^b = 8$

$e^b = \dfrac{8}{9}$

$b = \ln\left(\dfrac{8}{9}\right) = \ln 8 - \ln 9$

49. (a) When $t = 1$, $S = \sum_{n=0}^{\infty} \left(\frac{1}{2}\right)^n = \frac{1}{1 - \left(\frac{1}{2}\right)} = 2$.

(b) S converges when $\left|\frac{t}{1+t}\right| <$ 1, or $|t| < |1 + t|$.

For $t < -1$, this inequality is equivalent to

$-t < -(1 + t)$, which is always false.

For $-1 \leq t < 0$, the inequality is equivalent to

$-t < 1 + t$, which is true when $t > -\frac{1}{2}$.

For $t \geq 0$, the inequality is equivalent to $t < 1 + t$,

which is always true.

Thus, S converges for all $t > -\frac{1}{2}$.

(c) For $t > -\frac{1}{2}$, we have

$S = \sum_{n=0}^{\infty} \left(\frac{t}{1+t}\right)^n = \frac{1}{1 - \frac{t}{1+t}} = \frac{1+t}{(1+t)-t} = 1 + t$, so

$S > 10$ when $t > 9$.

50. (a) Comparing $f(t) = \frac{4}{1+t^2}$ with $\frac{a}{1-r}$, the first term

is $a = 4$ and the common ratio is $r = -t^2$.

First four terms: $4 - 4t^2 + 4t^4 - 4t^6$

General term: $(-1)^n(4t^{2n})$

(b) Note that $G(0) = 0$, so the constant term of the power

series for $G(x)$ will be 0. Integrate the terms for $f(x)$ to

obtain the terms for $G(x)$.

First four terms: $4x - \frac{4}{3}x^3 + \frac{4}{5}x^5 - \frac{4}{7}x^7$

General term: $(-1)^n\left(\frac{4}{2n+1}\right)x^{2n+1}$

(c) The series in part (a) converges when $|-t^2| < 1$, so the

interval of convergence is $(-1, 1)$.

(d) The two numbers are $x = \pm 1$, which result in the

convergent series

$G(1) = 4 - \frac{4}{3} + \frac{4}{5} - \frac{4}{7} + \cdots + (-1)^n\left(\frac{4}{2n+1}\right) + \cdots$

and

$G(-1)$

$= -4 + \frac{4}{3} - \frac{4}{5} + \frac{4}{7} - \cdots + (-1)^{n-1}\left(\frac{4}{2n+1}\right) + \cdots$,

respectively.

51. Since $\frac{1}{x} = 1 - (x - 1) + (x - 1)^2 - (x - 1)^3 + \cdots +$

$(-1)^n(x-1)^n + \cdots$, we may write $\ln x = \int_1^x \frac{1}{t}\, dt$

$= x - 1 - \frac{(x-1)^2}{2} + \frac{(x-1)^3}{3} - \frac{(x-1)^4}{4} + \cdots$

$+ \frac{(-1)^n(x-1)^n}{n}$

52. To determine our starting point, we note that

$\int f(x)\, dx = \int 2(1 - x)^{-3}\, dx = (1 - x)^{-2} + C$.

Using the result from Example 4, we have:

$(1 - x)^{-2} = 1 + 2x + 3x^2 + 4x^3 + \cdots + nx^{n-1} + \cdots$

$\frac{d}{dx}(1 - x)^{-2} = \frac{d}{dx}(1 + 2x + 3x^2 + 4x^3 + \cdots$

$+ nx^{n-1} + \cdots)$

$2(1 - x)^{-3} = 0 + 2 + 6x + 12x^2 + \cdots + n(n-1)x^{n-2} + \cdots$

Thus, $f(x) = 2 + 6x + 12x^2 + \cdots + n(n - 1)x^{n-2} + \cdots$.

Replacing n by $n + 2$, this may be written as

$f(x) = 2 + 6x + 12x^2 + (n + 2)(n + 1)x^n + \cdots$.

Interval: The series converges when $|x| < 1$, so the interval

of convergence is $(-1, 1)$.

53. (a) No, because if you differentiate it again, you would

have the original series for f, but by Theorem 1, that

would have to converge for $-2 < x < 2$, which

contradicts the assumption that the original series

converges only for $-1 < x < 1$.

(b) No, because if you integrate it again, you would have

the original series for f, but by Theorem 2, that would

have to converge for $-2 < x < 2$, which contradicts

the assumption that the original series converges only

for $-1 < x < 1$.

54. Let $L = \lim_{n\to\infty} a_n$. Then by definition of convergence, for $\frac{\epsilon}{2}$

there corresponds an N such that for all m and n,

$n, m > N \Rightarrow |a_m - L| < \frac{\epsilon}{2}$ and $|a_n - L| < \frac{\epsilon}{2}$.

Now,

$|a_m - a_n| = |a_m - L + L - a_n|$

$\leq |a_m - L| + |a_n - L| < \frac{\epsilon}{2} + \frac{\epsilon}{2} = \epsilon$

whenever $m > N$ and $n > N$.

55. Given an $\epsilon > 0$, by definition of convergence there corresponds an N such that for all $n < N$, $|L_1 - a_n| < \epsilon$ and $|L_2 - a_n| < \epsilon$. (There is one such number for each series, and we may let N be the larger of the two numbers.) Now

$$|L_2 - L_1| = |L_2 - a_n + a_n - L_1|$$
$$\leq |L_2 - a_n| + |a_n - L_1|$$
$$< \epsilon + \epsilon$$
$$= 2\epsilon.$$

$|L_2 - L_1| < 2\epsilon$ says that the difference between two fixed values is smaller than any positive number 2ϵ. The only nonnegative number smaller than every positive number is 0, so $|L_2 - L_1| = 0$ or $L_1 = L_2$.

56. Consider the two subsequences $a_{k(n)}$ and $a_{i(n)}$, where $\lim\limits_{n \to \infty} a_{k(n)} = L_1$, $\lim\limits_{n \to \infty} a_{i(n)} = L_2$, and $L_1 \neq L_2$. Given an $\epsilon > 0$ there corresponds an N_1 such that for $k(n) > N_1$, $|a_{k(n)} - L_1| < \epsilon$, and an N_2 such that for $i(n) > N_2$, $|a_{i(n)} - L_2| < \epsilon$. Assume a_n converges.

Let $N = \max\{N_1, N_2\}$. Then for $n > N$, we have that $|a_n - L_1| < \epsilon$ and $|a_n - L_2| < \epsilon$ for infinitely many n. This implies that $\lim\limits_{n \to \infty} a_n = L_1$ and $\lim\limits_{n \to \infty} a_n = L_2$ where $L_1 \neq L_2$. Since the limit of a sequence is unique (by Exercise 55), a_n does not converge and hence diverges.

57. **(a)** $\lim\limits_{n \to \infty} \dfrac{3n + 1}{n + 1} = 3$

(b) The line $y = 3$ is a horizontal asymptote of the graph of the function $f(x) = \dfrac{3x + 1}{x + 1}$, which means $\lim\limits_{x \to \infty} f(x) = 3$. Because $f(n) = a_n$ for all positive integers n, it follows that $\lim\limits_{n \to \infty} a_n$ must also be 3.

■ Section 9.2 Taylor Series (pp. 469–479)

Exploration 1   Designing a Polynomial to Specifications

1. Since $P(0) = 1$, we know that the constant coefficient is 1.

Since $P'(0) = 2$, we know that the coefficient of x is 2.

Since $P''(0) = 3$, we know that the coefficient of x^2 is $\dfrac{3}{2}$.

(The 2 in the denominator is needed to cancel the factor of 2 that results from differentiating x^2.) Similarly, we find the coefficients of x^3 and x^4 to be $\dfrac{4}{6}$ and $\dfrac{5}{24}$.

Thus, $P(x) = 1 + 2x + \dfrac{3}{2}x^2 + \dfrac{4}{6}x^3 + \dfrac{5}{24}x^4$.

Exploration 2   A Power Series for the Cosine

1. $\cos(0) = 1$
$\cos'(0) = -\sin(0) = 0$
$\cos''(0) = -\cos(0) = -1$
$\cos^{(3)}(0) = \sin(0) = 0$
etc.

The pattern $1, 0, -1, 0$ will repeat forever. Therefore,

$P_6(x) = 1 - \dfrac{x^2}{2} + \dfrac{x^4}{4!} - \dfrac{x^6}{6!}$, and the Taylor series is

$1 - \dfrac{x^2}{2} + \dfrac{x^4}{4!} - \dfrac{x^6}{6!} + \cdots + (-1)^n \dfrac{x^{2n}}{(2n)!} + \cdots$.

2. A clever shortcut is simply to differentiate the previously-discovered series for $\sin x$ term-by-term!

Exploration 3   Approximating sin 13

1. $0.4201670368\ldots$

4. 20 terms.

Quick Review 9.2

1. $f(x) = e^{2x}$
$f'(x) = 2e^{2x}$
$f''(x) = 4e^{2x}$
$f'''(x) = 8e^{2x}$
$f^{(n)}(x) = 2^n e^{2x}$

2. $f(x) = \dfrac{1}{x - 1}$

$f'(x) = -(x - 1)^{-2}$

$f''(x) = 2(x - 1)^{-3}$

$f'''(x) = -6(x - 1)^{-4}$

$f^{(n)}(x) = (-1)^n n!(x - 1)^{-(n+1)}$

3. $f(x) = 3^x$
$f'(x) = 3^x \ln 3$
$f''(x) = 3^x (\ln 3)^2$
$f'''(x) = 3^x (\ln 3)^3$
$f^{(n)}(x) = 3^x (\ln 3)^n$

4. $f(x) = \ln x$
$f'(x) = x^{-1}$
$f''(x) = -x^{-2}$
$f'''(x) = 2x^{-3}$
$f^{(4)}(x) = -6x^{-4}$
$f^{(n)}(x) = (-1)^{n-1}(n - 1)!x^{-n}$ for $n \geq 1$

5. $f(x) = x^n$

$f'(x) = nx^{n-1}$

$f''(x) = n(n - 1)x^{n-2}$

$f'''(x) = n(n - 1)(n - 2)x^{n-3}$

$f^{(k)}(x) = \dfrac{n!}{(n - k)!}x^{n-k}$

$f^{(n)}(x) = \dfrac{n!}{0!}x^0 = n!$

6. $\dfrac{dy}{dx} = \dfrac{d}{dx} \dfrac{x^n}{n!} = \dfrac{nx^{n-1}}{n!} = \dfrac{x^{n-1}}{(n - 1)!}$

7. $\dfrac{dy}{dx} = \dfrac{d}{dx} \dfrac{2^n(x - a)^n}{n!} = \dfrac{2^n n(x - a)^{n-1}}{n!} = \dfrac{2^n(x - a)^{n-1}}{(n - 1)!}$

8. $\dfrac{dy}{dx} = \dfrac{d}{dx}\left[(-1)^n\dfrac{x^{2n+1}}{(2n+1)!}\right] = (-1)^n\dfrac{(2n+1)x^{2n}}{(2n+1)!} = \dfrac{(-1)^nx^{2n}}{(2n)!}$

9. $\dfrac{dy}{dx} = \dfrac{d}{dx}\dfrac{(x+a)^{2n}}{(2n)!} = \dfrac{2n(x+a)^{2n-1}}{(2n)!} = \dfrac{(x+a)^{2n-1}}{(2n-1)!}$

10. $\dfrac{dy}{dx} = \dfrac{d}{dx}\dfrac{(1-x)^n}{n!} = \dfrac{n(1-x)^{n-1}(-1)}{n!} = -\dfrac{(1-x)^{n-1}}{(n-1)!}$

Section 9.2 Exercises

1. Substitute $2x$ for x in the Maclaurin series for $\sin x$ shown at the end of Section 9.2.

$\sin 2x = 2x - \dfrac{(2x)^3}{3!} + \dfrac{(2x)^5}{5!} - \cdots + (-1)^n\dfrac{(2x)^{2n+1}}{(2n+1)!} + \cdots$

$\qquad = 2x - \dfrac{4x^3}{3} + \dfrac{4x^5}{15} - \cdots + \dfrac{(-1)^n(2x)^{2n+1}}{(2n+1)!} + \cdots$

This series converges for all real x.

2. Substitute $-x$ for x in the Maclaurin series for $\ln(1+x)$ shown at the end of Section 9.2.

$\ln(1-x) = (-x) - \dfrac{(-x)^2}{2} + \dfrac{(-x)^3}{3} - \cdots$
$\qquad\qquad + (-1)^{n-1}\dfrac{(-x)^n}{n} + \cdots$

$\qquad\quad = -x - \dfrac{x^2}{2} - \dfrac{x^3}{3} - \cdots - \dfrac{x^n}{n} - \cdots$

This series converges when $-1 \le -x < 1$, so the interval of convergence is $[-1, 1)$.

3. Substitute x^2 for x in the Maclaurin series for $\tan^{-1} x$ shown at the end of Section 9.2.

$\tan^{-1} x^2 = x^2 - \dfrac{(x^2)^3}{3} + \dfrac{(x^2)^5}{5} - \cdots + (-1)^n\dfrac{(x^2)^{2n+1}}{2n+1} + \cdots$

$\qquad\quad = x^2 - \dfrac{x^6}{3} + \dfrac{x^{10}}{5} - \cdots + \dfrac{(-1)^nx^{4n+2}}{2n+1} + \cdots$

This series converges when $\left|x^2\right| \le 1$, so the interval of convergence is $[-1, 1]$.

4. $7xe^x = 7x\left(1 + x + \dfrac{x^2}{2!} + \cdots + \dfrac{x^n}{n!} + \cdots\right)$

$\qquad = 7x + 7x^2 + \dfrac{7x^3}{2!} + \cdots + \dfrac{7x^{n+1}}{n!}$

This series converges for all real x.

5. $\cos(x+2) = (\cos 2)(\cos x) - (\sin 2)(\sin x)$

$= (\cos 2)\left[1 - \dfrac{x^2}{2!} + \dfrac{x^4}{4!} - \cdots + (-1)^n\dfrac{x^{2n}}{(2n)!} + \cdots\right]$

$\quad - (\sin 2)\left[x - \dfrac{x^3}{3!} + \dfrac{x^5}{5!} - \cdots + (-1)^n\dfrac{x^{2n+1}}{(2n+1)!} + \cdots\right]$

$= (\cos 2) - (\sin 2)x - \dfrac{(\cos 2)x^2}{2!} + \dfrac{(\sin 2)x^3}{3!} + \dfrac{(\cos 2)x^4}{4!}$

$\quad - \dfrac{(\sin 2)x^5}{5!} - \cdots$

We need to write an expression for the coefficient of x^k.

If k is even, the coefficient is $\dfrac{(-1)^n(\cos 2)}{(2n)!}$ where $2n = k$.

Thus the coefficient is

$\dfrac{(-1)^{k/2}(\cos 2)}{k!}$, which is the same as $\dfrac{(-1)^{\mathrm{int}[(k+1)/2]}(\cos 2)}{k!}$.

If k is odd, the coefficient is $\dfrac{(-1)^{n+1}(\sin 2)}{(2n+1)!}$ where

$2n + 1 = k$. Thus the coefficient is

$\dfrac{(-1)^{(k+1)/2}(\sin 2)}{(2n+1)!}$, which is the same as $\dfrac{(-1)^{\mathrm{int}[(k+1)/2]}(\cos 2)}{k!}$.

Hence the general term is $\dfrac{(-1)^A Bx^n}{n!}$, where $A = \mathrm{int}\left(\dfrac{n+1}{2}\right)$,

and $B = \sin 2$ if n is odd and

$B = \cos 2$ if n is even.

Another way to handle the general term is to observe that

$-\sin 2 = \cos\left(2 + \dfrac{\pi}{2}\right), \ -\cos 2 = \cos(2 + \pi)$,

and so on, so the general term is $\left[\dfrac{1}{n!}\cos\left(2 + \dfrac{n\pi}{2}\right)\right]x^n$.

The series converges for all real x.

6. $x^2\cos x = x^2\left(1 - \dfrac{x^2}{2!} + \dfrac{x^4}{4!} - \cdots + (-1)^n\dfrac{x^{2n}}{(2n)!} + \cdots\right)$

$\qquad\quad = x^2 - \dfrac{x^4}{2} + \dfrac{x^6}{24} - \cdots + \dfrac{(-1)^nx^{2n+2}}{(2n)!} + \cdots$

The series converges for all real x.

7. Factor out x and substitute x^3 for x in the Maclaurin series for $\dfrac{1}{1-x}$ shown at the end of Section 9.2.

$\dfrac{x}{1-x^3} = x\left(\dfrac{1}{1-x^3}\right)$

$\qquad = x[1 + x^3 + (x^3)^2 + \cdots + (x^3)^n + \cdots]$

$\qquad = x + x^4 + x^7 + \cdots + x^{3n+1} + \cdots$

The series converges for $\left|x^3\right| < 1$, so the interval of convergence is $(-1, 1)$.

8. Substitute $-2x$ for x in the Maclaurin series for e^x shown at the end of Section 9.2.

$$e^{-2x} = 1 + (-2x) + \frac{(-2x)^2}{2!} + \cdots + \frac{(-2x)^n}{n!} + \cdots$$
$$= 1 - 2x + 2x^2 - \cdots + \frac{(-1)^n 2^n x^n}{n!} + \cdots$$

The series converges for all real x.

9. $f(2) = \left.\dfrac{1}{x}\right|_{x=2} = \dfrac{1}{2}$

$f'(2) = \left.-x^{-2}\right|_{x=2} = -\dfrac{1}{4}$

$f''(2) = \left.2x^{-3}\right|_{x=2} = \dfrac{1}{4}$, so $\dfrac{f''(2)}{2!} = \dfrac{1}{8}$

$f'''(2) = \left.-6x^{-4}\right|_{x=2} = -\dfrac{3}{8}$, so $\dfrac{f'''(2)}{3!} = -\dfrac{1}{16}$

$P_0(x) = \dfrac{1}{2}$

$P_1(x) = \dfrac{1}{2} - \dfrac{x-2}{4}$

$P_2(x) = \dfrac{1}{2} - \dfrac{x-2}{4} + \dfrac{(x-2)^2}{8}$

$P_3(x) = \dfrac{1}{2} - \dfrac{x-2}{4} + \dfrac{(x-2)^2}{8} - \dfrac{(x-2)^3}{16}$

10. $f\left(\dfrac{\pi}{4}\right) = \left.\sin x\right|_{x=\pi/4} = \dfrac{\sqrt{2}}{2}$

$f'\left(\dfrac{\pi}{4}\right) = \left.\cos x\right|_{x=\pi/4} = \dfrac{\sqrt{2}}{2}$

$f''\left(\dfrac{\pi}{4}\right) = \left.-\sin x\right|_{x=\pi/4} = -\dfrac{\sqrt{2}}{2}$, so $\dfrac{f''\left(\frac{\pi}{4}\right)}{2!} = -\dfrac{\sqrt{2}}{4}$

$f'''\left(\dfrac{\pi}{4}\right) = \left.-\cos x\right|_{x=\pi/4} = -\dfrac{\sqrt{2}}{2}$, so $\dfrac{f'''\left(\frac{\pi}{4}\right)}{3!} = -\dfrac{\sqrt{2}}{12}$

$P_0(x) = \dfrac{\sqrt{2}}{2}$

$P_1(x) = \dfrac{\sqrt{2}}{2} + \left(\dfrac{\sqrt{2}}{2}\right)\left(x - \dfrac{\pi}{4}\right)$

$P_2(x) = \dfrac{\sqrt{2}}{2} + \left(\dfrac{\sqrt{2}}{2}\right)\left(x - \dfrac{\pi}{4}\right) - \left(\dfrac{\sqrt{2}}{4}\right)\left(x - \dfrac{\pi}{4}\right)^2$

$P_3(x) = \dfrac{\sqrt{2}}{2} + \left(\dfrac{\sqrt{2}}{2}\right)\left(x - \dfrac{\pi}{4}\right) - \left(\dfrac{\sqrt{2}}{4}\right)\left(x - \dfrac{\pi}{4}\right)^2$
$\qquad - \left(\dfrac{\sqrt{2}}{12}\right)\left(x - \dfrac{\pi}{4}\right)^3$

11. $f\left(\dfrac{\pi}{4}\right) = \left.\cos x\right|_{x=\pi/4} = \dfrac{\sqrt{2}}{2}$

$f'\left(\dfrac{\pi}{4}\right) = \left.-\sin x\right|_{x=\pi/4} = -\dfrac{\sqrt{2}}{2}$

$f''\left(\dfrac{\pi}{4}\right) = \left.-\cos x\right|_{x=\pi/4} = -\dfrac{\sqrt{2}}{2}$, so $\dfrac{f''\left(\frac{\pi}{4}\right)}{2!} = -\dfrac{\sqrt{2}}{4}$

$f'''\left(\dfrac{\pi}{4}\right) = \left.\sin x\right|_{x=\pi/4} = \dfrac{\sqrt{2}}{2}$, so $\dfrac{f'''\left(\frac{\pi}{4}\right)}{3!} = \dfrac{\sqrt{2}}{12}$

$P_0(x) = \dfrac{\sqrt{2}}{2}$

$P_1(x) = \dfrac{\sqrt{2}}{2} - \left(\dfrac{\sqrt{2}}{2}\right)\left(x - \dfrac{\pi}{4}\right)$

$P_2(x) = \dfrac{\sqrt{2}}{2} - \left(\dfrac{\sqrt{2}}{2}\right)\left(x - \dfrac{\pi}{4}\right) - \left(\dfrac{\sqrt{2}}{4}\right)\left(x - \dfrac{\pi}{4}\right)^2$

$P_3(x) = \dfrac{\sqrt{2}}{2} - \left(\dfrac{\sqrt{2}}{2}\right)\left(x - \dfrac{\pi}{4}\right) - \left(\dfrac{\sqrt{2}}{4}\right)\left(x - \dfrac{\pi}{4}\right)^2$
$\qquad + \left(\dfrac{\sqrt{2}}{12}\right)\left(x - \dfrac{\pi}{4}\right)^3$

12. $f(4) = \left.x^{1/2}\right|_{x=4} = 2$

$f'(4) = \left.\dfrac{1}{2}x^{-1/2}\right|_{x=4} = \dfrac{1}{4}$

$f''(4) = \left.-\dfrac{1}{4}x^{-3/2}\right|_{x=4} = -\dfrac{1}{32}$, so $\dfrac{f''(4)}{2!} = -\dfrac{1}{64}$

$f'''(4) = \left.\dfrac{3}{8}x^{-5/2}\right|_{x=4} = \dfrac{3}{256}$, so $\dfrac{f'''(4)}{3!} = \dfrac{1}{512}$

$P_0(x) = 2$

$P_1(x) = 2 + \dfrac{x-4}{4}$

$P_2(x) = 2 + \dfrac{x-4}{4} - \dfrac{(x-4)^2}{64}$

$P_3(x) = 2 + \dfrac{x-4}{4} - \dfrac{(x-4)^2}{64} + \dfrac{(x-4)^3}{512}$

13. (a) Since f is a cubic polynomial, it is its own Taylor polynomial of order 3.
$$P_3(x) = x^3 - 2x + 4 \text{ or } 4 - 2x + x^3$$

(b) $f(1) = \left.x^3 - 2x + 4\right|_{x=1} = 3$

$f'(1) = \left.3x^2 - 2\right|_{x=1} = 1$

$f''(1) = \left.6x\right|_{x=1} = 6$, so $\dfrac{f''(1)}{2!} = 3$

$f'''(1) = \left.6\right|_{x=1} = 6$, so $\dfrac{f'''(1)}{3!} = 1$

$P_3(x) = 3 + (x-1) + 3(x-1)^2 + (x-1)^3$

14. (a) Since f is a cubic polynomial, it is its own Taylor polynomial of order 3.
$$P_3(x) = 2x^3 + x^2 + 3x - 8 \text{ or } -8 + 3x + x^2 + 2x^3$$

(b) $f(1) = \left.2x^3 + x^2 + 3x - 8\right|_{x=1} = -2$

$f'(1) = \left.6x^2 + 2x + 3\right|_{x=1} = 11$

$f''(1) = \left.12x + 2\right|_{x=1} = 14$, so $\dfrac{f''(1)}{2!} = 7$

$f'''(1) = \left.12\right|_{x=1} = 12$, so $\dfrac{f'(1)}{3!} = 2$

$P_3(x) = -2 + 11(x-1) + 7(x-1)^2 + 2(x-1)^3$

15. (a) Since $f(0) = f'(0) = f''(0) = f'''(0) = 0$, the Taylor polynomial of order 3 is $P_3(0) = 0$.

(b) $f(1) = \left.x^4\right|_{x=1} = 1$

$f'(1) = \left.4x^3\right|_{x=1} = 4$

$f''(1) = \left.12x^2\right|_{x=1} = 12$, so $\dfrac{f''(1)}{2!} = 6$

$f'''(1) = \left.24x\right|_{x=1} = 24$, so $\dfrac{f'''(1)}{3!} = 4$

$P_3(x) = 1 + 4(x-1) + 6(x-1)^2 + 4(x-1)^3$

16. (a) $P_3(x) = 4 + 5x + \dfrac{-8}{2!}x^2 + \dfrac{6}{3!}x^3$

$\qquad = 4 + 5x - 4x^2 + x^3$

$f(0.2) \approx P_3(0.2) = 4.848$

16. continued

(b) Since the Taylor series of $f'(x)$ can be obtained by differentiating the terms of the Taylor series of $f(x)$, the second order Taylor polynomial of $f'(x)$ is given by $5 - 8x + 3x^2$. Evaluating at $x = 0.2$,

$$f'(0.2) \approx 3.52$$

17. (a) $P_3(x) = 4 + (-1)(x - 1) + \dfrac{3}{2!}(x - 1)^2 + \dfrac{2}{3!}(x - 1)^3$

$$= 4 - (x - 1) + \frac{3}{2}(x - 1)^2 + \frac{1}{3}(x - 1)^3$$

$$f(1.2) \approx P_3(1.2) \approx 3.863$$

(b) Since the Taylor series of $f'(x)$ can be obtained by differentiating the terms of the Taylor series of $f(x)$, the second order Taylor polynomial of $f'(x)$ is given by $-1 + 3(x - 1) + (x - 1)^2$. Evaluating at $x = 1.2$,

$$f'(1.2) \approx -0.36$$

18. (a) Since $f'(0)x = \dfrac{x}{2!}, f'(0) = \dfrac{1}{2!} = \dfrac{1}{2}$.

Since $\dfrac{f^{(10)}(0)}{10!}x^{10} = \dfrac{x^{10}}{11!}, f^{(10)}(0) = \dfrac{10!}{11!} = \dfrac{1}{11}$.

(b) Multiply each term of $f(x)$ by x.

$$g(x) = x + \frac{x^2}{2!} + \frac{x^3}{3!} + \frac{x^4}{4!} + \cdots + \frac{x^{n+1}}{(n + 1)!} + \cdots$$

(c) $g(x) = e^x - 1$

19. (a) Substitute $\dfrac{x}{2}$ for x in the Maclaurin series for e^x shown at the end of Section 9.2

$$e^{x/2} = 1 + \frac{x}{2} + \frac{\left(\frac{x}{2}\right)^2}{2} + \cdots + \frac{\left(\frac{x}{2}\right)^n}{n!} + \cdots$$

$$= 1 + \frac{x}{2} + \frac{x^2}{8} + \cdots + \frac{x^n}{2^n \cdot n!}$$

(b) $g(x) = \dfrac{e^x - 1}{x}$

$$= \frac{1}{x}\left[\left(1 + x + \frac{x^2}{2!} + \frac{x^3}{3!} + \cdots + \frac{x^n}{n!} + \cdots\right) - 1\right]$$

$$= \frac{1}{x}\left(x + \frac{x^2}{2!} + \frac{x^3}{3!} + \cdots + \frac{x^n}{n!} + \cdots\right)$$

$$= 1 + \frac{x}{2!} + \frac{x^2}{3!} + \cdots + \frac{x^{n-1}}{n!} + \cdots$$

This can also be written as

$$1 + \frac{x}{2!} + \frac{x^2}{3!} + \cdots + \frac{x^n}{(n + 1)!} + \cdots.$$

(c) $g'(x) = \dfrac{d}{dx}\dfrac{e^x - 1}{x} = \dfrac{(x)(e^x) - (e^x - 1)(1)}{x^2}$

$$= \frac{xe^x - e^x + 1}{x^2}$$

$$g'(1) = \frac{e - e + 1}{1} = 1$$

From the series,

$$g'(x) = \frac{d}{dx}\left(1 + \frac{x}{2!} + \frac{x^2}{3!} + \frac{x^3}{4!} + \cdots + \frac{x^n}{(n + 1)!} + \cdots\right)$$

$$= \frac{1}{2!} + \frac{2x}{3!} + \frac{3x^2}{4!} + \cdots + \frac{nx^{n-1}}{(n + 1)!} + \cdots$$

$$= \sum_{n=1}^{\infty} \frac{nx^{n-1}}{(n + 1)!}$$

Therefore, $g'(1) = \displaystyle\sum_{n=1}^{\infty} \frac{n}{(n + 1)!}$, which means

$$\sum_{n=1}^{\infty} \frac{n}{(n + 1)!} = 1.$$

20. (a) Factor out 2 and substitute t^2 for x in the Maclaurin series for $\dfrac{1}{1 - x}$ at the end of Section 9.2.

$$f(t) = \frac{2}{1 - t^2}$$

$$= 2\left(\frac{1}{1 - t^2}\right)$$

$$= 2[1 + t^2 + (t^2)^2 + (t^2)^3 + \cdots + (t^2)^n + \cdots]$$

$$= 2 + 2t^2 + 2t^4 + 2t^6 + \cdots + 2t^{2n} + \cdots$$

(b) Since $G(0) = 0$, the constant term is zero and we may find $G(x)$ by integrating the terms of the series for $f(x)$.

$$G(x) = 2x + \frac{2x^3}{3} + \frac{2x^5}{5} + \frac{2x^7}{7} + \cdots + \frac{2x^{2n+1}}{2n + 1} + \cdots$$

21. (a) $f(0) = (1 + x)^{1/2}\big|_{x=0} = 1$

$$f'(0) = \frac{1}{2}(1 + x)^{-1/2}\Big|_{x=0} = \frac{1}{2}$$

$$f''(0) = -\frac{1}{4}(1 + x)^{-3/2}\Big|_{x=0} = -\frac{1}{4}, \text{ so } \frac{f''(0)}{2!} = -\frac{1}{8}$$

$$f'''(0) = \frac{3}{8}(1 + x)^{-5/2}\Big|_{x=0} = \frac{3}{8}, \text{ so } \frac{f'''(0)}{3!} = \frac{1}{16}$$

$$P_4(x) = 1 + \frac{x}{2} - \frac{x^2}{8} + \frac{x^3}{16}$$

(b) Since $g(x) = f(x^2)$, the first four terms are

$$1 + \frac{x^2}{2} - \frac{x^4}{8} + \frac{x^6}{16}.$$

(c) Since $h(0) = 5$, the constant term is 5. The next three terms are obtained by integrating the first three terms of the answer to part (b). The first four terms of the series for $h(x)$ are $5 + x + \dfrac{x^3}{6} - \dfrac{x^5}{40}$.

22. (a) $a_0 = 1$

$$a_1 = \frac{3}{1}a_0 = 3 \cdot 1 = 3$$

$$a_2 = \frac{3}{2}a_1 = \frac{3}{2} \cdot 3 = \frac{9}{2}$$

$$a_3 = \frac{3}{3}a_2 = a_2 = \frac{9}{2}$$

Since each term is obtained by multiplying the previous

term by $\frac{3}{n}$, $a_n = \frac{3^n}{n!}$.

$$\sum_{n=0}^{\infty} a_n x^n = 1 + 3x + \frac{9}{2}x^2 + \frac{9}{2}x^3 + \cdots + \frac{3^n}{n!}x^n + \cdots$$

(b) Since the series can be written as $\displaystyle\sum_{n=0}^{\infty} \frac{(3x)^n}{n!}$, it represents

the function $f(x) = e^{3x}$.

(c) $f'(1) = 3e^{3x}\Big|_{x=1} = 3e^3$

23. First, note that $\cos 18 \approx 0.6603$.

Using $\cos x = \displaystyle\sum_{n=0}^{\infty} (-1)^n \frac{x^{2n}}{(2n)!}$, enter the following two-step

commands on your home screen and continue to hit

ENTER.

```
0→N:1→T
                        1
N+1→N:T+(-1)^N*1
8^(2N)/(2N)!→T
                     -161
                     4213
                  -43026.2
■
```

The sum corresponding to $N = 25$ is about 0.6582 (not within 0.001 of the exact value), and the sum corresponding to $N = 26$ is about 0.6606, which is within 0.001 of the exact value. Since we began with $N = 0$, it takes a total of 27 terms (or, up to and including the 52nd degree term).

24. One possible answer: Because the end behavior of a polynomial must be unbounded and $\sin x$ is not unbounded. Another: Because $\sin x$ has an infinite number of local extrema, but a polynomial can have only a finite number.

25. (1) $\sin x$ is odd and $\cos x$ is even
(2) $\sin 0 = 0$ and $\cos 0 = 1$

26. Replace x by $3x$ in series for $\sin x$. Therefore, we have

$\dfrac{(3x)^5}{5!}$ so $\dfrac{3^5}{5!} = \dfrac{81}{40}$.

27. Since $\dfrac{d^3}{dx^3} \ln x = 2x^{-3}$, which is $\dfrac{1}{4}$ at $x = 2$, the coefficient

is $\dfrac{\frac{1}{4}}{3!} = \dfrac{1}{24}$.

28. The linearization of f at a is the first order Taylor polynomial generated by f at $x = a$.

29. (a) Since $f'(x) = \dfrac{d}{dx} \dfrac{4x}{x^2 + 1}$

$$= \frac{(x^2 + 1)(4) - (4x)(2x)}{(x^2 + 1)^2}$$

$$= \frac{4 - 4x^2}{(x^2 + 1)^2},$$

we have $f(0) = 0$, $f'(0) = 4$, $f(\sqrt{3}) = \sqrt{3}$ and

$f'(\sqrt{3}) = -\dfrac{1}{2}$, so the linearizations are $L_1(x) = 4x$ and

$$L_2(x) = \sqrt{3} - \frac{1}{2}(x - \sqrt{3}) = -\frac{1}{2}x + \frac{3}{2}\sqrt{3},$$

respectively.

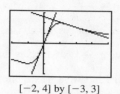

[−2, 4] by [−3, 3]

(b) $f''(a)$ must be 0 because of the inflection point, so the second degree term in the Taylor series of f at $x = a$ is zero.

30. The series represents $\tan^{-1} x$. When $x = 1$, it converges to

$\tan^{-1} 1 = \dfrac{\pi}{4}$. When $x = -1$, it converges to

$\tan^{-1}(-1) = -\dfrac{\pi}{4}$.

31. (a) $f(x) = \dfrac{1}{x}(\sin x)$

$$= \frac{1}{x}\left(x - \frac{x^3}{3!} + \frac{x^5}{5!} - \cdots + (-1)^n\frac{x^{2n+1}}{(2n+1)!} + \cdots\right)$$

$$= 1 - \frac{x^2}{3!} + \frac{x^4}{5!} - \cdots + (-1)^n\frac{x^{2n}}{(2n+1)!} + \cdots$$

(b) Because f is undefined at $x = 0$.

(c) $k = 1$

32. Note that the Maclaurin series for $\dfrac{1}{1-x}$ is

$1 + x + x^2 + \cdots + x^n + \cdots$. If we differentiate this series

and multiply by x, we obtain the desired Maclaurin series

$x + 2x^2 + 3x^3 + \cdots + nx^n + \cdots$. Therefore, the desired

function is

$$f(x) = x\frac{d}{dx}\frac{1}{1-x} = x\frac{1}{(1-x)^2} = \frac{x}{(x-1)^2}.$$

33. (a) $f(x) = (1 + x)^m$

$$f'(x) = m(1 + x)^{m-1}$$

$$f''(x) = m(m-1)(1 + x)^{m-2}$$

$$f'''(x) = m(m-1)(m-2)(1 + x)^{m-3}$$

(b) Differentiating $f(x)$ k times gives
$f^{(k)}(x) = m(m-1)(m-2) \cdots (m - k + 1)(1 + x)^{m-k}$.
Substituting 0 for x, we have
$f^{(k)}(0) = m(m-1)(m-2) \cdots (m - k + 1)$.

33. continued

(c) The coefficient is

$$\frac{f^{(k)}(0)}{k!} = \frac{m(m-1)(m-2)\cdots(m-k+1)}{k!}$$

(d) $f(0) = 1, f'(0) = m$, and we're done by part (c).

34. Because $f(x) = (1+x)^m$ is a polynomial of degree m. Alternately, observe that $f^{(k)}(0) = 0$ for $k \geq m+1$.

■ Section 9.3 Taylor's Theorem (pp. 480–487)

Exploration 1   Your Turn

1. We need to consider what happens to $R_n(x)$ as $n \to \infty$. By Taylor's Theorem, $R_n(x) = \frac{f^{(n+1)}(c)}{(n+1)!}(x-0)^n$, where $f^{(n+1)}(c)$ is the $(n+1)$st derivative of cos x evaluated at some c between x and 0. As with sin x, we can say that $f^{(n+1)}(c)$ lies between -1 and 1 inclusive. Therefore, no matter what x is, we have

$$|R_n(x)| = \left|\frac{f^{(n+1)}(c)}{(n+1)!}(x-0)^n\right| \leq \left|\frac{1}{(n+1)!}x^n\right| = \frac{|x|^n}{(n+1)!}.$$

The factorial growth in the denominator, as noted in Example 3, eventually outstrips the power growth in the numerator, and we have $\frac{|x|^n}{(n+1)!} \to 0$ for all x. This means that $R_n(x) \to 0$ for all x, which completes the proof.

Exploration 2   Euler's Formula

1. $e^{ix} = 1 + ix + \frac{(ix)^2}{2!} + \frac{(ix)^3}{3!} + \cdots + \frac{(ix)^n}{n!} + \cdots$

$$= 1 + ix - \frac{x^2}{2!} - i\frac{x^3}{3!} + \frac{x^4}{4!} + i\frac{x^5}{5!} - \cdots + (i)^n\frac{x^n}{n!} + \cdots$$

2. If we isolate the terms in the series that have i as a factor, we get:

$$e^{ix} = 1 + ix - \frac{x^2}{2!} - i\frac{x^3}{3!} + \frac{x^4}{4!} + i\frac{x^5}{5!} - \cdots + (i)^n\frac{x^n}{n!} + \cdots$$

$$= 1 - \frac{x^2}{2!} + \frac{x^4}{4!} - \frac{x^6}{6!} + \cdots + (-1)^n\frac{x^{2n}}{(2n)!} + \cdots$$

$$+ i\left(x - \frac{x^3}{3!} + \frac{x^5}{5!} - \frac{x^7}{7!} + \cdots + (-1)^n\frac{x^{2n+1}}{(2n+1)!} + \cdots\right)$$

$$= \cos x + i \sin x.$$

(We are assuming here that we can rearrange the terms of a convergent series without affecting the sum. It happens to be true in this case, but we will see in Section 9.5 that it is not always true.)

3. $e^{i\pi} = \cos \pi + i \sin \pi = -1 + 0 = -1$
Thus, $e^{i\pi} + 1 = 0$

Quick Review 9.3

1. Since $|f(x)| = |2\cos(3x)| \leq 2$ on $[-2\pi, 2\pi]$ and $f(0) = 2$, $M = 2$.

2. Since $f(x)$ is increasing and positive on $[1, 2]$, $M = f(2) = 7$.

3. Since $f(x)$ is increasing and positive on $[-3, 0]$, $M = f(0) = 1$.

4. Since the minimum value of $f(x)$ is $f(-1) = -\frac{1}{2}$ and the maximum value of $f(x)$ is $f(1) = \frac{1}{2}$, $M = \frac{1}{2}$.

5. On $[-3, 1]$, the minimum value of $f(x)$ is $f(-3) = -7$ and the maximum value of $f(x)$ is $f(0) = 2$. On $(1, 3]$, f is increasing and positive, so the maximum value of f is $f(3) = 5$. Thus $|f(x)| \leq 7$ on $[-3, 3]$ and $M = 7$.

6. Yes, since each expression for an nth derivative given by the Quotient Rule will be a rational function whose denominator is a power of $x + 1$.

7. No, since the function $f(x) = |x^2 - 4|$ has a corner at $x = 2$.

8. Yes, since the derivatives of all orders for sin x and cos x are defined for all values of x.

9. Yes, since the function $f(x) = e^{-x}$ has derivatives of the form $f^{(n)}(x) = -e^{-x}$ for odd values of n and $f^{(n)}(x) = e^{-x}$ for even values of n, and both of these expressions are defined for all values of x.

10. No, since $f(x) = x^{3/2}$, we have $f'(x) = \frac{3}{2}x^{1/2}$ and $f''(x) = \frac{3}{4}x^{-1/2}$, so $f''(0)$ is undefined.

Section 9.3 Exercises

1. $f(0) = e^{-2x}\big|_{x=0} = 1$

$f'(0) = -2e^{-2x}\big|_{x=0} = -2$

$f''(0) = 4e^{-2x}\big|_{x=0} = 4$, so $\frac{f''(0)}{2!} = 2$

$f'''(0) = -8e^{-2x}\big|_{x=0} = -8$, so $\frac{f'''(0)}{3!} = -\frac{4}{3}$

$f^{(4)}(0) = 16e^{-2x}\big|_{x=0} = 16$, so $\frac{f^{(4)}(0)}{4!} = \frac{2}{3}$

$P_4(x) = 1 - 2x + 2x^2 - \frac{4}{3}x^3 + \frac{2}{3}x^4$

$f(0.2) \approx P_4(0.2) = 0.6704$

2. $f(0) = \cos\frac{\pi x}{2}\big|_{x=0} = 1$

$f'(0) = -\frac{\pi}{2}\sin\frac{\pi x}{2}\big|_{x=0} = 0$

$f''(0) = -\frac{\pi^2}{4}\cos\frac{\pi x}{2}\big|_{x=0} = -\frac{\pi^2}{4}$, so $\frac{f''(0)}{2!} = -\frac{\pi^2}{8}$

$f'''(0) = \frac{\pi^3}{8}\sin\frac{\pi x}{2}\big|_{x=0} = 0$, so $\frac{f'''(0)}{3!} = 0$

$f^{(4)}(0) = \frac{\pi^4}{16}\cos\frac{\pi x}{2}\big|_{x=0} = \frac{\pi^4}{16}$, so $\frac{f^{(4)}(0)}{4!} = \frac{\pi^4}{384}$

$P_4(x) = 1 - \frac{\pi^2}{8}x^2 + \frac{\pi^4}{384}x^4$

$f(0.2) \approx P_4(0.2) \approx 0.9511$

3. $f(0) = 5 \sin(-x)\big|_{x=0} = -5 \sin x\big|_{x=0} = 0$

$f'(0) = -5 \cos x\big|_{x=0} = -5$

$f''(0) = 5 \sin x\big|_{x=0} = 0$, so $\dfrac{f''(0)}{2!} = 0$

$f'''(0) = 5 \cos x\big|_{x=0} = 5$, so $\dfrac{f'''(0)}{3!} = \dfrac{5}{6}$

$f^{(4)}(0) = -5 \sin x\big|_{x=0} = 0$, so $\dfrac{f^{(4)}(0)}{4!} = 0$

$P_4(x) = -5x + \dfrac{5}{6}x^3$

$f(0.2) \approx P_4(0.2) = -\dfrac{149}{150} \approx -0.9933$

4. Substituting x^2 for x in the Maclaurin series given for

$\ln(1 + x)$ at the end of Section 9.2, we have

$\ln(1 + x^2) = x^2 - \dfrac{(x^2)^2}{2} + \dfrac{(x^2)^3}{3} - \cdots + (-1)^{n-1}\dfrac{(x^2)^n}{n} + \cdots$

$= x^2 - \dfrac{x^4}{2} + \dfrac{x^6}{3} - \cdots + (-1)^{n-1}\dfrac{x^{2n}}{n} + \cdots$

Therefore, $P_4(x) = x^2 - \dfrac{x^4}{2}$ and $f(0.2) \approx P_4(0.2) = 0.0392$.

5. $f(0) = (1 - x)^{-2}\big|_{x=0} = 1$

$f'(0) = 2(1 - x)^{-3}\big|_{x=0} = 2$

$f''(0) = 6(1 - x)^{-4}\big|_{x=0} = 6$, so $\dfrac{f''(0)}{2!} = 3$

$f'''(0) = 24(1 - x)^{-5}\big|_{x=0} = 24$, so $\dfrac{f'''(0)}{3!} = 4$

$f^{(4)}(0) = 120(1 - x)^{-6}\big|_{x=0} = 120$, so $\dfrac{f^{(4)}(0)}{4!} = 5$

$P_4(x) = 1 + 2x + 3x^2 + 4x^3 + 5x^4$

$f(0.2) \approx P_4(0.2) = 1.56$

6. $xe^x = x\left(1 + x + \dfrac{x^2}{2!} + \cdots + \dfrac{x^n}{n!} + \cdots\right)$

$= x + x^2 + \dfrac{x^3}{2!} + \cdots + \dfrac{x^{n+1}}{n!} + \cdots$

7. $\sin x - x + \dfrac{x^3}{3!}$

$= \left(x - \dfrac{x^3}{3!} + \dfrac{x^5}{5!} - \cdots + (-1)^n\dfrac{x^{2n+1}}{(2n+1)!} + \cdots\right) - x + \dfrac{x^3}{3!}$

$= \dfrac{x^5}{5!} - \dfrac{x^7}{7!} + \dfrac{x^9}{9!} - \cdots + (-1)^n\dfrac{x^{2n+1}}{(2n+1)!} + \cdots$

Note: By replacing n with $n + 2$, the general term can be

written as $(-1)^n\dfrac{x^{2n+5}}{(2n+5)!}$.

8. $\cos^2 x = \dfrac{1}{2} + \dfrac{1}{2}\cos(2x)$

$= \dfrac{1}{2} + \dfrac{1}{2}\left(1 - \dfrac{(2x)^2}{2!} + \dfrac{(2x)^4}{4!} - \cdots + (-1)^n\dfrac{(2x)^{2n}}{(2n)!} + \cdots\right)$

$= 1 - \dfrac{4x^2}{2 \cdot 2!} + \dfrac{16x^4}{2 \cdot 4!} - \cdots + (-1)^n\dfrac{2^{2n}x^{2n}}{2 \cdot (2n)!} + \cdots$

$= 1 - x^2 + \dfrac{x^4}{3} - \cdots + (-1)^n\dfrac{2^{2n-1}x^{2n}}{(2n)!} + \cdots$

9. $\sin^2 x = \dfrac{1}{2} - \dfrac{1}{2}\cos(2x)$

$= \dfrac{1}{2} - \dfrac{1}{2}\left(1 - \dfrac{(2x)^2}{2!} + \dfrac{(2x)^4}{4!} - \dfrac{(2x)^6}{6!} + \cdots\right.$

$\left. + (-1)^n\dfrac{(2x)^{2n}}{(2n)!} + \cdots\right)$

$= \dfrac{4x^2}{2 \cdot 2!} - \dfrac{16x^4}{2 \cdot 4!} + \dfrac{64x^6}{2 \cdot 6!} - \cdots$

$+ (-1)^{n-1}\dfrac{2^{2n}\,x^{2n}}{2 \cdot (2n)!} + \cdots$

$= x^2 - \dfrac{x^4}{3} + \dfrac{2x^6}{45} - \cdots + (-1)^{n-1}\dfrac{2^{2n-1}\,x^{2n}}{(2n)!} + \cdots$

Note: By replacing n with $n + 1$, the general term can be

written as $(-1)^n\dfrac{2^{2n+1}\,x^{2n+2}}{(2n + 2)!}$.

10. $\dfrac{x^2}{1 - 2x} = x^2\left(\dfrac{1}{1 - 2x}\right)$

$= x^2[1 + 2x + (2x)^2 + \cdots + (2x)^n + \cdots]$

$= x^2 + 2x^3 + 4x^4 + \cdots + 2^n x^{n+2} + \cdots$

11. Let $f(x) = \sin x$. Then $P_4(x) = P_3(x) = x - \dfrac{x^3}{6}$, so we use

the Remainder Estimation Theorem with $n = 4$. Since

$|f^{(5)}(x)| = |\cos x| \le 1$ for all x, we may use $M = r = 1$,

giving $|R_4(x)| \le \dfrac{|x|^5}{5!}$, so we may assure that

$|R_4(x)| \le 5 \times 10^{-4}$ by requiring $\dfrac{|x|^5}{5!} \le 5 \times 10^{-4}$, or

$|x| \le \sqrt[5]{0.06} \approx 0.5697$. Thus, the absolute error is no

greater than 5×10^{-4} when

$-0.56 < x < 0.56$ (approximately).

Alternate method: Using graphing techniques,

$\left|\sin x - \left(x - \dfrac{x^3}{6}\right)\right| \le 5 \times 10^{-4}$ when $-0.57 < x < 0.57$.

12. Let $f(x) = \cos x$. Then $P_3(x) = P_2(x) = 1 - \dfrac{x^2}{2}$, so we may

use the Remainder Estimation Theorem with $n = 3$. Since

$|f^{(4)}(x)| = |\cos x| \le 1$ for all x, we may use $M = r = 1$,

giving $|R_3(x)| \le \dfrac{|x|^4}{4!}$. For $|x| < 0.5$, the absolute error is less

than $\dfrac{(0.5)^4}{4!} \approx 0.0026$ (approximately).

12. continued

Alternate method: Using graphing techniques, we find that

when $|x| < 0.5$,

$$|\text{error}| = \left|\cos x - \left(1 - \frac{x^2}{2}\right)\right|$$
$$< \left|\cos 0.5 - \left(1 - \frac{0.5^2}{2}\right)\right|$$
$$\approx 0.002583.$$

The quantity $1 - \frac{x^2}{2}$ tends to be too small, as shown by the

graphs of $y = \cos x$ and $y = 1 - \frac{x^2}{2}$.

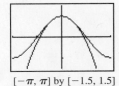

$[-\pi, \pi]$ by $[-1.5, 1.5]$

13. Let $f(x) = \sin x$. Then $P_2(x) = P_1(x) = x$, so we may use

the Remainder Estimation Theorem with $n = 2$. Since

$|f'''(x)| = |-\cos x| \le 1$ for all x, we may use $M = r = 1$,

giving $|R_2(x)| \le \frac{|x|^3}{3!}$. Thus, for $|x| < 10^{-3}$, the maximum

possible error is about $\frac{(10^{-3})^3}{3!} \approx 1.67 \times 10^{-10}$.

Alternate method:

Using graphing techniques, we find that when $|x| < 10^{-3}$,

$|\text{error}| = |\sin x - x| \le |\sin 10^{-3} - 10^{-3}| \approx 1.67 \times 10^{-10}$.

The inequality $x < \sin x$ is true for $x < 0$, as we may see

by graphing $y = \sin x - x$.

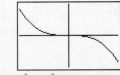

$[-10^{-3}, 10^{-3}]$ by $[-2 \times 10^{-10}, 2 \times 10^{-10}]$

14. Let $f(x) = \sqrt{1 + x}$. Then $P_1(x) = 1 + \frac{x}{2}$, so we may use

the Remainder Estimation Theorem with $n = 1$. Since

$|f''(x)| = \left|-\frac{1}{4}(1 + x)^{-3/2}\right|$, which is less than 0.2538 for

$|x| < 0.01$, we may use $M = 0.2538$ and $r = 1$, giving

$|R_1(x)| \le \frac{0.2538|x|^2}{2!}$. Thus, for $|x| < 0.01$ the maximum

possible absolute error is about

$\frac{0.2538(0.01)^2}{2!} \approx 1.27 \times 10^{-5}$.

Alternate method:

Using graphing techniques, we find that when $|x| < 0.01$,

$$|\text{error}| = \left|\sqrt{1 + x} - \left(1 + \frac{x}{2}\right)\right|$$
$$\le \left|\sqrt{1 - 0.01} - \left(1 - \frac{0.01}{2}\right)\right|$$
$$\approx 1.26 \times 10^{-5}.$$

15. Note that $1 + x + \frac{x^2}{2}$ is the second order Taylor polynomial

for $f(x) = e^x$ at $x = 0$, so we may use the Remainder

Estimation Theorem with $n = 2$. Since $|f'''(x)| = e^x$, which

is less than $e^{0.1}$ when $|x| < 0.1$ and $r = 1$, giving

$|R_2(x)| \le \frac{e^{0.1}|x|^3}{3!}$. Thus, for $|x| < 0.1$, the maximum possible

error is about $\frac{e^{0.1}(0.1)^3}{3!} \approx 1.842 \times 10^{-4}$.

16. Note that $e^x = 1 + x + \frac{x^2}{2!} + \cdots + \frac{x^n}{n!} + \cdots$ and

$e^{-x} = 1 - x + \frac{x^2}{2!} - \cdots + (-1)^n\frac{x^n}{n!} + \cdots$

Thus the terms with n even will cancel for

$\sinh x = \frac{1}{2}(e^x - e^{-x})$, and the terms with n odd will cancel

for $\cosh x = \frac{1}{2}(e^x + e^{-x})$.

$\sinh x = x + \frac{x^3}{3!} + \frac{x^5}{5!} + \cdots + \frac{x^{2n+1}}{(2n+1)!} + \cdots$

$\cosh x = 1 + \frac{x^2}{2!} + \frac{x^4}{4!} + \cdots + \frac{x^{2n}}{(2n)!} + \cdots$

17. All of the derivatives of $\cosh x$ are either $\cosh x$ or $\sinh x$.

For any real x, $\cosh x$ and $\sinh x$ are both bounded by $e^{|x|}$.

So for any real x, let $M = e^{|x|}$ and $r = 1$ in the Remainder

Estimation Theorem. This gives $|R_n(x)| \le \frac{e^{|x|}|x|^{n+1}}{(n+1)!}$

But for any fixed value of x, $\lim_{n \to \infty} \frac{e^{|x|}|x|^{n+1}}{(n+1)!} = 0$. It follows

that the series converges to $\cosh x$ for all real values of x.

18. For $n = 0$, Taylor's Theorem with Remainder says that if f

has derivatives of all orders in an open interval I containing

a, then for each x in I,

$f(x) = f(a) + R(x)$, where $R(x) = f'(c)(x - a)$, so

$f(x) = f(a) + f'(c)(x - a)$ for some c between a and x.

Letting $b = x$ this equation is $f(b) = f(a) + f'(c)(b - a)$,

which is equivalent to $f'(c) = \frac{f(b) - f(a)}{b - a}$ for some c

between a and b. Thus, for the class of functions that have

derivatives of all orders in an open interval containing a

and b, the Mean Value Theorem can be considered a special

case of Taylor's Theorem.

19. $f(0) = \ln(\cos x)\big|_{x=0} = \ln 1 = 0$

$f'(0) = \dfrac{1}{\cos x}(-\sin x)\big|_{x=0} = -\tan x\big|_{x=0} = 0$

$f''(0) = -\sec^2 x\big|_{x=0} = -1$ so $\dfrac{f''(0)}{2!} = -\dfrac{1}{2}$

(a) $L(x) = 0$

(b) $P_2(x) = -\dfrac{1}{2}x^2$

(c) The graphs of the linear and quadratic approximations fit the graph of the function near $x = 0$.

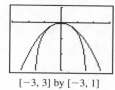

$[-3, 3]$ by $[-3, 1]$

20. $f(0) = e^{\sin x}\big|_{x=0} = e^0 = 1$

$f'(0) = e^{\sin x}\cos x\big|_{x=0} = 1$

$f''(0) = \left[(e^{\sin x})(-\sin x) + (\cos x)(e^{\sin x}\cos x)\right]\big|_{x=0} = 1$,

so $\dfrac{f''(0)}{2!} = \dfrac{1}{2}$

(a) $L(x) = 1 + x$

(b) $P_2(x) = 1 + x + \dfrac{x^2}{2}$

(c) The graphs of the linear and quadratic approximations fit the graph of the function near $x = 0$.

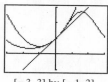

$[-3, 3]$ by $[-1, 3]$

21. $f(0) = (1 - x^2)^{-1/2}\big|_{x=0} = 1$

$f'(0) = -\dfrac{1}{2}(1 - x^2)^{-3/2}(-2x)\big|_{x=0} = x(1 - x^2)^{-3/2}\big|_{x=0} = 0$

$f''(0) = (x)\left[-\dfrac{3}{2}(1 - x^2)^{-5/2}(-2x)\right] + (1 - x^2)^{-3/2}\big|_{x=0} = 1$,

so $\dfrac{f''(0)}{2!} = \dfrac{1}{2}$

(a) $L(x) = 1$

(b) $P_2(x) = 1 + \dfrac{x^2}{2}$

(c) The graphs of the linear and quadratic approximations fit the graph of the function near $x = 0$.

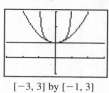

$[-3, 3]$ by $[-1, 3]$

22. $f(0) = \sec x\big|_{x=0} = 1$

$f'(0) = \sec x \tan x\big|_{x=0} = 0$

$f''(0) = (\sec x)(\sec^2 x) + (\tan x)(\sec x \tan x)\big|_{x=0} = 1$,

so $\dfrac{f''(0)}{2!} = \dfrac{1}{2}$

(a) $L(x) = 1$

(b) $P_2(x) = 1 + \dfrac{x^2}{2}$

(c) The graphs of the linear and quadratic approximations fit the graph of the function near $x = 0$.

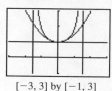

$[-3, 3]$ by $[-1, 3]$

23. $f(0) = \tan x\big|_{x=0} = 0$

$f'(0) = \sec^2 x\big|_{x=0} = 1$

$f''(0) = (2 \sec x)(\sec x \tan x)\big|_{x=0} = 0$, so $\dfrac{f''(0)}{2!} = 0$

(a) $L(x) = x$

(b) $P_2(x) = x$

(c) The graphs of the linear and quadratic approximations fit the graph of the function near $x = 0$.

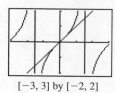

$[-3, 3]$ by $[-2, 2]$

24. $f(0) = (1 + x)^k\big|_{x=0} = 1$

$f'(0) = k(1 + x)^{k-1}\big|_{x=0} = k$

$f''(0) = k(k - 1)(1 + x)^{k-2}\big|_{x=0} = k(k - 1)$,

so $\dfrac{f''(0)}{2!} = \dfrac{k(k - 1)}{2}$

$P_2(x) = 1 + kx + \dfrac{k(k - 1)}{2}x^2$

For $k = 3$, we have $f(x) = (1 + x)^3$ and $f'''(x) = 6$. We may use the Remainder Estimation Theorem with $n = 2$, $M = 6$, and $r = 1$, giving $R_2(x) \le \dfrac{6|x|^3}{3!} = |x|^3$. (In this particular case it is actually true that $R_2(x) = x^3$, since $f(x)$ is a cubic polynomial.) Thus the absolute error is less than $\dfrac{1}{100}$ whenever $|x|^3 < 0.01$. In the interval $[0, 1]$, this occurs when $0 \le x < \sqrt[3]{0.01} \approx 0.215$.

Alternate method:

Note that $P_2(x) = 1 + 3x + 3x^2$. Using graphing techniques,

$\left|(1 + x)^3 - (1 + 3x + 3x^2)\right| < \dfrac{1}{100}$ when $|x| < 0.215$.

25. Let $f(x) = e^x$. Then $P_3(x) = 1 + x + \dfrac{x^2}{2} + \dfrac{x^3}{6}$, so we may

use the Remainder Estimation Theorem with $n = 3$. Since

$\left|f^{(4)}(x)\right| = e^x$, which is no more than $e^{0.1}$ when $|x| \le 0.1$, we

may use $M = e^{0.1}$ and $r = 1$, giving $|R_3(x)| \le \dfrac{e^{0.1}|x|^4}{4!}$. Thus,

for $|x| \le 0.1$, the maximum possible absolute error is about

$\dfrac{e^{0.1}(0.1)^4}{24} \approx 4.605 \times 10^{-6}$.

Alternate method:

Using graphing techniques, when $|x| \le 0.1$,

$$|\text{error}| = \left| e^x - \left(1 + x + \frac{x^2}{2} + \frac{x^3}{6} \right) \right|$$

$$\le \left| e^{0.1} - \left(1 + 0.1 + \frac{0.01}{2} + \frac{0.001}{6} \right) \right|$$

$$\approx 4.251 \times 10^{-6}.$$

26. Since the Maclaurin series is

$$\frac{1}{1-x} = 1 + x + x^2 + \cdots + x^n + \cdots,$$

$$P_3(x) = 1 + x + x^2 + x^3.$$

Since $\left|f^{(4)}(x)\right| = 24(1-x)^{-5}$, which is no more than

$24(0.9)^{-5}$ when $|x| \le 0.1$, we may use $M = 24(0.9)^{-5}$ and

$r = 1$, giving $|R_3(x)| \le \dfrac{24(0.9)^{-5}|x|^4}{4!} = \dfrac{|x|^4}{0.9^5}$. Thus, for

$|x| \le 0.1$, an upper bound for the magnitude of the

approximation error is $\dfrac{0.1^4}{0.9^5} \approx 1.694 \times 10^{-4}$. Rounding up

to be safe, an upper bound is 1.70×10^{-4}.

Alternate method:

Using graphing techniques, when $|x| \le 0.1$,

$$|\text{error}| = \left| \frac{1}{1-x} - (1 + x + x^2 + x^3) \right|$$

$$\le \left| \frac{1}{1-0.1} - 1.111 \right| \approx 1.11 \times 10^{-4}.$$

27. (a) No

(b) Yes, since

$$\frac{dy}{dx} = e^{-x^2}$$

$$= 1 + (-x^2) + \frac{(-x^2)^2}{2!} + \cdots + \frac{(-x^2)^n}{n!} + \cdots$$

$$= 1 - x^2 + \frac{x^4}{2!} - \cdots + (-1)^n \frac{x^{2n}}{n!} + \cdots.$$

The constant term of y is $y(0) = 2$, and we may obtain

the remaining terms of y by integrating the above

series.

$$y = 2 + x - \frac{x^3}{3} + \frac{x^5}{10} - \cdots + (-1)^n \frac{x^{2n+1}}{(2n+1)n!} + \cdots$$

By substituting $n - 1$ for n, the general term may also

be written as $(-1)^{n-1} \dfrac{x^{2n-1}}{(2n-1)(n-1)!}$.

(c) The power series equals the function y for all real
values of x. This is because the series for e^{-x^2}
converges for all real values of x, so Theorem 2 of
Section 9.1 implies that the new series also converges
for all x.

28. (a) Substitute $-x$ for x in the Maclaurin series for

$\ln (1 + x)$ given at the end of Section 9.2.

$$\ln (1 - x) = -x - \frac{x^2}{2} - \frac{x^3}{3} - \cdots - \frac{x^n}{n} - \cdots$$

(b) $\ln \dfrac{1+x}{1-x} = \ln (1 + x) - \ln (1 - x)$

$$= \left(x - \frac{x^2}{2} + \frac{x^3}{3} - \cdots + (-1)^{n-1}\frac{x^n}{n} + \cdots \right)$$

$$+ \left(x + \frac{x^2}{2} + \frac{x^3}{3} + \cdots + \frac{x^n}{n} \right)$$

$$= 2x + \frac{2x^3}{3} + \frac{2x^5}{5} + \cdots + \frac{2x^{2n+1}}{2n+1} + \cdots$$

29. (a)

$\left[-\dfrac{\pi}{2}, \dfrac{\pi}{2} \right]$ by $[-2, 2]$

The series approximates $\tan x$.

(b)

$\left[-\dfrac{\pi}{2}, \dfrac{\pi}{2} \right]$ by $[-1, 4]$

The series approximates $\sec x$.

30. (a) $\sin^2 x = \frac{1}{2}(1 - \cos 2x)$

$$= \frac{1}{2} - \frac{1}{2}\left(1 - \frac{(2x)^2}{2!} + \frac{(2x)^4}{4!} - \frac{(2x)^6}{6!} + \cdots \right.$$

$$\left. + (-1)^n\frac{(2x)^{2n}}{(2n)!} + \cdots \right)$$

$$= \frac{4x^2}{2 \cdot 2!} - \frac{16x^4}{2 \cdot 4!} + \frac{64x^6}{2 \cdot 6!} - \frac{256x^8}{2 \cdot 8!}$$

$$+ \frac{1024x^{10}}{2 \cdot 10!} - \cdots$$

$$= x^2 - \frac{x^4}{3} + \frac{2x^6}{45} - \frac{x^8}{315} + \frac{2x^{10}}{14,175} - \cdots$$

(b) derivative $= 2x - \frac{4x^3}{3} + \frac{4x^5}{15} - \frac{8x^7}{315} + \cdots$

(c) part (b) $= 2x - \frac{(2x)^3}{3!} + \frac{(2x)^5}{5!} - \frac{(2x)^7}{7!} + \cdots = \sin 2x$

31. (a) It works. For example, let $n = 2$. Then $P = 3.14$ and $P + \sin P \approx 3.141592653$, which is accurate to more than 6 decimal places.

(b) Let $P = \pi + x$ where x is the error in the original estimate. Then

$$P + \sin P = (\pi + x) + \sin(\pi + x) = \pi + x - \sin x$$

But by the Remainder Theorem, $|x - \sin x| < \frac{|x|^3}{6}$.

Therefore, the difference between the new estimate $P + \sin P$ and π is less than $\frac{|x|^3}{6}$.

32. (a) $\frac{e^{i\theta} + e^{-i\theta}}{2} = \frac{(\cos\theta + i\sin\theta) + (\cos(-\theta) + i\sin(-\theta))}{2}$

$$= \frac{\cos\theta + i\sin\theta + \cos\theta - i\sin\theta}{2}$$

$$= \frac{2\cos\theta}{2} = \cos\theta$$

(b) $\frac{e^{i\theta} - e^{-i\theta}}{2i} = \frac{(\cos\theta + i\sin\theta) - (\cos(-\theta) + i\sin(-\theta))}{2i}$

$$= \frac{(\cos\theta + i\sin\theta) - (\cos\theta - i\sin\theta)}{2i}$$

$$= \frac{2i\sin\theta}{2i} = \sin\theta$$

33. $\frac{d}{dx}[e^{ax}(\cos bx + i\sin bx)]$

$$= (e^{ax})(-b\sin bx + bi\cos bx) + (ae^{ax})(\cos bx + i\sin bx)$$

$$= (e^{ax})[(bi^2\sin bx + bi\cos bx) + a(\cos bx + i\sin bx)]$$

$$= (e^{ax})[bi(\cos bx + i\sin bx) + a(\cos bx + i\sin bx)]$$

$$= (a + bi)(e^{ax})(\cos bx + i\sin bx)$$

$$= (a + bi)e^{(a+bi)x}$$

34. (a) The derivative of the right-hand side is

$$\frac{a - bi}{a^2 + b^2}(a + bi)e^{(a+bi)x}$$

$$= \frac{a^2 - (bi)^2}{a^2 + b^2}e^{(a+bi)x}$$

$$= \frac{a^2 + b^2}{a^2 + b^2}e^{(a+bi)x} = e^{(a+bi)x},$$

which confirms the antiderivative formula.

(b) $\int e^{ax}\cos bx\, dx + i\int e^{ax}\sin bx\, dx$

$$= \int e^{(a+bi)x}\, dx$$

$$= \frac{a - bi}{a^2 + b^2}e^{(a+bi)x}$$

$$= \frac{a - bi}{a^2 + b^2}e^{ax}(\cos bx + i\sin bx)$$

$$= \left(\frac{e^{ax}}{a^2 + b^2}\right)(a\cos bx + b\sin bx - bi\cos bx$$

$$+ ai\sin bx)$$

$$= \left(\frac{e^{ax}}{a^2 + b^2}\right)[(a\cos bx + b\sin bx)$$

$$+ i(a\sin bx - b\cos bx)]$$

Separating the real and imaginary parts gives

$$\int e^{ax}\cos bx\, dx = \frac{e^{ax}}{a^2 + b^2}(a\cos bx + b\sin bx) \text{ and}$$

$$\int e^{ax}\sin bx\, dx = \frac{e^{ax}}{a^2 + b^2}(a\sin bx - b\cos bx)$$

■ Section 9.4 Radius of Convergence
(pp. 487–496)

Exploration 1   Finishing the Proof of the Ratio Test

1. For $\sum\frac{1}{n}$: $L = \lim_{n\to\infty} \frac{\frac{1}{n+1}}{\frac{1}{n}} = \lim_{n\to\infty}\frac{n}{n+1} = 1$.

For $\sum\frac{1}{n^2}$: $L = \lim_{n\to\infty} \frac{\frac{1}{(n+1)^2}}{\frac{1}{n^2}} = \lim_{n\to\infty}\frac{n^2}{(n+1)^2} = 1$.

2. (a) $\int_1^\infty \frac{1}{x}\, dx = \lim_{k\to\infty}\left(\ln x\Big|_1^k\right) = \lim_{k\to\infty}\ln k = \infty$.

(b) $\int_1^\infty \frac{1}{x^2}\, dx = \lim_{k\to\infty}\left(-x^{-1}\Big|_1^k\right) = \lim_{k\to\infty}\left(-\frac{1}{k} + 1\right) = 1$.

3. Figure 9.14a shows that $\sum\frac{1}{n}$ is greater than $\int_1^\infty \frac{1}{x}\, dx$. Since the integral diverges, so must the series.

Figure 9.14b shows that $\sum\frac{1}{n^2}$ is less than $1 + \int_1^\infty \frac{1}{x^2}\, dx$. Since the integral converges, so must the series.

4. These two examples prove that $L = 1$ can be true for either a divergent series or a convergent series. The Ratio Test itself is therefore inconclusive when $L = 1$.

Exploration 2   Revisiting a Maclaurin Series

1. $L = \lim_{n\to\infty}\frac{|x|^{n+1}}{n+1} \cdot \frac{n}{|x|^n} = \lim_{n\to\infty}\frac{n}{n+1}|x| = |x|$. The series converges absolutely when $|x| < 1$, so the radius of convergence is 1.

2. When $x = -1$, the series becomes

$$-1 - \frac{1}{2} - \frac{1}{3} - \cdots - \frac{1}{n} - \cdots.$$

Each term in this series is the negative of the corresponding term in the divergent series of Figure 9.14a. Just as $\sum\frac{1}{n}$ diverges to $+\infty$, this series diverges to $-\infty$.

3. Geometrically, we chart the progress of the partial sums as in the figure below:

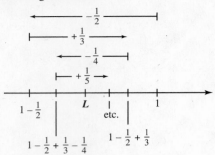

4. The series converges at the right-hand endpoint. As shown in the picture above, the partial sums are closing in on some limit L as they oscillate left and right by constantly decreasing amounts.

5. We know that the series does not converge absolutely at the right-hand endpoint, because $\sum \frac{1}{n}$ diverges (Exploration 1 of this section).

Quick Review 9.4

1. $\lim\limits_{n\to\infty} \frac{n|x|}{n+1} = |x| \lim\limits_{n\to\infty} \frac{n}{n+1} = |x|$

2. $\lim\limits_{n\to\infty} \frac{n^2|x-3|}{n(n+1)} = |x-3| \lim\limits_{n\to\infty} \frac{n^2}{n^2+n} = |x-3|$

3. $\lim\limits_{n\to\infty} \frac{|x|^n}{n!} = 0$

   (Note: This limit is similar to the limit which is discussed at the end of Example 3 in Section 9.3.)

4. $\lim\limits_{n\to\infty} \frac{(n+1)^4 x^2}{(2n)^4} = x^2 \lim\limits_{n\to\infty} \frac{n^4 + 4n^3 + 6n^2 + 4n + 1}{16n^4}$

   $= x^2\left(\frac{1}{16}\right) = \frac{x^2}{16}$

5. $\lim\limits_{n\to\infty} \frac{|2x+1|^{n+1} 2^n}{2^{n+1}|2x+1|^n} = \lim\limits_{n\to\infty} \frac{|2x+1|}{2} = \frac{|2x+1|}{2}$

6. Since $n^2 > 5n$ for $n \geq 6$, $a_n = n^2$, $b_n = 5n$, and $N = 6$.

7. Since $5^n > n^5$ for $n \geq 6$, $a_n = 5^n$, $b_n = n^5$ and $N = 6$.

8. Since $\sqrt{n} > \ln n$ for $n \geq 1$, $a_n = \sqrt{n}$, $b_n = \ln n$, and $N = 1$.

9. Since $10^n < n!$ $\left(\text{and hence } \frac{1}{10^n} > \frac{1}{n!}\right)$ for $n \geq 25$,

   $a_n = \frac{1}{10^n}$, $b_n = \frac{1}{n!}$, and $N = 25$.

10. Since $n^2 < n^3$ $\left(\text{and hence } \frac{1}{n^2} > n^{-3}\right)$ for

    $n \geq 2$, $a_n = \frac{1}{n^2}$, $b_n = n^{-3}$, and $N = 2$.

Section 9.4 Exercises

1. Diverges by the nth-Term Test, since $\lim\limits_{n\to\infty} \frac{n}{n+1} = 1 \neq 0$.

2. Diverges by the nth-Term Test, since $\lim\limits_{n\to\infty} \frac{2^n}{n+1} = \infty$. (The Ratio Test can also be used.)

3. Converges by the Ratio Test, since

   $\lim\limits_{n\to\infty} \frac{a_{n+1}}{a_n} = \lim\limits_{n\to\infty} \frac{(n+1)^2 - 1}{2^{n+1}} \cdot \frac{2^n}{n^2 - 1} = \frac{1}{2} < 1$.

4. Converges, because it is a geometric series with $r = \frac{1}{8}$, so $|r| < 1$.

5. Converges by the Ratio Test, since

   $\lim\limits_{n\to\infty} \frac{a_{n+1}}{a_n} = \lim\limits_{n\to\infty} \frac{2^{n+1}}{(3^{n+1} + 1)} \cdot \frac{3^n + 1}{2^n} = \frac{2}{3} < 1$.

   Alternately, note that $\frac{2^n}{3^n + 1} < \left(\frac{2}{3}\right)^n$ for all n.

   Since $\sum\limits_{n=1}^{\infty} \left(\frac{2}{3}\right)^n$ converges, $\sum\limits_{n=1}^{\infty} \frac{2^n}{3^n + 1}$ converges by the Direct Comparison Test.

6. Diverges by the nth-Term Test, since

   $\lim\limits_{n\to\infty} n \sin\left(\frac{1}{n}\right) = 1 \neq 0$

7. Converges by the Ratio Test, since

   $\lim\limits_{n\to\infty} \frac{a_{n+1}}{a_n} = \lim\limits_{n\to\infty} \frac{(n+1)^2 e^{-n-1}}{n^2 e^{-n}} = e^{-1} < 1$.

8. Converges by the Ratio Test, since

   $\lim\limits_{n\to\infty} \frac{a_{n+1}}{a_n} = \lim\limits_{n\to\infty} \frac{(n+1)^{10}}{10^{n+1}} \cdot \frac{10^n}{n^{10}} = \frac{1}{10} < 1$.

9. Converges by the Ratio Test, since

   $\lim\limits_{n\to\infty} \frac{a_{n+1}}{a_n} = \lim\limits_{n\to\infty} \frac{(n+4)!}{3!(n+1)!3^{n+1}} \cdot \frac{3!n!\, 3^n}{(n+3)!}$

   $= \lim\limits_{n\to\infty} \frac{n+4}{3(n+1)}$

   $= \frac{1}{3} < 1$.

10. Diverges by the nth-Term Test, since

    $\lim\limits_{n\to\infty} \left(1 + \frac{1}{n}\right)^n = e \neq 0$.

11. Converges, because it is a geometric series with $r = -\frac{2}{3}$, so $|r| < 1$.

12. Diverges by the Ratio Test, since

    $\lim\limits_{n\to\infty} \frac{a_{n+1}}{a_n} = \lim\limits_{n\to\infty} \frac{(n+1)!e^{-n-1}}{n!e^{-n}} = \lim\limits_{n\to\infty} (n+1)e^{-1} = \infty$.

    (The nth-Term Test can also be used.)

13. Diverges by the Ratio Test, since

$$\lim_{n\to\infty} \frac{a_{n+1}}{a_n} = \lim_{n\to\infty} \frac{3^{n+1}}{(n+1)^3 \, 2^{n+1}} \cdot \frac{n^3 2^n}{3^n}$$
$$= \lim_{n\to\infty} \frac{3n^3}{(n+1)^3 (2)}$$
$$= \frac{3}{2} > 1.$$

(The nth = Term Test can also be used.)

14. Converges by the Ratio Test, since

$$\lim_{n\to\infty} \frac{a_{n+1}}{a_n} = \lim_{n\to\infty} \frac{(n+1)\ln(n+1)}{2^{n+1}} \cdot \frac{2^n}{n \ln n}$$
$$= \lim_{n\to\infty} \frac{1}{2} \cdot \frac{n+1}{n} \cdot \frac{\ln(n+1)}{\ln n}$$
$$= \frac{1}{2} < 1.$$

15. Converges by the Ratio Test, since

$$\lim_{n\to\infty} \frac{a_{n+1}}{a_n} = \lim_{n\to\infty} \frac{(n+1)!}{(2n+3)!} \cdot \frac{(2n+1)!}{n!}$$
$$= \lim_{n\to\infty} \frac{n+1}{(2n+3)(2n+2)}$$
$$= \lim_{n\to\infty} \frac{1}{2(2n+3)} = 0 < 1.$$

16. Converges by the Ratio Test, since

$$\lim_{n\to\infty} \frac{a_{n+1}}{a_n} = \lim_{n\to\infty} \frac{(n+1)!}{(n+1)^{n+1}} \cdot \frac{n^n}{n!}$$
$$= \lim_{n\to\infty} \frac{(n+1)n^n}{(n+1)(n+1)^n}$$
$$= \lim_{n\to\infty} \left(\frac{n}{n+1}\right)^n$$
$$= \lim_{n\to\infty} \frac{1}{(1+1/n)^n}$$
$$= \frac{1}{e} < 1$$

17. One possible answer: $\sum_{n=1}^{\infty} \frac{1}{n}$ diverges (see Exploration 1 in this section) even though $\lim_{n\to\infty} \frac{1}{n} = 0$.

18. One possible answer:

Let $a_n = 2^{-n}$ and $b_n = 3^{-n}$

Then $\sum a_n$ and $\sum b_n$ are convergent geometric series, but $\sum \frac{a_n}{b_n} = \sum \left(\frac{3}{2}\right)^n$ is a divergent geometric series.

19. This is a geometric series which converges only for $|x| < 1$, so the radius of convergence is 1.

20. This is a geometric series which converges only for $|x + 5| < 1$, so the radius of convergence is 1.

21. This is a geometric series which converges only for $|-(4x + 1)| < 1$, or $\left|x + \frac{1}{4}\right| < \frac{1}{4}$, so the radius of convergence is $\frac{1}{4}$.

22. $\lim_{n\to\infty} \left|\frac{a_{n+1}}{a_n}\right| = \lim_{n\to\infty} \frac{|3x-2|^{n+1}}{n+1} \cdot \frac{n}{|3x-2|^n} = |3x-2|$

The series converges for $|3x - 2| < 1$, or $\left|x - \frac{2}{3}\right| < \frac{1}{3}$, and diverges for $\left|x - \frac{2}{3}\right| > \frac{1}{3}$, so the radius of convergence is $\frac{1}{3}$.

23. This is a geometric series which converges only for $\left|\frac{x-2}{10}\right| < 1$, or $|x - 2| < 10$, so the radius of convergence is 10.

24. $\lim_{n\to\infty} \left|\frac{a_{n+1}}{a_n}\right| = \lim_{n\to\infty} \frac{(n+1)|x|^{n+1}}{n+3} \cdot \frac{n+2}{n|x|^n} = \lim_{n\to\infty} |x| = |x|$

The series converges for $|x| < 1$ and diverges for $|x| > 1$, so the radius of convergence is 1.

25. $\lim_{n\to\infty} \left|\frac{a_{n+1}}{a_n}\right| = \lim_{n\to\infty} \frac{|x|^{n+1}}{(n+1)\sqrt{n+1}\,3^{n+1}} \cdot \frac{n\sqrt{n}\,3^n}{|x|^n}$
$$= \lim_{n\to\infty} \frac{|x|}{3} = \frac{|x|}{3}$$

The series converges for $|x| < 3$ and diverges for $|x| > 3$, so the radius of convergence is 3.

26. $\lim_{n\to\infty} \left|\frac{a_{n+1}}{a_n}\right| = \lim_{n\to\infty} \frac{|x|^{2n+3}}{(n+1)!} \cdot \frac{n!}{|x|^{2n+1}} = \lim_{n\to\infty} \frac{x^2}{n+1} = 0$

The series converges for all values of x, so the radius of convergence is ∞.

27. $\lim_{n\to\infty} \left|\frac{a_{n+1}}{a_n}\right| = \lim_{n\to\infty} \frac{(n+1)|x+3|^{n+1}}{5^{n+1}} \cdot \frac{5^n}{n|x+3|^n}$
$$= \lim_{n\to\infty} \frac{|x+3|}{5} = \frac{|x+3|}{5}$$

The series converges for $|x + 3| < 5$ and diverges for $|x + 3| > 5$, so the radius of convergence is 5.

28. $\lim_{n\to\infty} \left|\frac{a_{n+1}}{a_n}\right| = \lim_{n\to\infty} \frac{(n+1)|x|^{n+1}}{4^{n+1}[(n+1)^2+1]} \cdot \frac{4^n(n^2+1)}{n|x|^n}$
$$= \lim_{n\to\infty} \frac{|x|}{4} = \frac{|x|}{4}$$

The series converges for $|x| < 4$ and diverges for $|x| > 4$, so the radius of convergence is 4.

29. $\lim_{n\to\infty} \left|\frac{a_{n+1}}{a_n}\right| = \lim_{n\to\infty} \frac{\sqrt{n+1}\,|x|^{n+1}}{3^{n+1}} \cdot \frac{3^n}{\sqrt{n}\,|x|^n} = \lim_{n\to\infty} \frac{|x|}{3} = \frac{|x|}{3}$

The series converges for $|x| < 3$ and diverges for $|x| > 3$, so the radius of convergence is 3.

30. $\lim\limits_{n\to\infty}\left|\dfrac{a_{n+1}}{a_n}\right| = \lim\limits_{n\to\infty} \dfrac{(n+1)!|x-4|^{n+1}}{n!|x-4|^n}$

$\qquad = \lim\limits_{n\to\infty} (n+1)|x-4|$

$\qquad = \infty \ (x \neq 4)$

The series converges only for $x = 4$, so the radius of

convergence is 0.

31. $\lim\limits_{n\to\infty}\left|\dfrac{a_{n+1}}{a_n}\right| = \lim\limits_{n\to\infty} \dfrac{|(-2)^{n+1}|(n+2)|x-1|^{n+1}}{|-2^n|(n+1)|x-1|^n}$

$\qquad = \lim\limits_{n\to\infty} 2|x-1|$

$\qquad = 2|x-1|$

The series converges for $|x-1| < \dfrac{1}{2}$ and diverges for

$|x-1| > \dfrac{1}{2}$, so the radius of convergence is $\dfrac{1}{2}$.

32. $\lim\limits_{n\to\infty}\left|\dfrac{a_{n+1}}{a_n}\right| = \lim\limits_{n\to\infty} \dfrac{|4x-5|^{2n+3}}{(n+1)^{3/2}} \cdot \dfrac{n^{3/2}}{|4x-5|^{2n+1}}$

$\qquad = \lim\limits_{n\to\infty} (4x-5)^2$

$\qquad = (4x-5)^2$

The series converges for $(4x-5)^2 < 1$, which is equivalent

to $|4x-5| < 1$, or $\left|x - \dfrac{5}{4}\right| < \dfrac{1}{4}$ and diverges for

$\left|x - \dfrac{5}{4}\right| > \dfrac{1}{4}$. The radius of convergence is $\dfrac{1}{4}$.

33. $\lim\limits_{n\to\infty}\left|\dfrac{a_{n+1}}{a_n}\right| = \lim\limits_{n\to\infty} \dfrac{|x+\pi|^{n+1}}{\sqrt{n+1}} \cdot \dfrac{\sqrt{n}}{|x+\pi|^n}$

$\qquad = \lim\limits_{n\to\infty} |x+\pi|$

$\qquad = |x+\pi|$

The series converges for $|x+\pi| < 1$ and diverges for

$|x+\pi| > 1$, so the radius of convergence is 1.

34. $\lim\limits_{n\to\infty}\left|\dfrac{a_{n+1}}{a_n}\right| = \lim\limits_{n\to\infty} \dfrac{|x-\sqrt{2}|^{2n+3}}{2^{n+1}} \cdot \dfrac{2^n}{|x-\sqrt{2}|^{2n+1}}$

$\qquad = \lim\limits_{n\to\infty} \dfrac{1}{2}(x-\sqrt{2})^2$

$\qquad = \dfrac{1}{2}(x-\sqrt{2})^2$

The series converges for $\dfrac{1}{2}(x-\sqrt{2})^2 < 1$, which is

equivalent to $|x-\sqrt{2}| < \sqrt{2}$, and diverges for

$|x-\sqrt{2}| > \sqrt{2}$. The radius of convergence is $\sqrt{2}$.

35. This is a geometric series with first term $a = 1$ and

common ratio $r = \dfrac{(x-1)^2}{4}$. It converges only when

$\left|\dfrac{(x-1)^2}{4}\right| < 1$, so the interval of convergence is

$-1 < x < 3$.

$\text{Sum} = \dfrac{a}{1-r} = \dfrac{1}{1 - \dfrac{(x-1)^2}{4}}$

$\qquad = \dfrac{4}{4 - (x-1)^2}$

$\qquad = \dfrac{4}{-x^2 + 2x + 3}$

$\qquad = -\dfrac{4}{x^2 - 2x - 3}$

36. This is a geometric series with first term $a = 1$ and

common ratio $r = \dfrac{(x+1)^2}{9}$. It converges only when

$\left|\dfrac{(x+1)^2}{9}\right| < 1$, so the interval of convergence is

$-4 < x < 2$.

$\text{Sum} = \dfrac{a}{1-r}$

$\qquad = \dfrac{1}{1 - \dfrac{(x+1)^2}{9}}$

$\qquad = \dfrac{9}{9 - (x+1)^2}$

$\qquad = \dfrac{9}{-x^2 - 2x + 8} = -\dfrac{9}{x^2 + 2x - 8}$

37. This is a geometric series with first term $a = 1$ and

common ratio $r = \dfrac{\sqrt{x}}{2} - 1$. It converges only when

$\left|\dfrac{\sqrt{x}}{2} - 1\right| < 1$, so the interval of convergence is

$0 < x < 16$.

$\text{Sum} = \dfrac{a}{1-r} = \dfrac{1}{1 - \left(\dfrac{\sqrt{x}}{2} - 1\right)} = \dfrac{2}{4 - \sqrt{x}}$

38. This is a geometric series with first term $a = 1$ and

common ratio $r = \ln x$. It converges only when $|\ln x| < 1$,

so the interval of convergence is $\dfrac{1}{e} < x < e$.

$\text{Sum} = \dfrac{a}{1-r} = \dfrac{1}{1 - \ln x}$

39. This is a geometric series with first term $a = 1$ and

common ratio $\dfrac{x^2 - 1}{3}$. It converges only when $\left|\dfrac{x^2 - 1}{3}\right| < 1$,

so the interval of convergence is $-2 < x < 2$.

$\text{Sum} = \dfrac{a}{1-r} = \dfrac{1}{1 - \dfrac{x^2 - 1}{3}} = \dfrac{3}{3 - (x^2 - 1)} = \dfrac{3}{4 - x^2}$

40. This is a geometric series with first term $a = 1$ and

common ratio $\dfrac{\sin x}{2}$. Since $\left|\dfrac{\sin x}{2}\right| < 1$ for all x, the interval

of convergence is $-\infty < x < \infty$.

$$\text{Sum} = \frac{a}{1 - r} = \frac{1}{1 - \dfrac{\sin x}{2}} = \frac{2}{2 - \sin x}$$

41. Almost, but the Ratio Test won't determine whether there is convergence or divergence at the endpoints of the interval.

42. (a) For $k \le N$, it's obvious that

$$a_1 + \cdots + a_k \le a_1 + \cdots + a_N + \sum_{n=N+1}^{\infty} c_n.$$

For all $k > N$,

$$a_1 + \cdots + a_k = a_1 + \cdots + a_N + a_{N+1} + \cdots + a_k$$

$$\le a_1 + \cdots + a_N + c_{N+1} + \cdots + c_k$$

$$\le a_1 + \cdots + a_N + \sum_{n=N+1}^{\infty} c_n$$

(b) Since all of the a_n are nonnegative, the partial sums of the series form a nondecreasing sequence of real numbers. Part (a) shows that the sequence is bounded above, so it must converge to a limit.

43. (a) For $k \le N$, it's obvious that

$$d_1 + \cdots + d_k \le d_1 + \cdots + d_N + \sum_{n=N+1}^{\infty} a_n.$$

For all $k > N$,

$$d_1 + \cdots + d_k = d_1 + \cdots + d_N + d_{N+1} + \cdots + d_k$$

$$\le d_1 + \cdots + d_N + a_{N+1} + \cdots + a_k$$

$$\le d_1 + \cdots + d_N + \sum_{n=N+1}^{\infty} a_n$$

(b) If $\sum a_n$ converged, that would imply that $\sum d_n$ was also convergent.

44. Answers will vary.

45. $\displaystyle\sum_{n=1}^{\infty} \frac{4}{(4n - 3)(4n + 1)} = \sum_{n=1}^{\infty}\left(\frac{1}{4n - 3} - \frac{1}{4n + 1}\right)$

$s_1 = 1 - \dfrac{1}{5}$

$s_2 = \left(1 - \dfrac{1}{5}\right) + \left(\dfrac{1}{5} - \dfrac{1}{9}\right) = 1 - \dfrac{1}{9}$

$s_3 = \left(1 - \dfrac{1}{5}\right) + \left(\dfrac{1}{5} - \dfrac{1}{9}\right) + \left(\dfrac{1}{9} - \dfrac{1}{13}\right) = 1 - \dfrac{1}{13}$

$s_n = 1 - \dfrac{1}{4n + 1}$

$S = \lim\limits_{n\to\infty} s_n = 1$

46. $\displaystyle\sum_{n=1}^{\infty} \frac{6}{(2n - 1)(2n + 1)} = \sum_{n=1}^{\infty}\left(\frac{3}{2n - 1} - \frac{3}{2n + 1}\right)$

$s_1 = 3 - \dfrac{3}{3}$

$s_2 = (3 - 1) + \left(1 - \dfrac{3}{5}\right) = 3 - \dfrac{3}{5}$

$s_3 = (3 - 1) + \left(1 - \dfrac{3}{5}\right) + \left(\dfrac{3}{5} - \dfrac{3}{7}\right) = 3 - \dfrac{3}{7}$

$s_n = 3 - \dfrac{3}{2n + 1}$

$S = \lim\limits_{n\to\infty} s_n = 3$

47. $\displaystyle\sum_{n=1}^{\infty} \frac{40n}{(2n-1)^2(2n+1)^2} = \sum_{n=1}^{\infty}\left[\frac{5}{(2n - 1)^2} - \frac{5}{(2n + 1)^2}\right]$

$s_1 = 5 - \dfrac{5}{9}$

$s_2 = \left(5 - \dfrac{5}{9}\right) + \left(\dfrac{5}{9} - \dfrac{5}{25}\right) = 5 - \dfrac{5}{25}$

$s_3 = \left(5 - \dfrac{5}{9}\right) + \left(\dfrac{5}{9} - \dfrac{5}{25}\right) + \left(\dfrac{5}{25} - \dfrac{5}{49}\right) = 5 - \dfrac{5}{49}$

$s_n = 5 - \dfrac{5}{(2n + 1)^2}$

$S = \lim\limits_{n\to\infty} s_n = 5$

48. $\displaystyle\sum_{n=1}^{\infty} \frac{2n + 1}{n^2(n + 1)^2} = \sum_{n=1}^{\infty}\left(\frac{1}{n^2} - \frac{1}{(n + 1)^2}\right)$

$s_1 = 1 - \dfrac{1}{4}$

$s_2 = \left(1 - \dfrac{1}{4}\right) + \left(\dfrac{1}{4} - \dfrac{1}{9}\right) = 1 - \dfrac{1}{9}$

$s_3 = \left(1 - \dfrac{1}{4}\right) + \left(\dfrac{1}{4} - \dfrac{1}{9}\right) + \left(\dfrac{1}{9} - \dfrac{1}{16}\right) = 1 - \dfrac{1}{16}$

$s_n = 1 - \dfrac{1}{(n + 1)^2}$

$S = \lim\limits_{n\to\infty} s_n = 1$

49. $s_1 = 1 - \dfrac{1}{\sqrt{2}}$

$s_2 = \left(1 - \dfrac{1}{\sqrt{2}}\right) + \left(\dfrac{1}{\sqrt{2}} - \dfrac{1}{\sqrt{3}}\right) = 1 - \dfrac{1}{\sqrt{3}}$

$s_3 = \left(1 - \dfrac{1}{\sqrt{2}}\right) + \left(\dfrac{1}{\sqrt{2}} - \dfrac{1}{\sqrt{3}}\right) + \left(\dfrac{1}{\sqrt{3}} - \dfrac{1}{\sqrt{4}}\right) = 1 - \dfrac{1}{\sqrt{4}}$

$s_n = 1 - \dfrac{1}{\sqrt{n + 1}}$

$S = \lim\limits_{n\to\infty} s_n = 1$

50. $s_1 = \dfrac{1}{\ln 3} - \dfrac{1}{\ln 2}$

$s_2 = \left(\dfrac{1}{\ln 3} - \dfrac{1}{\ln 2}\right) + \left(\dfrac{1}{\ln 4} - \dfrac{1}{\ln 3}\right) = \dfrac{1}{\ln 4} - \dfrac{1}{\ln 2}$

$s_3 = \left(\dfrac{1}{\ln 3} - \dfrac{1}{\ln 2}\right) + \left(\dfrac{1}{\ln 4} - \dfrac{1}{\ln 3}\right) + \left(\dfrac{1}{\ln 5} - \dfrac{1}{\ln 4}\right)$

$\quad = \dfrac{1}{\ln 5} - \dfrac{1}{\ln 2}$

$s_n = \dfrac{1}{\ln(n + 2)} - \dfrac{1}{\ln 2}$

$S = \lim\limits_{n\to\infty} s_n = -\dfrac{1}{\ln 2}$

51. $s_1 = \tan^{-1} 1 - \tan^{-1} 2 = \dfrac{\pi}{4} - \tan^{-1} 2$

$s_2 = (\tan^{-1} 1 - \tan^{-1} 2) + (\tan^{-1} 2 - \tan^{-1} 3)$

$\quad = \dfrac{\pi}{4} - \tan^{-1} 3$

$s_3 = (\tan^{-1} 1 - \tan^{-1} 2) + (\tan^{-1} 2 - \tan^{-1} 3)$

$\quad\quad + (\tan^{-1} 3 - \tan^{-1} 4)$

$\quad = \dfrac{\pi}{4} - \tan^{-1} 4$

$s_n = \dfrac{\pi}{4} - \tan^{-1} (n + 1)$

$S = \lim\limits_{n\to\infty} s_n = \dfrac{\pi}{4} - \lim\limits_{n\to\infty} \tan^{-1} n = \dfrac{\pi}{4} - \dfrac{\pi}{2} = -\dfrac{\pi}{4}$

52. $\dfrac{1}{1 - x} = \sum\limits_{n=0}^{\infty} x^n$

Differentiate:

$\dfrac{1}{(1 - x)^2} = \sum\limits_{n=0}^{\infty} nx^{n-1}$

Multiply by x:

$\dfrac{x}{(1 - x)^2} = \sum\limits_{n=0}^{\infty} nx^n$

Differentiate:

$\dfrac{d}{dx} \dfrac{x}{(1 - x)^2} = \dfrac{(1 - x)^2(1) - (x)(2)(1 - x)(-1)}{(1 - x)^4}$

$\quad = \dfrac{(1 - x) + 2x}{(1 - x)^3}$

$\quad = \dfrac{x + 1}{(1 - x)^3}$

$\dfrac{x + 1}{(1 - x)^3} = \sum\limits_{n=0}^{\infty} n^2 x^{n-1}$

Multiply by x:

$\dfrac{x(x + 1)}{(1 - x)^3} = \sum\limits_{n=0}^{\infty} n^2 x^n$

Let $x = \dfrac{1}{2}$:

$\dfrac{\dfrac{1}{2}\left(\dfrac{3}{2}\right)}{\left(\dfrac{1}{2}\right)^3} = \sum\limits_{n=0}^{\infty} n^2 \left(\dfrac{1}{2}\right)^n$

$6 = \sum\limits_{n=0}^{\infty} \dfrac{n^2}{2^n}$

The sum is 6.

■ Section 9.5 Testing Convergence at Endpoints (pp. 496–508)

Exploration 1   The *p*-Series Test

1. We first note that the Integral Test applies to any series of the form $\sum \dfrac{1}{n^p}$ where p is positive. This is because the function $f(x) = x^{-p}$ is continuous and positive for all $x > 0$, and $f'(x) = -p \cdot x^{-p-1}$ is negative for all $x > 0$.

If $p > 1$:

$\displaystyle\int_1^{\infty} \dfrac{1}{x^p}\, dx = \lim_{k\to\infty} \int_1^k \dfrac{1}{x^p}\, dx = \lim_{k\to\infty} \left(\dfrac{x^{-p+1}}{-p+1}\Big]_1^k \right)$

$\quad = \lim\limits_{k\to\infty}\left(\dfrac{1}{1-p} \cdot \left(\dfrac{1}{k^{p-1}} - 1 \right) \right)$

$\quad = 0 + \dfrac{1}{p-1} \text{ (since } p-1 > 0)$

$\quad = \dfrac{1}{p-1} < \infty.$

The series converges by the Intergral Test.

2. If $0 < p < 1$:

$\displaystyle\int_1^{\infty} \dfrac{1}{x^p}\, dx = \lim_{k\to\infty} \int_1^k \dfrac{1}{x^p}\, dx$

$\quad = \lim\limits_{k\to\infty}\left(\dfrac{x^{-p+1}}{-p+1}\Big]_1^k \right)$

$\quad = \lim\limits_{k\to\infty}\left(\dfrac{1}{1-p} \cdot (k^{1-p} - 1) \right)$

$\quad = \infty \text{ (since } 1 - p > 0).$

The series diverges by the Integral Test.

If $p \leq 0$, the series diverges by the nth Term Test. This completes the proof for $p < 1$.

3. If $p = 1$:

$\displaystyle\int_1^{\infty} \dfrac{1}{x^p}\, dx = \lim_{k\to\infty} \int_1^k \dfrac{1}{x}\, dx$

$\quad = \lim\limits_{k\to\infty}\left(\ln x \Big]_1^k \right)$

$\quad = \lim\limits_{k\to\infty} \ln k = \infty.$

The series diverges by the Integral Test.

Exploration 2   The Maclaurin Series of a Strange Function

1. Since $f^{(n)}(0) = 0$ for all n, the Maclaurin Series for f has all zero coefficients! The series is simply $\sum\limits_{n=0}^{\infty} 0 \cdot x^n = 0$.

2. The series converges (to 0) for all values of x.

3. Since $f(x) = 0$ only at $x = 0$, the only place that this series actually converges to its f-value is at $x = 0$.

Quick Review 9.5

1. Converges, since it is of the form $\int_1^\infty \frac{1}{x^p}\,dx$ with $p > 1$

2. Diverges, limit comparison test with integral of $\frac{1}{x}$

3. Diverges, comparison test with integral of $\frac{1}{x}$

4. Converges, comparison test with integral of $\frac{2}{x^2}$

5. Diverges, limit comparison test with integral of $\frac{1}{\sqrt{x}}$

6. Yes, for $N = 0$

7. Yes, for $N = 2\sqrt{2}$

8. No, neither positive nor decreasing for $x > \sqrt{3}$

9. No, oscillates

10. No, not positive for $x \geq 1$

Section 9.5 Exercises

1. Diverges by the Integral Test, since $\int_1^\infty \frac{5}{x+1}\,dx$ diverges.

2. Diverges because $\sum_{n=1}^\infty \frac{3}{\sqrt{n}} = 3\sum_{n=1}^\infty \frac{1}{n^{1/2}}$, which diverges by the p-series Test.

3. Diverges by the Direct Comparison Test, since $\frac{\ln n}{n} > \frac{1}{n}$ for $n \geq 2$ and $\sum_{n=2}^\infty \frac{1}{n}$ diverges.

4. Diverges by the Integral Test, since $\int_1^\infty \frac{1}{2x-1}\,dx$ diverges.

5. Diverges, since it is a geometric series with
$r = \frac{1}{\ln 2} \approx 1.44.$

6. Converges, since it is a geometric series with
$r = \frac{1}{\ln 3} \approx 0.91.$

7. Diverges by the nth-Term Test, since $\lim_{n\to\infty} n \sin \frac{1}{n} = 1.$

8. Converges by the Direct Comparison Test, since
$\frac{e^n}{1+e^{2n}} < e^{-n}$ for $n \geq 0$, and $\sum_{n=0}^\infty e^{-n}$ converges as a geometric series with $r = e^{-1} \approx 0.37.$

9. Converges by the Direct Comparison Test, since
$\frac{\sqrt{n}}{n^2+1} < \frac{1}{n^{3/2}}$ for $n \geq 1$, and $\sum_{n=1}^\infty \frac{1}{n^{3/2}}$ converges as a p-series with $p = \frac{3}{2}.$

10. Converges by the Limit Comparison Test, since
$$\lim_{n\to\infty} \frac{\frac{5n^3-3n}{n^2(n+2)(n^2+5)}}{\frac{1}{n^2}} = 5, \text{ and } \sum_{n=1}^\infty \frac{1}{n^2}$$
converges as a p-series with $p = 2.$

11. Diverges by the nth-Term Test, since
$$\lim_{n\to\infty} \frac{3^{n-1}+1}{3^n} = \frac{1}{3} \neq 0.$$

12. Converges by the Alternating Series Test. If $u_n = \frac{1}{\ln n}$, then $\{u_n\}$ is a decreasing sequence of positive terms with
$$\lim_{n\to\infty} u_n = 0.$$

13. Diverges by the nth-Term Test, since $\lim_{n\to\infty} \frac{10^n}{n^{10}} = \infty.$

14. Converges by the Alternating Series Test. If $u_n = \frac{\sqrt{n}+1}{n+1}$, then $\{u_n\}$ is a decreasing sequence of positive terms with $\lim_{n\to\infty} u_n = 0$. (To show that u_n is decreasing, let
$f(x) = \frac{\sqrt{x}+1}{x+1}$ and observe that
$$f'(x) = \frac{(x+1)\left(\frac{1}{2\sqrt{x}}\right) - (\sqrt{x}+1)(1)}{(x+1)^2} = \frac{1-x-2\sqrt{x}}{2(x+1)^2\sqrt{x}},$$
which is negative, at least for $x \geq 1$.)

15. Diverges by the nth-Term Test since $\frac{\ln n}{\ln n^2} = \frac{\ln n}{2\ln n} = \frac{1}{2}$, which means each term is $\pm\frac{1}{2}$.

16. Diverges by the Limit Comparison Test.
Let $a_n = \frac{1}{n} - \frac{1}{n^2}$ and $b_n = \frac{1}{n}$.
Then $a_n > 0$ and $b_n > 0$ for $n \geq 2$ and
$$\lim_{n\to\infty} \frac{a_n}{b_n} = \lim_{n\to\infty} \frac{\frac{1}{n}-\frac{1}{n^2}}{\frac{1}{n}} = \lim_{n\to\infty} \frac{n-1}{n} = \lim_{n\to\infty}\left(1-\frac{1}{n}\right) = 1.$$
Since $\sum_{n=1}^\infty b_n$ diverges, $\sum_{n=1}^\infty a_n$ also diverges.

17. Converges absolutely, because, absolutely, it is a geometric series with
$r = 0.1.$

18. Converges conditionally:
If $u_n = \frac{1+n}{n^2} = \frac{1}{n} + \frac{1}{n^2}$, then $\{u_n\}$ is a decreasing sequence of positive terms with $\lim_{n\to\infty} u_n = 0$, so $\sum_{n=1}^\infty (-1)^{n+1}\frac{1+n}{n^2}$ converges by the Alternating Series Test.

But $\sum_{n=1}^\infty \frac{1+n}{n^2}$ diverges by the Direct Comparison Test, since $\frac{1+n}{n^2} \geq \frac{1}{n}$ for $n \geq 1$ and $\sum_{n=1}^\infty \frac{1}{n}$ diverges.

19. Converges absolutely, since $\displaystyle\sum_{n=1}^{\infty} n^2\left(\frac{2}{3}\right)^n$ converges by the

Ratio Test:

$$\lim_{n\to\infty}\left|\frac{a_{n+1}}{a_n}\right| = (n+1)^2\left(\frac{2}{3}\right)^{n+1} \cdot \frac{1}{n^2}\left(\frac{3}{2}\right)^n = \frac{2}{3} < 1.$$

20. Converges conditionally.

If $u_n = \dfrac{1}{n \ln n}$, then $\{u_n\}$ is a decreasing sequence of

positive terms with $\displaystyle\lim_{n\to\infty} u_n = 0$, so $\displaystyle\sum_{n=2}^{\infty} (-1)^{n+1}\frac{1}{n \ln n}$

converges by the Alternating Series Test.

But $\displaystyle\sum_{n=2}^{\infty} \frac{1}{n \ln n}$ diverges by the integral test, since

$$\int_2^{\infty} \frac{1}{x \ln x}\,dx = \lim_{b\to\infty}\left[\ln|\ln x|\right]_2^b = \infty.$$

21. Diverges by the nth-Term Test, since $\displaystyle\lim_{n\to\infty} \frac{n!}{2^n} = \infty$ and so the

terms do not approach 0.

22. Converges absolutely, since $\displaystyle\sum_{n=1}^{\infty} \left|\frac{\sin n}{n^2}\right|$ converges by direct

comparison to $\displaystyle\sum_{n=1}^{\infty} \frac{1}{n^2}$, which converges as a p-series with

$p = 2$.

23. Converges conditionally:

If $u_n = \dfrac{1}{1 + \sqrt{n}}$, then $\{u_n\}$ is a decreasing sequence of

positive terms with $\displaystyle\lim_{n\to\infty} u_n = 0$, so $\displaystyle\sum_{n=1}^{\infty} \frac{(-1)^n}{1 + \sqrt{n}}$ converges

by the Alternating Series Test.

But $\displaystyle\sum_{n=1}^{\infty} \frac{1}{1 + \sqrt{n}}$ diverges by direct comparison to $\displaystyle\sum_{n=1}^{\infty} \frac{1}{n^{1/2}}$,

which diverges as a p-series with $p = \dfrac{1}{2}$.

24. Converges absolutely, since $\displaystyle\sum_{n=1}^{\infty} \left|\frac{\cos n\pi}{n\sqrt{n}}\right| = \sum_{n=1}^{\infty} \frac{1}{n^{3/2}}$, which

converges as a p-series.

25. Converges conditionally, since $\displaystyle\sum_{n=1}^{\infty} \frac{\cos n\pi}{n} = -\sum_{n=1}^{\infty} \frac{(-1)^{n+1}}{n}$.

(See Examples 2 and 4.)

26. Converges conditionally:

If $u_n = \dfrac{1}{\sqrt{n} + \sqrt{n+1}}$, then $\{u_n\}$ is a decreasing sequence

of positive terms with $\displaystyle\lim_{n\to\infty} u_n = 0$, so $\displaystyle\sum_{n=1}^{\infty} \frac{(-1)^n}{\sqrt{n} + \sqrt{n+1}}$

converges by the Alternating Series Test.

But $\displaystyle\sum_{n=1}^{\infty} u_n$ diverges by the Limit Comparison Test:

If $v_n = \dfrac{1}{n^{1/2}}$, then $\displaystyle\lim_{n\to\infty} \frac{u_n}{v_n} = \lim_{n\to\infty} \frac{n^{1/2}}{\sqrt{n} + \sqrt{n+1}} = \frac{1}{2}$.

Since $\displaystyle\sum_{n=1}^{\infty} v_n$ diverges as a p-series with $p = \dfrac{1}{2}$, $\displaystyle\sum_{n=1}^{\infty} u_n$ also

diverges.

27. This is a geometric series which converges only for $|x| < 1$.

(a) $(-1, 1)$

(b) $(-1, 1)$

(c) None

28. This is a geometric series which converges only for $|x + 5| < 1$, or $-6 < x < -4$.

(a) $(-6, -4)$

(b) $(-6, -4)$

(c) None

29. This is a geometric series which converges only for $|4x + 1| < 1$, or $-\dfrac{1}{2} < x < 0$.

(a) $\left(-\dfrac{1}{2}, 0\right)$

(b) $\left(-\dfrac{1}{2}, 0\right)$

(c) None

30. $\displaystyle\lim_{n\to\infty}\left|\frac{a_{n+1}}{a_n}\right| = \lim_{n\to\infty}\frac{|3x - 2|^{n+1}}{n+1} \cdot \frac{n}{|3x - 2|^n} = |3x - 2|$

The series converges absolutely when $|3x - 2| < 1$, or

$\dfrac{1}{3} < x < 1$. Check $x = \dfrac{1}{3}$: $\displaystyle\sum_{n=1}^{\infty} \frac{(-1)^n}{n}$ converges

conditionally. Check $x = 1$: $\displaystyle\sum_{n=1}^{\infty} \frac{1^n}{n} = \sum_{n=1}^{\infty} \frac{1}{n}$ diverges.

(a) $\left[\dfrac{1}{3}, 1\right)$

(b) $\left(\dfrac{1}{3}, 1\right)$

(c) At $x = \dfrac{1}{3}$

31. This is a geometric series which converges only for

$\left|\dfrac{x - 2}{10}\right| < 1$, or $-8 < x < 12$.

(a) $(-8, 12)$

(b) $(-8, 12)$

(c) None

32. $\displaystyle\lim_{n\to\infty}\left|\frac{a_{n+1}}{a_n}\right| = \lim_{n\to\infty}\frac{(n+1)|x|^{n+1}}{n+3} \cdot \frac{n+2}{n|x|^n} = |x|$

The series converges absolutely when $|x| < 1$, or

$-1 < x < 1$. For $|x| \geq 1$, the series diverges by the

nth-Term Test.

(a) $(-1, 1)$

(b) $(-1, 1)$

(c) None

33. $\lim\limits_{n \to \infty} \left| \dfrac{a_{n+1}}{a_n} \right| = \lim\limits_{n \to \infty} \dfrac{|x|^{n+1}}{(n+1)\sqrt{n+1} \cdot 3^{n+1}} \cdot \dfrac{n\sqrt{n}\, 3^n}{|x|^n} = \dfrac{|x|}{3}$

The series converges absolutely for $|x| < 3$. Furthermore,

when $|x| = 3$, $\displaystyle\sum_{n=1}^{\infty} \left| \dfrac{x^n}{n\sqrt{n}\, 3^n} \right| = \sum_{n=1}^{\infty} \dfrac{1}{n^{3/2}}$, which also converges

as a p-series with $p = \dfrac{3}{2}$.

(a) $[-3, 3]$

(b) $[-3, 3]$

(c) None

34. $\lim\limits_{n \to \infty} \left| \dfrac{a_{n+1}}{a_n} \right| = \lim\limits_{n \to \infty} \dfrac{|x|^{2n+3}}{(n+1)!} \cdot \dfrac{n!}{|x|^{2n+1}} = \lim\limits_{n \to \infty} \dfrac{x^2}{n+1} = 0$

The series converges absolutely for all real numbers.

(a) All real numbers

(b) All real numbers

(c) None

35. $\lim\limits_{n \to \infty} \left| \dfrac{a_{n+1}}{a_n} \right| = \lim\limits_{n \to \infty} \dfrac{(n+1)|x+3|^{n+1}}{5^{n+1}} \cdot \dfrac{5^n}{n|x+3|^n} = \dfrac{|x+3|}{5}$

The series converges absolutely for $\dfrac{|x+3|}{5} < 1$,

or $-8 < x < 2$. For $\dfrac{|x+3|}{5} \geq 1$, the series diverges by

the nth-Term Test.

(a) $(-8, 2)$

(b) $(-8, 2)$

(c) None

36. $\lim\limits_{n \to \infty} \left| \dfrac{a_{n+1}}{a_n} \right| = \lim\limits_{n \to \infty} \dfrac{(n+1)|x|^{n+1}}{4^{n+1}[(n+1)^2+1]} \cdot \dfrac{4^n(n^2+1)}{n|x|^n} = \dfrac{|x|}{4}$

The series converges absolutely for $\dfrac{|x|}{4} < 1$, or $-4 < x < 4$.

Check $x = -4$:

$\displaystyle\sum_{n=0}^{\infty} \dfrac{(-1)^n n}{n^2+1}$ converges by the Alternating Series Test.

Check $x = 4$:

$\displaystyle\sum_{n=0}^{\infty} \dfrac{n}{n^2+1}$ diverges by the Limit Comparison Test

with $\displaystyle\sum_{n=1}^{\infty} \dfrac{1}{n}$.

(a) $[-4, 4)$

(b) $(-4, 4)$

(c) At $x = -4$

37. $\lim\limits_{n \to \infty} \left| \dfrac{a_{n+1}}{a_n} \right| = \lim\limits_{n \to \infty} \dfrac{\sqrt{n+1}\,|x|^{n+1}}{3^{n+1}} \cdot \dfrac{3^n}{\sqrt{n}\,|x|^n} = \dfrac{|x|}{3}$

The series converges absolutely for $|x| < 3$, or $-3 < x < 3$.

For $|x| \geq 3$, the series diverges by the nth-Term Test.

(a) $(-3, 3)$

(b) $(-3, 3)$

(c) None

38. $\lim\limits_{n \to \infty} \left| \dfrac{a_{n+1}}{a_n} \right| = \lim\limits_{n \to \infty} \dfrac{(n+1)!\,|x-4|^{n+1}}{n!\,|x-4|^n}$

$= \lim\limits_{n \to \infty} (n+1)|x-4|$

$= \begin{cases} 0, & x = 4 \\ \infty, & x \neq 4 \end{cases}$

(a) Only at $x = 4$

(b) At $x = 4$

(c) None

39. $\lim\limits_{n \to \infty} \left| \dfrac{a_{n+1}}{a_n} \right| = \lim\limits_{n \to \infty} \dfrac{|-2|^{n+1}(n+2)|x-1|^{n+1}}{|-2|^n(n+1)|x-1|^n} = |2(x-1)|$

The series converges absolutely for $|2(x-1)| < 1$, or

$\dfrac{1}{2} < x < \dfrac{3}{2}$. For $|2(x-1)| \geq 1$, the series diverges by the

nth-Term Test.

(a) $\left(\dfrac{1}{2}, \dfrac{3}{2} \right)$

(b) $\left(\dfrac{1}{2}, \dfrac{3}{2} \right)$

(c) None

40. $\lim\limits_{n \to \infty} \left| \dfrac{a_{n+1}}{a_n} \right| = \lim\limits_{n \to \infty} \dfrac{|4x-5|^{2n+3}}{(n+1)^{3/2}} \cdot \dfrac{n^{3/2}}{|4x-5|^{2n+1}} = (4x-5)^2$

The series converges absolutely for $(4x-5)^2 < 1$, or

$1 < x < \dfrac{3}{2}$. Check $x = 1$: $\displaystyle\sum_{n=1}^{\infty} \dfrac{(-1)^{2n+1}}{n^{3/2}} = -\sum_{n=1}^{\infty} \dfrac{1}{n^{3/2}}$

converges as a p-series with $p = \dfrac{3}{2}$. Check $x = \dfrac{3}{2}$:

$\displaystyle\sum_{n=1}^{\infty} \dfrac{1^{2n+1}}{n^{3/2}}$ converges as a p-series with $p = \dfrac{3}{2}$.

(a) $\left[1, \dfrac{3}{2} \right]$

(b) $\left[1, \dfrac{3}{2} \right]$

(c) None

41. $\lim\limits_{n \to \infty} \left| \dfrac{a_{n+1}}{a_n} \right| = \lim\limits_{n \to \infty} \dfrac{|x+\pi|^{n+1}}{\sqrt{n+1}} \cdot \dfrac{\sqrt{n}}{|x+\pi|^n} = |x+\pi|$

The series converges absolutely for $|x+\pi| < 1$, or

$-\pi - 1 < x < -\pi + 1$.

Check $x = -\pi - 1$:

$\displaystyle\sum_{n=1}^{\infty} \dfrac{(-1)^n}{\sqrt{n}}$ converges by Alternating Series Test.

Check $x = -\pi + 1$:

$\displaystyle\sum_{n=1}^{\infty} \dfrac{1}{\sqrt{n}}$ diverges as a p-series with $p = \dfrac{1}{2}$.

(a) $[-\pi - 1, -\pi + 1)$

(b) $(-\pi - 1, -\pi + 1)$

(c) At $x = -\pi - 1$

42. This is a geometric series which converges only for

$|\ln x| < 1$, or $\dfrac{1}{e} < x < e$.

(a) $\left(\dfrac{1}{e}, e\right)$

(b) $\left(\dfrac{1}{e}, e\right)$

(c) None

43. $n = 13 \times 10^9 \cdot 365 \cdot 24 \cdot 3600 = 4.09968 \times 10^{17}$
$\ln(n+1) < \text{sum} < 1 + \ln n$
$\ln(4.09968 \times 10^{17} + 1) < \text{sum} < 1 + \ln(4.09968 \times 10^{17})$
$40.5548... < \text{sum} < 41.5548...$
$40.554 < \text{sum} < 41.555$

44. Comparing areas in the figures, we have for all $n \geq 1$,

$$\int_1^{n+1} f(x)\, dx < a_1 + \cdots + a_n < a_1 + \int_1^n f(x)\, dx.$$

If the integral diverges, it must go to infinity, and the first inequality forces the partial sums of the series to go to infinity as well, so the series is divergent. If the integral converges, then the second inequality puts an upper bound on the partial sums of the series, and since they are a nondecreasing sequence, they must converge to a finite sum for the series. (See the explanation preceding Exercise 42 in Section 9.4.)

45.

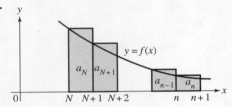

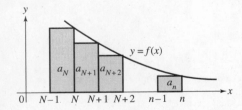

Comparing areas in the figures, we have for all $n \geq N$,

$$\int_N^{n+1} f(x)\, dx < a_N + \cdots + a_n < a_N + \int_N^n f(x)\, dx.$$

If the integral diverges, it must go to infinity, and the first inequality forces the partial sums of the series to go to infinity as well, so the series is divergent. If the integral converges, then the second inequality puts an upper bound on the partial sums of the series, and since they are a nondecreasing sequence, they must converge to a finite sum for the series. (See the explanation preceding Exercise 42 in Section 9.4.)

46. (a) Diverges by the Limit Comparison Test.

Let $a_k = \dfrac{1}{\sqrt{2k+7}}$ and $b_k = \dfrac{1}{k^{1/2}}$. Then $a_k > 0$ and $b_k > 0$ for $k \geq 1$ and $\lim\limits_{k\to\infty} \dfrac{a_k}{b_k} = \lim\limits_{k\to\infty} \dfrac{k^{1/2}}{\sqrt{2k+7}} = \dfrac{1}{\sqrt{2}}$.
Since $\sum\limits_{k=1}^{\infty} b_k$ diverges as a p-series with $p = \dfrac{1}{2}$, $\sum\limits_{k=1}^{\infty} a_k$ also diverges.

(b) Diverges by the nth-Term Test, since

$$\lim_{k\to\infty}\left(1 + \frac{1}{k}\right)^k = e \neq 0.$$

(c) Converges absolutely by the Comparison Test, since

$\left|\dfrac{\cos k}{k^2 + \sqrt{k}}\right| < \dfrac{1}{k^2}$ for $k \geq 1$ and $\sum\limits_{k=1}^{\infty} \dfrac{1}{k^2}$ converges as a p-series with $p = 2$.

(d) Diverges by the integral test, since

$$\int_3^\infty \frac{18}{x\ln x}\, dx = \lim_{b\to\infty}\left[18\ln|\ln x|\right]_3^b = \infty$$

47. One possible answer: $\sum\limits_{n=3}^{\infty} \dfrac{1}{n\ln n}$

This series diverges by the integral test, since

$\int_3^\infty \dfrac{1}{x\ln x}\, dx = \lim\limits_{b\to\infty}\left[\ln|\ln x|\right]_3^b = \infty$. Its partial sums are roughly $\ln(\ln n)$, so they are much smaller than the partial sums for the harmonic series, which are about $\ln n$.

48. (a) $a_k = (-1)^{k+1}\displaystyle\int_0^{1/k} 6(kx)^2\, dx$

$= (-1)^{k+1}\left[2k^2 x^3\right]_0^{1/k}$

$= (-1)^{k+1}\left(\dfrac{2}{k}\right)$

(b) The series converges by the Alternating Series Test.

(c) The first few partial sums are:

$S_1 = 2,\ S_2 = 1,\ S_3 = \dfrac{5}{3},\ S_4 = \dfrac{7}{6},\ S_5 = \dfrac{47}{30},\ S_6 = \dfrac{37}{30},$
$S_7 = \dfrac{319}{210},\ S_8 = \dfrac{533}{420},\ S_9 = \dfrac{1879}{1260}$. For an alternating series, the sum is between any two adjacent partial sums, so $1 < S_8 \leq \text{sum} \leq S_9 < \dfrac{3}{2}$.

49. (a) Diverges by the Limit Comparison Test. Let

$a_n = \dfrac{n}{3n^2 + 1}$ and $b_n = \dfrac{1}{n}$. Then $a_n > 0$ and $b_n > 0$ for $n \geq 1$, and $\lim\limits_{n\to\infty} \dfrac{a_n}{b_n} = \lim\limits_{n\to\infty} \dfrac{n^2}{3n^2 + 1} = \dfrac{1}{3}$. Since $\sum\limits_{n=1}^{\infty} b_n$ diverges, $\sum\limits_{n=1}^{\infty} a_n$ diverges.

(b) $S = \sum_{n=1}^{\infty} \dfrac{n}{3n^2 + 1} \cdot \dfrac{3}{n} = \sum_{n=1}^{\infty} \dfrac{3}{3n^2 + 1}$.

This series converges by the Direct Comparison Test,

since $\dfrac{3}{3n^2 + 1} < \dfrac{1}{n^2}$ and $\sum_{n=1}^{\infty} \dfrac{1}{n^2}$ is convergent as a

p-series with $p = 2$.

50. (a) From the list of Maclaurin series in Section 9.2,

$\ln(1 + x) = x - \dfrac{x^2}{2} + \dfrac{x^3}{3} - \cdots + (-1)^{n+1} \dfrac{x^n}{n} + \cdots$.

(b) $-1 < x \leq 1$

(c) To estimate $\ln \dfrac{3}{2}$, we would let $x = \dfrac{1}{2}$

The truncation error is less than the magnitude of the

sixth nonzero term, or

$\left| -\dfrac{x^6}{6} \right| = \dfrac{1}{2^6 \cdot 6} = \dfrac{1}{384} < 0.002605$

Thus, a bound for the (absolute) truncation error is

0.002605.

(d) $\sum_{n=1}^{\infty} \dfrac{(-1)^{n+1} x^{2n}}{2n} = \dfrac{1}{2} \sum_{n=1}^{\infty} \dfrac{(-1)^{n+1} (x^2)^n}{n} = \dfrac{1}{2} \ln(1 + x^2)$

51. $\lim_{k \to \infty} \left| \dfrac{a_{k+1}}{a_k} \right| = \lim_{k \to \infty} \dfrac{2^{k+1} |x|^{k+1}}{\ln(k+3)} \cdot \dfrac{\ln(k+2)}{2^k |x|^k} = 2|x|$

The series converges absolutely for $|x| < \dfrac{1}{2}$,

or $-\dfrac{1}{2} < x < \dfrac{1}{2}$.

Check $x = -\dfrac{1}{2}$:

$\sum_{k=0}^{\infty} \dfrac{(-1)^k}{\ln(k+2)}$ converges by the Alternating Series Test.

Check $x = \dfrac{1}{2}$:

$\sum_{k=0}^{\infty} \dfrac{1}{\ln(k+2)}$ diverges by the Direct Comparison Test, since

$\dfrac{1}{\ln(k+2)} > \dfrac{1}{k}$ for $k \geq 2$ and $\sum_{k=2}^{\infty} \dfrac{1}{k}$ diverges. The original

series converges for $-\dfrac{1}{2} \leq x < \dfrac{1}{2}$.

52. (a) The series converges by the Direct Comparison Test,

since $\dfrac{1}{n^p \ln n} < \dfrac{1}{n^p}$ for $n \geq 3$, and $\sum_{n=3}^{\infty} \dfrac{1}{n^p}$ converges as a

p-series when $p > 1$.

(b) For $p = 1$, the series is $\sum_{n=2}^{\infty} \dfrac{1}{n \ln n}$, which diverges by the

Integral Test, since $\displaystyle\int_2^{\infty} \dfrac{1}{x \ln x}\, dx = \lim_{b \to \infty} \Big[\ln(\ln x) \Big]_2^b = \infty$.

(c) For $0 \leq p < 1$, we have $\dfrac{1}{n^p \ln n} > \dfrac{1}{n \ln n}$, so

$\sum_{n=2}^{\infty} \dfrac{1}{n^p \ln n}$ diverges by the Direct Comparison Test with

$\dfrac{1}{n \ln n}$ from part (b).

53. $\ln(1 + x) = \sum_{n=1}^{\infty} (-1)^{n+1} \dfrac{x^n}{n}$, so at $x = 1$, the series is

$\sum_{n=1}^{\infty} \dfrac{(-1)^{n+1}}{n}$. This series converges by the Alternating Series

Test.

54. $\arctan x = \sum_{n=0}^{\infty} (-1)^n \dfrac{x^{2n+1}}{2n + 1}$

At $x = -1$, the sequence is

$\sum_{n=0}^{\infty} \dfrac{(-1)^n (-1)^{2n+1}}{2n + 1} = -\sum_{n=0}^{\infty} \dfrac{(-1)^n}{2n + 1}$, which converges by the

Alternating Series Test. At $x = 1$, the sequence is

$\sum_{n=0}^{\infty} \dfrac{(-1)^n}{2n + 1}$, which converges by the Alternating Series Test.

55. (a) It fails to satisfy $u_n \geq u_{n+1}$ for all $n \geq N$.

(b) The sum is $\left(\sum_{n=1}^{\infty} \dfrac{1}{3^n} \right) - \left(\sum_{n=1}^{\infty} \dfrac{1}{2^n} \right) = \dfrac{1/3}{1 - 1/3} - \dfrac{1/2}{1 - 1/2}$

$= \dfrac{1}{2} - 1$

$= -\dfrac{1}{2}$.

56. Answers will vary.

57. (a) $\lim_{n \to \infty} \sqrt[n]{a_n} = \lim_{n \to \infty} \sqrt[n]{\dfrac{n^2}{2^n}} = \lim_{n \to \infty} \dfrac{(\sqrt[n]{n})^2}{2} = \dfrac{1}{2}$

The series converges.

(b) $\lim_{n \to \infty} \sqrt[n]{a_n} = \lim_{n \to \infty} \sqrt[n]{\left(\dfrac{n}{2n-1} \right)^n} = \lim_{n \to \infty} \dfrac{n}{2n - 1} = \dfrac{1}{2}$

The series converges.

(c) $\lim_{n \to \infty, \, n \text{ odd}} \sqrt[n]{a_n} = \lim_{n \to \infty, \, n \text{ odd}} \sqrt[n]{\dfrac{n}{2^n}}$

$= \lim_{n \to \infty, \, n \text{ odd}} \dfrac{\sqrt[n]{n}}{2} = \dfrac{1}{2}$

$\lim_{n \to \infty, \, n \text{ even}} \sqrt[n]{a_n} = \lim_{n \to \infty, \, n \text{ even}} \sqrt[n]{\dfrac{1}{2^n}} = \dfrac{1}{2}$

Thus, $\lim_{n \to \infty} \sqrt[n]{a_n} = \dfrac{1}{2}$, so the series converges.

58. (a) $\lim_{n \to \infty} \sqrt[n]{|a_n|} = \lim_{n \to \infty} \sqrt[n]{\dfrac{|x - 1|^n}{4^n}} = \dfrac{|x - 1|}{4}$

The series converges absolutely if $\dfrac{|x - 1|}{4} < 1$, or

$-3 < x < 5$.

Check $x = -3$: $\sum_{n=0}^{\infty} (-1)^n$ diverges.

Check $x = 5$: $\sum_{n=0}^{\infty} 1^n$ diverges.

The interval of convergence is $(-3, 5)$.

58. continued

(b) $\lim\limits_{n\to\infty} \sqrt[n]{|a_n|} = \lim\limits_{n\to\infty} \sqrt[n]{\dfrac{|x-2|^n}{n\cdot 3^n}} = \lim\limits_{n\to\infty} \dfrac{|x-2|}{\sqrt[n]{n}\cdot 3} = \dfrac{|x-2|}{3}$

The series converges absolutely if $\dfrac{|x-2|}{3} < 1$, or

$-1 < x < 5$.

Check $x = -1$: $\sum\limits_{n=1}^{\infty} \dfrac{(-1)^n}{n}$ converges.

Check $x = 5$: $\sum\limits_{n=1}^{\infty} \dfrac{1}{n}$ diverges.

The interval of convergence is $[-1, 5)$.

(c) $\lim\limits_{n\to\infty} \sqrt[n]{|a_n|} = \lim\limits_{n\to\infty} \sqrt[n]{2^n|x|^n} = 2|x|$

The series converges absolutely if

$2|x| < 1$, or $-\dfrac{1}{2} < x < \dfrac{1}{2}$.

Check $x = -\dfrac{1}{2}$: $\sum\limits_{n=1}^{\infty} (-1)^n$ diverges.

Check $x = \dfrac{1}{2}$: $\sum\limits_{n=1}^{\infty} 1$ diverges.

The interval of convergence is $\left(-\dfrac{1}{2}, \dfrac{1}{2}\right)$.

(d) $\lim\limits_{n\to\infty} \sqrt[n]{|a_n|} = \lim\limits_{n\to\infty} \sqrt[n]{|\ln x|^n} = |\ln x|$

The series converges absolutely if $|\ln x| < 1$, or

$\dfrac{1}{e} < x < e$.

Check: $x = \dfrac{1}{e}$: $\sum\limits_{n=0}^{\infty} \left(\ln \dfrac{1}{e}\right)^n = \sum\limits_{n=0}^{\infty} (-1)^n$ diverges.

Check $x = e$: $\sum\limits_{n=0}^{\infty} (\ln e)^n = \sum\limits_{n=0}^{\infty} 1^n$ diverges.

The interval of convergence is $\left(\dfrac{1}{e}, e\right)$.

■ Chapter 9 Review Exercises

(pp. 509–511)

1. $\lim\limits_{n\to\infty} \left|\dfrac{a_{n+1}}{a_n}\right| = \lim\limits_{n\to\infty} \dfrac{|-x|^{n+1}}{(n+1)!} \cdot \dfrac{n!}{|-x|^n} = \lim\limits_{n\to\infty} \dfrac{|x|}{n+1} = 0$

The series converges absolutely for all x.

(a) ∞

(b) All real numbers

(c) All real numbers

(d) None

2. $\lim\limits_{n\to\infty} \left|\dfrac{a_{n+1}}{a_n}\right| = \lim\limits_{n\to\infty} \dfrac{|x+4|^{n+1}}{(n+1)3^{n+1}} \cdot \dfrac{n3^n}{|x+4|^n} = \dfrac{|x+4|}{3}$

The series converges absolutely for $\dfrac{|x+4|}{3} < 1$,

or $-7 < x < -1$.

Check $x = -7$: $\sum\limits_{n=1}^{\infty} \dfrac{(-1)^n}{n}$ converges

Check $x = -1$: $\sum\limits_{n=1}^{\infty} \dfrac{1}{n}$ diverges.

(a) 3

(b) $[-7, -1)$

(c) $(-7, -1)$

(d) At $x = -7$

3. This is a geometric series, so it converges absolutely when

$|r| < 1$ and diverges for all other values of x. Since

$r = \dfrac{2}{3}(x-1)$, the series converges absolutely when

$\left|\dfrac{2}{3}(x-1)\right| < 1$, or $-\dfrac{1}{2} < x < \dfrac{5}{2}$.

(a) $\dfrac{3}{2}$

(b) $\left(-\dfrac{1}{2}, \dfrac{5}{2}\right)$

(c) $\left(-\dfrac{1}{2}, \dfrac{5}{2}\right)$

(d) None

4. $\lim\limits_{n\to\infty} \left|\dfrac{a_{n+1}}{a_n}\right| = \lim\limits_{n\to\infty} \dfrac{|x-1|^{2n}}{(2n+1)!} \cdot \dfrac{(2n-1)!}{|x-1|^{2n-2}}$

$= \lim\limits_{n\to\infty} \dfrac{|x-1|^2}{(2n+1)(2n)} = 0$

The series converges absolutely for all x.

(a) ∞

(b) All real numbers

(c) All real numbers

(d) None

5. $\lim\limits_{n\to\infty} \left|\dfrac{a_{n+1}}{a_n}\right| = \lim\limits_{n\to\infty} \dfrac{|3x-1|^{n+1}}{(n+1)^2} \cdot \dfrac{n^2}{|3x-1|^n} = |3x-1|$

The series converges absolutely for

$|3x-1| < 1$, or $0 < x < \dfrac{2}{3}$. Furthermore, when

$|3x-1| = 1$, we have $|a_n| = \dfrac{1}{n^2}$ and

$\sum\limits_{n=1}^{\infty} \dfrac{1}{n^2}$ converges as a p-series with $p = 2$, so $\sum\limits_{n=1}^{\infty} a_n$ also

converges absolutely at the interval endpoints.

(a) $\dfrac{1}{3}$

(b) $\left[0, \dfrac{2}{3}\right]$

(c) $\left[0, \dfrac{2}{3}\right]$

(d) None

6. $\displaystyle\lim_{n\to\infty}\left|\frac{a_{n+1}}{a_n}\right| = \lim_{n\to\infty}\frac{(n+2)|x|^{3n+3}}{(n+1)|x|^{3n}} = |x|^3$

The series converges absolutely for $|x|^3 < 1$, or

$-1 < x < 1$. When $|x| \geq 1$, the series diverges by the nth

Term Test.

(a) 1

(b) $(-1, 1)$

(c) $(-1, 1)$

(d) None

7. $\displaystyle\lim_{n\to\infty}\left|\frac{a_{n+1}}{a_n}\right| = \lim_{n\to\infty}\frac{(n+2)|2x+1|^{n+1}}{(2n+3)2^{n+1}} \cdot \frac{(2n+1)2^n}{(n+1)|2x+1|^n}$

$\qquad = \dfrac{|2x+1|}{2}$

The series converges absolutely for $\dfrac{|2x+1|}{2} < 1$, or

$-\dfrac{3}{2} < x < \dfrac{1}{2}$. When $\dfrac{|2x+1|}{2} \geq 1$, the series diverges by the

nth-Term Test.

(a) 1

(b) $\left(-\dfrac{3}{2}, \dfrac{1}{2}\right)$

(c) $\left(-\dfrac{3}{2}, \dfrac{1}{2}\right)$

(d) None

8. $\displaystyle\lim_{n\to\infty}\left|\frac{a_{n+1}}{a_n}\right| = \lim_{n\to\infty}\frac{|x|^{n+1}}{(n+1)^{n+1}} \cdot \frac{n^n}{|x|^n} = |x|\lim_{n\to\infty}\frac{n^n}{(n+1)(n+1)^n}$

$\qquad = |x|\lim_{n\to\infty}\dfrac{1}{(n+1)\left(1+\dfrac{1}{n}\right)^n} = \dfrac{|x|}{e}\lim_{n\to\infty}\dfrac{1}{n+1} = 0$

The series converges absolutely for all x.

Another way to see that the series must converge is to

observe that for $n \geq 2x$, we have $\left|\dfrac{x^n}{n^n}\right| \leq \left(\dfrac{1}{2}\right)^n$, so the terms

are (eventually) bounded by the terms of a convergent

geometric series.

A third way to solve this exercise is to use the nth Root

Test (see Exercises 57–58 in Section 9.5).

(a) ∞

(b) All real numbers

(c) All real numbers

(d) None

9. $\displaystyle\lim_{n\to\infty}\left|\frac{a_{n+1}}{a_n}\right| = \lim_{n\to\infty}\frac{|x|^{n+1}}{\sqrt{n+1}} \cdot \frac{\sqrt{n}}{|x|^n} = |x|$

The series converges absolutely for $|x| < 1$, or $-1 < x < 1$.

Check $x = -1$:

$\displaystyle\sum_{n=1}^{\infty}\frac{(-1)^n}{n}$ converges by the Alternating Series Test.

Check $x = 1$:

$\displaystyle\sum_{n=1}^{\infty}\frac{1}{\sqrt{n}}$ diverges as a p-series with $p = \dfrac{1}{2}$.

(a) 1

(b) $[-1, 1)$

(c) $(-1, 1)$

(d) At $x = -1$

10. $\displaystyle\lim_{n\to\infty}\left|\frac{a_{n+1}}{a_n}\right| = \lim_{n\to\infty}\frac{e^{n+1}|x|^{n+1}}{(n+1)^e} \cdot \frac{n^e}{e^n|x|^n} = e|x|$

The series converges absolutely for $e|x| < 1$,

or $-\dfrac{1}{e} < x < \dfrac{1}{e}$.

Furthermore, when $e|x| = 1$, we have $|a_n| = \dfrac{1}{n^e}$ and $\displaystyle\sum_{n=1}^{\infty}\frac{1}{n^e}$

converges as a p-series with $p = e$, so $\displaystyle\sum_{n=1}^{\infty}a_n$ also converges

absolutely at the interval endpoints.

(a) $\dfrac{1}{e}$

(b) $\left[-\dfrac{1}{e}, \dfrac{1}{e}\right]$

(c) $\left[-\dfrac{1}{e}, \dfrac{1}{e}\right]$

(d) None

11. $\displaystyle\lim_{n\to\infty}\left|\frac{a_{n+1}}{a_n}\right| = \lim_{n\to\infty}\frac{(n+2)|x|^{2n+1}}{3^{n+1}} \cdot \frac{3^n}{(n+1)|x|^{2n-1}} = \dfrac{x^2}{3}$

The series converges absolutely when $\dfrac{x^2}{3} < 1$,

or $-\sqrt{3} < x < \sqrt{3}$.

When $|x| \geq \sqrt{3}$, the series diverges by the nth Term Test.

(a) $\sqrt{3}$

(b) $(-\sqrt{3}, \sqrt{3})$

(c) $(-\sqrt{3}, \sqrt{3})$

(d) None

12. $\lim\limits_{n\to\infty}\left|\dfrac{a_{n+1}}{a_n}\right| = \lim\limits_{n\to\infty}\dfrac{|x-1|^{2n+3}}{2n+3}\cdot\dfrac{2n+1}{|x-1|^{2n+1}} = |x-1|^2$

The series converges absolutely when $|x-1|^2 < 1$,

or $0 < x < 2$.

Check $x = 0$: $\displaystyle\sum_{n=0}^{\infty}\dfrac{(-1)^n(-1)^{2n-1}}{2n+1} = -\sum_{n=0}^{\infty}\dfrac{(-1)^n}{2n+1}$ converges

conditionally by the Alternating Series Test.

Check $x = 2$: $\displaystyle\sum_{n=0}^{\infty}\dfrac{(-1)^n}{2n+1}$ converges conditionally by the

Alternating Series Test.

(a) 1

(b) $[0, 2]$

(c) $(0, 2)$

(d) At $x = 0$ and $x = 2$

13. $\lim\limits_{n\to\infty}\left|\dfrac{a_{n+1}}{a_n}\right| = \lim\limits_{n\to\infty}\dfrac{(n+1)!\,|x|^{2n+2}}{2^{n+1}}\cdot\dfrac{2^n}{n!\,|x|^{2n}}$

$= \lim\limits_{n\to\infty}\dfrac{(n+1)x^2}{2} = \begin{cases}0, & x = 0 \\ \infty, & x \neq 0\end{cases}$

The series converges only at $x = 0$.

(a) 0

(b) $x = 0$ only

(c) $x = 0$

(d) None

14. $\lim\limits_{n\to\infty}\left|\dfrac{a_{n+1}}{a_n}\right| = \lim\limits_{n\to\infty}\dfrac{|10x|^{n+1}}{\ln(n+1)}\cdot\dfrac{\ln n}{|10x|^n} \doteq |10x|$

The series converges absolutely for $|10x| < 1$,

or $-\dfrac{1}{10} < x < \dfrac{1}{10}$.

Check $n = -\dfrac{1}{10}$: $\displaystyle\sum_{n=2}^{\infty}\dfrac{(-1)^n}{\ln n}$ converges by the Alternating

Series Test.

Check $n = \dfrac{1}{10}$: $\displaystyle\sum_{n=2}^{\infty}\dfrac{1}{\ln n}$ diverges by the Direct Comparison

Test, since $\dfrac{1}{\ln n} > \dfrac{1}{n}$ for $n \geq 2$ and $\displaystyle\sum_{n=2}^{\infty}\dfrac{1}{n}$ diverges.

(a) $\dfrac{1}{10}$

(b) $\left[-\dfrac{1}{10}, \dfrac{1}{10}\right)$

(c) $\left(-\dfrac{1}{10}, \dfrac{1}{10}\right)$

(d) At $x = -\dfrac{1}{10}$

15. $\lim\limits_{n\to\infty}\left|\dfrac{a_{n+1}}{a_n}\right| = \lim\limits_{n\to\infty}\dfrac{(n+2)!\,|x|^{n+1}}{(n+1)!\,|x|^n} = \lim\limits_{n\to\infty}(n+2)|x| = \infty \;(x \neq 0)$

The series converges only at $x = 0$.

(a) 0

(b) $x = 0$ only

(c) $x = 0$

(d) None

16. This is a geometric series with $r = \dfrac{x^2-1}{2}$, so it converges

absolutely when $\left|\dfrac{x^2-1}{2}\right| < 1$, or $-\sqrt{3} < x < \sqrt{3}$. It

diverges for all other values of x.

(a) $\sqrt{3}$

(b) $(-\sqrt{3}, \sqrt{3})$

(c) $(-\sqrt{3}, \sqrt{3})$

(d) None

17. $f(x) = \dfrac{1}{1+x} = 1 - x + x^2 - \cdots + (-1)^n x^n + \cdots$,

evaluated at $x = \dfrac{1}{4}$. Sum $= \dfrac{1}{1+\left(\frac{1}{4}\right)} = \dfrac{4}{5}$.

18. $f(x) = \ln(1+x) = x - \dfrac{x^2}{2} + \dfrac{x^3}{3} - \cdots + (-1)^{n-1}\dfrac{x^n}{n}$,

evaluated at $x = \dfrac{2}{3}$. Sum $= \ln\left(1 + \dfrac{2}{3}\right) = \ln\left(\dfrac{5}{3}\right)$.

19. $f(x) = \sin x = x - \dfrac{x^3}{3!} + \dfrac{x^5}{5!} - \cdots + (-1)^n\dfrac{x^{2n+1}}{(2n+1)!} + \cdots$,

evaluated at $x = \pi$. Sum $= \sin \pi = 0$.

20. $f(x) = \cos x = 1 - \dfrac{x^2}{2!} + \dfrac{x^4}{4!} - \cdots + (-1)^n\dfrac{x^{2n}}{(2n)!} + \cdots$,

evaluated at $x = \dfrac{\pi}{3}$. Sum $= \cos\dfrac{\pi}{3} = \dfrac{1}{2}$.

21. $f(x) = e^x = 1 + x + \dfrac{x^2}{2!} + \cdots + \dfrac{x^n}{n!} + \cdots$, evaluated at

$x = \ln 2$. Sum $= e^{\ln 2} = 2$.

22. $f(x) = \tan^{-1}x = x - \dfrac{x^3}{3} + \dfrac{x^5}{5} - \cdots + (-1)^n\dfrac{x^{2n+1}}{2n+1} + \cdots$,

evaluated at $x = \dfrac{1}{\sqrt{3}}$. Sum $= \tan^{-1}\left(\dfrac{1}{\sqrt{3}}\right) = \dfrac{\pi}{6}$. (Note that

when n is replaced by $n-1$, the general term of $\tan^{-1}x$

becomes $(-1)^{n-1}\dfrac{x^{2n-1}}{2n-1}$, which matches the general term

given in the exercise.)

23. Replace x by $6x$ in the Maclaurin series for $\dfrac{1}{1-x}$ given at

the end of Section 9.2.

$\dfrac{1}{1-6x} = 1 + (6x) + (6x)^2 + \cdots + (6x)^n + \cdots$

$\qquad = 1 + 6x + 36x^2 + \cdots + (6x)^n + \cdots$

24. Replace x by x^3 in the Maclaurin series for $\dfrac{1}{1+x}$ given at

the end of Section 9.2.

$\dfrac{1}{1+x^3} = 1 - (x^3) + (x^3)^2 - \cdots + (-x^3)^n + \cdots$

$\qquad = 1 - x^3 + x^6 - \cdots + (-1)^n x^{3n} + \cdots$

25. The Maclaurin series for a polynomial is the polynomial

itself: $1 - 2x^2 + x^9$.

26. $\dfrac{4x}{1-x} = 4x\left(\dfrac{1}{1-x}\right)$

$\quad = 4x(1 + x + x^2 + \cdots + x^n + \cdots)$

$\quad = 4x + 4x^2 + 4x^3 + \cdots + 4x^{n+1} + \cdots$

27. Replace x by πx in the Maclaurin series for $\sin x$ given at the end of Section 9.2.

$\sin \pi x = \pi x - \dfrac{(\pi x)^3}{3!} + \dfrac{(\pi x)^5}{5!} - \cdots + (-1)^n \dfrac{(\pi x)^{2n+1}}{(2n+1)!} + \cdots$

28. Replace x by $\dfrac{2x}{3}$ in the Maclaurin series for $\sin x$ given at the end of Section 9.2

$-\sin \dfrac{2x}{3} = -\left(\dfrac{2x}{3} - \dfrac{\left(\dfrac{2x}{3}\right)^3}{3!} + \dfrac{\left(\dfrac{2x}{3}\right)^5}{5!} - \cdots + (-1)^n \dfrac{\left(\dfrac{2x}{3}\right)^{2n+1}}{(2n+1)!}\right)$

$\quad = -\dfrac{2x}{3} + \dfrac{4x^3}{81} - \dfrac{4x^5}{3645} + \cdots + \dfrac{(-1)^{n+1}\left(\dfrac{2x}{3}\right)^{2n+1}}{(2n+1)!}$

29. $-x + \sin x = -x + \left(x - \dfrac{x^3}{3!} + \dfrac{x^5}{5!} - \dfrac{x^7}{7!} + \cdots\right.$

$\quad \left. + (-1)^n \dfrac{x^{2n+1}}{(2n+1)!} + \cdots\right)$

$\quad = -\dfrac{x^3}{3!} + \dfrac{x^5}{5!} - \dfrac{x^7}{7!} + \cdots + (-1)^n \dfrac{x^{2n+1}}{(2n+1)!} + \cdots$

30. $\dfrac{e^x + e^{-x}}{2} = \dfrac{1}{2}\left(1 + x + \dfrac{x^2}{2!} + \cdots + \dfrac{x^n}{n!} + \cdots\right)$

$\quad + \dfrac{1}{2}\left(1 - x + \dfrac{x^2}{2!} + \cdots + (-1)^n\dfrac{x^n}{n!} + \cdots\right)$

$\quad = 1 + \dfrac{x^2}{2!} + \dfrac{x^4}{4!} + \cdots + \dfrac{x^{2n}}{(2n)!} + \cdots$

31. Replace x by $\sqrt{5x}$ in the Maclaurin series for $\cos x$ given at the end of Section 9.2.

$\cos \sqrt{5x} = 1 - \dfrac{(\sqrt{5x})^2}{2!} + \dfrac{(\sqrt{5x})^4}{4!} - \cdots$

$\quad + (-1)^n \dfrac{(\sqrt{5x})^{2n}}{(2n)!} + \cdots$

$\quad = 1 - \dfrac{5x}{2!} + \dfrac{(5x)^2}{4!} - \cdots + (-1)^n \dfrac{(5x)^n}{(2n)!} + \cdots$

32. Replace x by $\dfrac{\pi x}{2}$ in the Maclaurin series for e^x given at the end of Section 9.2.

$e^{\pi x/2} = 1 + \dfrac{\pi x}{2} + \dfrac{\left(\dfrac{\pi x}{2}\right)^2}{2!} + \cdots + \dfrac{\left(\dfrac{\pi x}{2}\right)^n}{n!} + \cdots$

$\quad = 1 + \dfrac{\pi x}{2} + \dfrac{\pi^2 x^2}{8} + \cdots + \dfrac{1}{n!}\left(\dfrac{\pi x}{2}\right)^n + \cdots$

33. Use the Maclaurin series for e^x given at the end of Section 9.2.

$xe^{-x^2} = x\left[1 + (-x^2) + \dfrac{(-x^2)^2}{2!} + \cdots + \dfrac{(-x^2)^n}{n!} + \cdots\right]$

$\quad = x - x^3 + \dfrac{x^5}{2!} - \cdots + (-1)^n\dfrac{x^{2n+1}}{n!} + \cdots$

34. Replace x by $3x$ in the Maclaurin series for $\tan^{-1} x$ given at the end of Section 9.2.

$\tan^{-1} 3x = 3x - \dfrac{(3x)^3}{3} + \dfrac{(3x)^5}{5} - \cdots + (-1)^n\dfrac{(3x)^{2n+1}}{2n+1} + \cdots$

35. Replace x by $-2x$ in the Maclaurin series for $\ln(1+x)$ given at the end of Section 9.2.

$\ln(1-2x) = -2x - \dfrac{(-2x)^2}{2} + \dfrac{(-2x)^3}{3} - \cdots$

$\quad + (-1)^{n-1}\dfrac{(-2x)^n}{n} + \cdots$

$\quad = -2x - 2x^2 - \dfrac{8x^3}{3} - \cdots - \dfrac{(2x)^n}{n} - \cdots.$

36. Use the Maclaurin series for $\ln(1+x)$ given at the end of Section 9.2.

$x\ln(1-x) = x\ln[1 + (-x)]$

$\quad = x\left[-x - \dfrac{(-x)^2}{2} + \dfrac{(-x)^3}{3} - \cdots + (-1)^{n-1}\dfrac{(-x)^n}{n} + \cdots\right]$

$\quad = -x^2 - \dfrac{x^3}{2} - \dfrac{x^4}{3} - \cdots - \dfrac{x^{n+1}}{n} - \cdots$

37. $f(2) = (3-x)^{-1}\big|_{x=2} = 1$

$f'(2) = (3-x)^{-2}\big|_{x=2} = 1$

$f''(2) = 2(3-x)^{-3}\big|_{x=2} = 2$, so $\dfrac{f''(2)}{2!} = 1$

$f'''(2) = 6(3-x)^{-4}\big|_{x=2} = 6$, so $\dfrac{f'''(2)}{3!} = 1$

$f^{(n)}(2) = n!(3-x)^{-n-1}\big|_{x=2} = n!$, so $\dfrac{f^{(n)}(2)}{n!} = 1$

$\dfrac{1}{3-x} = 1 + (x-2) + (x-2)^2 + (x-2)^3 + \cdots$

$\quad + (x-2)^n + \cdots$

38. $f(-1) = (x^3 - 2x^2 + 5)\big|_{x=-1} = 2$

$f'(-1) = (3x^2 - 4x)\big|_{x=-1} = 7$

$f''(-1) = (6x - 4)\big|_{x=-1} = -10$, so $\dfrac{f''(-1)}{2!} = -5$

$f'''(-1) = 6\big|_{x=-1} = 6$, so $\dfrac{f'''(-1)}{3!} = 1$

$f^{(n)}(-1) = 0$ for $n \geq 4$.

$x^3 - 2x^2 + 5 = 2 + 7(x+1) - 5(x+1)^2 + (x+1)^3$

This is a finite series and the general term for $n \geq 4$ is 0.

39. $f(3) = \dfrac{1}{x}\Big|_{x=3} = \dfrac{1}{3}$

$f'(3) = -x^{-2}\Big|_{x=3} = -\dfrac{1}{9}$

$f''(3) = 2x^{-3}\Big|_{x=3} = \dfrac{2}{27}$, so $\dfrac{f''(3)}{2!} = \dfrac{1}{27}$

$f'''(3) = -6x^{-4}\Big|_{x=3} = -\dfrac{2}{27}$, so $\dfrac{f'''(3)}{3!} = -\dfrac{1}{81}$

$\dfrac{f^{(n)}(3)}{n!} = \dfrac{(-1)^n}{3^{n+1}}$

$\dfrac{1}{x} = \dfrac{1}{3} - \dfrac{1}{9}(x-3) + \dfrac{1}{27}(x-3)^2 - \dfrac{1}{81}(x-3)^3 + \cdots$

$\qquad + (-1)^n \dfrac{(x-3)^n}{3^{n+1}}$

40. $f(\pi) = \sin x\Big|_{x=\pi} = 0$

$f'(\pi) = \cos x\Big|_{x=\pi} = -1$

$f''(\pi) = -\sin x\Big|_{x=\pi} = 0$, so $\dfrac{f''(\pi)}{2!} = 0$

$f'''(\pi) = -\cos x\Big|_{x=\pi} = 1$, so $\dfrac{f'''(\pi)}{3!} = \dfrac{1}{6}$

$f^{(k)}(\pi) = \begin{cases} 0, & \text{if } k \text{ is even} \\ -1, & \text{if } k = 2n+1, \ n \text{ even} \\ 1, & \text{if } k = 2n+1, \ n \text{ odd} \end{cases}$

$\sin x = -(x-\pi) + \dfrac{1}{3!}(x-\pi)^3 - \dfrac{1}{5!}(x-\pi)^5$

$\qquad + \dfrac{1}{7!}(x-\pi)^7 - \cdots$

$\qquad + (-1)^{n+1}\dfrac{1}{(2n+1)!}(x-\pi)^{2n+1} + \cdots$

41. Diverges, because it is -5 times the harmonic series:

$\displaystyle\sum_{n=1}^{\infty} \dfrac{-5}{n} = -5\sum_{n=1}^{\infty}\dfrac{1}{n} = -\infty$

42. Converges conditionally.

If $u_n = \dfrac{1}{\sqrt{n}}$, then $\{u_n\}$ is a decreasing sequence of positive terms with $\lim\limits_{n\to\infty} u_n = 0$, so $\displaystyle\sum \dfrac{(-1)^n}{\sqrt{n}}$ converges by the Alternating Series Test. The convergence is conditional because $\displaystyle\sum_{n=1}^{\infty} \dfrac{1}{\sqrt{n}}$ is a divergent p-series $\left(p = \dfrac{1}{2}\right)$.

43. Converges absolutely by the Direct Comparison Test, since

$0 \le \dfrac{\ln n}{n^3} < \dfrac{1}{n^2}$ for $n \ge 1$ and $\displaystyle\sum_{n=1}^{\infty}\dfrac{1}{n^2}$ converges as a p-series with $p = 2$.

44. Converges absolutely by the Ratio Test, since

$\lim\limits_{n\to\infty}\left|\dfrac{a_{n+1}}{a_n}\right| = \lim\limits_{n\to\infty}\dfrac{n+2}{(n+1)!}\cdot\dfrac{n!}{n+1} = \lim\limits_{n\to\infty}\dfrac{n+2}{(n+1)^2} = 0.$

45. Converges conditionally:

If $u_n = \dfrac{1}{\ln(n+1)}$, then $\{u_n\}$ is a decreasing sequence of positive terms with $\lim\limits_{n\to\infty} u_n = 0$, so $\displaystyle\sum_{n=1}^{\infty}\dfrac{(-1)^n}{\ln(n+1)}$ converges by the Alternating Series Test. The convergence is conditional because $\dfrac{1}{\ln(n+1)} > \dfrac{1}{n}$ for $n \ge 1$ and $\displaystyle\sum_{n=1}^{\infty}\dfrac{1}{n}$ diverges, so $\displaystyle\sum_{n=1}^{\infty}\dfrac{1}{\ln(n+1)}$ diverges by the Direct Comparison Test.

46. Converges absolutely by the Integral Test, because

$\displaystyle\int_2^{\infty}\dfrac{1}{x(\ln x)^2}\,dx = \lim\limits_{b\to\infty}\left[-\dfrac{1}{\ln x}\right]_2^b = \dfrac{1}{\ln 2}.$

47. Converges absolutely the the Ratio Test, because

$\lim\limits_{n\to\infty}\left|\dfrac{a_{n+1}}{a_n}\right| = \lim\limits_{n\to\infty}\dfrac{|-3|^{n+1}}{(n+1)!}\cdot\dfrac{n!}{|-3|^n} = \lim\limits_{n\to\infty}\dfrac{3}{n+1} = 0.$

48. Converges absolutely by the Direct Comparison Test, since

$\dfrac{2^n 3^n}{n^n} \le \left(\dfrac{1}{2}\right)^n$ for $n \ge 12$ and $\displaystyle\sum_{n=1}^{\infty}\left(\dfrac{1}{2}\right)^n$ is a convergent geometric series. Alternately, we may use the Ratio Test or the nth-Root Test (see Exercise 57 and 58 in Section 9.5).

49. Diverges by the nth-Term Test, since

$\lim\limits_{n\to\infty}\dfrac{(-1)^n(n^2+1)}{2n^2+n-1}$ does not exist.

50. Converges absolutely by the Direct Comparison Test, since

$\dfrac{1}{\sqrt{n(n+1)(n+2)}} < \dfrac{1}{n^{3/2}}$ and $\displaystyle\sum_{n=1}^{\infty}\dfrac{1}{n^{3/2}}$ converges as a p-series with $p = \dfrac{3}{2}$.

51. Converges absolutely by the Limit Comparison Test.

Let $a_n = \dfrac{1}{n\sqrt{n^2-1}}$ and $b_n = \dfrac{1}{n^2}$.

Then $\lim\limits_{n\to\infty}\dfrac{a_n}{b_n} = \lim\limits_{n\to\infty}\dfrac{n^2}{n\sqrt{n^2-1}} = 1$ and $\displaystyle\sum_{n=2}^{\infty}\dfrac{1}{n^2}$ converges as a p-series $(p = 2)$. Therefore $\displaystyle\sum_{n=2}^{\infty} a_n$ converges.

52. Diverges by the nth-Term Test, since

$\lim\limits_{n\to\infty}\left(\dfrac{n}{n+1}\right)^n = \lim\limits_{n\to\infty}\left(1+\dfrac{1}{n}\right)^{-n} = \dfrac{1}{e} \ne 0.$

53. This is a telescoping series.

$$\sum_{n=3}^{\infty}\frac{1}{(2n-3)(2n-1)} = \sum_{n=3}^{\infty}\left(\frac{1}{2(2n-3)} - \frac{1}{2(2n-1)}\right)$$

$$s_1 = \frac{1}{2(2\cdot 3 - 3)} - \frac{1}{2(2\cdot 3 - 1)} = \frac{1}{6} - \frac{1}{10}$$

$$s_2 = \left(\frac{1}{6} - \frac{1}{10}\right) + \left(\frac{1}{10} - \frac{1}{14}\right) = \frac{1}{6} - \frac{1}{14}$$

$$s_3 = \left(\frac{1}{6} - \frac{1}{10}\right) + \left(\frac{1}{10} - \frac{1}{14}\right) + \left(\frac{1}{14} - \frac{1}{18}\right) = \frac{1}{6} - \frac{1}{18}$$

$$s_n = \frac{1}{6} - \frac{1}{2(2n-1)}$$

$$S = \lim_{n\to\infty} s_n = \frac{1}{6}$$

54. This is a telescoping series.

$$\sum_{n=2}^{\infty}\frac{-2}{n(n+1)} = \sum_{n=2}^{\infty}\left(-\frac{2}{n} + \frac{2}{n+1}\right)$$

$$s_1 = -\frac{2}{2} + \frac{2}{3} = -1 + \frac{2}{3}$$

$$s_2 = \left(-1 + \frac{2}{3}\right) + \left(-\frac{2}{3} + \frac{2}{4}\right) = -1 + \frac{2}{4}$$

$$s_3 = \left(-1 + \frac{2}{3}\right) + \left(-\frac{2}{3} + \frac{2}{4}\right) + \left(-\frac{2}{4} + \frac{2}{5}\right) = -1 + \frac{2}{5}$$

$$s_n = -1 + \frac{2}{n+2}$$

$$S = \lim_{n\to\infty} s_n = -1$$

55. (a) $P_3(x) = f(3) + f'(3)(x-3) + \frac{f''(3)}{2!}(x-3)^2$

$$+ \frac{f'''(3)}{3!}(x-3)^3$$

$$= 1 + 4(x-3) + 3(x-3)^2 + 2(x-3)^3$$

$$f(3.2) \approx P_3(3.2) = 1.936$$

(b) Since the Taylor series for f' can be obtained by term-by-term differentiation of the Taylor Series for f, the second order Taylor polynomial for f' at $x=3$ is $4 + 6(x-3) + 6(x-3)^2$. Evaluated at $x = 2.7$, $f'(2.7) \approx 2.74$.

(c) It underestimates the values, since $f''(3) = 6$, which means the graph of f is concave up near $x = 3$.

56. (a) Since the constant term is $f(4)$, $f(4) = 7$. Since

$$-2 = \frac{f'''(4)}{3!}, f'''(4) = -12.$$

(b) Note that
$P_4{}'(x) = -3 + 10(x-4) - 6(x-4)^2 + 24(x-4)^3$.
The second degree polynomial for f' at $x = 4$ is given by the first three terms of this expression, namely $-3 + 10(x-4) - 6(x-4)^2$. Evaluating at $x = 4.3$, $f'(4.3) \approx -0.54$.

(c) The fourth order Taylor polynomial for $g(x)$ at $x = 4$ is

$$\int_4^x [7 - 3(t-4) + 5(t-4)^2 - 2(t-4)^3]\, dx$$

$$= \left[7t - \frac{3}{2}(t-4)^2 + \frac{5}{3}(t-4)^3 - \frac{1}{2}(t-4)^4\right]_4^x$$

$$= 7(x-4) - \frac{3}{2}(x-4)^2 + \frac{5}{3}(x-4)^3 - \frac{1}{2}(x-4)^4$$

(d) No. One would need the entire Taylor series for $f(x)$, and it would have to converge to $f(x)$ at $x = 3$.

57. (a) Use the Maclaurin series for $\sin x$ given at the end of Section 9.2.

$$5\sin\left(\frac{x}{2}\right)$$

$$= 5\left[\frac{x}{2} - \frac{(x/2)^3}{3!} + \frac{(x/2)^5}{5!} - \cdots + (-1)^n\frac{(x/2)^{2n+1}}{(2n+1)!} + \cdots\right]$$

$$= \frac{5x}{2} - \frac{5x^3}{48} + \frac{x^5}{768} - \cdots + (-1)^n\frac{5}{(2n+1)!}\left(\frac{x}{2}\right)^{2n+1} + \cdots$$

(b) The series converges for all real numbers, according to the Ratio Test:

$$\lim_{n\to\infty}\left|\frac{a_{n+1}}{a_n}\right| = \lim_{n\to\infty}\frac{5}{(2n+3)!}\left|\frac{x}{2}\right|^{2n+3} \cdot \frac{(2n+1)!}{5}\left|\frac{2}{x}\right|^{2n+1}$$

$$= \lim_{n\to\infty}\frac{|x/2|^2}{(2n+3)(2n+2)} = 0$$

(c) Note that the absolute value of $f^{(n)}(x)$ is bounded by $\frac{5}{2^n}$ for all x and all $n = 1, 2, 3, \cdots$.

We may use the Remainder Estimation Theorem with $M = 5$ and $r = \frac{1}{2}$.

So if $-2 < x < 2$, the truncation error using P_n is bounded by

$$\frac{5}{2^{n+1}} \cdot \frac{2^{n+1}}{(n+1)!} = \frac{5}{(n+1)!}.$$

To make this less than 0.1 requires $n \geq 4$. So, two terms (up through degree 4) are needed.

58. (a) Substitute $2x$ for x in the Maclaurin series for $\frac{1}{1-x}$ given at the end of Section 9.2.

$$\frac{1}{1-2x} = 1 + 2x + (2x)^2 + (2x)^3 + \cdots + (2x)^n + \cdots$$

$$= 1 + 2x + 4x^2 + 8x^3 + \cdots + (2x)^n + \cdots$$

(b) $\left(-\frac{1}{2}, \frac{1}{2}\right)$. The series for $\frac{1}{1-t}$ is known to converge for $-1 < t < 1$, so by substituting $t = 2x$, we find the resulting series converges for $-1 < 2x < 1$.

58. continued

(c) $f\left(-\dfrac{1}{4}\right) = \dfrac{2}{3}$, so one percent is approximately 0.0067. It takes 7 terms (up through degree 6). This can be found by trial and error. Also, for $x = -\dfrac{1}{4}$, the series is the alternating series $\displaystyle\sum_{n=0}^{\infty}\left(-\dfrac{1}{2}\right)^n$. If you use the Alternating Series Estimation Theorem, it shows that 8 terms (up through degree 7) are sufficient since $\left|-\dfrac{1}{2}\right|^8 < 0.0067$. It is also a geometric series, and you could use the remainder formula for a geometric series to determine the number of terms needed. (See Example 2 in Section 9.3.)

59. (a) $\displaystyle\lim_{n\to\infty}\left|\dfrac{a_{n+1}}{a_n}\right| = \lim_{n\to\infty}\dfrac{|x|^{n+1}(n+1)^{n+1}}{(n+1)!}\cdot\dfrac{n!}{|x|^n n^n}$

$= \displaystyle\lim_{n\to\infty}\dfrac{|x|(n+1)^{n+1}}{(n+1)n^n}$

$= |x|\displaystyle\lim_{n\to\infty}$

$\left(\dfrac{n+1}{n}\right)^n = |x|e$

The series converges for $|x|e < 1$, or $|x| < \dfrac{1}{e}$, so the radius of convergence is $\dfrac{1}{e}$.

(b) $f\left(-\dfrac{1}{3}\right) \approx -\dfrac{1}{3}\cdot\dfrac{1}{1} + \left(-\dfrac{1}{3}\right)^2\cdot\dfrac{2^2}{2!} + \left(-\dfrac{1}{3}\right)^3\cdot\dfrac{3^3}{3!}$

$= -\dfrac{1}{3} + \dfrac{2}{9} - \dfrac{1}{6}$

$= -\dfrac{5}{18} \approx -0.278$

(c) By the Alternating Series Estimation Theorem the error is no more than the magnitude of the next term, which is $\left|\left(-\dfrac{1}{3}\right)^4\cdot\dfrac{4^4}{4!}\right| = \dfrac{32}{243} \approx 0.132$.

60. (a) $f(3) = (x-2)^{-1}\big|_{x=3} = 1$

$f'(3) = -(x-2)^{-2}\big|_{x=3} = -1$

$f''(3) = 2(x-2)^{-3}\big|_{x=3} = 2$, so $\dfrac{f''(3)}{2!} = 1$

$f'''(3) = -6(x-2)^{-4}\big|_{x=3} = -6$, so $\dfrac{f'''(3)}{3!} = -1$

$f^{(n)}(3) = (-1)^n n!$, so $\dfrac{f^{(n)}(3)}{n!} = (-1)^n$

$f(x) = 1 - (x-3) + (x-3)^2 - (x-3)^3 + \cdots$

$\qquad + (-1)^n(x-3)^n + \cdots$

(b) Integrate term by term.

$\ln|x-2| = \displaystyle\int_3^x \dfrac{1}{t-2}\,dt$

$= \left[t - \dfrac{1}{2}(t-3)^2 + \dfrac{1}{3}(t-3)^3 - \dfrac{1}{4}(t-3)^4 + \cdots\right.$

$\qquad \left. + (-1)^n\dfrac{(t-3)^{n+1}}{n+1} + \cdots\right]_3^x$

$= (x-3) - \dfrac{(x-3)^2}{2} + \dfrac{(x-3)^3}{3} - \dfrac{(x-3)^4}{4} + \cdots$

$\qquad + (-1)^n\dfrac{(x-3)^{n+1}}{n+1} + \cdots$

(c) Evaluate at $x = 3.5$. This is the alternating series

$\dfrac{1}{2} - \dfrac{1}{2^2\cdot 2} + \dfrac{1}{2^3\cdot 3} - \cdots + (-1)^n\dfrac{1}{2^{n+1}(n+1)} + \cdots$

By the Alternating Series Estimation Theorem, since the size of the third term is $\dfrac{1}{24} < 0.05$, the first two terms will suffice. The estimate for $\ln\left(\dfrac{3}{2}\right)$ is 0.375.

61. (a) Substitute $-2x^2$ for x in the Maclaurin series for e^x given at the end of Section 9.2.

$e^{-2x^2} = 1 + (-2x^2) + \dfrac{(-2x^2)^2}{2!} + \dfrac{(-2x^2)^3}{3!}$

$\qquad + \cdots + \dfrac{(-2x^2)^n}{n!} + \cdots$

$= 1 - 2x^2 + 2x^4 - \dfrac{4x^6}{3} + \cdots$

$\qquad + (-1)^n\dfrac{2^n x^{2n}}{n!} + \cdots$

(b) Use the Ratio Test:

$\displaystyle\lim_{n\to\infty}\left|\dfrac{a_{n+1}}{a_n}\right| = \lim_{n\to\infty}\dfrac{2^{n+1}x^{2n+2}}{(n+1)!}\cdot\dfrac{n!}{2^n x^{2n}}$

$= \displaystyle\lim_{n\to\infty}\dfrac{2x^2}{n+1} = 0$

The series converges for all real numbers, so the interval of convergence is $(-\infty, \infty)$.

(c) This is an alternating series. The difference will be bounded by the magnitude of the fifth term, which is $\dfrac{(2x^2)^4}{4!} = \dfrac{2x^8}{3}$. Since $-0.6 \le x \le 0.6$, this term is less than $\dfrac{2(0.6)^8}{3}$ which is less than 0.02.

62. (a) $f(x) = x^2\left(\dfrac{1}{1+x}\right)$

$= x^2(1 - x + x^2 + \cdots + (-x)^n + \cdots)$

$= x^2 - x^3 + x^4 + \cdots + (-1)^n x^{n+2} + \cdots$

(b) No. At $x = 1$, the series is $\displaystyle\sum_{n=0}^{\infty}(-1)^n$ and the partial sums form the sequence $1, 0, 1, 0, 1, 0, \ldots$, which has no limit.

63. (a) Substituting x^2 for x in the Maclaurin series for $\sin x$ given at the end of Section 9.2,

$$\sin x^2 = x^2 - \frac{x^6}{3!} + \frac{x^{10}}{5!} - \cdots + (-1)^n \frac{x^{4n+2}}{(2n+1)!}.$$

Integrating term-by-term and observing that the constant term is 0,

$$\int_0^x \sin t^2\, dt = \frac{x^3}{3} - \frac{x^7}{7(3!)} + \frac{x^{11}}{11(5!)} - \cdots$$
$$+ (-1)^n \frac{x^{4n+3}}{(4n+3)(2n+1)!} + \cdots$$

(b) $\displaystyle\int_0^1 \sin x\, dx = \frac{1}{3} - \frac{1}{7(3!)} + \frac{1}{11(5!)} - \cdots$
$$+ (-1)^n \frac{1}{(4n+3)(2n+1)!} + \cdots.$$

Since the third term is $\dfrac{1}{11(5!)} = \dfrac{1}{1320} < 0.001$, it suffices to use the first two nonzero terms (through degree 7).

(c) NINT$(\sin x^2, x, 0, 1) \approx 0.31026830$

(d) $\dfrac{1}{3} - \dfrac{1}{7(3!)} + \dfrac{1}{11(5!)} - \dfrac{1}{15(7!)} = \dfrac{258,019}{831,600} \approx 0.31026816$

This is within 1.5×10^{-7} of the answer in (c).

64. (a) Let $f(x) = x^2 e^x\, dx$.

$$\int_0^1 x^2 e^x\, dx = \int_0^1 f(x)\, dx$$
$$\approx \frac{h}{2}\Big[f(0) + 2f(0.5) + f(1) \Big]$$
$$= \frac{1}{4}\Big[0 + 2\frac{e^{0.5}}{4} + e \Big]$$
$$= \frac{e^{0.5}}{8} + \frac{e}{4}$$
$$\approx 0.88566$$

(b) $x^2 e^x = x^2\Big(1 + x + \frac{x^2}{2!} + \cdots + \frac{x^n}{n!} + \cdots \Big)$
$$= x^2 + x^3 + \frac{x^4}{2!} + \cdots + \frac{x^{n+2}}{n!} + \cdots$$
$$P_4(x) = x^2 + x^3 + \frac{x^4}{2}$$
$$\int_0^1 P_4(x) = \Big[\frac{x^3}{3} + \frac{x^4}{4} + \frac{x^5}{10} \Big]_0^1 = \frac{41}{60} \approx 0.68333$$

(c) Since f is concave up, the trapezoids used to estimate the area lie above the curve, and the estimate is too large.

(d) Since all the derivatives are positive (and $x > 0$), the remainder, $R_n(x)$, must be positive. This means that $P_n(x)$ is smaller than $f(x)$.

(e) Let $u = x^2 \qquad dv = e^x\, dx$

$\quad du = 2x\, dx \qquad v = e^x$

$$\int x^2 e^x\, dx = x^2 e^x - \int 2x\, e^x\, dx$$

Let $u = 2x \qquad dv = e^x\, dx$

$\quad du = 2\, dx \qquad v = e^x$

$$x^2 e^x - \int 2x e^x\, dx = x^2 e^x - \Big[2x e^x - \int 2e^x\, dx \Big]$$
$$= x^2 e^x - 2x e^x + 2e^x + C$$
$$= (x^2 - 2x + 2)e^x + C$$
$$\int_0^1 x^2 e^x\, dx = (x^2 - 2x + 2)e^x \Big|_0^1 = e - 2 \approx 0.71828$$

65. (a) Because $[\$1000(1.08)^{-n}](1.08)^n = \$1000$ will be available after n years.

(b) Assume that the first payment goes to the charity at the end of the first year.
$$1000(1.08)^{-1} + 1000(1.08)^{-2} + 1000(1.08)^{-3} + \cdots$$

(c) This is a geometric series with sum equal to
$$\frac{1000/1.08}{1 - (1/1.08)} = \frac{1000}{0.08} = 12,500.$$ This means that $\$12,500$ should be invested today in order to completely fund the perpetuity forever.

66. We again assume that the first payment occurs at the end of the year.

Present value $= 1000(1.06)^{-1} + 1000(1.06)^{-2}$
$$+ 1000(1.06)^{-3} + \cdots$$
$$= \frac{1000/1.06}{1 - (1/1.06)} = \frac{1000}{1.06 - 1} \approx 16,666.67$$

The present value is $\$16,666.67$.

67. (a)

Sequence of Tosses	Payoff ($)	Probability	Term of Series
T	0	$\frac{1}{2}$	$0\left(\frac{1}{2}\right)$
HT	1	$\left(\frac{1}{2}\right)^2$	$1\left(\frac{1}{2}\right)^2$
HHT	2	$\left(\frac{1}{2}\right)^3$	$2\left(\frac{1}{2}\right)^3$
HHHT	3	$\left(\frac{1}{2}\right)^4$	$3\left(\frac{1}{2}\right)^4$
⋮	⋮	⋮	⋮

Expected payoff

$$= 0\left(\frac{1}{2}\right) + 1\left(\frac{1}{2}\right)^2 + 2\left(\frac{1}{2}\right)^3 + 3\left(\frac{1}{2}\right)^4 + \cdots$$

(b) $\dfrac{1}{(1-x)^2} = 1 + 2x + 3x^2 + \cdots + nx^{n-1} + \cdots$

(c) $\dfrac{x^2}{(1-x)^2} = x^2(1 + 2x + 3x^2 + \cdots + nx^{n-1} + \cdots)$

$$= x^2 + 2x^3 + 3x^4 + \cdots + nx^{n+1} + \cdots$$

(d) If $x = \dfrac{1}{2}$, the formula in part (c) matches the nonzero terms of the series in part (a). Since $\dfrac{(1/2)^2}{[1-(1/2)]^2} = 1$, the expected payoff is $1.

68. (a) The area of an equilateral triangle whose sides have length s is $\dfrac{1}{2}(s)\left(\dfrac{\sqrt{3}s}{2}\right) = \dfrac{s^2\sqrt{3}}{4}$. The sequence of areas removed from the original triangle is

$$\frac{b^2\sqrt{3}}{4} + 3\left(\frac{b}{2}\right)^2\frac{\sqrt{3}}{4} + 9\left(\frac{b}{4}\right)^2\frac{\sqrt{3}}{4} + \cdots$$

$$+ 3^n\left(\frac{b}{2^n}\right)^2\frac{\sqrt{3}}{4} + \cdots \text{ or}$$

$$\frac{b^2\sqrt{3}}{4} + \frac{3b^2\sqrt{3}}{4^2} + \frac{3^2b^2\sqrt{3}}{4^3} + \cdots + \frac{3^nb^2\sqrt{3}}{4^{n+1}} + \cdots.$$

(b) This is a geometric series with initial term $a = \dfrac{b^2\sqrt{3}}{4}$ and common ratio $r = \dfrac{3}{4}$, so the sum is $\dfrac{b^2\sqrt{3}/4}{1-(3/4)} = b^2\sqrt{3}$, which is the same as the area of the original triangle.

(c) No, not every point is removed. For example, the vertices of the original triangle are not removed. But the remaining points are "isolated" enough that there are no regions and hence no area remaining.

69. $\dfrac{1}{1-x} = 1 + x + x^2 + x^3 + \cdots$

Differentiate both sides.

$$\frac{1}{(1-x)^2} = 1 + 2x + 3x^2 + 4x^3 + 5x^4 + \cdots$$

Substitute $x = \dfrac{1}{2}$ to get the desired result.

70. (a) Note that $\displaystyle\sum_{n=1}^{\infty} x^{n+1}$ is a geometric series with first term $a = x^2$ and common ratio $r = x$, which explains the identity $\displaystyle\sum_{n=1}^{\infty} x^{n+1} = \frac{x^2}{1-x}$ (for $|x| < 1$).

Differentiate.

$$\sum_{n=1}^{\infty} (n+1)x^n = \frac{(1-x)(2x) - (x^2)(-1)}{(1-x)^2} = \frac{2x - x^2}{(1-x)^2}$$

Differentiate again.

$$\sum_{n=1}^{\infty} n(n+1)x^{n-1}$$

$$= \frac{(1-x)^2(2-2x) - (2x-x^2)(2)(1-x)(-1)}{(1-x)^4}$$

$$= \frac{(1-x)(2-2x) + 2(2x-x^2)}{(1-x)^3}$$

$$= \frac{2}{(1-x)^3}$$

Multiply by x.

$$\sum_{n=1}^{\infty} n(n+1)x^n = \frac{2x}{(1-x)^3}$$

Replace x by $\dfrac{1}{x}$.

$$\sum_{n=1}^{\infty} \frac{n(n+1)}{x^n} = \frac{\dfrac{2}{x}}{\left(1 - \dfrac{1}{x}\right)^3} = \frac{2x^2}{(x-1)^3}, |x| > 1$$

(b) Solve $x = \dfrac{2x^2}{(x-1)^3}$ to get $x \approx 2.769$ for $x > 1$.

Chapter 10
Vectors

■ Section 10.1 Parametric Functions
(pp. 513–520)

Exploration 1 Investigating Cycloids

1.

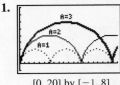

[0, 20] by [−1, 8]

2. $x = 2na\pi$ for any integer n.

3. $a > 0$ and $1 - \cos t \geq 0$ so $y \geq 0$.

4. An arch is produced by one complete turn of the wheel. Thus, they are congruent.

5. The maximum value of y is $2a$ and occurs when $x = (2n+1)a\pi$ for any integer n.

6. The function represented by the cycloid is periodic with period $2a\pi$, and each arch represents one period of the graph. In each arch, the graph is concave down, has an absolute maximum of $2a$ at the midpoint, and an absolute minimum of 0 at the two endpoints.

Quick Review 10.1

1. $(\cos(0), \sin(0)) = (1, 0)$

2. $\left(\cos\left(\dfrac{3\pi}{2}\right), \sin\left(\dfrac{3\pi}{2}\right)\right) = (0, -1)$

3. $x^2 + y^2 = 1$ (since $\cos^2 t + \sin^2 t = 1$)

4. The portion in the first three quadrants, moving counter-clockwise as t increases.

5. $x = t, y = t^2 + 1, -1 \le t \le 3$

6. The graph is a circle with radius 2 centered at $(2, 3)$. Modify the $x = \cos t, y = \sin t$ parameterization correspondingly:
$x = 2\cos t + 2, y = 2\sin t + 3, 0 \le t \le 2\pi$.

7. $\dfrac{dy}{dx} = \dfrac{dy/dt}{dx/dt} = \dfrac{3\cos t}{-2\sin t}$,
which at $t = \dfrac{3\pi}{4}$ equals $\dfrac{3(-\sqrt{2}/2)}{-2(\sqrt{2}/2)} = \dfrac{3}{2}$.

8. $y = \dfrac{3}{2}x + C$. For $t = \dfrac{3\pi}{4}, x = -\sqrt{2}$ and $y = \dfrac{3\sqrt{2}}{2}$, so
$\dfrac{3\sqrt{2}}{2} = \dfrac{3}{2}(-\sqrt{2}) + C$ and $C = 3\sqrt{2}$.
Thus, $y = \dfrac{3}{2}x + 3\sqrt{2}$.

9. $y = -\dfrac{2}{3}x + C$. For $t = \dfrac{3\pi}{4}, x = -\sqrt{2}$ and $y = \dfrac{3\sqrt{2}}{2}$, so
$\dfrac{3\sqrt{2}}{2} = -\dfrac{2}{3}(-\sqrt{2}) + C$ and $C = \dfrac{5\sqrt{2}}{6}$.
Thus, $y = -\dfrac{2}{3}x + \dfrac{5\sqrt{2}}{6}$.

10. $y' = \dfrac{3}{2}\sqrt{x}$, so
$$\text{Length} = \int_0^3 \sqrt{1 + \left(\dfrac{3}{2}\sqrt{x}\right)^2} \, dx$$
$$= \int_0^3 \sqrt{1 + \dfrac{9}{4}x} \, dx$$
$$= \left[\dfrac{8}{27}\left(1 + \dfrac{9}{4}x\right)^{3/2}\right]_0^3 = \dfrac{31^{3/2} - 8}{27}.$$

Section 10.1 Exercises

1. (a) $\dfrac{dy}{dx} = y' = \dfrac{dy/dt}{dx/dt} = \dfrac{-2\sin t}{4\cos t} = -\dfrac{1}{2}\tan t$

(b) $\dfrac{d^2y}{dx^2} = \dfrac{dy'/dt}{dx/dt} = \dfrac{-\frac{1}{2}\sec^2 t}{4\cos t} = -\dfrac{1}{8}\sec^3 t$

2. (a) $\dfrac{dy}{dx} = y' = \dfrac{dy/dt}{dx/dt} = \dfrac{-\sqrt{3}\sin t}{-\sin t} = \sqrt{3}$

(b) $\dfrac{d^2y}{dx^2} = \dfrac{dy'/dt}{dx/dt} = \dfrac{0}{-\sin t} = 0$

3. (a) $\dfrac{dy}{dx} = y' = \dfrac{dy/dt}{dx/dt}$
$= \dfrac{3/(2\sqrt{3t})}{-1/(2\sqrt{t+1})}$
$= -\dfrac{3\sqrt{t+1}}{\sqrt{3t}}$
$= -\sqrt{3 + \dfrac{3}{t}}$

(b) $\dfrac{d^2y}{dx^2} = \dfrac{dy'/dt}{dx/dt} = \dfrac{3/(2t^2\sqrt{3 + 3/t})}{-1/(2\sqrt{t+1})} = -\dfrac{3\sqrt{t+1}}{t^2\sqrt{3 + 3/t}}$
$= -\dfrac{\sqrt{3}}{t^{3/2}}$

4. (a) $\dfrac{dy}{dx} = y' = \dfrac{dy/dt}{dx/dt} = \dfrac{1/t}{-1/t^2} = -t$

(b) $\dfrac{d^2y}{dx^2} = \dfrac{dy'/dt}{dx/dt} = \dfrac{-1}{-1/t^2} = t^2$

5. (a) $\dfrac{dy}{dx} = y' = \dfrac{dy/dt}{dx/dt} = \dfrac{3t^2}{2t - 3}$

(b) $\dfrac{d^2y}{dx^2} = \dfrac{dy'/dt}{dx/dt}$
$= \dfrac{[(2t-3)(6t) - (3t^2)(2)]/(2t-3)^2}{2t - 3}$
$= \dfrac{12t^2 - 18t - 6t^2}{(2t-3)^3}$
$= \dfrac{6t^2 - 18t}{(2t-3)^3}$

6. (a) $\dfrac{dy}{dx} = y' = \dfrac{dy/dt}{dx/dt} = \dfrac{2t - 1}{2t + 1}$

(b) $\dfrac{d^2y}{dx^2} = \dfrac{dy'/dt}{dx/dt}$
$= \dfrac{[(2t+1)(2) - (2t-1)(2)]/(2t+1)^2}{2t + 1}$
$= \dfrac{4}{(2t+1)^3}$

7. $\dfrac{dy}{dx} = \dfrac{dy/dt}{dx/dt} = \dfrac{\cos t}{-\sin t} = -\cot t$

(a) $-\cot = 0$ when $t = \dfrac{\pi}{2} + k\pi$ (k any integer). Then
$(x, y) = \left(2 + \cos\left(\dfrac{\pi}{2} + k\pi\right), -1 + \sin\left(\dfrac{\pi}{2} + k\pi\right)\right)$
$= (2, -1 \pm 1)$. The points are $(2, 0)$ and $(2, -2)$.

(b) $-\cot$ is undefined when $t = k\pi$ (k any integer). Then
$(x, y) = (2 + \cos(k\pi), -1 + \sin(k\pi)) = (2 \pm 1, -1)$.
The points are $(1, -1)$ and $(3, -1)$.

8. $\dfrac{dy}{dx} = \dfrac{dy/dt}{dx/dt} = \dfrac{\sec^2 t}{\sec t \tan t} = \csc t$

    (a) Nowhere, since $\csc t$ never equals zero.

    (b) $\csc t$ is undefined when $t = k\pi$ (k any integer). Then $(x, y) = (\sec (k\pi), \tan (k\pi)) = (\pm1, 0)$.
    The points are $(1, 0)$ and $(-1, 0)$.

9. $\dfrac{dy}{dx} = \dfrac{dy/dt}{dx/dt} = \dfrac{3t^2 - 4}{-1} = 4 - 3t^2$

    (a) $4 - 3t^2 = 0$ when $t = \pm\sqrt{\dfrac{4}{3}} = \pm\dfrac{2}{\sqrt{3}}$.

    Then $(x, y) = \left(2 \mp \dfrac{2}{\sqrt{3}}, \pm\left(\dfrac{2}{\sqrt{3}}\right)^3 \mp 4\left(\dfrac{2}{\sqrt{3}}\right)\right)$

    $= \left(2 \mp \dfrac{2}{\sqrt{3}}, \pm\dfrac{8}{3\sqrt{3}} \mp \dfrac{8}{\sqrt{3}}\right)$,

    which evaluates to $\approx (0.845, -3.079)$ and $\approx (3.155, 3.079)$.

    (b) Nowhere, since $4 - 3t^2$ is never undefined.

10. $\dfrac{dy}{dx} = \dfrac{dy/dt}{dx/dt} = \dfrac{3 \cos t}{-3 \sin t} = -\cot t$

    (a) $-\cot t = 0$ when $t = \dfrac{\pi}{2} + k\pi$ (k any integer).

    Then (x, y)

    $= \left(-2 + 3 \cos\left(\dfrac{\pi}{2} + k\pi\right), 1 + 3 \sin\left(\dfrac{\pi}{2} + k\pi\right)\right)$

    $= (-2, 1 \pm 3)$. The points are $(-2, 4)$ and $(-2, -2)$.

    (b) $-\cot t$ is undefined when $t = k\pi$ (k any integer). Then

    $(x, y) = (-2 + 3 \cos (k\pi), 1 + 3 \sin (k\pi))$

    $= (-2 \pm 3, 1)$. The points are $(1, 1)$ and $(-5, 1)$.

11. $x' = -\sin t$, $y' = 1 + \cos t$, so

    $\text{length} = \displaystyle\int_0^\pi \sqrt{(-\sin t)^2 + (1 + \cos t)^2}\, dt$

    $= \displaystyle\int_0^\pi \sqrt{2(1 + \cos t)}\, dt$

    $= \displaystyle\int_0^\pi \sqrt{4 \cos^2\left(\dfrac{t}{2}\right)}\, dt$

    $= \displaystyle\int_0^\pi 2 \cos\left(\dfrac{t}{2}\right) dt$

    $= 2\left[2 \sin\left(\dfrac{t}{2}\right)\right]_0^\pi = 4$

12. $x' = \sqrt{2t + 3}$, $y' = 1 + t$, so

    $\text{Length} = \displaystyle\int_0^3 \sqrt{(\sqrt{2t + 3})^2 + (1 + t)^2}\, dt$

    $= \displaystyle\int_0^3 (t + 2)\, dt = \left[\dfrac{1}{2}t^2 + 2t\right]_0^3 = \dfrac{21}{2}$

13. $x' = t^2$, $y' = t$, so

    $\text{Length} = \displaystyle\int_0^1 \sqrt{(t^2)^2 + t^2}\, dt$

    $= \displaystyle\int_0^1 t\sqrt{t^2 + 1}\, dt$

    $= \left[\dfrac{1}{3}(t^2 + 1)^{3/2}\right]_0^1$

    $= \dfrac{1}{3}(2^{3/2} - 1)$

    $= \dfrac{2\sqrt{2} - 1}{3} \approx 0.609$

14. $x' = 8t \cos t$, $y' = 8t \sin t$, so

    $\text{Length} = \displaystyle\int_0^{\pi/2} \sqrt{(8t \cos t)^2 + (8t \sin t)^2}\, dt$

    $= \displaystyle\int_0^{\pi/2} 8t\, dt$

    $= \left[4t^2\right]_0^{\pi/2} = \pi^2$

15. $x' = \dfrac{\sec t \tan t + \sec^2 t}{\sec t + \tan t} - \cos t = \sec t - \cos t$,

    $y' = -\sin t$, so

    $\text{Length} = \displaystyle\int_0^{\pi/3} \sqrt{(\sec t - \cos t)^2 + (-\sin t)^2}\, dt$

    $= \displaystyle\int_0^{\pi/3} \sqrt{\sec^2 t - 1}\, dt$

    $= \displaystyle\int_0^{\pi/3} \tan t\, dt$

    $= \left[\ln |\sec t|\right]_0^{\pi/3} = \ln 2$

16. $x' = e^t - 2t$, $y' = 1 - e^{-t}$, so

    $\text{Length} = \displaystyle\int_{-1}^2 \sqrt{(e^t - 2t)^2 + (1 - e^{-t})^2}\, dt$,

    which using NINT evaluates to ≈ 4.497.

17. $x' = -\sin t$, $y' = \cos t$, so

    $\text{Area} = \displaystyle\int_0^{2\pi} 2\pi(2 + \sin t)\sqrt{(-\sin t)^2 + \cos^2 t}\, dt$

    $= 2\pi \displaystyle\int_0^{2\pi} (2 + \sin t)\, dt$

    $= 2\pi\left[2t - \cos t\right]_0^{2\pi} = 8\pi^2$

18. $x' = \sqrt{t}$, $y' = \dfrac{1}{\sqrt{t}}$, so

    $\text{Area} = \displaystyle\int_0^2 2\pi\left(\dfrac{2}{3}t^{3/2}\right)\sqrt{(\sqrt{t})^2 + \left(\dfrac{1}{\sqrt{t}}\right)^2}\, dt$

    $= \dfrac{4\pi}{3} \displaystyle\int_0^2 t\sqrt{t^2 + 1}\, dt$

    $= \dfrac{4\pi}{3}\left[\dfrac{1}{3}(t^2 + 1)^{3/2}\right]_0^2$

    $= \dfrac{4\pi(5\sqrt{5} - 1)}{9} \approx 14.214$

19. $x' = 1$, $y' = 2t$, so

    $\text{Area} = \displaystyle\int_0^3 2\pi(t + 1)\sqrt{1 + (2t)^2}\, dt$,

    which using NINT evaluates to ≈ 178.561.

20. $x' = \sec t - \cos t$ (see Ex. 15), $y' = -\sin t$, so

$$\text{Length} = \int_0^{\pi/3} 2\pi(\cos t)\sqrt{(\sec t - \cos t)^2 + (-\sin t)^2}\, dx$$
$$= \int_0^{\pi/3} 2\pi \cos t\, \sqrt{\tan^2 t}\, dt$$
$$= 2\pi \int_0^{\pi/3} \sin t\, dt$$
$$= 2\pi\left[-\cos t\right]_0^{\pi/3} = \pi.$$

21. (a) $x(t) = 2t$, $y(t) = t + 1$, $0 \le t \le 1$

(b) $x' = 2$, $y' = 1$, so

$$\text{Area} = \int_0^1 2\pi(t + 1)\sqrt{2^2 + 1^2}\, dt$$
$$= 2\pi\sqrt{5}\int_0^1 (t + 1)\, dt$$
$$= 2\pi\sqrt{5}\left[\frac{1}{2}t^2 + t\right]_0^1$$
$$= 3\pi\sqrt{5}$$

(c) Slant height $= \sqrt{2^2 + 1^2} = \sqrt{5}$, so

$$\text{Area} = \pi(1 + 2)\sqrt{5} = 3\pi\sqrt{5}$$

22. (a) Because these values for $x(t)$ and $y(t)$ satisfy $y = \frac{r}{h}x$, which is the equation of the line through the origin and (h, r), and this range of t-values gives the correct initial and terminal points.

(b) $x' = h$, $y' = r$, so

$$\text{Area} = \int_0^1 2\pi(rt)\sqrt{h^2 + r^2}\, dt$$
$$= \pi r\sqrt{h^2 + r^2}\left[t^2\right]_0^1$$
$$= \pi r\sqrt{r^2 + h^2}.$$

(c) Slant height $= \sqrt{r^2 + h^2}$, so Area $= \pi r\sqrt{r^2 + h^2}$

23. (a) $x' = -2 \sin 2t$, $y' = 2 \cos 2t$, so

$$\text{Length} = \int_0^{\pi/2} \sqrt{(-2 \sin 2t)^2 + (2 \cos 2t)^2}$$
$$= \int_0^{\pi/2} 2\, dt = \pi.$$

(b) $x' = \pi \cos \pi t$, $y' = -\pi \sin \pi t$, so

$$\text{Length} = \int_{-1/2}^{1/2} \sqrt{(\pi \cos \pi t)^2 + (-\pi \sin \pi t)^2}\, dt$$
$$= \int_{-1/2}^{1/2} \pi\, dt = \pi.$$

24. $x' = -3 \sin t$, $y' = 4 \cos t$, so

$$\text{Length} = \int_0^{2\pi} \sqrt{(-3 \sin t)^2 + (4 \cos t)^2}\, dt$$

which using NINT evaluates to ≈ 22.103.

25. In the first integral, replace t with x. Then $\dfrac{dx}{dt}$ becomes $\dfrac{dx}{dx} = 1$.

26. Parameterize the curve as $x = g(y)$, $y = y$, $c \le y \le d$. The parameter is y itself, so replace t with y in the general formula. Then $\dfrac{dy}{dt}$ becomes $\dfrac{dy}{dy} = 1$.

27. $x' = t$, $y' = \sqrt{2t + 1}$, so

$$\text{Total length} = \int_0^4 \sqrt{t^2 + (\sqrt{2t + 1})^2}\, dt$$
$$= \int_0^4 (t + 1)\, dt$$
$$= \left[\frac{1}{2}t^2 + t\right]_0^4 = 12.$$

Now solve $\left[\dfrac{1}{2}t^2 + t\right]_0^m = \dfrac{12}{2}$ for m:

$\dfrac{1}{2}m^2 + m = 6$, or $m^2 + 2m - 12 = 0$, and

$m = \dfrac{-2 \pm \sqrt{4 + 48}}{2} = -1 \pm \sqrt{13}$. Take the positive solution. The midpoint is at $t = \sqrt{13} - 1$, which gives

$$(x, y) = \left(\frac{(\sqrt{13} - 1)^2}{2}, \frac{1}{3}(2\sqrt{13} - 1)^{3/2}\right) \approx (3.394, 5.160).$$

28.

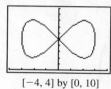

$[-4, 4]$ by $[0, 10]$

Use the right half of the curve, $0 \le t \le \pi$.

$x' = 3 \cos t$, $y' = 6 \cos 2t$, so

$$\text{Area} = \int_0^\pi 2\pi(3 \sin t)\sqrt{(3 \cos t)^2 + (6 \cos 2t)^2}\, dt,$$

which using NINT evaluates to ≈ 159.485.

29.

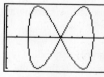

$[0, 9]$ by $[-3, 3]$

Use the top half of the curve, and make use of the shape's symmetry.

$x' = 3 \cos t$, $y' = 6 \cos 2t$, so

$$\text{Area} = 2\int_0^{\pi/2} 2\pi(3 \sin 2t)\sqrt{(3 \cos t)^2 + (6 \cos 2t)^2}\, dt$$

which using NINT, evaluates to ≈ 144.513.

30. $y = 0$ for $t = 0$ and $t = 2\pi$. $x' = a - a \cos t$, $y' = a \sin t$,

so

$$\text{Area} = \int_0^{2\pi} 2\pi[a(1 - \cos t)]\sqrt{(a - a \cos t)^2 + (a \sin t)^2}\, dt$$

$$= 2\pi a^2 \int_0^{2\pi} (1 - \cos t)\sqrt{2 - 2 \cos t}\, dt$$

$$= 2\pi a^2 \int_0^{2\pi} \left(2 \sin^2\left(\frac{t}{2}\right)\right)\sqrt{4 \sin^2\left(\frac{t}{2}\right)}\, dt$$

$$= 8\pi a^2 \int_0^{2\pi} \sin^3\left(\frac{t}{2}\right) dt$$

$$= 8\pi a^2 \int_0^{2\pi} \left(1 - \cos^2\left(\frac{t}{2}\right)\right) \sin\left(\frac{t}{2}\right) dt$$

$$= 8\pi a^2 \left[-2 \cos\left(\frac{t}{2}\right) + \frac{2}{3} \cos^3\left(\frac{t}{2}\right)\right]_0^{2\pi}$$

$$= \frac{64\pi a^2}{3}$$

31. $\dfrac{dx}{dt} = a(1 - \cos t)$

(Note: integrate with respect to x from 0 to $2a\pi$; integrate

with respect to t from 0 to 2π.)

$$\text{Area} = \int_0^{2a\pi} y\, dx$$

$$= \int_0^{2\pi} a(1 - \cos t)a(1 - \cos t)\, dt$$

$$= a^2 \int_0^{2\pi} (1 - 2 \cos t + \cos^2 t)\, dt$$

$$= a^2 \left[t - 2 \sin t + \frac{t}{2} + \frac{1}{4}\sin 2t\right]_0^{2\pi} = 3\pi a^2$$

32. $\dfrac{dx}{dt} = a(1 - \cos t)$, so

$$\text{Volume} = \int_0^{2\pi} \pi[a(1 - \cos t)]^2 a(1 - \cos t)\, dt$$

$$= \pi a^3 \int_0^{2\pi} (1 - 3 \cos t + 3 \cos^2 t - \cos^3 t)\, dt$$

$$= \pi a^3 \left[t - 3 \sin t + \frac{3}{2}t + \frac{3}{4}\sin 2t \right.$$
$$\left. -\left(\sin t - \frac{1}{3} \sin^3 t\right)\right]_0^{2\pi}$$

$$= 5\pi^2 a^3$$

33. (a) $\overline{QP}$ has length t, so P can be obtained by starting at Q and moving $t \sin t$ units right and $t \cos t$ units downward.
(If either quantity is negative, the corresponding direction is reversed.) Since $Q = (\cos t, \sin t)$, the coordinates of P are
$x = \cos t + t \sin t$ and $y = \sin t - t \cos t$.

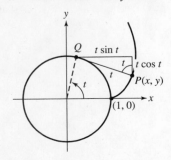

(b) $x' = t \cos t$, $y' = t \sin t$, so

$$\text{Length} = \int_0^{2\pi} \sqrt{(t \cos t)^2 + (t \sin t)^2}\, dt = \int_0^{2\pi} t\, dt$$

$$= 2\pi^2$$

34. All distances are a times as big as before.

(a) $x = a(\cos t + t \sin t)$, $y = a(\sin t - t \cos t)$

(b) Length $= 2a\pi^2$

For exercises 35–38, $x' = v_0 \cos \theta$ and $y' = v_0 \sin \theta - 32t$, and $y = 0$ for $t = 0$ or $t = \dfrac{v_0 \sin \theta}{16}$. The maximum height is attained in mid-flight at $t = \dfrac{v_0 \sin \theta}{32}$. To find the path length, evaluate $\int_0^{v_0 \sin \theta/16} \sqrt{(v_0 \cos \theta)^2 + (v_0 \sin \theta - 32t)^2}\, dt$ using NINT. To find the

maximum height, calculate

$$y_{max} = (v_0 \sin \theta)\left(\frac{v_0 \sin \theta}{32}\right) - 16\left(\frac{v_0 \sin \theta}{32}\right)^2.$$

35. (a) The projectile hits the ground when $y = 0$.

$$y = t(150 \sin 20° - 16t) = 0$$

$$t = 0 \text{ or } t = \frac{75}{8} \sin 20° \approx 3.206$$

$$x' = 150 \cos 20°, y' = 150 \sin 20° - 32t$$

$$\text{Length} = \int_0^{(75 \sin 20°)/8} \sqrt{(150 \cos 20°)^2 + (150 \sin 20° - 32t)^2}$$

dt which, using NINT, evaluates to ≈ 461.749 ft

(b) The maximum height of the projectile occurs when

$y' = 0$,

so $t = \dfrac{75}{16} \sin 20°$, $y\left(\dfrac{75}{16} \sin 20°\right) \approx 41.125$ ft

36. (a) ≈ 641.236 ft

(b) $\dfrac{5625}{64} \approx 87.891$ ft

37. (a) ≈ 840.421 ft

(b) $\dfrac{16,875}{64} \approx 263.672$ ft

38. (a) It is not necessary to use NINT.

$$\text{Length} = \int_0^{75/8} (150 - 32t)\, dt = \left[150t - 16t^2\right]_0^{75/8}$$

$$= \frac{5625}{8} = 703.125 \text{ ft}$$

(b) $\dfrac{5625}{16} = 351.5625$

39. In the integral $\int_a^b 2\pi y \sqrt{\left(\dfrac{dx}{dt}\right)^2 + \left(\dfrac{dy}{dt}\right)^2}\, dt$, replace t with x

and y with $f(x)$.

Then $\dfrac{dx}{dt}$ becomes $\dfrac{dx}{dx} = 1$.

40. $\frac{dy}{dx} = e^x$, so Area $= \int_0^3 2\pi e^x \sqrt{1 + (e^x)^2}\, dx$ which using

NINT evaluates to ≈ 1273.371.

41. $\frac{dy}{dx} = -\frac{1}{x^2}$, so Area $= \int_1^4 2\pi \left(\frac{1}{x}\right) \sqrt{1 + \left(-\frac{1}{x^2}\right)^2}\, dx$, which,

using NINT, evaluates to ≈ 9.417.

42. $\frac{dy}{dx} = (\ln 2)2^x - (\ln 2)2^{-x} = (\ln 2)(2^x - 2^{-x})$, so

Area $= \int_{-2}^2 2\pi(2^x + 2^{-x})\sqrt{1 + (\ln 2)^2(2^x - 2^{-x})^2}\, dx$ which

using NINT evaluates to ≈ 116.687.

■ Section 10.2 Vectors in the Plane
(pp. 520–529)

Quick Review 10.2

1. $\sqrt{(5-1)^2 + (3-2)^2} = \sqrt{17}$

2. $\frac{3-2}{5-1} = \frac{1}{4}$

3. Solve $\frac{3-b}{5-3} = -4$: $b = 11$.

4. Slope of $\overline{AB}$ = Slope of $\overline{CD}$, so $\frac{3-0}{1-0} = \frac{3-0}{5-a}$ and $a = 4$.

5. Slope of $\overline{AB}$ = Slope of $\overline{CD}$, so $\frac{5-1}{3-1} = \frac{2-b}{6-8}$ = and $b = 6$.

6. (a) $\theta = 120°$

   (b) $\theta = \frac{2\pi}{3}$

7. (a) $\theta = -30°$

   (b) $\theta = -\frac{\pi}{6}$

8. (a) $\theta = -45°$

   (b) $\theta = -\frac{\pi}{4}$

9. $c^2 = 3^2 + 5^2 - 2(3)(5)\cos(30°) = 34 - 15\sqrt{3}$, so

$c = \sqrt{34 - 15\sqrt{3}} \approx 2.832$

10. $24^2 = 27^2 + 19^2 - 2(27)(19)\cos\theta$, so

$\cos\theta = \frac{24^2 - 27^2 - 19^2}{-2(27)(19)} = \frac{257}{513}$ and

$\theta = \cos^{-1}\frac{257}{513} \approx 1.046$ radians or $59.935°$.

Section 10.2 Exercises

1. (a) $\langle 3(3),\ 3(-2)\rangle = \langle 9,\ -6\rangle$

   (b) $\sqrt{9^2 + (-6)^2} = \sqrt{117} = 3\sqrt{13}$

2. (a) $\langle -2(-2),\ -2(5)\rangle = \langle 4,\ -10\rangle$

   (b) $\sqrt{4^2 + (-10)^2} = \sqrt{116} = 2\sqrt{29}$

3. (a) $\langle 3 + (-2),\ -2 + 5\rangle = \langle 1,\ 3\rangle$

   (b) $\sqrt{1^2 + 3^2} = \sqrt{10}$

4. (a) $\langle 3 - (-2),\ -2 - 5\rangle = \langle 5,\ -7\rangle$

   (b) $\sqrt{5^2 + (-7)^2} = \sqrt{74}$

5. (a) $2\mathbf{u} = \langle 2(3),\ 2(-2)\rangle = \langle 6,\ -4\rangle$

$3\mathbf{v} = \langle 3(-2),\ 3(5)\rangle = \langle -6,\ 15\rangle$

$2\mathbf{u} - 3\mathbf{v} = \langle 6 - (-6),\ -4 - 15\rangle = \langle 12,\ -19\rangle$

   (b) $\sqrt{12^2 + (-19)^2} = \sqrt{505}$

6. (a) $-2\mathbf{u} = \langle -2(3),\ -2(-2)\rangle = \langle -6,\ 4\rangle$

$5\mathbf{v} = \langle 5(-2),\ 5(5)\rangle = \langle -10,\ 25\rangle$

$-2\mathbf{u} + 5\mathbf{v} = \langle -6 + (-10),\ 4 + 25\rangle = \langle -16,\ 29\rangle$

   (b) $\sqrt{(-16)^2 + 29^2} = \sqrt{1097}$

7. (a) $\frac{3}{5}\mathbf{u} = \left\langle \frac{3}{5}(3),\ \frac{3}{5}(-2)\right\rangle = \left\langle \frac{9}{5},\ -\frac{6}{5}\right\rangle$

$\frac{4}{5}\mathbf{v} = \left\langle \frac{4}{5}(-2),\ \frac{4}{5}(5)\right\rangle = \left\langle -\frac{8}{5},\ 4\right\rangle$

$\frac{3}{5}\mathbf{u} + \frac{4}{5}\mathbf{v} = \left\langle \frac{9}{5} + \left(-\frac{8}{5}\right),\ -\frac{6}{5} + 4\right\rangle = \left\langle \frac{1}{5},\ \frac{14}{5}\right\rangle$

   (b) $\sqrt{\left(\frac{1}{5}\right)^2 + \left(\frac{14}{5}\right)^2} = \frac{\sqrt{197}}{5}$

8. (a) $-\frac{5}{13}\mathbf{u} = \left\langle -\frac{5}{13}(3),\ -\frac{5}{13}(-2)\right\rangle = \left\langle -\frac{15}{13},\ \frac{10}{13}\right\rangle$

$\frac{12}{13}\mathbf{v} = \left\langle \frac{12}{13}(-2),\ \frac{12}{13}(5)\right\rangle = \left\langle -\frac{24}{13},\ \frac{60}{13}\right\rangle$

$-\frac{5}{13}\mathbf{u} + \frac{12}{13}\mathbf{v} = \left\langle -\frac{15}{13} + \left(-\frac{24}{13}\right),\ \frac{10}{13} + \frac{60}{13}\right\rangle = \left\langle -3,\ \frac{70}{13}\right\rangle$

   (b) $\sqrt{(-3)^2 + \left(\frac{70}{13}\right)^2} = \frac{\sqrt{6421}}{13}$

9. $\langle 2 - 1,\ -1 - 3\rangle = \langle 1,\ -4\rangle$

10. $\left\langle \frac{2 + (-4)}{2} - 0,\ \frac{-1 + 3}{2} - 0\right\rangle = \langle -1,\ 1\rangle$

11. $\langle 0 - 2,\ 0 - 3\rangle = \langle -2,\ -3\rangle$

12. $\overrightarrow{AB} = \langle 2 - 1,\ 0 - (-1)\rangle = \langle 1,\ 1\rangle$

$\overrightarrow{CD} = \langle -2 - (-1),\ 2 - 3\rangle = \langle -1,\ -1\rangle$

$\overrightarrow{AB} + \overrightarrow{CD} = \langle 1 + (-1),\ 1 + (-1)\rangle = \langle 0,\ 0\rangle$

13. $\left\langle \cos\frac{2\pi}{3},\ \sin\frac{2\pi}{3}\right\rangle = \left\langle -\frac{1}{2},\ \frac{\sqrt{3}}{2}\right\rangle$

14. $\left\langle \cos\left(-\frac{3\pi}{4}\right),\ \sin\left(-\frac{3\pi}{4}\right)\right\rangle = \left\langle -\frac{1}{\sqrt{2}},\ -\frac{1}{\sqrt{2}}\right\rangle$

15. This is the unit vector which makes an angle of

$120 + 90 = 210°$ with the positive x-axis;

$\langle \cos 210°,\ \sin 210°\rangle = \left\langle -\frac{\sqrt{3}}{2},\ -\frac{1}{2}\right\rangle$

16. $\langle \cos 135°,\ \sin 135°\rangle = \left\langle -\frac{1}{\sqrt{2}},\ \frac{1}{\sqrt{2}}\right\rangle$

17. The vector **v** is horizontal and 1 in. long. The vectors **u** and **w** are $\frac{11}{16}$ in. long. **w** is vertical and **u** makes a 45° angle with the horizontal. All vectors must be drawn to scale.

(a)

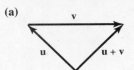

(b)

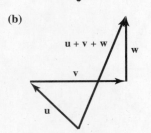

(c)

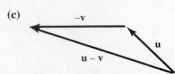

(d)

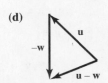

18. The angles between the vectors is 120° and vector **u** is horizontal. They are all 1 in. long. Draw to scale.

(a)

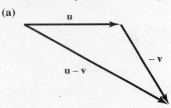

(b)

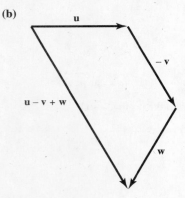

(c)

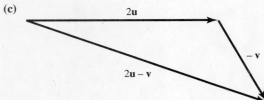

(d)

$$\mathbf{u} + \mathbf{v} + \mathbf{w} = \mathbf{0}$$

19. $\sqrt{3^2 + 4^2} = 5;\ \frac{1}{5}\langle 3, 4\rangle = \left\langle \frac{3}{5}, \frac{4}{5}\right\rangle$

20. $\sqrt{4^2 + (-3)^2} = 5;\ \frac{1}{5}\langle 4, -3\rangle = \left\langle \frac{4}{5}, -\frac{3}{5}\right\rangle$

21. $\sqrt{(-15)^2 + 8^2} = 17;\ \frac{1}{17}\langle -15, 8\rangle = \left\langle -\frac{15}{17}, \frac{8}{17}\right\rangle$

22. $\sqrt{(-5)^2 + (-2)^2} = \sqrt{29};$

$$\frac{1}{\sqrt{29}}\langle -5, -2\rangle = \left\langle -\frac{5}{\sqrt{29}}, -\frac{2}{\sqrt{29}}\right\rangle$$

23. $x' = \frac{1}{2\sqrt{t}},\ y' = 1 + \frac{1}{\sqrt{t}};$ for $t = 1,\ x' = \frac{1}{2},\ y' = 2,$ and

$\sqrt{(x')^2 + (y')^2} = \frac{\sqrt{17}}{2}.$

Tangent: $\pm\frac{2}{\sqrt{17}}\left\langle \frac{1}{2}, 2\right\rangle = \pm\left\langle \frac{1}{\sqrt{17}}, \frac{4}{\sqrt{17}}\right\rangle,$

Normal: $\pm\frac{2}{\sqrt{17}}\left\langle 2, -\frac{1}{2}\right\rangle = \pm\left\langle \frac{4}{\sqrt{17}}, -\frac{1}{\sqrt{17}}\right\rangle.$

24. $x' = \frac{1}{t-1},\ y' = 1;$ for $t = 3,\ x' = \frac{1}{2},\ y' = 1,$ and

$\sqrt{(x')^2 + (y')^2} = \frac{\sqrt{5}}{2}.$

Tangent: $\pm\frac{2}{\sqrt{5}}\left\langle \frac{1}{2}, 1\right\rangle = \pm\left\langle \frac{1}{\sqrt{5}}, \frac{2}{\sqrt{5}}\right\rangle,$

Normal $= \pm\frac{2}{\sqrt{5}}\left\langle 1, -\frac{1}{2}\right\rangle = \pm\left\langle \frac{2}{\sqrt{5}}, -\frac{1}{\sqrt{5}}\right\rangle.$

25. $x' = -4\sin t,\ y' = 5\cos t;$ for $t = \frac{\pi}{3},\ x' = -2\sqrt{3},$

$y' = \frac{5}{2},$ and $\sqrt{(x')^2 + (y')^2} = \frac{\sqrt{73}}{2}.$

Tangent $= \pm\frac{2}{\sqrt{73}}\left\langle -2\sqrt{3}, \frac{5}{2}\right\rangle = \pm\left\langle -\frac{12}{\sqrt{219}}, \frac{5}{\sqrt{73}}\right\rangle$

$\approx \pm\langle -0.811, 0.585\rangle,$

Normal $= \pm\frac{2}{\sqrt{73}}\left\langle \frac{5}{2}, 2\sqrt{3}\right\rangle = \pm\left\langle \frac{5}{\sqrt{73}}, \frac{12}{\sqrt{219}}\right\rangle$

$\approx \pm\langle 0.585, 0.811\rangle.$

26. $x' = -3 \sin t$, $y' = 3 \cos t$; for $t = -\dfrac{\pi}{4}$, $x' = \dfrac{3}{\sqrt{2}}$,

$y' = \dfrac{3}{\sqrt{2}}$, and $\sqrt{(x')^2 + (y')^2} = 3$.

Tangent: $\pm\dfrac{1}{3}\left\langle \dfrac{3}{\sqrt{2}}, \dfrac{3}{\sqrt{2}} \right\rangle = \pm\left\langle \dfrac{1}{\sqrt{2}}, \dfrac{1}{\sqrt{2}} \right\rangle$,

Normal: $\pm\dfrac{1}{3}\left\langle \dfrac{3}{\sqrt{2}}, -\dfrac{3}{\sqrt{2}} \right\rangle = \pm\left\langle \dfrac{1}{\sqrt{2}}, -\dfrac{1}{\sqrt{2}} \right\rangle$.

27. $\overrightarrow{AB} = \langle 3, 1 \rangle$, $\overrightarrow{BC} = \langle -1, -3 \rangle$, and $\overrightarrow{AC} = \langle 2, -2 \rangle$.

$\overrightarrow{BA} = \langle -3, -1 \rangle$, $\overrightarrow{CB} = \langle 1, 3 \rangle$, and $\overrightarrow{CA} = \langle -2, 2 \rangle$.

$|\overrightarrow{AB}| = |\overrightarrow{BA}| = \sqrt{10}$, $|\overrightarrow{BC}| = |\overrightarrow{CB}| = \sqrt{10}$, and

$|\overrightarrow{AC}| = |\overrightarrow{CA}| = 2\sqrt{2}$.

Angle at $A = \cos^{-1}\left(\dfrac{\overrightarrow{AB} \cdot \overrightarrow{AC}}{|\overrightarrow{AB}||\overrightarrow{AC}|} \right)$

$= \cos^{-1}\left(\dfrac{3(2) + 1(-2)}{(\sqrt{10})(2\sqrt{2})} \right)$

$= \cos^{-1}\left(\dfrac{1}{\sqrt{5}} \right) \approx 63.435°$,

Angle at $B = \cos^{-1}\left(\dfrac{\overrightarrow{BC} \cdot \overrightarrow{BA}}{|\overrightarrow{BC}||\overrightarrow{BA}|} \right)$

$= \cos^{-1}\left(\dfrac{(-1)(-3) + (-3)(-1)}{(\sqrt{10})(\sqrt{10})} \right)$

$= \cos^{-1}\left(\dfrac{3}{5} \right) \approx 53.130°$, and

Angle at $C = \cos^{-1}\left(\dfrac{\overrightarrow{CB} \cdot \overrightarrow{CA}}{|\overrightarrow{CB}||\overrightarrow{CA}|} \right)$

$= \cos^{-1}\left(\dfrac{1(-2) + 3(2)}{(\sqrt{10})(2\sqrt{2})} \right)$

$= \cos^{-1}\left(\dfrac{1}{\sqrt{5}} \right) \approx 63.435°$.

28. $\overrightarrow{AC} = \langle 2, 4 \rangle$ and $\overrightarrow{BD} = \langle 4, -2 \rangle$.

$\overrightarrow{AC} \cdot \overrightarrow{BD} = 2(4) + 4(-2) = 0$, so the angle measures 90°.

29. (a) $\mathbf{u} \cdot (\mathbf{v} + \mathbf{w}) = u_1(v_1 + w_1) + u_2(v_2 + w_2)$
$= (u_1 v_1 + u_1 w_1) + (u_2 v_2 + u_2 w_2)$
$= (u_1 v_1 + u_2 v_2) + (u_1 w_1 + u_2 w_2)$
$= \mathbf{u} \cdot \mathbf{v} + \mathbf{u} \cdot \mathbf{w}$

(b) $(\mathbf{u} + \mathbf{v}) \cdot \mathbf{w} = (u_1 + v_1)w_1 + (u_2 + v_2)w_2$
$= (u_1 w_1 + v_1 w_1) + (u_2 w_2 + v_2 w_2)$
$= (u_1 w_1 + u_2 w_2) + (v_1 w_1 + v_2 w_2)$
$= \mathbf{u} \cdot \mathbf{w} + \mathbf{v} \cdot \mathbf{w}$

30. $\mathbf{u} \cdot \mathbf{u} = u_1^2 + u_2^2 = (\sqrt{u_1^2 + u_2^2})^2 = |\mathbf{u}|^2$

31. $(\mathbf{u} + \mathbf{v}) \cdot (\mathbf{u} - \mathbf{v})$

$= (u_1 + v_1)(u_1 - v_1) + (u_2 + v_2)(u_2 - v_2)$
$= u_1^2 - v_1^2 + u_2^2 - v_2^2$
$= (u_1^2 + u_2^2) - (v_1^2 + v_2^2)$
$= |\mathbf{u}|^2 - |\mathbf{v}|^2$

32. Since $\mathbf{u}$ and $\mathbf{v}$ are nonzero, we know that $|\mathbf{u}| \neq 0$ and $|\mathbf{v}| \neq 0$. Therefore, the dot product $\mathbf{u} \cdot \mathbf{v} = |\mathbf{u}| \, |\mathbf{v}| \cos\theta$ is 0 if and only if $\cos\theta = 0$, which occurs if and only if $\mathbf{u}$ and $\mathbf{v}$ are orthogonal $\left(\theta = \dfrac{\pi}{2}\right)$.

33.

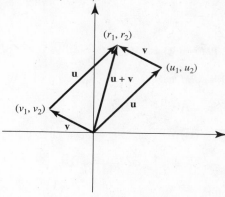

$r_1 - v_1 = u_1$ so $r_1 = u_1 + v_1$
$r_2 - v_2 = u_2$ so $r_2 = u_2 + v_2$

34. (a) To find $\mathbf{u} - \mathbf{v}$, place both vectors with their initial points at the origin. The vector drawn from the terminal point of $\mathbf{v}$ to the terminal point of $\mathbf{u}$ is $\mathbf{u} - \mathbf{v}$. Or, add $\mathbf{u}$ and $-\mathbf{v}$ according to the parallelogram law.

(b)

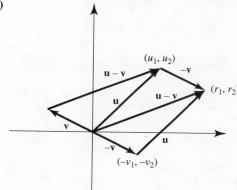

$r_1 - (-v_1) = u_1 \rightarrow r_1 = u_1 - v_1$
$r_2 - (-v_2) = u_2 \rightarrow r_2 = u_2 - v_2$

35. (a) Let $P = (a, b)$ and $Q = (c, d)$. Then

$\left(\dfrac{1}{2}\right)\overrightarrow{OP} + \left(\dfrac{1}{2}\right)\overrightarrow{OQ} = \left(\dfrac{1}{2}\right)\langle a, b \rangle + \left(\dfrac{1}{2}\right)\langle c, d \rangle$

$= \left\langle \dfrac{(a + c)}{2}, \dfrac{(b + d)}{2} \right\rangle = \overrightarrow{OM}$

(b) $\overrightarrow{OM} = \left(\dfrac{2}{3}\right)\overrightarrow{OP} + \left(\dfrac{1}{3}\right)\overrightarrow{OQ}$

(c) $\overrightarrow{OM} = \left(\dfrac{1}{3}\right)\overrightarrow{OP} + \left(\dfrac{2}{3}\right)\overrightarrow{OQ}$

35. continued

(d) *M is a fraction of the way from P to Q. Let d be this*

fraction. Then

$$\overrightarrow{OM} = d\overrightarrow{OQ} + (1-d)\overrightarrow{OP}.$$

Proof: $\overrightarrow{PM} = d\overrightarrow{PQ}$ and $\overrightarrow{MQ} = (1-d)\overrightarrow{PQ}$,

so $\overrightarrow{PQ} = \dfrac{1}{d}\overrightarrow{PM}$ and $\overrightarrow{PQ} = \dfrac{1}{1-d}\overrightarrow{MQ}$.

Therefore, $\dfrac{1}{d}\overrightarrow{PM} = \dfrac{1}{1-d}\overrightarrow{MQ}$.

But $\overrightarrow{PM} = \overrightarrow{OM} - \overrightarrow{OP}$ and $\overrightarrow{MQ} = \overrightarrow{OQ} - \overrightarrow{OM}$, so

$$\frac{1}{d}\overrightarrow{OM} - \frac{1}{d}\overrightarrow{OP} = \frac{1}{1-d}\overrightarrow{OQ} - \frac{1}{1-d}\overrightarrow{OM}.$$

Therefore,

$$\frac{1}{d}\overrightarrow{OM} + \frac{1}{1-d}\overrightarrow{OM} = \frac{1}{d}\overrightarrow{OP} + \frac{1}{1-d}\overrightarrow{OQ}.$$

$$\Rightarrow \overrightarrow{OM}\left(\frac{1}{d(1-d)}\right) = \frac{1}{d}\overrightarrow{OP} + \frac{1}{1-d}\overrightarrow{OQ}$$

$$\Rightarrow \overrightarrow{OM} = (1-d)\overrightarrow{OP} + d\overrightarrow{OQ}.$$

36. $\overrightarrow{CA} = -\mathbf{u} - \mathbf{v}$ and $\overrightarrow{CB} = \mathbf{u} - \mathbf{v}$. Since $|\mathbf{v}| = |\mathbf{u}|$, these vectors are orthogonal, as $(-\mathbf{u} - \mathbf{v})\cdot(\mathbf{u} - \mathbf{v}) = |\mathbf{v}|^2 - |\mathbf{u}|^2 = 0$.

37. Two adjacent sides of the rhombus can be given by two vectors of the same length, $\mathbf{u}$ and $\mathbf{v}$. Then the diagonals of the rhombus are $(\mathbf{u} + \mathbf{v})$ and $(\mathbf{u} - \mathbf{v})$. These two vectors are orthogonal since $|\mathbf{u}| = |\mathbf{v}|$ so $(\mathbf{u} + \mathbf{v})\cdot(\mathbf{u} - \mathbf{v}) = |\mathbf{u}|^2 - |\mathbf{v}|^2 = 0$.

38. Two adjacent sides of a rectangle can be given by two vectors $\mathbf{u}$ and $\mathbf{v}$. The diagonals are then $(\mathbf{u} + \mathbf{v})$ and $(\mathbf{u} - \mathbf{v})$. These two vectors will be orthogonal if and only if $\mathbf{u}$ and $\mathbf{v}$ are the same length, since $(\mathbf{u} + \mathbf{v})\cdot(\mathbf{u} - \mathbf{v}) = |\mathbf{u}|^2 - |\mathbf{v}|^2$.

39. Let two adjacent sides of the parallelogram be given by two vectors $\mathbf{u}$ and $\mathbf{v}$. The diagonals are then $(\mathbf{u} + \mathbf{v})$ and $(\mathbf{u} - \mathbf{v})$. So the lengths of the diagonals satisfy

$$|\mathbf{u} + \mathbf{v}|^2 = (\mathbf{u} + \mathbf{v})\cdot(\mathbf{u} + \mathbf{v})$$
$$= |\mathbf{u}|^2 + 2\mathbf{u}\cdot\mathbf{v} + |\mathbf{v}|^2$$

and $|\mathbf{u} - \mathbf{v}|^2 = (\mathbf{u} - \mathbf{v})\cdot(\mathbf{u} - \mathbf{v})$
$$= |\mathbf{u}|^2 - 2\mathbf{u}\cdot\mathbf{v} + |\mathbf{v}|^2.$$

The two lengths will be the same if and only if $\mathbf{u}\cdot\mathbf{v} = 0$, which means that $\mathbf{u}$ and $\mathbf{v}$ are perpendicular and the parallelogram is a rectangle.

40. The indicated diagonal is $(\mathbf{u} + \mathbf{v})$. The cosine of the angle between the diagonal and $\mathbf{u}$ is

$$\frac{(\mathbf{u} + \mathbf{v})\cdot\mathbf{u}}{|\mathbf{u} + \mathbf{v}|\,|\mathbf{u}|} = \frac{|\mathbf{u}|^2 + \mathbf{v}\cdot\mathbf{u}}{|\mathbf{u} + \mathbf{v}|\,|\mathbf{u}|}.$$

But the cosine of the angle between the diagonal and $\mathbf{v}$ is

$$\frac{(\mathbf{u} + \mathbf{v})\cdot\mathbf{v}}{|\mathbf{u} + \mathbf{v}|\,|\mathbf{v}|} = \frac{\mathbf{u}\cdot\mathbf{v} + |\mathbf{v}|^2}{|\mathbf{u} + \mathbf{v}|\,|\mathbf{v}|}.$$

If $\mathbf{u}$ and $\mathbf{v}$ are the same length then these two quantities are equal, and the diagonal makes the same angle with both sides.

41. The slopes are the same.

42. $\mathbf{v} = \mathbf{0}$ since any other vector has positive magnitude.

43. 25° west of north is $90 + 25 = 115°$ north of east. $800\langle\cos 115°, \sin 115°\rangle \approx \langle -338.095, 725.046\rangle$

44. 10° east of south is $270 + 10 = 280°$ "north" of east. $600\langle\cos 280°, \sin 280°\rangle \approx \langle 104.189, -590.885\rangle$

45. Initial velocity is 70° north of east:

$325\langle\cos 70°, \sin 70°\rangle \approx \langle 111.157, 305.400\rangle$.

Wind velocity is 130° north of east:

$40\langle\cos 130°, \sin 130°\rangle \approx \langle -25.712, 30.642\rangle$.

Add the two vectors to get $\approx \langle 85.445, 336.042\rangle$.

The speed is the magnitude, ≈ 346.735 mph.

The direction is $\tan^{-1}\left(\dfrac{336.042}{85.445}\right) \approx 75.734°$ north of east, or $\approx 14.266°$ east of north.

46. $|\mathbf{w}|\cos(33° - 15°) = 2.5$ lb, so $|\mathbf{w}| = \dfrac{2.5\text{ lb}}{\cos 18°}$.

Then $\mathbf{w} \approx \dfrac{2.5\text{ lb}}{\cos 18°}\langle\cos 33°, \sin 33°\rangle \approx \langle 2.205, 1.432\rangle$.

47. Juana's pull $= 23\langle\cos 18°, \sin 18°\rangle \approx \langle 21.874, 7.107\rangle$; Diego's pull $= 18\langle\cos(-15°), \sin(-15°)\rangle \approx \langle 17.387, -4.659\rangle$. Add to get the combined pull of the children: $\approx \langle 39.261, 2.449\rangle$. The puppy pulls with an opposite force of the same magnitude: $\sqrt{39.261^2 + 2.449^2} \approx 39.337$ lb.

48. (a) $7\langle\cos 45°, \sin 45°\rangle$ has its terminal point at $\approx(4.950, 4.950)$.

(b) $7\langle\cos 45°, \sin 45°\rangle + 8\langle\cos 210°, \sin 210°\rangle$ has its terminal point at $\approx(-1.978, 0.950)$.

49. $\overrightarrow{AB} = \langle -3 - 0, 4 - 0\rangle = \langle -3, 4\rangle = \langle 1 - 4, 5 - 1\rangle = \overrightarrow{CD}$

50. $\overrightarrow{AB} = \langle -2 - (-4), -2 - 3\rangle$
$= \langle 2, -5\rangle$
$= \langle 3 - 1, -4 - 1\rangle = \overrightarrow{CD}$

51. $\mathbf{u} = \langle u_1, u_2 \rangle$, $\mathbf{v} = \langle v_1, v_2 \rangle$, $\mathbf{w} = \langle w_1, w_2 \rangle$

   (i) $\mathbf{u} + \mathbf{v} = \langle u_1 + v_1, u_2 + v_2 \rangle$
            $= \langle v_1 + u_1, v_2 + u_2 \rangle = \mathbf{v} + \mathbf{u}$

  (ii) $(\mathbf{u} + \mathbf{v}) + \mathbf{w}$
            $= \langle u_1 + v_1, u_2 + v_2 \rangle + \langle w_1, w_2 \rangle$
            $= \langle (u_1 + v_1) + w_1, (u_2 + v_2) + w_2 \rangle$
            $= \langle u_1 + (v_1 + w_1), u_2 + (v_2 + w_2) \rangle$
            $= \mathbf{u} + (\mathbf{v} + \mathbf{w})$

 (iii) $\mathbf{u} + \mathbf{0} = \langle u_1, u_2 \rangle + \langle 0, 0 \rangle = \langle u_1 + 0, u_2 + 0 \rangle$
            $= \langle u_1, u_2 \rangle = \mathbf{u}$

 (iv) $\mathbf{u} + (-\mathbf{u}) = \langle u_1, u_2 \rangle + \langle -u_1, -u_2 \rangle$
            $= \langle u_1 - u_1, u_2 - u_2 \rangle = \langle 0, 0 \rangle = \mathbf{0}$

  (v) $0\mathbf{u} = 0\langle u_1, u_2 \rangle = \langle 0u_1, 0u_2 \rangle = \langle 0, 0 \rangle = \mathbf{0}$

 (vi) $1\mathbf{u} = 1\langle u_1, u_2 \rangle = \langle 1u_1, 1u_2 \rangle = \langle u_1, u_2 \rangle = \mathbf{u}$

 (vii) $a(b\mathbf{u}) = a(b\langle u_1, u_2 \rangle) = a\langle bu_1, bu_2 \rangle$
            $= \langle abu_1, abu_2 \rangle = ab\langle u_1, u_2 \rangle = (ab)\mathbf{u}$

(viii) $a(\mathbf{u} + \mathbf{v}) = a\langle u_1 + v_1, u_2 + v_2 \rangle$
            $= \langle au_1 + av_1, au_2 + av_2 \rangle$
            $= \langle au_1, au_2 \rangle + \langle av_1, av_2 \rangle$
            $= a\langle u_1, u_2 \rangle + a\langle v_1, v_2 \rangle$
            $= a\mathbf{u} + a\mathbf{v}$

 (ix) $(a + b)\mathbf{u} = (a + b)\langle u_1, u_2 \rangle$
            $= \langle (a + b)u_1, (a + b)u_2 \rangle$
            $= \langle au_1 + bu_1, au_2 + bu_2 \rangle$
            $= \langle au_1, au_2 \rangle + \langle bu_1, bu_2 \rangle = a\mathbf{u} + b\mathbf{u}$

52. Write the two vectors as $a\langle 1, 1 \rangle$ and $b\langle 1, -1 \rangle$. Then their

    sum is $\langle a + b, a - b \rangle$, so solve $a + b = 3$, $a - b = 4$ to get

    $a = \dfrac{7}{2}$, $b = -\dfrac{1}{2}$. So $\langle 3, 4 \rangle = \left\langle \dfrac{7}{2}, \dfrac{7}{2} \right\rangle + \left\langle -\dfrac{1}{2}, \dfrac{1}{2} \right\rangle$.

53. **(a)** Slope $= -\dfrac{1}{1} = -1$, so $y - y_1 = m(x - x_1)$ becomes

        $y - 1 = -(x + 2)$ or $y = -x - 1$.

    (b) Slope $= 1$, so $y - y_1 = m(x - x_1)$ becomes
        $y - 1 = x + 2$ or $y = x + 3$.

54. The slopes of the lines are $\dfrac{3}{4}$ and 1, which means that

    vectors $\langle 4, 3 \rangle$ and $\langle 1, 1 \rangle$ are parallel to the respective lines.

    $\theta = \cos^{-1}\left(\dfrac{4 \cdot 1 + 3 \cdot 1}{5\sqrt{2}} \right) = \cos^{-1}\left(\dfrac{7\sqrt{2}}{10} \right) \approx 8.130°$.

■ Section 10.3 Vector-valued Functions
(pp. 529–539)

Quick Review 10.3

1. $f'(x) = -\dfrac{x}{\sqrt{4 - x^2}}$, so for $x = 1$, $f(x) = \sqrt{3}$ and

    $f'(x) = -\dfrac{1}{\sqrt{3}}$. Then $y - \sqrt{3} = -\dfrac{1}{\sqrt{3}}(x - 1)$ or

    $y = \left(-\dfrac{1}{\sqrt{3}} \right)x + \dfrac{4}{\sqrt{3}}$.

2. $f'(x) = -\dfrac{x}{\sqrt{4 - x^2}}$, so for $x = 1$, $f(x) = \sqrt{3}$ and

    $f'(x) = -\dfrac{1}{\sqrt{3}}$. Then $y - \sqrt{3} = \sqrt{3}(x - 1)$ or $y = \sqrt{3}x$.

3. $\dfrac{dy}{dx} = \dfrac{dy/dt}{dx/dt} = \dfrac{5\cos t}{-4\sin t}$, which for $t = \dfrac{\pi}{2}$ equals zero.

4. $\dfrac{dy}{dx} = \dfrac{dy/dt}{dx/dt} = \dfrac{5\cos t}{-4\sin t}$, which for $t = \pi$ is undefined:

    the tangent line is vertical.

5. $\dfrac{dy}{dx} = \dfrac{dy/dt}{dx/dt} = \dfrac{5\cos t}{-4\sin t}$, which for $t = \dfrac{\pi}{6}$ equals $-\dfrac{5\sqrt{3}}{4}$.

    Also, at $t = \dfrac{\pi}{6}$, $x = 2\sqrt{3}$ and $y = \dfrac{5}{2}$. The equation for the

    tangent line is $y - \dfrac{5}{2} = -\dfrac{5\sqrt{3}}{4}(x - 2\sqrt{3})$, or

    $y = \left(-\dfrac{5\sqrt{3}}{4} \right)x + 10$.

6. $\dfrac{dy}{dx} = \dfrac{dy/dt}{dx/dt} = \dfrac{5\cos t}{-4\sin t}$, which for $t = \dfrac{\pi}{6}$ equals $-\dfrac{5\sqrt{3}}{4}$.

    Also, at $t = \dfrac{\pi}{6}$, $x = 2\sqrt{3}$ and $y = \dfrac{5}{2}$. The equation for the

    normal line is $y - \dfrac{5}{2} = \dfrac{4}{5\sqrt{3}}(x - 2\sqrt{3})$, or

    $y = \left(\dfrac{4\sqrt{3}}{15} \right)x + \dfrac{9}{10}$.

7. $\displaystyle\lim_{x \to 2} \dfrac{x - 2}{x^2 - 4} = \lim_{x \to 2} \dfrac{x - 2}{(x + 2)(x - 2)} = \lim_{x \to 2} \dfrac{1}{x + 2} = \dfrac{1}{4}$

8. $y' = 3 - 2x$, and Length $= \displaystyle\int_0^2 \sqrt{1 + (3 - 2x)^2}\, dx$, which

    using NINT evaluates to ≈ 3.400.

9. $x' = t\cos t + \sin t$, and $y' = -t\sin t + \cos t$, and

    Length $= \displaystyle\int_0^2 \sqrt{(t\cos t + \sin t)^2 + (-t\sin t + \cos t)^2}\, dt$

    $= \displaystyle\int_0^2 \sqrt{t^2 + 1}\, dt$,

    which using NINT evaluates to ≈ 2.958.

10. $y = xe^x - e^x + C$ (use integration by parts), so
    $2 = 0 - e^0 + C$ and $C = 3$:
    $y = xe^x - e^x + 3$

Section 10.3 Exercises

1. $[5 - (-1)]\mathbf{i} + (1 - 4)\mathbf{j} = 6\mathbf{i} - 3\mathbf{j}$

2. $(0 - 3)\mathbf{i} + [0 - (-4)]\mathbf{j} = -3\mathbf{i} + 4\mathbf{j}$

3. $\overrightarrow{AB} = [0 - (-3)]\mathbf{i} + (2 - 0)\mathbf{j} = 3\mathbf{i} + 2\mathbf{j}$ and
    $\overrightarrow{CD} = (0 - 4)\mathbf{i} + (-3 - 0)\mathbf{j} = -4\mathbf{i} - 3\mathbf{j}$.

    (a) $[3 + (-4)]\mathbf{i} + [2 + (-3)]\mathbf{j} = -\mathbf{i} - \mathbf{j}$

    (b) $[3 - (-4)]\mathbf{i} + [2 - (-3)]\mathbf{j} = 7\mathbf{i} + 5\mathbf{j}$

4. **(a)** $(5 + 3)\mathbf{i} + [(-2) + 4]\mathbf{j} = 8\mathbf{i} + 2\mathbf{j}$

    (b) $(5 - 3)\mathbf{i} + [(-2) - 4]\mathbf{j} = 2\mathbf{i} - 6\mathbf{j}$

    (c) $3(5)\mathbf{i} + 3(-2)\mathbf{j} = 15\mathbf{i} - 6\mathbf{j}$

    (d) $[2(5)\mathbf{i} + 2(-2)\mathbf{j}] - [3(3)\mathbf{i} + 3(4)\mathbf{j}] = \mathbf{i} - 16\mathbf{j}$

5. (a)

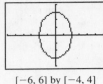

$[-6, 6]$ by $[-4, 4]$

(b) $\mathbf{v}(t) = \dfrac{d}{dt}(2 \cos t)\mathbf{i} + \dfrac{d}{dt}(3 \sin t)\mathbf{j}$

$= (-2 \sin t)\mathbf{i} + (3 \cos t)\mathbf{j}$

$\mathbf{a}(t) = \dfrac{d}{dt}(-2 \sin t)\mathbf{i} + \dfrac{d}{dt}(3 \cos t)\mathbf{j}$

$= (-2 \cos t)\mathbf{i} - (3 \sin t)\mathbf{j}$

(c) $\mathbf{v}\left(\dfrac{\pi}{2}\right) = \langle -2, 0 \rangle$; speed $= \sqrt{(-2)^2 + 0^2} = 2$,

direction $= \dfrac{1}{2}\langle -2, 0 \rangle = \langle -1, 0 \rangle$

(d) Velocity $= 2\langle -1, 0 \rangle$

6. (a)

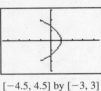

$[-4.5, 4.5]$ by $[-3, 3]$

(b) $\mathbf{v}(t) = \dfrac{d}{dt}(\cos 2t)\mathbf{i} + \dfrac{d}{dt}(2 \sin t)\mathbf{j}$

$= (-2 \sin 2t)\mathbf{i} + (2 \cos t)\mathbf{j}$

$\mathbf{a}(t) = \dfrac{d}{dt}(-2 \sin 2t)\mathbf{i} + \dfrac{d}{dt}(2 \cos t)\mathbf{j}$

$= (-4 \cos t)\mathbf{i} - (2 \sin t)\mathbf{j}$

(c) $\mathbf{v}(0) = \langle 0, 2 \rangle$; speed $= \sqrt{0^2 + 2^2} = 2$,

direction $= \dfrac{1}{2}\langle 0, 2 \rangle = \langle 0, 1 \rangle$

(d) Velocity $= 2\langle 0, 1 \rangle$

7. (a)

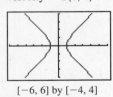

$[-6, 6]$ by $[-4, 4]$

(b) $\mathbf{v}(t) = \dfrac{d}{dt}(\sec t)\mathbf{i} + \dfrac{d}{dt}(\tan t)\mathbf{i} = (\sec t \tan t)\mathbf{i} + (\sec^2 t)\mathbf{j}$

$\mathbf{a}(t) = \dfrac{d}{dt}(\sec t \tan t)\mathbf{i} + \dfrac{d}{dt}(\sec^2 t)\mathbf{j}$

$= (\sec t \tan^2 t + \sec^3 t)\mathbf{i} + (2 \sec^2 t \tan t)\mathbf{j}$

(c) $\mathbf{v}\left(\dfrac{\pi}{6}\right) = \left\langle \dfrac{2}{3}, \dfrac{4}{3} \right\rangle$; speed $= \sqrt{\left(\dfrac{2}{3}\right)^2 + \left(\dfrac{4}{3}\right)^2} = \dfrac{2\sqrt{5}}{3}$,

direction $= \dfrac{3}{2\sqrt{5}}\left\langle \dfrac{2}{3}, \dfrac{4}{3} \right\rangle = \left\langle \dfrac{1}{\sqrt{5}}, \dfrac{2}{\sqrt{5}} \right\rangle$

(d) Velocity $= \dfrac{2\sqrt{5}}{3}\left\langle \dfrac{1}{\sqrt{5}}, \dfrac{2}{\sqrt{5}} \right\rangle$

8. (a)

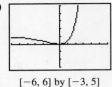

$[-6, 6]$ by $[-3, 5]$

(b) $\mathbf{v}(t) = \dfrac{d}{dt}(2 \ln (t + 1))\mathbf{i} + \dfrac{d}{dt}(t^2)\mathbf{j}$

$= \left(\dfrac{2}{t + 1}\right)\mathbf{i} + (2t)\mathbf{j}$

$\mathbf{a}(t) = \dfrac{d}{dt}\left(\dfrac{2}{t + 1}\right)\mathbf{i} + \dfrac{d}{dt}(2t)\mathbf{j} = \left(-\dfrac{2}{(t + 1)^2}\right)\mathbf{i} + 2\mathbf{j}$

(c) $\mathbf{v}(1) = \langle 1, 2 \rangle$; speed $= \sqrt{1^2 + 2^2} = \sqrt{5}$,

direction $= \dfrac{1}{\sqrt{5}}\langle 1, 2 \rangle = \left\langle \dfrac{1}{\sqrt{5}}, \dfrac{2}{\sqrt{5}} \right\rangle$

(d) Velocity $= \sqrt{5}\left\langle \dfrac{1}{\sqrt{5}}, \dfrac{2}{\sqrt{5}} \right\rangle$

9. $\mathbf{v}(t) = (\cos t)\mathbf{i} + (2t + \sin t)\mathbf{j}$, $\mathbf{r}(0) = -\mathbf{j}$ and $\mathbf{v}(0) = \mathbf{i}$.

So the slope is zero (the velocity vector is horizontal).

(a) The horizontal line through $(0, -1)$: $y = -1$.

(b) The vertical line through $(0, -1)$: $x = 0$.

10. $\mathbf{v}(t) = (-2 \sin t)\mathbf{i} + (3 \cos t)\mathbf{j}$,

$\mathbf{r}\left(\dfrac{\pi}{4}\right) = (\sqrt{2} - 3)\mathbf{i} + \left(\dfrac{3}{\sqrt{2}} + 1\right)\mathbf{j}$ and

$\mathbf{v}\left(\dfrac{\pi}{4}\right) = (-\sqrt{2})\mathbf{i} + \left(\dfrac{3}{\sqrt{2}}\right)\mathbf{j}$. So the slope is $\dfrac{3/\sqrt{2}}{-\sqrt{2}} = -\dfrac{3}{2}$.

(a) $y - \left(\dfrac{3}{\sqrt{2}} + 1\right) = -\dfrac{3}{2}[x - (\sqrt{2} - 3)]$ or

$y = -\dfrac{3}{2}x + \dfrac{6\sqrt{2} - 7}{2}$

(b) $y - \left(\dfrac{3}{\sqrt{2}} + 1\right) = \dfrac{2}{3}[x - (\sqrt{2} - 3)]$ or

$y = \dfrac{2}{3}x + \dfrac{5\sqrt{2} + 18}{6}$

11. $\left(\displaystyle\int_1^2 (6 - 6t)\, dt\right)\mathbf{i} + \left(\displaystyle\int_1^2 3\sqrt{t}\, dt\right)\mathbf{j}$

$= \left[6t - 3t^2\right]_1^2 \mathbf{i} + \left[2t^{3/2}\right]_1^2 \mathbf{j}$

$= -3\mathbf{i} + (4\sqrt{2} - 2)\mathbf{j}$

12. $\left(\displaystyle\int_{-\pi/4}^{\pi/4} \sin t\, dt\right)\mathbf{i} + \left(\displaystyle\int_{-\pi/4}^{\pi/4} (1 + \cos t)\, dt\right)\mathbf{j}$

$= \left[-\cos t\right]_{-\pi/4}^{\pi/4} \mathbf{i} + \left[t + \sin t\right]_{-\pi/4}^{\pi/4} \mathbf{j}$

$= \left(\sqrt{2} + \dfrac{\pi}{2}\right)\mathbf{j}$

13. $\left(\int \sec t \tan t \, dt\right)\mathbf{i} + \left(\int \tan t \, dt\right)\mathbf{j}$

$= (\sec t + C_1)\mathbf{i} + (\ln|\sec t| + C_2)\mathbf{j}$

$= (\sec t)\mathbf{i} + (\ln|\sec t|)\mathbf{j} + \mathbf{C}$

14. $\left(\int \dfrac{1}{t} \, dt\right)\mathbf{i} + \left(\int \dfrac{1}{5-t} \, dt\right)\mathbf{j}$

$= (\ln|t| + C_1)\mathbf{i} + (-\ln|5-t| + C_2)\mathbf{j}$

$= (\ln|t|)\mathbf{i} - (\ln|5-t|)\mathbf{j} + \mathbf{C}$

15. $\mathbf{r}(t) = (t+1)^{3/2}\mathbf{i} - e^{-t}\mathbf{j} + \mathbf{C}$, and
$\mathbf{r}(0) = \mathbf{i} - \mathbf{j} + \mathbf{C} = \mathbf{0}$, so $\mathbf{C} = -(\mathbf{i} - \mathbf{j}) = -\mathbf{i} + \mathbf{j}$
$\mathbf{r}(t) = ((t+1)^{3/2} - 1)\mathbf{i} - (e^{-t} - 1)\mathbf{j}$

16. $\mathbf{r}(t) = \left(\dfrac{t^4}{4} + 2t^2\right)\mathbf{i} + \left(\dfrac{t^2}{2}\right)\mathbf{j} + \mathbf{C}$, and $\mathbf{r}(0) = \mathbf{C} = \mathbf{i} + \mathbf{j}$, so

$\mathbf{r}(t) = \left(\dfrac{t^4}{4} + 2t^2 + 1\right)\mathbf{i} + \left(\dfrac{t^2}{2} + 1\right)\mathbf{j}$.

17. $\dfrac{d\mathbf{r}}{dt} = (-32t)\mathbf{j} + \mathbf{C}_1$ and $\mathbf{r}(t) = (-16t^2)\mathbf{j} + \mathbf{C}_1 t + \mathbf{C}_2$.

$\mathbf{r}(0) = \mathbf{C}_2 = 100\mathbf{i}$, and $\left.\dfrac{d\mathbf{r}}{dt}\right|_{t=0} = \mathbf{C}_1 = 8\mathbf{i} + 8\mathbf{j}$. So

$\mathbf{r}(t) = (-16t^2)\mathbf{j} + (8\mathbf{i} + 8\mathbf{j})t + 100\mathbf{i}$

$= (8t + 100)\mathbf{i} + (-16t^2 + 8t)\mathbf{j}$.

18. $\dfrac{d\mathbf{r}}{dt} = -t\mathbf{i} - t\mathbf{j} + \mathbf{C}_1$, and

$\mathbf{r}(t) = \left(-\dfrac{t^2}{2}\right)\mathbf{i} + \left(-\dfrac{t^2}{2}\right)\mathbf{j} + \mathbf{C}_1 t + \mathbf{C}_2$

$\mathbf{r}(0) = \mathbf{C}_2 = 10\mathbf{i} + 10\mathbf{j}$, and

$\left.\dfrac{d\mathbf{r}}{dt}\right|_{t=0} = \mathbf{C}_1 = \mathbf{0}$, so

$\mathbf{r}(t) = \left(-\dfrac{t^2}{2}\right)\mathbf{i} + \left(-\dfrac{t^2}{2}\right)\mathbf{j} + (10\mathbf{i} + 10\mathbf{j})$

$= \left(-\dfrac{t^2}{2} + 10\right)\mathbf{i} + \left(-\dfrac{t^2}{2} + 10\right)\mathbf{j}$

19. $\mathbf{v}(t) = (1 - \cos t)\mathbf{i} + (\sin t)\mathbf{j}$ and $\mathbf{a}(t) = (\sin t)\mathbf{i} + (\cos t)\mathbf{j}$.
Solve $\mathbf{v} \cdot \mathbf{a} = 0$: $(\sin t - \sin t \cos t) + (\sin t \cos t) = 0$
implies $\sin t = 0$, which is true for $t = 0$, π, or 2π.

20. $\mathbf{v}(t) = (\cos t)\mathbf{i} + \mathbf{j}$, and $\mathbf{a}(t) = (-\sin t)\mathbf{i}$.

Solve $\mathbf{v} \cdot \mathbf{a} = 0$: $-\sin t \cos t = 0$, which is true for

$t = \dfrac{k\pi}{2}$, k any nonnegative integer.

21. $\mathbf{v}(t) = (-3 \sin t)\mathbf{i} + (4 \cos t)\mathbf{j}$, and

$\mathbf{a}(t) = (-3 \cos t)\mathbf{i} + (-4 \sin t)\mathbf{j}$.

Solve $\mathbf{v} \cdot \mathbf{a} = 0$: $(9 \sin t \cos t) - (16 \sin t \cos t) = 0$, is

true when $\sin t = 0$ or $\cos t = 0$, i.e., for

$t = \dfrac{k\pi}{2}$, k any nonnegative integer.

22. $\mathbf{v}(t) = (-5 \sin t)\mathbf{i} + (5 \cos t)\mathbf{j}$, and

$\mathbf{a}(t) = (-5 \cos t)\mathbf{i} + (-5 \sin t)\mathbf{j}$.

Solve $\mathbf{v} \cdot \mathbf{a} = 0$: $(25 \sin t \cos t) + (-25\sin t \cos t) = 0$,

which is true for all values of t.

23. $\mathbf{v}(t) = (-2 \sin t)\mathbf{i} + (\cos t)\mathbf{j}$, and

$\mathbf{a}(t) = (-2 \cos t)\mathbf{i} + (-\sin t)\mathbf{j}$. So

$\mathbf{v}\left(\dfrac{\pi}{4}\right) = (-\sqrt{2})\mathbf{i} + \left(\dfrac{1}{\sqrt{2}}\right)\mathbf{j}$, and

$\mathbf{a}\left(\dfrac{\pi}{4}\right) = (-\sqrt{2})\mathbf{i} + \left(-\dfrac{1}{\sqrt{2}}\right)\mathbf{j}$.

Then $|\mathbf{v}| = |\mathbf{a}| = \sqrt{\dfrac{5}{2}}$,

$\mathbf{v} \cdot \mathbf{a} = \dfrac{3}{2}$, and

$\theta = \cos^{-1}\left(\dfrac{\mathbf{v} \cdot \mathbf{a}}{|\mathbf{v}||\mathbf{a}|}\right) = \cos^{-1}\left(\dfrac{3}{5}\right) \approx 53.130°$.

24. $\mathbf{v}(t) = 3\mathbf{i} + (2t)\mathbf{j}$, and $\mathbf{a}(t) = 2\mathbf{j}$. So $\mathbf{v}(0) = 3\mathbf{i}$, and $\mathbf{a}(0) = 2\mathbf{j}$. These are perpendicular, i.e., the angle between them measures 90°.

25. (a) Both components are continuous at $t = 3$, so the limit

is $3\mathbf{i} + \left(\dfrac{3^2 - 9}{3^2 + 3(3)}\right)\mathbf{j} = 3\mathbf{i}$.

(b) Continuous so long as $t^2 + 3t \neq 0$, i.e., $t \neq 0, -3$

(c) Discontinuous when $t^2 + 3t = 0$, i.e., $t = 0$ or -3

26. (a) Use L'Hôpital's Rule for the **i**-component:

$\lim_{t \to 0}\left(\dfrac{\sin 2t}{t}\right)\mathbf{i} + \lim_{t \to 0}(\ln(t+1))\mathbf{j}$

$= \lim_{t \to 0}\left(\dfrac{2 \cos 2t}{1}\right)\mathbf{i} + \lim_{t \to 0}(\ln(t+1))\mathbf{j}$

$= 2\mathbf{i} + 0\mathbf{j} = 2\mathbf{i}$.

(b) Continuous so long as $t \neq 0$ and $t + 1 > 0$, i.e.,
$(-1, 0) \cup (0, \infty)$.

(c) Discontinuous when $t = 0$ or $t + 1 \leq 0$, i.e.,
$(-\infty, -1] \cup \{0\}$.

27. $\mathbf{v}(t) = (\sin t)\mathbf{i} + (1 - \cos t)\mathbf{j}$, i.e.,

$\dfrac{dx}{dt} = \sin t$, and $\dfrac{dy}{dt} = 1 - \cos t$

$\text{Distance} = \int_0^{2\pi/3} \sqrt{(\sin t)^2 + (1 - \cos t)^2} \, dt$

$= \int_0^{2\pi/3} \sqrt{2 - 2 \cos t} \, dt$

$= \int_0^{2\pi/3} 2 \sin\left(\dfrac{t}{2}\right) dt$

$= \left[-4 \cos\left(\dfrac{t}{2}\right)\right]_0^{2\pi/3} = 2$

28. (a) $\mathbf{r}(0) = \left(\frac{1}{4}e^0 - 0\right)\mathbf{i} + (e^0)\mathbf{j}$

$= \frac{1}{4}\mathbf{i} + \mathbf{j}$,

$\mathbf{r}(2) = \left(\frac{1}{4}e^8 - 2\right)\mathbf{i} + (e^4)\mathbf{j}$

Initial $= \left(\frac{1}{4}, 1\right)$, terminal $= \left(\frac{1}{4}e^8 - 2, e^4\right)$

(b) $\mathbf{v}(t) = (e^{4t} - 1)\mathbf{i} + (2e^{2t})\mathbf{j}$; $\frac{dx}{dt} = e^{4t} - 1$, and

$\frac{dy}{dt} = 2e^{2t}$.

Length $= \int_0^2 \sqrt{(e^{4t} - 1)^2 + (2e^{2t})^2}\, dt$

$= \int_0^2 \sqrt{(e^{4t} + 1)^2}\, dt$

$= \int_0^2 (e^{4t} + 1)\, dt$

$= \left[\frac{1}{4}e^{4t} + t\right]_0^2$

$= \frac{e^8 + 7}{4} \approx 746.989$

(c) $\int_0^2 2\pi\left(\frac{1}{4}e^{4t} - t\right)\sqrt{(e^{4t} - 1)^2 + (2e^{2t})^2}\, dt$

$= 2\pi\int_0^2 \left(\frac{1}{4}e^{4t} - t\right)(e^{4t} + 1)\, dt$

$= 2\pi\int_0^2 \left(\frac{1}{4}e^{8t} + \frac{1}{4}e^{4t} - te^{4t} - t\right) dt$

$= 2\pi\left[\frac{1}{32}e^{8t} + \frac{1}{16}e^{4t} - \frac{1}{16}(4t - 1)e^{4t} - \frac{1}{2}t^2\right]_0^2$

$= \pi\left(\frac{e^{16} - 12e^8 - 69}{16}\right) \approx 1{,}737{,}746.456$

29. (a) $\mathbf{v}(t) = (\cos t)\mathbf{i} - (2 \sin 2t)\mathbf{j}$

(b) $\mathbf{v}(t) = \mathbf{0}$ when both $\cos t = 0$ and $\sin 2t = 0$. $\cos t = 0$

at $t = \frac{\pi}{2}$ and $\frac{3\pi}{2}$; $\sin 2t = 0$ at $t = 0, \frac{\pi}{2}, \pi, \frac{3\pi}{2}$, and 2π.

So $\mathbf{v}(t) = \mathbf{0}$ at $t = \frac{\pi}{2}, \frac{3\pi}{2}$.

(c) $x = \sin t$, $y = \cos 2t$. Relate the two using the identity $\cos 2u = 1 - 2\sin^2 u$: $y = 1 - 2x^2$, where as t ranges over all possible values, $-1 \le x \le 1$. When t increases from 0 to 2π, the particle starts at $(0, 1)$, goes to $(1, -1)$, then goes to $(-1, -1)$, and then goes to $(0, 1)$, tracing the curve twice.

30. (a) $\frac{dy}{dx} = \frac{dy/dt}{dx/dt} = \frac{3t^2 - 12}{6t^2 - 6t} = \frac{t^2 - 4}{2t^2 - 2t}$

(b) Horizontal tangents: $t^2 - 4 = 0$ for $t = \pm 2$.
Vertical tangents: $2t^2 - 2t = 0$ for $t = 0, 1$.
Plugging the t-values into $x = 2t^3 - 3t^2$ and $y = t^3 - 12t$ produces the x- and y-coordinates of the critical points.
$t = -2$: horizontal tangent at $(-28, 16)$
$t = 0$: vertical tangent at $(0, 0)$
$t = 1$: vertical tangent at $(-1, -11)$
$t = 2$: horizontal tangent at $(4, -16)$

31. $\mathbf{a}(t) = 3\mathbf{i} - \mathbf{j}$, so $\mathbf{v}(t) = (3t)\mathbf{i} - t\mathbf{j} + \mathbf{C}_1$ and

$\mathbf{r}(t) = \left(\frac{3}{2}t^2\right)\mathbf{i} - \left(\frac{1}{2}t^2\right)\mathbf{j} + \mathbf{C}_1 t + \mathbf{C}_2$. $\mathbf{r}(0) = \mathbf{C}_2 = \mathbf{i} + 2\mathbf{j}$,

and since $\mathbf{v}(0)$ must point directly from $(1, 2)$ toward $(4, 1)$

with magnitude 2,

$\mathbf{v}(0) = \mathbf{C}_1 = 2\left(\frac{(4 - 1)\mathbf{i} + (1 - 2)\mathbf{j}}{\sqrt{(4 - 1)^2 + (1 - 2)^2}}\right)$

$= \frac{6}{\sqrt{10}}\mathbf{i} - \frac{2}{\sqrt{10}}\mathbf{j}$

$= \frac{3\sqrt{10}}{5}\mathbf{i} - \frac{\sqrt{10}}{5}\mathbf{j}$

So $\mathbf{r}(t) = \left(\frac{3}{2}t^2 + \frac{3\sqrt{10}}{5}t + 1\right)\mathbf{i} + \left(-\frac{1}{2}t^2 - \frac{\sqrt{10}}{5}t + 2\right)\mathbf{j}$.

32. (a) $\frac{dx}{dt} = 1 - \frac{2}{t^2} = 0$ when $t = \sqrt{2}$. That corresponds to

point $\left(\sqrt{2} + \frac{2}{\sqrt{2}}, 3(\sqrt{2})^2\right) = (2\sqrt{2}, 6)$.

(b) $\frac{dy}{dx} = y' = \frac{dy/dt}{dx/dt} = \frac{6t}{1 - 2/t^2}$, which for $t = 1$ equals -6.

(c) When $y = 12$, $t = 2$.

$\frac{d^2y}{dx^2} = \frac{dy'}{dx} = \frac{dy'/dt}{dx/dt} = \frac{(1 - 2/t^2)6 - (4/t^3)6t}{(1 - 2/t^2)^3}$,

which for $t = 2$ equals -24.

33. (a) The $\mathbf{j}$-component is zero at $t = 0$ and $t = 160$: 160 seconds.

(b) $-\frac{3}{64}(40)(40 - 160) = 225$ m

(c) $\frac{d}{dt}\left[-\frac{3}{64}t(t - 160)\right] = -\frac{3}{32}t + \frac{15}{2}$, which for $t = 40$

equals $\frac{15}{4}$ m per second.

(d) $\mathbf{v}(t) = -\frac{3}{32}t + \frac{15}{2}$ equals 0 at $t = 80$ seconds (and is

negative after that time).

34. (a) Solve $t - 3 = \frac{3t}{2} - 4$: $t = 2$. Then check that

$(t - 3)^2 = \frac{3t}{2} - 2$ for $t = 2$: it does.

(b) First particle: $\mathbf{v}_1(t) = \mathbf{i} + 2(t - 3)\mathbf{j}$, so $\mathbf{v}_1(2) = \mathbf{i} - 2\mathbf{j}$

and the direction unit vector $\mathbf{v}_1$ is $\left\langle\frac{1}{\sqrt{5}}, -\frac{2}{\sqrt{5}}\right\rangle$.

Second particle: $\mathbf{v}_2(t) = \frac{3}{2}\mathbf{i} + \frac{3}{2}\mathbf{j}$, which is constant, and

the direction unit vector is $\left\langle\frac{1}{\sqrt{2}}, \frac{1}{\sqrt{2}}\right\rangle$.

35. (a) Referring to the figure, look at the circular arc from the point where $t = 0$ to the point "m". On one hand, this arc has length given by $r_0\theta$, but it also has length given by vt. Setting those two quantities equal gives the result.

(b) $\mathbf{v}(t) = \left(-v\sin\dfrac{vt}{r_0}\right)\mathbf{i} + \left(v\cos\dfrac{vt}{r_0}\right)\mathbf{j}$, and

$\mathbf{a}(t) = \left(-\dfrac{v^2}{r_0}\cos\dfrac{vt}{r_0}\right)\mathbf{i} + \left(-\dfrac{v^2}{r_0}\sin\dfrac{vt}{r_0}\right)\mathbf{j}$

$= -\dfrac{v^2}{r_0}\left[\left(\cos\dfrac{vt}{r_0}\right)\mathbf{i} + \left(\sin\dfrac{vt}{r_0}\right)\mathbf{j}\right]$

(c) From part (b) above, $\mathbf{a}(t) = -\left(\dfrac{v}{r_0}\right)^2\mathbf{r}(t)$.

So, by Newton's second law, $\mathbf{F} = -m\left(\dfrac{v}{r_0}\right)^2\mathbf{r}$.

Substituting for $\mathbf{F}$ in the law of gravitation gives the result.

(d) Set $\dfrac{vT}{r_0} = 2\pi$ and solve for vT.

(e) Substitute $\dfrac{2\pi r_0}{T}$ for v in $v^2 = \dfrac{GM}{r_0}$ and solve for T^2:

$$\left(\dfrac{2\pi r_0}{T}\right)^2 = \dfrac{GM}{r_0}$$

$$\dfrac{4\pi^2 r_0^2}{T^2} = \dfrac{GM}{r_0}$$

$$\dfrac{1}{T^2} = \dfrac{GM}{4\pi^2 r_0^3}$$

$$T^2 = \dfrac{4\pi^2}{GM}r_0^3$$

36. Solve both equations for t: $t = e^x - 1$ and $t = \sqrt{y + 1}$. Now eliminate the t and solve for y: $e^x - 1 = \sqrt{y + 1}$, $y = (e^x - 1)^2 - 1$, or $y = e^{2x} - 2e^x$, where $t \geq 0$ so $x \geq 0$.

37. (a) Apply Corollary 3 to each component separately. If the components all differ by scalar constants, the difference vector is a constant vector.

(b) Follows immediately from (a) since any two anti-derivatives of $\mathbf{r}(t)$ must have identical derivatives, namely $\mathbf{r}(t)$.

38. $\dfrac{d}{dt}|\mathbf{v}|^2 = \dfrac{d}{dt}(\mathbf{v}\cdot\mathbf{v}) = \mathbf{v}'\cdot\mathbf{v} + \mathbf{v}\cdot\mathbf{v}' = 2\mathbf{v}\cdot\mathbf{v}' = 0$.

Therefore, $|\mathbf{v}|$ is constant.

39. Let $\mathbf{C} = \langle C_1, C_2\rangle$. $\dfrac{d\mathbf{C}}{dt} = \left\langle\dfrac{dC_1}{dt}, \dfrac{dC_2}{dt}\right\rangle = \langle 0, 0\rangle$.

40. (a) Suppose $\mathbf{u} = \langle u_1(t), u_2(t)\rangle$.

$\dfrac{d}{dt}(c\mathbf{u}) = \dfrac{d}{dt}\langle cu_1(t), cu_2(t)\rangle$

$= \left\langle\dfrac{d}{dt}(cu_1(t)), \dfrac{d}{dt}(cu_2(t))\right\rangle$

$= \left\langle c\dfrac{du_1}{dt}, c\dfrac{du_2}{dt}\right\rangle = c\left\langle\dfrac{du_1}{dt}, \dfrac{du_2}{dt}\right\rangle = c\dfrac{d\mathbf{u}}{dt}$

(b) $\dfrac{d}{dt}(f\mathbf{u}) = \dfrac{d}{dt}\langle fu_1, fu_2\rangle$

$= \langle fu_1' + f'u_1, fu_2' + f'u_2\rangle$

$= \langle fu_1', fu_2'\rangle + \langle f'u_1, f'u_2\rangle$

$= f\mathbf{u}' + f'\mathbf{u}$

41. $\mathbf{u} = \langle u_1, u_2\rangle$, $\mathbf{v} = \langle v_1, v_2\rangle$

(a) $\dfrac{d}{dt}(\mathbf{u} + \mathbf{v}) = \dfrac{d}{dt}(\langle u_1 + v_1, u_2 + v_2\rangle)$

$= \left\langle\dfrac{d}{dt}(u_1 + v_1), \dfrac{d}{dt}(u_2 + v_2)\right\rangle$

$= \langle u_1' + v_1', u_2' + v_2'\rangle$

$= \langle u_1', u_2'\rangle + \langle v_1', v_2'\rangle = \dfrac{d\mathbf{u}}{dt} + \dfrac{d\mathbf{v}}{dt}$

(b) $\dfrac{d}{dt}(\mathbf{u} - \mathbf{v}) = \dfrac{d}{dt}(\langle u_1 - v_1, u_2 - v_2\rangle)$

$= \left\langle\dfrac{d}{dt}(u_1 - v_1), \dfrac{d}{dt}(u_2 - v_2)\right\rangle$

$= \langle u_1' - v_1', u_2' - v_2'\rangle$

$= \langle u_1', u_2'\rangle - \langle v_1', v_2'\rangle$

$= \dfrac{d\mathbf{u}}{dt} - \dfrac{d\mathbf{v}}{dt}$

42. $\dfrac{d\mathbf{r}}{dt} = \dfrac{df}{dt}\mathbf{i} + \dfrac{dg}{dt}\mathbf{j}$

$\left(\dfrac{d\mathbf{r}}{dt}\right)\left(\dfrac{dt}{ds}\right) = \left(\dfrac{df}{dt}\mathbf{i} + \dfrac{dg}{dt}\mathbf{j}\right)\left(\dfrac{dt}{ds}\right)$

$= \left(\dfrac{df}{dt}\cdot\dfrac{dt}{ds}\right)\mathbf{i} + \left(\dfrac{dg}{dt}\cdot\dfrac{dt}{ds}\right)\mathbf{j}$

$= \dfrac{df}{ds}\mathbf{i} + \dfrac{dg}{ds}\mathbf{j}$

$= \dfrac{d\mathbf{r}}{ds}$

43. $f(t)$ and $g(t)$ differentiable at $c \Rightarrow f(t)$ and $g(t)$ continuous at $c \Rightarrow \mathbf{r}(t) = f(t)\mathbf{i} + g(t)\mathbf{j}$ is continuous at c.

44. (a) Let $\mathbf{r}(t) = \langle x(t), y(t) \rangle$.

$$\int_a^b k\mathbf{r}(t)\,dt = \int_a^b \langle kx(t), ky(t) \rangle\,dt = \left\langle \int_a^b kx(t)\,dt, \int_a^b ky(t)\,dt \right\rangle$$

$$= \left\langle k\int_a^b x(t)\,dt, k\int_a^b y(t)\,dt \right\rangle$$

$$= k\left\langle \int_a^b x(t)\,dt, \int_a^b y(t)\,dt \right\rangle = k\int_a^b \langle x(t), y(t) \rangle\,dt$$

$$= k\int_a^b \mathbf{r}(t)\,dt$$

(b) Let $\mathbf{r}_1(t) = \langle x_1(t), y_1(t) \rangle$ and $\mathbf{r}_2(t) = \langle x_2(t), y_2(t) \rangle$.

$$\int_a^b (\mathbf{r}_1(t) \pm \mathbf{r}_2(t))\,dt = \int_a^b (\langle x_1(t), y_1(t) \rangle \pm \langle x_2(t), y_2(t) \rangle)\,dt$$

$$= \int_a^b \langle x_1(t) \pm x_2(t), y_1(t) \pm y_2(t) \rangle\,dt$$

$$= \left\langle \int_a^b (x_1(t) \pm x_2(t))\,dt, \int_a^b (y_1(t) \pm y_2(t))\,dt \right\rangle$$

$$= \left\langle \int_a^b x_1(t)\,dt \pm \int_a^b x_2(t)\,dt, \int_a^b y_1(t)\,dt \pm \int_a^b y_2(t)\,dt \right\rangle$$

$$= \left\langle \int_a^b x_1(t)\,dt, \int_a^b y_1(t)\,dt \right\rangle \pm \left\langle \int_a^b x_2(t)\,dt, \int_a^b y_2(t)\,dt \right\rangle$$

$$= \int_a^b \mathbf{r}_1(t)\,dt \pm \int_a^b \mathbf{r}_2(t)\,dt$$

(c) Let $\mathbf{C} = \langle C_1, C_2 \rangle$, $\mathbf{r}(t) = \langle x(t), y(t) \rangle$.

$$\int_a^b \mathbf{C} \cdot \mathbf{r}(t)\,dt = \int_a^b (C_1 x(t) + C_2 y(t))\,dt$$

$$= C_1 \int_a^b x(t)\,dt + C_2 \int_a^b y(t)\,dt$$

$$= \langle C_1, C_2 \rangle \cdot \left\langle \int_a^b x(t)\,dt, \int_a^b y(t)\,dt \right\rangle$$

$$= \mathbf{C} \cdot \int_a^b \mathbf{r}(t)\,dt$$

45. (a) Let $\mathbf{r}(t) = f(t)\mathbf{i} + g(t)\mathbf{j}$. Then

$$\frac{d}{dt}\int_a^t \mathbf{r}(q)\,dq = \frac{d}{dt}\int_a^t [f(q)\mathbf{i} + g(q)\mathbf{j}]\,dq$$

$$= \frac{d}{dt}\left[\left(\int_a^t f(q)\,dq\right)\mathbf{i} + \left(\int_a^t g(q)\,dq\right)\mathbf{j}\right]$$

$$= \left(\frac{d}{dt}\int_a^t f(q)\,dq\right)\mathbf{i} + \left(\frac{d}{dt}\int_a^t g(q)\,dq\right)\mathbf{j}$$

$$= f(t)\mathbf{i} + g(t)\mathbf{j} = \mathbf{r}(t).$$

(b) Let $S(t) = \int_a^t \mathbf{r}(q)\,dq$. Then part (a) shows that $\mathbf{S}(t)$ is an antiderivative of $\mathbf{r}(t)$. Let $\mathbf{R}(t)$ be any antiderivative of $\mathbf{r}(t)$. Then according to 37(b), $\mathbf{S}(t) = \mathbf{R}(t) + \mathbf{C}$.

Letting $t = a$, we have $0 = \mathbf{S}(a) = \mathbf{R}(a) + \mathbf{C}$.

Therefore, $\mathbf{C} = -\mathbf{R}(a)$ and $\mathbf{S}(t) = \mathbf{R}(t) - \mathbf{R}(a)$.

The result follows by letting $t = b$.

■ Section 10.4 Modeling Projectile Motion
(pp. 539–552)

Exploration 1 Hitting a Home Run

1. The graphs of the parametric equations
   $x = (152 \cos 20° - 8.8)t$, $y = 3 + (152 \sin 20°)t - 16t^2$
   and the fence are shown in the window [0, 450] by
   [−20, 60]. The fence was obtained using the line command
   "Line(". You can zoom in as shown in the second figure to
   see that the ball does just clear the fence.

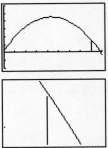

   You can also use algebraic methods to show that $t \approx 2.984$
   when $x = 400$, and that $y \approx 15.647$ for this value of t.

2.

angle (degrees)	25	30	45
range (ft)	≈523.707	≈588.279	≈665.629
flight time (sec)	≈4.061	≈4.789	≈6.745

3. Using the same window of part (1) we can see that the ball
   clears the fence.

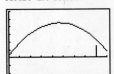

4.

angle (degrees)	25	30	45
range (ft)	≈559.444	≈630.424	≈724.988
flight time (sec)	≈4.061	≈4.789	≈6.745

■ Exploration 2 Hitting a Baseball

1. $x = \dfrac{152}{0.05}(1 - e^{-0.05t})\cos 20°$

   $y = 3 + \dfrac{152}{0.05}(1 - e^{-0.05t})\sin 20°$

   $\qquad + \dfrac{32}{0.05^2}(1 - 0.05t - e^{-0.05t})$

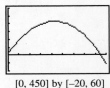

   [0, 450] by [−20, 60]

2. The ball reaches a maximum height of about 43.07 ft when
   t is about 1.56 sec.

3. The range is about 425.47 ft and the flight time is about
   3.23 sec.

Quick Review 10.4

1. $\langle 50 \cos 25°, 50 \sin 25° \rangle \approx \langle 45.315, 21.131 \rangle$

2. $\langle 80 \cos 120°, 80 \sin 120° \rangle = \langle -40, 40\sqrt{3} \rangle$

3. To find the x-intercepts, solve $2x^2 + 11x - 40 = 0$ using

the quadratic formula: $x = \dfrac{-11 \pm \sqrt{11^2 - 4(2)(-40)}}{2(2)}$

$= \dfrac{5}{2}$ or -8. The x-intercepts are $\left(\dfrac{5}{2}, 0\right)$ and $(-8, 0)$. For the

y-intercept, find $f(0) = 2(0)^2 + 11(0) - 40 = -40$. The

y-intercept is $(0, -40)$.

4. At the vertex, $f'(x) = 4x + 11 = 0$ and $x = -\dfrac{11}{4}$. Then the

vertex is $\left(-\dfrac{11}{4}, 2\left(-\dfrac{11}{4}\right)^2 + 11\left(-\dfrac{11}{4}\right) - 40\right)$

$= \left(-\dfrac{11}{4}, -\dfrac{441}{8}\right)$.

5. To find the x-intercepts, solve $20x - x^2 = 0$: $x = 0$ or 20.
The x-intercepts are $(0, 0)$ and $(20, 0)$. For the y-intercept,
find $y(0)$: it is already known to be 0. So the y-intercept is
$(0, 0)$.

6. At the vertex, $g'(x) = 20 - 2x = 0$ and $x = 10$. Then the
vertex is $(10, 20(10) - 10^2) = (10, 100)$.

7. $y = -\cos x + C$. $y\left(\dfrac{\pi}{2}\right) = -\cos\left(\dfrac{\pi}{2}\right) + C = C = 2$, so

$y = -\cos x + 2$.

8. $y' = t^2 + C_1$ and $y = \dfrac{1}{3}t^3 + C_1 t + C_2$

$y'(-1) = (-1)^2 + C_1 = 1 + C_1 = 4$, so $C_1 = 3$.

$y(-1) = \dfrac{1}{3}(-1)^3 + 3(-1) + C_2 = -\dfrac{10}{3} + C_2 = 5$, so

$C_2 = \dfrac{25}{3}$

$y = \dfrac{t^3}{3} + 3t + \dfrac{25}{3}$

9. $\displaystyle\int \dfrac{dy}{16 - y} = \int dt$

$-\ln|16 - y| = t + C$

$16 - y = ke^{-t}$

$y(0) = 16 - k = 20$ so $k = -4$

$y = 16 + 4e^{-t}$

10. $\displaystyle\int \dfrac{dy}{4 - 2y} = \int x\, dx$

$-\dfrac{1}{2}\ln|4 - 2y| = \dfrac{1}{2}x^2 + C$

$4 - 2y = ke^{-x^2}$

$y = 2 - \dfrac{k}{2}e^{-x^2}$

$y(0) = 2 - \dfrac{k}{2} = 1$ so $k = 2$

$y = 2 - e^{-x^2}$

Section 10.4 Exercises

1. Solve $v_x t = (840 \cos 60°)t = 21{,}000$ for t: $t = 50$ seconds.

2. Use $R = \dfrac{v_0^2}{g}\sin 2\alpha$; solve $24{,}500 = \dfrac{v_0^2}{9.8}\sin 90°$

for v_0: $v_0 = 490$ m/sec.

3. (a) $t = \dfrac{2v_0 \sin \alpha}{g} = \dfrac{2(500)\sin 45°}{9.8} \approx 72.154$ seconds;

$R = \dfrac{v_0^2}{g}\sin 2\alpha = \dfrac{500^2}{9.8}\sin 90° \approx 25{,}510$ m

$= 25.510$ km downrange

(b) $y = -\left(\dfrac{g}{2v_0^2 \cos^2\alpha}\right)x^2 + (\tan \alpha)x$

$= -\left(\dfrac{9.8}{2(500)^2 \cos^2 45°}\right)5000^2 + (\tan 45°)5000 = 4020$ m

(c) $y_{max} = \dfrac{(v_0 \sin \alpha)^2}{2g} = \dfrac{(500 \sin 45°)^2}{2(9.8)} \approx 6377.551$ m

4. With the origin at the launch point

(so the ground is $t = 2$ when $y = -32$), use

$y = (v_0 \sin \alpha)t - \dfrac{1}{2}gt^2$.

$-32 = (32 \sin 30°)t - \dfrac{1}{2}(32)t^2$

$-2 = t - t^2$

$t = 2$ seconds

Then $x = (v_0 \cos \alpha)t = (32 \cos 30°)2 = 32\sqrt{3} \approx 55.426$

feet away (horizontally).

5. Use $y = (v_0 \sin \alpha)t - \dfrac{1}{2}gt^2 + 6.5$.

$16t^2 - 22\sqrt{2}t - 6.5 = 0$

$t = \dfrac{11\sqrt{2} + \sqrt{346}}{16} \approx 2.135$ seconds (by the quadratic

formula). Substitute that into $x = (v_0 \cos \alpha)t$

$= (44 \sin 45°)t$ to obtain $x \approx 66.4206$. 66.421 feet from the

stopboard.

6. With the origin at the launch point, use

$y = (v_0 \sin \alpha)t - \dfrac{1}{2}gt^2$. $-6.5 = (44 \sin 40°)t - 16t^2$

$t = \dfrac{(44 \sin 40°) + \sqrt{(44 \sin 40°)^2 + 416}}{32} \approx 1.974$ sec

At $t \approx 1.974$, $x = (44 \cos 40°)t \approx 66.5193$ ft

Thus the shot would have gone ≈ 0.0987 feet ≈ 1.18 inches

farther.

7. (a) Use $R = \dfrac{v_0{}^2}{g}\sin 2\alpha$; solve $10 = \dfrac{v_0{}^2}{9.8}\sin 90°$ for v_0:

$v_0 = 7\sqrt{2} \approx 9.899$ m/sec.

(b) Solve $6 = \dfrac{(7\sqrt{2})^2}{9.8}\sin 2\alpha$ for α: $\sin 2\alpha = 0.6$, so

$2\alpha = \sin^{-1} 0.6 \approx 36.870°$ and $\alpha \approx 18.435°$ or

$2\alpha = 180° - \sin^{-1} 0.6 \approx 143.130$ and $\alpha \approx 71.565°$.

8. $t = \dfrac{40 \times 10^{-2}\text{ m}}{5 \times 10^6\text{ m/sec}} = 8 \times 10^{-8}$ sec. Then y (taking down as

positive) is $\frac{1}{2}gt^2 \approx \frac{1}{2}(9.8)(8 \times 10^{-8})^2 = 3.136 \times 10^{-14}$

meters or 3.136×10^{-12} cm.

9. $R = \dfrac{v_0{}^2}{g}\sin 2\alpha$

$(248.8\text{ yd})(3\text{ ft/yd}) = \dfrac{v_0{}^2}{32\text{ ft/sec}^2}\sin 18°$

$v_0 \approx 278.016$ ft/sec or ≈ 189.556 mph.

10. $R = \dfrac{v_0{}^2}{g}\sin 2\alpha \Rightarrow 200 = \dfrac{\left(\frac{80\sqrt{10}}{3}\right)^2}{32}\sin 2\alpha \Rightarrow \sin 2\alpha = 0.9.$

Taking the smaller of the two possible angles,

$\alpha = \frac{1}{2}\sin^{-1} 0.9 \approx 32.079°$. Then

$y_{\max} \approx \dfrac{\left(\frac{80\sqrt{10}}{3}\right)^2 \sin^2 32.079}{2(32)} \approx 31.339$, which is well below

the ceiling height.

11. No. For $\alpha = 30°$, $v_0 = 90$ ft/sec, and $x = 135$ ft,

$y = -\left(\dfrac{32}{2v_0{}^2\cos^2\alpha}\right)x^2 + (\tan\alpha)x$ evaluates to ≈ 29.942

feet above the ground, which is not quite high enough.

12. Use $y = -\left(\dfrac{32}{2(116)^2\cos^2 45°}\right)x^2 + (\tan 45°)x$

$= -\dfrac{2}{841}x^2 + x$. Set $y = 45$, then solve for x using the

quadratic formula and taking the larger of the two values:

$x = \dfrac{1 + \sqrt{\frac{481}{841}}}{\frac{4}{841}} \approx 369.255$ ft, which is ≈ 0.255 ft ≈ 3.059

inches beyond the pin.

13. (a) With the origin at the launch point, use

$y = -\left(\dfrac{32}{2v_0{}^2\cos^2 20°}\right)x^2 + (\tan 20°)x$. Set $x = 315$ and

$y = 37 - 3 = 34$, then solve to find

$v_0 = \dfrac{1260}{\cos 20°\sqrt{315\tan 20° - 34}} \approx 149.307$ ft/sec.

(b) Solve $v_0(\cos 20°)t \approx 149.307(\cos 20°)t = 315$ to find

$t \approx 2.245$ seconds.

14. In the formula for range, $\sin 2\alpha = \sin 2(90 - \alpha)$.

15. Use $R = \dfrac{v_0{}^2}{g}\sin 2\alpha$: $\sin 2\alpha = \dfrac{(9.8)(16,000)}{400^2} = 0.98$;

$\alpha = \dfrac{\sin^{-1} 0.98}{2} \approx 39.261°$ or $\alpha = 90 - \dfrac{\sin^{-1} 0.98}{2}$

$\approx 50.739°$.

16. (a) Substitute $2v_0$ for v_0 in the formula for range.

(b) To increase the range (and height) by a factor of 2, increase v_0 by a factor of $\sqrt{2} \approx 1.41$. That is an increase of $\approx 41\%$.

17. With the origin at the launch point,

$y = -\left(\dfrac{32}{2v_0{}^2\cos^2 40°}\right)x^2 + (\tan 40°)x$. Setting $x = 73\frac{5}{6}$ and

$y = -6.5$ and solving for v_0 yields $v_0 \approx 46.597$ ft/sec.

18. $y(t) = v_0(\sin\alpha)t - \frac{1}{2}gt^2$, and we know the maximum height

is $\dfrac{(v_0\sin\alpha)^2}{2g}$ and it occurs when $t = \dfrac{v_0\sin\alpha}{g}$. Substituting

$t = \dfrac{v_0\sin\alpha}{2g}$ into the equation for $y(t)$ gives a height of

$\dfrac{3(v_0\sin\alpha)^2}{8g}$, which is three-fourths of the maximum height.

19. Integrating, $\dfrac{d}{dt}\mathbf{r}(t) = c_1\mathbf{i} + (-gt + c_2)\mathbf{j}$. The initial

condition on the velocity gives $c_1 = v_0\cos\alpha$

and $c_2 = v_0\sin\alpha$. Integrating again,

$\mathbf{r}(t) = ((v_0\cos\alpha)t + c_3)\mathbf{i} + \left(-\frac{1}{2}gt^2 + (v_0\sin\alpha)t + c_4\right)\mathbf{j}$.

The initial condition on the position gives

$c_3 = x_0$ and $c_4 = y_0$.

20. With the origin at the launch point, $y_{\max} = 68$ ft. Then

$v_0 = \dfrac{\sqrt{2y_{\max}g}}{\sin\alpha} \approx v_0 = \dfrac{\sqrt{2(68)(32)}}{\sin 56.505°} \approx 79.107$ ft/sec.

21. The horizontal distance is $30\text{ yd} - 6\text{ ft} = 84$ ft. Then

$84 = (v_0\cos\alpha)t$, where $\alpha = \tan^{-1}\left(\dfrac{68}{45}\right) \approx 56.5°$ and

$v_0 = \dfrac{16\sqrt{17}}{\sin\alpha}$ (from Exercise 20). So $t = \dfrac{84}{v_0\cos\alpha}$

$= \dfrac{84\tan\alpha}{16\sqrt{17}} = \dfrac{21\left(\frac{68}{45}\right)}{4\sqrt{17}} = \dfrac{119}{15\sqrt{17}} \approx 1.924$ seconds. Then

$y = (v_0\sin\alpha)t - \frac{1}{2}gt^2$

$= (16\sqrt{17})\left(\dfrac{119}{15\sqrt{17}}\right) - \frac{1}{2}(32)\left(\dfrac{119}{15\sqrt{17}}\right)^2 \approx 67.698$ ft.

The height above the ground is 6 ft more than that, ≈ 73.698, and the height above the rim is about $73.698 - 70 = 3.698$ feet.

22. The projectile rises straight up and then falls straight down, returning to the firing point.

23. Angle is $\alpha \approx 62°$ (measurements may vary slightly). For

flight time $t = \dfrac{2v_0 \sin \alpha}{g} = 1$ sec, $y_{max} = \dfrac{(v_0 \sin \alpha)^2}{2g} = \dfrac{1}{8}gt^2$

$= \dfrac{1}{8}(32)(1)^2 = 4$ ft (independent of the measured angle).

$v_0 = \dfrac{gt}{2 \sin \alpha}$, so speed of engine $= v_0 \cos \alpha = \dfrac{gt}{2 \tan \alpha}$

$\approx \dfrac{32(1)}{2 \tan (62°)} \approx 8.507$ ft/sec (changes with the angle).

24. The height of A is given by $y_A = (v \sin \alpha)t - \dfrac{1}{2}gt^2$ and the

height of B is given by $y_B = R \tan \alpha - \dfrac{1}{2}gt^2$. The second

terms in y_A and y_B $\left(-\dfrac{1}{2}gt^2\right)$ are equal for any value of t. But

A moves R units horizontally to B's line of fall in $\dfrac{R}{v \cos \alpha}$

time units, and the first terms in y_A and y_B are also equal at

that time: $(v \sin \alpha)\left(\dfrac{R}{v \cos \alpha}\right) = R \tan \alpha$. Therefore, A and B

will always be at the same height when A reaches B's line

of fall.

25. (a)

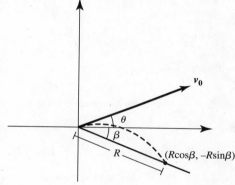

$x = (v_0 \cos \theta)t$

$y = (v_0 \sin \theta)t - \dfrac{1}{2}gt^2$

$x = R \cos \beta \Rightarrow R \cos \beta = (v_0 \cos \theta)t$

$\Rightarrow t = \dfrac{R \cos \beta}{v_0 \cos \theta}$. Then $y = -R \sin \beta$

$\Rightarrow -R \sin \beta = \dfrac{(v_0 \sin \theta) R \cos \beta}{v_0 \cos \theta} - \dfrac{g}{2}\dfrac{R^2 \cos^2 \beta}{v_0^2 \cos^2 \theta}$

$\Rightarrow R = \dfrac{2v_0^2}{g \cos^2 \beta} \cos \theta \sin (\theta + \beta)$.

Let $f(\theta) = \cos \theta \sin (\theta + \beta)$.

$f'(\theta) = \cos \theta \cos (\theta + \beta) - \sin \theta \sin (\theta + \beta)$

$f'(\theta) = 0 \Rightarrow \tan \theta \tan (\theta + \beta) = 1$

$\Rightarrow \tan \theta = \cot (\theta + \beta)$

$\Rightarrow \theta + \beta = 90° - \theta$. Note that $f''(\theta) < 0$, so R is

maximum when $\alpha = \theta + \beta = 90° - \theta$. Thus the initial

velocity bisects angle AOR.

(b)

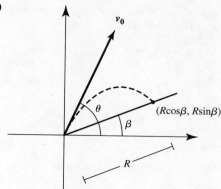

$R = \dfrac{2v_0^2}{g \cos^2 \beta} \cos \theta \sin (\theta - \beta)$ is maximum when

$\tan \theta = \cot (\theta - \beta)$,

so $\theta - \beta = 90° - \theta$.

The initial velocity vector bisects the angle between the
hill and the vertical for max range.

26. (a) $\mathbf{r}(t) = (x(t))\mathbf{i} + (y(t))\mathbf{j}$, where
   $x(t) = (145 \cos 23° - 14)t$ and
   $y(t) = 2.5 + (145 \sin 23°)t - 16t^2$.

(b) $y_{max} = \dfrac{(v_0 \sin \alpha)^2}{2g} + 2.5 = \dfrac{(145 \sin 23°)^2}{64} + 2.5$

≈ 52.655 feet , which is reached at $t = \dfrac{v_0 \sin \alpha}{g}$

$= \dfrac{145 \sin 23°}{32} \approx 1.771$ seconds.

(c) For the time, solve

$y = 2.5 + (145 \sin 23°)t - 16t^2 = 0$ for t, using the

quadratic formula:

$t = \dfrac{145 \sin 23° + \sqrt{(145 \sin 23°)^2 + 160}}{32} \approx 3.585$ sec.

Then the range at $t \approx 3.585$ is about

$x = (145 \cos 23° - 14)(3.585) \approx 428.262$ feet.

(d) For the time, solve $y = 2.5 + (145 \sin 23°)t - 16t^2$

$= 20$ for t, using the quadratic formula:

$t = \dfrac{145 \sin 23° \pm \sqrt{(145 \sin 23°)^2 - 1120}}{32} \approx 0.342$ and

3.199 seconds. At those times the ball is about

$x(0.342) = (145 \cos 23° - 14)(0.342) \approx 40.847$ feet

and $x(3.199) = (145 \cos 23° - 14)(3.199) \approx 382.208$

feet from home plate.

(e) Yes. According to part (d), the ball is still 20 feet above
the ground when it is 382 feet from home plate.

27. (a) (Assuming that "x" is zero at the point of impact.)

$\mathbf{r}(t) = (x(t))\mathbf{i} + (y(t))\mathbf{j}$, where

$x(t) = (35 \cos 27°)t$ and

$y(t) = 4 + (35 \sin 27°)t - 16t^2$.

(b) $y_{max} = \dfrac{(v_0 \sin \alpha)^2}{2g} + 4 = \dfrac{(35 \sin 27°)^2}{64} + 4 \approx 7.945$ feet,

which is reached at $t = \dfrac{v_0 \sin \alpha}{g} = \dfrac{35 \sin 27°}{32}$

≈ 0.497 seconds.

(c) For the time, solve $y = 4 + (35 \sin 27°)t - 16t^2 = 0$

for t, using the quadratic formula:

$t = \dfrac{35 \sin 27° + \sqrt{(-35 \sin 27°)^2 + 256}}{32}$

≈ 1.201 seconds.

Then the range is about $x(1.201) = (35 \cos 27°)(1.201)$

≈ 37.460 feet.

(d) For the time, solve $y = 4 + (35 \sin 27°)t - 16t^2 = 7$

for t, using the quadratic formula:

$t = \dfrac{35 \sin 27° \pm \sqrt{(-35 \sin 27°)^2 - 192}}{32} \approx 0.254$ and

0.740 seconds. At those times the ball is about

$x(0.254) = (35 \cos 27°)(0.254) \approx 7.906$ feet and

$x(0.740) = (35 \cos 27°)(0.740) \approx 23.064$ feet from the

impact point, or about $37.460 - 7.906 \approx 29.554$ feet

and $37.460 - 23.064 \approx 14.396$ feet from the landing

spot.

(e) Yes. It changes things because the ball won't clear the

net ($y_{max} \approx 7.945$ ft).

28. (a) $\mathbf{r}(t) = (x(t))\mathbf{i} + (y(t))\mathbf{j}$, where

$x(t) = \left(\dfrac{152}{0.12}\right)(1 - e^{-0.12t})(\cos 20°)$ and

$y(t) = 3 + \left(\dfrac{152}{0.12}\right)(1 - e^{-0.12t})(\sin 20°)$

$+ \left(\dfrac{32}{0.12^2}\right)(1 - 0.12t - e^{-0.12t})$

(b) Solve graphically: enter $y(t)$ for Y_1 (where X stands in

for t), then use the maximum function to find that at

$t \approx 1.484$ seconds the ball reaches a maximum height

of about 40.435 feet.

(c) Use the zero function to find that $y = 0$ when the ball

has traveled for ≈ 3.126 seconds. The range is about

$x(3.126) = \left(\dfrac{152}{0.12}\right)(1 - e^{-0.12(3.126)})(\cos 20°)$

≈ 372.323 feet.

(d) Graph $Y_2 = 30$ and use the intersect function to find

that $y = 30$ for $t \approx 0.689$ and 2.305 seconds, at which

times the ball is about $x(0.689) \approx 94.513$ feet and

$x(2.305) \approx 287.628$ feet from home plate.

(e) Yes, the batter has hit a home run since a graph in

parametric mode shows that the ball is more than

14 feet above the ground when it passes over the fence.

29. (a) $\mathbf{r}(t) = (x(t))\mathbf{i} + (y(t))\mathbf{j}$, where

$x(t) = \left(\dfrac{1}{0.08}\right)(1 - e^{-0.08t})(152 \cos 20° - 17.6)$ and

$y(t) = 3 + \left(\dfrac{152}{0.08}\right)(1 - e^{-0.08t})(\sin 20°)$

$+ \left(\dfrac{32}{0.08^2}\right)(1 - 0.08t - e^{-0.08t})$

(b) Solve graphically: enter $y(t)$ for Y_1 (where X stands in

for t), then use the maximum function to find that at

$t \approx 1.527$ seconds the ball reaches a maximum height

of about 41.893 feet.

(c) Use the zero function to find that $y = 0$ when the ball

has traveled for ≈ 3.181 seconds. The range is about

$x(3.181)$

$= \left(\dfrac{1}{0.08}\right)(1 - e^{-0.08(3.181)})(152 \cos 20° - 17.6)$

≈ 351.734 feet

(d) Graph $Y_2 = 35$ and use the interesect function to find

that $y = 35$ for $t \approx 0.877$ and 2.190 seconds, at which

times the ball is about $\approx x(0.877) \approx 106.028$ feet and

$x(2.190) \approx 251.530$ feet from home plate.

(e) No; the range is less than 380 feet. To find the wind

needed for a home run, first use the method of part (d)

to find that $y = 20$ at $t \approx 0.376$ and 2.716 seconds.

Then define

$x(w) = \left(\dfrac{1}{0.08}\right)(1 - e^{-0.08(2.716)})(152 \cos 20° + w)$,

and solve $x(w) = 380$ to find $w \approx 12.846$ ft/sec. This is

the speed of a wind gust needed in the direction of the

hit for the ball to clear the fence for a home run.

30. (a) To save time, enter one expression for $x(t)$ in the main window, then use the ENTRY function to repeat it six times in the parametric Y = menu. Do the same for $y(t)$, then make appropriate modifications.

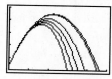

[0, 500] by [0, 50]

Now replace T with X in all the $y(t)$ expressions in the parametric Y = menu, then change to function mode and enter Y_{1T} for Y_1, Y_{2T} for Y_2, and so on. Use the functions in the CALC menu to fill in the tables for parts (b) and (c).

(b)

drag coeff	time at max ht	max ht
$k = 0.01$	$t \approx 1.612$	44.777
$k = 0.02$	$t \approx 1.599$	44.336
$k = 0.10$	$t \approx 1.505$	41.149
$k = 0.15$	$t \approx 1.454$	39.419
$k = 0.20$	$t \approx 1.407$	37.854
$k = 0.25$	$t \approx 1.363$	36.431

(c) After flight times using the zero function, plug the x-intercepts into T and read the ranges out as X_{1T}, X_{2T}, etc.

drag coeff	flight time	range
$k = 0.01$	$t \approx 3.289$	462.152
$k = 0.02$	$t \approx 3.273$	452.478
$k = 0.10$	$t \approx 3.153$	386.274
$k = 0.15$	$t \approx 3.088$	352.983
$k = 0.20$	$t \approx 3.028$	324.410
$k = 0.25$	$t \approx 2.974$	299.661

(d) This follows from the following two limits (as $k \to 0$):

$$\lim_{k \to 0} \frac{1 - e^{-kt}}{k} = t, \text{ and}$$

$$\lim_{k \to 0} \frac{1 - kt - e^{-kt}}{k^2} = -\frac{t^2}{2}.$$

As $k \to 0$, the air resistance approaches 0.

31. The points in question are $(x, y) = \left(\frac{R}{2}, y_{\max}\right)$. So,

$$x = \frac{v_0^2 \sin \alpha \cos \alpha}{g}, \text{ and } y = \frac{(v_0 \sin \alpha)^2}{2g}. \text{ Then}$$

$$x^2 + 4\left(y - \frac{v_0^2}{4g}\right)^2$$

$$= \left(\frac{v_0^2 \sin \alpha \cos \alpha}{g}\right)^2 + 4\left(\frac{(v_0 \sin \alpha)^2}{2g} - \frac{v_0^2}{4g}\right)^2$$

$$= \frac{v_0^4}{g^2}\left[\sin^2 \alpha \cos^2 \alpha + 4\left(\frac{\sin^2 \alpha}{2} - \frac{1}{4}\right)^2\right]$$

$$= \frac{v_0^4}{g^2}\left[\sin^2 \alpha \cos^2 \alpha + 4\left(\frac{\sin^4 \alpha}{4} - \frac{\sin^2 \alpha}{4} + \frac{1}{16}\right)\right]$$

$$= \frac{v_0^4}{g^2}\left[\sin^2 \alpha \cos^2 \alpha + (\sin^2 \alpha)(1 - \cos^2 \alpha) - \sin^2 \alpha + \frac{1}{4}\right]$$

$$= \frac{v_0^4}{g^2}\left(\frac{1}{4}\right) = \frac{v_0^4}{4g^2},$$

so the point (x, y) lies on the ellipse.

32. $\dfrac{d\mathbf{r}}{dt} = (v_0 e^{-kt} \cos \alpha)\mathbf{i} + (v_0 e^{-kt} \sin \alpha + \dfrac{g}{k}e^{-kt} - \dfrac{g}{k})\mathbf{j}$

$\dfrac{d^2\mathbf{r}}{dt} = (-kv_0 e^{-kt} \cos \alpha)\mathbf{i} + (-kv_0 e^{-kt} \sin \alpha - ge^{-kt})\mathbf{j}$

$= -g\mathbf{j} - k\dfrac{d\mathbf{r}}{dt}$

The initial conditions are also satisfied, since

$\mathbf{r}(0) = \dfrac{v_0}{k}(1 - e^0)(\cos \alpha)\mathbf{i} +$

$\qquad\qquad \left[\dfrac{v_0}{k}(1 - e^0)(\sin \alpha) + \dfrac{g}{k^2}(1 - 0 - e^0)\right]\mathbf{j}$

$= 0\mathbf{i} + 0\mathbf{j} = \mathbf{0}$,

and $\dfrac{d\mathbf{r}}{dt}\bigg|_{t=0} = (v_0 e^0 \cos \alpha)\mathbf{i} + \left(v_0 e^0 \sin \alpha + \dfrac{g}{k}e^0 - \dfrac{g}{k}\right)\mathbf{j}$

$= (v_0 \cos \alpha)\mathbf{i} + (v_0 \sin \alpha)\mathbf{j}$

■ Section 10.5 Polar Coordinates and Polar Graphs (pp. 552–559)

Exploration 1   Investigating Polar Graphs

1. The graph is drawn in the decimal window $[-4.7, 4.7]$ by $[-3.1, 3.1]$ with $-\dfrac{\pi}{2} \le \theta \le \dfrac{\pi}{2}$.

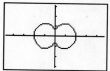

2. r_1 and r_2 are 0 for $\theta = \dfrac{\pi}{2}$.

3. π

4. If (r, θ) is a solution of $r^2 = 4 \cos \theta$, then so is $(r, -\theta)$ because $\cos(-\theta) = \cos \theta$. Thus, the graph is symmetric about the x-axis.
If (r, θ) is a solution of $r^2 = 4 \cos \theta$, then so is $(-r, -\theta)$ because $(-r)^2 = r^2$ and $\cos(-\theta) = \cos \theta$. Thus, the graph is symmetric about the y-axis.
The graph is symmetric about the origin because it is symmetric about both the x- and y-axes. You can also give a direct proof by showing that $(-r, \theta)$ lies on the graph if (r, θ) does.

Exploration 2 Graphing Rose Curves

All graphs are drawn in the window $[-4.7, 4.7]$ by $[-3.1, 3.1]$.

1. The graphs are rose curves with 4 petals when $n = \pm 2$, 8 petals when $n = \pm 4$, and 12 petals when $n = \pm 6$.

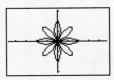

$$n = \pm 2$$

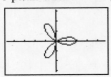

$$n = \pm 4$$

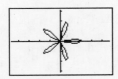

$$n = \pm 6$$

2. 2π

3. The graph is a rose curve with $2|n|$ petals.

4. The graphs are rose curves with 3 petals when $n = \pm 3$, 5 petals when $n = \pm 5$, and 7 petals when $n = \pm 7$.

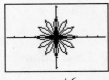

$$n = \pm 3$$

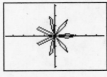

$$n = \pm 5$$

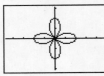

$$n = \pm 7$$

5. π

6. The graph is a rose cuve with $|n|$ petals.

Quick Review 10.5

1. Slope $= \dfrac{-1 - 4}{3 - (-2)} = -1$,

so $y - 4 = -1[x - (-2)]$ or $y = -x + 2$.

2. $(x - 0)^2 + (y - 0)^2 = 3^2$, or $x^2 + y^2 = 9$.

3. $[x - (-2)]^2 + (y - 4)^2 = 2^2$, or $(x + 2)^2 + (y - 4)^2 = 4$.

4. (a) No; y is a function of x and is not the zero function.

   (b) No;
   $$y(-x) = (-x)^3 - (-x) = -x^3 + x = -(x^3 - x) \neq y(x)$$

   (c) Yes; $y(-x) = -y(x)$ (see part (b))

5. (a) No; y is a function of x and is not the zero function.

   (b) No; $y(-x) = (-x)^2 - (-x) = x^2 + x \neq y(x)$

   (c) No; $y(-x) \neq -y(x)$ (see part (b))

6. (a) No; y is a function of x and is not the zero function.

   (b) Yes; $y(-x) = \cos(-x) = \cos x = y(x)$

   (c) No; $y(-x) \neq -y(x)$ (see part (b))

7. (a) Yes; Substitute $-y$ for y in the equation to get the original equation.

   (b) Yes; Substitute $-x$ for x in the equation to get the original equation.

   (c) Yes; since the curve is symmetric with respect to both the x-axis and y-axis, it is symmetric with respect to the origin. (Also, substitute $-x$ for x and $-y$ for y in the equation to get the original equation.)

8. Solve for y: $y = (x - 2)^{1/2}$ or $-(x - 2)^{1/2}$.
   Enter the first expression for Y_1, the second for Y_2.

9. Solve for y: $y = \left(\dfrac{4 - x^2}{3}\right)^{1/2}$ or $-\left(\dfrac{4 - x^2}{3}\right)^{1/2}$.

   Enter the first expression for Y_1, the second for Y_2.

10. $(x^2 - 4x) + (y^2 + 6y + 9) = 0$
    $(x^2 - 4x + 4) + (y^2 + 6y + 9) = 4$
    $(x - 2)^2 + (y + 3)^2 = 2^2$.
    Center $= (2, -3)$, Radius $= 2$.

Section 10.5 Exercises

For Exercises 1 and 2, two pairs of polar coordinates label the same point if the r-coordinates are the same and the θ-coordinates differ by an even multiple of π, or if the r-coordinates are opposites and the θ-coordinates differ by an odd multiple of π.

1. (a) and (e) are the same.
   (b) and (g) are the same.
   (c) and (h) are the same.
   (d) and (f) are the same.

2. (a) and (f) are the same.
   (b) and (h) are the same.
   (c) and (g) are the same.
   (d) and (e) are the same.

3.

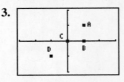

$$[-3, 3] \text{ by } [-2, 2]$$

(a) $\left(\sqrt{2} \cos \dfrac{\pi}{4}, \sqrt{2} \sin \dfrac{\pi}{4}\right) = (1, 1)$

(b) $(1 \cos 0, 1 \sin 0) = (1, 0)$

(c) $\left(0 \cos \dfrac{\pi}{2}, 0 \sin \dfrac{\pi}{2}\right) = (0, 0)$

(d) $\left(-\sqrt{2} \cos \dfrac{\pi}{4}, -\sqrt{2} \sin \dfrac{\pi}{4}\right) = (-1, -1)$

4.

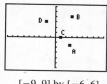

[−9, 9] by [−6, 6]

(a) $\left(-3\cos\frac{5\pi}{6}, -3\sin\frac{5\pi}{6}\right) = \left(\frac{3\sqrt{3}}{2}, -\frac{3}{2}\right)$

(b) $\left(5\cos\left(\tan^{-1}\left(\frac{4}{3}\right)\right), 5\sin\left(\tan^{-1}\left(\frac{4}{3}\right)\right)\right) = (3, 4)$

(c) $(-1\cos 7\pi, -1\sin 7\pi) = (1, 0)$

(d) $\left(2\sqrt{3}\cos\frac{2\pi}{3}, 2\sqrt{3}\sin\frac{2\pi}{3}\right) = (-\sqrt{3}, 3)$

5.

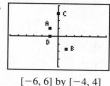

[−6, 6] by [−4, 4]

(a) $r = \sqrt{(-1)^2 + 1^2} = \sqrt{2}$, $\tan\theta = \frac{1}{-1} = -1$ with θ in quadrant II. The coordinates are $\left(\sqrt{2}, \frac{3\pi}{4}\right)$. $\left(\sqrt{2}, -\frac{5\pi}{4}\right)$ also works, since r is the same and θ differs by 2π.

(b) $r = \sqrt{1^2 + (-\sqrt{3})^2} = 2$, $\tan\theta = -\frac{\sqrt{3}}{1} = -\sqrt{3}$ with θ in quadrant IV. The coordinates are $\left(2, -\frac{\pi}{3}\right)$. $\left(-2, \frac{2\pi}{3}\right)$ also works, since r has the opposite sign and θ differs by π.

(c) $r = \sqrt{0^2 + 3^2} = 3$, $\tan\theta = \frac{3}{0}$ is undefined with θ on the positive y-axis. The coordinates are $\left(3, \frac{\pi}{2}\right)$. $\left(3, \frac{5\pi}{2}\right)$ also works, since r is the same and θ differs by 2π.

(d) $r = \sqrt{(-1)^2 + 0^2} = 1$, $\tan\theta = \frac{0}{-1} = 0$ with θ on the negative x-axis. The coordinates are $(1, \pi)$. $(-1, 0)$ also works, since r has the opposite sign and θ differs by π.

6.

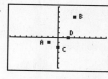

[−9, 9] by [−6, 6]

(a) $r = \sqrt{(-\sqrt{3})^2 + (-1)^2} = 2$, $\tan\theta = \frac{-1}{-\sqrt{3}} = \frac{1}{\sqrt{3}}$ with θ in quadrant III. The coordinates are $\left(2, \frac{7\pi}{6}\right)$. $\left(-2, \frac{\pi}{6}\right)$ also works, since r has the opposite sign and θ differs by π.

(b) $r = \sqrt{3^2 + 4^2} = 5$, $\tan\theta = \frac{4}{3}$ with θ in quadrant I. The coordinates are $\left(5, \tan^{-1}\frac{4}{3}\right)$. $\left(-5, \pi + \tan^{-1}\frac{4}{3}\right)$ also works, since r has the opposite sign and θ differs by π.

(c) $r = \sqrt{0 + (-2)^2} = 2$, $\tan\theta = -\frac{2}{0}$ is undefined with θ on the negative y-axis. The coordinates are $\left(2, \frac{3\pi}{2}\right)$. $\left(2, -\frac{\pi}{2}\right)$ also works, since r is the same and θ differs by 2π.

(d) $r = \sqrt{2^2 + 0^2} = 2$, $\tan\theta = \frac{0}{2} = 0$ with θ on the positive x-axis. The coordinates are $(2, 0)$. $(2, 2\pi)$ also works, since r is the same and θ differs by 2π.

7.

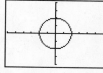

[−6, 6] by [−4, 4]

8.

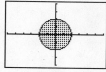

[−6, 6] by [−4, 4]

9.

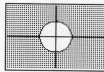

[−3, 3] by [−2, 2]

10.

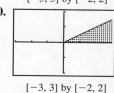

[−3, 3] by [−2, 2]

11.

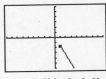

$[-9, 9]$ by $[-6, 6]$

12.

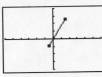

$[-6, 6]$ by $[-4, 4]$

13.

$[-3, 3]$ by $[-2, 2]$

14.

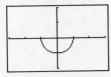

$[-3, 3]$ by $[-2, 2]$

15.

$[-3, 3]$ by $[-2, 2]$

16.

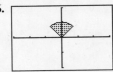

$[-3, 3]$ by $[-2, 2]$

17.

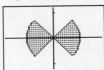

$[-1.8, 1.8]$ by $[-1.2, 1.2]$

18.

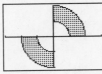

$[-3, 3]$ by $[-2, 2]$

19. $y = r \sin \theta$, so the equation is $y = 0$, which is the x-axis.

20. $x = r \cos \theta$, so the equation is $x = 0$, which is the y-axis.

21. $r = 4 \csc \theta$

$r \sin \theta = 4$

$y = r \sin \theta$, so the equation is $y = 4$, a horizontal line.

22. $r = -3 \sec \theta$

$r \cos \theta = -3$

$x = r \cos \theta$, so the equation is $x = -3$, a vertical line.

23. $x = r \cos \theta$ and $y = r \sin \theta$, so the equation is $x + y = 1$, a line (slope $= -1$, y-intercept $= 1$).

24. $x^2 + y^2 = r^2$, so the equation is $x^2 + y^2 = 1$, a circle (center $= (0, 0)$, radius $= 1$).

25. $x^2 + y^2 = r^2$ and $y = r \sin \theta$, so the equation is $x^2 + y^2 = 4y \Rightarrow x^2 + (y - 2)^2 = 4$, a circle (center $= (0, 2)$, radius $= 2$).

26. $r = \dfrac{5}{\sin \theta - 2 \cos \theta}$

$r \sin \theta - 2r \cos \theta = 5$

$x = r \cos \theta$ and $y = r \sin \theta$, so the equation is $y - 2x = 5$, a line (slope $= 2$, y-intercept $= 5$).

27. $r^2 \sin 2\theta = 2$

$2r^2 \sin \theta \cos \theta = 2$

$(r \sin \theta)(r \cos \theta) = 1$

$x = r \cos \theta$ and $y = r \sin \theta$, so the equation is $xy = 1$ $\left(\text{or}, y = \dfrac{1}{x}\right)$, a hyperbola.

28. $r = \cot \theta \csc \theta$

$r \sin \theta = \cot \theta$

$y = r \sin \theta$ and $\dfrac{x}{y} = \cot \theta$, so the equation is $y^2 = x$, a parabola.

29. $r = \csc \theta \, e^{r\cos\theta}$

$r \sin \theta = e^{r\cos\theta}$

$x = r \cos \theta$ and $y = r \sin \theta$, so the equation is $y = e^x$, the exponential curve.

30. $\cos^2 \theta = \sin^2 \theta$

$(r \cos \theta)^2 = (r \sin \theta)^2$

$x = r \cos \theta$ and $y = r \sin \theta$, so the equation is $x^2 = y^2$ or $y = \pm x$, the union of two lines.

31. $r \sin \theta = \ln r + \ln \cos \theta$

$r \sin \theta = \ln (r \cos \theta)$

$y = \ln x$, the logarithmic curve.

32. $r^2 + 2r^2 \cos \theta \sin \theta = 1$

$r^2 + 2(r \cos \theta)(r \sin \theta) = 1$

$x^2 + y^2 + 2xy = 1$

$(x + y)^2 = 1$

$x + y = \pm 1$, the union of two lines.

33. $r^2 = -4r \cos \theta$

$x^2 + y^2 = -4x$

$(x + 2)^2 + y^2 = 4$, a circle (center $= (-2, 0)$, radius $= 2$).

34. $r = 8 \sin \theta$

$r^2 = 8r \sin \theta$

$x^2 + y^2 = 8y$

$x^2 + (y - 4)^2 = 16$, a circle (center $= (0, 4)$, radius $= 4$).

35. $r = 2 \cos \theta + 2 \sin \theta$

$r^2 = 2r \cos \theta + 2r \sin \theta$

$x^2 + y^2 = 2x + 2y$

$(x - 1)^2 + (y - 1)^2 = 2$, a circle (center $= (1, 1)$, radius $= \sqrt{2}$).

36. $r \sin\left(\theta + \dfrac{\pi}{6}\right) = 2$

$r\left(\sin\theta \cos\dfrac{\pi}{6} + \cos\theta \sin\dfrac{\pi}{6}\right) = 2$

$\dfrac{\sqrt{3}}{2} r \sin\theta + \dfrac{1}{2} r \cos\theta = 2$

$\dfrac{\sqrt{3}}{2} y + \dfrac{1}{2} x = 2$

$x + \sqrt{3} y = 4$, a line $\left(\text{slope} = -\dfrac{1}{\sqrt{3}}, \ y\text{-intercept} = \dfrac{4}{\sqrt{3}}\right)$.

37. $x = 7$

$r \cos\theta = 7$. The graph is a vertical line.

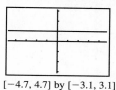

$[-9.4, 9.4]$ by $[-6.2, 6.2]$

38. $y = 1$

$r \sin\theta = 1$

The graph is a horiztonal line.

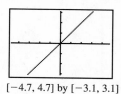

$[-4.7, 4.7]$ by $[-3.1, 3.1]$

39. $x = y \Rightarrow r \cos\theta = r \sin\theta \Rightarrow \tan\theta = 1 \Rightarrow \theta = \dfrac{\pi}{4}$

More generally, $\theta = \dfrac{\pi}{4} + 2k\pi$ for any integer k.

The graph is a slanted line.

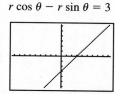

$[-4.7, 4.7]$ by $[-3.1, 3.1]$

40. $x - y = 3$

$r \cos\theta - r \sin\theta = 3$

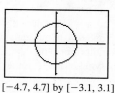

$[-9.4, 9.4]$ by $[-6.2, 6.2]$

41. $x^2 + y^2 = 4$

$r^2 = 4$ or $r = 2$ (or $r = -2$)

$[-4.7, 4.7]$ by $[-3.1, 3.1]$

42. $x^2 - y^2 = 1$

$r^2 \cos^2\theta - r^2 \sin^2\theta = 1$

$r^2(\cos^2\theta - \sin^2\theta) = 1$

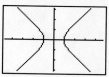

$[-4.7, 4.7]$ by $[-3.1, 3.1]$

43. $\dfrac{x^2}{9} + \dfrac{y^2}{4} = 1$

$\dfrac{r^2 \cos^2\theta}{9} + \dfrac{r^2 \sin^2\theta}{4} = 1$

$r^2(4 \cos^2\theta + 9 \sin^2\theta) = 36$

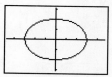

$[-4.7, 4.7]$ by $[-3.1, 3.1]$

44. $xy = 2$

$(r \cos\theta)(r \sin\theta) = 2$

$r^2 \cos\theta \sin\theta = 2$

$r^2\, 2 \cos\theta \sin\theta = 4$

$r^2 \sin 2\theta = 4$

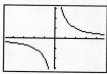

$[-4.7, 4.7]$ by $[-3.1, 3.1]$

45. $y^2 = 4x$

$r^2 \sin^2\theta = 4r \cos\theta$

$r \sin^2\theta = 4 \cos\theta$

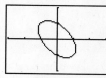

$[-4.7, 4.7]$ by $[-3.1, 3.1]$

46. $x^2 + xy + y^2 = 1$

$(r \cos\theta)^2 + (r \cos\theta)(r \sin\theta) + (r \sin\theta)^2 = 1$

$r^2(1 + \cos\theta \sin\theta) = 1$

$[-3, 3]$ by $[-2, 2]$

47. $x^2 + (y - 2)^2 = 4$

$r^2 \cos^2 \theta + (r \sin \theta - 2)^2 = 4$

$r^2 \cos^2 \theta + r^2 \sin^2 \theta - 4r \sin \theta + 4 = 4$

$r^2 - 4r \sin \theta = 0$

$r = 4 \sin \theta$.

The graph is a circle centered at (0, 2) with radius 2.

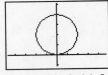

[−4.7, 4.7] by [−1.1, 5.1]

48. $(x - 3)^2 + (y + 1)^2 = 4$

$(r \cos \theta - 3)^2 + (r \sin \theta + 1)^2 = 4$

$r^2 \cos^2 \theta - 6r \cos \theta + 9 + r^2 \sin^2 \theta + 2r \sin \theta + 1 = 4$

$r^2 - 6r \cos \theta + 2r \sin \theta + 6 = 0$

$r = \dfrac{6 \cos \theta - 2 \sin \theta \pm \sqrt{(6 \cos \theta - 2 \sin \theta)^2 - 24}}{2}$

$r = 3 \cos \theta - \sin \theta \pm \sqrt{(3 \cos \theta - \sin \theta)^2 - 6}$

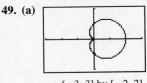

[−6, 6] by [−4, 4]

In Exercises 49–58, find the minimum θ-interval by trying different intervals on a graphing calculator.

49. (a)

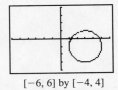

[−3, 3] by [−2, 2]

(b) Length of interval = 2π

50. (a)

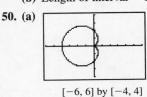

[−6, 6] by [−4, 4]

(b) Length of interval = 2π

51. (a)

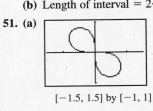

[−1.5, 1.5] by [−1, 1]

(b) Length of interval = $\dfrac{\pi}{2}$

52. (a)

[−3, 3] by [−2, 2]

(b) Length of interval = 2π

53. (a)

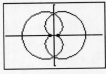

[−3.75, 3.75] by [−2, 3]

(b) Length of interval = 2π

54. (a)

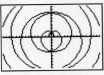

[−1.5, 1.5] by [−1, 1]

(b) Length of interval = 4π

55. (a)

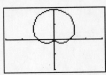

[−15, 15] by [−10, 10]

(b) Required interval = $(-\infty, \infty)$

56. (a)

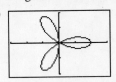

[−3, 3] by [−2, 2]

(b) Length of interval = 2π

57. (a)

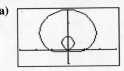

[−3, 3] by [−2, 2]

(b) Length of interval = π

58. (a)

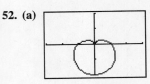

[−3, 3] by [−1, 3]

(b) Length of interval = 2π

59. If (r, θ) is a solution, so is $(-r, \theta)$. Therefore, the curve is symmetric about the origin. And if (r, θ) is a solution, so is $(r, -\theta)$. Therefore, the curve is symmetric about the x-axis. And since any curve with x-axis and origin symmetry also has y-axis symmetry, the curve is symmetric about the y-axis.

60. If (r, θ) is a solution, so is $(-r, \theta)$. Therefore, the curve is symmetric about the origin. The curve does not have x-axis or y-axis symmetry.

61. If (r, θ) is a solution, so is $(r, \pi - \theta)$. Therefore, the curve is symmetric about the y-axis. The curve does not have x-axis or origin symmetry.

62. If (r, θ) is a solution, so is $(-r, \theta)$. Therefore, the curve is symmetric about the origin. And if (r, θ) is a solution, so is $(r, -\theta)$. Therefore, the curve is symmetric about the x-axis. And since any curve with x-axis and origin symmetry also has y-axis symmetry, the curve is symmetric about the y-axis.

63. (a) Because $r = a \sec \theta$ is equivalent to $r \cos \theta = a$, which is equivalent to the Cartesian equation $x = a$.

(b) $r = a \csc \theta$ is equivalent to $y = a$.

64. (a) The graph is the same for $n = 2$ and $n = -2$, and in general, it's the same for $n = 2k$ and $n = -2k$. The graphs for $n = 2, 4$, and 6 are roses with 4, 8, and 12 "petals" respectively.
The graphs for $n = \pm 2$ and $n = \pm 6$ are shown below.

$n = \pm 2$

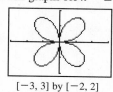

[−3, 3] by [−2, 2]

$n = \pm 6$

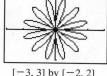

[−3, 3] by [−2, 2]

(b) 2π

(c) The graph is a rose with $2|n|$ "petals".

(d) The graphs are roses with 3, 5, and 7 "petals" respectively. The "center petal" points upward if $n = -3, +5$, or -7.
The graphs for $n = 3$ and $n = -3$ are shown below.

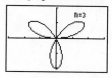

[−3, 3] by [−2, 2]

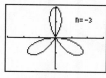

[−3, 3] by [−2, 2]

(e) π

(f) The graph is a rose with $|n|$ "petals".

65. (a) We have $x = r \cos \theta$ and $y = r \sin \theta$. By taking $t = \theta$, we have $r = f(t)$, so $x = f(t) \cos t$ and $y = f(t) \sin t$.

(b) $x = 3 \cos t, y = 3 \sin t$

(c) $x = (1 - \cos t) \cos t, y = (1 - \cos t) \sin t$

(d) $x = (3 \sin 2t) \cos t, y = (3 \sin 2t) \sin t$

66. (a)

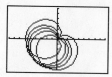

[−9, 9] by [−6, 6]

The graph of r_2 is the graph of r_1 rotated by angle α counterclockwise about the origin.

(b)

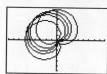

[−9, 9] by [−6, 6]

The graph of r_2 is the graph of r_1 rotated by angle $-\alpha$ clockwise about the origin.

(c) The graph of r_2 is the graph of r_1 rotated counterclockwise about the origin by the angle α.

67. $d = \sqrt{(x_2 - x_1)^2 + (y_1 - y_2)^2}$

$= [(r_2 \cos \theta_2 - r_1 \cos \theta_1)^2 + (r_2 \sin \theta_2 - r_1 \sin \theta_1)^2]^{1/2}$

$= [r_2^2 \cos^2 \theta_2 - 2r_2 r_1 \cos \theta_2 \cos \theta_1 + r_1^2 \cos^2 \theta_1$
$\quad + r_2^2 \sin^2 \theta_2 - 2r_2 r_1 \sin \theta_2 \sin \theta_1 + r_1^2 \sin^2 \theta_1]^{1/2}$

$= \sqrt{r_1^2 + r_2^2 - 2r_1 r_2 \cos(\theta_1 - \theta_2)}$

68. (a)

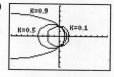

[−9, 9] by [−6, 6]

The graphs are ellipses.

(b) Graphs for $0 < k < 1$ are ellipses. As $k \to 0^+$, the graph approaches the circle of radius 2 centered at the origin.

69. (a)

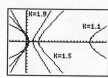

[−5, 25] by [−10, 10]

The graphs are hyperbolas.

(b) Graphs for $k > 1$ are hyperbolas. As $k \to 1^+$, the right branch of the hyperbola goes to infinity and "disappears". The left branch approaches the parabola $y^2 = 4 - 4x$.

70. (a)

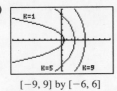

[−9, 9] by [−6, 6]

The graphs are parabolas.

(b) As $k \to 0^+$, the limit of the graph is the negative x-axis.

■ Section 10.6 Calculus of Polar Curves
(pp. 559–568)

Quick Review 10.6

1. $\dfrac{dy}{dx} = \dfrac{dy/dt}{dx/dt} = \dfrac{5 \cos t}{-3 \sin t} = -\dfrac{5}{3} \cot t$

2. $-\dfrac{5}{3} \cot 2 \approx 0.763$

3. Solve $\cot t = 0$: $t = \dfrac{\pi}{2}$ or $\dfrac{3\pi}{2}$;

the corresponding points are $\left(3 \cos \dfrac{\pi}{2}, 5 \sin \dfrac{\pi}{2}\right) = (0, 5)$

and $\left(3 \cos \dfrac{3\pi}{2}, 5 \sin \dfrac{3\pi}{2}\right) = (0, -5)$

4. $-\dfrac{5}{3} \cot t$ is undefined when $t = 0$, π, or 2π;

the corrresponding points are

$(3 \cos 0, 5 \sin 0) = (3 \cos 2\pi, 5 \sin 2\pi) = (3, 0)$ and

$(3 \cos \pi, 5 \sin \pi) = (-3, 0)$.

5. Length $= \displaystyle\int_0^\pi \sqrt{\left(\dfrac{dx}{dt}\right)^2 + \left(\dfrac{dy}{dt}\right)^2}\, dt$

$= \displaystyle\int_0^\pi \sqrt{9 \sin^2 t + 25 \cos^2 t}\, dt,$

which using NINT evaluates to ≈ 12.763.

For questions 6–8, the graph is:

[−2, 4] by [−2, 2]

6. The upper half of the outer loop

7. The inner loop

8. The lower half of the outer loop

9. $y = 0$ for $x = 0$ or 6.

Area $= \displaystyle\int_0^6 (6x - x^2)\, dx = \left[3x^2 - \dfrac{1}{3}x^3\right]_0^6 = 36$

10. Use a graphing calculator's intersect function to find that

the curves cross at $x \approx 0.270$ and $x \approx 2.248$, then use

NINT to find

Area $= \displaystyle\int_{0.270}^{2.248} [2 \sin x - (x^2 - 2x + 1)]\, dx \approx 2.403$.

Section 10.6 Exercises

1. $\dfrac{dy}{dx} = \dfrac{f'(\theta) \sin \theta + f(\theta) \cos \theta}{f'(\theta) \cos \theta - f(\theta) \sin \theta}$

$= \dfrac{\cos \theta \sin \theta + (-1 + \sin \theta)\cos \theta}{\cos \theta \cos \theta - (-1 + \sin \theta)\sin \theta}$

$= \dfrac{2 \sin \theta \cos \theta - \cos \theta}{\cos^2 \theta - \sin^2 \theta + \sin \theta}$

$\left.\dfrac{dy}{dx}\right|_{\theta=0} = -\dfrac{1}{1} = -1,\ \left.\dfrac{dy}{dx}\right|_{\theta=\pi} = \dfrac{1}{1} = 1$

2. $\dfrac{dy}{dx} = \dfrac{f'(\theta) \sin \theta + f(\theta) \cos \theta}{f'(\theta) \cos \theta - f(\theta) \sin \theta} = \dfrac{-2 \sin 2\theta \sin \theta + \cos 2\theta \cos \theta}{-2 \sin 2\theta \cos \theta - \cos 2\theta \sin \theta}.$

$\left.\dfrac{dy}{dx}\right|_{\theta=0} = \dfrac{1}{0}$, which is undefined; $\left.\dfrac{dy}{dx}\right|_{\theta=\pm\pi/2} = \dfrac{\pm 0}{1} = 0$;

and $\left.\dfrac{dy}{dx}\right|_{\theta=\pi} = -\dfrac{1}{0}$, which is undefined.

3. $\dfrac{dy}{dx} = \dfrac{f'(\theta) \sin \theta + f(\theta) \cos \theta}{f'(\theta) \cos \theta - f(\theta) \sin \theta}$

$= \dfrac{-3 \cos \theta \sin \theta + (2 - 3 \sin \theta) \cos \theta}{-3 \cos \theta \cos \theta - (2 - 3 \sin \theta) \sin \theta}$

$= \dfrac{2 \cos \theta - 6 \sin \theta \cos \theta}{-2 \sin \theta - 3(\cos^2 \theta - \sin^2 \theta)}$

$\left.\dfrac{dy}{dx}\right|_{(2, 0)} = \left.\dfrac{dy}{dx}\right|_{\theta=0} = \dfrac{2}{-3} = -\dfrac{2}{3},$

$\left.\dfrac{dy}{dx}\right|_{(-1, \pi/2)} = \left.\dfrac{dy}{dx}\right|_{\theta=\pi/2} = \dfrac{0}{1} = 0,$

$\left.\dfrac{dy}{dx}\right|_{(2, \pi)} = \left.\dfrac{dy}{dx}\right|_{\theta=\pi} = \dfrac{2}{3},$ and

$\left.\dfrac{dy}{dx}\right|_{(5, 3\pi/2)} = \left.\dfrac{dy}{dx}\right|_{\theta=3\pi/2} = \dfrac{0}{5} = 0.$

4. $\dfrac{dy}{dx} = \dfrac{f'(\theta) \sin \theta + f(\theta) \cos \theta}{f'(\theta) \cos \theta - f(\theta) \sin \theta}$

$= \dfrac{3 \sin^2 \theta + 3 \cos \theta(1 - \cos \theta)}{3 \sin \theta \cos \theta - 3 \sin \theta(1 - \cos \theta)}$

$= \dfrac{\cos \theta - (\cos^2 \theta - \sin^2 \theta)}{2 \sin \theta \cos \theta - \sin \theta}$

$\left.\dfrac{dy}{dx}\right|_{(1.5, \pi/3)} = \dfrac{\dfrac{1}{2} - \left(-\dfrac{1}{2}\right)}{\dfrac{\sqrt{3}}{2} - \dfrac{\sqrt{3}}{2}}$, which is undefined;

$\left.\dfrac{dy}{dx}\right|_{(4.5, 2\pi/3)} = \dfrac{-\dfrac{1}{2} - \left(-\dfrac{1}{2}\right)}{-\dfrac{\sqrt{3}}{2} - \dfrac{\sqrt{3}}{2}} = 0;$

$\left.\dfrac{dy}{dx}\right|_{(6, \pi)} = \dfrac{-1 - 1}{0 - 0}$, which is undefined; and

$\left.\dfrac{dy}{dx}\right|_{(3, 3\pi/2)} = \dfrac{0 - (-1)}{0 - (-1)} = 1.$

5.

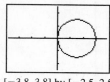

[−3.8, 3.8] by [−2.5, 2.5]

The graph passes through the pole when $r = 3 \cos \theta = 0$, which occurs when $\theta = \dfrac{\pi}{2}$ and when $\theta = \dfrac{3\pi}{2}$. Since the θ-interval $0 \le \theta \le \pi$ produces the entire graph, we need only consider $\theta = \dfrac{\pi}{2}$. At this point, there appears to be a vertical tangent line with equation $\theta = \dfrac{\pi}{2}$ (or $x = 0$).

Confirm analytically:

$x = (3 \cos \theta) \cos \theta = 3 \cos^2 \theta$

$y = (3 \cos \theta) \sin \theta$

$\dfrac{dy}{d\theta} = (-3 \sin \theta) \sin \theta + (3 \cos \theta) \cos \theta = 3(\cos^2 \theta - \sin^2 \theta)$

and $\dfrac{dx}{d\theta} = 6 \cos \theta (-\sin \theta)$.

At $\left(0, \dfrac{\pi}{2}\right)$, $\dfrac{dx}{d\theta}\Big|_{\theta = \pi/2} = 0$, and

$\dfrac{dy}{d\theta}\Big|_{\theta = \pi/2} = 3(0^2 - 1^2) = -3$. So at $\left(0, \dfrac{\pi}{2}\right)$, $\dfrac{dx}{d\theta} = 0$

and $\dfrac{dy}{d\theta} \ne 0$, so $\dfrac{dy}{dx}$ is undefined and the tangent line is

vertical.

6.

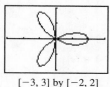

[−3, 3] by [−2, 2]

A trace of the graph suggests three tangent lines, one with positive slope for $\theta = \dfrac{\pi}{6}$, a vertical one for $\theta = \dfrac{\pi}{2}$, and one with negative slope for $\theta = \dfrac{5\pi}{6}$.

Confirm analytically:

$\dfrac{dy}{d\theta} = -6 \sin 3\theta \sin \theta + 2 \cos 3\theta \cos \theta$ and

$\dfrac{dx}{d\theta} = -6 \sin 3\theta \cos \theta - 2 \cos 3\theta \sin \theta$.

$\left(0, \dfrac{\pi}{6}\right)$, $\left(0, \dfrac{\pi}{2}\right)$, and $\left(0, \dfrac{5\pi}{6}\right)$ are all solutions.

$\dfrac{dy}{dx} = \dfrac{dy/d\theta}{dx/d\theta}$, and so

$\dfrac{dy}{dx}\Big|_{\theta = \pi/6} = \dfrac{-6(1)(1/2) + 2(0)(\sqrt{3}/2)}{-6(1)(\sqrt{3}/2) - 2(0)(1/2)} = \dfrac{1}{\sqrt{3}}$;

$\dfrac{dy}{dx}\Big|_{\theta = \pi/2} = \dfrac{-6(-1)(1) + 2(0)(0)}{-6(-1)(0) - 2(0)(1)}$, which is undefined; and

$\dfrac{dy}{dx}\Big|_{\theta = 5\pi/6} = \dfrac{-6(1)(1/2) + 2(0)(-\sqrt{3}/2)}{-6(1)(-\sqrt{3}/2) - 2(0)(1/2)} = -\dfrac{1}{\sqrt{3}}$. The tangent

lines have equations $\theta = \dfrac{\pi}{6} \left[y = \dfrac{1}{\sqrt{3}} x \right]$, $\theta = \dfrac{\pi}{2} [x = 0]$,

and $\theta = \dfrac{5\pi}{6} \left[y = -\dfrac{1}{\sqrt{3}} x \right]$.

7.

[−1.5, 1.5] by [−1, 1]

The polar solutions are $\left(0, \dfrac{k\pi}{5}\right)$ for $k = 0, 1, 2, 3, 4$, and for a given k, the line $\theta = \dfrac{k\pi}{5}$ appears to be tangent to the curve at $\left(0, \dfrac{k\pi}{5}\right)$. This can be confirmed analytically by noting that the slope of the curve, $\dfrac{dy}{dx}$, equals the slope of the line, $\tan \dfrac{k\pi}{5}$. So the tangent lines are $\theta = 0$ $[y = 0]$,

$\theta = \dfrac{\pi}{5} \left[y = \left(\tan \dfrac{\pi}{5}\right) x \right]$, $\theta = \dfrac{2\pi}{5} \left[y = \left(\tan \dfrac{2\pi}{5}\right) x \right]$,

$\theta = \dfrac{3\pi}{5} \left[y = \left(\tan \dfrac{3\pi}{5}\right) x \right]$, and $\theta = \dfrac{4\pi}{5} \left[y = \left(\tan \dfrac{4\pi}{5}\right) x \right]$.

8.

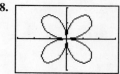

[−3, 3] by [−2, 2]

The polar solutions are $\left(0, \dfrac{k\pi}{2}\right)$ for $k = 0, 1, 2, 3, 4$, and for a given k, the line $\theta = \dfrac{k\pi}{2}$ appears to be tangent to the curve at $\left(0, \dfrac{k\pi}{2}\right)$. This can be confirmed analytically by noting that the slope of the curve, $\dfrac{dy}{dx}$, equals the slope of the line, $\tan \dfrac{k\pi}{2}$. So the tangent lines are $\theta = 0$ $[y = 0]$ and $\theta = \dfrac{\pi}{2}$ $[x = 0]$. $\left(\theta = \pi, \theta = \dfrac{3\pi}{2}$ and $\theta = 2\pi$ are duplicate solutions.$\right)$

9. $\dfrac{dy}{d\theta} = \cos\theta\sin\theta + (-1 + \sin\theta)\cos\theta$

$\qquad = \cos\theta(2\sin\theta - 1)$

$\qquad = \sin 2\theta - \cos\theta$

$\dfrac{dx}{d\theta} = \cos^2\theta - (-1 + \sin\theta)\sin\theta$

$\qquad = \cos^2\theta + \sin\theta - \sin^2\theta$

$\qquad = -2\sin^2\theta + \sin\theta + 1$

$\dfrac{dy}{d\theta} = 0$ when $\theta = \dfrac{\pi}{2}, \dfrac{3\pi}{2}$ ($\cos\theta = 0$) or when

$\theta = \dfrac{\pi}{6}, \dfrac{5\pi}{6}$ ($2\sin\theta - 1 = 0$). $\dfrac{dx}{d\theta} = 0$ when

$\sin\theta = \dfrac{-1 \pm \sqrt{9}}{-4} = -\dfrac{1}{2}$ or 1, i.e., when $\theta = \dfrac{7\pi}{6}, \dfrac{11\pi}{6}$, or

$\dfrac{\pi}{2}$. So there is a horizontal tangent line for $\theta = \dfrac{3\pi}{2}$, $r = -2$

$\left[\text{the line } y = -2\sin\dfrac{3\pi}{2} = 2\right]$, for $\theta = \dfrac{\pi}{6}$, $r = -\dfrac{1}{2}$

$\left[\text{the line } y = -\dfrac{1}{2}\sin\dfrac{\pi}{6} = -\dfrac{1}{4}\right]$ and for $\theta = \dfrac{5\pi}{6}$, $r = -\dfrac{1}{2}$

$\left[\text{again, the line } y = -\dfrac{1}{2}\sin\dfrac{5\pi}{6} = -\dfrac{1}{4}\right]$.

There is a vertical tangent line for $\theta = \dfrac{7\pi}{6}$, $r = -\dfrac{3}{2}$

$\left[\text{the line } x = -\dfrac{3}{2}\cos\dfrac{7\pi}{6} = \dfrac{3\sqrt{3}}{4}\right]$ and for

$\theta = \dfrac{11\pi}{6}$, $r = -\dfrac{3}{2}\left[\text{the line } x = -\dfrac{3}{2}\cos\dfrac{11\pi}{6} = -\dfrac{3\sqrt{3}}{4}\right]$.

For $\theta = \dfrac{\pi}{2}$, $\dfrac{dy}{d\theta} = \dfrac{dx}{d\theta} = 0$, but

$\dfrac{d}{d\theta}\left(\dfrac{dy}{d\theta}\right) = 2\cos 2\theta + \sin\theta = -1$ for $\theta = \dfrac{\pi}{2}$ and

$\dfrac{d}{d\theta}\left(\dfrac{dx}{d\theta}\right) = -4\sin\theta\cos\theta + \cos\theta = 0$ for $\theta = \dfrac{\pi}{2}$, so by

L'Hôpital's rule $\dfrac{dy}{dx}$ is undefined and the tangent line is

vertical at $\theta = \dfrac{\pi}{2}$, $r = 0$ [the line $x = 0$].

This information can be summarized as follows.

Horizontal at: $\left(-\dfrac{1}{2}, \dfrac{\pi}{6}\right)\ \left[y = -\dfrac{1}{4}\right]$,

$\qquad\qquad \left(-\dfrac{1}{2}, \dfrac{5\pi}{6}\right)\ \left[y = -\dfrac{1}{4}\right]$,

$\qquad\qquad \left(-2, \dfrac{3\pi}{2}\right)\ \left[y = 2\right]$

Vertical at: $\quad \left(0, \dfrac{\pi}{2}\right)\ [x = 0]$,

$\qquad\qquad \left(-\dfrac{3}{2}, \dfrac{7\pi}{6}\right)\ \left[x = \dfrac{3\sqrt{3}}{4}\right]$,

$\qquad\qquad \left(-\dfrac{3}{2}, \dfrac{11\pi}{6}\right)\ \left[x = -\dfrac{3\sqrt{3}}{4}\right]$

10. $\dfrac{dy}{d\theta} = -\sin^2\theta + (1 + \cos\theta)\cos\theta$

$\qquad = \cos^2\theta + \cos\theta - \sin^2\theta$

$\qquad = 2\cos^2\theta + \cos\theta - 1$

$\dfrac{dx}{d\theta} = -\sin\theta\cos\theta - (1 + \cos\theta)\sin\theta$

$\qquad = -\sin\theta(1 + 2\cos\theta)$

$\qquad = -\sin 2\theta - \sin\theta$

$\dfrac{dy}{d\theta} = 0$ when $\cos\theta = \dfrac{-1 \pm \sqrt{9}}{4} = -1$ or $\dfrac{1}{2}$, i.e., when

$\theta = \pi, \dfrac{\pi}{3}$ or $\dfrac{5\pi}{3}$. $\dfrac{dx}{d\theta} = 0$ when $\theta = 0, \pi, 2\pi$

(then $\sin\theta = 0$) or when $\theta = \dfrac{2\pi}{3}, \dfrac{4\pi}{3}$

(then $1 + 2\cos\theta = 0$). So there is a horizontal tangent line

for $\theta = \dfrac{\pi}{3}$, $r = \dfrac{3}{2}\left[\text{the line } y = \dfrac{3}{2}\sin\dfrac{\pi}{3} = \dfrac{3\sqrt{3}}{4}\right]$ and for

$\theta = \dfrac{5\pi}{3}$, $r = \dfrac{3}{2}\left[\text{the line } y = \dfrac{3}{2}\sin\dfrac{5\pi}{3} = -\dfrac{3\sqrt{3}}{4}\right]$. There is a

vertical tangent line for $\theta = 0$, $r = 2$

[the line $x = 2\cos 0 = 2$], for $\theta = 2\pi$, $r = 2$ [again, the

line $x = 2\cos 2\pi = 2$], for $\theta = \dfrac{2\pi}{3}$, $r = \dfrac{1}{2}$

[the line $x = \dfrac{1}{2}\cos\dfrac{2\pi}{3} = -\dfrac{1}{4}$] and for $\theta = \dfrac{4\pi}{3}$, $r = \dfrac{1}{2}$

$\left[\text{again, the line } x = \dfrac{1}{2}\cos\dfrac{2\pi}{3} = -\dfrac{1}{4}\right]$.

For $\theta = \pi$, $\dfrac{dy}{d\theta} = \dfrac{dx}{d\theta} = 0$, but

$\dfrac{d}{d\theta}\left(\dfrac{dy}{d\theta}\right) = -4\cos\theta\sin\theta - \sin\theta = 0$ for $\theta = \pi$, and

$\dfrac{d}{d\theta}\left(\dfrac{dx}{d\theta}\right) = -2\cos 2\theta - \cos\theta = -1$ for $\theta = \pi$,

so by L'Hôpital's rule $\dfrac{dy}{dx} = 0$ and the tangent line is hori-

zontal at $\theta = \pi$, $r = 0$ [the line $y = 0$].

This information can be summarized as follows.

Horizontal at: $\left(\dfrac{3}{2}, \dfrac{\pi}{3}\right)\ \left[y = \dfrac{3\sqrt{3}}{4}\right]$,

$\qquad\qquad (0, \pi)\ [y = 0]$,

$\qquad\qquad \left(\dfrac{3}{2}, \dfrac{5\pi}{3}\right)\ \left[y = -\dfrac{3\sqrt{3}}{4}\right]$

Vertical at: $\quad (2, 0)\ [x = 2]$,

$\qquad\qquad \left(\dfrac{1}{2}, \dfrac{2\pi}{3}\right)\ \left[x = -\dfrac{1}{4}\right]$,

$\qquad\qquad \left(\dfrac{1}{2}, \dfrac{4\pi}{3}\right)\ \left[x = -\dfrac{1}{4}\right]$,

$\qquad\qquad (2, 2\pi)\ [x = 2]$

11. $y = 2 \sin^2 \theta$

$\dfrac{dy}{d\theta} = 4 \sin \theta \cos \theta$

$\qquad = 2 \sin 2\theta$

$x = 2 \sin \theta \cos \theta$

$\qquad = \sin 2\theta$

$\dfrac{dy}{d\theta} = 2 \cos 2\theta$

$\dfrac{dy}{d\theta} = 0$ when $\theta = 0, \dfrac{\pi}{2}, \pi$, and $\dfrac{dx}{d\theta} = 0$ when

$\theta = \dfrac{\pi}{4}, \dfrac{3\pi}{4}$. They are never both zero.

For $\theta = 0, \dfrac{\pi}{2}, \pi$ the curve has horizontal asymptotes

at $(0, 0)$ $[y = 0 \sin 0 = 0]$, $\left(2, \dfrac{\pi}{2}\right) \left[y = 2 \sin \dfrac{\pi}{2} = 2\right]$, and

$(0, \pi)$ $[y = 0 \sin \pi = 0]$. For $\theta = \dfrac{\pi}{4}, \dfrac{3\pi}{4}$ the curve has

vertical asymptotes at $\left(\sqrt{2}, \dfrac{\pi}{4}\right)$ $[x = \sqrt{2} \cos \dfrac{\pi}{4} = 1]$ and

$\left(\sqrt{2}, \dfrac{3\pi}{4}\right) \left[x = \sqrt{2} \cos \dfrac{3\pi}{4} = -1\right]$.

This information can be summarized as follows.

Horizontal at: $(0, 0)$ $[y = 0]$,

$\qquad\qquad \left(2, \dfrac{\pi}{2}\right)$ $[y = 2]$,

$\qquad\qquad (0, \pi)$ $[y = 0]$

Vertical at: $\left(\sqrt{2}, \dfrac{\pi}{4}\right)$ $[x = 1]$,

$\qquad\qquad \left(\sqrt{2}, \dfrac{3\pi}{4}\right)$ $[x = -1]$

12. $\dfrac{dy}{d\theta} = 4 \sin^2 \theta + (3 - 4 \cos \theta)\cos \theta$

$\qquad = 4(\sin^2 \theta - \cos^2 \theta) + 3 \cos \theta$

$\qquad = -8 \cos^2 \theta + 3 \cos \theta + 4$

$\dfrac{dx}{d\theta} = 4 \sin \theta \cos \theta - (3 - 4 \cos \theta)\sin \theta$

$\qquad = \sin \theta(8 \cos \theta - 3)$

$\qquad = 4 \sin 2\theta - 3 \sin \theta$

$\dfrac{dy}{d\theta} = 0$ when $\cos \theta = \dfrac{-3 \pm \sqrt{137}}{-16}$, i.e., when

$\theta \approx 0.405, 2.146, 4.137$, or 5.878 (values solved for with a

graphing calculator). $\dfrac{dx}{d\theta} = 0$ when $\theta = 0, \pi$ or 2π

(then $\sin \theta = 0$) or when $\theta = \cos^{-1}\left(\dfrac{3}{8}\right) \approx 1.186$ or

$2\pi - \cos^{-1}\left(\dfrac{3}{8}\right) \approx 5.097$ (then $8 \cos \theta - 3 = 0$). So there

is a horizontal tangent line for $\theta \approx 0.405, r \approx -0.676$

[the line $y \approx -0.676 \sin 0.405 \approx -0.267$], for $\theta \approx 2.146$,

$r \approx 5.176$ [the line $y \approx 5.176 \sin 2.146 \approx 4.343$], for

$\theta \approx 4.137, r \approx 5.176$

[the line $y \approx 5.176 \sin 4.137 \approx -4.343$], and for

$\theta \approx 5.878, r \approx -0.676$

[the line $y \approx -0.676 \sin 5.878 \approx 0.267$]. There is a vertical

tangent for $\theta = 0, r = -1$ [the line $x = -1 \cos 0 = -1$],

for $\theta = \pi, r = 7$ [the line $x = 7 \cos \pi = -7$], for $\theta = 2\pi$,

$r = -1$ [again, the line $x = -1 \cos 2\pi = -1$], for

$\theta = \cos^{-1}\left(\dfrac{3}{8}\right), r = \dfrac{3}{2}$ $\left[\text{the line } x = \dfrac{9}{16}\right]$, and for

$\theta = 2\pi - \cos^{-1}\left(\dfrac{3}{8}\right), r = \dfrac{3}{2}$ $\left[\text{again, the line } x = \dfrac{9}{16}\right]$.

This information can be summarized as follows.

Horizontal at: $(-0.676, 0.405)$ $[y \approx -0.267]$,

$\qquad\qquad (5.176, 2.146)$ $[y \approx 4.343]$,

$\qquad\qquad (5.176, 4.137)$ $[y \approx -4.343]$,

$\qquad\qquad (-0.676, 5.878)$ $[y \approx 0.267]$

Vertical at: $(-1, 0)$ $[x = -1]$,

$\qquad\qquad (1.5, 1.186)$ $\left[x = \dfrac{9}{16}\right]$,

$\qquad\qquad (7, \pi)$ $[x = -7]$,

$\qquad\qquad (1.5, 5.097)$ $\left[x = \dfrac{9}{16}\right]$,

$\qquad\qquad (-1, 2\pi)$ $[x = -1]$

13. The curve is complete for $0 \le \theta \le 2\pi$ (as can be verified by graphing). The area is

$$\int_0^{2\pi} \frac{1}{2}(4 + 2\cos\theta)^2 \, d\theta$$
$$= 2\int_0^{2\pi}(4 + 4\cos\theta + \cos^2\theta) \, d\theta$$
$$= 2\left[4\theta + 4\sin\theta + \frac{1}{2}\theta + \frac{1}{4}\sin 2\theta\right]_0^{2\pi} = 18\pi$$

14. The curve is complete for $0 \le \theta \le 2\pi$ (as can be verified by graphing). The area is

$$\int_0^{2\pi} \frac{1}{2}a^2(1 + \cos\theta)^2 \, d\theta$$
$$= \frac{1}{2}a^2\int_0^{2\pi}(1 + 2\cos\theta + \cos^2\theta) \, d\theta$$
$$= \frac{1}{2}a^2\left[\theta + 2\sin\theta + \frac{1}{2}\theta + \frac{1}{4}\sin 2\theta\right]_0^{2\pi} = \frac{3}{2}\pi a^2$$

15. Use $r = \sqrt{2a^2\cos 2\theta}$. One lobe is complete for $-\frac{\pi}{4} \le \theta \le \frac{\pi}{4}$. The total area is

$$2\int_{-\pi/4}^{\pi/4} \frac{1}{2}(\sqrt{2a^2\cos 2\theta})^2 \, d\theta = 2a^2\int_{-\pi/4}^{\pi/4}\cos 2\theta \, d\theta$$
$$= 2a^2\left[\frac{1}{2}\sin 2\theta\right]_{-\pi/4}^{\pi/4}$$
$$= 2a^2$$

(Integrating from 0 to 2π will not work, because r is not defined over the entire interval.)

16. One leaf covers $-\frac{\pi}{4} \le \theta \le \frac{\pi}{4}$. Its area is

$$\int_{-\pi/4}^{\pi/4} \frac{1}{2}\cos^2 2\theta \, d\theta = \left[\frac{1}{4}\theta + \frac{1}{16}\sin 4\theta\right]_{-\pi/4}^{\pi/4} = \frac{\pi}{8}.$$

17. Use $r = \sqrt{4\sin 2\theta}$. One loop is complete for $0 \le \theta \le \frac{\pi}{2}$.

Its area is $\int_0^{\pi/2} \frac{1}{2}(\sqrt{4\sin 2\theta})^2 \, d\theta = \int_0^{\pi/2} 2\sin 2\theta \, d\theta$
$$= \left[-\cos 2\theta\right]_0^{\pi/2} = 2.$$

18. Use $r = \sqrt{2\sin 3\theta}$. One leaf is complete for $0 \le \theta \le \frac{\pi}{3}$.

The total area is

$$6\int_0^{\pi/3} \frac{1}{2}(\sqrt{2\sin 3\theta})^2 \, d\theta = 6\int_0^{\pi/3} \sin 3\theta \, d\theta$$
$$= 2\left[-\cos 3\theta\right]_0^{\pi/3} = 4.$$

19.

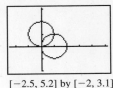

$[-2.5, 5.2]$ by $[-2, 3.1]$

The circles intersect at (x, y) coordinates $(0, 0)$ and $(1, 1)$. The area shared is twice the area inside the circle $r = 2\sin\theta$ between $\theta = 0$ and $\theta = \frac{\pi}{4}$.

$$\text{Shared area} = 2\int_0^{\pi/4} \frac{1}{2}(2\sin\theta)^2 \, d\theta$$
$$= \int_0^{\pi/4} 4\sin^2\theta \, d\theta$$
$$= 4\left[\frac{1}{2}\theta - \frac{1}{4}\sin 2\theta\right]_0^{\pi/4}$$
$$= 4\left(\frac{\pi}{8} - \frac{1}{4}\right) = \frac{\pi}{2} - 1.$$

20.

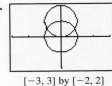

$[-3, 3]$ by $[-2, 2]$

The circles intersect at $\left(1, \frac{\pi}{6}\right)$ and $\left(1, \frac{5\pi}{6}\right)$. The shared area is $2\int_0^{\pi/6} \frac{1}{2}(2\sin\theta)^2 \, d\theta + 2\int_{\pi/6}^{\pi/2} \frac{1}{2}(1)^2 \, d\theta$

$$= 4\int_0^{\pi/6}\sin^2\theta \, d\theta + \int_{\pi/6}^{\pi/2} d\theta$$
$$= 4\left[\frac{1}{2}\theta - \frac{1}{4}\sin 2\theta\right]_0^{\pi/6} + \left[\theta\right]_{\pi/6}^{\pi/2} = \left(\frac{\pi}{3} - \frac{\sqrt{3}}{2}\right) + \frac{\pi}{3}$$
$$= \frac{2\pi}{3} - \frac{\sqrt{3}}{2}$$

21.

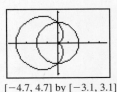

$[-4.7, 4.7]$ by $[-3.1, 3.1]$

The shared area is half the circle plus two lobelike regions:

$$\frac{1}{2}\pi(2)^2 + 2\int_0^{\pi/2} \frac{1}{2}[2(1 - \cos\theta)]^2 \, d\theta$$
$$= 2\pi + \int_0^{\pi/2}(4 - 8\cos\theta + 4\cos^2\theta) \, d\theta$$
$$= 2\pi + 4\left[\theta - 2\sin\theta + \frac{1}{2}\theta + \frac{1}{4}\sin 2\theta\right]_0^{\pi/2}$$
$$= 5\pi - 8$$

22.

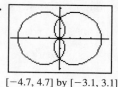

[−4.7, 4.7] by [−3.1, 3.1]

Use the symmetries of the graphs: the shared area is

$$4\int_0^{\pi/2}\frac{1}{2}[2(1-\cos\theta)]^2\,d\theta$$

$$=8\int_0^{\pi/2}(1-2\cos\theta+\cos^2\theta)\,d\theta$$

$$=8\left[\theta-2\sin\theta+\frac{1}{2}\theta+\frac{1}{4}\sin2\theta\right]_0^{\pi/2}=6\pi-16$$

23. For $a=1$:

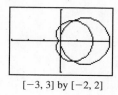

[−3, 3] by [−2, 2]

The curves intersect at the origin and when

$$3a\cos\theta=a(1+\cos\theta)$$

$$2\cos\theta=1$$

$$\theta=\pm\frac{\pi}{3}.$$

Use the symmetries of the curves: the area in question is

$$2\int_0^{\pi/3}\frac{1}{2}[(3a\cos\theta)^2-a^2(1+\cos\theta)^2]\,d\theta$$

$$=a^2\int_0^{\pi/3}(9\cos^2\theta-1-2\cos\theta-\cos^2\theta)\,d\theta$$

$$=a^2\int_0^{\pi/3}(8\cos^2\theta-2\cos\theta-1)\,d\theta$$

$$=a^2\left[4\theta+2\sin2\theta-2\sin\theta-\theta\right]_0^{\pi/3}=a^2\pi$$

24.

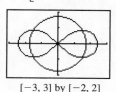

[−3, 3] by [−2, 2]

The curves intersect when

$$6\cos2\theta=3$$

$$\theta=\pm\frac{\pi}{6}\text{ or }\pm\frac{5\pi}{6}.$$

Use the symmetries of the curves. The area in question is

$$4\int_0^{\pi/6}\frac{1}{2}(6\cos2\theta-3)\,d\theta=6\left[\sin2\theta-\theta\right]_0^{\pi/6}=3\sqrt{3}-\pi.$$

25.

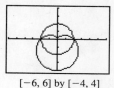

[−6, 6] by [−4, 4]

The area in question is half the circle minus two lobelike regions:

$$\frac{1}{2}\pi(2)^2-2\int_0^{\pi/2}\frac{1}{2}[2(1-\sin\theta)]^2\,d\theta$$

$$=2\pi-\int_0^{\pi/2}(4-8\sin\theta+4\sin^2\theta)\,d\theta$$

$$=2\pi-4\left[\theta+2\cos\theta+\frac{1}{2}\theta-\frac{1}{4}\sin2\theta\right]_0^{\pi/2}=8-\pi$$

26.

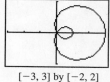

[−3, 3] by [−2, 2]

(a) To find the integration limits, solve

$$2\cos\theta+1=0$$

$$\theta=\pm\frac{2\pi}{3}.$$

Because of the curve's symmetry, the area inside the outer loop is

$$2\int_0^{2\pi/3}\frac{1}{2}(2\cos\theta+1)^2\,d\theta$$

$$=\int_0^{2\pi/3}(4\cos^2\theta+4\cos\theta+1)\,d\theta$$

$$=\left[2\theta+\sin2\theta+4\sin\theta+\theta\right]_0^{2\pi/3}$$

$$=\frac{3\sqrt{3}}{2}+2\pi$$

(b) Again, use the curve's symmetry. The inner loop's area is

$$2\int_{2\pi/3}^{\pi}\frac{1}{2}(2\cos\theta+1)^2\,d\theta$$

$$=\left[2\theta+\sin2\theta+4\sin\theta+\theta\right]_{2\pi/3}^{\pi}=\pi-\frac{3\sqrt{3}}{2}.$$

Subtract this from the answer in (a) to get $3\sqrt{3}+\pi$.

27.

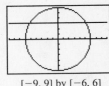

[−9, 9] by [−6, 6]

To find the integration limits, solve

$3 \csc \theta = 6$

$\theta = \dfrac{\pi}{6}, \dfrac{5\pi}{6}$. The area in question is

$\displaystyle\int_{\pi/6}^{5\pi/6} \frac{1}{2}(6^2 - 3^2 \csc^2 \theta)\, d\theta$

$= \dfrac{1}{2}\left[36\theta + 9 \cot \theta\right]_{\pi/6}^{5\pi/6}$

$= 12\pi - 9\sqrt{3}$

28.

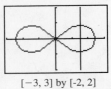

[−3, 3] by [−2, 2]

To find the intersection points, solve

$6 \cos 2\theta = \dfrac{9}{4} \sec^2 \theta$

$48 \cos^4 \theta - 24 \cos^2 \theta - 9 = 0$

$\cos^2 \theta = \dfrac{3}{4}$

$\theta = \pm\dfrac{\pi}{6}$.

By the symmetry of the curves, the area in question is

$2\displaystyle\int_0^{\pi/6} \frac{1}{2}\left(6 \cos 2\theta - \frac{9}{4} \sec^2 \theta\right) d\theta$

$= \left[3 \sin 2\theta - \dfrac{9}{4} \tan \theta\right]_0^{\pi/6} = \dfrac{3\sqrt{3}}{4}$.

29. (a) Find the area of the right half in two parts, then double the result: Right half area

$= \displaystyle\int_0^{\pi/4} \frac{1}{2} \tan^2 \theta\, d\theta + \int_{\pi/4}^{\pi/2} \frac{1}{2}\left(\frac{1}{2} \csc^2 \theta\right) d\theta$

$= \dfrac{1}{2}\left[\tan \theta - \theta\right]_0^{\pi/4} + \dfrac{1}{4}\left[-\cot \theta\right]_{\pi/4}^{\pi/2}$

$= \dfrac{1}{2}\left(1 - \dfrac{\pi}{4}\right) + \dfrac{1}{4}(0 + 1) = \dfrac{3}{4} - \dfrac{\pi}{8}$.

Total area is twice that, or $\dfrac{3}{2} - \dfrac{\pi}{4}$.

(b) Yes. $x = \tan \theta \cos \theta \Rightarrow x = \sin \theta$

$y = \tan \theta \sin \theta \Rightarrow y = \dfrac{\sin^2 \theta}{\cos \theta}$

$\displaystyle\lim_{\theta \to -\pi/2^+} x = -1, \quad \lim_{\theta \to -\pi/2^+} y = \infty$

$\displaystyle\lim_{\theta \to \pi/2^-} x = 1, \quad \lim_{\theta \to \pi/2^-} y = \infty$

30. The integral given is incorrect because $r = \cos \theta$ sweeps out the circle twice as θ goes from 0 to 2π. Or, you can't use equation (2) from the text on the interval $[0, 2\pi]$ because $r = \cos \theta$ is negative for $\dfrac{\pi}{2} < \theta < \dfrac{3\pi}{2}$. The correct area is $\dfrac{5\pi}{4}$, which can be found by computing the areas of the cardioid $\dfrac{3\pi}{2}$ and the circle $\dfrac{\pi}{4}$ separately and subtracting.

31. $\dfrac{dr}{d\theta} = 2\theta$, so

Length $= \displaystyle\int_0^{\sqrt{5}} \sqrt{(\theta^2)^2 + (2\theta)^2}\, d\theta$

$= \displaystyle\int_0^{\sqrt{5}} \theta\sqrt{\theta^2 + 4}\, d\theta$

$= \left[\dfrac{1}{3}(\theta^2 + 4)^{3/2}\right]_0^{\sqrt{5}}$

$= \dfrac{1}{3}(27 - 8) = \dfrac{19}{3}$

32. $\dfrac{dr}{d\theta} = \dfrac{e^\theta}{\sqrt{2}}$, so

Length $= \displaystyle\int_0^\pi \sqrt{\left(\dfrac{e^\theta}{\sqrt{2}}\right)^2 + \left(\dfrac{e^\theta}{\sqrt{2}}\right)^2}\, d\theta$

$= \displaystyle\int_0^\pi e^\theta\, d\theta$

$= \left[e^\theta\right]_0^\pi = e^\pi - 1$

33. $\dfrac{dr}{d\theta} = -\sin \theta$, so

Length $= \displaystyle\int_0^{2\pi} \sqrt{(1 + \cos \theta)^2 + (-\sin \theta)^2}\, d\theta$

$= \displaystyle\int_0^{2\pi} \sqrt{2 + 2 \cos \theta}\, d\theta,$

$= \displaystyle\int_0^{2\pi} \sqrt{2 + 4\cos^2\left(\dfrac{\theta}{2}\right) - 2}\, d\theta$

$= \displaystyle\int_0^{2\pi} 2\left|\cos\left(\dfrac{\theta}{2}\right)\right| d\theta$

$= 4\displaystyle\int_0^\pi \cos\left(\dfrac{\theta}{2}\right) d\theta$

$= 8\left[\sin\left(\dfrac{\theta}{2}\right)\right]_0^\pi = 8$

34. $\dfrac{dr}{d\theta} = a \sin\left(\dfrac{\theta}{2}\right) \cos\left(\dfrac{\theta}{2}\right)$, so

Length $= \displaystyle\int_0^\pi \sqrt{a^2 \sin^4\left(\dfrac{\theta}{2}\right) + a^2 \sin^2\left(\dfrac{\theta}{2}\right) \cos^2\left(\dfrac{\theta}{2}\right)}\, d\theta$

$= a\displaystyle\int_0^\pi \sqrt{\sin^2\left(\dfrac{\theta}{2}\right)}\, d\theta$

$= 2a\left[-\cos\left(\dfrac{\theta}{2}\right)\right]_0^\pi = 2a$

35. $\dfrac{dr}{d\theta} = \dfrac{6 \sin \theta}{(1 + \cos \theta)^2}$, so

Length $= \displaystyle\int_0^{\pi/2} \sqrt{\dfrac{6^2}{(1 + \cos \theta)^2} + \dfrac{6^2 \sin^2 \theta}{(1 + \cos \theta)^4}}\, d\theta$, which using

NINT evaluates to ≈ 6.887.

(Note: the integrand can simplify to $3 \sec^3\left(\dfrac{\theta}{2}\right)$.)

36. $\dfrac{dr}{d\theta} = -\dfrac{2 \sin \theta}{(1 - \cos \theta)^2}$, so

Length $= \displaystyle\int_{\pi/2}^{\pi} \sqrt{\dfrac{2^2}{(1 - \cos \theta)^2} + \dfrac{2^2 \sin^2 \theta}{(1 - \cos \theta)^4}}\, d\theta$, which using

NINT evalutes to ≈ 2.296.

(Note: the integrand can simplify to $\csc^3\left(\dfrac{\theta}{2}\right)$).

37. $\dfrac{dr}{d\theta} = -\cos^2\left(\dfrac{\theta}{3}\right) \sin\left(\dfrac{\theta}{3}\right)$, so

Length $= \displaystyle\int_0^{\pi/4} \sqrt{\cos^6\left(\dfrac{\theta}{3}\right) + \cos^4\left(\dfrac{\theta}{3}\right) \sin^2\left(\dfrac{\theta}{3}\right)}\, d\theta$

$= \displaystyle\int_0^{\pi/4} \sqrt{\cos^4\left(\dfrac{\theta}{3}\right)}\, d\theta$

$= \left[\dfrac{1}{2}\theta + \dfrac{3}{4}\sin\left(\dfrac{2\theta}{3}\right)\right]_0^{\pi/4} = \dfrac{\pi + 3}{8}$.

38. $\dfrac{dr}{d\theta} = \dfrac{\cos 2\theta}{\sqrt{1 + \sin 2\theta}}$, so

Length $= \displaystyle\int_0^{\pi\sqrt{2}} \sqrt{\dfrac{\cos^2 2\theta}{1 + \sin 2\theta} + 1 + \sin 2\theta}\, d\theta$

$= \displaystyle\int_0^{\pi\sqrt{2}} \sqrt{\dfrac{\cos^2 2\theta + (1 + \sin 2\theta)^2}{1 + \sin 2\theta}}\, d\theta$

$= \displaystyle\int_0^{\pi\sqrt{2}} \sqrt{2}\, d\theta = 2\pi$.

39. $\dfrac{dr}{d\theta} = \dfrac{1}{2\sqrt{\cos 2\theta}}(-\sin 2\theta)(2) = -\dfrac{\sin 2\theta}{\sqrt{\cos 2\theta}}$, so

Surface area

$= \displaystyle\int_0^{\pi/4} 2\pi \sqrt{\cos 2\theta}\, \cos \theta \sqrt{(\sqrt{\cos 2\theta})^2 + \left(-\dfrac{\sin 2\theta}{\sqrt{\cos 2\theta}}\right)^2}\, d\theta$

$= 2\pi \displaystyle\int_0^{\pi/4} \cos \theta \sqrt{\cos^2 2\theta + \sin^2 2\theta}\, d\theta$

$= 2\pi \displaystyle\int_0^{\pi/4} \cos \theta\, d\theta$

$= 2\pi \left[\sin \theta\right]_0^{\pi/4} = \pi\sqrt{2} \approx 4.443$.

40. $\dfrac{dr}{d\theta} = \left(\dfrac{\sqrt{2}}{2}\right)e^{\theta/2}$, so surface area

$= \displaystyle\int_0^{\pi/2} 2\pi\sqrt{2}e^{\theta/2} \sin \theta \sqrt{(\sqrt{2}e^{\theta/2})^2 + \left(\dfrac{\sqrt{2}}{2}\right)^2 (e^{\theta/2})^2}\, d\theta$

$= \displaystyle\int_0^{\pi/2} 2\pi e^{\theta} \sin \theta \sqrt{5}\, d\theta$

$= 2\sqrt{5}\pi\left[\dfrac{1}{2}e^{\theta}(\sin \theta - \cos \theta)\right]_0^{\pi/2}$

$= \sqrt{5}\pi(e^{\pi/2} + 1) \approx 40.818$

41.

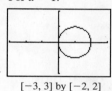

$[-1.5, 1.5]$ by $[-1, 1]$

$2r\dfrac{dr}{d\theta} = -2 \sin 2\theta$

$\dfrac{dr}{d\theta} = \dfrac{-\sin 2\theta}{\sqrt{\cos 2\theta}}$.

Use the curve's symmetry and note that r is defined for

$0 \le \theta \le \dfrac{\pi}{4}$: Surface area

$= 2\displaystyle\int_0^{\pi/4} 2\pi \sqrt{\cos 2\theta} \sin \theta \sqrt{\cos 2\theta + \dfrac{\sin^2 2\theta}{\cos 2\theta}}\, d\theta$

$= 2\displaystyle\int_0^{\pi/4} 2\pi \sin \theta\, d\theta$

$= 4\pi\left[-\cos \theta\right]_0^{\pi/4} = (4 - 2\sqrt{2})\pi \approx 3.681$

42. For $a = 1$:

$[-3, 3]$ by $[-2, 2]$

$\dfrac{dr}{d\theta} = -2a \sin \theta$, so surface area

$= 2\displaystyle\int_0^{\pi/2} 2\pi(2a \cos \theta) \cos \theta \sqrt{4a^2 \cos^2 \theta + 4a^2 \sin^2 \theta}\, d\theta$

$= 16a^2\pi\displaystyle\int_0^{\pi/2} \cos^2 \theta\, d\theta$

$= 16a^2\pi\left[\dfrac{1}{2}\theta + \dfrac{1}{4}\sin 2\theta\right]_0^{\pi/2} = 4a^2\pi^2$

43. $\left(\dfrac{dx}{d\theta}\right)^2 + \left(\dfrac{dy}{d\theta}\right)^2$

$= (f'(\theta) \cos \theta - f(\theta) \sin \theta)^2$

$\qquad + (f'(\theta) \sin \theta + f(\theta) \cos \theta)^2$

$= (f'(\theta) \cos \theta)^2 + (f(\theta) \sin \theta)^2 + (f'(\theta) \sin \theta)^2$

$\qquad + (f(\theta) \cos \theta)^2$

$= (f(\theta))^2(\cos^2 \theta + \sin^2 \theta)$

$\qquad + (f'(\theta))^2(\cos^2 \theta + \sin^2 \theta)$

$= (f(\theta))^2 + (f'(\theta))^2 = r^2 + \left(\dfrac{dr}{d\theta}\right)^2$

44. (a) $\dfrac{1}{2\pi - 0}\displaystyle\int_0^{2\pi} a(1 - \cos \theta)\, d\theta = \dfrac{a}{2\pi}\left[\theta - \sin \theta\right]_0^{2\pi} = a$

(b) $\dfrac{1}{2\pi - 0}\displaystyle\int_0^{2\pi} a\, d\theta = \dfrac{a}{2\pi}\left[\theta\right]_0^{2\pi} = a$

(c) $\dfrac{1}{\pi/2 - (-\pi/2)}\displaystyle\int_{-\pi/2}^{\pi/2} a \cos \theta\, d\theta = \dfrac{a}{\pi}\left[\sin \theta\right]_{-\pi/2}^{\pi/2} = \dfrac{2a}{\pi}$

45. If $g(\theta) = 2f(\theta)$, then
$\sqrt{(g(\theta)^2 + g'(\theta)^2} = 2\sqrt{(f(\theta)^2 + f'(\theta)^2)}$, so the length of
g is 2 times the length of f.

46. If $g(\theta) = 2f(\theta)$, then
$$2\pi\, g(\theta) \sin\theta\, \sqrt{(g(\theta)^2 + g'(\theta)^2)}$$
$$= 4[2\pi f(\theta) \sin\theta\, \sqrt{(f(\theta)^2 + f'(\theta)^2)}],$$
so the area generated by g is 4 times that of f.

47. (a) Let $r = 1.75 + \dfrac{0.06\theta}{2\pi}$.

(b) Since $\dfrac{dr}{d\theta} = \dfrac{b}{2\pi}$, this is just Equation 4 for the

length of the curve.

(c) Using NINT, $\displaystyle\int_0^{80\pi} \sqrt{\left(1.75 + \frac{0.06\theta}{2\pi}\right)^2 + \left(\frac{0.06}{2\pi}\right)^2}\, d\theta$

evaluates to ≈ 741.420 cm ≈ 7.414 m.

(d) $\left(r^2 + \left(\dfrac{b}{2\pi}\right)^2\right)^{1/2} = r\left(1 + \left(\dfrac{b}{2\pi r}\right)^2\right)^{1/2} \approx r$

since $\left(\dfrac{b}{2\pi r}\right)^2$ is a very small quantity squared.

(e) $L \approx 741.420$ cm (from part (c)),

$$L_a = \int_0^{80\pi} \left(1.75 + \frac{0.06\theta}{2\pi}\right) d\theta$$

$$= \left[1.75\theta + \frac{0.03\theta^2}{2\pi}\right]_0^{80\pi} = 236\pi \approx 741.416 \text{ cm}$$

48. (a) Use the approximation, L_a, from 47(e). If the reel has

made n complete turns, then the angle is $2\pi n$. So from

the integral, $L_a = \pi b n^2 + 2\pi r_0 n$. Solving for n gives

$$n = \left(\frac{r_0}{b}\right)\left(\sqrt{\frac{bL}{r_0^2 \pi} + 1} - 1\right).$$

(b) The take up reel slows down as time progresses.

(c) Since L is proportional to time, the formula in part (a)
shows that n will grow roughly as the square root of
time.

49. $\dfrac{2}{3}\displaystyle\int_0^{2\pi} a^3(1 + \cos\theta)^3 \cos\theta\, d\theta$

$$= \frac{2}{3}a^3 \int_0^{2\pi} (\cos\theta + 3\cos^2\theta + 3\cos^3\theta + \cos^4\theta)\, d\theta$$

$$= \frac{2}{3}a^3 \left[3\sin\theta + \frac{15}{8}\sin\theta\cos\theta + \frac{15}{8}\theta + \cos^2\theta\sin\theta\right.$$

$$\left. + \frac{1}{4}\cos^3\theta\sin\theta\right]_0^{2\pi}$$

$$= \frac{5}{2}\pi a^3, \text{ and } \int_0^{2\pi} a^2(1 + \cos\theta)^2\, d\theta$$

$$= a^2 \int_0^{2\pi} (1 + 2\cos\theta + \cos^2\theta)\, d\theta$$

$$= a^2\left[\frac{3}{2}\theta + 2\sin\theta + \frac{1}{4}\sin 2\theta\right]_0^{2\pi} = 3\pi a^2.$$

So $\bar{x} = \dfrac{\frac{5}{2}\pi a^3}{3\pi a^2} = \dfrac{5a}{6}$.

By symmetry, $\bar{y} = 0$, so the centroid is $\left(\dfrac{5a}{6}, 0\right)$.

50. $\dfrac{2}{3}\displaystyle\int_0^{\pi} a^3 \sin\theta\, d\theta = \dfrac{2}{3}a^3\left[-\cos\theta\right]_0^{\pi} = \dfrac{4}{3}a^3$, and

$\displaystyle\int_0^{\pi} a^2\, d\theta = \pi a^2$. So

$$\bar{y} = \frac{\frac{4}{3}a^3}{\pi a^2} = \frac{4a}{3\pi}.$$ By symmetry, $\bar{x} = 0$, so the centroid is

$\left(0, \dfrac{4a}{3\pi}\right)$.

■ Chapter 10 Review Exercises
(pp. 569–572)

1. (a) $3\langle -3, 4\rangle - 4\langle 2, -5\rangle = \langle -9 - 8, 12 + 20\rangle$
$= \langle -17, 32\rangle$

(b) $\sqrt{17^2 + 32^2} = \sqrt{1313}$

2. (a) $\langle -3 + 2, 4 - 5\rangle = \langle -1, -1\rangle$

(b) $\sqrt{1^2 + 1^2} = \sqrt{2}$

3. (a) $\langle -2(-3), -2(4)\rangle = \langle 6, -8\rangle$

(b) $\sqrt{6^2 + 8^2} = 10$

4. (a) $\langle 5(2), 5(-5)\rangle = \langle 10, -25\rangle$

(b) $\sqrt{10^2 + 25^2} = \sqrt{725} = 5\sqrt{29}$

5. $\dfrac{\pi}{6}$ radians below the negative x-axis: $\left\langle -\dfrac{\sqrt{3}}{2}, -\dfrac{1}{2}\right\rangle$

[assuming counterclockwise].

6. $\left\langle \dfrac{\sqrt{3}}{2}, \dfrac{1}{2}\right\rangle$

7. $2\left(\dfrac{1}{\sqrt{4^2 + 1^2}}\right)\langle 4, -1\rangle = \left\langle \dfrac{8}{\sqrt{17}}, -\dfrac{2}{\sqrt{17}}\right\rangle$

8. $-5\left(\dfrac{1}{\sqrt{(3/5)^2 + (4/5)^2}}\right)\left\langle \dfrac{3}{5}, \dfrac{4}{5}\right\rangle = \langle -3, -4\rangle$

9. (a) $\dfrac{dy}{dx} = \dfrac{dy/dt}{dx/dt} = \dfrac{(1/2)\sec t \tan t}{(1/2)\sec^2 t} = \sin t$

For $t = \dfrac{\pi}{3}$; $x = \dfrac{\sqrt{3}}{2}$, $y = 1$, and $\dfrac{dy}{dx} = \dfrac{\sqrt{3}}{2}$. So the

tangent line is $y - 1 = \dfrac{\sqrt{3}}{2}\left(x - \dfrac{\sqrt{3}}{2}\right)$ or

$y = \dfrac{\sqrt{3}}{2}x + \dfrac{1}{4}$.

(b) $\dfrac{d^2y}{dx^2} = \dfrac{dy'}{dx} = \dfrac{dy'/dt}{dx/dt} = \dfrac{\cos t}{(1/2)\sec^2 t} = 2\cos^3 t$,

which for $t = \dfrac{\pi}{3}$ equals $\dfrac{1}{4}$.

10. (a) $\dfrac{dy}{dx} = \dfrac{dy/dt}{dx/dt} = \dfrac{3/t^2}{-2/t^3} = -\dfrac{3}{2}t$

For $t = 2$: $x = \dfrac{5}{4}$, $y = -\dfrac{1}{2}$, and $\dfrac{dy}{dx} = -3$.

So the tangent line is $y + \dfrac{1}{2} = -3\left(x - \dfrac{5}{4}\right)$ or

$y = -3x + \dfrac{13}{4}$.

(b) $\dfrac{d^2y}{dx^2} = \dfrac{dy'}{dx} = \dfrac{dy'/dt}{dx/dt} = \dfrac{-3/2}{-2/t^3} = \dfrac{3t^3}{4}$, which for $t = 2$

equals 6.

11. $\frac{dy}{dt} = \frac{1}{2}\tan t \sec t$ equals zero for $t = k\pi$, where k is any integer. $\frac{dx}{dt} = \frac{1}{2}\sec^2 t$ never equals zero.

(a) Horizontal tangents at $\left(\frac{1}{2}\tan 0, \frac{1}{2}\sec 0\right) = \left(0, \frac{1}{2}\right)$ and $\left(\frac{1}{2}\tan \pi, \frac{1}{2}\sec \pi\right) = \left(0, -\frac{1}{2}\right)$.

(b) There are no vertical tangents, since $\frac{dx}{dt}$ never equals zero.

12. $\frac{dy}{dt} = 2\cos t$ equals zero for $\theta = \frac{k\pi}{2}$, where k is any odd integer. $\frac{dx}{dt} = 2\sin t$ equals zero for $t = k\pi$, where k is any integer.

(a) Horizontal tangents at $\left(-2\cos\frac{\pi}{2}, 2\sin\frac{\pi}{2}\right) = (0, 2)$ and $\left(-2\cos\frac{3\pi}{2}, 2\sin\frac{3\pi}{2}\right) = (0, -2)$.

(b) Vertical tangents at $(-2\cos 0, 2\sin 0) = (-2, 0)$ and $(-2\cos \pi, 2\sin \pi) = (2, 0)$.

13. $\frac{dy}{dt} = -2\sin t \cos t = -\sin 2t$ equals zero for $t = \frac{k\pi}{2}$, where k is any integer. $\frac{dx}{dt} = \sin t$ equals zero for $t = k\pi$, where k is any integer. Where they are both zero, use L'Hôpital's rule:

$$\lim_{t\to k\pi}\frac{dy/dt}{dx/dt} = \lim_{t\to k\pi}\frac{-\sin 2t}{\sin t} = \lim_{t\to k\pi}\frac{-2\cos 2t}{\cos t} = \pm 2.$$

(a) Horizontal tangent at $\left(-\cos\frac{\pi}{2}, \cos^2\frac{\pi}{2}\right) = (0, 0)$.

(b) There are no vertical tangents.

14. $\frac{dy}{dt} = 9\cos t$ equals zero for $t = \frac{k\pi}{2}$, where k is any odd integer. $\frac{dx}{dt} = -4\sin t$ equals zero for $t = k\pi$, where k is any integer.

(a) Horizontal tangents at $\left(4\cos\frac{\pi}{2}, 9\sin\frac{\pi}{2}\right) = (0, 9)$ and $\left(4\cos\frac{3\pi}{2}, 9\sin\frac{3\pi}{2}\right) = (0, -9)$.

(b) Vertical tangents at $(4\cos 0, 9\sin 0) = (4, 0)$ and $(4\cos \pi, 9\sin \pi) = (-4, 0)$.

15.

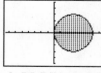

$[-7.5, 7.5]$ by $[-5, 5]$

16.

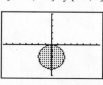

$[-7.5, 7.5]$ by $[-5, 5]$

17. (a)

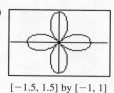

$[-1.5, 1.5]$ by $[-1, 1]$

(b) 2π

18. (a)

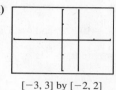

$[-3, 3]$ by $[-2, 2]$

(b) π

19. (a)

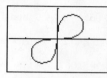

$[-1.5, 1.5]$ by $[-1, 1]$

(b) $\frac{\pi}{2}$

20. (a)

$[-1.5, 1.5]$ by $[-1, 1]$

(b) π

21. $\frac{dy}{dx} = \frac{f'(\theta)\sin\theta + f(\theta)\cos\theta}{f'(\theta)\cos\theta - f(\theta)\sin\theta}$

$= \frac{-2\sin 2\theta\sin\theta + \cos 2\theta\cos\theta}{-2\sin 2\theta\cos\theta - \cos 2\theta\sin\theta}$

$\left(0, \frac{\pi}{4}\right), \left(0, \frac{3\pi}{4}\right), \left(0, \frac{5\pi}{4}\right)$ and $\left(0, \frac{7\pi}{4}\right)$ are polar solutions.

$\frac{dy}{dx}\Big|_{\theta=\pi/4} = \frac{-2/\sqrt{2}}{-2/\sqrt{2}} = 1, \ \frac{dy}{dx}\Big|_{\theta=3\pi/4} = \frac{2/\sqrt{2}}{-2/\sqrt{2}} = -1,$

$\frac{dy}{dx}\Big|_{\theta=5\pi/4} = \frac{2/\sqrt{2}}{2/\sqrt{2}} = 1, \ \frac{dy}{dx}\Big|_{\theta=7\pi/4} = \frac{-2\sqrt{2}}{2\sqrt{2}} = -1.$

The Cartesian equations are $y = \pm x$.

22. $\frac{dy}{dx} = \frac{f'(\theta)\sin\theta + f(\theta)\cos\theta}{f'(\theta)\cos\theta - f(\theta)\sin\theta}$

$= \frac{-2\sin 2\theta\sin\theta + (1 + \cos 2\theta)\cos\theta}{-2\sin 2\theta\cos\theta - (1 + \cos 2\theta)\sin\theta}$

$= \frac{-4\sin^2\theta\cos\theta + \cos\theta + 2\cos^3\theta - \cos\theta}{-4\cos^2\theta\sin\theta - \sin\theta - 2\cos^2\theta\sin\theta + \sin\theta}$

$= \frac{-4\sin^2\theta + 2\cos^2\theta}{-6\cos\theta\sin\theta}$

$= \frac{4\sin^2\theta - 2\cos^2\theta}{3\sin 2\theta}.$

$\left(0, \frac{\pi}{2}\right)$ and $\left(0, \frac{3\pi}{2}\right)$ are polar solutions.

$\frac{dy}{dx}\Big|_{\theta=\pi/2} = \frac{dy}{dx}\Big|_{\theta=3\pi/2} = \frac{4}{0}$ is undefined, so the tangent lines

are vertical with equation $x = 0$.

23. $\dfrac{dy}{d\theta} = \dfrac{d}{d\theta}\left[\left(1 - \cos\left(\dfrac{\theta}{2}\right)\right)\sin\theta\right]$

$\qquad = \dfrac{1}{2}\sin\left(\dfrac{\theta}{2}\right)\sin\theta + \cos\theta - \cos\left(\dfrac{\theta}{2}\right)\cos\theta$

$\dfrac{dx}{d\theta} = \dfrac{d}{d\theta}\left[\left(1 - \cos\left(\dfrac{\theta}{2}\right)\right)\cos\theta\right]$

$\qquad = \dfrac{1}{2}\sin\left(\dfrac{\theta}{2}\right)\cos\theta - \sin\theta + \cos\left(\dfrac{\theta}{2}\right)\sin\theta$

Solve $\dfrac{dy}{d\theta} = 0$ for θ with a graphing calculator: the solutions

are 0, ≈ 2.243, ≈ 4.892, ≈ 7.675, ≈ 10.323, and 4π. Using

the middle four solutions to $y = r\sin\theta$ reveals

horizontal tangent lines at $y \approx \pm 0.443$ and $y \approx \pm 1.739$.

Solve $\dfrac{dx}{d\theta} = 0$ for θ with a graphing calculator: the solutions

are 0, ≈ 1.070, ≈ 3.531, 2π, ≈ 9.035, ≈ 11.497, and 4π.

Using the middle five solutions to find $x = r\cos\theta$ reveals

vertical tangent lines at $x = 2$, $x \approx 0.067$, and $x \approx -1.104$.

Where $\dfrac{dy}{dt}$ and $\dfrac{dx}{dt}$ both equal zero ($\theta = 0, 4\pi$), close

inspection of the plot shows that the tangent lines are

horizontal, with equation $y = 0$. (This can be confirmed

using L'Hôpital's rule.)

24. $\dfrac{dy}{d\theta} = \dfrac{d}{d\theta}[2(1 - \sin\theta)\sin\theta] = -4\sin\theta\cos\theta + 2\cos\theta$

$\dfrac{dx}{d\theta} = \dfrac{d}{d\theta}[2(1 - \sin\theta)\cos\theta]$

$\qquad = -2\cos^2\theta - 2\sin\theta + 2\sin^2\theta$

$\qquad = 4\sin^2\theta - 2\sin\theta - 2$

Solve $\dfrac{dy}{d\theta} = 0$ for θ:

the solutions are $\dfrac{\pi}{6}, \dfrac{\pi}{2}, \dfrac{5\pi}{6},$ and $\dfrac{3\pi}{2}$.

Using the first, third, and fourth solutions to find

$y = r\sin\theta$ reveals horizontal tangent lines at $y = \dfrac{1}{2}$ and

$y = -4$.

Solve $\dfrac{dx}{d\theta} = 0$ for θ (by first using the quadratic formula to

find $\sin\theta$): the solutions are $\dfrac{\pi}{2}, \dfrac{7\pi}{6},$ and $\dfrac{11\pi}{6}$. Using the last

two solutions to find $x = r\cos\theta$ reveals vertical tangent

lines at $x = \pm\dfrac{3\sqrt{3}}{2} \approx \pm 2.598$. Where $\dfrac{dy}{dt}$ and $\dfrac{dx}{dt}$ both equal

zero $\left(\theta = \dfrac{\pi}{2}\right)$, inspection of the plot shows that the tangent

line is vertical, with equation $x = 0$. (This can be confirmed

using L'Hôpital's rule.)

25.

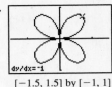

$[-1.5, 1.5]$ by $[-1, 1]$

The tips have Cartesian coordinates $\left(\dfrac{1}{\sqrt{2}}, \dfrac{1}{\sqrt{2}}\right)$,

$\left(-\dfrac{1}{\sqrt{2}}, \dfrac{1}{\sqrt{2}}\right)$, $\left(-\dfrac{1}{\sqrt{2}}, -\dfrac{1}{\sqrt{2}}\right)$, and $\left(\dfrac{1}{\sqrt{2}}, -\dfrac{1}{\sqrt{2}}\right)$. From the

curve's symmetries, it is evident that the tangent lines at

those points have slopes of $-1, 1, -1,$ and 1, respectively.

So the equations of the tangent lines are

$y - \dfrac{1}{\sqrt{2}} = -\left(x - \dfrac{1}{\sqrt{2}}\right)$ or

$y = -x + \sqrt{2}$,

$y - \dfrac{1}{\sqrt{2}} = x + \dfrac{1}{\sqrt{2}}$ or

$y = x + \sqrt{2}$,

$y + \dfrac{1}{\sqrt{2}} = -\left(x + \dfrac{1}{\sqrt{2}}\right)$ or

$y = -x - \sqrt{2}$, and

$y + \dfrac{1}{\sqrt{2}} = x - \dfrac{1}{\sqrt{2}}$ or

$y = x - \sqrt{2}$

26.

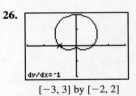

$[-3, 3]$ by $[-2, 2]$

As the plot shows, the curve crosses the x-axis at

(x, y)-coordinates $(-1, 0)$ and $(1, 0)$, with slope -1 and 1,

respectively. (This can be confirmed analytically.) So the

equations of the tangent lines are

$y - 0 = -(x + 1)$

$y = -x - 1$ and

$y - 0 = x - 1$

$y = x - 1$.

27. $r\cos\theta = r\sin\theta$

$\quad x = y$, a line

28. $r = 3\cos\theta$

$\quad r^2 = 3r\cos\theta$

$\quad x^2 + y^2 = 3x$

$\quad x^2 - 3x + \dfrac{9}{4} + y^2 = \dfrac{9}{4}$

$\quad \left(x - \dfrac{3}{2}\right)^2 + y^2 = \left(\dfrac{3}{2}\right)^2$

$\quad$ a circle $\left(\text{center} = \left(\dfrac{3}{2}, 0\right), \text{radius} = \dfrac{3}{2}\right)$

29. $r = 4 \tan \theta \sec \theta$

$$r \cos \theta = 4 \frac{r \sin \theta}{r \cos \theta}$$

$x = 4\frac{y}{x}$ or $x^2 = 4y$, a parabola

30. $r \cos\left(\theta + \frac{\pi}{3}\right) = 2\sqrt{3}$

$$r \cos \theta \cos\left(\frac{\pi}{3}\right) - r \sin \theta \sin\left(\frac{\pi}{3}\right) = 2\sqrt{3}$$

$$\frac{1}{2} r \cos \theta - \frac{\sqrt{3}}{2} r \sin \theta = 2\sqrt{3}$$

$$\frac{1}{2}x - \frac{\sqrt{3}}{2}y = 2\sqrt{3}$$

$x - \sqrt{3}y = 4\sqrt{3}$ or $y = \frac{x}{\sqrt{3}} - 4$, a line

31. $x^2 + y^2 + 5y = 0$
$r^2 + 5r \sin \theta = 0$
$r = -5 \sin \theta$

32. $x^2 + y^2 - 2y = 0$
$r^2 - 2r \sin \theta = 0$
$r = 2 \sin \theta$

33. $x^2 + 4y^2 = 16$

$$(r \cos \theta)^2 + 4(r \sin \theta)^2 = 16$$

$r^2 \cos^2 \theta + 4r^2 \sin^2 \theta = 16$, or $r^2 = \dfrac{16}{\cos^2 \theta + 4 \sin^2 \theta}$

34. $(x + 2)^2 + (y - 5)^2 = 16$
$(r \cos \theta + 2)^2 + (r \sin \theta - 5)^2 = 16$

35. $\dfrac{dx}{dt} = 2e^{2t} - \dfrac{1}{8}, \dfrac{dy}{dt} = e^t$, so

$$\text{Length} = \int_0^{\ln 2} \sqrt{\left(2e^{2t} - \frac{1}{8}\right)^2 + (e^t)^2}\, dt$$

$$= \int_0^{\ln 2} \sqrt{4e^{4t} - \frac{1}{2}e^{2t} + \frac{1}{64} + e^{2t}}\, dt$$

$$= \int_0^{\ln 2} \sqrt{\left(2e^{2t} + \frac{1}{8}\right)^2}\, dt$$

$$= \left[e^{2t} + \frac{t}{8}\right]_0^{\ln 2}$$

$$= 4 + \frac{\ln 2}{8} - 1$$

$$= 3 + \frac{\ln 2}{8} = \frac{\ln 2 + 24}{8} \approx 3.087.$$

36. $\dfrac{dx}{dt} = 2t, \dfrac{dy}{dt} = t^2 - 1$, so

$$\text{Length} = \int_{-\sqrt{3}}^{\sqrt{3}} \sqrt{(2t)^2 + (t^2 - 1)^2}\, dt$$

$$= \int_{-\sqrt{3}}^{\sqrt{3}} \sqrt{4t^2 + t^4 - 2t^2 + 1}\, dt$$

$$= \int_{-\sqrt{3}}^{\sqrt{3}} \sqrt{(t^2 + 1)^2}\, dt$$

$$= \left[\left(\frac{t^3}{3}\right) + t\right]_{-\sqrt{3}}^{\sqrt{3}} = 4\sqrt{3}.$$

37. $\dfrac{dr}{d\theta} = -\sin \theta$, so

$$\text{Length} = \int_0^{2\pi} \sqrt{(-1 + \cos \theta)^2 + (-\sin \theta)^2}\, d\theta$$

$$= \int_0^{2\pi} \sqrt{2 - 2 \cos \theta}\, d\theta$$

$$= \int_0^{2\pi} \sqrt{4 \sin^2 \frac{\theta}{2}}\, d\theta = \left[-4 \cos \frac{\theta}{2}\right]_0^{2\pi} = 8.$$

38. $\dfrac{dr}{d\theta} = 2 \cos \theta - 2 \sin \theta$, so Length

$$= \int_0^{\pi/2} \sqrt{(2 \sin \theta + 2 \cos \theta)^2 + (2 \cos \theta - 2 \sin \theta)^2}\, d\theta$$

$$= \int_0^{\pi/2} \sqrt{8 \sin^2 \theta + 8 \cos^2 \theta}\, d\theta$$

$$= \int_0^{\pi/2} 2\sqrt{2}\, d\theta = \pi\sqrt{2}.$$

39. $\dfrac{dr}{d\theta} = 8 \sin^2\left(\dfrac{\theta}{3}\right) \cos\left(\dfrac{\theta}{3}\right)$, so

$$\text{Length} = \int_0^{\pi/4} \sqrt{\left(8 \sin^3\left(\frac{\theta}{3}\right)\right)^2 + \left(8 \sin^2\left(\frac{\theta}{3}\right) \cos\left(\frac{\theta}{3}\right)\right)^2}\, d\theta$$

$$= \int_0^{\pi/4} 8 \sin^2\left(\frac{\theta}{3}\right) \sqrt{\sin^2\left(\frac{\theta}{3}\right) + \cos^2\left(\frac{\theta}{3}\right)}\, d\theta$$

$$= \int_0^{\pi/4} 8 \sin^2\left(\frac{\theta}{3}\right) d\theta$$

$$= 8\left[\frac{1}{2}\theta - \frac{3}{4} \sin\left(\frac{2\theta}{3}\right)\right]_0^{\pi/4} = \pi - 3$$

40. $\dfrac{dr}{d\theta} = \dfrac{-\sin 2\theta}{\sqrt{1 + \cos 2\theta}}$, so Length

$$= \int_{-\pi/2}^{\pi/2} \sqrt{(\sqrt{1 + \cos 2\theta})^2 + \left(\frac{-\sin 2\theta}{\sqrt{1 + \cos 2\theta}}\right)^2}\, d\theta$$

$$= \int_{-\pi/2}^{\pi/2} \sqrt{\frac{(1 + \cos 2\theta)^2}{1 + \cos 2\theta} + \frac{\sin^2 2\theta}{1 + \cos 2\theta}}\, d\theta$$

$$= \int_{-\pi/2}^{\pi/2} \sqrt{\frac{1 + 2 \cos 2\theta + \cos^2 2\theta + \sin^2 2\theta}{1 + \cos 2\theta}}\, d\theta$$

$$= \int_{-\pi/2}^{\pi/2} \sqrt{2}\, d\theta = \pi\sqrt{2}$$

41. $\dfrac{dx}{dt} = -2 \sin t, \dfrac{dy}{dt} = 2t$, so

$$\text{Length} = \int_0^{\pi/2} \sqrt{(-2 \sin t)^2 + (2t)^2}\, dt$$

$$= \int_0^{\pi/2} 2\sqrt{t^2 + \sin^2 t}\, dt,$$

which using NINT evaluates to ≈ 3.183.

42. $\dfrac{dx}{dt} = 3 \cos t, \dfrac{dy}{dt} = 3\sqrt{t}$, so

$$\text{Length} = \int_0^3 \sqrt{(3 \cos t)^2 + (3\sqrt{t})^2}\, dt = \int_0^3 3\sqrt{t + \cos^2 t}\, dt,$$

which using NINT evaluates to ≈ 12.363.

43. $\text{Area} = \int_0^{2\pi} \dfrac{1}{2}(2 - \cos \theta)^2\, d\theta$

$$= \frac{1}{2}\int_0^{2\pi} (4 - 4 \cos \theta + \cos^2 \theta)\, d\theta$$

$$= \frac{1}{2}\left[4\theta - 4 \sin \theta + \frac{1}{2}\theta + \frac{1}{4} \sin 2\theta\right]_0^{2\pi} = \frac{9\pi}{2}$$

44. Area $= \int_0^{\pi/3} \frac{1}{2} \sin^2 3\theta \; d\theta = \frac{1}{2}\left[\frac{1}{2}\theta - \frac{1}{12}\sin(6\theta)\right]_0^{\pi/3} = \frac{\pi}{12}$

45.

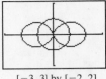

$[-3, 3]$ by $[-2, 2]$

The curves cross where $\cos 2\theta = 0$, such as $\theta = \frac{\pi}{4}$. Using

the curves' symmetry,

$\text{Length} = 4\int_0^{\pi/4} \frac{1}{2}[(1 + \cos 2\theta)^2 - 1] \; d\theta$

$= 2\int_0^{\pi/4} (\cos^2 2\theta + 2\cos 2\theta) \; d\theta$

$= 2\left[\frac{1}{8}\sin 4\theta + \frac{1}{2}\theta + \sin 2\theta\right]_0^{\pi/4}$

$= \frac{\pi}{4} + 2$

46.

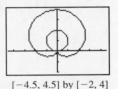

$[-4.5, 4.5]$ by $[-2, 4]$

Since the two curves are covered over different θ-intervals,

find the two areas separately. Then

$\text{Area} = \int_0^{2\pi} \frac{1}{2}[2(1 + \sin \theta)]^2 \; d\theta - \pi r^2$

$= 2\int_0^{2\pi} (1 + 2\sin \theta + \sin^2 \theta) \; d\theta - \pi$

$= 2\left[\theta - 2\cos \theta + \frac{1}{2}\theta - \frac{1}{4}\sin 2\theta\right]_0^{2\pi} - \pi = 5\pi$

47. $\frac{dx}{dt} = t, \frac{dy}{dt} = 2$, so

$\text{Area} = \int_0^{\sqrt{5}} 2\pi(2t)\sqrt{t^2 + 2^2} \; dt$

$= \left[\frac{4\pi}{3}(t^2 + 4)^{3/2}\right]_0^{\sqrt{5}} = \frac{76\pi}{3}$

48. $\frac{dx}{dt} = 2t - \frac{1}{2t^2}, \frac{dy}{dt} = 4$, so

$\text{Area} = \int_{1/\sqrt{2}}^1 2\pi\left(t^2 + \frac{1}{2t}\right)\sqrt{\left(2t - \frac{1}{2t^2}\right)^2 + 4^2} \; dt$,

which using NINT evaluates to ≈ 10.110.

49. $\frac{dr}{d\theta} = \frac{-\sin 2\theta}{\sqrt{\cos 2\theta}}$, so

$\text{Area} = \int_0^{\pi/4} 2\pi \sqrt{\cos 2\theta} \sin \theta \sqrt{\cos 2\theta + \frac{\sin^2 2\theta}{\cos 2\theta}} \; d\theta$

$= \int_0^{\pi/4} 2\pi \sin \theta \; d\theta$

$= 2\pi\left[-\cos \theta\right]_0^{\pi/4} = \pi(2 - \sqrt{2}) \approx 1.840$

50.

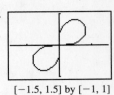

$[-1.5, 1.5]$ by $[-1, 1]$

$r = \pm\sqrt{\sin 2\theta}$ and $\frac{dr}{d\theta} = \pm\frac{\cos 2\theta}{\sqrt{\sin 2\theta}}$, where $0 \le \theta \le \frac{\pi}{2}$, so

$\text{Area} = 2\int_0^{\pi/2} 2\pi \sqrt{\sin 2\theta} \cos \theta \sqrt{\sin 2\theta + \frac{\cos^2 2\theta}{\sin 2\theta}} \; d\theta$

$= 4\pi\int_0^{\pi/2} \cos \theta \; d\theta$

$= 4\pi\left[\sin \theta\right]_0^{\pi/2} = 4\pi$

51. (a) $\mathbf{v}(t) = \frac{d}{dt}[(4\cos t)\mathbf{i} + (\sqrt{2}\sin t)\mathbf{j}]$

$= (-4\sin t)\mathbf{i} + (\sqrt{2}\cos t)\mathbf{j}$

$\mathbf{a}(t) = \frac{d}{dt}[(-4\sin t)\mathbf{i} + (\sqrt{2}\cos t)\mathbf{j}]$

$= (-4\cos t)\mathbf{i} + (-\sqrt{2}\sin t)\mathbf{j}$

(b) $\left|\mathbf{v}\left(\frac{\pi}{4}\right)\right| = \sqrt{\left(-4\sin\frac{\pi}{4}\right)^2 + \left(\sqrt{2}\cos\frac{\pi}{4}\right)^2}$

$= \sqrt{8 + 1} = 3$

(c) At $t = \frac{\pi}{4}$, $\mathbf{v} = -2\sqrt{2}\mathbf{i} + \mathbf{j}$, $\mathbf{a} = -2\sqrt{2}\mathbf{i} - \mathbf{j}$, and

$\theta = \cos^{-1}\frac{\mathbf{v}\cdot\mathbf{a}}{|\mathbf{v}||\mathbf{a}|}$

$= \cos^{-1}\frac{8 - 1}{(3)(3)}$

$= \cos^{-1}\frac{7}{9} \approx 38.94°$.

52. (a) $\mathbf{v}(t) = \frac{d}{dt}[(\sqrt{3}\sec t)\mathbf{i} + (\sqrt{3}\tan t)\mathbf{j}]$

$= (\sqrt{3}\sec t \tan t)\mathbf{i} + (\sqrt{3}\sec^2 t)\mathbf{j}$

$\mathbf{a}(t) = \frac{d}{dt}[(\sqrt{3}\sec t \tan t)\mathbf{i} + (\sqrt{3}\sec^2 t)\mathbf{j}]$

$= \sqrt{3}(\sec t \tan^2 t + \sec^3 t)\mathbf{i} + (2\sqrt{3}\sec^2 t \tan t)\mathbf{j}$

(b) $|\mathbf{v}(0)| = \sqrt{3\sec^2 0 \tan^2 0 + 3\sec^4 0} = \sqrt{0 + 3} = \sqrt{3}$

(c) At $t = 0$, $\mathbf{v} = \sqrt{3}\mathbf{j}$, $\mathbf{a} = \sqrt{3}\mathbf{i}$

$\theta = \cos^{-1}\frac{\mathbf{v}\cdot\mathbf{a}}{|\mathbf{v}||\mathbf{a}|} = \frac{0 + 0}{(\sqrt{3})(\sqrt{3})} = \cos^{-1} 0 = 90°$

53. $\mathbf{v}(t) = -\frac{t}{(1 + t^2)^{3/2}}\mathbf{i} + \frac{1}{(1 + t^2)^{3/2}}\mathbf{j}$

$\left|\frac{d\mathbf{r}}{dt}\right| = |\mathbf{v}(t)| = \sqrt{\left(-\frac{t}{(1 + t^2)^{3/2}}\right)^2 + \left(\frac{1}{(1 + t^2)^{3/2}}\right)^2} = \frac{1}{1 + t^2}$,

which is at a maximum of 1 when $t = 0$.

54. $\mathbf{v}(t) = \dfrac{d\mathbf{r}}{dt} = (e^t \cos t - e^t \sin t)\mathbf{i} + (e^t \sin t + e^t \cos t)\mathbf{j}$

$\quad \mathbf{a}(t) = \dfrac{d\mathbf{x}}{dt} = (e^t \cos t - e^t \sin t - e^t \sin t - e^t \cos t)\mathbf{i}$

$\qquad\qquad + (e^t \sin t + e^t \cos t + e^t \cos t - e^t \sin t)\mathbf{j}$

$\qquad = (-2e^t \sin t)\mathbf{i} + (2e^t \cos t)\mathbf{j}$

$\quad \mathbf{r}(t) \cdot \mathbf{a}(t) = (e^t \cos t)(-2e^t \sin t) + (e^t \sin t)(2e^t \cos t) = 0$

for all t. The angle between $\mathbf{r}$ and $\mathbf{a}$ is always $90°$.

55. $\left(\displaystyle\int_0^1 (3 + 6t)\, dt\right)\mathbf{i} + \left(\displaystyle\int_0^1 6\pi \cos \pi t\, dt\right)\mathbf{j}$

$\quad = \left[3t + 3t^2\right]_0^1 \mathbf{i} + \left[6 \sin \pi t\right]_0^1 \mathbf{j} = 6\mathbf{i}$

56. $\left(\displaystyle\int_e^{e^2} \dfrac{2 \ln t}{t}\, dt\right)\mathbf{i} + \left(\displaystyle\int_e^{e^2} \dfrac{1}{t \ln t}\, dt\right)\mathbf{j}$

$\quad = \left[\ln^2 t\right]_e^{e^2} \mathbf{i} + \left[\ln (\ln t)\right]_e^{e^2} \mathbf{j} = 3\mathbf{i} + (\ln 2)\mathbf{j}$

57. $\mathbf{r}(t) = \displaystyle\int \dfrac{d\mathbf{r}}{dt}\, dt = (\cos t)\mathbf{i} + (\sin t)\mathbf{j} + \mathbf{C}$

$\quad \mathbf{r}(0) = \mathbf{i} + \mathbf{C} = \mathbf{j}$, so $\mathbf{C} = -\mathbf{i} + \mathbf{j}$, and

$\quad \mathbf{r}(t) = (\cos t - 1)\mathbf{i} + (\sin t + 1)\mathbf{j}$

58. $\mathbf{r}(t) = \displaystyle\int \dfrac{d\mathbf{r}}{dt}\, dt = (\tan^{-1} t)\mathbf{i} + \sqrt{t^2 + 1}\,\mathbf{j} + \mathbf{C}$

$\quad \mathbf{r}(0) = \mathbf{j} + \mathbf{C} = \mathbf{i} + \mathbf{j}$, so $\mathbf{C} = \mathbf{i}$ and

$\quad \mathbf{r}(t) = (\tan^{-1} t + 1)\mathbf{i} + \sqrt{t^2 + 1}\,\mathbf{j}$

59. $\dfrac{d\mathbf{r}}{dt} = \displaystyle\int \dfrac{d^2\mathbf{r}}{dt^2}\, dt = 2t\mathbf{j} + \mathbf{C}_1$, $\mathbf{r}(t) = \displaystyle\int \dfrac{d\mathbf{r}}{dt}\, dt = t^2\mathbf{j} + \mathbf{C}_1 t + \mathbf{C}_2$

$\quad \dfrac{d\mathbf{r}}{dt}\bigg|_{t=0} = \mathbf{C}_1 = \mathbf{0}$, so $\mathbf{r}(t) = t^2\mathbf{j} + \mathbf{C}_2$. And $\mathbf{r}(0) = \mathbf{C}_2 = \mathbf{i}$, so

$\quad \mathbf{r}(t) = \mathbf{i} + t^2\mathbf{j}$

60. $\dfrac{d\mathbf{r}}{dt} = \displaystyle\int \dfrac{d^2\mathbf{r}}{dt^2}\, dt = (-2t)\mathbf{i} + (-2t)\mathbf{j} + \mathbf{C}_1$,

$\quad \mathbf{r}(t) = \displaystyle\int \dfrac{d\mathbf{r}}{dt}\, dt = -t^2\mathbf{i} - t^2\mathbf{j} + \mathbf{C}_1 t + \mathbf{C}_2$

$\quad \dfrac{d\mathbf{r}}{dt}\bigg|_{t=1} = -2\mathbf{i} - 2\mathbf{j} + \mathbf{C}_1 = 4\mathbf{i}$, so $\mathbf{C}_1 = 6\mathbf{i} + 2\mathbf{j}$ and

$\quad \mathbf{r}(t) = (-t^2 + 6t)\mathbf{i} + (-t^2 + 2t)\mathbf{j} + \mathbf{C}_2$

$\quad \mathbf{r}(1) = 5\mathbf{i} + \mathbf{j} + \mathbf{C}_2 = 3\mathbf{i} + 3\mathbf{j}$, so $\mathbf{C}_2 = -2\mathbf{i} + 2\mathbf{j}$, and

$\quad \mathbf{r}(t) = (-t^2 + 6t - 2)\mathbf{i} + (-t^2 + 2t + 2)\mathbf{j}$

61. (a) $\mathbf{v}(t) = \left\langle \dfrac{dx}{dt}, \dfrac{dy}{dt} \right\rangle = \left\langle -\dfrac{3\pi}{4} \sin \dfrac{\pi}{4}t, \dfrac{5\pi}{4} \cos \dfrac{\pi}{4}t \right\rangle$,

$\quad \mathbf{v}(3) = \left\langle -\dfrac{3\pi}{4\sqrt{2}}, -\dfrac{5\pi}{4\sqrt{2}} \right\rangle$, and

$\quad |\mathbf{v}(3)| = \sqrt{\dfrac{9\pi^2}{32} + \dfrac{25\pi^2}{32}} = \dfrac{\pi\sqrt{34}}{4\sqrt{2}} = \dfrac{\pi\sqrt{17}}{4} \approx 3.238$

(b) x-component: $\dfrac{d^2x}{dt^2}\bigg|_{t=3} = -\dfrac{3\pi^2}{16} \cos\left(\dfrac{\pi}{4} \cdot 3\right) = \dfrac{3\pi^2}{16\sqrt{2}}$

$\quad y$-component: $\dfrac{d^2y}{dt^2}\bigg|_{t=3} = \dfrac{-5\pi^2}{16} \sin\left(\dfrac{\pi}{4} \cdot 3\right) = -\dfrac{5\pi^2}{16\sqrt{2}}$

(c) $\dfrac{x}{3} = \cos \dfrac{\pi}{4}t$ and $\dfrac{y}{5} = \sin \dfrac{\pi}{4}t$, so $\left(\dfrac{x}{3}\right)^2 + \left(\dfrac{y}{5}\right)^2 = 1$ or $\dfrac{x^2}{9} + \dfrac{y^2}{25} = 1$.

62. (a) $\dfrac{dx}{dt} = \dfrac{1}{2}$ and $\dfrac{dy}{dt} = 5 - t$ so

$\quad \text{Length} = \displaystyle\int_0^{10} \sqrt{\left(\dfrac{1}{2}\right)^2 + (5 - t)^2}\, dt$, which using NINT

evaluates to ≈ 25.874.

(b) $\text{Volume} = \displaystyle\int_0^{10} \pi y^2 \dfrac{dx}{dt}\, dt$

$\quad = \dfrac{\pi}{2} \displaystyle\int_0^{10} \left(\dfrac{t(10 - t)}{2}\right)^2 dt$

$\quad = \dfrac{\pi}{8} \displaystyle\int_0^{10} (100t^2 - 20t^3 + t^4)\, dt$

$\quad = \dfrac{\pi}{8}\left[\dfrac{100}{3}t^3 - 5t^4 + \dfrac{1}{5}t^5\right]_0^{10} = \dfrac{1250\pi}{3}$

(c) $\text{Area} = \displaystyle\int_0^{10} 2\pi \dfrac{t(10 - t)}{2} \sqrt{\left(\dfrac{1}{2}\right)^2 + (5 - t)^2}\, dt$, which

using NINT evaluates to ≈ 1040.728.

63. (a) $\dfrac{dy}{dx} = \dfrac{dy/dt}{dx/dt} = \dfrac{e^t \sin t + e^t \cos t}{e^t \cos t - e^t \sin t} = \dfrac{\cos t + \sin t}{\cos t - \sin t}$

$\quad \dfrac{dy}{dx}\bigg|_{t=\pi} = \dfrac{-1}{-1} = 1$

(b) $\dfrac{dy}{dt} = e^t(\sin t + \cos t)$, $\dfrac{dx}{dt} = e^t(\cos t - \sin t)$

$\quad \left(\dfrac{dy}{dt}\right)^2 = e^{2t}(\sin^2 t + 2 \sin t \cos t + \cos^2 t)$

$\qquad = e^{2t}(1 + 2 \sin t \cos t)$

$\quad \left(\dfrac{dx}{dt}\right)^2 = e^{2t}(\cos^2 t - 2 \cos t \sin t + \sin^2 t)$

$\qquad = e^2(1 - 2 \cos t \sin t)$

$\quad |\mathbf{v}(t)| = e^t\sqrt{2}$

$\quad |\mathbf{v}(3)| = e^3\sqrt{2}$

(c) $\text{Distance} = \displaystyle\int_0^3 |\mathbf{v}(t)|\, dt$

$\quad = \displaystyle\int_0^3 e^t\sqrt{2}$

$\quad = \sqrt{2}\left[e^t\right]_0^3$

$\quad = (e^3 - 1)\sqrt{2}$

64. (a) $\mathbf{v}(t) = \left\langle \dfrac{dx}{dt}, \dfrac{dy}{dt} \right\rangle = \left\langle 2t, \dfrac{6}{5}t^2 \right\rangle$, $\mathbf{v}(4) = \left\langle 8, \dfrac{96}{5} \right\rangle$, and

$$|\mathbf{v}(4)| = \sqrt{8^2 + \left(\frac{96}{5} \right)^2} = \frac{104}{5}$$

(b) Distance $= \displaystyle\int_0^4 \sqrt{(2t)^2 + \left(\frac{6}{5}t^2 \right)^2}\, dt$

$$= \int_0^4 \frac{2}{5}t\sqrt{25 + 9t^2}\, dt$$

$$= \left[\frac{2}{135}(25 + 9t^2)^{3/2} \right]_0^4 = \frac{4144}{135}$$

(c) $t = \sqrt{x + 2}$, so $\dfrac{dy}{dx} = \dfrac{dy/dt}{dx/dt} = \dfrac{6t^2/5}{2t} = \dfrac{3}{5}t = \dfrac{3}{5}\sqrt{x + 2}$

65. x degrees east of north is $(90 - x)$ degrees north of east.

Add the vectors:

$\langle 540\cos 10°, 540\sin 10° \rangle + \langle 55\cos(-10°), 55\sin(-10°) \rangle$

$= \langle 595\cos 10°, 485\sin 10° \rangle$

$\approx \langle 585.961, 84.219 \rangle.$

Speed $\approx \sqrt{585.961^2 + 84.219^2} \approx 591.982$ mph.

Direction $\approx \tan^{-1}\left(\dfrac{585.961}{84.219} \right) \approx 81.821°$ east of north

66. Add the vectors:

$\langle 120\cos 20°, 120\sin 20° \rangle + \langle 300\cos(-5°), 300\sin(-5°) \rangle$

$\approx \langle 411.622, 14.896 \rangle.$

Direction $\approx \tan^{-1}\left(\dfrac{14.896}{411.622} \right) \approx 2.073°$

Length $\approx \sqrt{411.622^2 + 14.896^2} \approx 411.891$ lbs

67. Taking the launch point as the origin,
$y = (44\sin 45°)t - 16t^2$ equals -6.5 when $t \approx 2.135$ sec (as can be determined graphically or using the quadratic formula). Then $x \approx (44\cos 45°)(2.135) \approx 66.421$ horizontal feet from where it left the thrower's hand. Assuming it doesn't bounce or roll, it will still be there 3 seconds after it was thrown.

68. $y_{\max} = \dfrac{(80\sin 45°)^2}{2(32)} + 7 = 57$ feet

69. (a)

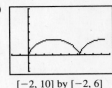

$[-2, 10]$ by $[-2, 6]$

(b) $\mathbf{v}(t) = \left\langle \dfrac{dx}{dt}, \dfrac{dy}{dt} \right\rangle = \langle \pi - \pi\cos\pi t, \pi\sin\pi t \rangle$

$\mathbf{a}(t) = \left\langle \dfrac{d^2x}{dt^2}, \dfrac{d^2y}{dt^2} \right\rangle = \langle \pi^2\sin\pi t, \pi^2\cos\pi t \rangle$

$\mathbf{v}(0) = \langle 0, 0 \rangle$	$\mathbf{v}(1) = \langle 2\pi, 0 \rangle$
$\mathbf{a}(0) = \langle 0, \pi^2 \rangle$	$\mathbf{a}(1) = \langle 0, -\pi^2 \rangle$
$\mathbf{v}(2) = \langle 0, 0 \rangle$	$\mathbf{v}(3) = \langle 2\pi, 0 \rangle$
$\mathbf{a}(2) = \langle 0, \pi^2 \rangle$	$\mathbf{a}(3) = \langle 0, -\pi^2 \rangle$

(c) Topmost point: 2π ft/sec
center of wheel: π ft/sec
Reasons: Since the wheel rolls half a circumference, or π feet every second, the center of the wheel will move π feet every second. Since the rim of the wheel is turning at a rate of π ft/sec about the center, the velocity of the topmost point relative to the center is π ft/sec, giving it a total velocity of 2π ft/sec.

70. $v_0 = \sqrt{\dfrac{Rg}{\sin 2\alpha}}$, where $\alpha = 45°$, $g = 32$, and

$R = $ range

for 4325 yds $= 12{,}975$ ft: $v_0 \approx 644.360$ ft/sec

for 4752 yds $= 14{,}256$ ft: $v_0 \approx 675.420$ ft/sec

71. (a) $v_0 = \sqrt{\dfrac{Rg}{\sin 2\alpha}} = \sqrt{(109.5)(32)} \approx 59.195$ ft/sec

(b) The cork lands at $y = -4$, $x = 177.75$.

Solve $y = -\left(\dfrac{g}{2v_0^2\cos^2\alpha} \right)x^2 + (\tan\alpha)x$ for v_0, with

$\alpha = 45°$: $v_0 = \sqrt{-\dfrac{gx^2}{y - x}} \approx 74.584$ ft/sec

72. (a) The javelin lands at $y = -6.5$, $x = 262\dfrac{5}{12}$.

Solve $y = -\left(\dfrac{g}{2v_0^2\cos^2\alpha} \right)x^2 + (\tan\alpha)x$ for v_0, with

$\alpha = 40°$:

$v_0 = \sqrt{-\dfrac{gx^2}{(2\cos^2 40°)(y - x\tan 40°)}} \approx 91.008$ ft/sec

(b) $y_{\max} = \dfrac{(v_0\sin\alpha)^2}{2g} + 6.5$

$\approx \dfrac{(91.008\sin 40°)^2}{64} + 6.5 \approx 59.970$ ft

73. We have $x = (v_0 t)\cos\alpha$ and

$y + \dfrac{gt^2}{2} = (v_0 t)\sin\alpha$. Squaring and adding gives

$x^2 + \left(y + \dfrac{gt^2}{2} \right)^2 = (v_0 t)^2(\cos^2\alpha + \sin^2\alpha) = v_0^2 t^2.$

74. (a) $\mathbf{r}(t) = (155 \cos 18° - 11.7)t\mathbf{i}$
$\qquad\qquad + (4 + 155 \sin 18°t - 16t^2)\mathbf{j}$
$\qquad x(t) = (155 \cos 18° - 11.7)t$
$\qquad y(t) = 4 + 155 \sin 18°t - 16t^2$

(b) $y_{max} = \dfrac{(155 \sin 18°)^2}{2(32)} + 4 \approx 39.847$ feet, reached at

$\qquad t_{max} = \dfrac{155 \sin 18°}{32} \approx 1.497$ sec

(c) $y(t) = 0$ when $t \approx 3.075$ sec (found using the quadratic formula), and then
$\qquad x \approx (155 \cos 18° - 11.7)(3.075) \approx 417.307$ ft.

(d) Solve $y(t) = 25$ using the quadratic formula:
$\qquad t = \dfrac{-155 \sin 18° \pm \sqrt{155^2 \sin^2 18° - 4(16)(21)}}{-32}$
$\qquad \approx 0.534$ and 2.460 seconds.

$\qquad$ At those times, $x = (155 \cos 18° - 11.7)t$ equals
$\qquad \approx 72.406$ and ≈ 333.867 feet from home plate.

(e) Yes, the batter has hit a home run. When the ball is 380 feet from home plate (at $t \approx 2.800$ seconds), it is approximately 12.673 feet off the ground and therefore clears the fence by at least two feet.

75. (a) $\mathbf{r}(t) = \left[(155 \cos 18° - 11.7)\dfrac{1}{0.09}(1 - e^{-0.09t}) \right]\mathbf{i}$
$\qquad + \left[4 + \left(\dfrac{155 \sin 18°}{0.09} \right)(1 - e^{-0.09t}) \right.$
$\qquad \left. + \dfrac{32}{0.09^2}(1 - 0.09t - e^{-0.09t}) \right]\mathbf{j}$
$\qquad x(t) = (155 \cos 18° - 11.7)\dfrac{1}{0.09}(1 - e^{-0.09t})$
$\qquad y(t) = 4 + \left(\dfrac{155 \sin 18°}{0.09} \right)(1 - e^{-0.09t})$
$\qquad + \dfrac{32}{0.09^2}(1 - 0.09t - e^{-0.09t})$

(b) Plot $y(t)$ and use the maximum function to find $y \approx 36.921$ feet at $t \approx 1.404$ seconds.

(c) Plot $y(t)$ and find that $y(t) = 0$ at $t \approx 2.959$, then plug this into the expression for $x(t)$ to find $x(2.959) \approx 352.520$ ft.

(d) Plot $y(t)$ and find that $y(t) = 30$ at $t \approx 0.753$ and 2.068 seconds. At those times, $x \approx 98.799$ and 256.138 feet (from home plate).

(e) No, the batter has not hit a home run. If the drag coefficient k is less than ≈ 0.011, the hit will be a home run.
(This result can be found by trying different k-values until the parametrically plotted curve has $y \geq 10$ for $x = 380$.)

76. (a) $\overrightarrow{BD} = \overrightarrow{AD} - \overrightarrow{AB}$

(b) $\overrightarrow{AP} = \overrightarrow{AB} + \dfrac{1}{2}\overrightarrow{BD} = \dfrac{1}{2}\overrightarrow{AB} + \dfrac{1}{2}\overrightarrow{AD}$

(c) $\overrightarrow{AC} = \overrightarrow{AB} + \overrightarrow{AD}$, so by part (b), $\overrightarrow{AP} = \dfrac{1}{2}\overrightarrow{AC}$.

77. The widths between the successive turns are constant and are given by $2\pi a$.

Cumulative Review Exercises
(pp. 573–576)

1. Since the function has no discontinuity at $x = 1$, the limit is
$\dfrac{2(1)^2 - 1 - 1}{1^2 + 1 - 12} = 0.$

2. By l'Hôpital's Rule, $\lim\limits_{x \to 0} \dfrac{\sin 3x}{4x} = \lim\limits_{x \to 0} \dfrac{3 \cos 3x}{4} = \dfrac{3}{4}.$

3. By l'Hôpital's Rule, $\lim\limits_{x \to 0} \dfrac{\frac{1}{x+1} - 1}{x} = \lim\limits_{x \to 0} \dfrac{-\frac{1}{(x+1)^2}}{1} = -1.$

4. By l'Hôpital's Rule, $\lim\limits_{x \to \infty} \dfrac{x + e^x}{x - e^x} = \lim\limits_{x \to \infty} \dfrac{1 + e^x}{1 - e^x}$
$= \lim\limits_{x \to \infty} \dfrac{e^x}{-e^x} = -1.$

5. By l'Hôpital's Rule, $\lim\limits_{t \to 0} \dfrac{t(1 - \cos t)}{t - \sin t}$
$= \lim\limits_{t \to 0} \dfrac{t \sin t + (1 - \cos t)}{1 - \cos t} = \lim\limits_{t \to 0} \dfrac{t \cos t + 2 \sin t}{\sin t}$
$= \lim\limits_{t \to 0} \dfrac{-t \sin t + 3 \cos t}{\cos t} = 3$

6. By l'Hôpital's Rule, $\lim\limits_{x \to 0^+} \dfrac{\ln (e^x - 1)}{\ln x} = \lim\limits_{x \to 0^+} \dfrac{\frac{e^x}{(e^x - 1)}}{\frac{1}{x}}$
$= \lim\limits_{x \to 0^+} \dfrac{xe^x}{e^x - 1} = \lim\limits_{x \to 0^+} \dfrac{xe^x + e^x}{e^x} = 1$

7. Use $f(x) = (e^x + x)^{1/x}$. Then $\ln f(x) = \dfrac{\ln (e^x + x)}{x}$, and
$\lim\limits_{x \to 0} \dfrac{\ln (e^x + x)}{x} = \lim\limits_{x \to 0} \dfrac{(e^x + 1)/(e^x + x)}{1} = 2.$
So $\lim\limits_{x \to 0} (e^x + x)^{1/x} = \lim\limits_{x \to 0} e^{\ln f(x)} = e^2.$

8. $\lim\limits_{x \to 0} \left(\dfrac{3x + 1}{x} - \dfrac{1}{\sin x} \right) = \lim\limits_{x \to 0} \dfrac{(3x + 1) \sin x - x}{x \sin x}$
$= \lim\limits_{x \to 0} \dfrac{(3x + 1) \cos x + 3 \sin x - 1}{x \cos x + \sin x}$
$= \lim\limits_{x \to 0} \dfrac{-(3x + 1) \sin x + 6 \cos x}{-x \sin x + 2 \cos x} = 3$

9. (a) $2(1) - 1^2 = 1$

(b) $2 - 1 = 1$

(c) 1 [from (a) and (b)]

(d) Yes, since $\lim_{x \to 1} f(x) = f(1) = 1$

(e) No.
Left-hand derivative:

$$\lim_{h \to 0^-} \frac{f(1+h) - f(1)}{h} = \lim_{h \to 0^-} \frac{2(1+h) - (1+h)^2 - 1}{h}$$
$$= \lim_{h \to 0^-} \frac{2 + 2h - 1 - 2h - h^2 - 1}{h}$$
$$= \lim_{h \to 0^-} -\frac{h^2}{h}$$
$$= \lim_{h \to 0^-} -h = 0$$

Right-hand derivative:

$$\lim_{h \to 0^+} \frac{f(1+h) - f(1)}{h} = \lim_{h \to 0^+} \frac{2 - (1+h) - 1}{h}$$
$$= \lim_{h \to 0^+} \frac{-h}{h} = -1$$

Since the left- and right-hand derivatives are not equal, f is not differentiable at $x = 1$.

10. Solve $4 - x^2 \leq 0$: all $x \leq -2$ and $x \geq 2$.

11. Horizontal: since as $x \to \pm\infty$, $2x^2 - x \to +\infty$ while $-1 \leq \cos x \leq 1$, the end behavior at both ends is $y = 0$.
Vertical: solve $2x^2 - x = 0$ to find $x = 0$, $x = \frac{1}{2}$.

12. One possible function is $y = \begin{cases} -3 + \dfrac{1}{(2-x)}, & x < 2 \\ 3 - \dfrac{8}{x}, & x \geq 2 \end{cases}$

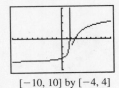

$[-10, 10]$ by $[-4, 4]$

13. $\dfrac{f(5) - f(0)}{5 - 0} = \dfrac{\sqrt{9} - \sqrt{4}}{5} = \dfrac{1}{5}$

14. $y' = \dfrac{(x-2)(1) - (x+1)(1)}{(x-2)^2} = -\dfrac{3}{(x-2)^2}$

15. $y' = -\sin(\sqrt{1-3x}) \left[\dfrac{1}{2}(1-3x)^{-1/2} \right](-3)$

$$= \dfrac{3 \sin \sqrt{1-3x}}{2\sqrt{1-3x}}$$

16. $y' = \sin x \sec^2 x + \tan x \cos x = \dfrac{\sin x}{\cos^2 x} + \sin x$

$$= \dfrac{(\sin x)(1 + \cos^2 x)}{\cos^2 x}$$

17. $y' = \left(\dfrac{1}{x^2 + 1} \right)(2x) = \dfrac{2x}{x^2 + 1}$

18. $y' = (e^{x^2 - x})(2x - 1) = (2x - 1)e^{x^2 - x}$

19. $y' = 2x \tan^{-1} x + \dfrac{x^2}{1 + x^2}$

20. $y' = -3x^{-4}e^x + e^x x^{-3} = (x^{-3} - 3x^{-4})e^x$

21. $y' = 3\left(\dfrac{\csc x}{1 + \cos x} \right)^2 \left(\dfrac{(1 + \cos x)(-\csc x \cot x) + \csc x \sin x}{(1 + \cos x)^2} \right)$

$$= \dfrac{3 \csc^2 x}{(1 + \cos x)^4} (1 - \csc x \cot x - \cos x \csc x \cot x)$$
$$= \dfrac{3 \csc^2 x}{(1 + \cos x)^4} (1 - \cot x \csc x - \cot^2 x)$$
$$= \dfrac{3 \csc^2 x}{(1 + \cos x)^4} (1 - \csc^2 x + \csc^2 x - \cot x \csc x - \cot^2 x)$$
$$= \dfrac{3 \csc^2 x}{(1 + \cos x)^4} (\csc^2 x - \cot x \csc x - 2 \cot^2 x)$$
$$= \left(\dfrac{3}{(\sin^2 x)(1 + \cos x)^4} \right) \left(\dfrac{1 - \cos x - 2 \cos^2 x}{\sin^2 x} \right)$$
$$= \left(\dfrac{3}{(\sin^2 x)(1 + \cos x)^4} \right) \left(\dfrac{(1 + \cos x)(1 - 2 \cos x)}{\sin^2 x} \right)$$
$$= \dfrac{3(1 - 2 \cos x)}{(\sin^4 x)(1 + \cos x)^3}$$

22. $y' = \dfrac{d}{dx}\left(\dfrac{\pi}{2} - \sin^{-1} x \right) - \dfrac{d}{dx}\left(\dfrac{\pi}{2} - \tan^{-1} x \right)$

$$= -\dfrac{1}{\sqrt{1 - x^2}} + \dfrac{1}{1 + x^2}$$

23. $\dfrac{d}{dx}[\cos(xy) + y^2 - \ln x] = \dfrac{d}{dx}(0)$

$$-\sin(xy)(xy' + y) + 2yy' - \dfrac{1}{x} = 0$$
$$y' = \dfrac{\dfrac{1}{x} + y \sin(xy)}{-x \sin(xy) + 2y} = \dfrac{1 + xy \sin(xy)}{2xy - x^2 \sin(xy)}$$

24. $y' = \dfrac{1}{2}|x|^{-1/2} \dfrac{d}{dx}|x| = \dfrac{1}{2\sqrt{|x|}}\left(\dfrac{|x|}{x} \right) = \dfrac{|x|}{2x\sqrt{|x|}}$

25. $\dfrac{dy}{dx} = \dfrac{dy/dt}{dx/dt} = \dfrac{-\cos t}{-\sin t} = \cot t = \dfrac{x - 1}{1 - y}$

26. $\ln y = \ln[(\cos x)^x]$

$\ln y = x \ln(\cos x)$

$\dfrac{1}{y}\dfrac{dy}{dx} = x\left(\dfrac{1}{\cos x} \right)(-\sin x) + \ln \cos x$

$\dfrac{dy}{dx} = y \cdot \left(\ln(\cos x) - \dfrac{x \sin x}{\cos x} \right)$

$= (\cos x)^x\left(\ln(\cos x) - \dfrac{x \sin x}{\cos x} \right)$

$= (\cos x)^{x-1} [\cos x \ln(\cos x) - x \sin x]$

27. By the Fundamental theorem of Calculus,
$y' = \sqrt{1 + x^3}$.

28. $y = \left[-\cos t \right]_{2x}^{x^2} = -\cos(x^2) + \cos(2x)$;

$y' = 2x \sin(x^2) - 2 \sin(2x)$

29. $\dfrac{d}{dx}(y^2 + 2y) = \dfrac{d}{dx}(\sec x)$

$2yy' + 2y' = \sec x \tan x,$

$y' = \dfrac{\sec x \tan x}{2y + 2},$

$y'' = \dfrac{(2y + 2)(\sec^3 x + \sec x \tan^2 x) - 2y' \sec x \tan x}{(2y + 2)^2}$

$\quad = \dfrac{(2y + 2)^2(\sec^3 x + \sec x \tan^2 x) - 2 \sec^2 x \tan^2 x}{(2y + 2)^3}$

30. $\left.\dfrac{(1 + v)u' - uv'}{(1 + v)^2}\right|_{x=0} = \dfrac{(1 - 3)(-1) - (2)(3)}{(1 - 3)^2} = -1$

31. **(a)** $v = \dfrac{dx}{dt} = 3t^2 - 12t + 9$

$\quad a = \dfrac{dv}{dt} = 6t - 12$

(b) Solve $v = 0$ for t: $3(t - 1)(t - 3) = 0$; $t = 1$ or $t = 3.$

(c) Right: $v > 0$ for $0 \le t < 1$, $3 < t \le 5$
left: $v < 0$ for $1 < t < 3$

(d) $a = 0$ at $t = 2$, and at that instant
$v = 3(2)^2 - 12(2) + 9 = -3$ m/sec

32. For $x = 1$, $y = -1$ and

$\dfrac{dy}{dx} = 6(1)^2 - 12(1) + 4 = -2$

(a) $y + 1 = -2(x - 1)$ or $y = -2x + 1$

(b) $y + 1 = \dfrac{1}{2}(x - 1)$ or $y = \dfrac{1}{2}x - \dfrac{3}{2}$

33. For $x = \dfrac{\pi}{3}$, $y = \dfrac{\pi}{3} \cos \dfrac{\pi}{3} = \dfrac{\pi}{6}$ and

$\dfrac{dy}{dx} = -\dfrac{\pi}{3} \sin \dfrac{\pi}{3} + \cos \dfrac{\pi}{3} = -\dfrac{\pi\sqrt{3}}{6} + \dfrac{1}{2} = \dfrac{3 - \pi\sqrt{3}}{6}.$

(a) $y - \dfrac{\pi}{6} = \left(\dfrac{3 - \pi\sqrt{3}}{6}\right)\left(x - \dfrac{\pi}{3}\right)$ or

$y = \left(\dfrac{3 - \pi\sqrt{3}}{6}\right)\left(x - \dfrac{\pi}{3}\right) + \dfrac{\pi}{6} \approx -0.407x + 0.950$

(b) $y - \dfrac{\pi}{6} = \left(\dfrac{6}{\pi\sqrt{3} - 3}\right)\left(x - \dfrac{\pi}{3}\right)$ or

$y = \left(\dfrac{6}{\pi\sqrt{3} - 3}\right)\left(x - \dfrac{\pi}{3}\right) + \dfrac{\pi}{6} \approx 2.458x - 2.050$

34. $\dfrac{1}{4}(2x) + \dfrac{1}{9}(2yy') = 0$; $y' = -\dfrac{\frac{x}{2}}{\frac{2y}{9}} = -\dfrac{9x}{4y}.$

At $x = 1$, $y = \dfrac{3\sqrt{3}}{2}$, the slope is $y' = -\dfrac{\sqrt{3}}{2}.$

(a) $y - \dfrac{3\sqrt{3}}{2} = -\dfrac{\sqrt{3}}{2}(x - 1)$ or

$y = -\dfrac{\sqrt{3}}{2}x + 2\sqrt{3} \approx -0.866x + 3.464$

(b) $y - \dfrac{3\sqrt{3}}{2} = \dfrac{2}{\sqrt{3}}(x - 1)$

or $y = \dfrac{2}{\sqrt{3}}x + \dfrac{5}{2\sqrt{3}} \approx 1.155x + 1.443$

35. At $t = \dfrac{\pi}{3}$: $x = 1$, $y = \dfrac{3\sqrt{3}}{2}$, and

$\dfrac{dy}{dx} = \dfrac{dy/dt}{dx/dt} = \dfrac{3 \cos (\pi/3)}{-2 \sin (\pi/3)} = -\dfrac{\sqrt{3}}{2}.$

(a) $y - \dfrac{3\sqrt{3}}{2} = -\dfrac{\sqrt{3}}{2}(x - 1)$ or

$y = -\dfrac{\sqrt{3}}{2}x + 2\sqrt{3} \approx -0.866x + 3.464$

(b) $y - \dfrac{3\sqrt{3}}{2} = \dfrac{2}{\sqrt{3}}(x - 1)$ or

$y = \dfrac{2}{\sqrt{3}}x + \dfrac{5}{2\sqrt{3}} \approx 1.155x + 1.443$

36. At $t = \dfrac{\pi}{4}$: $\mathbf{r} = \sec\left(\dfrac{\pi}{4}\right)\mathbf{i} + \tan\left(\dfrac{\pi}{4}\right)\mathbf{j} = \sqrt{2}\mathbf{i} + \mathbf{j}$ and

$\mathbf{r}' = \sec\left(\dfrac{\pi}{4}\right)\tan\left(\dfrac{\pi}{4}\right)\mathbf{i} + \sec^2\left(\dfrac{\pi}{4}\right)\mathbf{j} = \sqrt{2}\mathbf{i} + 2\mathbf{j}$, so that

$\dfrac{dy}{dx} = \dfrac{2}{\sqrt{2}} = \sqrt{2}.$

(a) $y - 1 = \sqrt{2}(x - \sqrt{2})$ or $y = \sqrt{2}x - 1 \approx 1.414x - 1$

(b) $y - 1 = -\dfrac{1}{\sqrt{2}}(x - \sqrt{2})$ or

$y = -\dfrac{1}{\sqrt{2}}x + 2 \approx -0.707x + 2$

37. With $f(x) = \begin{cases} -x + C_1, x < 3 \\ 2x + C_2, x > 3 \end{cases}$, choose C_1, C_2 so that

$-3 + C_1 = 2(3) + C_2 = 1.$

$f(x) = \begin{cases} -x + 4, x \le 3 \\ 2x - 5, x > 3 \end{cases}.$

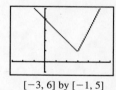

$[-3, 6]$ by $[-1, 5]$

38. **(a)** $x \ne 0, 2$

(b) $x = 0$

(c) $x = 2$

(d) Absolute maximum of 2 at $x = 0$:
absolute minimum of 0 at $x = -2, 2, 3$

39. According to the Mean Value Theorem the driver's speed at

some time was $\dfrac{111}{1.5} = 74$ mph.

40. (a) Increasing in $[-0.7, 2]$ (where $f' \geq 0$), decreasing in $[-2, -0.7]$ (where $f' \leq 0$), and has a local minimum at $x \approx -0.7$.

(b) $y \approx -2x^2 + 3x + 3$

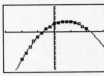

$[-3, 3]$ by $[-15, 10]$

(c) $f(x) = -\frac{2}{3}x^3 + \frac{3}{2}x^2 + 3x + C$; choose C so that

$f(0) = 1: f(x) = -\frac{2}{3}x^3 + \frac{3}{2}x^2 + 3x + 1$.

41. $f(x) = x^2 - 3x - \cos x + C$; choose C so that $f(0) = -2$: $f(x) = x^2 - 3x - \cos x - 1$.

42.

$[-2.35, 2.35]$ by $[-0.5, 3.5]$

$f(x)$ is defined on $[-2, 2]$.

$f'(x) = 2x\sqrt{4 - x^2} - \frac{x^3}{\sqrt{4 - x^2}} = \frac{8x - 3x^3}{\sqrt{4 - x^2}}$; solve

$f'(x) = 0$ for x to find $x = 0$, $x = \pm\frac{2\sqrt{6}}{3}$.

The graph of $y = f'(x)$ is shown.

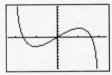

$[-2.35, 2.35]$ by $[-10, 10]$

(a) $\left[-2, -\frac{2\sqrt{6}}{3}\right], \left[0, \frac{2\sqrt{6}}{3}\right]$

(b) $\left[-\frac{2\sqrt{6}}{3}, 0\right], \left[\frac{2\sqrt{6}}{3}, 2\right]$

Use NDER to plot $f''(x)$ and find that $f''(x) = 0$ for $x \approx \pm1.042$.

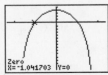

Zero
X=-1.041703 Y=0

$[-2.35, 2.35]$ by $[-15, 5]$

(c) Approximately $(-1.042, 1.042)$

(d) Approximately $(-2, -1.042), (1.042, 2)$

(e) Local (and absolute) maximum of approximately

3.079 at

$x = -\frac{2\sqrt{6}}{3}$ and $x = \frac{2\sqrt{6}}{3}$;

local (and absolute) minimum of 0 at $x = 0$ and

at $x = \pm2$

(f) $\approx(\pm1.042, 1.853)$

43. (a) f has an absolute maximum at $x = 1$ and an absolute minimum at $x = 3$.

(b) f has a point of inflection at $x = 2$.

(c) The function $f(x) = \begin{cases} -\frac{1}{2}(x - 1)^2 + 3, & -1 \leq x \leq 2 \\ -\frac{7}{2}\sqrt{x - 2} + \frac{3}{2}, & 2 < x \leq 3 \end{cases}$

is one example of a function with the given properties.

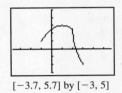

$[-3.7, 5.7]$ by $[-3, 5]$

44. $y = 2\sqrt{1 - \frac{x^2}{16}}$, and the area of the rectangle for $x > 0$ is

$A(x) = 4x\sqrt{1 - \frac{x^2}{16}} = x\sqrt{16 - x^2}$.

$A'(x) = \sqrt{16 - x^2} - \frac{x^2}{\sqrt{16 - x^2}} = \frac{2(8 - x^2)}{\sqrt{16 - x^2}}$, and so

$A'(x) = 0$ when $x = \pm2\sqrt{2}$ and $y = \sqrt{2}$. The maximum

possible area is $A(2\sqrt{2}) = 8$, with dimensions

$4\sqrt{2}$ by $\sqrt{2}$.

45. $f\left(\frac{\pi}{4}\right) = \sqrt{2}$ and $f'\left(\frac{\pi}{4}\right) = \sec\left(\frac{\pi}{4}\right)\tan\left(\frac{\pi}{4}\right) = \sqrt{2}$. The

equation is $y - \sqrt{2} = \sqrt{2}\left(x - \frac{\pi}{4}\right)$ or

$y = \sqrt{2}\left(x - \frac{\pi}{4}\right) + \sqrt{2} \approx 1.414x + 0.303$

46. $V = s^3$

$dV = 3s^2\, ds$

Since $|ds| = 0.01s$, the error of the volume calculation is

approximately $|dV| = 3s^2(0.01s) = 0.03s^3 = 0.03V$, or 3%.

47. Let s be the rope length remaining and x be the horizontal distance from the dock.

(a) $x = \sqrt{s^2 - 5^2}$, $\dfrac{ds}{dt} = -1.5$, and $\dfrac{dx}{dt} = \dfrac{s}{\sqrt{s^2 - 25}} \dfrac{ds}{dt}$,

which means that for $s = 8$ ft,

$$\text{speed} = -\frac{dx}{dt} = -\frac{8}{\sqrt{64 - 25}}(-1.5) \approx 1.9 \text{ ft/sec}$$

(b) $\theta = \sec^{-1}\left(\dfrac{s}{5}\right)$, so $\dfrac{d\theta}{dt} = \dfrac{5}{|s|\sqrt{s^2 - 25}} \dfrac{ds}{dt}$, which for

$s = 8$ ft becomes $\dfrac{5}{8\sqrt{64 - 25}}(-1.5) = -0.15$ rad/sec.

Since $\dfrac{d\theta}{dt}$ is negative, the angle is decreasing at a rate of

0.15 rad/sec.

48. (a) Let h be the level of the coffee in the pot, and let V be

the volume of the coffee in the pot.

$$h = \frac{V}{16\pi}, \text{ so } \frac{dh}{dt} = \frac{dV/dt}{16\pi} = \frac{9}{16\pi} \approx 0.179 \text{ in./min.}$$

(b) Now let h be the level of the coffee in the cone, and let

V be the volume of the coffee in the cone.

$$V = \frac{1}{3}\pi\left(\frac{h}{2}\right)^2 h = \frac{\pi}{12}h^3, \text{ so } \frac{dV}{dt} = \left(\frac{\pi}{4}h^2\right)\left(\frac{dh}{dt}\right) \text{ and } \frac{dh}{dt}$$

$$= \left(\frac{4}{\pi h^2}\right)\left(\frac{dV}{dt}\right) = \left(\frac{4}{25\pi}\right)(-9) = -\frac{36}{25\pi}$$

$$\approx -0.458 \text{ in./min.}$$

Since $\dfrac{dh}{dt}$ is negative, the level in the cone is falling at

the rate of about 0.458 in./min.

49. (a) $(1)(0 + 1.8 + 6.4 + \cdots + 16.2) = 165$ in.
(b) $(1)(1.8 + 6.4 + 12.6 + \cdots + 0) = 165$ in.

50. $\displaystyle\int_{-2}^{1} |x| \, dx = \int_{-2}^{0} -x \, dx + \int_{0}^{1} x \, dx = \left[-\frac{1}{2}x^2\right]_{-2}^{0} + \left[\frac{1}{2}x^2\right]_{0}^{1}$

$= 2 + \dfrac{1}{2} = 2.5$

51. Using Number 29 in the Table of Integrals, with $a = 2$,

$$\int_{-2}^{2} \sqrt{4 - x^2} \, dx = \left[\frac{x}{2}\sqrt{4 - x^2} + 2\sin^{-1}\left(\frac{x}{2}\right)\right]_{-2}^{2}$$

$= \pi - (-\pi) = 2\pi.$

Alternately, observe that the region under the curve and

above the x-axis is a semicircle of radius 2, so the area is

$\dfrac{1}{2}\pi(2)^2 = 2\pi.$

52. $\displaystyle\int_{1}^{3}\left(x^2 + \frac{1}{x}\right) dx = \left[\frac{1}{3}x^3 + \ln x\right]_{1}^{3} = 9 + \ln 3 - \frac{1}{3}$

$= \ln 3 + \dfrac{26}{3} \approx 9.765$

53. $\displaystyle\int_{0}^{\pi/4} \sec^2 x \, dx = \Big[\tan x\Big]_{0}^{\pi/4} = 1$

54. $\displaystyle\int_{1}^{4} \frac{2 + \sqrt{x}}{\sqrt{x}} \, dx = \int_{1}^{4}\left(\frac{2}{\sqrt{x}} + 1\right) dx = \left[4\sqrt{x} + x\right]_{1}^{4} = 12 - 5$

$= 7$

55. Let $u = \ln x$, so $du = \dfrac{1}{x}\, dx$.

Then $\displaystyle\int \frac{dx}{x(\ln x)^2} = \int u^{-2}\, du = -\frac{1}{u} + C = -\frac{1}{\ln x} + C.$

Therefore, $\displaystyle\int_{e}^{2e} \frac{dx}{x(\ln x)^2} =$

$\left[-\dfrac{1}{\ln x}\right]_{e}^{2e} = \left[-\dfrac{1}{1 + \ln 2} + \dfrac{1}{1}\right] = \dfrac{\ln 2}{1 + \ln 2} \approx 0.409$

56. $\displaystyle\int\left[(3 - 2t)\mathbf{i} + \left(\frac{1}{t}\right)\mathbf{j}\right] dt =$

$\left[(3t - t^2)\mathbf{i} + (\ln t)\mathbf{j}\right]_{1}^{3} = (\ln 3)\mathbf{j} - 2\mathbf{i} = -2\mathbf{i} + (\ln 3)\mathbf{j}$

57. Let $u = e^x + 1$, so $du = e^x \, dx$.

Use the identity $\cot^2 u = \csc^2 u - 1$.

$\displaystyle\int e^x \cot^2(e^x + 1) \, dx = \int \cot^2 u \, du$

$\qquad\qquad = \displaystyle\int (\csc^2 u - 1)\, du$

$\qquad\qquad = -\cot u - u + C$

$\qquad\qquad = -\cot(e^x + 1) - (e^x + 1) + C$

Since $-1 + C$ is an arbitrary constant, we may redefine C

and write the solution as $-\cot(e^x + 1) - e^x + C$.

58. Let $u = \dfrac{s}{2}$, so $du = \dfrac{ds}{2}$.

$\displaystyle\int \frac{ds}{s^2 + 4} = \int \frac{ds}{4(s/2)^2 + 4} = \frac{1}{2}\int \frac{ds}{2[(s/2)^2 + 1]} = \frac{1}{2}\int \frac{du}{u^2 + 1}$

$= \dfrac{1}{2}\tan^{-1} u + C = \dfrac{1}{2}\tan^{-1}\left(\dfrac{s}{2}\right) + C$

59. Let $u = \cos(x - 3)$, so $du = -\sin(x - 3)\, dx$.

$\displaystyle\int \frac{\sin(x - 3)}{\cos^3(x - 3)} \, dx = \int (-u^{-3})\, du = \frac{1}{2}u^{-2} + C$

$= \dfrac{1}{2\cos^2(x - 3)} + C$

60. Use integration by parts.

$$u = e^{-x} \qquad dv = \cos 2x \, dx$$

$$du = -e^{-x} \, dx \qquad v = \frac{1}{2} \sin 2x$$

$$\int e^{-x} \cos 2x \, dx = \frac{1}{2} e^{-x} \sin 2x + \int \frac{1}{2} e^{-x} \sin 2x \, dx$$

Now let

$$u = e^{-x} \qquad dv = \frac{1}{2} \sin 2x \, dx$$

$$du = -e^{-x} \, dx \qquad v = -\frac{1}{4} \cos 2x$$

Then

$$\int e^{-x} \cos 2x \, dx$$

$$= \frac{1}{2} e^{-x} \sin 2x - \frac{1}{4} e^{-x} \cos 2x - \frac{1}{4} \int e^{-x} \cos 2x \, dx$$

so

$$\int e^{-x} \cos 2x \, dx = \frac{e^{-x}}{5} (2 \sin 2x - \cos 2x) + C$$

61. $\dfrac{x+2}{x^2 - 5x - 6} = \dfrac{x+2}{(x+1)(x-6)} = \dfrac{A}{x+1} + \dfrac{B}{x-6}$

$$x + 2 = A(x - 6) + B(x + 1) = (A + B)x + (B - 6A)$$

Solving $A + B = 1$, $B - 6A = 2$ yields $A = -\dfrac{1}{7}$, $B = \dfrac{8}{7}$ so

$\dfrac{x+2}{x^2 - 5x - 6} = \dfrac{8}{7(x-6)} - \dfrac{1}{7(x+1)}$. Then

$$\int \frac{x+2}{x^2 - 5x - 6} \, dx = \int \left(\frac{8}{7(x-6)} - \frac{1}{7(x+1)} \right) dx$$

$$= \frac{8}{7} \ln |x - 6| - \frac{1}{7} \ln |x + 1| + C = \frac{1}{7} \ln \frac{(x-6)^8}{|x+1|} + C$$

62. Area $\approx \dfrac{5}{2}[3 + 2(8.3) + 2(9.9) + \cdots + 2(8.3) + 3] = 359;$

Volume $\approx 25 \times 359 = 8975 \text{ ft}^3$

63. $y = -(t+1)^{-1} - \dfrac{1}{2} e^{-2t} + C; \, y(0) = -1 - \dfrac{1}{2} + C = 2$, so

$C = \dfrac{7}{2}$ and $y = -\dfrac{1}{t+1} - \dfrac{1}{2} e^{-2t} + \dfrac{7}{2}.$

64. $y' = -\dfrac{1}{2} \cos 2\theta - \sin \theta + C_1$, and $y'\left(\dfrac{\pi}{2}\right) = 0 \Rightarrow$

$y' = -\dfrac{1}{2} \cos 2\theta - \sin \theta + \dfrac{1}{2}.$

$y = -\dfrac{1}{4} \sin 2\theta + \cos \theta + \dfrac{1}{2} \theta + C_2$, and $y\left(\dfrac{\pi}{2}\right) = 0$

$\Rightarrow y = -\dfrac{1}{4} \sin 2\theta + \cos \theta + \dfrac{1}{2} \theta - \dfrac{\pi}{4}$

65. Use integration by parts.

$$u = x^2 \qquad dv = \sin x \, dx$$

$$du = 2x \, dx \qquad v = -\cos x$$

$$\int x^2 \sin x \, dx = -x^2 \cos x + \int 2x \cos x \, dx$$

Now let

$$u = x \qquad dv = 2 \cos x \, dx$$

$$du = dx \qquad v = 2 \sin x$$

$$\int x^2 \sin x \, dx = -x^2 \cos x + 2x \sin x - \int 2 \sin x \, dx$$

$$= -x^2 \cos x + 2x \sin x + 2 \cos x + C$$

$$= (2 - x^2) \cos x + 2x \sin x + C$$

The graph of the slope field of the differential equation

$\dfrac{dy}{dx} = x^2 \sin x$ and the antiderivative $y = (2 - x^2) \cos x +$

$2x \sin x$ is shown below.

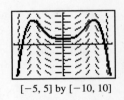

$[-5, 5]$ by $[-10, 10]$

66. Use integration by parts.

$$u = x \qquad dv = e^x \, dx$$

$$du = dx \qquad v = e^x$$

$$\int x \, e^x \, dx = xe^x - \int e^x \, dx = xe^x - e^x + C = e^x(x - 1) + C$$

Confirm by differentiation:

$$\frac{d}{dx}[e^x(x-1) + C] = e^x + (x-1)e^x = xe^x$$

67. (a) $y = Ce^{kt}$, with $6{,}000 = Ce^{k(2)}$ and $10{,}000 = Ce^{k(5)}$.

Then $\dfrac{10{,}000}{6{,}000} = e^{k(5-2)}$, so $\dfrac{5}{3} = e^{3k}$ and therefore

$$k = \frac{\ln\left(\dfrac{5}{3}\right)}{3} \approx 0.170.$$

Furthermore, $C = \dfrac{6{,}000}{e^{2k}} \approx 4268$. The approximate number

of bacteria is given by $y = 4268e^{0.170t}$.

(b) About 4268

68. Let t be the time in minutes where $t = 0$ represents right now, and let $T(t)$ be the number of degrees above room temperature. Then we may write $T(t) = T_0 e^{-kt}$ where $T(0) = 50$ and $T(-15) = 65$, giving $T_0 = 50$ and

$$k = \frac{1}{15} \ln \frac{13}{10} \approx 0.0175.$$

(a) $50e^{-k(120)} \approx 6.13°C$ above room temperature.

(b) Solving $5 = 50e^{-kt}$ gives $t = \frac{\ln 0.1}{-k} \approx 131.6$ minutes, or about 2 hours and 12 minutes from now.

69. $\dfrac{dy}{dx} = 0.08y\left(1 - \dfrac{y}{500}\right)$

$$\frac{500\, dy}{y(500 - y)} = 0.08\, dx$$

$$\frac{(500 - y) + y}{y(500 - y)}\, dy = 0.08\, dx$$

$$\left(\frac{1}{y} + \frac{1}{500 - y}\right) dy = 0.08\, dx$$

Integrate both sides.

$$\ln |y| - \ln |500 - y| = 0.08x + C_1$$

$$\frac{y}{500 - y} = C_2 e^{0.08x}$$

$$y \cdot (1 + C_2 e^{0.08x}) = 500 C_2 e^{0.08x}$$

$$y = \frac{500}{1 + Ce^{-0.08x}}$$

70. $\dfrac{dy}{dx} = (y - 4)(x + 3)$

$$\frac{dy}{y - 4} = (x + 3)\, dx$$

$$\int \frac{dy}{y - 4} = \int (x + 3)\, dx$$

$$\ln |y - 4| = \frac{x^2}{2} + 3x + C_1$$

$$y - 4 = e^{C_1} e^{(x^2/2) + 3x} + 4$$

$$y = Ce^{(x^2/2) + 3x} + 4$$

71. Use EULERT.

x	y
0	0
0.1	0.1
0.2	0.2095
0.3	0.3285
0.4	0.4568
0.5	0.5946
0.6	0.7418
0.7	0.8986
0.8	1.0649
0.9	1.2411
1.0	1.4273

72. The region has four congruent portions, so

$$\text{Area} = 4\int_0^{\pi/2} \sin 2x \, dx = 4\left[-\frac{1}{2}\cos 2x\right]_0^{\pi/2} = 4$$

73. Solve $5 - x^2 = x^2 - 3$ to find the integration limits:

$$2x^2 = 8 \Rightarrow x = \pm 2. \text{ Then}$$

$$\text{Area} = \int_{-2}^{2} [(5 - x^2) - (x^2 - 3)]\, dx = \int_{-2}^{2} (8 - 2x^2)\, dx$$

$$= \left[8x - \frac{2}{3}x^3\right]_{-2}^{2} = \frac{64}{3}$$

74. Solve $y^2 - 3 = y + 2$ to find the integration limits:

$$y^2 - y - 5 = 0 \Rightarrow y = \frac{1 \pm \sqrt{21}}{2}. \text{ Then}$$

$$\text{Area} = \int_{(1 - \sqrt{21})/2}^{(1 + \sqrt{21})/2} [(y + 2) - (y^2 - 3)]\, dy \approx 16.039.$$

75. $\text{Area} = \dfrac{1}{2}\displaystyle\int_0^{2\pi} r^2\, d\theta = \dfrac{1}{2}\int_0^{2\pi} 9(1 + \cos\theta)^2\, d\theta$

$$= \frac{9}{2}\int_0^{2\pi} (1 + 2\cos\theta + \cos^2\theta)\, d\theta$$

$$= \frac{9}{2}\int_0^{2\pi} \left(1 + 2\cos\theta + \frac{1 + \cos 2\theta}{2}\right) d\theta$$

$$= \frac{9}{2}\int_0^{2\pi} \left(\frac{3}{2} + \cos\theta + \frac{1}{2}\cos 2\theta\right) d\theta$$

$$= \frac{9}{2}\left[\frac{3}{2}\theta + 2\sin\theta - \frac{1}{4}\sin 2\theta\right]_0^{2\pi}$$

$$= \frac{9}{2}(3\pi - 0) = \frac{27\pi}{2} \approx 42.412$$

76. $\text{Volume} = \displaystyle\int_{-1}^{1} \pi\left(\frac{x^3}{2}\right)^2 dx = \frac{\pi}{4}\left[\frac{1}{7}x^7\right]_{-1}^{1} = \frac{\pi}{14} \approx 0.224$

77. Solve $4x - x^2 = 0$ to find the limit of integration:

$x = 0$ or $x = 4$. By the cylindrical shell method,

$$\text{Volume} = \int_0^4 2\pi x(4x - x^2)\, dx = 2\pi \int_0^4 (4x^2 - x^3)\, dx$$

$$= 2\pi\left[\frac{4}{3}x^3 - \frac{1}{4}x^4\right]_0^4 = \frac{128\pi}{3}$$

$$\approx 134.041.$$

78. The average value is the integral divided by the interval length. Using NINT,

$$\text{average value} = \frac{1}{\pi}\int_0^\pi \sqrt{\sin x}\, dx \approx 0.763$$

79. $y' = \sec^2 x$, so we may use NINT to obtain

$$\text{Length} = \int_{-\pi/4}^{\pi/4} \sqrt{1 + (\sec^2 x)^2}\, dx \approx 2.556.$$

80. $\dfrac{dx}{dt} = \cos t$ and $\dfrac{dy}{dt} = 1 - \sin t$, so we may use NINT to obtain

$$\text{Length} = \int_{-\pi/2}^{\pi/2} \sqrt{\cos^2 t + (1 - \sin t)^2}\, dt$$

$$= \int_{-\pi/2}^{\pi/2} \sqrt{2 - 2\sin t}\, dt = 4.$$

81. Using NINT,

$$\text{Length} = \int_0^\pi \sqrt{\theta^2 + \left(\frac{dr}{d\theta}\right)^2}\, d\theta = \int_0^\pi \sqrt{1 + \theta^2}\, d\theta \approx 6.110.$$

82. $\dfrac{dy}{dx} = -\dfrac{1}{2}e^{-x/2}$, so we may use NINT to obtain

$$\text{Area} = \int_0^2 2\pi e^{-x/2}\sqrt{1 + \left(\frac{-e^{-x/2}}{2}\right)^2}\, dx$$

$$= \int_0^2 \pi e^{-x/2}\sqrt{4 + e^{-x}}\, dx \approx 8.423.$$

83. $\dfrac{dx}{dt} = \cos t$ and $\dfrac{dy}{dt} = 1 - \sin t$, so

$$\text{Area} = \int_0^{\pi/2} 2\pi \sin t \sqrt{\cos^2 t + (1 - \sin t)^2}\, dt$$

$$= \int_0^{\pi/2} 2\pi \sin t \sqrt{2 - 2\sin t}\, dt \approx 3.470.$$

84. $\dfrac{dr}{d\theta} = 1$, so we may use NINT to obtain

$$\text{Area} = \int_{\pi/2}^{\pi} 2\pi\theta \sin\theta \sqrt{\theta^2 + 1}\, d\theta \approx 32.683.$$

85. $\text{Volume} = \displaystyle\int_0^1 \pi\left(\frac{\sqrt{x} - x^2}{2}\right)^2 dx$

$$= \int_0^1 \frac{\pi}{4}(x - 2x^{5/2} + x^4)\, dx$$

$$= \frac{\pi}{4}\left[\frac{1}{2}x^2 - \frac{4}{7}x^{7/2} + \frac{1}{5}x^5\right]_0^1$$

$$= \frac{9\pi}{280} \approx 0.101.$$

86. Use the region's symmetry:

$$\text{Volume} = 2\int_0^{\pi/4} \pi(2\tan x)^2\, dx$$

$$= 8\pi \int_0^{\pi/4} \tan^2 x\, dx$$

$$= 8\pi \int_0^{\pi/4} (\sec^2 x - 1)\, dx$$

$$= 8\pi\left[\tan x - x\right]_0^{\pi/4}$$

$$= 8\pi\left(1 - \frac{\pi}{4}\right)$$

$$= 8\pi - 2\pi^2 \approx 5.394.$$

87. (a) $F = kx \Rightarrow 200 = k(0.8) \Rightarrow k = 250$ N/m, so for

$$F = 300 \text{ N}, \quad x = \frac{300}{250} = 1.2 \text{ m}.$$

(b) $\text{Work} = \displaystyle\int_0^{1.2} 250x\, dx = \left[125x^2\right]_0^{1.2} = 180$ J

88. (a) The work required to raise a thin disk at height y from the bottom is

$$(\text{weight})(\text{distance}) = \left[60\pi\left(\frac{y}{2}\right)^2 dy\right](12 - y).$$

$$\text{Total work} = \int_0^{10} 15\pi y^2(12 - y)\, dy$$

$$= 15\pi \int_0^{10} (-y^3 + 12y^2)\, dy = 15\pi\left[-\frac{1}{4}y^4 + 4y^3\right]_0^{10}$$

$$= 22{,}500\pi \approx 70{,}686 \text{ ft-lb.}$$

(b) $\dfrac{22{,}500\pi}{275} \approx 257 \text{ sec} = 4 \text{ min, } 17 \text{ sec}$

89. The sideways force exerted by a thin disk at depth y is its edge area times the pressure, or

$$(2\pi\, dy)(849y) = 1698\pi y\, dy.$$

$$\text{Total force} = \int_0^H 1698\pi y\, dy = 849\pi H^2, \text{ where } H \text{ is depth.}$$

Solve: $40{,}000 = 849\pi H^2$

$$\Rightarrow H = \sqrt{\frac{40{,}000}{849\pi}} \text{ and } V = \pi H \approx 12.166 \text{ ft}^3.$$

90. Use l'Hôpital's Rule: $\displaystyle\lim_{x\to\infty} \frac{\ln x}{\sqrt{x}} = \lim_{x\to\infty} \frac{\frac{1}{x}}{\frac{x^{-1/2}}{2}} = \lim_{x\to\infty} \frac{2}{\sqrt{x}} = 0.$

$f(x) = \ln x$ grows slower than $g(x) = \sqrt{x}$.

91. Use the limit comparison test with $f(t) = \dfrac{1}{t^2 - 4}$ and

$g(t) = \dfrac{1}{t^2}$. Since f and g are both continuous on $[3, \infty)$,

$\displaystyle\lim_{t\to\infty} \frac{f(t)}{g(t)} = 1$, and $\displaystyle\int_3^\infty g(t)\, dt$ converges, we conclude that

$\displaystyle\int_3^\infty f(t)\, dt = \int_3^\infty \frac{dt}{t^2 - 4}$ converges.

92. Use the comparison test: for $x \ge 2$, $\dfrac{1}{\ln x} > \dfrac{1}{x}$, and

$\displaystyle\lim_{b\to\infty} \int_2^b \frac{dx}{x} = \lim_{b\to\infty} (\ln b - \ln 2) = \infty.$ Both integrals diverge.

93. $\displaystyle\int_{-\infty}^\infty e^{-|x|}\, dx = \int_{-\infty}^0 e^x\, dx + \int_0^\infty e^{-x}\, dx = 2\int_0^\infty e^{-x}\, dx$

Since $\displaystyle\int_0^\infty e^{-x}\, dx = \lim_{b\to\infty} \int_0^b e^{-x}\, dx = \lim_{b\to\infty}\left[-e^{-x}\right]_0^b = 1$, the original integral converges.

94. $\displaystyle\int_0^1 \frac{4r\, dr}{\sqrt{1 - r^2}} = \lim_{b\to 1^-} \int_0^b \frac{4r\, dr}{\sqrt{1 - r^2}} = \lim_{b\to 1^-}\left[-4\sqrt{1 - r^2}\right]_0^b$

$= \displaystyle\lim_{b\to 1^-} (-4\sqrt{1 - b^2} + 4) = 4.$ The integral converges.

95. $\displaystyle\int_0^{10} \frac{dx}{1 - x} = \int_0^1 \frac{dx}{1 - x} + \int_1^{10} \frac{dx}{1 - x}$

Since $\displaystyle\int_0^1 \frac{dx}{1 - x} = \lim_{b\to 1^-} \int_0^b \frac{dx}{1 - x}$

$= \displaystyle\lim_{b\to 1^-}\left[-\ln(1 - x)\right]_0^b = \infty$, the original integral diverges.

96. $\int_0^2 \dfrac{dx}{\sqrt[3]{x-1}} = \int_0^1 \dfrac{dx}{\sqrt[3]{x-1}} + \int_1^2 \dfrac{dx}{\sqrt[3]{x-1}}$

$= \lim_{b\to 1^-} \int_0^b \dfrac{dx}{\sqrt[3]{x-1}} + \lim_{a\to 1^+} \int_a^2 \dfrac{dx}{\sqrt[3]{x-1}}$

$= \lim_{b\to 1^-} \left[\dfrac{3}{2}(x-1)^{2/3}\right]_0^b + \lim_{a\to 1^+} \left[\dfrac{3}{2}(x-1)^{2/3}\right]_a^2 = 0.$

The whole integral converges.

97. We know that

$\dfrac{1}{1+x} = 1 - x + x^2 - x^3 + \cdots + (-1)^n x^n + \cdots$

for $-1 < x < 1$. Substituting $2x$ for x yields

$\dfrac{1}{1+2x} = 1 - 2x + 4x^2 - 8x^3 + \cdots + (-1)^n 2^n x^n + \cdots$

for $-1 < 2x < 1$, so the interval of convergence is

$-\dfrac{1}{2} < x < \dfrac{1}{2}.$

98. (a)

$\cos t^2 = 1 - \dfrac{(t^2)^2}{2!} + \dfrac{(t^2)^4}{4!} - \dfrac{(t^2)^6}{6!} + \cdots + (-1)^n \dfrac{(t^2)^{2n}}{(2n)!} + \cdots$

$= 1 - \dfrac{t^4}{2!} + \dfrac{t^8}{4!} - \dfrac{t^{12}}{6!} + \cdots + (-1)^n \dfrac{t^{4n}}{(2n)!}$

Integrating each term with respect to t from 0 to x

yields

$x - \dfrac{x^5}{5(2!)} + \dfrac{x^9}{9(4!)} - \dfrac{x^{13}}{13(6!)} + \cdots + (-1)^n \dfrac{x^{4n+1}}{(4n+1)(2n)!} + \cdots.$

(b) $-\infty < x < \infty$; Since the cosine series converges for all

real numbers, so does the integrated series, by, the

term-by-term integration theorem (Section 9.1,

Theorem 2).

99. $\ln(2+2x) = \ln[2(x+1)] = \ln 2 + \ln(x+1)$

$= \ln 2 + x - \dfrac{x^2}{2} + \dfrac{x^3}{3} - \dfrac{x^4}{4} + \cdots + (-1)^{n-1}\dfrac{x^n}{n} + \cdots$

Since by the Ratio Test $\lim_{n\to\infty} \left|\dfrac{a_{n+1}}{a_n}\right| = \lim_{n\to\infty} \left|\dfrac{n}{n+1}x\right| = |x|$, the

series

converges for $-1 < x \le 1$.

$\left(\sum_{n=1}^{\infty} \dfrac{(-1)^n}{n} \text{ converges, but } \sum_{n=1}^{\infty} -\dfrac{1}{n} \text{ does not.}\right)$

100. Let $f(x) = \sin x$. Then $f'(x) = \cos x$, $f''(x) = -\sin x$,

$f'''(x) = -\cos x$, $f^{(4)}(x) = \sin x$, and so on. At $x = 2\pi$ the

sine terms are zero and the cosine terms alternate between

1 and -1, so the Taylor series is

$(x-2\pi) - \dfrac{(x-2\pi)^3}{3!} + \dfrac{(x-2\pi)^5}{5!} - \cdots$

$\quad + (-1)^n \dfrac{(x-2\pi)^{2n+1}}{(2n+1)!} + \cdots.$

101. The first six terms of the Maclaurin series are

$1 - x + \dfrac{x^2}{2!} - \dfrac{x^3}{3!} + \dfrac{x^4}{4!} - \dfrac{x^5}{5!} + \dfrac{x^6}{6!}$. By the Alternating

Series Estimation Theorem, $|\text{error}| \le \left|\dfrac{x^7}{7!}\right| \le \dfrac{1}{7!} < 0.001.$

102. $f(0) = 1, f'(0) = \dfrac{1}{3(0+1)^{2/3}} = \dfrac{1}{3}$,

$f''(0) = -\dfrac{2}{9(0+1)^{2/3}} = -\dfrac{2}{9}$,

$\cdots f^{(n)}(0) = (-1)^{n-1}\dfrac{2\cdot 5\cdot\cdots\cdot(3n-4)}{3^n}$, so the

Taylor series is

$1 + \dfrac{1}{3}x - \dfrac{2}{2!\cdot 3^2}x^2 + \dfrac{2\cdot 5}{3!\cdot 3^3}x^3 - \dfrac{2\cdot 5\cdot 8}{4!\cdot 3^4}x^4 + \cdots$

$\quad + (-1)^{n-1}\dfrac{2\cdot 5\cdot\cdots\cdot(3n-4)}{n!\cdot 3^n}x^n + \cdots.$

Since by the Ratio Test

$\lim_{n\to\infty} \left|\dfrac{a_{n+1}}{a_n}\right|$

$= \lim_{n\to\infty} \left|\dfrac{2\cdot 5\cdot\cdots\cdot(3n-4)(3n-1)x^{n+1}}{(n+1)!3^{n+1}} \cdot \dfrac{n!3^n}{2\cdot 5\cdot\cdots\cdot(3n-4)x^n}\right|$

$= \lim_{n\to\infty} \left|\dfrac{(3n-1)x}{(n+1)(3)}\right| = |x|$, the radius of convergence is 1.

103. Using the Ratio Test, $\lim_{n\to\infty} \left|\dfrac{a_{n+1}}{a_n}\right| = \lim_{n\to\infty} \left|\dfrac{2}{3^{n+1}} \cdot \dfrac{3^n}{2}\right| = \dfrac{1}{3}$, so

the series converges.

104. Note that $a_n > \dfrac{1}{n}$ for every n. By the Direct Comparison

Test, since $\displaystyle\sum_{n=1}^{\infty} \dfrac{1}{n}$ diverges, so does $\displaystyle\sum_{n=1}^{\infty} \dfrac{2}{\sqrt{n}}$.

105. Use the alternating series test.

Note that $\displaystyle\sum_{n=0}^{\infty} \dfrac{(-1)^n}{n+1} = \sum_{n=0}^{\infty} (-1)^n u_n$, where $u_n = \dfrac{1}{n+1}$.

Since each u_n is positive, $u_n > u_{n+1}$ for all n, and

$\lim_{n\to\infty} u_n = 0$, the original series converges.

106. Using the Ratio Test,

$\lim_{n\to\infty} \left|\dfrac{a_{n+1}}{a_n}\right| = \lim_{n\to\infty} \left|\dfrac{3^{n+1}}{(n+1)!} \cdot \dfrac{n!}{3^n}\right| = \lim_{n\to\infty} \dfrac{3}{n+1} = 0$, and the

series converges.

107. (a) Using the Ratio Test,

$$\lim_{n\to\infty}\left|\frac{a^{n+1}}{a_n}\right| = \lim_{n\to\infty}\left|\frac{(x+2)^{n+1}}{n+1}\cdot\frac{n}{(x+2)^n}\right| = |x+2|, \text{ which}$$

means that the series converges for $-1 < x + 2 < 1$,

or $-3 < x < -1$. Furthermore, at $x = -3$, the series

is $\displaystyle\sum_{n=1}^{\infty}\frac{1}{n}$, which diverges, and at $x = -1$, the series is

$\displaystyle\sum_{n=1}^{\infty}\frac{(-1)^n}{n}$, which converges. The interval of

convergence is $-3 < x \le -1$ and the radius of

convergence is 1.

(b) $-3 < x < -1$

(c) At $x = -1$

108. (a) Using the Ratio Test, $\displaystyle\lim_{n\to\infty}\left|\frac{a^{n+1}}{a_n}\right|$

$$= \lim_{n\to\infty}\left|\frac{x^{n+1}}{(n+1)\ln^2(n+1)}\cdot\frac{n\ln^2 n}{x^n}\right|$$

$$= \lim_{n\to\infty}\left|\frac{nx\ln^2(n)}{(n+1)\ln^2(n+1)}\right|$$

$$= |x|\left(\lim_{n\to\infty}\frac{n}{n+1}\right)\left(\lim_{n\to\infty}\frac{\ln n}{\ln(n+1)}\right)^2 = |x|, \text{ which means}$$

that the series converges for $-1 < x < 1$. At $x = \pm 1$,

the series converges by the Integral Test:

$$\int_2^{\infty}\frac{1}{x(\ln x)^2}\,dx = \lim_{b\to\infty}\int_2^{b}\frac{1}{x(\ln x)^2}\,dx = \left[-\frac{1}{\ln x}\right]_2^{b}$$

$$= \lim_{b\to\infty}\left(-\frac{1}{\ln b} + \frac{1}{\ln 2}\right) = \frac{1}{\ln 2}. \text{ So the}$$

convergence interval is $-1 \le x \le 1$ and the radius of

convergence is 1.

(b) $-1 \le x \le 1$

(c) Nowhere

109. $\displaystyle\frac{1}{\sqrt{2^2 + (-3)^2}}\langle 2, -3\rangle = \left\langle\frac{2}{\sqrt{13}}, -\frac{3}{\sqrt{13}}\right\rangle$

110. $\displaystyle\left\langle 1\cos\frac{\pi}{3}, 1\sin\frac{\pi}{3}\right\rangle = \left\langle\frac{1}{2}, \frac{\sqrt{3}}{2}\right\rangle$

111. $\displaystyle\frac{dy}{dx}\bigg|_{t=3\pi/4} = \frac{dy/dt}{dx/dt}\bigg|_{t=3\pi/4} = \frac{-3\sin t}{4\cos t}\bigg|_{t=3\pi/4} = \frac{3}{4}.$ The

tangent vectors are $\displaystyle\frac{1}{\sqrt{3^2 + 4^2}}\langle 4, 3\rangle = \left\langle\frac{4}{5}, \frac{3}{5}\right\rangle$ and

$\left\langle-\frac{4}{5}, -\frac{3}{5}\right\rangle$. The normal vectors are $\left\langle\frac{3}{5}, -\frac{4}{5}\right\rangle$ and $\left\langle-\frac{3}{5}, \frac{4}{5}\right\rangle$.

112. (a) $\displaystyle\mathbf{v}(t) = \frac{d\mathbf{r}}{dt} = (-\cos t)\mathbf{i} + (1 + \sin t)\mathbf{j}$

$\displaystyle\mathbf{a}(t) = \frac{d\mathbf{v}}{dt} = (\sin t)\mathbf{i} + (\cos t)\mathbf{j}$

(b) Using NINT, the distance traveled is

$$\int_{\pi/2}^{3\pi/2}|\mathbf{v}(t)|\,dt = \int_{\pi/2}^{3\pi/2}\sqrt{(-\cos t)^2 + (1 + \sin t)^2}\,dt$$

$$= \int_{\pi/2}^{3\pi/2}\sqrt{2 + 2\sin t}\,dt = 4.$$

113. Yes. The path of the ball is given by

$x = 100(\cos 45°)t = 50\sqrt{2}t$ and

$y = -16t^2 + 100(\sin 45°)t = -16t^2 + 50\sqrt{2}t.$

When $x = 130$, we have $t = \dfrac{13}{5\sqrt{2}}$ and so

$y = -16\left(\dfrac{13}{5\sqrt{2}}\right)^2 + 50\sqrt{2}\left(\dfrac{13}{5\sqrt{2}}\right) = 75.92$ ft, high enough

to easily clear the 35-ft tree.

114. Since $r\cos\theta = x$, $r\sin\theta = y$, the Cartesian equation is $x - y = 2$. The graph is a line with slope 1 and y-intercept -2.

115.

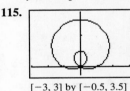

$[-3, 3]$ by $[-0.5, 3.5]$

The shortest possible θ-interval has length 2π.

116. $x = r\cos\theta = \cos\theta - \cos^2\theta,$

$y = r\sin\theta = \sin\theta - \sin\theta\cos\theta$

$$\frac{dy}{dx} = \frac{dy/d\theta}{dx/d\theta} = \frac{\cos\theta + \sin^2\theta - \cos^2\theta}{-\sin\theta + 2\sin\theta\cos\theta}$$

Zeros of $\dfrac{dy}{d\theta}$:

$\cos\theta + \sin^2\theta - \cos^2\theta = 0$

$\cos\theta + 1 - 2\cos^2\theta = 0$

$(2\cos\theta + 1)(\cos\theta - 1) = 0$

$\theta = 0, \theta = \dfrac{2\pi}{3}, \theta = \dfrac{4\pi}{3}, \text{ or } \theta = 2\pi$

Zeros of $\dfrac{dx}{d\theta}$:

$-\sin\theta + 2\sin\theta\cos\theta = 0$

$\sin\theta = 0 \text{ or } \cos\theta = \dfrac{1}{2}$

$\theta = 0, \theta = \pi, \theta = \dfrac{\pi}{3} \text{ or } \theta = \dfrac{5\pi}{3}, \theta = 2\pi$

There are horizontal tangents $\left(\dfrac{dy}{d\theta} = 0, \dfrac{dx}{d\theta} \neq 0\right)$ at $\theta = \dfrac{2\pi}{3}$ and at $\theta = \dfrac{4\pi}{3}$, and vertical tangents $\left(\dfrac{dx}{d\theta} = 0, \dfrac{dy}{d\theta} \neq 0\right)$ at $\theta = \dfrac{\pi}{3}$, at $\theta = \pi$, and at $\theta = \dfrac{5\pi}{3}$.

For $\theta = 0$ (or 2π), $\dfrac{dy}{dx}$ becomes $\dfrac{0}{0}$ and l'Hôpital's Rule leads to

$$\dfrac{dy}{dx}\bigg|_{\theta=0} = \dfrac{-\sin(0) + 4\sin(0)\cos(0)}{-\cos(0) + 2\cos^2(0) - 2\sin^2(0)} = 0,$$ so this is another horizontal tangent line.

Horizontal tangents:

At $\theta = 0$ or $\theta = 2\pi$, we have $r = 0$ and the Cartesian coordinates are $(0, 0)$, so the tangent is $y = 0$.

At $\theta = \dfrac{2\pi}{3}$, we have $r = \dfrac{3}{2}$ and the Cartesian coordinates are $\left(\dfrac{3}{2}\cos\dfrac{2\pi}{3}, \dfrac{3}{2}\sin\dfrac{2\pi}{3}\right) = \left(-\dfrac{3}{4}, \dfrac{3\sqrt{3}}{4}\right)$, so the tangent is $y = \dfrac{3\sqrt{3}}{4}$.

At $\theta = \dfrac{4\pi}{3}$, we again have $r = \dfrac{3}{2}$ and the Cartesian coordinates are $\left(\dfrac{3}{2}\cos\dfrac{4\pi}{3}, \dfrac{3}{2}\sin\dfrac{4\pi}{3}\right) = \left(-\dfrac{3}{4}, -\dfrac{3\sqrt{3}}{4}\right)$, so the tangent is $y = -\dfrac{3\sqrt{3}}{4}$.

Vertical tangents:

At $\theta = \dfrac{\pi}{3}$, we have $r = \dfrac{1}{2}$ and the Cartesian coordinates are $\left(\dfrac{1}{2}\cos\dfrac{\pi}{3}, \dfrac{1}{2}\sin\dfrac{\pi}{3}\right) = \left(\dfrac{1}{4}, \dfrac{\sqrt{3}}{4}\right)$, so the tangent is $x = \dfrac{1}{4}$.

At $\theta = \pi$, we have $r = 2$ and the Cartesian coordinates are $(2\cos\pi, 2\sin\pi) = (-2, 0)$, so the tangent is $x = -2$.

At $\theta = \dfrac{5\pi}{3}$, we have $r = \dfrac{1}{2}$ and the Cartesian coordinates are $\left(\dfrac{1}{2}\cos\dfrac{5\pi}{3}, \dfrac{1}{2}\sin\dfrac{5\pi}{3}\right) = \left(\dfrac{1}{4}, -\dfrac{\sqrt{3}}{4}\right)$, so the tangent is $x = \dfrac{1}{4}$. In summary, the horizontal tangents are $y = 0$, $y = -\dfrac{3\sqrt{3}}{4}$, and $y = \dfrac{3\sqrt{3}}{4}$, and the vertical tangents are $x = -2$ and $x = \dfrac{1}{4}$.

■ Appendix A2
(pp. 581–584)

1. Step 1: The formula holds for $n = 1$, because $|x_1| = |x_1|$.

Step 2: Suppose $|x_1 + x_2 + \cdots x_k| \leq |x_1| + |x_2| + \cdots + |x_k|$.
Then, $|x_1 + x_2 + \cdots + x_{k+1}|$
$$\leq |x_1 + x_2 + \cdots + x_k| + |x_{k+1}|$$ by the triangle inequality.

So, by the transitivity of $\leq$,
$$|x_1 + x_2 + \cdots + x_{k+1}| \leq |x_1| + |x_2| + \cdots + |x_{k+1}|.$$

The mathematical induction principle now guarantees the original formula for all n.

2. Step 1: The formula holds for $n = 1$, because
$$1 + r = \dfrac{(1 + r)(1 - r)}{1 - r} = \dfrac{1 - r^2}{1 - r}.$$

Step 2: Suppose $1 + r + r^2 + \cdots + r^k = \dfrac{1 - r^{k+1}}{1 - r}$. Then
$$1 + r + r^2 + \cdots + r^{k+1} = \dfrac{1 - r^{k+1}}{1 - r} + r^{k+1}$$
$$= \dfrac{1 - r^{k+1} + r^{k+1}(1 - r)}{1 - r} = \dfrac{1 - r^{k+2}}{1 - r}.$$

The mathematical induction principle now guarantees the original formula for every positive integer n.

3. Step 1: The formula holds for $n = 1$, because $\dfrac{d}{dx}(x) = 1$.

Step 2: Suppose $\dfrac{d}{dx}(x^k) = kx^{k-1}$. Then
$$\dfrac{d}{dx}(x^{k+1}) = \dfrac{d}{dx}(x \cdot x^k) = x \cdot \dfrac{d}{dx}(x^k) + x^k \cdot \dfrac{d}{dx}(x)$$
$$= x \cdot kx^{k-1} + x^k = kx^k + x^k = (k + 1)x^k.$$

The mathematical induction principle now guarantees the original formula for any positive integer n.

4. Step 1: The formula holds for $n = 1$, because $f(x_1) = f(x_1)$.

Step 2: Suppose
$$f(x_1 x_2 \cdots x_k) = f(x_1) + f(x_2) + \cdots + f(x_k).$$
Then by the given property,
$$f(x_1 x_2 \cdots x_{k+1}) = f(x_1 x_2 \cdots x_k) + f(x_{k+1})$$
$$= f(x_1) + f(x_2) + \cdots + f(x_{k+1}).$$

The mathematical induction principle now guarantees the original formula for every positive integer n.

5. Step 1: The formula holds for $n = 1$, because $\dfrac{2}{3} = 1 - \dfrac{1}{3}$.

Step 2: Suppose $\dfrac{2}{3^1} + \dfrac{2}{3^2} + \cdots + \dfrac{2}{3^k} = 1 - \dfrac{1}{3^k}$. Then
$$\dfrac{2}{3^1} + \dfrac{2}{3^2} + \cdots + \dfrac{2}{3^{k+1}} = 1 - \dfrac{1}{3^k} + \dfrac{2}{3^{k+1}}$$
$$= 1 - \dfrac{3 - 2}{3^{k+1}} = 1 - \dfrac{1}{3^{k+1}}.$$

The mathematical induction principle now guarantees the original formula for all positive integers n.

6. Experiment:

n	1	2	3	4	5	6	7
$n!$	1	2	6	24	120	720	5040
n^3	1	8	27	64	125	216	343

Step 1: The inequality holds for $n = 6$, because

$$720 > 216.$$

Step 2: Suppose $k! > k^3$. Then $(k + 1)! > (k + 1)k^3$.

For $k \geq 4$, $k > 1 + \dfrac{2}{k} + \dfrac{1}{k^2}$ (since $\dfrac{2}{k} < 2$ and $\dfrac{1}{k^2} < 1$), and so $k^3 > k^2 + 2k + 1 = (k + 1)^2$. So $(k + 1)k^3 > (k + 1)^3$, and thus by the transitivity of $>$, $(k + 1)! > (k + 1)^3$.

The mathematical induction principle now guarantees the original inequality for all $n \geq 6$.

7. Experiment:

n	1	2	3	4	5	6
2^n	2	4	8	16	32	64
n^2	1	4	9	16	25	36

Step 1: The inequality holds for $n = 5$, because $32 > 25$.

Step 2: Suppose $2^k > k^2$. For $k \geq 3$, $k > 2 + \dfrac{1}{k}$ $\left(\text{since } \dfrac{1}{k} < 1\right)$, and so $k^2 > 2k + 1$. Then by the transitivity of $>$, $2^k > 2k + 1$. And thus

$$2^{k+1} = 2^k + 2^k > k^2 + 2k + 1 = (k + 1)^2.$$

The mathematical induction principle now guarantees the original inequality for all $n \geq 5$.

8. Step 1: The inequality holds for $n = -3$, because $2^{-3} = \dfrac{1}{8}$.

Step 2: Suppose $2^k \geq \dfrac{1}{8}$. Then $2^{k+1} = 2 \cdot 2^k \geq \dfrac{2}{8} = \dfrac{1}{4}$, and by the transitivity of $\geq$ and the fact that $\dfrac{1}{4} \geq \dfrac{1}{8}$, $2^{k+1} \geq \dfrac{1}{8}$.

The mathematical induction principle now guarantees the original inequality for $n \geq -3$.

9. Step 1: The formula holds for $n = 1$, because

$$1^2 = \frac{1(1 + 1/2)(1 + 1)}{3} = 1.$$

Step 2: Suppose $1^2 + 2^2 + \cdots + k^2 = \dfrac{k(k + 1/2)(k + 1)}{3}$.

Then $1^2 + 2^2 + \cdots + (k + 1)^2$

$$= \frac{k(k + 1/2)(k + 1)}{3} + (k + 1)^2$$

$$= \frac{k(k + 1/2)(k + 1) + 3(k + 1)^2}{3}$$

$$= \frac{k^3 + (9/2)k^2 + (13/2)k + 3}{3}$$

$$= \frac{(k + 1)(k + 3/2)(k + 2)}{3}$$

$$= \frac{(k + 1)[(k + 1) + 1/2][(k + 1) + 1]}{3}.$$

The mathematical induction principle now guarantees the original formula for all positive integers n.

10. Step 1: The formula holds for $n = 1$, because

$$1^3 = \left(\frac{1(1 + 1)}{2}\right)^2 = 1.$$

Step 2: Suppose $1^3 + 2^3 + \cdots + k^3 = \left(\dfrac{k(k + 1)}{2}\right)^2$.

Then $1^3 + 2^3 + \cdots + (k + 1)^3$

$$= \left(\frac{k(k + 1)}{2}\right)^2 + (k + 1)^3$$

$$= \frac{k^2(k + 1)^2}{4} + (k + 1)(k + 1)^2$$

$$= \left(\frac{k^2}{4} + k + 1\right)(k + 1)^2 = \left[\frac{(k + 2)^2}{4}\right](k + 1)^2$$

$$= \left(\frac{(k + 1)(k + 2)}{2}\right)^2.$$

The mathematical induction principle now guarantees the original formula for all positive integers n.

11. (a) Step 1: The formula holds for $n = 1$, because

$$\sum_{k=1}^{1} (a_k + b_k) = \sum_{k=1}^{1} a_k + \sum_{k=1}^{1} b_k = a_1 + b_1.$$

Step 2: Suppose $\displaystyle\sum_{k=1}^{i} (a_k + b_k) = \sum_{k=1}^{i} a_k + \sum_{k=1}^{i} b_k$. Then

$$\sum_{k=1}^{i+1} (a_k + b_k) = \left[\sum_{k=1}^{i} (a_k + b_k)\right] + (a_{i+1} + b_{i+1})$$

$$= \left[\sum_{k=1}^{i} a_k\right] + \left[\sum_{k=1}^{i} b_k\right] + a_{i+1} + b_{i+1}$$

$$= \sum_{k=1}^{i+1} a_k + \sum_{k=1}^{i+1} b_k.$$

The mathematical induction principle now guarantees the original formula for every positive integer n.

(b) Step 1: The formula holds for $n = 1$, because

$$\sum_{k=1}^{1}(a_k - b_k) = \sum_{k=1}^{1}a_k - \sum_{k=1}^{1}b_k = a_1 - b_1.$$

Step 2: Suppose $\sum_{k=1}^{i}(a_k - b_k) = \sum_{k=1}^{i}a_k - \sum_{k=1}^{i}b_k$. Then

$$\sum_{k=1}^{i+1}(a_k - b_k) = \left[\sum_{k=1}^{i}(a_k - b_k)\right] + (a_{i+1} - b_{i+1})$$

$$= \left[\sum_{k=1}^{i}a_k\right] - \left[\sum_{k=1}^{i}b_k\right] + a_{i+1} - b_{i+1}$$

$$= \sum_{k=1}^{i+1}a_k - \sum_{k=1}^{i+1}b_k.$$

The mathematical induction principle now guarantees the original formula for every positive integer n.

(c) Step 1: The formula holds for $n = 1$, because

$$\sum_{k=1}^{1}ca_k = c \cdot \sum_{k=1}^{1}a_k = ca_1.$$

Step 2: Suppose $\sum_{k=1}^{i}ca_k = c \cdot \sum_{k=1}^{i}a_k$. Then $\sum_{k=1}^{i+1}ca_{k+1}$

$$= \left[\sum_{k=1}^{i}ca_k\right] + ca_{k+1} = \left[c \cdot \sum_{k=1}^{i}a_k\right] + ca_{k+1}$$

$$= c\left[\left(\sum_{k=1}^{i}a_k\right) + a_{k+1}\right] = c \cdot \sum_{k=1}^{i+1}a_{k+1}.$$

The mathematical induction principle how guarantees the original formula for every positive integer n.

(d) Step 1: The formula $\sum_{k=1}^{n}c = n \cdot c$ holds for $n = 1$, because

$$\sum_{k=1}^{1}c = 1 \cdot c = c.$$

Step 2: Suppose $\sum_{k=1}^{i}c = i \cdot c$. Then

$$\sum_{k=1}^{i+1}c = i \cdot c + c = (i + 1) \cdot c.$$

The mathematical induction principle now guarantees the original formula for every positive integer n.

12. Step 1: The formula holds for $n = 1$ (and every real number x), because

$$|x^1| = |x|^1 = |x|.$$

Step 2: Suppose $|x^k| = |x|^k$. Then

$$|x^{k+1}| = |x^k \cdot x| = |x^k| \cdot |x| = |x|^k \cdot |x| = |x|^{k+1}.$$

The mathematical induction principle now guarantees the original formula for every positive integer n (and every real number x).

■ Appendix A3

(pp. 584–592)

1.

Step 1: $\left|x - \dfrac{1}{2}\right| < \delta \Rightarrow -\delta < x - \dfrac{1}{2} < \delta$

$\Rightarrow -\delta + \dfrac{1}{2} < x < \delta + \dfrac{1}{2}$

Step 2: $-\delta + \dfrac{1}{2} = \dfrac{4}{9} \Rightarrow \delta = \dfrac{1}{18}$, or $\delta + \dfrac{1}{2} = \dfrac{4}{7} \Rightarrow \delta = \dfrac{1}{14}$.

The value of δ which assures $\left|x - \dfrac{1}{2}\right| < \delta$

$\Rightarrow \dfrac{4}{9} < x < \dfrac{4}{7}$ is the smaller value, $\delta = \dfrac{1}{18}$.

2.

Step 1: $|x - 3| < \delta \Rightarrow -\delta < x - 3 < \delta$

$\Rightarrow -\delta + 3 < x < \delta + 3$

Step 2: $-\delta + 3 = 2.7591 \Rightarrow \delta = 0.2409$,

or $\delta + 3 = 3.2391 \Rightarrow \delta = 0.2391$.

The value of δ which assures $|x - 3| < \delta$

$\Rightarrow 2.7591 < x < 3.2391$ is the smaller value,

$\delta = 0.2391$.

3. Step 1: $|x - 3| < \delta \Rightarrow -\delta < x - 3 < \delta$

$\Rightarrow -\delta + 3 < x < \delta + 3$

Step 2: From the graph, $-\delta + 3 = 2.61 \Rightarrow \delta = 0.39$,

or $\delta + 3 = 3.41 \Rightarrow \delta = 0.41$; thus $\delta = 0.39$.

4. Step 1: $|x - (-1)| < \delta \Rightarrow -\delta < x + 1 < \delta$

$\Rightarrow -\delta - 1 < x < \delta - 1$

Step 2: From the graph, $-\delta - 1 = -\dfrac{16}{9} \Rightarrow \delta = \dfrac{7}{9}$

≈ 0.77, or $\delta - 1 = -\dfrac{16}{25} \Rightarrow \dfrac{9}{25} = 0.36$; thus

$\delta = \dfrac{9}{25} = 0.36$.

5. Step 1: $|(2x - 2) - (-6)| < 0.02 \Rightarrow |2x + 4| < 0.02$

$\Rightarrow -0.02 < 2x + 4 < 0.02$

$\Rightarrow -4.02 < 2x < -3.98 \Rightarrow -2.01 < x < -1.99$

Step 2: $|x - (-2)| < \delta \Rightarrow -\delta < x + 2 < \delta$

$\Rightarrow -\delta - 2 < x < \delta - 2 \Rightarrow \delta = 0.01$.

6. Step 1: $|\sqrt{x + 1} - 1| < 0.1 \Rightarrow -0.1 < \sqrt{x + 1} - 1 < 0.1$

$\Rightarrow 0.9 < \sqrt{x + 1} < 1.1 \Rightarrow 0.81 < x + 1 < 1.21$

$\Rightarrow -0.19 < x < 0.21$

Step 2: $|x - 0| < \delta \Rightarrow -\delta < x < \delta \Rightarrow \delta = 0.19$.

7. Step 1: $\left|\sqrt{19-x}-3\right|<1 \Rightarrow -1<\sqrt{19-x}-3<1$
$\Rightarrow 2<\sqrt{19-x}<4 \Rightarrow 4<19-x<16$
$\Rightarrow -4>x-19>-16 \Rightarrow 15>x>3$
or $3<x<15$

Step 2: $\left|x-10\right|<\delta \Rightarrow -\delta<x-10<\delta$
$\Rightarrow -\delta+10<x<\delta+10.$
Then $-\delta+10=3 \Rightarrow \delta=7$, or $\delta+10=15$
$\Rightarrow \delta=5$; thus $\delta=5$.

8. Step 1: $\left|x^2-4\right|<0.5 \Rightarrow -0.5<x^2-4<0.5$
$\Rightarrow 3.5<x^2<4.5 \Rightarrow \sqrt{3.5}<\left|x\right|<\sqrt{4.5}$
$\Rightarrow -\sqrt{4.5}<x<-\sqrt{3.5}$, for x near -2.

Step 2: $\left|x-(-2)\right|<\delta \Rightarrow -\delta<x+2<\delta$
$\Rightarrow -\delta-2<x<\delta-2.$
Then $-\delta-2=-\sqrt{4.5}$
$\Rightarrow \delta=\sqrt{4.5}-2 \approx 0.1213,$
or $\delta-2=-\sqrt{3.5} \Rightarrow \delta=2-\sqrt{3.5} \approx 0.1292;$
thus $\delta=\sqrt{4.5}-2 \approx 0.121.$

9. (a) $\lim\limits_{x\to-5}\dfrac{x^2+6x+5}{x+5}=\lim\limits_{x\to-5}\dfrac{(x+5)(x+1)}{x+5}=\lim\limits_{x\to-5}(x+1)$
$=-4$, $x\neq-5.$

(b) Step 1: $\left|\left(\dfrac{x^2+6x+5}{x+5}\right)-(-4)\right|<0.05$
$\Rightarrow -0.05<\dfrac{(x+5)(x+1)}{x+5}+4<0.05$
$\Rightarrow -4.05<x+1<-3.95$, $x\neq-5$
$\Rightarrow -5.05<x<-4.95$, $x\neq-5.$

Step 2: $\left|x-(-5)\right|<\delta \Rightarrow -\delta<x+5<\delta$
$\Rightarrow -\delta-5<x<\delta-5.$
Then $-\delta-5=-5.05 \Rightarrow \delta=0.05$, or
$\delta-5=-4.95 \Rightarrow \delta=0.05$; thus $\delta=0.05.$

10. (a) $\lim\limits_{x\to1^-}f(x)=\lim\limits_{x\to1^-}(4-2x)=2$ and
$\lim\limits_{x\to1^+}f(x)=\lim\limits_{x\to1^+}(6x-4)=2$, so $\lim\limits_{x\to1}f(x)=2.$

(b) Step 1: $x<1$: $(4-2x)-2<0.5 \Rightarrow 2-2x<0.5$
$\Rightarrow x\geq\dfrac{2-0.5}{2}=\dfrac{3}{4};$
$x\geq1$: $(6x-4)-2<0.5 \Rightarrow 6x-6<0.5$
$\Rightarrow x<\dfrac{6+0.5}{6}=\dfrac{13}{12}.$

Step 2: $\left|x-1\right|<\delta \Rightarrow -\delta<x-1<\delta$
$\Rightarrow 1-\delta<x<1+\delta.$
Then $1-\delta=\dfrac{3}{4} \Rightarrow \delta=\dfrac{1}{4}$, or $1+\delta=\dfrac{13}{12}$
$\Rightarrow \delta=\dfrac{1}{12}$. Choose $\delta=\dfrac{1}{12}.$

11. (a) $\lim\limits_{x\to1}(\sin x)=\sin 1 \approx 0.841$

(b) Step 1: $\left|\sin x-\sin 1\right|<0.01$
$\Rightarrow -0.01<\sin x-\sin 1<0.01$
$\Rightarrow \sin 1-0.01<\sin x<\sin 1+0.01$
$\Rightarrow \sin^{-1}(\sin 1-0.01)<x$
$<\sin^{-1}(\sin 1+0.01)$

Step 2: $\left|x-1\right|<\delta \Rightarrow -\delta<x-1<\delta$
$\Rightarrow 1-\delta<x<1+\delta.$
Then $1-\delta=\sin^{-1}(\sin 1-0.01)$
$\Rightarrow \delta=1-\sin^{-1}(\sin 1-0.01) \approx 0.0182$, or
$1+\delta=\sin^{-1}(\sin 1+0.01)$
$\Rightarrow \delta=\sin^{-1}(\sin 1+0.01)-1 \approx 0.0188.$
Choose $\delta=0.018.$

Alternately, graph $y_1=\sin x$, $y_2=\sin 1-1$, and
$y_3=\sin 1+1$. The curve intersects the lines at
$x\approx0.98175=1-0.01825$ and at
$x\approx1.01878=1+0.01878.$ We may choose
$\delta=0.018.$

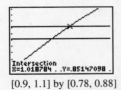

[0.9, 1.1] by [0.78, 0.88]

12. (a) $\lim\limits_{x \to -1} \dfrac{x}{x^2 - 4} = \dfrac{-1}{(-1)^2 - 4} = \dfrac{1}{3}$

   (b) Step 1: $\left| \dfrac{x}{x^2 - 4} - \dfrac{1}{3} \right| < 0.1$

   $\Rightarrow -0.1 < \dfrac{x}{x^2 - 4} - \dfrac{1}{3} < 0.1$

   $\Rightarrow \dfrac{7}{30} < \dfrac{x}{x^2 - 4} < \dfrac{13}{30}$

   $\Rightarrow \dfrac{7}{30}x^2 - \dfrac{28}{30} > x > \dfrac{13}{30}x^2 - \dfrac{52}{30}$ for x near -1.

   Then $\dfrac{7}{30}x^2 - x - \dfrac{28}{30} > 0 > \dfrac{13}{30}x^2 - x - \dfrac{52}{30}$,

   which using the quadratic formula implies

   $x < \dfrac{15 - \sqrt{421}}{7} \approx -0.7883$ or

   $x > \dfrac{15 + \sqrt{421}}{7} \approx 5.0740$, and also

   $\dfrac{15 - \sqrt{901}}{13} \approx -1.1551 < x < \dfrac{15 + \sqrt{901}}{13}$

   ≈ 3.4628. Thus $\dfrac{15 - \sqrt{901}}{13} < x < \dfrac{15 - \sqrt{421}}{7}$.

   Step 2: $|x - (-1)| < \delta \Rightarrow -\delta < x + 1 < \delta$

   $\Rightarrow -\delta - 1 < x < \delta - 1$.

   Then $-\delta - 1 = \dfrac{15 - \sqrt{901}}{13}$

   $\Rightarrow \delta = \dfrac{\sqrt{901} - 28}{13} \approx 0.1551$,

   or $\delta - 1 = \dfrac{15 - \sqrt{421}}{7}$

   $\Rightarrow \delta = \dfrac{22 - \sqrt{421}}{7} \approx 0.2117$.

   Choose $\delta = 0.155$.

   Alternately, graph $y_1 = \dfrac{x}{x^2 - 4}$, $y_2 = \dfrac{1}{3} - 0.1$, and

   $y_3 = \dfrac{1}{3} + 0.1$. The curve intersects the lines at

   $x \approx -1.15513 = -1 - 0.15513$ and at

   $x \approx -0.78833 = -1 + 0.21167$. We may choose

   $\delta = 0.155$.

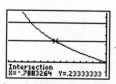

   Intersection
   X=-.7883264 Y=.23333333

   $[-1.5, 0]$ by $[-0.15, 0.55]$

13. Step 1: For $x \neq 1$, $|x^2 - 1| < \epsilon \Rightarrow -\epsilon < x^2 - 1 < \epsilon$

   $\Rightarrow 1 - \epsilon < x^2 < 1 + \epsilon$

   $\Rightarrow \sqrt{1 - \epsilon} < |x| < \sqrt{1 + \epsilon}$

   $\Rightarrow \sqrt{1 - \epsilon} < x < \sqrt{1 + \epsilon}$ near $x = 1$.

   Step 2: $|x - 1| < \delta \Rightarrow -\delta < x - 1 < \delta$

   $\Rightarrow -\delta + 1 < x < \delta + 1$.

   Then $-\delta + 1 = \sqrt{1 - \epsilon} \Rightarrow \delta = 1 - \sqrt{1 - \epsilon}$,

   or $\delta + 1 = \sqrt{1 + \epsilon} \Rightarrow \delta = \sqrt{1 + \epsilon} - 1$.

   Choose $\delta = \min\{1 - \sqrt{1 - \epsilon},\ \sqrt{1 + \epsilon} - 1\}$,

   that is, the smaller of the two distances.

14. Step 1: $\left| \dfrac{1}{x^2} - \dfrac{1}{3} \right| < \epsilon \Rightarrow -\epsilon < \dfrac{1}{x^2} - \dfrac{1}{3} < \epsilon$

   $\Rightarrow \dfrac{1}{3} - \epsilon < \dfrac{1}{x^2} < \dfrac{1}{3} + \epsilon$

   $\Rightarrow \dfrac{1 - 3\epsilon}{3} < \dfrac{1}{x^2} < \dfrac{1 + 3\epsilon}{3} \Rightarrow \dfrac{3}{1 - 3\epsilon} > x^2 > \dfrac{3}{1 + 3\epsilon}$

   $\Rightarrow \sqrt{\dfrac{3}{1 + 3\epsilon}} < |x| < \sqrt{\dfrac{3}{1 - 3\epsilon}}$,

   or $\sqrt{\dfrac{3}{1 + 3\epsilon}} < x < \sqrt{\dfrac{3}{1 - 3\epsilon}}$ for x near $\sqrt{3}$.

   Step 2: $|x - \sqrt{3}| < \delta \Rightarrow -\delta < x - \sqrt{3} < \delta$

   $\Rightarrow \sqrt{3} - \delta < x < \sqrt{3} + \delta$.

   Then $\sqrt{3} - \delta = \sqrt{\dfrac{3}{1 + 3\epsilon}} \Rightarrow \delta = \sqrt{3} - \sqrt{\dfrac{3}{1 + 3\epsilon}}$,

   or $\sqrt{3} + \delta = \sqrt{\dfrac{3}{1 - 3\epsilon}} \Rightarrow \delta = \sqrt{\dfrac{3}{1 - 3\epsilon}} - \sqrt{3}$.

   Choose

   $\delta = \min\left\{ \sqrt{3} - \sqrt{\dfrac{3}{1 + 3\epsilon}},\ \sqrt{\dfrac{3}{1 - 3\epsilon}} - \sqrt{3} \right\}$.

15. (a) $\sqrt{(5 + \delta) - 5} = \epsilon \Rightarrow \sqrt{\delta} = \epsilon \Rightarrow \delta = \epsilon^2$

   $\Rightarrow I = (5, 5 + \epsilon^2)$

   (b) $\lim\limits_{x \to 5^+} \sqrt{x - 5} = 0$

16. (a) $\sqrt{4 - (4 - \delta)} = \epsilon \Rightarrow \sqrt{\delta} = \epsilon \Rightarrow \delta = \epsilon^2$

   $\Rightarrow I = (4 - \epsilon^2, 4)$

   (b) $\lim\limits_{x \to 4^-} \sqrt{4 - x} = 0$

17. If L, c, and k are real numbers and $\lim\limits_{x \to c} f(x) = L$, show that

   for any $\epsilon > 0$, there is a $\delta > 0$ such that $0 < |x - c| < \delta$

   $\Rightarrow |k \cdot f(x) = k \cdot L| < \epsilon$.

   Proof: For any $\epsilon > 0$, let $\epsilon' = \dfrac{\epsilon}{|k|}$. Since $\lim\limits_{x \to c} f(x) = L$, there

   is a $\delta > 0$ such that $0 < |x - c| < \delta \Rightarrow |f(x) - L| < \epsilon'$

   $= \dfrac{\epsilon}{|k|}$. Therefore, $0 < |x - c| < \delta \Rightarrow |k \cdot f(x) - k \cdot L| < \epsilon$.

18. If L, M, and c are real numbers and $\lim\limits_{x \to c} f(x) = L$ and $\lim\limits_{x \to c} g(x) = M$, show that for any $\epsilon > 0$, there is a $\delta > 0$ such that $0 < |x - c| < \delta \Rightarrow |f(x) - g(x) - (L - M)| < \epsilon$.

Proof: $|f(x) - g(x) - (L - M)| = |f(x) - L + M - g(x)|$

$\leq |f(x) - L| + |M - g(x)| = |f(x) - L| + |g(x) - M|$ by the

triangle inequality. Since $\lim\limits_{x \to c} f(x) = L$, $\lim\limits_{x \to c} g(x) = M$, for

any ϵ there exist δ_1, δ_2 such that

$0 < |x - c| < \delta_1 \Rightarrow |f(x) - L| < \dfrac{\epsilon}{2}$ and

$0 < |x - c| < \delta_2 \Rightarrow |g(x) - M| < \dfrac{\epsilon}{2}$.

Choose $\delta = \min \{\delta_1, \delta_2\}$. Then

$0 < |x - c| < \delta \Rightarrow |f(x) - L| + |g(x) - M| < \dfrac{\epsilon}{2} + \dfrac{\epsilon}{2} = \epsilon$

$\Rightarrow |f(x) - g(x) - (L - M)| < \epsilon.$

19. $\lim\limits_{x \to c} [f_1(x) + f_2(x) + f_3(x)] = \lim\limits_{x \to c} [f_1(x) + f_2(x)] + L_3$

$= L_1 + L_2 + L_3$, by two applications of the Sum Rule.

To generalize:

Step 1 ($n = 1$): $\lim\limits_{x \to c} f_1(x) = L_1$ as given.

Step 2: Suppose $\lim\limits_{x \to c} [f_1(x) + f_2(x) + \cdots + f_k(x)]$

$= L_1 + L_2 + \cdots + L_k$. Then

$\lim\limits_{x \to c} [f_1(x) + f_2(x) + \cdots + f_{k+1}(x)]$

$= \lim [f_1(x) + f_2(x) + \cdots + f_k(x)] + L_{k+1}$

$= L_1 + L_2 + \cdots + L_{k+1}$, by the Sum Rule.

20. Step 1 ($n = 1$): $\lim\limits_{x \to c} f_1(x) = L_1$, as given.

Step 2: Suppose $\lim\limits_{x \to c} (f_1(x) \cdot f_2(x) \cdot \cdots \cdot f_k(x))$

$= L_1 \cdot L_2 \cdot \cdots \cdot L_k$. Then

$\lim\limits_{x \to c} (f_1(x) \cdot f_2(x) \cdot \cdots \cdot f_{k+1}(x))$

$= \lim\limits_{x \to c} (f_1(x)) \cdot f_2(x) \cdot \cdots \cdot f_k(x)) \cdot L_{k+1}$

$= L_1 \cdot L_2 \cdot \cdots \cdot L_{k+1}$, by the Product Rule.

21. $\lim\limits_{x \to c} x^n = \lim\limits_{x \to c} \underbrace{(x \cdot x \cdot \cdots \cdot x)}_{n \text{ factors}} = \underbrace{c \cdot c \cdot \cdots \cdot c}_{n \text{ factors}} = c^n$

22. $\lim\limits_{x \to c} f(x) = \lim\limits_{x \to c} (a_n x^n + a_{n-1} x^{n-1} + \cdots + a_1 x + a_0)$

$= \lim\limits_{x \to c} a_n x^n + \lim\limits_{x \to c} a_{n-1} x^{n-1} + \cdots + \lim\limits_{x \to c} a_1 x + \lim\limits_{x \to c} a_0$

$= a_n \lim\limits_{x \to c} x^n + a_{a-1} \lim\limits_{x \to c} x^{n-1} + \cdots + a_1 \lim\limits_{x \to c} x + \lim\limits_{x \to c} a_0$

$= a_n c^n + a_{n-1} c^{n-1} + \cdots a_1 c + a_0 = f(c)$, where in

addition to the items given in the problem, the Constant

Multiple Rule was used (to move the coefficients out of the

scope of the limit signs).

23. By the Quotient Rule, $\lim\limits_{x \to c} \dfrac{f(x)}{g(x)} = \dfrac{\lim\limits_{x \to c} f(x)}{\lim\limits_{x \to c} g(x)} = \dfrac{f(c)}{g(c)}$.

24. From the continuity of g, for any $\epsilon > 0$ there is a $\delta > 0$

such that $0 < |f(x) - f(c)| < \delta \Rightarrow |g(f(x)) - g(f(c))| < \epsilon$.

The second inequality also holds when $f(x) = f(c)$, so

$|f(x) - f(c)| < \delta \Rightarrow |g(f(x)) - g(f(c))| < \epsilon$. But from the

continuity of f, there is a $\gamma > 0$ such that

$0 < |x - c| < \gamma \Rightarrow |f(x) - f(c)| < \delta$. So for any $\epsilon > 0$

there is a $\gamma > 0$ such that

$0 < |x - c| < \gamma \Rightarrow |g(f(x)) - g(f(c))| < \epsilon$, which means

that $g(f(x)) = g \circ f$ is continuous at c.

■ Appendix A5.1

(pp. 593–606)

1. $(x - h)^2 + (y - k)^2 = a^2$
$(x - 0)^2 + (y - 2)^2 = 2^2$
$x^2 + (y - 2)^2 = 4$

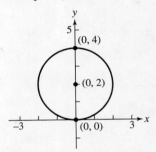

2. $(x - h)^2 + (y - k)^2 = a^2$
$[x - (-1)]^2 + (y - 5)^2 = (\sqrt{10})^2$
$(x + 1)^2 + (y - 5)^2 = 10$

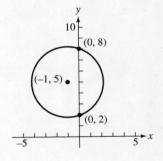

3. Complete the squares.
$$x^2 + y^2 + 4x - 4y + 4 = 0$$
$$x^2 + 4x + 4 + y^2 - 4y + 4 = 4$$
$$(x + 2)^2 + (y - 2)^2 = 2^2$$
Center $= (-2, 2)$; radius $= 2$

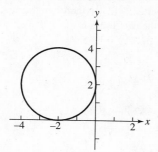

4. Complete the squares.
$$x^2 + y^2 - 4x + 4y = 0$$
$$x^2 - 4x + 4 + y^2 + 4y + 4 = 8$$
$$(x - 2)^2 + (y + 2)^2 = (2\sqrt{2})^2$$
Center $= (2, -2)$; radius $= 2\sqrt{2}$

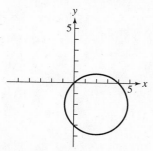

5. The circle with center at $(1, 0)$ and radius 2 plus its interior.

6. The region exterior to the unit circle and interior to the circle with center at $(0, 0)$ and radius 2.

7. $y^2 = 8x \Rightarrow 4p = 8 \Rightarrow p = 2$; focus is $(2, 0)$, directrix is $x = -2$

8. $y^2 = -4x \Rightarrow 4p = 4 \Rightarrow p = 1$; focus is $(-1, 0)$, directrix is $x = 1$

9. $x^2 = -6y \Rightarrow 4p = 6 \Rightarrow p = \dfrac{3}{2}$; focus is $\left(0, -\dfrac{3}{2}\right)$, directrix is $y = \dfrac{3}{2}$

10. $x^2 = 2y \Rightarrow 4p = 2 \Rightarrow p = \dfrac{1}{2}$; focus is $\left(0, \dfrac{1}{2}\right)$, directrix is $y = -\dfrac{1}{2}$

11. $\dfrac{x^2}{4} - \dfrac{y^2}{9} = 1 \Rightarrow c = \sqrt{4 + 9} = \sqrt{13}$
$\Rightarrow$ foci are $(\pm\sqrt{13}, 0)$; vertices are $(\pm 2, 0)$;
asymptotes are $y = \pm\dfrac{3}{2}x$

12. $\dfrac{x^2}{4} + \dfrac{y^2}{9} = 1 \Rightarrow c = \sqrt{9 - 4} = \sqrt{5} \Rightarrow$ foci are $(0, \pm\sqrt{5})$;
vertices are $(0, \pm 3)$

13. $\dfrac{x^2}{2} + y^2 = 1 \Rightarrow c = \sqrt{2 - 1} = 1 \Rightarrow$ foci are $(\pm 1, 0)$;
vertices are $(\pm\sqrt{2}, 0)$

14. $\dfrac{y^2}{4} - x^2 = 1 \Rightarrow c = \sqrt{4 + 1} = \sqrt{5} \Rightarrow$ foci are $(0, \pm\sqrt{5})$;
vertices are $(0, \pm 2)$; asymptotes are $y = \pm 2x$

15. $y^2 = 12x \Rightarrow 4p = 12 \Rightarrow p = 3$; focus is $(3, 0)$, directrix is
$x = -3$

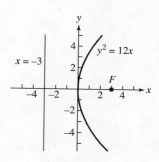

16. $y = 4x^2 \Rightarrow x^2 = \dfrac{1}{4}y \Rightarrow 4p = \dfrac{1}{4} \Rightarrow p = \dfrac{1}{16}$;
focus is $\left(0, \dfrac{1}{16}\right)$, directrix is $y = -\dfrac{1}{16}$

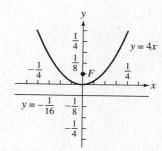

17. $16x^2 + 25y^2 = 400 \Rightarrow \dfrac{x^2}{25} + \dfrac{y^2}{16} = 1$
$\Rightarrow c = \sqrt{a^2 - b^2} = \sqrt{25 - 16} = 3$
foci are $(\pm 3, 0)$

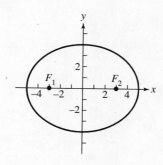

18. $3x^2 + 2y^2 = 6 \Rightarrow \dfrac{x^2}{2} + \dfrac{y^2}{3} = 1$

$\Rightarrow c = \sqrt{a^2 - b^2} = \sqrt{3 - 2} = 1$

foci are $(0, \pm 1)$

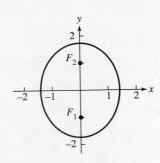

19. Foci: $(\pm\sqrt{2}, 0)$, Vertices: $(\pm 2, 0) \Rightarrow a = 2, c = \sqrt{2}$

$\Rightarrow b^2 = a^2 - c^2 = 4 - (\sqrt{2})^2 = 2 \Rightarrow \dfrac{x^2}{4} + \dfrac{y^2}{2} = 1$

20. Foci: $(0, \pm 4)$, Vertices: $(0, \pm 5) \Rightarrow a = 5, c = 4$

$\Rightarrow b^2 = 25 - 16 = 9 \Rightarrow \dfrac{x^2}{9} + \dfrac{y^2}{25} = 1$

21. $x^2 - y^2 = 1 \Rightarrow c = \sqrt{a^2 + b^2} = \sqrt{1 + 1} = \sqrt{2}$;
asymptotes are $y = \pm x$,
foci are $(\pm\sqrt{2}, 0)$

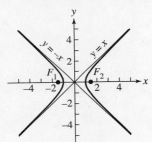

22. $8y^2 - 2x^2 = 16 \Rightarrow \dfrac{y^2}{2} - \dfrac{x^2}{8} = 1$

$\Rightarrow c = \sqrt{a^2 + b^2} = \sqrt{2 + 8} = \sqrt{10}$;

asymptotes are $y = \pm\dfrac{x}{2}$, foci are $(0, \pm\sqrt{10})$

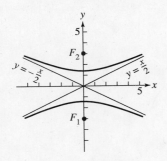

23. Foci: $(0, \pm\sqrt{2})$, Asymptotes: $y = \pm x \Rightarrow c = \sqrt{2}$

and $\dfrac{b}{a} = 1 \Rightarrow a = b \Rightarrow c^2 = a^2 + b^2 = 2a^2 \Rightarrow 2 = 2a^2$

$\Rightarrow a = 1 \Rightarrow b = 1 \Rightarrow y^2 - x^2 = 1$

24. Vertices: $(\pm 3, 0)$, Asymptotes: $y = \pm\dfrac{4}{3}x \Rightarrow a = 3$

and $\dfrac{b}{a} = \dfrac{4}{3} \Rightarrow b = \dfrac{4}{3}(3) = 4 \Rightarrow \dfrac{x^2}{9} - \dfrac{y^2}{16} = 1$

25. (a) $y^2 = 8x \Rightarrow 4p = 8 \Rightarrow p = 2 \Rightarrow$ directrix is $x = -2$,
focus is $(2, 0)$, and vertex is $(0, 0)$; therefore the new
directrix is $x = -1$, the new focus is $(3, -2)$, and the
new vertex is $(1, -2)$.

(b)

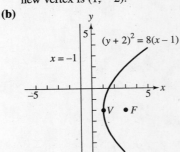

26. (a) $\dfrac{x^2}{16} + \dfrac{y^2}{9} = 1 \Rightarrow$ center is $(0, 0)$, vertices are $(-4, 0)$

and $(4, 0)$, $c = \sqrt{a^2 - b^2} = \sqrt{7} \Rightarrow$ foci are $(\sqrt{7}, 0)$

and $(-\sqrt{7}, 0)$; therefore the new center is $(4, 3)$, the

new vertices are $(0, 3)$ and $(8, 3)$, and the new foci are

$(4 \pm \sqrt{7}, 3)$.

(b)

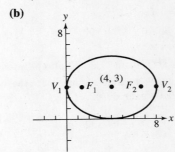

27. (a) $\dfrac{x^2}{16} - \dfrac{y^2}{9} = 1 \Rightarrow$ center is $(0, 0)$, vertices are $(-4, 0)$

and $(4, 0)$, and the asymptotes are $y = \pm\dfrac{3x}{4}$,

$c = \sqrt{a^2 + b^2} = \sqrt{25} = 5 \Rightarrow$ foci are $(-5, 0)$ and

$(5, 0)$; therefore the new center is $(2, 0)$, the new

vertices are $(-2, 0)$ and $(6, 0)$, the new foci are $(-3, 0)$

and $(7, 0)$, and the new asymptotes are $y = \pm\dfrac{3(x - 2)}{4}$.

(b)

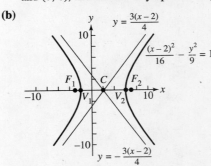

28. Original parabola: $y^2 = 4x$; vertex is $(0, 0)$; $y^2 = 4x$
$\Rightarrow 4p = 4 \Rightarrow p = 1$, so focus is $(1, 0)$ and directrix is
$x = -1$.
New parabola: $(y + 3)^2 = 4(x + 2)$; vertex is $(-2, -3)$,
focus is $(-1, -3)$, directrix is $x = -3$.

29. Original ellipse: $\dfrac{x^2}{6} + \dfrac{y^2}{9} = 1$; vertices are $(0, 3)$ and

$(0, -3)$; $c^2 = 9 - 6 \Rightarrow c = \sqrt{3} \Rightarrow$ foci are $(0, \pm\sqrt{3})$;

center is $(0, 0)$.

New ellipse: $\dfrac{(x + 2)^2}{6} + \dfrac{(y + 1)^2}{9} = 1$; vertices are

$(-2, 2)$ and $(-2, -4)$; foci are $(-2, -1 \pm \sqrt{3})$; center is

$(-2, -1)$.

30. Original hyperbola: $\dfrac{x^2}{4} - \dfrac{y^2}{5} = 1$; vertices are $(2, 0)$ and

$(-2, 0)$; $c^2 = 4 + 5 \Rightarrow c = 3 \Rightarrow$ foci are $(3, 0)$ and

$(-3, 0)$; center is $(0, 0)$; asymptotes are $y = \pm\dfrac{\sqrt{5}}{2}x$.

New hyperbola: $\dfrac{(x - 2)^2}{4} - \dfrac{(y - 2)^2}{5} = 1$; vertices are $(4, 2)$

and $(0, 2)$; foci are $(5, 2)$ and $(-1, 2)$; center is $(2, 2)$;

asymptotes are $y = \pm\dfrac{\sqrt{5}}{2}(x - 2) + 2$.

31. Original hyperbola: $y^2 - x^2 = 1$; vertices are $(0, 1)$ and
$(0, -1)$; $c^2 = 1 + 1 \Rightarrow c = \sqrt{2} \Rightarrow$ foci are $(0, \pm\sqrt{2})$;
center is $(0, 0)$; asymptotes are $y = \pm x$.
New hyperbola: $(y - 1)^2 - (x + 1)^2 = 1$; vertices are
$(-1, 2)$ and $(-1, 0)$; foci are $(-1, 1 \pm \sqrt{2})$; center is
$(-1, 1)$; asymptotes are $y = \pm(x + 1) + 1$.

32. $x^2 + 4x + y^2 = 12 \Rightarrow x^2 + 4x + 4 + y^2 = 12 + 4$
$\Rightarrow (x + 2)^2 + y^2 = 16$; this is a circle: center at $C(-2, 0)$,
$a = 4$

33. $2x^2 + 2y^2 - 28x + 12y + 114 = 0$
$\Rightarrow x^2 - 14x + 49 + y^2 + 6y + 9 = -57 + 49 + 9$
$\Rightarrow (x - 7)^2 + (y + 3)^2 = 1$; this is a circle: center at
$C(7, -3)$, $a = 1$

34. $x^2 + 2x + 4y - 3 = 0 \Rightarrow x^2 + 2x + 1 = -4y + 3 + 1$
$\Rightarrow (x + 1)^2 = -4(y - 1)$; this is a parabola:
$V(-1, 1)$, $F(-1, 0)$

35. $x^2 + 5y^2 + 4x = 1 \Rightarrow x^2 + 4x + 4 + 5y^2 = 4 + 1$

$\Rightarrow (x + 2)^2 + 5y^2 = 5 \Rightarrow \dfrac{(x + 2)^2}{5} + y^2 = 1$; this is an

ellipse: the center is $(-2, 0)$, the vertices are

$(-2 \pm \sqrt{5}, 0)$; $c = \sqrt{a^2 - b^2} = \sqrt{5 - 1} = 2$

$\Rightarrow$ the foci are $(-4, 0)$ and $(0, 0)$

36. $x^2 - y^2 - 2x + 4y = 4$
$\Rightarrow x^2 - 2x + 1 - (y^2 - 4y + 4) = 1$
$\Rightarrow (x - 1)^2 - (y - 2)^2 = 1$; this is a hyperbola: the center
is $(1, 2)$, the vertices are $(2, 2)$ and $(0, 2)$;
$c = \sqrt{a^2 + b^2} = \sqrt{1 + 1} = \sqrt{2} \Rightarrow$ the foci are
$(1 \pm \sqrt{2}, 2)$; the asymptotes are $y - 2 = \pm(x - 1)$

37. Volume of the Parabolic Solid:

$$V_1 = \int_0^{b/2} 2\pi x\left(h - \frac{4h}{b^2}x^2\right)dx = 2\pi h \int_0^{b/2}\left(x - \frac{4x^3}{b^2}\right)dx$$

$$= 2\pi h\left[\frac{x^2}{2} - \frac{x^4}{b^2}\right]_0^{b/2} = \frac{\pi h b^2}{8};$$

Volume of the Cone: $V_2 = \dfrac{1}{3}\pi\left(\dfrac{b}{2}\right)^2 h = \dfrac{1}{3}\pi\left(\dfrac{b^2}{4}\right)h = \dfrac{\pi h b^2}{12}$;

therefore $V_1 = \dfrac{3}{2}V_2$

38. (a) $y^2 = kx \Rightarrow x = \dfrac{y^2}{k}$; the volume of the solid formed by

revolving A about the y-axis is

$$V_1 = \int_0^{\sqrt{kx}} \pi\left(\frac{y^2}{k}\right)^2 dy = \frac{\pi}{k^2}\int_0^{\sqrt{kx}} y^4\, dy = \frac{\pi x^2\sqrt{kx}}{5};\text{ the}$$

volume of the right circular cylinder formed by

revolving the rectangle about the y-axis is

$V_2 = \pi x^2\sqrt{kx} \Rightarrow$ the volume of the solid formed by

revolving B about the y-axis is $V_3 = V_2 - V_1 =$

$\dfrac{4\pi x^2\sqrt{kx}}{5}$. Therefore we can see the ratio of V_3 to V_1 is

$4:1$.

(b) The volume of the solid formed by revolving B about

the x-axis is $V_1 = \int_0^x \pi(\sqrt{kt})^2\, dt = \pi k\int_0^x t\, dt = \dfrac{\pi k x^2}{2}$.

The volume of the right circular cylinder formed by

revolving the rectangle about the x-axis is

$V_2 = \pi(\sqrt{kx})^2 x = \pi k x^2 \Rightarrow$ the volume of the solid

formed by revolving A about the x-axis is

$V_3 = V_2 - V_1 = \pi k x^2 - \dfrac{\pi k x^2}{2} = \dfrac{\pi k x^2}{2}$. Therefore the

ratio of V_3 to V_1 is $1:1$.

39. Let $P_1(-p, y_1)$ be any point on $x = -p$, and let $P(x, y)$ be a

point where a tangent intersects $y^2 = 4px$. Now

$y^2 = 4px \Rightarrow 2y\dfrac{dy}{dx} = 4p \Rightarrow \dfrac{dy}{dx} = \dfrac{2p}{y}$; then the slope of a

tangent line from P_1 is $\dfrac{y - y_1}{x - (-p)} = \dfrac{dy}{dx} = \dfrac{2p}{y}$

$\Rightarrow y^2 - yy_1 = 2px + 2p^2$. Since $x = \dfrac{y^2}{4p}$, we have

$y^2 - yy_1 = 2p\left(\dfrac{y^2}{4p}\right) + 2p^2 \Rightarrow y^2 - yy_1 = \dfrac{1}{2}y^2 + 2p^2$

$\Rightarrow \dfrac{1}{2}y^2 - yy_1 - 2p^2 = 0$

$\Rightarrow y = \dfrac{2y_1 \pm \sqrt{4y_1{}^2 + 16p^2}}{2} = y_1 \pm \sqrt{y_1{}^2 + 4p^2}$. Therefore

the slopes of the two tangents from P_1 are

$m_1 = \dfrac{2p}{y_1 + \sqrt{y_1{}^2 + 4p^2}}$ and $m_2 = \dfrac{2p}{y_1 - \sqrt{y_1{}^2 + 4p^2}}$

$\Rightarrow m_1 m_2 = \dfrac{4p^2}{y_1{}^2 - (y_1{}^2 + 4p^2)} = -1 \Rightarrow$ the lines are

perpendicular.

40. Let $y = \sqrt{1 - \dfrac{x^2}{4}}$ on the interval $0 \le x \le 2$. The area of

the inscribed rectangle is given by

$A(x) = 2x\left(2\sqrt{1 - \dfrac{x^2}{4}}\right) = 4x\sqrt{1 - \dfrac{x^2}{4}}$ (since the length is $2x$

and the height is $2y$) $\Rightarrow A'(x) = 4\sqrt{1 - \dfrac{x^2}{4}} - \dfrac{x^2}{\sqrt{1 - \dfrac{x^2}{4}}}$.

Thus $A'(x) = 0 \Rightarrow 4\sqrt{1 - \dfrac{x^2}{4}} - \dfrac{x^2}{\sqrt{1 - \dfrac{x^2}{4}}} = 0$

$\Rightarrow 4\left(1 - \dfrac{x^2}{4}\right) - x^2 = 0 \Rightarrow x^2 = 2 \Rightarrow x = \sqrt{2}$ (only the

positive square root lies in the interval). Since

$A(0) = A(2) = 0$ we have that $A(\sqrt{2}) = 4$ is the maximum

area, when the length is $2\sqrt{2}$ and the height is $\sqrt{2}$.

41. (a) Around the x-axis: $9x^2 + 4y^2 = 36 \Rightarrow y^2 = 9 - \dfrac{9}{4}x^2$

$\Rightarrow y = \pm\sqrt{9 - \dfrac{9}{4}x^2}$ and we use the positive root

$\Rightarrow V = 2\displaystyle\int_0^2 \pi\left(\sqrt{9 - \dfrac{9}{4}x^2}\right)^2 dx = 2\displaystyle\int_0^2 \pi\left(9 - \dfrac{9}{4}x^2\right) dx$

$= 2\pi\left[9x - \dfrac{3}{4}x^3\right]_0^2 = 24\pi$

(b) Around the y-axis: $9x^2 + 4y^2 = 36 \Rightarrow x^2 = 4 - \dfrac{4}{9}y^2$

$\Rightarrow x = \pm\sqrt{4 - \dfrac{4}{9}y^2}$ and we use the positive root

$\Rightarrow V = 2\displaystyle\int_0^3 \pi\left(\sqrt{4 - \dfrac{4}{9}y^2}\right)^2 dy = 2\displaystyle\int_0^3 \pi\left(4 - \dfrac{4}{9}y^2\right) dy$

$= 2\pi\left[4y - \dfrac{4}{27}y^3\right]_0^3 = 16\pi$

42. $9x^2 - 4y^2 = 36 \Rightarrow y^2 = \dfrac{9x^2 - 36}{4} \Rightarrow y = \pm\dfrac{3}{2}\sqrt{x^2 - 4}$ on

the interval $2 \le x \le 4 \Rightarrow V = \displaystyle\int_2^4 \pi\left(\dfrac{3}{2}\sqrt{x^2 - 4}\right)^2 dx$

$= \dfrac{9\pi}{4}\displaystyle\int_2^4 (x^2 - 4)\, dx = \dfrac{9\pi}{4}\left[\dfrac{x^3}{3} - 4x\right]_2^4$

$= \dfrac{9\pi}{4}\left[\left(\dfrac{64}{3} - 16\right) - \left(\dfrac{8}{3} - 8\right)\right] = \dfrac{9\pi}{4}\left(\dfrac{56}{3} - 8\right)$

$= \dfrac{3\pi}{4}(56 - 24) = 24\pi$

43. $x^2 - y^2 = 1 \Rightarrow x = \pm\sqrt{1 + y^2}$ on the interval $-3 \le y \le 3$

$\Rightarrow V = \displaystyle\int_{-3}^3 \pi(\sqrt{1 + y^2})^2\, dy = 2\displaystyle\int_0^3 \pi(\sqrt{1 + y^2})^2\, dy$

$= 2\pi\displaystyle\int_0^3 (1 + y^2)\, dy = 2\pi\left[y + \dfrac{y^3}{3}\right]_0^3 = 24\pi$

44. $y = \displaystyle\int \dfrac{w}{H}x\, dx = \dfrac{w}{H}\left(\dfrac{x^2}{2}\right) + C = \dfrac{wx^2}{2H} + C$; $y = 0$ when

$x = 0 \Rightarrow 0 = \dfrac{w(0)^2}{2H} + C \Rightarrow C = 0$; therefore $y = \dfrac{wx^2}{2H}$ is the

equation of the cable's curve.

45. $\dfrac{dr_A}{dt} = \dfrac{dr_B}{dt} \Rightarrow \dfrac{d}{dt}(r_A - r_B) = 0$

$\Rightarrow r_A - r_B =$ a constant

46. PF will always equal PB because the string has constant
length $AB = FP + PA = AP + PB$.

■ Appendix A5.2
(pp. 606–611)

1. $16x^2 + 25y^2 = 400 \Rightarrow \dfrac{x^2}{25} + \dfrac{y^2}{16} = 1$

$\Rightarrow c = \sqrt{a^2 - b^2} = \sqrt{25 - 16} = 3$

$\Rightarrow e = \dfrac{c}{a} = \dfrac{3}{5}$; $F(\pm 3, 0)$; directrices are

$x = 0 \pm \dfrac{a}{e} = \pm\dfrac{5}{\left(\frac{3}{5}\right)} = \pm\dfrac{25}{3}$

2. $2x^2 + y^2 = 2 \Rightarrow x^2 + \dfrac{y^2}{2} = 1$

$\Rightarrow c = \sqrt{a^2 - b^2} = \sqrt{2 - 1} = 1$

$\Rightarrow e = \dfrac{c}{a} = \dfrac{1}{\sqrt{2}}$; $F(0, \pm 1)$; directrices are

$y = 0 \pm \dfrac{a}{e} = \pm\dfrac{\sqrt{2}}{\left(\frac{1}{\sqrt{2}}\right)} = \pm 2$

3. $3x^2 + 2y^2 = 6 \Rightarrow \dfrac{x^2}{2} + \dfrac{y^2}{3} = 1$

$\Rightarrow c = \sqrt{a^2 - b^2} = \sqrt{3 - 2} = 1 \Rightarrow e = \dfrac{c}{a} = \dfrac{1}{\sqrt{3}};$

$F(0, \pm 1);$ directrices are $y = 0 \pm \dfrac{a}{e} = \pm \dfrac{\sqrt{3}}{\left(\dfrac{1}{\sqrt{3}}\right)} = \pm 3$

4. $6x^2 + 9y^2 = 54 \Rightarrow \dfrac{x^2}{9} + \dfrac{y^2}{6} = 1$

$\Rightarrow c = \sqrt{a^2 - b^2} = \sqrt{9 - 6} = \sqrt{3} \Rightarrow e = \dfrac{c}{a} = \dfrac{\sqrt{3}}{3}$

$= \dfrac{1}{\sqrt{3}};\ F(\pm\sqrt{3}, 0);$ directrices are

$x = 0 \pm \dfrac{a}{e} = \pm \dfrac{3}{\left(\dfrac{1}{\sqrt{3}}\right)} = \pm 3\sqrt{3}$

5. Foci: $(0, \pm 3),\ e = 0.5 \Rightarrow c = 3$ and $a = \dfrac{c}{e} = \dfrac{3}{0.5} = 6$

$\Rightarrow b^2 = 36 - 9 = 27 \Rightarrow \dfrac{x^2}{27} + \dfrac{y^2}{36} = 1$

6. Foci: $(\pm 8, 0),\ e = 0.2 \Rightarrow c = 8$ and $a = \dfrac{c}{e} = \dfrac{8}{0.2} = 40$

$\Rightarrow b^2 = 1600 - 64 = 1536 \Rightarrow \dfrac{x^2}{1600} + \dfrac{y^2}{1536} = 1$

7. Vertices: $(\pm 10, 0),\ e = 0.24 \Rightarrow a = 10$ and

$c = ae = 10(0.24) = 2.4 \Rightarrow b^2 = 100 - 5.76 = 94.24$

$\Rightarrow \dfrac{x^2}{100} + \dfrac{y^2}{94.24} = 1$

8. Vertices: $(0, \pm 70),\ e = 0.1 \Rightarrow a = 70$

and $c = ae = 70(0.1) = 7 \Rightarrow b^2 = 4900 - 49 = 4851$

$\Rightarrow \dfrac{x^2}{4851} + \dfrac{y^2}{4900} = 1$

9. Focus: $(\sqrt{5}, 0),$ Directrix: $x = \dfrac{9}{\sqrt{5}} \Rightarrow c = ae = \sqrt{5}$ and

$\dfrac{a}{e} = \dfrac{9}{\sqrt{5}} \Rightarrow \dfrac{ae}{e^2} = \dfrac{9}{\sqrt{5}} \Rightarrow \dfrac{\sqrt{5}}{e^2} = \dfrac{9}{\sqrt{5}} \Rightarrow e^2 = \dfrac{5}{9} \Rightarrow e = \dfrac{\sqrt{5}}{3}.$

Then $PF = \dfrac{\sqrt{5}}{3}PD$

$\Rightarrow \sqrt{(x - \sqrt{5})^2 + (y - 0)^2} = \dfrac{\sqrt{5}}{3}\left|x - \dfrac{9}{\sqrt{5}}\right|$

$\Rightarrow (x - \sqrt{5})^2 + y^2 = \dfrac{5}{9}\left(x - \dfrac{9}{\sqrt{5}}\right)^2$

$\Rightarrow x^2 - 2\sqrt{5}x + 5 + y^2 = \dfrac{5}{9}\left(x^2 - \dfrac{18}{\sqrt{5}}x + \dfrac{81}{5}\right)$

$\Rightarrow \dfrac{4}{9}x^2 + y^2 = 4 \Rightarrow \dfrac{x^2}{9} + \dfrac{y^2}{4} = 1$

10. Focus: $(-4, 0),$ Directrix: $x = -16 \Rightarrow c = ae = 4$ and

$\dfrac{a}{e} = 16 \Rightarrow \dfrac{ae}{e^2} = 16 \Rightarrow \dfrac{4}{e^2} = 16 \Rightarrow e^2 = \dfrac{1}{4} \Rightarrow e = \dfrac{1}{2}.$ Then

$PF = \dfrac{1}{2}PD \Rightarrow \sqrt{(x + 4)^2 + (y - 0)^2} = \dfrac{1}{2}|x + 16|$

$\Rightarrow (x + 4)^2 + y^2 = \dfrac{1}{4}(x + 16)^2$

$\Rightarrow x^2 + 8x + 16 + y^2 = \dfrac{1}{4}(x^2 + 32x + 256)$

$\Rightarrow \dfrac{3}{4}x^2 + y^2 = 48 \Rightarrow \dfrac{x^2}{64} + \dfrac{y^2}{48} = 1$

11. $e = \dfrac{4}{5} \Rightarrow$ take $c = 4$ and $a = 5;\ c^2 = a^2 - b^2$

$\Rightarrow 16 = 25 - b^2 \Rightarrow b^2 = 9 \Rightarrow b = 3;$

therefore $\dfrac{x^2}{25} + \dfrac{y^2}{9} = 1$

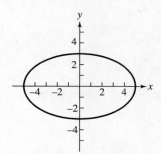

12. The eccentricity e for Pluto is $0.25,\ \Rightarrow e = \dfrac{c}{a} = 0.25 = \dfrac{1}{4}$

take $c = 1$ and $a = 4;\ c^2 = a^2 - b^2 \Rightarrow 1 = 16 - b^2$

$\Rightarrow b^2 = 15 \Rightarrow b = \sqrt{15};$ therefore, $\dfrac{x^2}{16} + \dfrac{y^2}{15} = 1$ is a model

of Pluto's orbit.

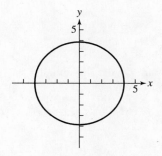

13. One axis is from $(1, 1)$ to $(1, 7)$ and is 6 units long; the

other axis is from $(3, 4)$ to $(-1, 4)$ and is 4 units long.

Therefore, $a = 3,\ b = 2$ and the major axis is vertical. The

center is the point $C(1, 4)$ and the ellipse is given by

$\dfrac{(x - 1)^2}{4} + \dfrac{(y - 4)^2}{9} = 1;\ c^2 = a^2 - b^2 = 3^2 - 2^2 = 5$

$\Rightarrow c = \sqrt{5};$ therefore the foci are $F(1, 4 \pm \sqrt{5}),$ the

eccentricity is $e = \dfrac{c}{a} = \dfrac{\sqrt{5}}{3},$ and the directrices are

$y = 4 \pm \dfrac{a}{e} = 4 \pm \dfrac{3}{\left(\dfrac{\sqrt{5}}{3}\right)} = 4 \pm \dfrac{9\sqrt{5}}{5}.$

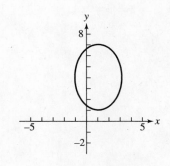

14. Using $PF = e \cdot PD$, we have $\sqrt{(x-4)^2 + y^2} = \frac{2}{3}|x - 9|$

$\Rightarrow (x-4)^2 + y^2 = \frac{4}{9}(x-9)^2$

$\Rightarrow x^2 - 8x + 16 + y^2 = \frac{4}{9}(x^2 - 18x + 81)$

$\Rightarrow \frac{5}{9}x^2 + y^2 = 20 \Rightarrow 5x^2 + 9y^2 = 180$ or $\frac{x^2}{36} + \frac{y^2}{20} = 1$.

15. $9x^2 - 16y^2 = 144 \Rightarrow \frac{x^2}{16} - \frac{y^2}{9} = 1$

$\Rightarrow c = \sqrt{a^2 + b^2} = \sqrt{16 + 9} = 5 \Rightarrow e = \frac{c}{a} = \frac{5}{4}$;

asymptotes are $y = \pm\frac{3}{4}x$; $F(\pm 5, 0)$; directrices are

$x = 0 \pm \frac{a}{e} = \pm\frac{16}{5}$.

16. $y^2 - x^2 = 8 \Rightarrow \frac{y^2}{8} - \frac{x^2}{8} = 1$

$\Rightarrow c = \sqrt{a^2 + b^2} = \sqrt{8 + 8} = 4 \Rightarrow e = \frac{c}{a} = \frac{4}{\sqrt{8}} = \sqrt{2}$;

asymptotes are $y = \pm x$; $F(0, \pm 4)$; directrices are

$y = 0 \pm \frac{a}{e} = \pm\frac{\sqrt{8}}{\sqrt{2}} = \pm 2$

17. $8x^2 - 2y^2 = 16 \Rightarrow \frac{x^2}{2} - \frac{y^2}{8} = 1$

$\Rightarrow c = \sqrt{a^2 + b^2} = \sqrt{2 + 8} = \sqrt{10}$

$\Rightarrow e = \frac{c}{a} = \frac{\sqrt{10}}{\sqrt{2}} = \sqrt{5}$; asymptotes are $y = \pm 2x$;

$F(\pm\sqrt{10}, 0)$; directrices are $x = 0 \pm \frac{a}{e} = \pm\frac{\sqrt{2}}{\sqrt{5}} = \pm\frac{2}{\sqrt{10}}$

18. $8y^2 - 2x^2 = 16 \Rightarrow \frac{y^2}{2} - \frac{x^2}{8} = 1$

$\Rightarrow c = \sqrt{a^2 + b^2} = \sqrt{2 + 8} = \sqrt{10}$

$\Rightarrow e = \frac{c}{a} = \frac{\sqrt{10}}{\sqrt{2}} = \sqrt{5}$; asymptotes are $y = \pm\frac{x}{2}$;

$F(0, \pm\sqrt{10})$; directrices are $y = 0 \pm \frac{a}{e} = \pm\frac{\sqrt{2}}{\sqrt{5}} = \pm\frac{2}{\sqrt{10}}$

19. Vertices $(0, \pm 1)$ and $e = 3 \Rightarrow a = 1$ and $e = \frac{c}{a} = 3$

$\Rightarrow c = 3a = 3 \Rightarrow b^2 = c^2 - a^2 = 9 - 1 = 8$

$\Rightarrow y^2 - \frac{x^2}{8} = 1$

20. Foci $(\pm 3, 0)$ and $e = 3 \Rightarrow c = 3$ and $e = \frac{c}{a} = 3 \Rightarrow c = 3a$

$\Rightarrow a = 1 \Rightarrow b^2 = c^2 - a^2 = 9 - 1 = 8 \Rightarrow x^2 - \frac{y^2}{8} = 1$

21. Focus $(4, 0)$ and directrix $x = 2 \Rightarrow c = ae = 4$ and $\frac{a}{e} = 2$

$\Rightarrow \frac{ae}{e^2} = 2 \Rightarrow \frac{4}{e^2} = 2 \Rightarrow e^2 = 2 \Rightarrow e = \sqrt{2}$.

Then $PF = \sqrt{2}PD \Rightarrow \sqrt{(x-4)^2 + (y-0)^2} = \sqrt{2}|x - 2|$

$\Rightarrow (x-4)^2 + y^2 = 2(x-2)^2$

$\Rightarrow x^2 - 8x + 16 + y^2 = 2(x^2 - 4x + 4)$

$\Rightarrow -x^2 + y^2 = -8 \Rightarrow \frac{x^2}{8} - \frac{y^2}{8} = 1$

22. Focus $(-2, 0)$ and directrix $x = -\frac{1}{2} \Rightarrow c = ae = 2$ and

$\frac{a}{e} = \frac{1}{2} \Rightarrow \frac{ae}{e^2} = \frac{1}{2} \Rightarrow \frac{2}{e^2} = \frac{1}{2} \Rightarrow e^2 = 4 \Rightarrow e = 2$.

Then $PF = 2PD \Rightarrow \sqrt{(x+2)^2 + (y-0)^2} = 2\left|x + \frac{1}{2}\right|$

$\Rightarrow (x+2)^2 + y^2 = 4\left(x + \frac{1}{2}\right)^2$

$\Rightarrow x^2 + 4x + 4 + y^2 = 4\left(x^2 + x + \frac{1}{4}\right)$

$\Rightarrow -3x^2 + y^2 = -3 \Rightarrow x^2 - \frac{y^2}{3} = 1$

23. $\sqrt{(x-1)^2 + (y+3)^2} = \frac{3}{2}|y - 2|$

$\Rightarrow x^2 - 2x + 1 + y^2 + 6y + 9 = \frac{9}{4}(y^2 - 4y + 4)$

$\Rightarrow 4x^2 - 5y^2 - 8x + 60y + 4 = 0$

$\Rightarrow 4(x^2 - 2x + 1) - 5(y^2 - 12y + 36) = -4 + 4 - 180$

$\Rightarrow \frac{(y-6)^2}{36} - \frac{(x-1)^2}{45} = 1$

24. $c^2 = a^2 + b^2 \Rightarrow b^2 = c^2 - a^2$; $e = \frac{c}{a} \Rightarrow c = ea$

$\Rightarrow c^2 = e^2 a^2 \Rightarrow b^2 = e^2 a^2 - a^2 = a^2(e^2 - 1)$;

thus, $\frac{x^2}{a^2} - \frac{y^2}{b^2} = 1 \Rightarrow \frac{x^2}{a^2} - \frac{y^2}{a^2(e^2 - 1)} = 1$; the asymptotes

of this hyperbola are $y = \pm\sqrt{e^2 - 1}\,x$. As e increases, the

slopes of the asymptotes increase and the hyperbola

approaches a single straight line.

25. The ellipse must pass through $(0, 0) \Rightarrow c = 0$; the point

$(-1, 2)$ lies on the ellipse $\Rightarrow -a + 2b = -8$. The ellipse is

tangent to the x-axis $\Rightarrow$ its center is on the y-axis, so $a = 0$

and $b = -4 \Rightarrow$ the equation is $4x^2 + y^2 - 4y = 0$. Next,

$4x^2 + y^2 - 4y + 4 = 4 \Rightarrow 4x^2 + (y - 2)^2 = 4$

$\Rightarrow x^2 + \frac{(y-2)^2}{4} = 1 \Rightarrow a = 2$ and $b = 1$ (now using the

standard symbols) $\Rightarrow c^2 = a^2 - b^2 = 4 - 1 = 3$

$\Rightarrow c = \sqrt{3} \Rightarrow e = \frac{c}{a} = \frac{\sqrt{3}}{2} = \frac{\sqrt{3}}{2}$.

26. We first prove a result which we will use: let m_1 and m_2 be the slopes of two nonparallel, nonperpendicular lines. Let α be the acute angle between the lines. Then $\tan \alpha = \dfrac{m_1 - m_2}{1 + m_1 m_2}$. (To see this result for positive-slope lines, let θ_1 be the angle of inclination of the line with slope m_1, and θ_2 be the angle of inclination of the line with slope m_2. Assume $m_1 > m_2$. Then $\theta_1 > \theta_2$ and we have $\alpha = \theta_1 - \theta_2$. Then $\tan \alpha = \tan(\theta_1 - \theta_2) = \dfrac{\tan \theta_1 - \tan \theta_2}{1 + \tan \theta_1 \tan \theta_2} = \dfrac{m_1 - m_2}{1 + m_1 m_2}$, since $m_1 = \tan \theta_1$ and $m_2 = \tan \theta_2$.)

Now we prove the reflective property of ellipses (see the accompanying figure):

$$2b^2 x + 2a^2 y y' = 0 \Rightarrow y' = -\frac{b^2 x}{a^2 y}.$$

Let $P(x_0, y_0)$ be any point on the ellipse

$$\Rightarrow y'(x_0) = -\frac{b x_0}{a\sqrt{a^2 - x_0^2}} = -\frac{b^2 x_0}{a^2 y_0}. \text{ Let } F_1(c, 0) \text{ and}$$

$F_2(-c, 0)$ be the foci. Then $m_{PF_1} = \dfrac{y_0}{x_0 - c}$ and $m_{PF_2} = \dfrac{y_0}{x_0 + c}$. Let α and β be the angles between the tangent line and PF_1 and PF_2 respectively. Then

$$\tan \alpha = \frac{\left(-\dfrac{b^2 x_0}{a^2 y_0} - \dfrac{y_0}{x_0 - c}\right)}{\left(1 - \dfrac{b^2 x_0 y_0}{a^2 y_0 (x_0 - c)}\right)}$$

$$= \frac{-b^2 x_0^2 + b^2 x_0 c - a^2 y_0^2}{a^2 y_0 x_0 - a^2 y_0 c - b^2 x_0 y_0}$$

$$= \frac{b^2 x_0 c - (b^2 x_0^2 + a^2 y_0^2)}{-a^2 y_0 c + (a^2 - b^2) x_0 y_0}$$

$$= \frac{b^2 x_0 c - a^2 b^2}{-a^2 y_0 c + c^2 x_0 y_0} = \frac{b^2}{c y_0}.$$

Similarly, $\tan \beta = \dfrac{b^2}{c y_0}$. Since $\tan \alpha = \tan \beta$, and α and β are both less than 90°, we have $\alpha = \beta$.

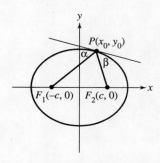

27. To prove the reflective property for hyperbolas:

$$b^2 x^2 - a^2 y^2 = a^2 b^2$$

$$2b^2 x - 2a^2 y y' = 0$$

$$y' = \frac{b^2 x}{a^2 y}$$

Let $P(x_0, y_0)$ be a point of tangency (see the accompanying figure). The slope from P to $F(-c, 0)$ is $\dfrac{y_0}{x_0 + c}$ and from P to $F_2(c, 0)$ it is $\dfrac{y_0}{x_0 - c}$. Let the tangent through P meet the x-axis in point A, and define the angles $\angle F_1 PA = \alpha$ and $\angle F_2 PA = \beta$. We will show that $\tan \alpha = \tan \beta$.

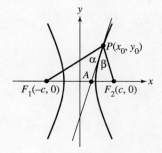

27. continued

From the preliminary result in Exercise 26,

$$\tan \alpha = \frac{\left(\dfrac{x_0 b^2}{y_0 a^2} - \dfrac{y_0}{x_0 + c}\right)}{1 + \left(\dfrac{x_0 b^2}{y_0 a^2}\right)\left(\dfrac{y_0}{x_0 + c}\right)}$$

$$= \frac{x_0^2 b^2 + x_0 b^2 c - y_0^2 a^2}{x_0 y_0 a^2 + y_0 a^2 c + x_0 y_0 b^2}$$

$$= \frac{a^2 b^2 + x_0 b^2 c}{x_0 y_0 c^2 + y_0 a^2 c} = \frac{b^2}{y_0 c}. \text{ In a similar manner,}$$

$$\tan \beta = \frac{\left(\dfrac{y_0}{x_0 - c} - \dfrac{x_0 b^2}{y_0 a^2}\right)}{1 + \left(\dfrac{y_0}{x_0 - c}\right)\left(\dfrac{x_0 b^2}{y_0 a^2}\right)} = \frac{b^2}{y_0 c}. \text{ Since } \tan \alpha = \tan \beta, \text{ and}$$

α and β are acute angles, we have $\alpha = \beta$.

28. The tangent to the ellipse of P bisects $\angle APC$, and the

tangent to the hyperbola at P bisects $\angle APB$. Since $\angle APC$

and $\angle APB$ are a linear pair, so that

$m\angle APC + m\angle APB = 180°$ and

$\dfrac{m\angle APC}{2} + \dfrac{m\angle LAPB}{2} = 90°$, the tangents to the ellipse and

hyperbola are perpendicular.

■ Appendix A5.3

(pp. 612–618)

1. $x^2 - 3xy + y^2 - x = 0$
$\Rightarrow B^2 - 4AC = (-3)^2 - 4(1)(1) = 5 > 0 \Rightarrow$ Hyperbola

2. $3x^2 - 18xy + 27y^2 - 5x + 7y = -4$
$\Rightarrow B^2 - 4AC = (-18)^2 - 4(3)(27) = 0 \Rightarrow$ Parabola

3. $3x^2 - 7xy + \sqrt{17}y^2 = 1$
$\Rightarrow B^2 - 4AC = (-7)^2 - 4(3)\sqrt{17} \approx -0.477 < 0$
$\Rightarrow$ Ellipse

4. $2x^2 - \sqrt{15}xy + 2y^2 + x + y = 0$
$\Rightarrow B^2 - 4AC = (-\sqrt{15})^2 - 4(2)(2) = -1 < 0 \Rightarrow$ Ellipse

5. $x^2 + 2xy + y^2 + 2x - y + 2 = 0$
$\Rightarrow B^2 - 4AC = 2^2 - 4(1)(1) = 0 \Rightarrow$ Parabola

6. $2x^2 - y^2 + 4xy - 2x + 3y = 6 \Rightarrow B^2 - 4AC$
$= 4^2 - 4(2)(-1) = 24 > 0 \Rightarrow$ Hyperbola

7. $x^2 + 4xy + 4y^2 - 3x = 6$
$\Rightarrow B^2 - 4AC = 4^2 - 4(1)(4) = 0 \Rightarrow$ Parabola

8. $x^2 + y^2 + 3x - 2y = 10$
$\Rightarrow B^2 - 4AC = 0^2 - 4(1)(1) = -4 < 0 \Rightarrow$ Ellipse (circle)

9. $xy + y^2 - 3x = 5 \Rightarrow B^2 - 4AC = 1^2 - 4(0)(1) = 1 > 0$
$\Rightarrow$ Hyperbola

10. $3x^2 + 6xy + 3y^2 - 4x + 5y = 12$
$\Rightarrow B^2 - 4AC = 6^2 - 4(3)(3) = 0 \Rightarrow$ Parabola

11. $3x^2 - 5xy + 2y^2 - 7x - 14y = -1$
$\Rightarrow B^2 - 4AC = (-5)^2 - 4(3)(2) = 1 > 0 \Rightarrow$ Hyperbola

12. $2x^2 - 4.9xy + 3y^2 - 4x = 7$
$\Rightarrow B^2 - 4AC = (-4.9)^2 - 4(2)(3) = 0.01 > 0$
$\Rightarrow$ Hyperbola

13. $x^2 - 3xy + 3y^2 + 6y = 7$
$\Rightarrow B^2 - 4AC = (-3)^2 - 4(1)(3) = -3 < 0 \Rightarrow$ Ellipse

14. $25x^2 + 21xy + 4y^2 - 350x = 0$
$\Rightarrow B^2 - 4AC = 21^2 - 4(25)(4) = 41 > 0 \Rightarrow$ Hyperbola

15. $6x^2 + 3xy + 2y^2 + 17y + 2 = 0$
$\Rightarrow B^2 - 4AC = 3^2 - 4(6)(2) = -39 < 0 \Rightarrow$ Ellipse

16. $3x^2 + 12xy + 12y^2 + 435x - 9y + 72 = 0$
$\Rightarrow B^2 - 4AC = 12^2 - 4(3)(12) = 0 \Rightarrow$ Parabola

17. $\cot 2\alpha = \dfrac{A - C}{B} = \dfrac{0}{1} = 0 \Rightarrow 2\alpha = \dfrac{\pi}{2} \Rightarrow \alpha = \dfrac{\pi}{4};$

therefore $x = x' \cos \alpha - y' \sin \alpha, y = x' \sin \alpha + y' \cos \alpha$

$\Rightarrow x = \dfrac{\sqrt{2}}{2}x' - \dfrac{\sqrt{2}}{2}y', y = \dfrac{\sqrt{2}}{2}x' + \dfrac{\sqrt{2}}{2}y'$

$\Rightarrow \left(\dfrac{\sqrt{2}}{2}x' - \dfrac{\sqrt{2}}{2}y'\right)\left(\dfrac{\sqrt{2}}{2}x' + \dfrac{\sqrt{2}}{2}y'\right) = 2$

$\Rightarrow \dfrac{1}{2}x'^2 - \dfrac{1}{2}y'^2 = 2 \Rightarrow x'^2 - y'^2 = 4 \Rightarrow$ Hyperbola

18. $\cot 2\alpha = \dfrac{A - C}{B} = \dfrac{1 - 1}{1} = 0 \Rightarrow 2\alpha = \dfrac{\pi}{2} \Rightarrow \alpha = \dfrac{\pi}{4};$

therefore $x = x' \cos \alpha - y' \sin, y = x' \sin \alpha + y' \cos \alpha$

$\Rightarrow x = \dfrac{\sqrt{2}}{2}x' - \dfrac{\sqrt{2}}{2}y', y = \dfrac{\sqrt{2}}{2}x' + \dfrac{\sqrt{2}}{2}y'$

$\Rightarrow \left(\dfrac{\sqrt{2}}{2}x' - \dfrac{\sqrt{2}}{2}y'\right)^2 + \left(\dfrac{\sqrt{2}}{2}x' + \dfrac{\sqrt{2}}{2}y'\right)\left(\dfrac{\sqrt{2}}{2}x' - \dfrac{\sqrt{2}}{2}y'\right)$
$\quad + \left(\dfrac{\sqrt{2}}{2}x' + \dfrac{\sqrt{2}}{2}y'\right)^2 = 1$

$\Rightarrow \dfrac{1}{2}x'^2 - x'y' + \dfrac{1}{2}y'^2 + \dfrac{1}{2}x'^2 - \dfrac{1}{2}y'^2 + \dfrac{1}{2}x'^2 + x'y'$
$\quad + \dfrac{1}{2}y'^2 = 1 \Rightarrow \dfrac{3}{2}x'^2 + \dfrac{1}{2}y'^2 = 1 \Rightarrow 3x'^2 + y'^2 = 2$

$\Rightarrow$ Ellipse

19. $\cot 2\alpha = \dfrac{A - C}{B} = \dfrac{3 - 1}{2\sqrt{3}} = \dfrac{1}{\sqrt{3}} \Rightarrow 2\alpha = \dfrac{\pi}{3} \Rightarrow \alpha = \dfrac{\pi}{6};$

therefore $x = x' \cos \alpha - y' \sin \alpha, y = x' \sin \alpha + y' \cos \alpha$

$\Rightarrow x = \dfrac{\sqrt{3}}{2}x' - \dfrac{1}{2}y', y = \dfrac{1}{2}x' + \dfrac{\sqrt{3}}{2}y'$

$\Rightarrow 3\left(\dfrac{\sqrt{3}}{2}x' - \dfrac{1}{2}y'\right)^2$
$\quad + 2\sqrt{3}\left(\dfrac{\sqrt{3}}{2}x' - \dfrac{1}{2}y'\right)\left(\dfrac{1}{2}x' + \dfrac{\sqrt{3}}{2}y'\right)$
$\quad + \left(\dfrac{1}{2}x' + \dfrac{\sqrt{3}}{2}y'\right)^2 - 8\left(\dfrac{\sqrt{3}}{2}x' - \dfrac{1}{2}y'\right)$
$\quad + 8\sqrt{3}\left(\dfrac{1}{2}x' + \dfrac{\sqrt{3}}{2}y'\right) = 0$

$\Rightarrow 4x'^2 + 16y' = 0 \Rightarrow$ Parabola

20. $\cot 2\alpha = \dfrac{A - C}{B} = \dfrac{1 - 2}{-\sqrt{3}} = \dfrac{1}{\sqrt{3}} \Rightarrow 2\alpha = \dfrac{\pi}{3} \Rightarrow \alpha = \dfrac{\pi}{6};$

therefore $x = x' \cos \alpha - y' \sin a,\ y = x' \sin \alpha + y' \cos \alpha$

$\Rightarrow x = \dfrac{\sqrt{3}}{2}x' - \dfrac{1}{2}y',\ y = \dfrac{1}{2}x' + \dfrac{\sqrt{3}}{2}y'$

$\Rightarrow \left(\dfrac{\sqrt{3}}{2}x' - \dfrac{1}{2}y'\right)^2 - \sqrt{3}\left(\dfrac{\sqrt{3}}{2}x' - \dfrac{1}{2}y'\right)\left(\dfrac{1}{2}x' + \dfrac{\sqrt{3}}{2}y'\right)$

$\qquad + 2\left(\dfrac{1}{2}x' + \dfrac{\sqrt{3}}{2}y'\right)^2 = 1$

$\Rightarrow \dfrac{1}{2}x'^2 + \dfrac{5}{2}y'^2 = 1 \Rightarrow x'^2 + 5y'^2 = 2 \Rightarrow$ ellipse

21. $\cot 2\alpha = \dfrac{A - C}{B} = \dfrac{1 - 1}{-2} = 0 \Rightarrow 2\alpha = \dfrac{\pi}{2} \Rightarrow \alpha = \dfrac{\pi}{4};$

therefore $x = x' \cos \alpha - y' \sin \alpha,\ y = x' \sin \alpha + y' \cos \alpha$

$\Rightarrow x = \dfrac{\sqrt{2}}{2}x' - \dfrac{\sqrt{2}}{2}y',\ y = \dfrac{\sqrt{2}}{2}x' + \dfrac{\sqrt{2}}{2}y'$

$\Rightarrow \left(\dfrac{\sqrt{2}}{2}x' - \dfrac{\sqrt{2}}{2}y'\right)^2$

$\qquad - 2\left(\dfrac{\sqrt{2}}{2}x' - \dfrac{\sqrt{2}}{2}y'\right)\left(\dfrac{\sqrt{2}}{2}x' + \dfrac{\sqrt{2}}{2}y'\right)$

$\qquad + \left(\dfrac{\sqrt{2}}{2}x' + \dfrac{\sqrt{2}}{2}y'\right)^2 = 2$

$\Rightarrow 2y'^2 = 2 \Rightarrow y'^2 = 1 \Rightarrow$ **Parallel horizontal lines**

22. $\cot 2\alpha = \dfrac{A - C}{B} = \dfrac{3 - 1}{-2\sqrt{3}} = -\dfrac{1}{\sqrt{3}} \Rightarrow 2\alpha = \dfrac{2\pi}{3} \Rightarrow \alpha = \dfrac{\pi}{3};$

therefore $x = x' \cos \alpha - y' \sin \alpha,\ y = x' \sin \alpha + y' \cos \alpha$

$\Rightarrow x = \dfrac{1}{2}x' - \dfrac{\sqrt{3}}{2}y',\ y = \dfrac{\sqrt{3}}{2}x' + \dfrac{1}{2}y'$

$\Rightarrow 3\left(\dfrac{1}{2}x' - \dfrac{\sqrt{3}}{2}y'\right)^2 - 2\sqrt{3}\left(\dfrac{1}{2}x' - \dfrac{\sqrt{3}}{2}y'\right)\left(\dfrac{\sqrt{3}}{2}x' + \dfrac{1}{2}y'\right)$

$\qquad + \left(\dfrac{\sqrt{3}}{2}x' + \dfrac{1}{2}y'\right)^2 = 1$

$\Rightarrow 4y'^2 = 1 \Rightarrow$ **Parallel horizontal lines**

23. $\cot 2\alpha = \dfrac{A - C}{B} = \dfrac{\sqrt{2} - \sqrt{2}}{2\sqrt{2}} = 0 \Rightarrow 2\alpha = \dfrac{\pi}{2} \Rightarrow \alpha = \dfrac{\pi}{4};$

therefore $x = x' \cos \alpha - y' \sin \alpha,\ y = x' \sin \alpha + y' \cos \alpha$

$\Rightarrow x = \dfrac{\sqrt{2}}{2}x' - \dfrac{\sqrt{2}}{2}y',\ y = \dfrac{\sqrt{2}}{2}x' + \dfrac{\sqrt{2}}{2}y'$

$\Rightarrow \sqrt{2}\left(\dfrac{\sqrt{2}}{2}x' - \dfrac{\sqrt{2}}{2}y'\right)^2$

$\qquad + 2\sqrt{2}\left(\dfrac{\sqrt{2}}{2}x' - \dfrac{\sqrt{2}}{2}y'\right)\left(\dfrac{\sqrt{2}}{2}x' + \dfrac{\sqrt{2}}{2}y'\right)$

$\qquad + \sqrt{2}\left(\dfrac{\sqrt{2}}{2}x' + \dfrac{\sqrt{2}}{2}y'\right)^2 - 8\left(\dfrac{\sqrt{2}}{2}x' - \dfrac{\sqrt{2}}{2}y'\right)$

$\qquad + 8\left(\dfrac{\sqrt{2}}{2}x' + \dfrac{\sqrt{2}}{2}y'\right) = 0$

$\Rightarrow 2\sqrt{2}x'^2 + 8\sqrt{2}y' = 0 \Rightarrow x'^2 + 4y' = 0 \Rightarrow$ **Parabola**

24. $\cot 2\alpha = \dfrac{A - C}{B} = \dfrac{0 - 0}{1} = 0 \Rightarrow 2\alpha = \dfrac{\pi}{2} \Rightarrow \alpha = \dfrac{\pi}{4};$

therefore $x = x' \cos \alpha - y' \sin \alpha,\ y = x' \sin \alpha + y' \cos \alpha$

$\Rightarrow x = \dfrac{\sqrt{2}}{2}x' - \dfrac{\sqrt{2}}{2}y',\ y = \dfrac{\sqrt{2}}{2}x' + \dfrac{\sqrt{2}}{2}y'$

$\Rightarrow \left(\dfrac{\sqrt{2}}{2}x' - \dfrac{\sqrt{2}}{2}y'\right)\left(\dfrac{\sqrt{2}}{2}x' + \dfrac{\sqrt{2}}{2}y'\right) - \left(\dfrac{\sqrt{2}}{2}x' + \dfrac{\sqrt{2}}{2}y'\right)$

$\qquad - \left(\dfrac{\sqrt{2}}{2}x' - \dfrac{\sqrt{2}}{2}y'\right) + 1$

$= 0 \Rightarrow \dfrac{1}{2}x'^2 - \dfrac{1}{2}y'^2 - \sqrt{2}x' + 1 = 0$

$\Rightarrow x'^2 - y'^2 - 2\sqrt{2}x' + 2 = 0 \Rightarrow$ hyperbola

25. $\cot 2\alpha = \dfrac{A - C}{B} = \dfrac{3 - 3}{2} = 0 \Rightarrow 2\alpha = \dfrac{\pi}{2} \Rightarrow \alpha = \dfrac{\pi}{4};$

therefore $x = x' \cos \alpha - y' \sin \alpha,$

$y = x' \sin \alpha + y' \cos \alpha \Rightarrow x = \dfrac{\sqrt{2}}{2}x' - \dfrac{\sqrt{2}}{2}y',$

$y = \dfrac{\sqrt{2}}{2}x' + \dfrac{\sqrt{2}}{2}y'$

$\Rightarrow 3\left(\dfrac{\sqrt{2}}{2}x' - \dfrac{\sqrt{2}}{2}y'\right)^2$

$\qquad + 2\left(\dfrac{\sqrt{2}}{2}x' - \dfrac{\sqrt{2}}{2}y'\right)\left(\dfrac{\sqrt{2}}{2}x' + \dfrac{\sqrt{2}}{2}y'\right)$

$\qquad + 3\left(\dfrac{\sqrt{2}}{2}x' + \dfrac{\sqrt{2}}{2}y'\right)^2 = 19$

$\Rightarrow 4x'^2 + 2y'^2 = 19 \Rightarrow$ **Ellipse**

26. $\cot 2\alpha = \dfrac{A - C}{B} = \dfrac{3 - (-1)}{4\sqrt{3}} = \dfrac{1}{\sqrt{3}} \Rightarrow 2\alpha = \dfrac{\pi}{3} \Rightarrow \alpha = \dfrac{\pi}{6};$

therefore $x = x' \cos \alpha - y' \sin \alpha,\ y = x' \sin \alpha + y' \cos \alpha$

$\Rightarrow x = \dfrac{\sqrt{3}}{2}x' - \dfrac{1}{2}y',\ y = \dfrac{1}{2}x' + \dfrac{\sqrt{3}}{2}y'$

$\Rightarrow 3\left(\dfrac{\sqrt{3}}{2}x' - \dfrac{1}{2}y'\right)^2 + 4\sqrt{3}\left(\dfrac{\sqrt{3}}{2}x' - \dfrac{1}{2}y'\right)\left(\dfrac{1}{2}x' + \dfrac{\sqrt{3}}{2}y'\right)$

$\qquad - \left(\dfrac{1}{2}x' + \dfrac{\sqrt{3}}{2}y'\right)^2 = 7$

$\Rightarrow 5x'^2 - 3y'^2 = 7 \Rightarrow$ **Hyperbola**

27. $\cot 2\alpha = \dfrac{A - C}{B} = \dfrac{14 - 2}{16} = \dfrac{3}{4} \Rightarrow \cos 2\alpha = \dfrac{3}{5}$ (if we

choose 2α in Quadrant I);

thus $\sin \alpha = \sqrt{\dfrac{1 - \cos 2\alpha}{2}} = \sqrt{\dfrac{1 - (3/5)}{2}} = \dfrac{1}{\sqrt{5}}$ and

$\cos \alpha = \sqrt{\dfrac{1 + \cos 2\alpha}{2}} = \sqrt{\dfrac{1 + (3/5)}{2}} = \dfrac{2}{\sqrt{5}}$

$\left(\text{or } \sin \alpha = -\dfrac{2}{\sqrt{5}} \text{ and } \cos \alpha = \dfrac{1}{\sqrt{5}}\right)$

28. $\cot 2\alpha = \dfrac{A - C}{B} = \dfrac{4 - 1}{-4} = -\dfrac{3}{4} \Rightarrow \cos 2\alpha = -\dfrac{3}{5}$ (if we

choose 2α in Quadrant II);

thus $\sin \alpha = \sqrt{\dfrac{1 - \cos 2\alpha}{2}} = \sqrt{\dfrac{1 + (3/5)}{2}} = \dfrac{2}{\sqrt{5}}$ and $\cos \alpha =$

$\sqrt{\dfrac{1 + \cos 2\alpha}{2}} = \sqrt{\dfrac{1 - (3/5)}{2}} = \dfrac{1}{\sqrt{5}}$

$\left(\text{or } \sin \alpha = -\dfrac{1}{\sqrt{5}} \text{ and } \cos \alpha = \dfrac{2}{\sqrt{5}}\right)$

29. $\tan 2\alpha = \dfrac{-1}{1 - 3} = \dfrac{1}{2} \Rightarrow 2\alpha \approx 26.57° \Rightarrow \alpha \approx 13.28°$

$\Rightarrow \sin \alpha \approx 0.23,\ \cos \alpha \approx 0.97;$ then $A' \approx 0.88,\ B' \approx 0.00,$

$C' \approx 3.12,\ D' \approx 0.74,\ E' \approx -1.20,$ and $F' = -3$

$\Rightarrow 0.88x'^2 + 3.12y'^2 + 0.74x' - 1.20y' - 3 = 0,$ an

ellipse

30. $\tan 2\alpha = \dfrac{1}{2 - (-3)} = \dfrac{1}{5} \Rightarrow 2\alpha \approx 11.31° \Rightarrow \alpha \approx 5.65°$

$\Rightarrow \sin \alpha \approx 0.10,\ \cos \alpha \approx 0.995;$ then $A' \approx 2.05,$

$B' \approx 0.00,\ C' \approx -3.05,\ D' \approx 2.99,\ E' \approx -0.30,$ and

$F' = -7$

$\Rightarrow 2.05x'^2 - 3.05y'^2 + 2.99x' - 0.30y' - 7 = 0,$ a

hyperbola

31. $\tan 2\alpha = \dfrac{-4}{1 - 4} = \dfrac{4}{3} \Rightarrow 2\alpha \approx 53.13° \Rightarrow \alpha \approx 26.57°$

$\Rightarrow \sin \alpha \approx 0.45,\ \cos \alpha \approx 0.89;$ then $A' \approx 0.00,\ B' \approx 0.00,$

$C' \approx 5.00,\ D' = 0,\ E' = 0,$ and $F' = -5$

$\Rightarrow 5.00y'^2 - 5 = 0$ or $y' = \pm 1.00,$ parallel lines

32. $\tan 2\alpha = \dfrac{-12}{2 - 18} = \dfrac{3}{4} \Rightarrow 2\alpha \approx 36.87° \Rightarrow \alpha \approx 18.43°$

$\Rightarrow \sin \alpha \approx 0.32,\ \cos \alpha \approx 0.95;$ then $A' \approx 0.00,\ B' \approx 0.00,$

$C' \approx 20.00,\ D' = 0,\ E' = 0,$ and $F' = -49$

$\Rightarrow 20.00y'^2 - 49 = 0,$ parallel lines

33. $\tan 2\alpha = \dfrac{5}{3 - 2} = 5 \Rightarrow 2\alpha \approx 78.69° \Rightarrow \alpha \approx 39.35°$

$\Rightarrow \sin \alpha \approx 0.63,\ \cos \alpha \approx 0.77;$ then $A' \approx 5.05,\ B' \approx 0.00,$

$C' \approx -0.05,\ D' \approx -5.07,\ E' \approx -6.19,$ and $F' = -1$

$\Rightarrow 5.05x'^2 - 0.05y'^2 - 5.07x' - 6.19y' - 1 = 0,$

a hyperbola

34. $\tan 2\alpha = \dfrac{7}{2 - 9} = -1 \Rightarrow 2\alpha = -45° \Rightarrow \alpha = -22.5°$

$\Rightarrow \sin \alpha \approx -0.38,\ \cos \alpha \approx 0.92;$

then $A' \approx 0.55,\ B' \approx 0.00,\ C' \approx 10.45,\ D' \approx 18.48,$

$E' \approx 7.65,$ and $F' = -86$

$\Rightarrow 0.55x'^2 + 10.45y'^2 + 18.48x' + 7.65y' - 86 = 0,$

an ellipse

35. **(a)** $A' = \cos 45° \sin 45° = \left(\dfrac{\sqrt{2}}{2}\right)\left(\dfrac{\sqrt{2}}{2}\right) = \dfrac{1}{2},\ B' = 0,$

$C' = -\sin 45° \cos 45° = -\dfrac{1}{2},\ F' = -1$

$\Rightarrow \dfrac{1}{2}x'^2 - \dfrac{1}{2}y'^2 = 1 \Rightarrow x'^2 - y'^2 = 2$

(b) $A' = \dfrac{1}{2},\ C' = -\dfrac{1}{2}$ (see part (a) above),

$D' = E' = B' = 0,\ F' = -a \Rightarrow \dfrac{1}{2}x'^2 - \dfrac{1}{2}y'^2 = a$

$\Rightarrow x'^2 - y'^2 = 2a$

36. Yes, the graph is a hyperbola: with $AC < 0$ we have $-4AC > 0$ and $B^2 - 4AC > 0.$

37. The one curve that meets all three of the stated criteria is the ellipse $x^2 + 4xy + 5y^2 - 1 = 0.$ The reasoning: The symmetry about the origin means that $(-x, -y)$ lies on the graph whenever (x, y) does. Adding $Ax^2 + Bxy + Cy^2 + Dx + Ey + F = 0$ and $A(-x)^2 + B(-x)(-y) + C(-y)^2 + D(-x) + E(-y) + F = 0$ and dividing the result by 2 produces the equivalent equation $Ax^2 + Bxy + Cy^2 + F = 0.$ Substituting $x = 1,$ $y = 0$ (because the point $(1, 0)$ lies on the curve) shows further that $A = -F.$ Then $-Fx^2 + Bxy + Cy^2 + F = 0.$ By implicit differentiation, $-2Fx + By + Bxy' + 2Cyy' = 0,$ so substituting $x = -2,$ $y = 1,$ and $y' = 0$ (from Property 3) gives $4F + B = 0$ $\Rightarrow B = -4F \Rightarrow$ the conic is $-Fx^2 - 4Fxy + Cy^2 + F = 0.$ Now substituting $x = -2$ and $y = 1$ again gives $-4F + 8F + C + F = 0 \Rightarrow C = -5F \Rightarrow$ the equation is now $-Fx^2 - 4Fxy - 5Fy^2 + F = 0.$ Finally, dividing through by $-F$ gives the equation $x^2 + 4xy + 5y^2 - 1 = 0.$

38. If $A = C,$ then $B' = B \cos 2\alpha + (C - A) \sin 2\alpha$

$= B \cos 2\alpha.$

Then $\alpha = \dfrac{\pi}{4} \Rightarrow 2\alpha = \dfrac{\pi}{2} \Rightarrow B' = B \cos \dfrac{\pi}{2} = 0$ so the

xy-term is eliminated.

39. $\alpha = 90° \Rightarrow x = x' \cos 90° - y' \sin 90° = -y'$
and $y = x' \sin 90° + y' \cos 90° = x'$

(a) $\dfrac{x'^2}{b^2} + \dfrac{y'^2}{a^2} = 1$

(b) $\dfrac{y'^2}{a^2} - \dfrac{x'^2}{b^2} = 1$

(c) $x'^2 + y'^2 = a^2$

(d) $y = mx \Rightarrow x' = m(-y') \Rightarrow y' = -\dfrac{1}{m}x'$

(e) $y = mx + b \Rightarrow x' = m(-y') + b \Rightarrow y' = -\dfrac{1}{m}x' + \dfrac{b}{m}$

40. $\alpha = 180° \Rightarrow x = x' \cos 180° - y' \sin 180° = -x'$

and $y = x' \sin 180° + y' \cos 180° = -y'$

   (a) $\dfrac{x'^2}{a^2} + \dfrac{y'^2}{b^2} = 1$

   (b) $\dfrac{x'^2}{a^2} - \dfrac{y'^2}{b^2} = 1$

   (c) $x'^2 + y'^2 = a^2$

   (d) $y = mx \Rightarrow -y' = m(-x') \Rightarrow y' = mx'$

   (e) $y = mx + b \Rightarrow -y' = m(-x') + b \Rightarrow y' = mx' - b$

41. (a) $B^2 - 4AC = 1 - 4(0)(0) = 1 \Rightarrow$ hyperbola

   (b) $xy + 2x - y = 0 \Rightarrow y(x-1) = -2x \Rightarrow y = -\dfrac{2x}{x-1}$

   (c) $y = -\dfrac{2x}{x-1} \Rightarrow \dfrac{dy}{dx} = \dfrac{2}{(x-1)^2}$ and we want

$$\dfrac{-1}{\left(\dfrac{dy}{dx}\right)} = -2, \text{ the slope of } y = -2x$$

$$\Rightarrow -2 = -\dfrac{(x-1)^2}{2} \Rightarrow (x-1)^2 = 4$$

$\Rightarrow x = 3$ or $x = -1$; $x = 3 \Rightarrow y = -3 \Rightarrow (3, -3)$ is a

point on the hyperbola where the line with

slope $m = -2$ is normal $\Rightarrow$ the line is

$y + 3 = -2(x - 3)$ or $y = -2x + 3$;

$x = -1 \Rightarrow y = -1 \Rightarrow (-1, -1)$ is a point on the

hyperbola where the line with slope $m = -2$ is normal

$\Rightarrow$ the line is $y + 1 = -2(x + 1)$ or $y = -2x - 3$

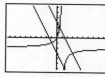

[−9.4, 9.4] by [−6.1, 6.1]

42. (a) False: let $A = C = 1$, $B = 2 \Rightarrow B^2 - 4AC = 0$
$\Rightarrow$ parabola

   (b) False: see part (a) above

   (c) True: $AC < 0 \Rightarrow -4AC > 0 \Rightarrow B^2 - 4AC > 0$
$\Rightarrow$ hyperbola

43. (a) $B^2 - 4AC = 4^2 - 4(1)(4) = 0$, so the discriminant indicates that this conic is a parabola.

   (b) The left-hand side of
$x^2 + 4xy + 4y^2 + 6x + 12y + 9 = 0$ factors as a perfect square:
$(x + 2y + 3)^2 = 0 \Rightarrow x + 2y + 3 = 0$
$\Rightarrow 2y = -x - 3$; thus the curve is a degenerate parabola (i.e., a straight line).

44. (a) $B^2 - 4AC = 6^2 - 4(9)(1) = 0$, so the discriminant indicates that this conic is a parabola.

   (b) The left-hand side of
$9x^2 + 6xy + y^2 - 12x - 4y + 4 = 0$ factors as a perfect square: $(3x + y - 2)^2 = 0 \Rightarrow 3x + y - 2 = 0$
$\Rightarrow y = -3x + 2$; thus the curve is a degenerate parabola (i.e., a straight line).

45. Assume the ellipse has been rotated to eliminate the

xy-term $\Rightarrow$ the new equation is $A'x'^2 + C'y'^2 = 1$

$\Rightarrow$ the semi-axes are $\sqrt{\dfrac{1}{A'}}$ and $\sqrt{\dfrac{1}{C'}}$ $\Rightarrow$ the area is

$$\pi\left(\sqrt{\dfrac{1}{A'}}\right)\left(\sqrt{\dfrac{1}{C'}}\right) = \dfrac{\pi}{\sqrt{A'C'}} = \dfrac{2\pi}{\sqrt{4A'C'}}.$$

Since $B^2 - 4AC = B'^2 - 4A'C' = -4A'C'$

(because $B' = 0$) we find that the area is $\dfrac{2\pi}{\sqrt{4AC - B^2}}$ as

claimed.

46. (a) $A' + C' = (A \cos^2\alpha + B \cos\alpha \sin\alpha + C \sin^2\alpha) +$
$(A \sin^2\alpha - B \cos\alpha \sin\alpha + C \cos^2\alpha)$
$= A(\cos^2\alpha + \sin^2\alpha) + C(\sin^2\alpha + \cos^2\alpha) = A + C$

   (b) $D'^2 + E'^2 = (D\cos\alpha + E\sin\alpha)^2 + (-D\sin\alpha + E\cos\alpha)^2$
$= D^2\cos^2\alpha + 2DE\cos\alpha\sin\alpha + E^2\sin^2\alpha$
$\quad + D^2\sin^2\alpha - 2DE\sin\alpha\cos\alpha + E^2\cos^2\alpha$
$= D^2(\cos^2\alpha + \sin^2\alpha) + E^2(\sin^2\alpha + \cos^2\alpha)$
$= D^2 + E^2$

■ Appendix A6

(pp. 618–627)

1. $\sinh x = -\dfrac{3}{4} \Rightarrow \cosh x = \sqrt{1 + \sinh^2 x} = \sqrt{1 + \left(-\dfrac{3}{4}\right)^2}$

$= \sqrt{1 + \dfrac{9}{16}} = \sqrt{\dfrac{25}{16}} = \dfrac{5}{4}$, $\tanh x = \dfrac{\sinh x}{\cosh x}$

$= \dfrac{\left(-\dfrac{3}{4}\right)}{\left(\dfrac{5}{4}\right)} = -\dfrac{3}{5}$, $\coth x = \dfrac{1}{\tanh x} = -\dfrac{5}{3}$, $\text{sech } x = \dfrac{1}{\cosh x}$

$= \dfrac{4}{5}$, and $\text{csch } x = \dfrac{1}{\sin x} = -\dfrac{4}{3}$

2. $\sinh x = \frac{4}{3} \Rightarrow \cosh x = \sqrt{1 + \sinh^2 x} = \sqrt{1 + \left(\frac{4}{3}\right)^2}$

$= \sqrt{1 + \frac{16}{9}} = \sqrt{\frac{25}{9}} = \frac{5}{3}$,

$\tanh x = \frac{\sinh x}{\cosh x} = \frac{\left(\frac{4}{3}\right)}{\left(\frac{5}{3}\right)} = \frac{4}{5}$,

$\coth x = \frac{1}{\tanh x} = \frac{5}{4}$, $\operatorname{sech} x = \frac{1}{\cosh x} = \frac{3}{5}$,

and $\operatorname{csch} x = \frac{1}{\sinh x} = \frac{3}{4}$

3. $\cosh x = \frac{17}{15}, x > 0 \Rightarrow \sinh x = \sqrt{\cosh^2 x - 1}$

$= \sqrt{\left(\frac{17}{15}\right)^2 - 1} = \sqrt{\frac{289}{225} - 1} = \sqrt{\frac{64}{225}} = \frac{8}{15}$,

$\tanh x = \frac{\sinh x}{\cosh x} = \frac{\left(\frac{8}{15}\right)}{\left(\frac{17}{15}\right)} = \frac{8}{17}$, $\coth x = \frac{1}{\tanh x}$

$= \frac{17}{8}$, $\operatorname{sech} x = \frac{1}{\cosh x} = \frac{15}{17}$, and $\operatorname{csch} x = \frac{1}{\sinh x} = \frac{15}{8}$

4. $\cosh x = \frac{13}{5}, x > 0 \Rightarrow \sinh x = \sqrt{\cosh^2 x - 1}$

$= \sqrt{\frac{169}{25} - 1} = \sqrt{\frac{144}{25}} = \frac{12}{5}$,

$\tanh x = \frac{\sinh x}{\cosh x} = \frac{\left(\frac{12}{5}\right)}{\left(\frac{13}{5}\right)} = \frac{12}{13}$, $\coth x = \frac{1}{\tanh x}$

$= \frac{13}{12}$, $\operatorname{sech} x = \frac{1}{\cosh x} = \frac{5}{13}$, and $\operatorname{csch} x = \frac{1}{\sinh x} = \frac{5}{12}$

In Exercises 5–10, graphical support may consist of showing that the graph of the original expression minus the simplified one is the line $y = 0$.

5. $2 \cosh (\ln x) = 2\left(\frac{e^{\ln x} + e^{-\ln x}}{2}\right) = e^{\ln x} + \frac{1}{e^{\ln x}} = x + \frac{1}{x}$

6. $\sinh (2 \ln x) = \frac{e^{2 \ln x} - e^{-2 \ln x}}{2} = \frac{e^{\ln x^2} - e^{\ln x^{-2}}}{2}$

$= \frac{\left(x^2 - \frac{1}{x^2}\right)}{2} = \frac{x^4 - 1}{2x^2}$

7. $\cosh 5x + \sinh 5x = \frac{e^{5x} + e^{-5x}}{2} + \frac{e^{5x} - e^{-5x}}{2} = e^{5x}$

8. $\cosh 3x - \sinh 3x = \frac{e^{3x} + e^{-3x}}{2} - \frac{e^{3x} - e^{-3x}}{2} = e^{-3x}$

9. $(\sinh x + \cosh x)^4 = \left(\frac{e^x - e^{-x}}{2} + \frac{e^x + e^{-x}}{2}\right)^4 = (e^x)^4 = e^{4x}$

10. $\ln (\cosh x + \sinh x) + \ln (\cosh x - \sinh x)$

$= \ln (\cosh^2 x - \sinh^2 x) = \ln 1 = 0$

11. (a) $\sinh 2x = \sinh (x + x) = \sinh x \cosh x + \cosh x \sinh x$
$= 2 \sinh x \cosh x$

(b) $\cosh 2x = \cosh (x + x) = \cosh x \cosh x + \sinh x \sinh x$
$= \cosh^2 x + \sinh^2 x$

12. $\cosh^2 x - \sinh^2 x = \left(\frac{e^x + e^{-x}}{2}\right)^2 - \left(\frac{e^x - e^{-x}}{2}\right)^2$

$= \frac{1}{4}\left[(e^x + e^{-x}) + (e^x - e^{-x})\right]\left[(e^x + e^{-x}) - (e^x - e^{-x})\right]$

$= \frac{1}{4}(2e^x)(2e^{-x}) = \frac{1}{4}(4e^0) = \frac{1}{4}(4) = 1$

13. $y = 6 \sinh \frac{x}{3} \Rightarrow \frac{dy}{dx} = 6\left(\cosh \frac{x}{3}\right)\left(\frac{1}{3}\right) = 2 \cosh \frac{x}{3}$

14. $y = \frac{1}{2} \sinh (2x + 1) \Rightarrow \frac{dy}{dx} = \frac{1}{2}[\cosh (2x + 1)](2)$

$= \cosh (2x + 1)$

15. $y = 2\sqrt{t} \tanh \sqrt{t} = 2t^{1/2} \tanh t^{1/2}$

$\Rightarrow \frac{dy}{dt} = [\operatorname{sech}^2(t^{1/2})]\left(\frac{1}{2}t^{-1/2}\right)(2t^{1/2}) + (\tanh t^{1/2})(t^{-1/2})$

$= \operatorname{sech}^2\sqrt{t} + \frac{\tanh \sqrt{t}}{\sqrt{t}}$

16. $y = t^2 \tanh \frac{1}{t} = t^2 \tanh t^{-1} \Rightarrow \frac{dy}{dt}$

$= [\operatorname{sech}^2 (t^{-1})](-t^{-2})(t^2) + (2t)(\tanh t^{-1})$

$= -\operatorname{sech}^2 \frac{1}{t} + 2t \tanh \frac{1}{t}$

17. $y = \ln (\sinh z) \Rightarrow \frac{dy}{dz} = \frac{\cosh z}{\sinh z} = \coth z$

18. $y = \ln (\cosh z) \Rightarrow \frac{dy}{dz} = \frac{\sinh z}{\cosh z} = \tanh z$

19. $y = (\operatorname{sech} \theta)(1 - \ln \operatorname{sech} \theta)$

$\Rightarrow \frac{dy}{d\theta} = \left(-\frac{-\operatorname{sech} \theta \tanh \theta}{\operatorname{sech} \theta}\right)(\operatorname{sech} \theta)$

$+ (-\operatorname{sech} \theta \tanh \theta)(1 - \ln \operatorname{sech} \theta)$

$= \operatorname{sech} \theta \tanh \theta - (\operatorname{sech} \theta \tanh \theta)(1 - \ln \operatorname{sech} \theta)$

$= (\operatorname{sech} \theta \tanh \theta)[1 - (1 - \ln \operatorname{sech} \theta)]$

$= (\operatorname{sech} \theta \tanh \theta)(\ln \operatorname{sech} \theta)$

20. $y = (\operatorname{csch} \theta)(1 - \ln \operatorname{csch} \theta)$

$\Rightarrow \frac{dy}{d\theta} = (\operatorname{csch} \theta)\left(-\frac{-\operatorname{csch} \theta \coth \theta}{\operatorname{csch} \theta}\right)$

$+ (1 - \ln \operatorname{csch} \theta)(-\operatorname{csch} \theta \coth \theta)$

$= \operatorname{csch} \theta \coth \theta - (1 - \ln \operatorname{csch} \theta)(\operatorname{csch} \theta \coth \theta)$

$= (\operatorname{csch} \theta \coth \theta)(1 - 1 + \ln \operatorname{csch} \theta)$

$= (\operatorname{csch} \theta \coth \theta)(\ln \operatorname{csch} \theta)$

21. $y = \ln \cosh x - \frac{1}{2} \tanh^2 x$

$\Rightarrow \frac{dy}{dx} = \frac{\sinh x}{\cosh x} - \left(\frac{1}{2}\right)(2 \tanh x)(\operatorname{sech}^2 x)$

$= \tanh x - (\tanh x)(\operatorname{sech}^2 x) = (\tanh x)(1 - \operatorname{sech}^2 x)$

$= (\tanh x)(\tanh^2 x) = \tanh^3 x$

22. $y = \ln \sinh x - \dfrac{1}{2} \coth^2 x$

$\Rightarrow \dfrac{dy}{dv} = \dfrac{\cosh x}{\sinh x} - \left(\dfrac{1}{2}\right)(2 \coth x)(-\text{csch}^2 x)$

$= \coth x + (\coth x)(\text{csch}^2 x) = (\coth x)(1 + \text{csch}^2 x)$

$= (\coth x)(\coth^2 x) = \coth^3 x$

23. $y = (x^2 + 1)\, \text{sech}\,(\ln x) = (x^2 + 1)\left(\dfrac{2}{e^{\ln x} + e^{-\ln x}}\right)$

$= (x^2 + 1)\left(\dfrac{2}{x + x^{-1}}\right) = (x^2 + 1)\left(\dfrac{2x}{x^2 + 1}\right) = 2x \Rightarrow \dfrac{dy}{dx} = 2$

24. $y = (4x^2 - 1)\, \text{csch}\,(\ln 2x) = (4x^2 - 1)\left(\dfrac{2}{e^{\ln 2x} - e^{-\ln 2x}}\right)$

$= (4x^2 - 1)\left(\dfrac{2}{2x - (2x)^{-1}}\right) = (4x^2 - 1)\left(\dfrac{4x}{4x^2 - 1}\right) = 4x$

$\Rightarrow \dfrac{dy}{dx} = 4$

25. $y = \sinh^{-1} \sqrt{x} = \sinh^{-1} (x^{1/2})$

$\Rightarrow \dfrac{dy}{dx} = \dfrac{\left(\dfrac{1}{2}\right)x^{-1/2}}{\sqrt{1 + (x^{1/2})^2}} = \dfrac{1}{2\sqrt{x}\sqrt{1 + x}} = \dfrac{1}{2\sqrt{x(1 + x)}}$

26. $y = \cosh^{-1} (2\sqrt{x + 1}) = \cosh^{-1} (2(x + 1)^{1/2})$

$\Rightarrow \dfrac{dy}{dx} = \dfrac{(2)\left(\dfrac{1}{2}\right)(x + 1)^{-1/2}}{\sqrt{[2(x + 1)^{1/2}]^2 - 1}} = \dfrac{1}{\sqrt{x + 1}\sqrt{4x + 3}}$

$= \dfrac{1}{\sqrt{4x^2 + 7x + 3}}$

27. $y = (1 - \theta) \tanh^{-1} \theta$

$\Rightarrow \dfrac{dy}{d\theta} = (1 - \theta)\left(\dfrac{1}{1 - \theta^2}\right) + (-1) \tanh^{-1} \theta$

$= \dfrac{1}{1 + \theta} - \tanh^{-1} \theta$

28. $y = (\theta^2 + 2\theta) \tanh^{-1} (\theta + 1)$

$\Rightarrow \dfrac{dy}{d\theta} = (\theta^2 + 2\theta)\left[\dfrac{1}{1 - (\theta + 1)^2}\right] + (2\theta + 2) \tanh^{-1} (\theta + 1)$

$= \dfrac{\theta^2 + 2\theta}{-\theta^2 - 2\theta} + (2\theta + 2) \tanh^{-1} (\theta + 1)$

$= (2\theta + 2) \tanh^{-1} (\theta + 1) - 1$

29. $y = (1 - t) \coth^{-1} \sqrt{t} = (1 - t) \coth^{-1} (t^{1/2})$

$\Rightarrow \dfrac{dy}{dt} = (1 - t)\left[\dfrac{(1/2)t^{-1/2}}{1 - (t^{1/2})^2}\right] + (-1) \coth^{-1} (t^{1/2})$

$= \dfrac{1}{2\sqrt{t}} - \coth^{-1} \sqrt{t}$

30. $y = (1 - t^2) \coth^{-1} t$

$\Rightarrow \dfrac{dy}{dt} = (1 - t^2)\left(\dfrac{1}{1 - t^2}\right) + (-2t) \coth^{-1} t$

$= 1 - 2t \coth^{-1} t$

31. $y = \cos^{-1} x - x\, \text{sech}^{-1} x$

$\Rightarrow \dfrac{dy}{dx} = \dfrac{-1}{\sqrt{1 - x^2}} - \left[x\left(\dfrac{-1}{x\sqrt{1 - x^2}}\right) + (1)\, \text{sech}^{-1} x\right]$

$= \dfrac{-1}{\sqrt{1 - x^2}} + \dfrac{1}{\sqrt{1 - x^2}} - \text{sech}^{-1} x = -\text{sech}^{-1} x$

32. $y = \ln x + \sqrt{1 - x^2}\, \text{sech}^{-1} x$

$= \ln x + (1 - x^2)^{1/2}\, \text{sech}^{-1} x$

$\Rightarrow \dfrac{dy}{dx} = \dfrac{1}{x} + (1 - x^2)^{1/2}\left(\dfrac{-1}{x\sqrt{1 - x^2}}\right)$

$\qquad + \left(\dfrac{1}{2}\right)(1 - x^2)^{-1/2}(-2x)\, \text{sech}^{-1} x$

$= \dfrac{1}{x} - \dfrac{1}{x} - \dfrac{x}{\sqrt{1 - x^2}}\, \text{sech}^{-1} x = -\dfrac{x}{\sqrt{1 - x^2}}\, \text{sech}^{-1} x$

33. $y = \text{csch}^{-1} \left(\dfrac{1}{2}\right)^{\theta}$

$\Rightarrow \dfrac{dy}{d\theta} = -\dfrac{\left[\ln\left(\dfrac{1}{2}\right)\right]\left[\left(\dfrac{1}{2}\right)^{\theta}\right]}{\left(\dfrac{1}{2}\right)^{\theta} \sqrt{1 + \left[\left(\dfrac{1}{2}\right)^{\theta}\right]^2}}$

$= -\dfrac{\ln (1) - \ln (2)}{\sqrt{1 + \left(\dfrac{1}{2}\right)^{2\theta}}} = \dfrac{\ln 2}{\sqrt{1 + \left(\dfrac{1}{2}\right)^{2\theta}}}$

34. $y = \text{csch}^{-1} 2^{\theta} \Rightarrow \dfrac{dy}{d\theta} = -\dfrac{(\ln 2)2^{\theta}}{2^{\theta}\sqrt{1 + (2^{\theta})^2}} = -\dfrac{\ln 2}{\sqrt{1 + 2^{2\theta}}}$

35. $y = \sinh^{-1} (\tan x) \Rightarrow \dfrac{dy}{dx} = \dfrac{\sec^2 x}{\sqrt{1 + (\tan x)^2}}$

$= \dfrac{\sec^2 x}{\sqrt{\sec^2 x}} = \dfrac{\sec^2 x}{|\sec x|} = \dfrac{|\sec x||\sec x|}{|\sec x|} = |\sec x|$

36. $y = \cosh^{-1} (\sec x) \Rightarrow \dfrac{dy}{dx} = \dfrac{(\sec x)(\tan x)}{\sqrt{\sec^2 x - 1}}$

$= \dfrac{(\sec x)(\tan x)}{\sqrt{\tan^2 x}} = \dfrac{(\sec x)(\tan x)}{|\tan x|} = \sec x,\, 0 < x < \dfrac{\pi}{2}$

37. (a) If $y = \tan^{-1} (\sinh x) + C$, then $\dfrac{dy}{dx}$

$= \dfrac{\cosh x}{1 + \sinh^2 x} = \dfrac{\cosh x}{\cosh^2 x} = \text{sech}\, x$, which verifies the

formula.

(b) If $y = \sin^{-1} (\tanh x) + C$, then $\dfrac{dy}{dx}$

$= \dfrac{\text{sech}^2 x}{\sqrt{1 - \tanh^2 x}} = \dfrac{\text{sech}^2 x}{\text{sech}\, x} = \text{sech}\, x$, which verifies the

formula.

38. If $y = \dfrac{x^2}{2}\, \text{sech}^{-1} x - \dfrac{1}{2}\sqrt{1 - x^2} + C$, then

$\dfrac{dy}{dx} = x\, \text{sech}^{-1} x + \dfrac{x^2}{2}\left(\dfrac{-1}{x\sqrt{1 - x^2}}\right) + \dfrac{2x}{4\sqrt{1 - x^2}}$

$= x\, \text{sech}^{-1} x$, which verifies the formula.

39. If $y = \dfrac{x^2 - 1}{2}\, \coth^{-1} x + \dfrac{x}{2} + C$, then

$\dfrac{dy}{dx} = x\, \coth^{-1} x + \left(\dfrac{x^2 - 1}{2}\right)\left(\dfrac{1}{1 - x^2}\right) + \dfrac{1}{2} = x\, \coth^{-1} x$,

which verifies the formula.

40. If $y = x \tanh^{-1} x + \frac{1}{2} \ln (1 - x^2) + C$,

then $\frac{dy}{dx} = \tanh^{-1} x + x\left(\frac{1}{1 - x^2}\right) + \frac{1}{2}\left(\frac{-2x}{1 - x^2}\right) = \tanh^{-1} x$,

which verifies the formula.

41. Let $u = 2x$ and $du = 2\ dx$.

$\int \sinh 2x\ dx = \frac{1}{2} \int \sinh u\ du = \frac{\cosh u}{2} + C = \frac{\cosh 2x}{2} + C$

42. Let $u = \frac{x}{5}$ and $du = \frac{1}{5} dx$.

$\int \sinh \frac{x}{5} dx = 5 \int \sinh u\ du = 5 \cosh u + C = 5 \cosh \frac{x}{5} + C$

43. Let $u = \frac{x}{2} - \ln 3$ and $du = \frac{1}{2} dx$.

$\int 6 \cosh\left(\frac{x}{2} - \ln 3\right) dx = 12 \int \cosh u\ du = 12 \sinh u + C$

$= 12 \sinh \left(\frac{x}{2} - \ln 3\right) + C$

44. Let $u = 3x - \ln 2$ and $du = 3\ dx$.

$\int 4 \cosh (3x - \ln 2)\ dx = \frac{4}{3} \int \cosh u\ du = \frac{4}{3} \sinh u + C$

$= \frac{4}{3} \sinh (3x - \ln 2) + C$

45. Let $u = \frac{x}{7}$ and $du = \frac{1}{7} dx$.

$\int \tanh \frac{x}{7} dx = 7 \int \frac{\sinh u}{\cosh u} du = 7 \ln |\cosh u| + C_1$

$= 7 \ln \left|\cosh \frac{x}{7}\right| + C_1$

$= 7 \ln \left|\frac{e^{x/7} + e^{-x/7}}{2}\right| + C_1$

$= 7 \ln \left|e^{x/7} + e^{-x/7}\right| - 7 \ln 2 + C_1$

$= 7 \ln \left|e^{x/7} + e^{-x/7}\right| + C$

46. Let $u = \frac{\theta}{\sqrt{3}}$ and $du = \frac{d\theta}{\sqrt{3}}$.

$\int \coth \frac{\theta}{\sqrt{3}} d\theta = \sqrt{3} \int \frac{\cosh u}{\sinh u} du = \sqrt{3} \ln |\sinh u| + C_1$

$= \sqrt{3} \ln \left|\sinh \frac{\theta}{\sqrt{3}}\right| + C_1 = \sqrt{3} \ln \left|\frac{e^{\theta/\sqrt{3}} - e^{-\theta/\sqrt{3}}}{2}\right| + C_1$

$= \sqrt{3} \ln \left|e^{\theta/\sqrt{3}} - e^{-\theta/\sqrt{3}}\right| - \sqrt{3} \ln 2 + C_1$

$= \sqrt{3} \ln \left|e^{\theta/\sqrt{3}} - e^{-\theta/\sqrt{3}}\right| + C$

47. Let $u = \left(x - \frac{1}{2}\right)$ and $du = dx$.

$\int \text{sech}^2 \left(x - \frac{1}{2}\right) dx = \int \text{sech}^2 u\ du = \tanh u + C$

$= \tanh \left(x - \frac{1}{2}\right) + C$

48. Let $u = (5 - x)$ and $du = -dx$.

$\int \text{csch}^2 (5 - x)\ dx = -\int \text{csch}^2 u\ du = -(-\coth u) + C$

$= \coth u + C$

$= \coth (5 - x) + C$

49. Let $u = \sqrt{t} = t^{1/2}$ and $du = \frac{dt}{2\sqrt{t}}$.

$\int \frac{\text{sech} \sqrt{t} \tanh \sqrt{t}}{\sqrt{t}} dt = 2 \int \text{sech}\ u \tanh u\ du$

$= 2(-\text{sech}\ u) + C = -2 \text{sech} \sqrt{t} + C$

50. Let $u = \ln t$ and $du = \frac{dt}{t}$.

$\int \frac{\text{csch} (\ln t) \coth (\ln t)}{t} dt = \int \text{csch}\ u \coth u\ du$

$= -\text{csch}\ u + C = -\text{csch} (\ln t) + C$

51. Let $u = \sinh x$, $du = \cosh x\ dx$, the lower limit is

$\sinh (\ln 2) = \frac{e^{\ln 2} - e^{-\ln 2}}{2} = \frac{2 - \left(\frac{1}{2}\right)}{2} = \frac{3}{4}$ and the upper

limit is $\sinh (\ln 4) = \frac{e^{\ln 4} - e^{-\ln 4}}{2} = \frac{4 - \left(\frac{1}{4}\right)}{2} = \frac{15}{8}$.

$\int_{\ln 2}^{\ln 4} \coth x\ dx = \int_{\ln 2}^{\ln 4} \frac{\cosh x}{\sinh x} dx = \int_{3/4}^{15/8} \frac{1}{u} du$

$= \left[\ln |u|\right]_{3/4}^{15/8} = \ln \left|\frac{15}{8}\right| - \ln \left|\frac{3}{4}\right| = \ln \left|\frac{15}{8} \cdot \frac{4}{3}\right| = \ln \frac{5}{2} \approx 0.916$

52. Let $u = \cosh 2x$, $du = 2 \sinh (2x)\ dx$, the lower limit is

$\cosh 0 = 1$ and the upper limit is

$\cosh (2 \ln 2) = \cosh (\ln 4) = \frac{e^{\ln 4} + e^{-\ln 4}}{2}$

$= \frac{4 + \left(\frac{1}{4}\right)}{2} = \frac{17}{8}$.

$\int_0^{\ln 2} \tanh 2x\ dx = \int_0^{\ln 2} \frac{\sinh 2x}{\cosh 2x} dx = \frac{1}{2} \int_1^{17/8} \frac{1}{u} du$

$= \frac{1}{2}\left[\ln |u|\right]_1^{17/8} = \frac{1}{2}\left[\ln \left(\frac{17}{8}\right) - \ln 1\right] = \frac{1}{2} \ln \frac{17}{8} \approx 0.377$

53. $\int_{-\ln 4}^{-\ln 2} 2e^\theta \cosh \theta\ d\theta = \int_{-\ln 4}^{-\ln 2} 2e^\theta \left(\frac{e^\theta + e^{-\theta}}{2}\right) d\theta$

$= \int_{-\ln 4}^{-\ln 2} (e^{2\theta} + 1)\ d\theta = \left[\frac{e^{2\theta}}{2} + \theta\right]_{-\ln 4}^{-\ln 2}$

$= \left(\frac{e^{-2 \ln 2}}{2} - \ln 2\right) - \left(\frac{e^{-2 \ln 4}}{2} - \ln 4\right)$

$= \left(\frac{1}{8} - \ln 2\right) - \left(\frac{1}{32} - \ln 4\right) = \frac{3}{32} - \ln 2 + 2 \ln 2$

$= \frac{3}{32} + \ln 2 \approx 0.787$

54. $\int_0^{\ln 2} 4e^{-\theta} \sinh \theta\ d\theta = \int_0^{\ln 2} 4e^{-\theta}\left(\frac{e^\theta - e^{-\theta}}{2}\right) d\theta$

$= 2 \int_0^{\ln 2} (1 - e^{-2\theta})\ d\theta = 2\left[\theta + \frac{e^{-2\theta}}{2}\right]_0^{\ln 2}$

$= 2\left[\left(\ln 2 + \frac{e^{-2 \ln 2}}{2}\right) - \left(0 + \frac{e^{-0}}{2}\right)\right]$

$= 2\left(\ln 2 + \frac{1}{8} - \frac{1}{2}\right) = 2 \ln 2 + \frac{1}{4} - 1 = \ln 4 - \frac{3}{4} \approx 0.636$

55. $\int_{-\pi/4}^{\pi/4} \cosh(\tan\theta)\sec^2\theta\,d\theta = \int_{-1}^{1}\cosh u\,du$

$= \Big[\sinh u\Big]_{-1}^{1} = \sinh(1) - \sinh(-1)$

$= \left(\dfrac{e^1 - e^{-1}}{2}\right) - \left(\dfrac{e^{-1}-e^1}{2}\right) = \dfrac{e - e^{-1} - e^{-1} + e}{2}$

$= e - e^{-1} \approx 2.350$, where $u = \tan\theta$, $du = \sec^2\theta\,d\theta$, the

lower limit is $\tan\left(-\dfrac{\pi}{4}\right) = -1$ and the upper limit is

$\tan\left(\dfrac{\pi}{4}\right) = 1$.

56. $\int_{0}^{\pi/2} 2\sinh(\sin\theta)\cos\theta\,d\theta = 2\int_{0}^{1}\sinh u\,du$

$= 2\Big[\cosh u\Big]_{0}^{1} = 2(\cosh 1 - \cosh 0) = 2\left(\dfrac{e + e^{-1}}{2} - 1\right)$

$= e + e^{-1} - 2 \approx 1.086$, where $u = \sin\theta$, $du = \cos\theta\,d\theta$,

the lower limit is $\sin 0 = 0$ and the upper limit is

$\sin\left(\dfrac{\pi}{2}\right) = 1$

57. $\int_{1}^{2} \dfrac{\cosh(\ln t)}{t}\,dt = \int_{0}^{\ln 2}\cosh u\,du = \Big[\sinh u\Big]_{0}^{\ln 2}$

$= \sinh(\ln 2) - \sinh(0) = \dfrac{e^{\ln 2} - e^{-\ln 2}}{2} - 0$

$= \dfrac{2 - \frac{1}{2}}{2} = \dfrac{3}{4}$, where $u = \ln t$, $du = \dfrac{1}{t}\,dt$, the lower limit is

$\ln 1 = 0$ and the upper limit is $\ln 2$

58. $\int_{1}^{4} \dfrac{8\cosh\sqrt{x}}{\sqrt{x}}\,dx = 16\int_{1}^{2}\cosh u\,du = 16\Big[\sinh u\Big]_{1}^{2}$

$= 16(\sinh 2 - \sinh 1)$

$= 16\left[\left(\dfrac{e^2 - e^{-2}}{2}\right) - \left(\dfrac{e - e^{-1}}{2}\right)\right]$

$= 8(e^2 - e^{-2} - e + e^{-1}) \approx 39.227$, where

$u = \sqrt{x} = x^{1/2}$, $du = \dfrac{1}{2}x^{-1/2}\,dx = \dfrac{dx}{2\sqrt{x}}$, the lower limit is

$\sqrt{1} = 1$ and the upper limit is $\sqrt{4} = 2$.

59. $\int_{-\ln 2}^{0} \cosh^2\left(\dfrac{x}{2}\right)dx = \int_{-\ln 2}^{0}\dfrac{\cosh x + 1}{2}\,dx$

$= \dfrac{1}{2}\int_{-\ln 2}^{0}(\cosh x + 1)\,dx = \dfrac{1}{2}\Big[\sinh x + x\Big]_{-\ln 2}^{0}$

$= \dfrac{1}{2}[(\sinh 0 + 0) - (\sinh(-\ln 2) - \ln 2)]$

$= \dfrac{1}{2}\left[(0 + 0) - \left(\dfrac{e^{-\ln 2} - e^{\ln 2}}{2} + \ln 2\right)\right]$

$= \dfrac{1}{2}\left[-\dfrac{(1/2) - 2}{2} + \ln 2\right]$

$= \dfrac{1}{2}\left(1 - \dfrac{1}{4} + \ln 2\right) = \dfrac{3}{8} + \dfrac{1}{2}\ln 2 = \dfrac{3}{8} + \ln\sqrt{2} \approx 0.722$

60. $\int_{0}^{\ln 10} 4\sinh^2\left(\dfrac{x}{2}\right)dx = \int_{0}^{\ln 10} 4\left(\dfrac{\cosh x - 1}{2}\right)dx$

$= 2\int_{0}^{\ln 10}(\cosh x - 1)\,dx = 2\Big[\sinh x - x\Big]_{0}^{\ln 10}$

$= 2[(\sinh(\ln 10) - \ln 10) - (\sinh 0 - 0)]$

$= e^{\ln 10} - e^{-\ln 10} - 2\ln 10 = 10 - \dfrac{1}{10} - 2\ln 10$

$= 9.9 - 2\ln 10 \approx 5.295$

61. $\cosh^2 x - \sinh^2 x = 1$, so $\int_{0}^{2}\pi(\cosh^2 x - \sinh^2 x)\,dx$

$= \pi\int_{0}^{2} 1\,dx = 2\pi$

62. $\int_{-\ln\sqrt{3}}^{\ln\sqrt{3}}\pi\,\text{sech}^2 x\,dx = \pi\Big[\tanh x\Big]_{-\ln\sqrt{3}}^{\ln\sqrt{3}}$

$= \pi\left(\dfrac{e^{\ln\sqrt{3}} - e^{-\ln\sqrt{3}}}{e^{\ln\sqrt{3}} + e^{-\ln\sqrt{3}}} - \dfrac{e^{-\ln\sqrt{3}} - e^{\ln\sqrt{3}}}{e^{-\ln\sqrt{3}} + e^{\ln\sqrt{3}}}\right)$

$= 2\pi\left(\dfrac{e^{\ln\sqrt{3}} - e^{-\ln\sqrt{3}}}{e^{\ln\sqrt{3}} + e^{-\ln\sqrt{3}}}\right) = 2\pi\left(\dfrac{\sqrt{3} - \frac{1}{\sqrt{3}}}{\sqrt{3} + \frac{1}{\sqrt{3}}}\right)$

$= 2\pi\left(\dfrac{3 - 1}{3 + 1}\right) = \pi$

63. $\int_{0}^{\ln\sqrt{199}}\pi(1 - \tanh x)^2\,dx$

$= \pi\int_{0}^{\ln\sqrt{199}}(1 - 2\tanh x + \tanh^2 x)\,dx$

$= \pi\int_{0}^{\ln\sqrt{199}}(2 - 2\tanh x - \text{sech}^2 x)\,dx$

$= \pi\Big[2x - 2\ln(\cosh x) - \tanh x\Big]_{0}^{\ln\sqrt{199}}$

$= \pi\Big[2\ln\sqrt{199} - 2\ln[\cosh(\ln\sqrt{199})] - \tanh(\ln\sqrt{199})\Big]$

$= \pi\left[2\ln\sqrt{199} - 2\ln\left(\dfrac{e^{\ln\sqrt{199}} + e^{-\ln\sqrt{199}}}{2}\right)\right.$

$\left. - \dfrac{e^{\ln\sqrt{199}} - e^{-\ln\sqrt{199}}}{e^{\ln\sqrt{199}} + e^{-\ln\sqrt{199}}}\right]$

$= \pi\left[\ln 199 - \ln\left(\dfrac{(\sqrt{199} + 1/\sqrt{199})^2}{4}\right) - \dfrac{\sqrt{199} - 1/\sqrt{199}}{\sqrt{199} + 1/\sqrt{199}}\right]$

$= \pi\left[\ln 199 - \ln\left(\dfrac{199 + 2 + 1/199}{4}\right) - \dfrac{199 - 1}{199 + 1}\right]$

$= \pi\left[\ln 199 - \ln\left(\dfrac{10{,}000}{199}\right) - \dfrac{99}{100}\right] = \left(2\ln\dfrac{199}{100} - \dfrac{99}{100}\right)\pi$

≈ 1.214

64. (a) $y = \frac{1}{2}\cosh 2x \Rightarrow y' = \sinh 2x \Rightarrow L$

$$= \int_0^{\ln\sqrt{5}} \sqrt{1 + (\sinh 2x)^2}\, dx = \int_0^{\ln\sqrt{5}} \cosh 2x\, dx$$

$$= \left[\frac{1}{2}\sinh 2x\right]_0^{\ln\sqrt{5}} = \left[\frac{1}{2}\left(\frac{e^{2x} - e^{-2x}}{2}\right)\right]_0^{\ln\sqrt{5}}$$

$$= \frac{1}{4}\left(5 - \frac{1}{5}\right) = \frac{6}{5}$$

(b) $y = \frac{1}{a}\cosh ax \Rightarrow 1 + (y')^2 = 1 + \sinh^2 ax = \cosh^2 ax$

$$\Rightarrow L = \int_0^b \sqrt{\cosh^2 ax}\, dx = \int_0^b \cosh ax\, dx$$

$$= \left[\frac{\sinh ax}{a}\right]_0^b = \frac{\sinh ab}{a}$$

65. (a) Let $E(x) = \frac{f(x) + f(-x)}{2}$ and $O(x) = \frac{f(x) - f(-x)}{2}$. Then

$$E(x) + O(x) = \frac{f(x) + f(-x)}{2} + \frac{f(x) - f(-x)}{2} = \frac{2f(x)}{2} =$$

$f(x)$. Also, $E(-x) = \frac{f(-x) + f(-(-x))}{2} = \frac{f(x) + f(-x)}{2} =$

$E(x) \Rightarrow E(x)$ is even, and $O(-x) = \frac{f(-x) - f(-(-x))}{2}$

$$= -\frac{f(x) - f(-x)}{2} = -O(x) \Rightarrow O(x) \text{ is odd.}$$

Consequently, $f(x)$ can be written as a sum of an even

and an odd function.

(b) Even part: $\frac{e^x + e^{-x}}{2} = \cosh x$

odd part: $\frac{e^x - e^{-x}}{2} = \sinh x$

66. (a) If f is even, then

$$\frac{f(x) + f(-x)}{2} + \frac{f(x) - f(-x)}{2}$$

$$= \frac{2f(x)}{2} + \frac{f(x) - f(x)}{2} = f(x) + 0$$

(b) If f is odd, then

$$\frac{f(x) + f(-x)}{2} + \frac{f(x) - f(-x)}{2}$$

$$= \frac{f(x) - f(x)}{2} + \frac{f(x) + f(x)}{2} = 0 + f(x)$$

67. Note that $\frac{dv}{dt} = \sqrt{\frac{mg}{k}}\,\text{sech}^2\left(\sqrt{\frac{gk}{m}}\,t\right)\left(\sqrt{\frac{gk}{m}}\right)$

$$= g\,\text{sech}^2\left(\sqrt{\frac{gk}{m}}\,t\right).$$

Then $m\frac{dv}{dt} = mg\,\text{sech}^2\left(\sqrt{\frac{gk}{m}}\,t\right)$ and

$$mg - kv^2 = mg - k\left[\sqrt{\frac{mg}{k}}\,\tanh\left(\sqrt{\frac{gk}{m}}\,t\right)\right]^2$$

$$= mg\left[1 - \tanh^2\left(\sqrt{\frac{gk}{m}}\,t\right)\right]$$

$$= mg\,\text{sech}^2\left(\sqrt{\frac{gk}{m}}\,t\right).$$

Thus, $m\frac{dv}{dt}$ and $mg - kv^2$ are equal to the same quantity, so

the differential equation is satisfied. Furthermore, the initial

condition is satisfied because $v(0) = \sqrt{\frac{mg}{k}}\tanh 0 = 0$.

68. (a) $s(t) = a\cos kt + b\sin kt$

$$\Rightarrow \frac{ds}{dt} = -ak\sin kt + bk\cos kt$$

$$\Rightarrow \frac{d^2s}{dt^2} = -ak^2\cos kt - bk^2\sin kt$$

$$= -k^2(a\cos kt + \sin kt) = -k^2 s(t) \Rightarrow \text{acceleration is}$$

proportional to s. The negative constant $-k^2$ implies

that the acceleration is directed toward the origin.

(b) $s(t) = a\cosh kt + b\sinh kt$

$$\Rightarrow \frac{ds}{dt} = ak\sinh kt + bk\cosh kt$$

$$\Rightarrow \frac{d^2s}{dt^2} = ak^2\cosh kt + bk^2\sinh kt$$

$$= k^2(a\cosh kt + \sinh kt) = k^2 s(t) \Rightarrow \text{acceleration is}$$

proportional to s. The positive constant k^2 implies that

the acceleration is directed away from the origin.

69. $\dfrac{dy}{dx} = \dfrac{-1}{x\sqrt{1 - x^2}} + \dfrac{x}{\sqrt{1 - x^2}}$

$$\Rightarrow y = \int \frac{-1}{x\sqrt{1 - x^2}}\, dx + \int \frac{x}{\sqrt{1 - x^2}}\, dx$$

$$\Rightarrow y = \text{sech}^{-1}(x) - \sqrt{1 - x^2} + C;\ x = 1 \text{ and}$$

$$y = 0 \Rightarrow C = 0 \Rightarrow y = \text{sech}^{-1}(x) - \sqrt{1 - x^2}$$

70. $y = 4\cosh\frac{x}{4} \Rightarrow 1 + \left(\frac{dy}{dx}\right)^2 = 1 + \sinh^2\left(\frac{x}{4}\right) = \cosh^2\left(\frac{x}{4}\right)$;

the surface area is $S = \int_{-\ln 16}^{\ln 81} 2\pi y \sqrt{1 + \left(\frac{dy}{dx}\right)^2}\, dx$

$$= 8\pi\int_{-\ln 16}^{\ln 81} \cosh^2\left(\frac{x}{4}\right)\, dx = 4\pi\int_{-\ln 16}^{\ln 81}\left(1 + \cosh\frac{x}{2}\right)\, dx$$

$$= 4\pi\left[x + 2\sinh\frac{x}{2}\right]_{-\ln 16}^{\ln 81}$$

$$= 4\pi\left[\left(\ln 81 + 2\sinh\left(\frac{\ln 81}{2}\right)\right)\right.$$

$$\left. - \left(-\ln 16 + 2\sinh\left(\frac{-\ln 16}{2}\right)\right)\right]$$

$$= 4\pi[\ln(81 \cdot 16) + 2\sinh(\ln 9) + 2\sinh(\ln 4)]$$

$$= 4\pi[\ln(9 \cdot 4)^2 + (e^{\ln 9} - e^{-\ln 9}) + (e^{\ln 4} - e^{-\ln 4})]$$

$$= 4\pi\left[2\ln 36 + \left(9 - \frac{1}{9}\right) + \left(4 - \frac{1}{4}\right)\right]$$

$$= 4\pi\left(4\ln 6 + \frac{80}{9} + \frac{15}{4}\right)$$

$$= 4\pi\left(4\ln 6 + \frac{320 + 135}{36}\right) = 16\pi\ln 6 + \frac{455\pi}{9} \approx 248.889$$

71. $y = a \cosh (x/a) \Rightarrow y' = \sinh (x/a)$

$\Rightarrow y'' = (1/a) \cosh (x/a) = (1/a)\sqrt{\cosh^2 (x/a)}$

$= (1/a)\sqrt{1 + \sinh^2 (x/a)} = (1/a)\sqrt{1 + (y')^2}.$

Also, $y'(0) = \sinh (0) = 0$ and $y(0) = a \cosh (0) = a.$

72. (a) Let the point located at $(\cosh x, 0)$ be called T. Then

$A(u)$ = area of the triangle $\triangle OTP$ minus the area under

the curve $y = \sqrt{x^2 - 1}$ from A to T

$\Rightarrow A(u) = \dfrac{1}{2} \cosh u \sinh u - \displaystyle\int_1^{\cosh u} \sqrt{x^2 - 1} \, dx.$

(b) $A(u) = \dfrac{1}{2} \cosh u \sinh u - \displaystyle\int_1^{\cosh u} \sqrt{x^2 - 1} \, dx$

$\Rightarrow A'(u)$

$= \dfrac{1}{2}(\cosh^2 u + \sinh^2 u) - (\sqrt{\cosh^2 u - 1})(\sinh u)$

$= \dfrac{1}{2} \cosh^2 u + \dfrac{1}{2} \sinh^2 u - \sinh^2 u$

$= \dfrac{1}{2}(\cosh^2 u - \sinh^2 u) = \left(\dfrac{1}{2}\right)(1) = \dfrac{1}{2}$

(c) $A'(u) = \dfrac{1}{2} \Rightarrow A(u) = \dfrac{u}{2} + C$, and from part (a) we have

$A(0) = 0 \Rightarrow C = 0 \Rightarrow A(u) = \dfrac{u}{2} \Rightarrow u = 2A(u)$